Teacher Edition

Volume 1

HARCOURT Math

NORTH CAROLINA EDITION

Harcourt

Orlando Austin Chicago New York Toronto London San Diego

Visit *The Learning Site!*
www.harcourtschool.com

Grateful acknowledgment is made to Flint Public Library, 1026 East Kearsley, MI, 48502-1994 for permission to reprint from "Cobbler, Cobbler" in *Ring a Ring o' Roses: Finger Plays for Pre-School Children,* Tenth Edition. Text copyright © 1996 by Flint Public Library.

Printed in the United States of America

ISBN 0-15-336623-0

3 4 5 6 7 8 9 10 030 10 09 08 07 06 05 04

Teacher's Edition Contents

Volume 1

Pupil Edition

UNIT 1 Understand Numbers and Operations Chapters 1–3

UNIT 2 Addition, Subtraction, Money, and Time Chapters 4–7

Multiplication Concepts and Facts Chapters 8–11

Volume 2

Pupil Edition

Division Concepts and Facts Chapters 12–14

Data and Measurement Chapters 15–18

Geometry Chapters 19–22

Volume 3

Pupil Edition

Patterns and Probability

Chapters 23–24

UNIT 8

Fractions and Decimals

Chapters 25–28

UNIT 9

Multiply and Divide by 1-Digit Numbers

Chapters 29–30

Authors

Senior Author

Evan M. Maletsky
Professor of Mathematics
Montclair State University
Upper Montclair, New Jersey

Angela Giglio Andrews
Math Teacher, Scott School
Naperville District #203
Naperville, Illinois

Jennie M. Bennett
Houston Independent School District
Houston, Texas

Grace M. Burton
Professor, Watson School of Education
University of North Carolina at Wilmington
Wilmington, North Carolina

Lynda A. Luckie
K-12 Mathematics Coordinator
Gwinnett County Public Schools
Lawrenceville, Georgia

Joyce C. McLeod
Visiting Professor
Rollins College
Winter Park, Florida

Tom Roby
Associate Professor of Mathematics
California State University
Hayward, California

Vicki Newman
Classroom Teacher
McGaugh Elementary School
Los Alamitos Unified School District
Seal Beach, California

Janet K. Scheer
Executive Director
Create A Vision
Foster City, California

Mathematics Advisors

The development of **HARCOURT MATH** was guided by prominent, accomplished mathematicians from across the United States. Their guidance helped ensure accurate mathematics and appropriate conceptual development.

Richard Askey
Professor of Mathematics
University of Wisconsin
Madison, Wisconsin
Grades 5–6

Tom Roby
Associate Professor of Mathematics
California State University
Hayward, California
Grade 4

David Singer
Professor of Mathematics
Case Western Reserve University
Cleveland, Ohio
Grade 3

Contributions to the Professional Handbook

Roger Howe
Professor of Mathematics
Yale University
New Haven, Connecticut

David Wright
Professor of Mathematics
Brigham Young University
Provo, Utah

Liping Ma
Mathematics Researcher and Educator
Palo Alto, California

Tom Roby
Associate Professor of Mathematics
Hayward, California

Marilee Sprenger
Educational Consultant
Two Rivers Professional Development Center
Edwards, Illinois

Program Consultants and Specialists

Janet S. Abbott
Mathematics Consultant
California

Elsie Babcock
Director, Mathematics and Science Center
Mathematics Consultant
Wayne Regional Educational Service Agency
Wayne, Michigan

William J. Driscoll
Professor of Mathematics
Department of Mathematical Sciences
Central Connecticut State University
New Britain, Connecticut

Lois Harrison-Jones
Education and Management Consultant
Dallas, Texas

Rebecca Valbuena
Language Development Specialist
Stanton Elementary School
Glendora, California

The Bag Ladies
Karen Simmons
Cindy Guinn
Palm Beach County, Florida
bagladiesonline.com

Reviewers and Field-Test Teachers

Britta Abinger
Teacher
Corkery School
Chicago, Illinois

Lynne D. Allen
Teacher
Wakefield Elementary
Raleigh, North Carolina

Ann Allison
Teacher
Woodward Elementary
Lock Haven, Pennsylvania

Elizabeth Arcement
DEEP Math Teacher/LINCS Coordinator
Iberia Parish Educational Center
New Iberia, Louisiana

Audrey A. Arellano-Davie
Assistant Principal
Side Creek Elementary
Aurora, Colorado

Angela M. Ascencio
Teacher
Bunche Elementary
Flint, Michigan

Sister Mary Berryman
Teacher
St. Peter Celestine School
Cherry Hill, New Jersey

Linda Bierkortte
Teacher
Parkmoor Urban Academy
Columbus, Ohio

Hazel Bills
Teacher
Corkery School
Chicago, Illinois

David A. Bond
Gifted and Talented Resource Teacher
Bollman Bridge Elementary
Ellicott City, Maryland

Henry Boyd
Teacher
Graham Elementary
Shelby, North Carolina

Kris Buechner
Teacher
Rowena Kyle Elementary School
Portage, Indiana

Wanda Bullock
Teacher
B.O. Barnes Elementary
Wilson, North Carolina

Stephanie Cahoon
Teacher
C. Wayne Collier Elementary
Hope Mills, North Carolina

Desiree A. Charles
Cayman Department of Education
Georgetown, Grand Cayman

Gail L. Clark
Teacher
Southhampton School #2
Delran, New Jersey

LaJuan Conley
Teacher
Burton Geo-World
Durham, North Carolina

Elizabeth Culpepper
Teacher
Princeton Elementary
Orlando, Florida

Carolyn A. Day
Director of Programs: Math/Science
Dayton Public Schools
Dayton, Ohio

Paul G. Dillenberger
Classroom 2000 Coordinator
Education Service Center
Minneapolis, Minnesota

Gail R. Englert
Teacher
Norfolk Public Schools/Sewells Point
Norfolk, Virginia

Judy Fisher
Teacher
James L. Dennis Elementary
Oklahoma City, Oklahoma

Kelly L. Fleming
Teacher
Windy Hill Elementary
Owings, Maryland

Mia Freeman
Teacher
Westchase Elementary School
Tampa, Florida

Ellen Galdieri
Teacher
Dowell Elementary
Huntingtown, Maryland

Susan Gaspich
Teacher
Chelsea Heights Elementary
Atlantic City, New Jersey

Kathryn George
Teacher
East Park Elementary
Danville, Illlinois

Lou Gerbi
Teacher
Westinghouse Elementary
Wilmerding, Pennsylvania

Elizabeth Q. Gilbert
Teacher
Roosevelt Elementary
West Palm Beach, Florida

James Giordano
Teacher
W.B. Powell Elementary
Washington, D.C.

Susan Googins
Teacher
Philip Schuyler Elementary
Albany, New York

Becky Hamilton
Teacher
Scull Elementary
North Huntingdon, Pennsylvania

Cheryl Harkins
Teacher
Bashaw Elementary
Bradenton, Florida

Elizabeth Harris
Teacher
Springfield Elementary
Providence, Rhode Island

Diane Hastings
Teacher
Thoreau Park
Parma, Ohio

Earl Heddle
Teacher
Richland Elementary
Gibsonia, Pennsylvania

Sarah Hillyer
Teacher
Craddock Elementary
Aurora, Ohio

Russell Hinson
Math Facilitator
Nathaniel Alexander
Charlotte, North Carolina

Tim Horton
Teacher
Quarryville Elementary
Quarryville, Pennsylvania

Heather Hunt
Teacher
Horizon Elementary
Hanover Park, Illinois

Travis Ivory
Teacher
Lyle Creek Elementary School
Conover, North Carolina

Michelle Jaronik
Coordinator, Gifted Math
Lincoln Center
Waukegan, Illinois

Catheline Jones
Teacher
Gateway Elementary
St. Louis, Missouri

Carolyn Rebecca Kniceley
Teacher
Breckinridge Elementary School
Fincastle, Virginia

Kim Lawrence
Teacher
Elmont Elementary
Ashland, Virginia

Jacqueline Leccia
Teacher
Timber Trace Elementary School
Palm Beach Gardens, Florida

Inell Lemon
Math Coordinator
Jensen Scholastic Academy
Chicago, Illinois

Carol C. Livingston
Teacher
Martin Luther King, Jr. Elementary
Woodbridge, Virginia

Arlene D. Loughlin
Teacher
Lake St. George
Palm Harbor, Florida

Ruth Loveland
Curriculum Director
Boundary County School District #101
Bonners Ferry, Idaho

Sarah Meadows
Title I Instructional Liaison
Topeka Public
Topeka, Kansas

Ruth Harbin Miles
Math Coordinator
Unified School District 233
Olathe, Kansas

Faye H. Miller
Teacher
Roosevelt Elementary
Plover, Wisconsin

Elaine Millie
Teacher
Bryant Elementary
Sioux City, Iowa

Susan Milstein
Teacher
Dag Hammerskjold School
Brooklyn, New York

Kathleen Mineau
Teacher
Public School # 19
Albany, New York

Ethel T. Munro
Teacher
Windom Elementary
Orchard Park, New York

Amy Musten
Teacher
Francisco Elementary School
Westfield, North Carolina

Patti Ogle
Teacher
Glen Arden Elementary School
Arden, North Carolina

Maritza Perez
Teacher
Huff Elementary
Elgin, Illinois

Jill E. Perkins
Teacher
Edwardsburg Primary
Cassopolis, Michigan

Kayanna Pitchford
Teacher
Alger B. Wilkins Elementary
Fayetteville, North Carolina

Paulette Prentice
Teacher
Anne Sullivan
Minneapolis, Minnesota

Suzanne Regali
Teacher
C.W. Holmes School
Derry, New Hampshire

Augustus Reid
Teacher
Greensboro, North Carolina

Pauline E. Robinson
Teacher
Star Hill Elementary
Dover, Delaware

Shana M. Runge
Teacher
Marion Intermediate School
Shelby, North Carolina

Telkia Rutherford
Mathematics Support Manager
Department of Instruction
Chicago, Illinois

Janae Shackelford
Teacher
Roosevelt Elementary
West Palm Beach, Florida

Therese Shields
Teacher
Parkside Elementary
Camden, New Jersey

Bonnie Short
Teacher
Snow Rogers Elementary
Gardendale, Alabama

Patti Smith
Teacher
Jefferson Elementary School
Ft. Riley, Kansas

Ivy Soffin
Teacher
Sunrise Park Elementary
Boca Raton, Florida

Ann H. Spencer
Teacher
Liberty Elementary
Shelbyville, Tennessee

Valerie J. Spindler
Teacher
L.V. Denti Elementary
Ava, New York

Ionia U. Stemple
Teacher
Norwood
Stonewood, West Virginia

Cathy L. Summa
Principal
Fountain City Elementary
Knoxville, Tennessee

Sylvia Teahan
Teacher
New Albany Elementary
Cinnaminson, New Jersey

Mary Thomas
Math Coordinator
Jersey Shore Area Junior High
Jersey Shore, Pennsylvania

Peter Tuttle
Teacher
Noble Elementary
Cleveland Heights, Ohio

Michelle Vancheri
Teacher
School #11
Paterson, New Jersey

Shelli Van Waes
K-1 Looping Teacher
Lyle Creek Elementary School
Conover, North Carolina

Suzanne Voos
Teacher
Roselawn-Condon Elementary
Cincinnati, Ohio

Beverly A. White
Teacher
Cecil Elementary
Cecil, Pennsylvania

Karen D. White
Teacher
Gardendale Elementary
Gardendale, Alabama

Lorraine White
Teacher
North Mami Elementary
North Miami, Florida

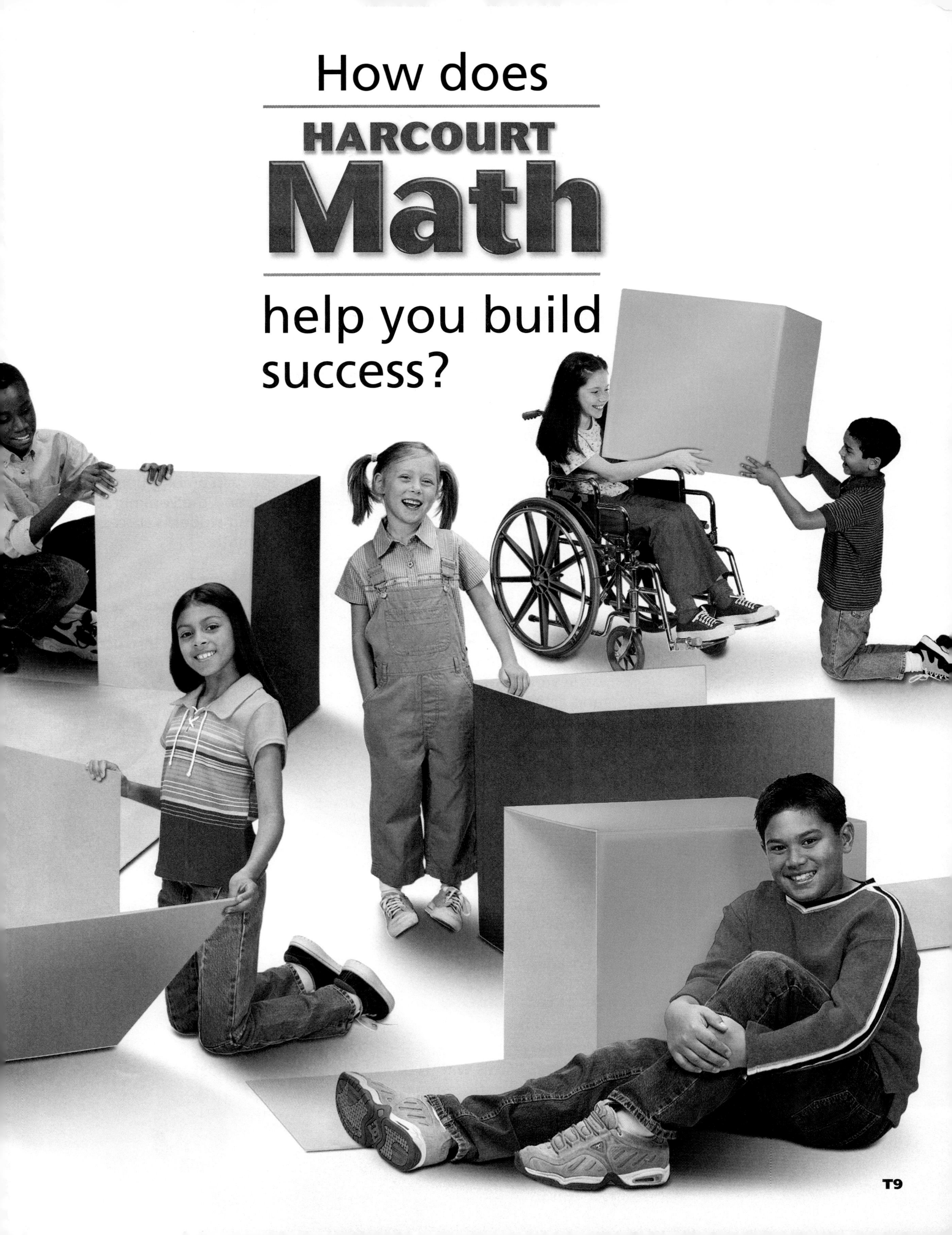
How does
HARCOURT
Math
help you build
success?

Building Success with

HARCOURT

Scientific Research Base

Harcourt Math provides a research-based instructional plan that ensures success for teachers and students.

Intervention

Harcourt Math includes daily intervention strategies for skills and for problem solving that diagnose students' difficulties with mathematics while providing intervention resources that will bring success for all learners.

Reaching All Learners

Harcourt Math provides a wide variety of strategies and activities to differentiate instruction so that all students can experience success in mathematics.

Algebra

The foundation for success in formal algebra at the middle school level begins with integrated lessons in Kindergarten and builds to complete chapters that develop algebraic concepts and thinking in grades 4 through 6.

Standards-Based Assessment

Harcourt Math assessment tools measure success with National and state-specific Standards before, during, and after instruction.

Customized Planning

Harcourt Math Teacher Editions, Electronic Lesson Planners, and Assessment Systems provide the tools to customize instruction.

School/Home Support

Harcourt Math builds a strong partnership among home, school, and the community that will bring students success in mathematics.

Technology

Harcourt Math increases student success by offering an array of technology-based instructional components that promote learning for all.

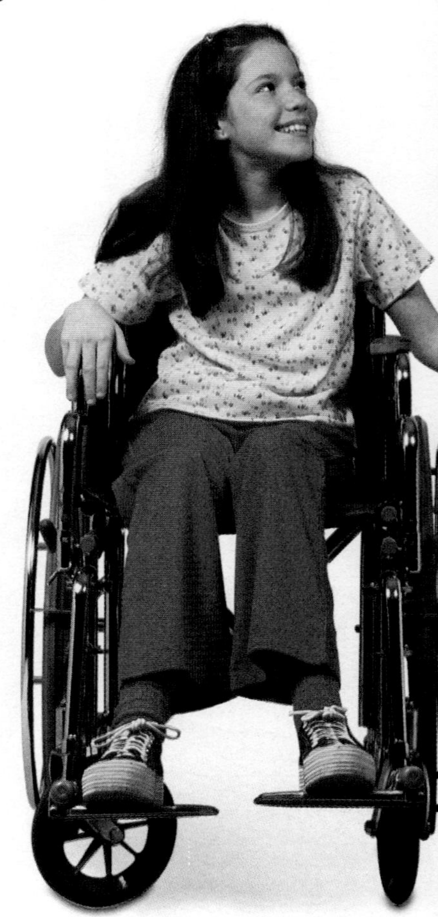

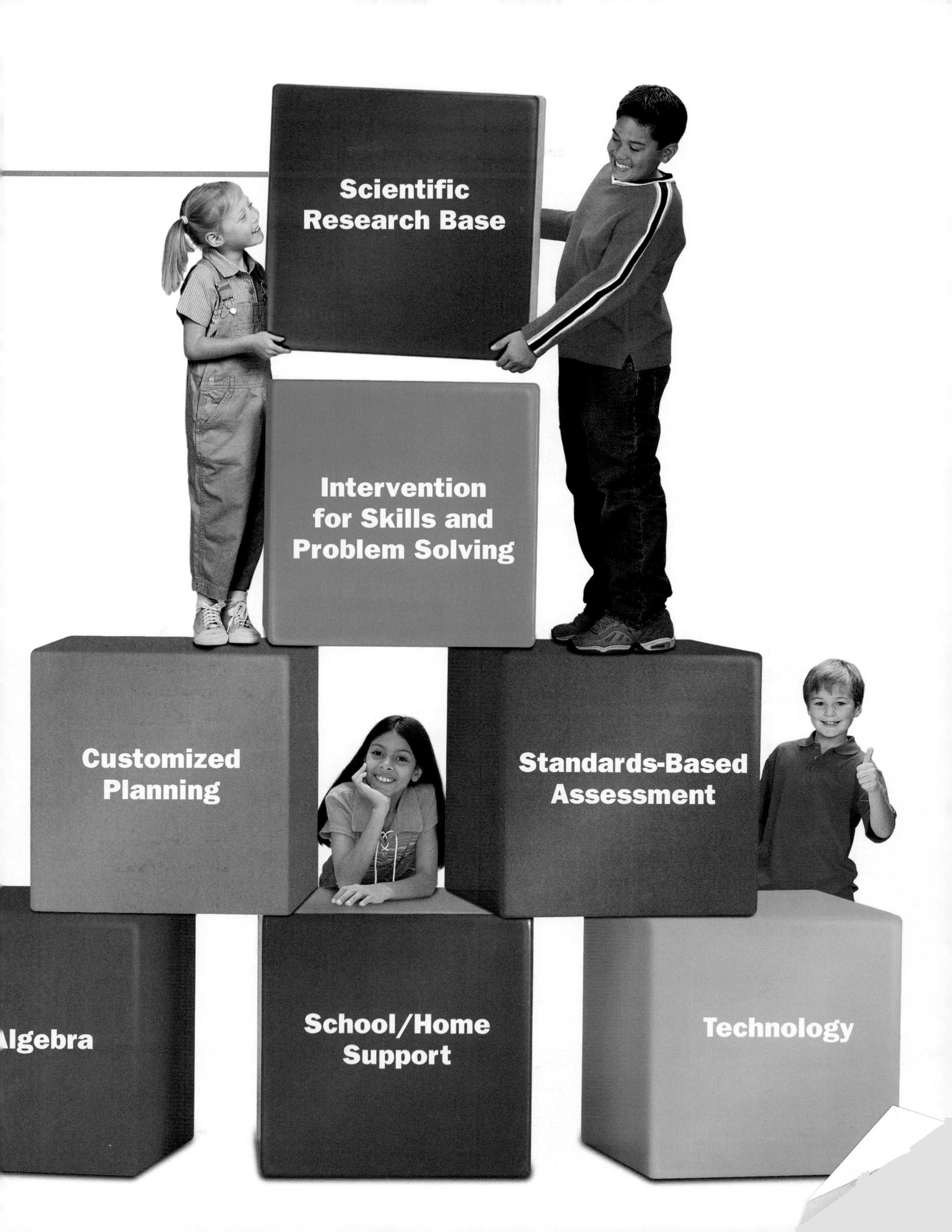
Scientific
Research Base
Intervention
for Skills and
Problem Solving
Customized
Planning
Standards-Based
Assessment
lgebra
School/Home
Support
Technology

Scientific Research Base

Building Success for All

Harcourt Math is based on scientific research that focuses on effective learning processes and instructional strategies that are essential for success in a wide range of learners. These processes and strategies include:

Explicit Instruction

The lesson plan in *Harcourt Math* is built upon the **three phases** of an **effective Mathematics lesson**:

1. Prior knowledge is activated and direct instruction takes place.
2. Guided practice transitions to independent work.
3. Concepts, skills, or strategies are applied, and assessment follows.

Conceptual Understanding

Visual Representation and Modeling promote students' abilities to make generalizations:

1. **Hands-on lessons** motivate and engage children.
2. **Step-by-step models** link concrete experiences to abstract representations and promote students' abilities to make generalizations.

Assessment Aligned with Intervention

Check What You Know quizzes:

1. Assess each student's prerequisite skills knowledge in preparation for chapter instruction.
2. Identify those who need intervention.
3. Allow for individualized instruction and reteaching.

Assess—the feature in each lesson—provides feedback and closure.

Assessment Aligned to State Standards

1. **Harcourt Assessment System (HAS)** provides assessment and practice by standard.
2. **HAS** allows teachers to generate customized tests to meet individual needs.

◀ illustrates how **Harcourt Math** is built on **scientific research**.

Professional Development

Through easy-to-follow professional development courses, teachers are informed about the scientific research-based learning processes and strategies that *Harcourt Math* is built on, and they become adept at incorporating these principles in their classrooms.

1. **Math Background and Instructional Strategies** support teachers and ensure daily teaching success.
2. **Professional Handbook** of articles written by mathematicians and educators supports teachers' knowledge of instructional approaches.
3. ***Professional Development for Math*** provides courses that focus on how children learn math and how to successfully use the instructional strategies in *Harcourt Math.*

Look for the apple to find instructional ideas from scientific research.

Intervention for Skills and Problem Solving

Building Success for All

Prerequisite Skills

A variety of intervention options provide direct instruction, conceptual models, scaffolded practice of missed skills, and challenging activities for those more capable. Built in assessment determines when a student is ready to move to the next level of instruction.

- **Assess readiness** for new learning and **diagnose students' difficulties** with mathematics: **Check What You Know**
- **Intervene or enrich**

Were students successful with Check What You Know?

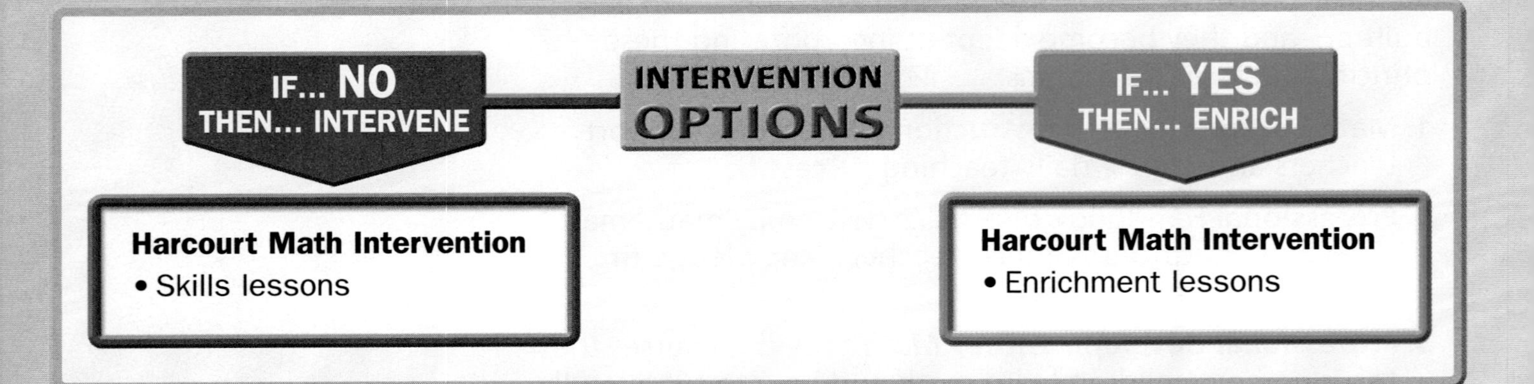

IF... NO
THEN... INTERVENE
INTERVENTION OPTIONS
IF... YES
THEN... ENRICH
Harcourt Math Intervention
• Skills lessons
Harcourt Math Intervention
• Enrichment lessons

Daily Intervention

A variety of intervention options exist in the daily Teacher Edition lesson plan:

- **Lesson Check**
- **Alternative Teaching Strategies**
- **Reteach Workbook**

Harcourt Math includes **intervention strategies** that diagnose students' difficulties with mathematics concepts, skills, and problem solving, and provides **intervention resources** to ensure success for all learners.

Problem Solving—

intervention help where the students need it the most!

Better problem solvers are better Test Takers.

- **Diagnose comprehension and readability problems**

  Each Problem Solving lesson in the Pupil Edition provides an opportunity to diagnose student difficulties in the critical area of problem solving.

- **Intervene with scaffolded instruction**

For students who have difficulty with:	How Harcourt Math Intervention helps:
Reading word problems	It uses language more accessible to students.
Comprehending word problems	It provides scaffolded instruction for problems.
Choosing the operation in problems	It uses unique graphic organizers called **Math Maps** to model the action in the problem.

- **Build confidence for all**

  ***Harcourt Math* Intervention Problem Solving can be used with all students** to strengthen their problem solving ability and to build confidence in their ability to solve problems and experience success on Standardized Tests.

Reaching All Learners

Harcourt Math offers a wide range of strategies and activities so that **all students experience success** in mathematics.

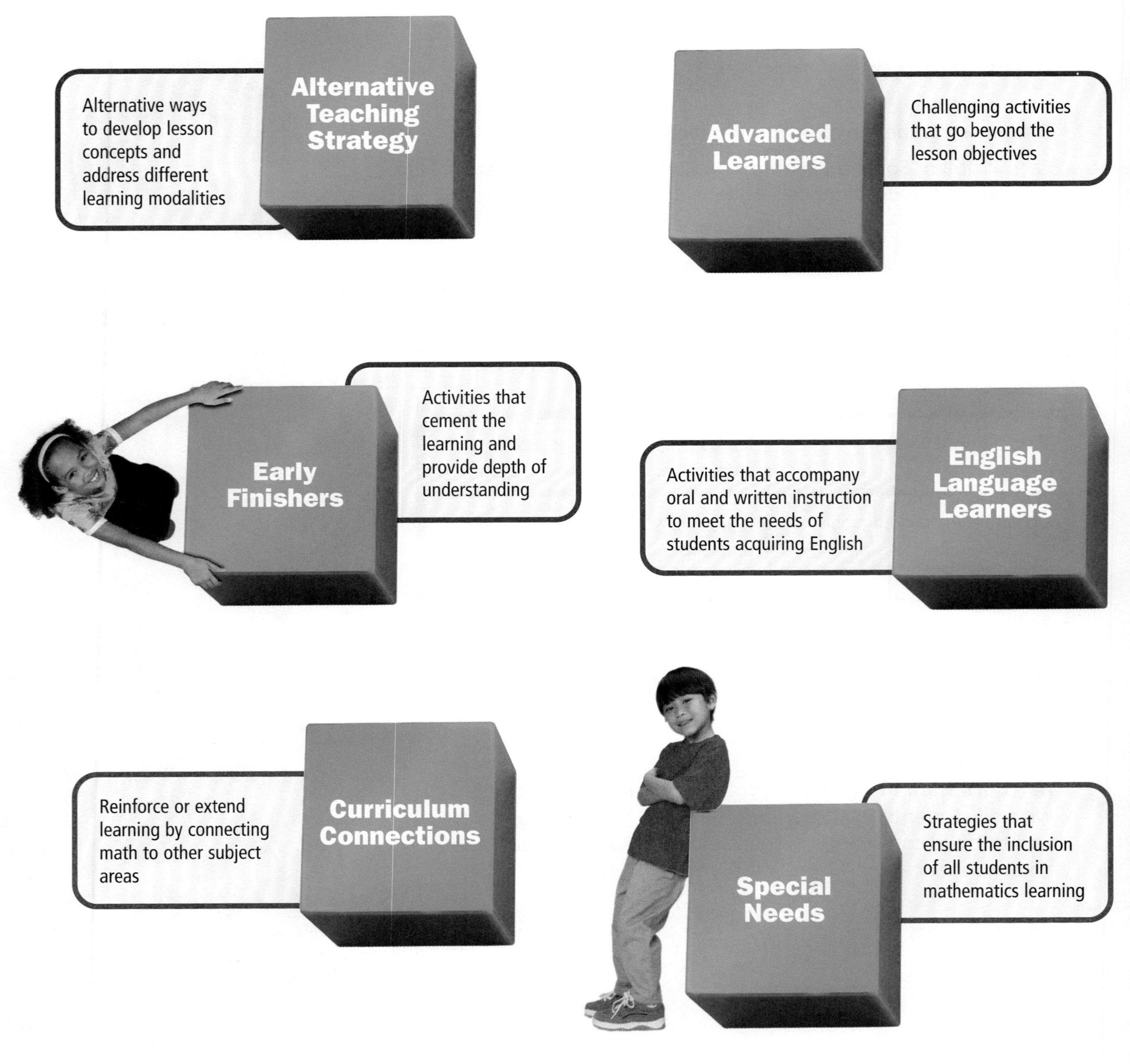

Alternative Teaching Strategy

Alternative ways to develop lesson concepts and address different learning modalities

Advanced Learners

Challenging activities that go beyond the lesson objectives

Early Finishers

Activities that cement the learning and provide depth of understanding

English Language Learners

Activities that accompany oral and written instruction to meet the needs of students acquiring English

Curriculum Connections

Reinforce or extend learning by connecting math to other subject areas

Special Needs

Strategies that ensure the inclusion of all students in mathematics learning

Algebra

Harcourt Math builds the foundation for **later success** with formal algebra courses.

Children begin with the study of patterns

- Early childhood students study simple shape, color, and number patterns.
- Patterns are connected to functions in lessons that ask students to find a missing number in a pattern or discover a rule for a pattern.
- Students explore graphing patterns.

Lessons and exercises connect algebra concepts to the mathematics skills they are learning

- Students find missing factors and evaluate number and algebraic expressions.
- Students develop rules or formulas for perimeter, area, and volume.

Chapters develop algebra concepts and provide practice of computational skills

- Students use addition and subtraction to learn about expressions and equations.
- Students graph and solve linear equations.
- Students explore and compute with integers and rational numbers.

Algebraic Thinking is developed at every grade level

- Algebraic thinking is a consistent part of the Teacher Edition lesson plan.
- In every lesson, reasoning questions and exercises require students to explain their thinking in class discussions or to write about it in their journals.

Assessment

Harcourt Math provides assessment tools that are **Standards-based** and modeled after widely-used **state assessment instruments**. They assess mastery of objectives before, during, and after instruction.

Assess Prior Knowledge

- **Inventory Test** in the Assessment Guide
- **Check What You Know** in the Pupil Edition
- **Chapter Pretests** (multiple choice or free response) in the Assessment Guide

Assess Mastery of grade-level objectives

Formal Assessment options:

- **Chapter Review/Test** in the Pupil Edition
- **Standardized Test Prep** in the Pupil Edition
- **Chapter Test, Forms A and B,** in the Assessment Guide
- **Unit Tests** in the Assessment Guide
- **Performance Assessment** in the Pupil Edition.

Monitor Progress toward Mastery

- **Daily Assessment, Quick Review,** and **Mixed Review and Test Prep** in the Pupil Edition
- **Assess** section and **Intervention and Extension Resources** in the Teacher Edition
- **Intervention** options in the *Harcourt Math Intervention* component
- **Student Self Assessment** in the Assessment Guide

Test Preparation

Multiple Test Prep opportunities in the Pupil Edition:

- **Mixed Review and Test Prep**
- **Standardized Test Prep**
- **Explain It**

Customized Planning

Harcourt Math provides the tools to allow you to **customize** the sequence, pace, and structure of **lesson plans** and **assessment**.

Harcourt Math Teacher Editions provide a variety of options to customize your daily lesson plans. They include:

- **Meaningful activities** to introduce, develop, and extend
- **Built-in questions** to develop Reasoning and Algebraic Thinking
- **Intervention and Extension Resources** and **Alternative Teaching Strategies** for instruction and extension using varying learning styles
- **Four point-of-use worksheets** for homework and for meeting individual needs

Harcourt Math ePlanner available on-line gives maximum flexibility of instruction and planning.

- **Sequence and pace instruction** to meet your State or District mandates
- **Teach by Standard** or compact the curriculum to prioritize instruction
- **Create daily, weekly,** and **yearly lesson plans** to match District needs and to meet diverse student needs
- **Preview workbook pages on-line** to plan homework, remediation, or challenge

The Harcourt Assessment System — (HAS) available on CD ROM :

- **Administer and grade Chapter and Unit Tests** electronically
- **Create your own test** based on grade-level objectives
- **Create Standards-based tests** from a bank of rich items
- **Create customized practice** by objective
- **Generate and print customized reports** using the HAS mini-manager

Technology

Harcourt Math increases student success by offering an array of **technology-based instructional components** that promote learning for all.

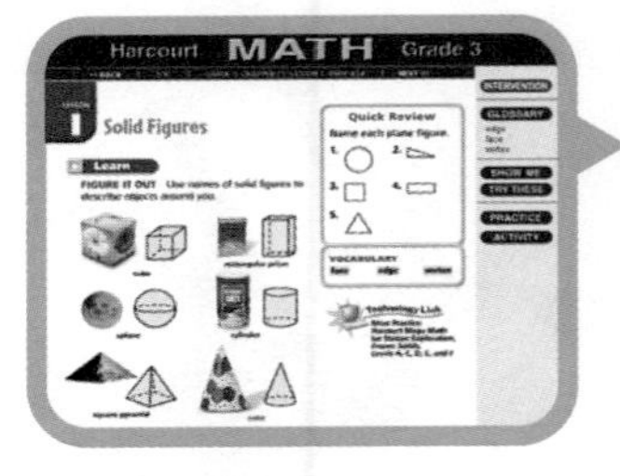

Harcourt Math eBook Student Edition provides an interactive replica of the student text with built-in intervention, a variety of practice activities, and the Multimedia Math Glossary. (Gr. 1–6)

Harcourt Math eBook Teacher Edition provides an online replica of the *Harcourt Math* Teacher Edition with links to a variety of resources. (Gr. 1–6)

Harcourt Math Intervention • Skills CD-ROM features animated, narrated lessons with conceptual models and scaffolded practice for students who lack prerequisite skills. (Gr. 1–6)

Harcourt Math Intervention • Problem Solving CD-ROM provides much-needed support for students who struggle to solve word problems. Math Maps help students understand and model the four operations.

Harcourt Mega Math CD-ROMs offer interactive learning for practice of basic facts, math skills from all strands, and problem solving. Students progress through the skills using a Grow Slide that advances automatically to offer more challenging problems. It also generates student reports.

Harcourt Assessment System CD-ROM offers computer-administered practice and testing. It allows for tests to be customized by Standards. Individual student and class reports aid teachers in tracking their students.

Harcourt Math Center™ is a learning management system that scores, tracks, and reports student progress in Harcourt Mega Math, Assessment System, Intervention Skills, and Intervention Problem Solving CD-ROMS.

Harcourt Math ePlanner provides online access allowing teachers to customize planning and pacing and to reorder content to meet their state, district, or local needs. (Gr. K–6)

The Harcourt Learning Site offers a variety of interactive experiences that reinforce grade-level math concepts. (Gr. K–6)

School/Home Support

Harcourt Math supports a strong **partnership** with **the home, the school,** and **the community** to help students experience success in mathematics.

Looking Back and *Looking Forward*

These pages at the beginning of each unit in the Primary Pupil Editions are sent home to inform the family of what mathematics will be studied in the coming unit and of ways to help the child during the learning process. They also provide a game that the child and family can play together, to practice the skills the child has just learned.

Family Involvement Activities

This component of **Harcourt Math** provides an informative, four-page family letter to accompany every chapter. Each letter provides:

- A family-friendly explanation of the expectations for student learning
- Models of chapter concepts and skills
- Tips that enable family members to assist students in the learning
- Homework practice
- A math game for family fun

The Learning Site

Harcourt's easy-to-use website offers family members interactive learning games, a Multimedia Math Glossary, and a special page with tips and ideas for parents.

School/Home
Support

Visit the **Harcourt Math** website at **www.harcourtschool.com.**

Components

	HARCOURT MATH COMPONENTS	PRE K	K	1	2	3	4	5	6
Daily Lesson Support	Student Edition		■	■	■	■	■	■	■
	Unit/Chapter Books		■	■	■				
	Activity Book	■							
	Big Book		■						
	Teacher Edition	■	■	■	■	■	■	■	■
	Reteach Workbook—Student and Teacher Editions			■	■	■	■	■	■
	Practice Workbook—Student and Teacher Editions		■	■	■	■	■	■	■
	Problem Solving and Reading Strategies Workbook—Student and Teacher Editions			■	■	■	■	■	■
	Challenge Workbook—Student and Teacher Editions		■	■	■	■	■	■	■
	Teacher's Resource Book		■	■	■	■	■	■	■
	Daily Transparencies			■	■	■	■	■	■
	Problem Solving Teaching Transparencies: Scaffolded Instruction			■	■	■	■	■	■
	Reading Transparencies			■	■	■	■	■	■
	Vocabulary Cards with Teacher's Activity Guide		■	■	■	■	■	■	■
	Success for English Language Learners, ESOL/ESL			■	■	■	■	■	■
	Poster Pack	■							
	Graphing Investigations Teacher Guide and Pack		■	■	■	■	■	■	■
Teacher Planning Support	On-line ePlanner		■	■	■	■	■	■	■
Intervention	Intervention • Skills			■	■	■	■	■	■
	Intervention • Problem Solving (Student and Teacher Editions)			■	■	■	■	■	■
Assessment Resources	Assessment Guide		■	■	■	■	■	■	■
	Performance Assessment			■	■	■	■	■	■
	Harcourt Assessment System CD-ROMs			■	■	■	■	■	■
Family Involvement	Family Involvement Activities		■	■	■	■	■	■	■
Literature and Music	Math Readers		■	■	■				
	Literature Big Books and Little Books	■	■						
	Literature Books on Tape		■						
	Math Jingles®		■	■	■	■	■	■	■
	Math Jingles® Copying Masters		■	■	■	■	■	■	■
Technology Resources	eBook and eBook Teacher Edition			■	■	■	■	■	■
	Harcourt Mega Math CD-ROMs		■	■	■	■	■	■	■
	Intervention • Skills CD-ROMs			■	■	■	■	■	■
	Intervention • Problem Solving CD-ROMs			■	■	■	■	■	■
	The Learning Site		■	■	■	■	■	■	■
Manipulative Options	My Manipulatives and Workmats/Student Manipulative Kit		■	■	■	■	■	■	■
	Core Manipulative Kit	■	■	■	■	■	■	■	■
	Teacher Modeling Kit		■	■	■	■	■	■	■
	Build-a-Kit® Manipulatives		■	■	■	■	■	■	■
	Concept Builder		■						

HARCOURT
Math
NORTH CAROLINA
EDITION
Harcourt
Orlando Austin Chicago New York Toronto London San Diego
Visit The Learning Site!
www.harcourtschool.com

Printed in the United States of America

ISBN 0-15-336607-9

2 3 4 5 6 7 8 9 10 032 10 09 08 07 06 05 04

Senior Author

Evan M. Maletsky
Professor of Mathematics
Montclair State University
Upper Montclair, New Jersey

Mathematics Advisor

David Singer
Professor of Mathematics
Case Western Reserve University
Cleveland, Ohio

Authors

Angela Giglio Andrews
Math Teacher, Scott School
Naperville District #203
Naperville, Illinois

Jennie M. Bennett
Houston Independent School District
Houston, Texas

Grace M. Burton
Professor, Watson School of Education
University of North Carolina
at Wilmington
Wilmington, North Carolina

Lynda A. Luckie
K–12 Mathematics Coordinator
Gwinnett County Public Schools
Lawrenceville, Georgia

Joyce C. McLeod
Visiting Professor
Rollins College
Winter Park, Florida

Vicki Newman
Classroom Teacher
McGaugh Elementary School
Los Alamitos Unified School District
Seal Beach, California

Tom Roby
Associate Professor of Mathematics
California State University
Hayward, California

Janet K. Scheer
Executive Director
Create A Vision
Foster City, California

Program Consultants and Specialist

Janet S. Abbott
Mathematics Consultant
California

Lois Harrison-Jones
Education and Management Consultant
Dallas, Texas

Elsie Babcock
Director, Mathematics and Science Center
Mathematics Consultant
Wayne Regional Educational Service Agency
Wayne, Michigan

William J. Driscoll
Professor of Mathematics
Department of Mathematical Sciences
Central Connecticut State University
New Britain, Connecticut

Rebecca Valbuena
Language Development Specialist
Stanton Elementary School
Glendora, California

iii

UNIT 1

CHAPTERS 1-3

Understand Numbers and Operations

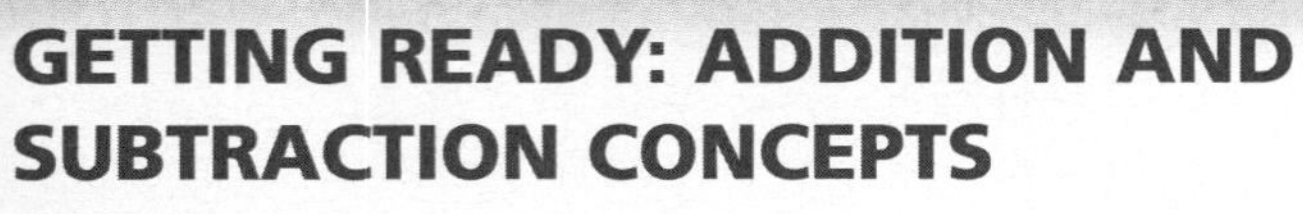

1 GETTING READY: ADDITION AND SUBTRACTION CONCEPTS

2 PLACE VALUE AND NUMBER SENSE 18

COMPARE, ORDER, AND ROUND NUMBERS . . 38

UNIT WRAPUP

Technology Link

Harcourt Mega Math
Chapter 1: pp. 2, 8; Chapter 2: pp. 22, 25
Chapter 3: p. 43
The Harcourt Learning Site:
www.harcourtschool.com
Multimedia Math Glossary:
www.harcourtschool.com/mathglossary

UNIT 2
CHAPTERS 4-7

Addition, Subtraction, Money, and Time

4 ADDITION .66

5 SUBTRACTION .86

Technology Link

Harcourt Mega Math
Chapter 4: pp. 70, 77; Chapter 5: p. 91
Chapter 6: pp. 111, 119; Chapter 7: pp. 134, 139
The Harcourt Learning Site: www.harcourtschool.com
Multimedia Math Glossary:
www.harcourtschool.com/mathglossary

USE MONEY ... 108

UNDERSTAND TIME ... 126

UNIT WRAPUP

vii

UNIT 3
CHAPTERS 8-11

Multiplication Concepts and Facts

Technology Link

Harcourt Mega Math
Chapter 8: pp. 158, 162; Chapter 9: p. 182
Chapter 10: p. 200; Chapter 11: pp. 213, 216
The Harcourt Learning Site:
www.harcourtschool.com
Multimedia Math Glossary:
www.harcourtschool.com/mathglossary

MULTIPLICATION FACTS AND STRATEGIES . . 192

MULTIPLICATION FACTS AND PATTERNS 210

UNIT WRAPUP

ix

UNIT 4
CHAPTERS 12-14

Division Concepts and Facts

Technology Link

Harcourt Mega Math
Chapter 12: pp. 242, 247; Chapter 13: p. 261
Chapter 14: pp. 274, 281
The Harcourt Learning Site:
www.harcourtschool.com
Multimedia Math Glossary:
www.harcourtschool.com/mathglossary

DIVISION FACTS THROUGH 10 272

UNIT WRAPUP

UNIT 5 Data and Measurement

CHAPTERS 15-18

15 COLLECT AND RECORD DATA .300

16 ANALYZE AND GRAPH DATA .320

Technology Link

Harcourt Mega Math
Chapter 15: pp. 311, 315; Chapter 16: pp. 325, 330
Chapter 17: p. 348; Chapter 18: p. 359
The Harcourt Learning Site:
www.harcourtschool.com
Multimedia Math Glossary:
www.harcourtschool.com/mathglossary

CUSTOMARY UNITS .336

METRIC UNITS AND TEMPERATURE .356

UNIT WRAPUP

xiii

UNIT 6 Geometry

CHAPTERS 19-22

GEOMETRIC FIGURES .382

CONGRUENCE AND SYMMETRY .406

Technology Link

Harcourt Mega Math
Chapter 19: p. 396; Chapter 20: pp. 408, 414
Chapter 21: p. 424; Chapter 22: p. 452
The Harcourt Learning Site:
www.harcourtschool.com
Multimedia Math Glossary:
www.harcourtschool.com/mathglossary

SOLID AND PLANE FIGURES 422

PERIMETER, AREA, AND VOLUME 442

UNIT WRAPUP

xv

UNIT 7 Patterns and Probability

CHAPTERS 23-24

Technology Link

Harcourt Mega Math
Chapter 23: p. 476
Chapter 24: pp. 489, 493
The Harcourt Learning Site:
www.harcourtschool.com
Multimedia Math Glossary:
www.harcourtschool.com/mathglossary

PROBABILITY

UNIT WRAPUP

xvii

UNIT 8 Fractions and Decimals

CHAPTERS 25-28

Technology Link

Harcourt Mega Math
Chapter 25: p. 527; Chapter 26: p. 547
Chapter 27: pp. 560, 562; Chapter 28: p. 580
The Harcourt Learning Site:
www.harcourtschool.com
Multimedia Math Glossary: www.harcourtschool.com/mathglossary

UNIT WRAPUP

xix

UNIT 9
CHAPTERS 29-30

Multiply and Divide by 1-Digit Numbers

Technology Link

Harcourt Mega Math
Chapter 29: p. 603
Chapter 30: p. 619
The Harcourt Learning Site:
www.harcourtschool.com
Multimedia Math Glossary:
www.harcourtschool.com/mathglossary

UNIT WRAPUP

STUDENT HANDBOOK

EOG TEST HANDBOOK

OTHER RESOURCES

xxi

Using Math In

North Carolina

▶ Building Success Now

You use math when you participate in sporting events. ▼

▲ You use math when you measure pieces of wood to build a tree house.

You use patterns in ▶ math when you play games or work with arts and crafts.

xxii

You will use the mathematics that you learn in **Harcourt Math** every day. The skills you learn will help you **build success** both now and in the future.

Building Success for the Future

◀ If you become a civil engineer, math skills will help you build bridges, like this one in New Bern.

▲ If you become a park ranger, you will use math skills to collect data about wildlife, weather, and hiking trail conditions in areas like the Outer Banks.

▲ If you become a scientist, math skills will help you conduct experiments.

Have a great year and enjoy learning Math!

xxiii

It's In The Bag

At the end of each Unit is a project-based activity that you can use to provide your students with practice of the skills and concepts taught in the unit.

Students will begin the year by making a holder for their projects out of an ordinary paper grocery bag. Each of the projects throughout the year is made from common materials and from copying masters in the *Teachers' Resource Book.*

Below are the materials needed for each unit's project that you can begin collecting now.

Materials List

Unit 1
Pocket Place Value

- 20-pocket plastic slide pages
- 5 colors of construction paper
- Square pattern
- Markers
- Scissors

Unit 2
My Coin Keeper

- 35-mm film canisters
- Eye screws
- Cord
- Beads
- Play coins and bills
- Product cards
- Labels for canisters
- Tape

Unit 3
Multiplication Rocks

- Small, flat rocks
- Permanent markers
- Paper lunch bags, or zip-type bags

Unit 4
Candy Bar Division

- Silver foil
- Construction paper
- Rulers
- $8\frac{1}{2}''$ x 11″ unlined paper
- Pencils
- Scissors
- Glue or tape
- Candy wrapper pattern

Unit 5
Stamp-O-Graph Math

- Spools of all sizes
- Water bottle lids
- Film canisters
- Precut foam shapes
- Colored ink pads or markers
- Grid paper
- Construction paper
- Scissors and glue

Unit 6
Pocketful of Polygons

- Construction paper
- Tape
- Polygon worksheets
- Scissors
- Crayons

Unit 7
Probability Clues

- CD cases
- Scissors
- Markers
- Spinner patterns
- Clue cards
- Brass fasteners
- Large paper clips

Unit 8
Fraction Trade Game

- Paper
- Scissors
- Markers or pencils
- Number cubes
- Small blank stickers

Unit 9
Multiply and Divide Start to Finish

- File folders
- Construction paper
- Game path pattern
- Markers, crayons, or color pencils
- Card stock
- Paper, pencils, scissors
- Dot cubes or number cubes
- Game pieces

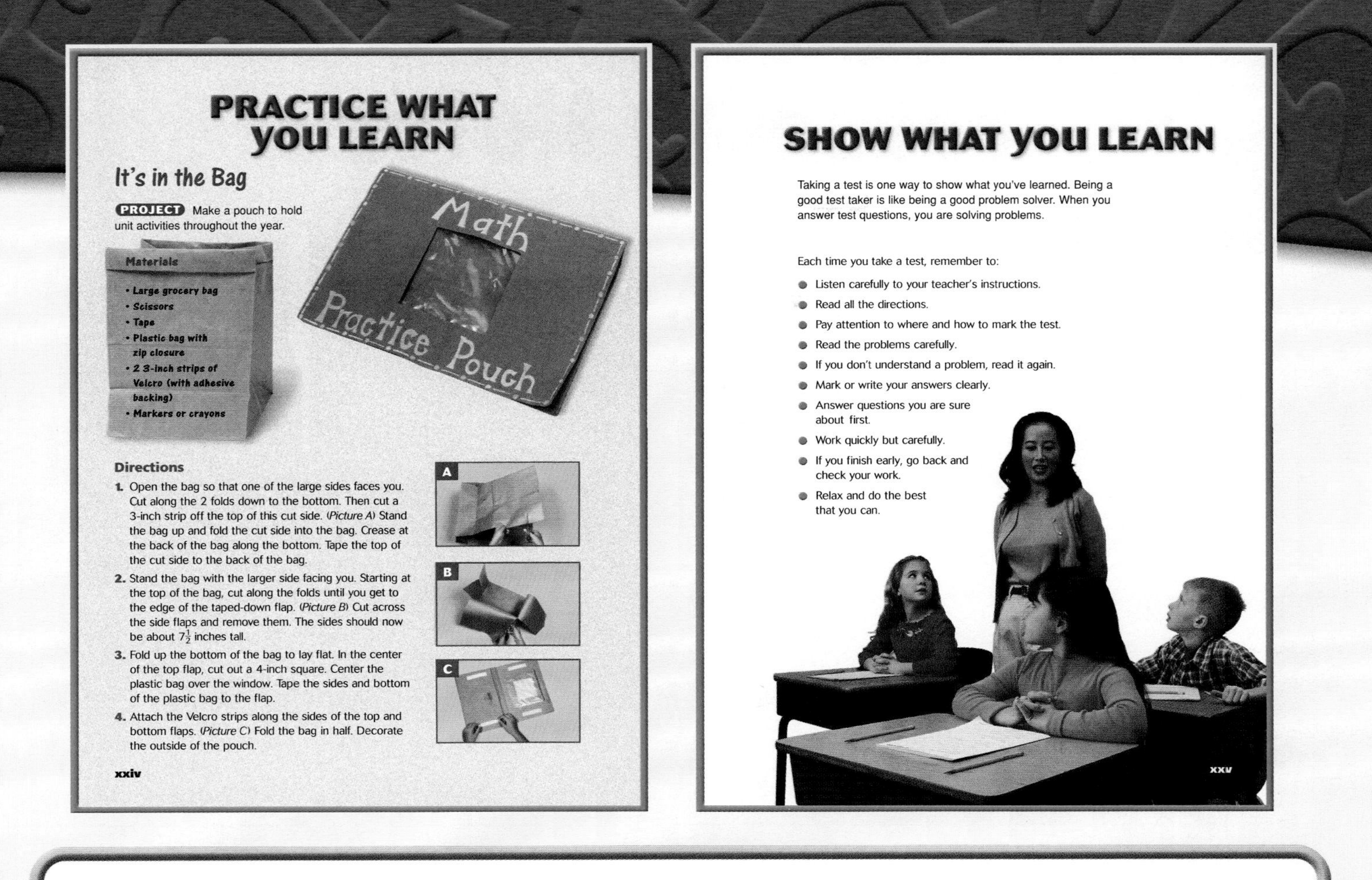

PRACTICE WHAT YOU LEARN

It's in the Bag

PROJECT Make a pouch to hold unit activities throughout the year.

Materials
- Large grocery bag
- Scissors
- Tape
- Plastic bag with zip closure
- 2 3-inch strips of Velcro (with adhesive backing)
- Markers or crayons

Directions

1. Open the bag so that one of the large sides faces you. Cut along the 2 folds down to the bottom. Then cut a 3-inch strip off the top of this cut side. (*Picture A*) Stand the bag up and fold the cut side into the bag. Crease at the back of the bag along the bottom. Tape the top of the cut side to the back of the bag.
2. Stand the bag with the larger side facing you. Starting at the top of the bag, cut along the folds until you get to the edge of the taped-down flap. (*Picture B*) Cut across the side flaps and remove them. The sides should now be about $7\frac{1}{2}$ inches tall.
3. Fold up the bottom of the bag to lay flat. In the center of the top flap, cut out a 4-inch square. Center the plastic bag over the window. Tape the sides and bottom of the plastic bag to the flap.
4. Attach the Velcro strips along the sides of the top and bottom flaps. (*Picture C*) Fold the bag in half. Decorate the outside of the pouch.

xxiv

SHOW WHAT YOU LEARN

Taking a test is one way to show what you've learned. Being a good test taker is like being a good problem solver. When you answer test questions, you are solving problems.

Each time you take a test, remember to:

- Listen carefully to your teacher's instructions.
- Read all the directions.
- Pay attention to where and how to mark the test.
- Read the problems carefully.
- If you don't understand a problem, read it again.
- Mark or write your answers clearly.
- Answer questions you are sure about first.
- Work quickly but carefully.
- If you finish early, go back and check your work.
- Relax and do the best that you can.

xxv

Practice What You Learn

Purpose

To make a pouch to hold the unit projects

Materials

For each student brown paper grocery bag, scissors, tape, markers, crayons, or color pencils, sandwich-size zip-lock bag, two 3-inch strips of Velcro with adhesive backing

Preparing the Materials

- Encourage each student to bring in a brown paper grocery bag. The bags should be blank on the outside. Have extra grocery bags available in case students make mistakes while cutting. Make a 4″ x 4″ cardboard pattern for students to use to trace and cut the "window" for their plastic bag. Have markers, crayons, and color pencils available for the students to use to label and decorate their bags.

Making the Project

- You may wish to have students complete steps 1 and 2 on one day and steps 3 and 4 on another day. Have students follow directions while you use a prepared model as an example. Be sure to model the activity slowly.

Teaching Notes

Additional Ideas:

Good Questions to Ask:

Additional Resources:

Notes for Next Time:

Unit at a Glance

CHAPTER 1

CHAPTER 2

CHAPTER 3

EXCERPTS FROM THE RESEARCH

"As is true with all higher-order skills, the development of good number sense takes time and begins at the earliest level. . . . It is a topic for every day, at every grade, with the most important foundation laid in the earliest years." (Van de Walle and Watkins, 1993)

Understand Numbers and Operations

Assessment Options

Assessing Prior Knowledge

Determine whether students have the required prerequisite concepts and skills.

Check What You Know, PE pp. 1, 19, 39

Test Preparation

Provide review and practice for chapter and standardized tests.

Getting Ready for the EOG Test, PE pp. 3, 5, 7, 9, 11, 16–17, 21, 23, 27, 31, 33, 36–37, 41, 45, 47, 51, 53, 56–57

Study Guide and Review, PE pp. 60–61

Formal Assessment

Assess students' mastery of chapter concepts and skills.

Chapter Review/Test, PE pp. 15, 35, 55

Pretest and Posttest Options

Chapter Test, Form A

pp. AG9–10, 13–14, 17–18

Chapter Test, Form B

pp. AG11–12, 15–16, 19–20

Unit 1 Test • Chapters 1–3

Form A, pp. AG21–24

Form B, pp. AG25–28

Daily Assessment

Obtain daily feedback on students' understanding of concepts.

Quick Review, See the first page of each PE lesson.

Getting Ready for the EOG Test

See the last page of each PE skill lesson.

Number of the Day

See the first page of each TE lesson.

Problem of the Day

See the first page of each TE lesson.

Lesson Quiz

See the *Assess* section of each TE lesson.

Performance Assessment

Assess students' understanding of concepts applied to real-world situations.

Performance Assessment (Tasks A–B), PE p. 62; pp. PA3–4

Student Self-Assessment

Have students evaluate their own work.

How Did I Do?, p. AGxvii

A Guide to My Math Portfolio, p. AGxix

Math Journal

See *Write* in the *Assess* section of each TE lesson and TE pages 4B, 24B, 46B.

Harcourt Assessment System

Make and grade chapter tests electronically.

This software includes:

- **multiple-choice items**
- **free-response items**
- **customizable tests**
- **the means to build your own tests from available items**
- **customizable student and class reports**

Portfolio

Portfolio opportunities appear throughout the Pupil and Teacher's Editions.

Suggested work samples:

Problem Solving Project, TE pp. xxvi, 18, 38

Write About It, PE pp. 3, 26, 49, 53

Chapter Review/Test, PE pp. 15, 35, 55

AG Assessment Guide **TE** Teacher's Edition **PA** Performance Assessment **PE** Pupil Edition

Correlation to STANDARDIZED TESTS

	LEARNING GOAL	TAUGHT IN LESSONS	CAT/ TERRA NOVA	CTBS/ TERRA NOVA	ITBS FORM A	MAT 8	STANFORD 10	NORTH CAROLINA STANDARDS
1A	To write addition and subtraction facts by using fact families	1.1	•	•	•	•	•	1.02
1B	To identify and write missing addends	1.2	•	•	•	•	•	1.02
1C	To write sums of 2 or 3 addends by using addition strategies such as the Order, Identity, and Grouping Properties of Addition	1.3	•	•	•	•	•	1.04
1D	To write sums and differences of two-digit numbers with and without regrouping	1.4, 1.5	•	•	•	•	•	1.02
1E	To solve problems by using an appropriate skill such as *choose the operation*	1.6	•	•	•	•	•	1.02
2A	To identify even and odd numbers	2.1	•	•	•	•	•	maintains (2) 1.06
2B	To read, write and identify the value of whole numbers through 9,999	2.2, 2.3	•	•	•	•	•	1.01
2C	To solve problems by using an appropriate strategy such as *use logical reasoning*	2.4	•	•	•	•	•	1.01
2D	To identify, extend, develop, and use number patterns	2.5	•	•	•	•	•	5.01
2E	To read, write and identify the value of whole numbers through 999,999	2.6	•	•	•	•	•	1.01
3A	To compare and order numbers to 999,999 using appropriate strategies	3.1, 3.2, 3.3	•	•	•	•	•	1.01
3B	To solve problems using an appropriate strategy such as *use a bar graph*	3.4	•	•	•	•	•	1.01
3C	To round numbers to the nearest 10, 100, and 1,000	3.5, 3.6	•	•	•	•	•	1.01

Technology Links

Harcourt Mega Math CD-ROM Series

The learning activities in this exciting, new comprehensive math software series complement, enrich, and enhance the Pupil Edition lessons.

Harcourt Mega Math Correlation		
Lesson	**Activity/Level**	**Skill**
1.1	Country Countdown, Counting Critters, Level U	Fact Families
1.2	Ice Station Exploration, Arctic Algebra, Level A	Algebra: Missing Addends
1.4 & 1.5	Country Countdown, Block Busters, Level M and R	2-Digit Addition and Subtraction
2.2 & 2.3	Country Countdown, Block Busters, Level S and T	Place Value • 3- and 4-Digit Numbers
2.5	The Number Games, Tiny's Think Tank, Level I	Number Patterns
2.6	The Number Games, Tiny's Think Tank, Level A; Fraction Action, Number Line Mine, Level A	Place Value • 5- and 6-Digit Numbers
3.2	Country Countdown, Harrison's Comparisons, Levels L and M; Fraction Action, Number Line Mine, Level A	Compare Numbers
3.5 & 3.6	Fraction Action, Number Line Mine, Level C	Round to the Nearest 10, 100, and 1,000

The Harcourt Learning Site

www.harcourtschool.com

Visit THE LEARNING SITE at **www.harcourtschool.com** for a variety of activities and resources that can be used to explore, reinforce, practice, and extend the learning of the chapter.

- Multimedia Math Glossary
- Activities and instructional resources
- E-Lab Activities
- Show Me math models

Intervention CD-ROMs

These CD-ROMs help you

- assess prerequisite concepts and skills for each chapter and assess problem-solving at point of use.
- diagnose to determine whether intervention is necessary or if enrichment is appropriate for a concept or skill.
- diagnose to determine whether intervention is necessary for a specific problem-solving strategy or skill.
- prescribe intervention for concepts, skills, and problem-solving strategies and skills.
- provide enrichment for students who mastered the prerequisite concepts and skills.

For the Student

The following technology can be used with students that need more instruction with skills or problem solving, and with students that will benefit from reinforcement, practice, and extension of skills from this chapter.

Intervention CD-ROMs

- Support and enrichment for prerequisite skills
- Support for problem solving

Harcourt Mega Math CD-ROMs

- Reinforcement, practice and extension

Block Busters
Skill Level T

Harrison's Comparisons
Skill Level M

The Harcourt Learning Site
www.harcourtschool.com

- Multimedia Math Glossary
- E-Lab activities
- Show Me math models
- Games and activities

For the Teacher

Intervention CD-ROMs

- Diagnose and prescribe intervention for prerequisite skills.
- Provide enrichment for prerequisite skills.
- Diagnose and prescribe intervention for problem-solving strategies and skills.

Harcourt Mega Math CD-ROMs

- Customize additional practice for each student in your class.
- The leveled activities increase in difficulty as students progress.

The Harcourt Learning Site
www.harcourtschool.com

- Find activities and other resources.

Harcourt Assessment System

This software includes:

- Online test taking and automatic scoring
- A bank of items from which to build tests
- Immediate feedback on students' performance
- Correlation of items to textbook and state standards
- Comprehensive program management and class reporting
- Prescriptive reports

ePlanner

This on-line resource allows you to:

- Customize planning and pacing.
- Select resources for daily instruction.
- Reorder content to meet your state, district, or local needs.

For the Parent

The Harcourt Learning Site
www.harcourtschool.com

Encourage parents to visit the Math section of the Harcourt Learning Site to help them reinforce mathematics vocabulary, concepts, and skills with their children.

- Multimedia Math Glossary
- E-Lab interactive learning experiences
- Show Me math models
- Family Involvement tips and activities

Cross-Curricular Connections

Use these topics to help integrate mathematics into your daily planning. See the pages indicated to find out more about each topic.

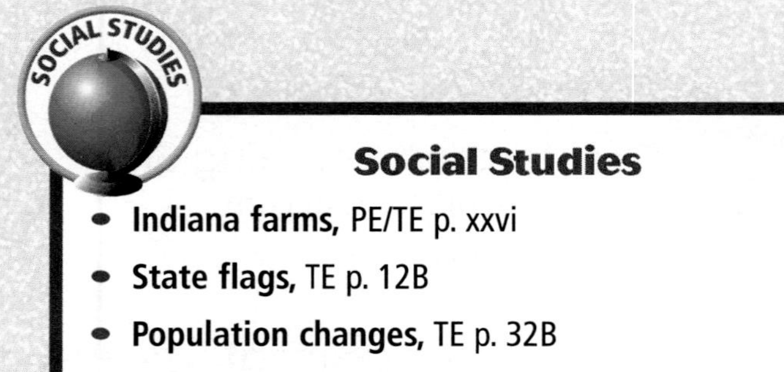

Social Studies

- **Indiana farms,** PE/TE p. xxvi
- **State flags,** TE p. 12B
- **Population changes,** TE p. 32B
- **Great Lakes,** TE/PE p. 38

Literature

- ***Bicycle Race*** by Donald Crews (Greenwillow Books, 1985), TE p. xxviG
- ***Nine for California*** by Sonia Levitin (Orchard Books, 1996), TE p. xxviG

Science

- **Land speeds of animals,** TE p. 10B
- **Livestock care,** PE/TE p. 18
- **Water usage,** TE p. 48B

Writing

- **Explain missing addends,** TE p. 4B
- **Explain place-value magnitudes,** TE p. 24B
- **Compare and contrast,** TE p. 46B

Language Arts/Reading

- **Draw conclusions,** TE p. 12B
- **Cause and effect,** TE p. 28B
- **Write a news story,** TE p. 40B
- **Word map,** TE p. 40B
- **Use graphic aids,** TE p. 48B
- **Semantic map,** TE p. 50B

Reaching All Learners

ACTIVITY WHEEL*

Write the least possible and the greatest possible 3-digit number using the digits 6, 2, and 0.

Describe a situation in which you have seen 3-digit numbers used. Think of places you have been and describe how the numbers were used.

Write a 2- to 4-sentence rhyme that explains how the value of each place-value position increases in a 2-digit number.

Differentiated Instruction

PURPOSE To demonstrate an understanding of place value in 3-digit numbers

USING THE ACTIVITY WHEEL Have each student choose one activity to complete independently. *Use after Lesson 2.2.*

*The Activity Wheel provides each student with a choice, according to learning style, for practicing an important skill.

Check students' work.

PRACTICE GAME

High Number

PURPOSE To compare numbers

MATERIALS *For each group* 0–9 spinner, p. TR70; game cards, p. TR71

ABOUT THE GAME

- Each player spins and records the number indicated on the spinner in the ones place on a game card.

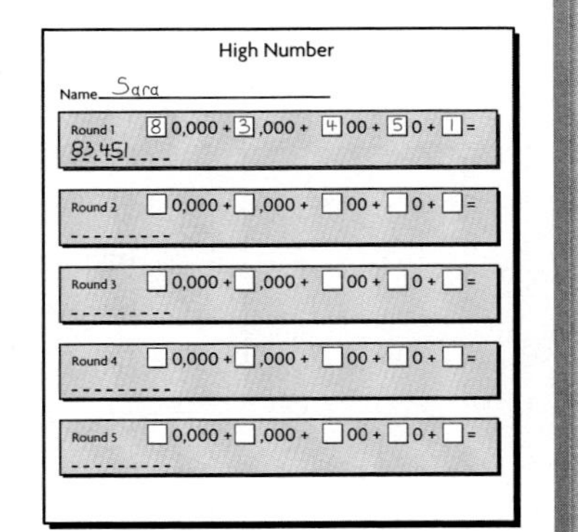
High Number

Name Sara

Round 1 [8]0,000 + [3],000 + [4]00 + [5]0 + [1] = 83,451

Round 2 [ ]0,000 + [ ],000 + [ ]00 + [ ]0 + [ ] =

Round 3 [ ]0,000 + [ ],000 + [ ]00 + [ ]0 + [ ] =

Round 4 [ ]0,000 + [ ],000 + [ ]00 + [ ]0 + [ ] =

Round 5 [ ]0,000 + [ ],000 + [ ]00 + [ ]0 + [ ] =

- Players take turns and continue to spin for numbers. They fill in the tens, hundreds, thousands, and ten-thousands places.
- Players write their numbers.
- The player with the greatest number wins the round and scores 1 point.
- The player with the greatest number of points after 5 rounds wins the game. *Use with Lesson 2.6.*

VISUAL; VISUAL/SPATIAL

Literature Connections

These books provide students with additional ways to explore ordinal numbers and addition.

Bicycle Race by Donald Crews (Greenwillow Books, 1985) is an exciting book that provides the perfect setting for a discussion about number position and ordinal numbers.

- Have students change the cardinal numbers to ordinal numbers as the race progresses and the order of the racers changes. *Use with Lesson 3.3.*

Nine for California by Sonia Levitin (Orchard Books, 1996) is an entertaining book in which many exciting events happen to Amanda and her family as they travel from Missouri to California to join their father.

- Have students add the items mama pulls from her sack. *Use with Lesson 1.4.*

Getting Ready: Addition and Subtraction Concepts

NCTM Standards 2000

1. Number and Operations
Lessons 1.1, 1.2, 1.3, 1.4, 1.5, 1.6
2. Algebra
Lessons 1.1, 1.2, 1.3, 1.6
3. Geometry
4. Measurement
5. Data Analysis and Probability
6. Problem Solving
Lessons 1.1, 1.2, 1.3, 1.4, 1.5, 1.6
7. Reasoning and Proof
Lessons 1.1, 1.2, 1.3, 1.5, 1.6
8. Communication
Lessons 1.1, 1.2, 1.3, 1.4, 1.5, 1.6
9. Connections
Lessons 1.2, 1.3, 1.4, 1.5, 1.6
10. Representation
Lessons 1.2, 1.3

Chapter Planner

Getting Ready for Chapter 1 • Assessing Prior Knowledge and INTERVENTION (See PE and TE page 1.)

LESSON	NORTH CAROLINA STANDARDS	PACING	VOCABULARY*	MATERIALS	RESOURCES AND TECHNOLOGY
1.1 Algebra: Fact Families pp. 2–3 **Objective** To identify and write related addition and subtraction facts	1.02c *also* 1.02a	1 Day	addend **fact family** **inverse operations**		Reteach, Practice, Problem Solving, Challenge 1.1 Transparency 1.1 **Intervention,** *Skills 5–7, 12–13* (CD or Book) **Harcourt Mega Math Country Countdown,** *Counting Critters*
1.2 Algebra: Missing Addends pp. 4–5 **Objective** To solve number sentences for missing addends	1.02a *also* 5.04, 1.02c	1 Day			Reteach, Practice, Problem Solving, Challenge 1.2 Transparency 1.2 **Intervention,** *Skills 5–7, 12–13* (CD or Book) **Harcourt Mega Math Ice Station Exploration,** *Arctic Algebra*
1.3 Algebra: Properties pp. 6–7 **Objective** To use properties of addition	1.04 *also* 1.02a, 1.06	1 Day	**Order Property of Addition** **Identity Property of Addition** **Grouping Property of Addition**		Reteach, Practice, Problem Solving, Challenge 1.3 Transparency 1.3 Scaffolded Instruction Transparency 1 **Intervention,** *Skills 5–7, 12–13* (CD or Book)
1.4 Two-Digit Addition pp. 8–9 **Objective** To add 2-digit numbers with and without regrouping	1.02a	1 Day			Reteach, Practice, Problem Solving, Challenge 1.4 Transparency 1.4 **Intervention,** *Skills 5–7* (CD or Book) **Harcourt Mega Math Country Countdown,** *Block Busters*
1.5 Two-Digit Subtraction pp. 10–11 **Objective** To subtract 2-digit numbers with and without regrouping	1.02a	1 Day			Reteach, Practice, Problem Solving, Challenge 1.5 Transparency 1.5 **Intervention,** *Skills 5–7, 12–13* (CD or Book) **Harcourt Mega Math Country Countdown,** *Block Busters*
1.6 Problem Solving Skill: Choose the Operation pp. 12–13 **Objective** To use the problem solving skill *choose the operation*	1.02a *also* 1.06	1 Day			Reteach, Practice, Reading Strategy, Challenge 1.6 Transparency 1.6 **Intervention • Problem Solving,** *Strategy/Skill 1* (CD or Book) Reading Transparency 1

Ending Chapter 1 • Extra Practice, p. 14 **• Chapter 1 Review/Test,** p. 15 **• Getting Ready for the EOG Test,** pp. 16–17

* **Boldfaced** terms are the key mathematical terms for the chapter. Other terms are review vocabulary.

Vocabulary Power

Review Vocabulary

To be ready for Chapter 1, students should know the following vocabulary term:

- **addend** (p. 1)—one of the numbers being added in an addition problem

Vocabulary Cards

Have students use the Vocabulary Cards on *Teacher's Resource Book* page TR141 for the key terms in the chapter. The cards can be added to a file of mathematics terms.

fact family

Develop Key Chapter Vocabulary

The **boldfaced** words are the key vocabulary terms in the chapter.

- **fact family** (p. 2)—a set of related addition and subtraction sentences
- **inverse operations** (p. 2)—operations that undo each other
- **Order Property of Addition** (p. 6)—two numbers can be added in any order and the sum is the same
- **Identity Property of Addition** (p. 6)—when adding zero to a number, the sum is that number
- **Grouping Property of Addition** (p. 6)—grouping addends in different ways does not change the sum

Multimedia Math Glossary

For vocabulary support, visit **www.harcourtschool.com/mathglossary**

Math Journal

Have students define the key vocabulary terms: *fact family, inverse operations, Order Property of Addition, Identity Property of Addition,* and *Grouping Property of Addition.* Have students use their own words and give an example of each.

MATH Word Work

Objective To reinforce vocabulary concepts
Use after Lesson 1.3.

Materials *For each student* counters, paper, colored pencils

Review the *Order Property of Addition*, the *Identity Property of Addition*, and the *Grouping Property of Addition.* Have students use counters to model each of the addition properties with at least one example. Ask students to explain each of the properties in their own words using their models. Have students draw their models and describe each property in writing. Discuss how the properties are similar and how they are different.

Order Property of Addition

You can add 2 numbers in any order and the sum will be the same.

Getting Ready: Addition and Subtraction Concepts

Mathematics Across the Grades

LOOKING BACK • Prerequisite Skills

To be ready for Chapter 1, students should have the following understandings and skills:

- **Addition Facts**—have ready knowledge and use of basic addition facts
- **Subtraction Facts**—have ready knowledge and use of basic subtraction facts

Check What You Know

Use page 1 to determine students' knowledge of prerequisite concepts and skills.

Intervention

Help students prepare for the chapter by using the intervention resources described on TE p. 1.

LOOKING AT CHAPTER 1 • Essential Skills

Students will

- relate addition and subtraction through the use of fact families.
- apply the concepts of inverse operations and fact families to solve number sentences with missing addends.
- use properties of addition to solve number sentences.
- **add and subtract two-digit numbers with and without regrouping.**
- name relationships between quantities in story problems in order to choose the correct operation to solve the problem.

Example

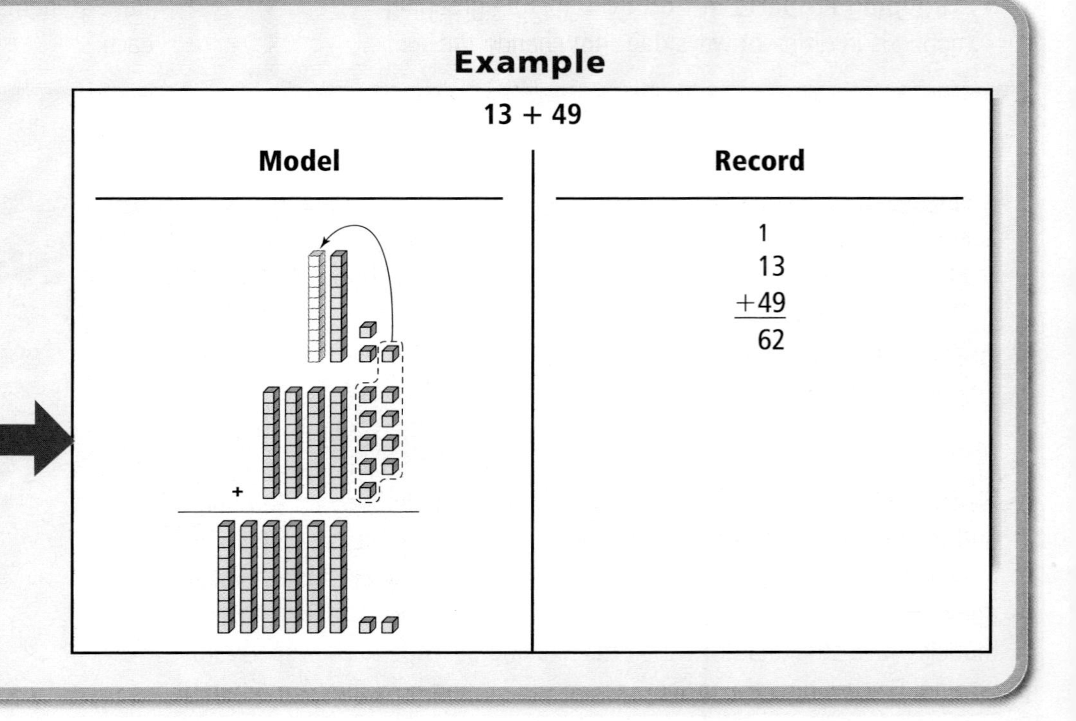

LOOKING AHEAD • Applications

Students will apply what they learn in Chapter 1 to the following new concepts:

- Solving multidigit addition problems (Chapter 4)
- Solving multidigit subtraction problems (Chapter 5)
- Connect addition and multiplication (Chapter 8)
- Subtraction and Division (Chapter 12)

Differentiated Instruction

Meeting the Needs of All Learners

Extra Support	Activities for All	Enrichment
Alternative Teaching Strategy TE Lessons 1.1, 1.2, 1.3, 1.4, 1.5, 1.6 **ESOL/ESL** TE Lessons 1.1, 1.2, 1.3, 1.4, 1.5, 1.6 **Special Needs** TE Lessons 1.1, 1.4, 1.5	**Cross-Curricular Connections** **Reading:** TE/PE Lesson 1.6 **Science:** TE/PE Lesson 1.5 **Social Studies:** PE Lesson 1.2, TE/PE Lesson 1.6 **Vocabulary:** TE p. xxviI, PE/TE p. 1 **Writing:** TE Lesson 1.2	**Advanced Learners** TE Lessons 1.2, 1.3 **Early Finishers** TE Lessons 1.1, 1.4

Combination and Multi-age Classrooms

Grade 2	Grade 3	Grade 4
Skills Trace Across the Grades		
Use strategies to learn basic addition and subtraction facts; use inverse operations and fact families to relate addition and subtraction; identify missing numbers by using addition and subtraction; find sums and differences of 1- and 2-digit numbers.	**Write addition and subtraction facts by using fact families; identify and write missing addends; write sums of 2- and 3-digit addends by using addition strategies; write sums and differences of 2-digit numbers with and without regrouping.**	Use addition properties to add; estimate sums and differences; write sums and differences of whole numbers up to 4-digits; write and interpret addition and subtraction equations; subtract across zeros.
Instructional Strategies		
Students on this level may require more time to build conceptual understanding. **Assignments** **Grade 3 Pupil Edition** • Skip Lesson 1.2. • Have students work in pairs on Lessons 1.4 and 1.5. **Grade 2 Pupil Edition**—pages 65–78, 81–96, 105–118, 121–138, 141–154, 157–174, 177–194	Students on this level should be able to complete all the lessons in the Pupil Edition and all the activities in the Teacher's Edition with minimal adjustments. **Assignment** **Grade 3 Pupil Edition**—pages 1–15	Students on this level will probably require less time to build conceptual understanding. **Assignments** **Grade 3 Pupil Edition** • Compact Lessons 1.1 and 1.2. • Compact Lessons 1.4 and 1.5. **Grade 4 Pupil Edition**—pages 38–59, 62–83

CHAPTER 1

Getting Ready: Addition and Subtraction Concepts

Introducing the Chapter

Explain that basic addition and subtraction facts form the foundation of operations students will learn. Have students use mental math to find out how many more goats and chickens there are than cows. 7 more goats and chickens

Using Data

To begin the study of this chapter, have students

- Find the three numbers in the pictograph whose ones digits total 10. 3, 5, and 12
- Describe 3 ways you can group the numbers of animals to find how many there are in all. Possible answers: $3 + 5 = 8$, $8 + 12 = 20$, $20 + 10 = 30$; $3 + 10 = 13$, $13 + 5 = 18$, $18 + 12 = 30$; $10 + 5 = 15$, $15 + 12 = 27$, $27 + 3 = 30$

Problem Solving Project

Purpose To use addition and subtraction fact families to express relationships in a pictograph

Grouping pairs

Background Indiana ranks 15th in the United States in the number of dairy cows.

UNDERSTAND • PLAN • SOLVE • CHECK

Have students

- Make a pictograph to show their classmates' favorite dairy foods.
- Have one student write an addition word problem using the information in the pictograph.
- Then have the partner write a subtraction problem using the same numbers. The result will be a set of word problems using a fact family.

Graphing Investigations
Begin Week 1.

CHAPTER 1

Getting Ready: Addition and Subtraction Concepts

FAST FACT • SOCIAL STUDIES
The state of Indiana has about 63,000 farms. Some of these farms are dairy farms with cows like this Holstein cow. The Holstein is the largest type of dairy cow.

PROBLEM SOLVING **The pictograph shows the number of animals on one Indiana farm. How many animals are there in all?**

ANIMALS ON AN INDIANA FARM

Sheep	
Cows	
Goats	
Chickens	

Key: Each (symbol) = 2 animals.

30 animals

WHY LEARN MATH? Farmers use math to determine how much food to buy for their animals. Ask: If 1 chicken eats 4 ounces of feed each day, how much feed will 2 chickens eat in 7 days? Explain. 56 ounces; $4 + 4 + 4 + 4 + 4 + 4 + 4 = 28$ ounces; $28 + 28 = 56$ ounces of feed

Family Involvement Activities

These activities provide:

- Letter to the Family
- Math Vocabulary
- Family Game
- Practice (Homework)

Family Involvement Activities, p. FA1

HARCOURT MATH
GRADE 3
Chapter 1
WHAT WE ARE LEARNING
Addition and Subtraction Concepts

VOCABULARY
Here are the vocabulary words we use in class:
Fact family A set of related addition and subtraction number sentences that use the same numbers
Inverse operations Opposite operations, such as addition and subtraction
Order Property of Addition A property that states that you can add two or more numbers in any order and get the same sum
Identity Property of Addition A property that states that when you add zero to a number, the sum is that number
Grouping Property of Addition A property that states that you can group addends in different ways and still get the same sum

Name
Date

Dear Family,

Your child is learning important concepts about addition and subtraction.

First, your child is learning about how related facts make up a fact family. Number sentences in a fact family use the same numbers. In this example, each number sentence uses the numbers 5, 7, and 12.

$5 + 7 = 12$ $12 - 5 = 7$
$7 + 5 = 12$ $12 - 7 = 5$

Your child can use related facts to solve problems. For example, your child can use the related addition fact, $7 + \blacksquare = 12$, to find the answer to $12 - 7 = \blacksquare$.

Properties help your child solve problems and simplify computation. The Order Property involves the order of two numbers. If your child knows the sum of 9 and 2, then your child knows the sum of 2 and 9.

The Grouping Property involves three or more numbers. Your child can group numbers together to find easy-to-add subtotals.

$5 + 7 + 3 + 5 = (5 + 5) + (7 + 3) = 10 + 10$

Finally, your child adds and subtracts two-digit numbers, regrouping when necessary.

$59 + 73 = 132$ $63 - 4 = 59$

To check the subtraction, your child can use the inverse operation, addition. $59 + 4 = 63$

Use the examples above and the pages that follow to talk about and practice addition and subtraction. Doing math with you is one way your child gains confidence and understanding. Enjoy your time together!

Sincerely,

Family Involvement Activities FA1

CHECK WHAT YOU KNOW

Use this page to help you review and remember important skills needed for Chapter 1.

ADDITION FACTS

Find the sum.

1. 8 + 2 = 10
2. 7 + 3 = 10
3. 1 + 6 = 7
4. 6 + 5 = 11
5. 3 + 4 = 7
6. 7 + 7 = 14
7. 4 + 8 = 12
8. 9 + 5 = 14
9. 8 + 6 = 14
10. 8 + 9 = 17
11. 5 + 4 = 9
12. 3 + 6 = 9
13. 4 + 7 = 11
14. 8 + 1 = 9
15. 6 + 7 = 13

SUBTRACTION FACTS

Find the difference.

16. 7 − 2 = 5
17. 9 − 3 = 6
18. 8 − 1 = 7
19. 10 − 5 = 5
20. 9 − 6 = 3
21. 12 − 7 = 5
22. 13 − 5 = 8
23. 11 − 5 = 6
24. 14 − 6 = 8
25. 15 − 8 = 7

VOCABULARY POWER

REVIEW

addend [a'dend] *noun*

Addend comes from the Latin word *addendum*. By the end of the 1600s, *addends* meant all the numbers being added. In the number sentence 8 + 5 = 13, what numbers are the addends? 8, 5

PREVIEW

fact family
inverse operations
Order Property of Addition
Identity Property of Addition
Grouping Property of Addition

GO ON-LINE www.harcourtschool.com/mathglossary

Assessing Prior Knowledge

Use the **Check What You Know** page to determine whether your students have mastered the prerequisite skills critical for this chapter.

Intervention

- **Diagnose and Prescribe**
  Evaluate your students' performance on this page to determine whether intervention is necessary or if enrichment is appropriate. Options that provide instruction, practice, and a check are listed in the chart below.

CHECK WHAT YOU KNOW RESOURCES

Intervention Copying Masters or CD-ROMs

Enrichment Copying Masters

VOCABULARY POWER

For activities and information about the vocabulary in this chapter, see page xxviI.

Were students successful with CHECK WHAT YOU KNOW?

IF . . . NO THEN . . . INTERVENE — INTERVENTION OPTIONS — IF . . . YES THEN . . . ENRICH

Skill/Items	Missed more than	Intervene with
Addition Facts, 1–15	4	• *Intervention*, Skills 5, 6, 7
Subtraction Facts, 16–25	3	• *Intervention*, Skills 12, 13

Skill/Items	Missed fewer than	Enrich with
Addition Facts, 1–15	5	• *Intervention*, Enrichment p. IN329
Subtraction Facts, 16–25	4	• *Intervention*, Enrichment p. IN330

Lesson 1.1

Algebra: Fact Families

Lesson Planning

Objective To identify and write related addition and subtraction facts

NCTM Standards

1. Number and Operations
2. Algebra
6. Problem Solving
7. Reasoning and Proof
8. Communication

Math Background

These ideas will help students understand related addition and subtraction facts.

- Two numbers and their sum can be used to make four related number sentences.
- All four related number sentences are called a fact family.
- A fact family uses the inverse operations of addition and subtraction.

Vocabulary

fact family a set of related addition and subtraction number sentences that use the same numbers

inverse operations operations that undo each other, such as addition and subtraction

Warm-Up Resources

Build Number Sense

Number of the Day

Transparency 1.1

The number of the day is the number of days in a week. Write a number sentence using that number. Possible answer: $7 + 4 = 11$

Daily Facts Practice

Have students practice addition facts by completing Set A of *Teacher's Resource Book*, p. TR83.

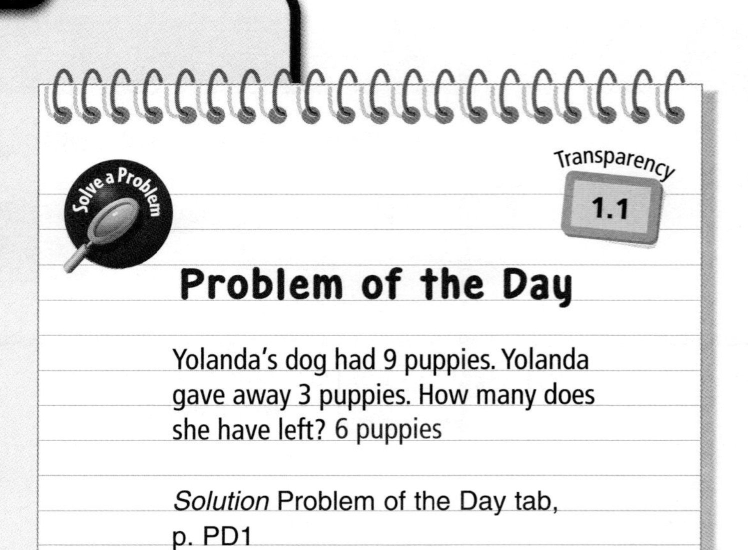

Problem of the Day

Yolanda's dog had 9 puppies. Yolanda gave away 3 puppies. How many does she have left? 6 puppies

Solution Problem of the Day tab, p. PD1

Intervention and Extension Resources

Alternative Teaching Strategy

ESOL/ESL

MATERIALS *For each group* dominoes, paper

Use dominoes to help students **understand fact families.** Explain that all 3 numbers of a fact family are contained on one domino: one number is on the left, one number is on the right, and the third number is the sum of the two numbers.

Have students take turns picking up a domino, naming the three numbers, and then writing the related addition and subtraction sentences. Check students' work.

KINESTHETIC

VERBAL/LINGUISTIC; LOGICAL/MATHEMATICAL

Multistep and Strategy Problems

The following multistep or strategy problem is provided in Lesson 1.1:

Page	Item
3	21

Special Needs

MATERIALS *For each group* base-ten unit blocks, paper

Have students **model fact families.** Give each group of students two different numbers such as 3 and 4. Have one student model the two addition sentences with base-ten blocks.

Have another student record the number sentences. Then have the first student model the two related subtraction sentences. Ask the second student to record the number sentences.

KINESTHETIC

LOGICAL/MATHEMATICAL

Early Finishers

MATERIALS *For each pair* index cards, counters

Help students **review fact families** by playing a game. Have students take turns. The student who plays first writes one addition or subtraction sentence on an index card. The second student writes the 3 related number sentences on another index card. Students earn one counter for each correct sentence. For an incorrect sentence, students lose one counter. The first student to earn 20 counters wins the game.

VISUAL

VERBAL/LINGUISTIC; LOGICAL/MATHEMATICAL

Technology Link

Intervention, *Skills 5–7, 12–13*

The Harcourt Learning Site www.harcourtschool.com

Harcourt Mega Math Country Countdown, *Counting Critters,* Level U

Lesson 1.1 Organizer

Objective To identify and write related addition and subtraction facts

Vocabulary fact family, inverse operations

1 INTRODUCE

QUICK REVIEW provides review of prerequisite skills.

WHY LEARN THIS? Knowing fact families helps you understand the relationship between addition and subtraction. *Share the lesson objective with students.*

2 TEACH

Guided Instruction

- *Have students read the Learn section.*
  Why do you skip-count by twos to find the number of ducks and chickens? The key shows that each tractor equals 2 animals.
  Why do you think the graph was made with the tractor symbol standing for 2 animals instead of 1 animal? Possible answer: so there would be fewer symbols to count.
  REASONING Why aren't there always four number sentences in a fact family? Give an example. If 2 of the numbers are the same, there are only 2 number sentences; $8 + 8 = 16$, $16 - 8 = 8$.
  MODIFYING INSTRUCTION Have students model the problem with counters. Give 14 counters to each student. Ask a volunteer to demonstrate the fact families for the class.
- *Direct students' attention to the Math Idea.*
  REASONING How can the word *reverse* help you remember the word *inverse*? *Reverse* can mean "to move in the opposite direction." Inverse means "the opposite operation."

LESSON 1

Algebra: Fact Families

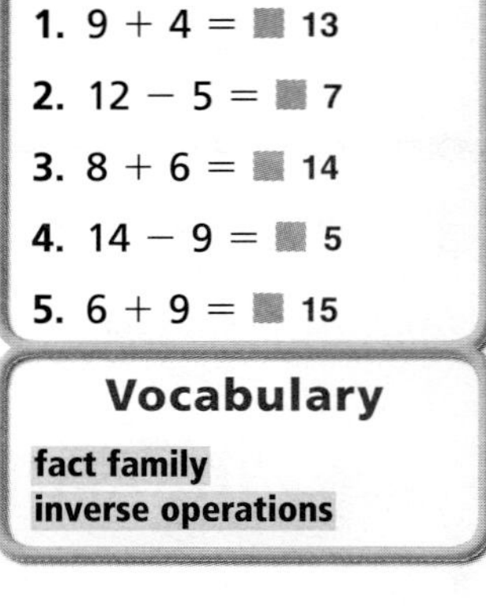
Quick Review
1. 9 + 4 = ■ 13
2. 12 − 5 = ■ 7
3. 8 + 6 = ■ 14
4. 14 − 9 = ■ 5
5. 6 + 9 = ■ 15

Vocabulary
fact family
inverse operations

Learn

FARM ANIMALS The pictograph shows some of the animals on Brittany's farm.

ANIMALS ON BRITTANY'S FARM	
Chickens	🚜 🚜 🚜
Cows	🚜 🚜 🚜 🚜 🚜
Ducks	🚜 🚜 🚜 🚜
Sheep	🚜 🚜 🚜
Key: Each 🚜 = 2 animals.	

How many ducks and chickens are there?

Look at the pictograph. Find the symbols for ducks. Then skip-count by twos. There are 8 ducks. Now skip-count the symbols for chickens. There are 6 chickens.

$$8 + 6 = 14 \text{ or } 6 + 8 = 14$$

So, there are 14 ducks and chickens in all.

The numbers 6, 8, and 14 can be used to make a fact family. A **fact family** is a set of related addition and subtraction number sentences that use the same numbers.

$8 + 6 = 14$ $\quad$ $6 + 8 = 14$

$14 - 6 = 8$ $\quad$ $14 - 8 = 6$

Technology Link
More Practice:
Harcourt Mega Math
Country Countdown,
Counting Critters,
Level U

- Write another fact family that uses the number 8.
  Possible answer: 8 + 4 = 12, 4 + 8 = 12, 12 – 4 = 8, 12 – 8 = 4
- What is the fact family for 6, 6, and 12? Why are there only two facts?
  6 + 6 = 12, 12 – 6 = 6; because both addends are the same

MATH IDEA Addition and subtraction are opposite or **inverse operations**. Fact families are examples of inverse operations.

$5 + 7 = 12$ $\quad$ $7 + 5 = 12$

$12 - 7 = 5$ $\quad$ $12 - 5 = 7$

2

Reteach 1.1

Algebra: Fact Families

Use addition and subtraction to tell about the fruit in different ways.

Use addition to tell how many pieces of fruit there are in all.
Add bananas to apples. $5 + 8 = 13$ pieces of fruit
Add apples to bananas. $8 + 5 = 13$ pieces of fruit

Use subtraction to tell the number of each kind of fruit.
There are 13 pieces of fruit in all.
Subtract apples to tell about bananas. $13 - 5 = 8$ bananas
Subtract bananas to tell about apples. $13 - 8 = 5$ apples

The same numbers are used in all the facts. These related addition and subtraction facts are called a **fact family**.

Write the fact family for each group. The first two have been started for you.

1. $3 + 8 = 11$; $8 + 3 = 11$; $11 - 3 = 8$; $11 - 8 = 3$
2. $9 + 8 = 17$; $8 + 9 = 17$; $17 - 8 = 9$; $17 - 9 = 8$
3. $6 + 8 = 14$; $8 + 6 = 14$; $14 - 6 = 8$; $14 - 8 = 6$
4. $4 + 9 = 13$; $9 + 4 = 13$; $13 - 4 = 9$; $13 - 9 = 4$

Reteach RW1

Practice 1.1

Algebra: Fact Families

Complete.

1. $7 + 4 = 11$, so $11 - 7 =$ 4
2. $16 - 7 = 9$, so $9 +$ 7 $= 16$
3. $6 + 8 = 14$, so $14 -$ 8 $= 6$
4. $12 - 6 = 6$, so 6 $+ 6 = 12$
5. $15 - 9 = 6$, so 6 + 9 $= 15$ (or 9 and 6)
6. $7 + 7 = 14$, so $14 -$ 7 $=$ 7

Write the fact family for each set of numbers.

7. 6, 7, 13: $6 + 7 = 13$; $7 + 6 = 13$; $13 - 6 = 7$; $13 - 7 = 6$
8. 9, 9, 18: $9 + 9 = 18$; $18 - 9 = 9$
9. 3, 9, 12: $3 + 9 = 12$; $9 + 3 = 12$; $12 - 3 = 9$; $12 - 9 = 3$
10. 7, 8, 15: $7 + 8 = 15$; $8 + 7 = 15$; $15 - 7 = 8$; $15 - 8 = 7$

Mixed Review

Add or subtract.

11. $4 + 7 =$ 11
12. $14 - 7 =$ 7
13. $11 - 3 =$ 8
14. $7 + 9 =$ 16
15. $10 - 3 =$ 7
16. $9 + 5 =$ 14
17. $12 - 4 =$ 8
18. $5 + 6 =$ 11
19. $15 - 6 =$ 9
20. $17 - 8 =$ 9
21. $8 + 7 =$ 15
22. $6 + 4 =$ 10

Practice PW1

Check

1. Explain why 7, 9, and 16 can be used to make a fact family.
   Possible answer: Since two addition and two subtraction sentences can be made using 7, 9, and 16, the numbers make a fact family.

Complete.

2. 6 + 7 = 13, so 13 − ■ = 7. 6
3. 15 − 7 = 8, so ■ + ■ = 15. 7, 8 or 8, 7

Write the fact family for each set of numbers.

4. 4, 7, 11 — 4 + 7 = 11, 7 + 4 = 11, 11 − 4 = 7, 11 − 7 = 4
5. 7, 7, 14 — 7 + 7 = 14, 14 − 7 = 7
6. 5, 9, 14 — 5 + 9 = 14, 9 + 5 = 14, 14 − 5 = 9, 14 − 9 = 5
7. 6, 9, 15 — 6 + 9 = 15, 9 + 6 = 15, 15 − 6 = 9, 15 − 9 = 6

Practice and Problem Solving

Extra Practice, page 14, Set A

18. Possible problem: David has 9 superhero comic books, and his brother Daniel has 3. How many superhero comic books do the brothers have in all? 9 + 3 = 12

Complete.

8. 5 + 8 = 13, so 13 − 5 = ■. 8
9. 16 − 8 = 8, so 8 + ■ = 16. 8
10. 12 − 8 = 4, so ■ + 8 = 12. 4
11. 4 + 9 = 13, so 13 − ■ = 9. 4
12. 9 + 9 = 18, so 18 − ■ = ■. 9, 9
13. 17 − 9 = 8, so ■ + ■ = 17. 8, 9 or 9, 8

14. 5 + 6 = 11, 6 + 5 = 11, 11 − 5 = 6, 11 − 6 = 5
16. 7 + 9 = 16, 9 + 7 = 16, 16 − 7 = 9, 16 − 9 = 7
17. 5 + 7 = 12, 7 + 5 = 12, 12 − 5 = 7, 12 − 7 = 5

Write the fact family for each set of numbers.

14. 5, 6, 11 See above.
15. 8, 8, 16 8 + 8 = 16, 16 − 8 = 8
16. 7, 9, 16 See above.
17. 5, 7, 12 See above.
18. **Write a problem** using the number sentence 9 + 3 = 12. See above.
19. **Write About It** Write two fact families using the number 7. See below.
20. **Vocabulary Power** Left is the opposite of right. Addition and subtraction are opposite operations. What other math words do you know that are opposites? Possible responses: even and odd, greater than and less than
21. Jared had 6 red marbles, 7 blue marbles, and 3 green marbles. He lost 4 blue marbles. How many marbles does Jared have now? 12 marbles

19. Possible answer: 7 + 5 = 12, 5 + 7 = 12, 12 − 5 = 7, 12 − 7 = 5; 7 + 8 = 15, 8 + 7 = 15, 15 − 7 = 8, 15 − 8 = 7

Getting Ready for the EOG Test

22. Alex has 8 fish in his fish tank. He buys 3 more fish. How many fish does he have in all? A

    A 11 C 8
    B 10 D 5

23. Jennifer found 7 shells at the beach. Then she found 6 more shells. How many shells does Jennifer have in all? C

    A 11 C 13
    B 12 D 14

North Carolina Standards 1.02 Develop fluency with multi-digit addition and subtraction ough 9,999 using: c) Relationships between operations. *also* 1.02a

Challenge 1.1

Fact Family Search

Find the fact family in each square.
The number above each square is the greatest number in the fact family.
You will find facts across and down. Not all numbers are a part of each fact family.
Write +, −, and = signs between the numbers.
The first one has been done for you.

12

6		8	+	4	=	12
				+		−
12	−	4	=	8		8
				=		=
6		4		12		4
8		12		10		2

17

8		17	−	8	=	9
+						+
9		10		7		8
=						=
17	−	9	=	8		17
8		7		15		9

14

5		9		5		4
		+		+		
14	−	5	=	9		5
−		=		=		
9		14		14		9
=						
5		7		7		4

13

6		13		7		3
		−				
7		6	+	7	=	13
+		=				−
6		7		10		7
=						=
13		7		3		6

16

7		7	+	9	=	16
9		16		6		10
+		−				
7		9		7		4
=		=				
16	−	7	=	9		6

15

15		7		7		15
−						−
7	+	8	=	15		8
=						=
8	+	7	=	15		7
5		10		8		1

Make up your own fact family search. Give it to another student to solve.

Challenge CW1

Problem Solving 1.1

Algebra: Fact Families Understand → Plan → Solve → Check

Write the correct answer.

1. What number sentence is missing from this fact family?
   4 + 8 = 12   12 − 8 = 4
   8 + 4 = 12
   12 − 4 = 8
2. Kathleen has 5 birds, 7 fish, and 3 dogs. How many pets does she have in all?
   15 pets
3. Sonya wrote only two number sentences in the fact family for 5, 5, and 10. Why?
   There are only two different numbers.
4. What is the missing number?
   7 + 6 = 13, so 13 − _?_ = 6
   7

Choose the letter of the correct answer.

5. Which number sentence does **not** belong in the fact family for 6, 9, and 15?
   A 15 − 9 = 6
   (B) 6 + 3 = 9
   C 9 + 6 = 15
   D 15 − 6 = 9
6. Aaron caught 14 fish. He threw 6 back. Which number sentence shows how many fish Aaron kept?
   F 14 − 6 = 7
   G 14 − 8 = 6
   (H) 14 − 6 = 8
   J 14 + 6 = 20
7. The lockers in the hallway are numbered 102, 104, and 106. What should the next locker be numbered?
   A 105 (C) 108
   B 107 D 110
8. Which number is missing in the pattern 9, 12, 15, _?_, 21, 24, 27?
   (F) 18 H 20
   G 19 J 21
9. **Write About It** In Problem 5, how did you decide which number sentence did not belong?
   Possible answer: The number sentence 6 + 3 = 9 contains 6 and 9, but not 15.

Problem Solving PS1

3 PRACTICE

Guided Practice

Do Check Exercises 1–7 with your students. Identify students who are having difficulty and choose appropriate lesson resources to provide assistance.

Independent Practice

Note that Exercise 21 is a **multistep or strategy problem.** Assign Exercises 8–21.

Vocabulary Power In math, an operation involves a change in a quantity. In addition, 2 or more numbers are joined. In subtraction, 2 numbers are separated.

Summarize the lesson by having students:

Discuss Explain why 4, 5, and 10 cannot be used to make a fact family. How could you change one number so that you could write a fact family? The numbers do not make a fact family because the sum of 4 and 5 is 9, not 10. You could change the 5 to a 6. 4 + 6 = 10 is one number sentence in a fact family.

Write Write a problem using the number sentence 7 + 8 = 15 and the inverse, 15 − 7 = 8. Answers will vary.

LESSON QUIZ Transparency 1.1

Write the fact family for each set of numbers.

1. 6, 7, 13 6 + 7 = 13; 7 + 6 = 13; 13 − 6 = 7; 13 − 7 = 6
2. 4, 8, 12 4 + 8 = 12; 8 + 4 = 12; 12 − 8 = 4; 12 − 4 = 8

Complete.

3. 9 + 4 = 13, so 13 − 4 = ■ 9
4. 9 + 8 = 17, so 17 − 8 = ■ 9

Lesson 1.2

Algebra: Missing Addends

Lesson Planning

Objective To solve number sentences for missing addends

NCTM Standards

1. Number and Operations
2. Algebra
6. Problem Solving
7. Reasoning and Proof
8. Communication
9. Connections
10. Representation

Math Background

These ideas will help students understand how to find missing addends.

- You can find a missing addend by using an addition basic fact.
- You can also find missing addends by using related subtraction facts.
- Knowing fact families can help you solve for missing addends.

Warm-Up Resources

Build Number Sense

Number of the Day

The number of the day is the number of toes on two feet. Using the addends 1–9, write 5 number sentences whose sums are the number of the day. $1 + 9 = 10, 2 + 8 = 10, 3 + 7 = 10, 4 + 6 = 10, 5 + 5 = 10$

Review Basic Facts

Daily Facts Practice

Have students practice addition facts by completing Set B of *Teacher's Resource Book*, p. TR83.

Solve a Problem

Problem of the Day

Evan had 20 cents. Then he borrowed a dime from his sister and a nickel from his brother. How much money does he have now? 35 cents

Solution Problem of the Day tab, p. PD1

Intervention and Extension Resources

Alternative Teaching Strategy

MATERIALS *For each pair* 34 counters

Help students **find missing addends** by modeling number sentences with counters. Have one student in each pair place 17 counters on the desk to represent the sum. Then have the student count and place a lesser quantity of counters to the left of the 17 counters. Ask: How many counters do you need to add to make a total of 17? Answers will vary. Students should be encouraged to count on to find the missing addend and record the addition sentence. Next have the partner place 17 counters on the desk. Then have that student remove the same number of counters as the first student used. Ask: How many counters are left? Answers will vary but should match the first answer. Have the student record the subtraction sentence. Remind students that the addition and subtraction sentences demonstrate inverse operations.

KINESTHETIC

LOGICAL/MATHEMATICAL

Multistep and Strategy Problems

The following multistep or strategy problem is provided in Lesson 1.2:

Page	Item
5	20

Writing in Mathematics

Help students **reinforce their understanding of missing addends** by having them write a problem like the one on page 4. Have students explain how to solve the problem by using an addition fact and by using a related subtraction fact. Check students' work.

VISUAL

LOGICAL/MATHEMATICAL

Advanced Learners

Provide students with a few extended missing addend problems. Explain that they are solved exactly the same way as the missing addend problems that use basic facts.

$30 + ■ = 50$ 20 $\quad$ $10 + ■ = 100$ 90

$40 + ■ = 60$ 20 $\quad$ $20 + ■ = 70$ 50

$50 + ■ = 80$ 30 $\quad$ $60 + ■ = 90$ 30

VISUAL

LOGICAL/MATHEMATICAL

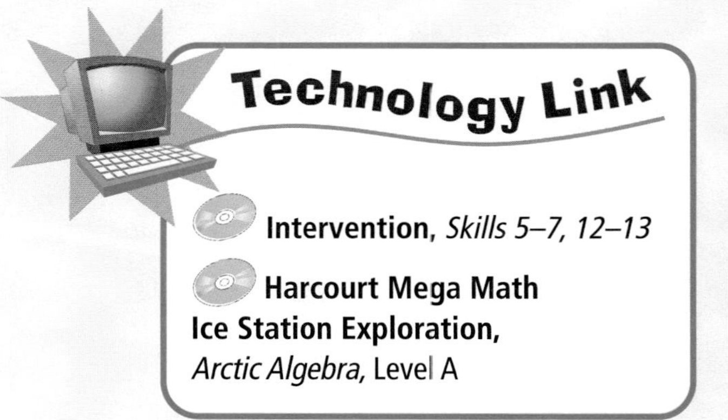

Technology Link

Intervention, *Skills 5–7, 12–13*

Harcourt Mega Math Ice Station Exploration, *Arctic Algebra,* Level A

Lesson 1.2 Organizer

Objective To solve number sentences for missing addends

1 INTRODUCE

QUICK REVIEW provides review of prerequisite skills.

WHY LEARN THIS? Gaining confidence with basic addition and subtraction facts, including finding missing addends, will help build number sense. *Share the lesson objective with students.*

2 TEACH

Guided Instruction

- *Direct students' attention to One Way.*
  REASONING What addition strategy could you use to help you find the missing addend? You could count up or count on to 14.
  If you don't want to count up or count on, how else could you find the answer? Possible answer: You can think, "What number added to 9 equals 14?"
- *Direct students' attention to Another Way.*
  REASONING How can knowing about fact families help you with this method? If you know one fact, you also know three related facts.
  Why is the answer the same in One Way as in Another Way? The numbers 5, 9, and 14 make a fact family.

LESSON 2

Algebra: Missing Addends

Quick Review

1. $5 + 6 = \blacksquare$ 11
2. $7 + 8 = \blacksquare$ 15
3. $6 + 9 = \blacksquare$ 15
4. $8 + 8 = \blacksquare$ 16
5. $5 + 7 = \blacksquare$ 12

Learn

HORSEBACK RIDING Aaron's family went horseback riding in the Greene-Sullivan State Forest in Dugger, Indiana. They rode on two trails that are a total of 14 miles long. The Yellow Loop trail is 9 miles long. How long is the Orange Loop trail?

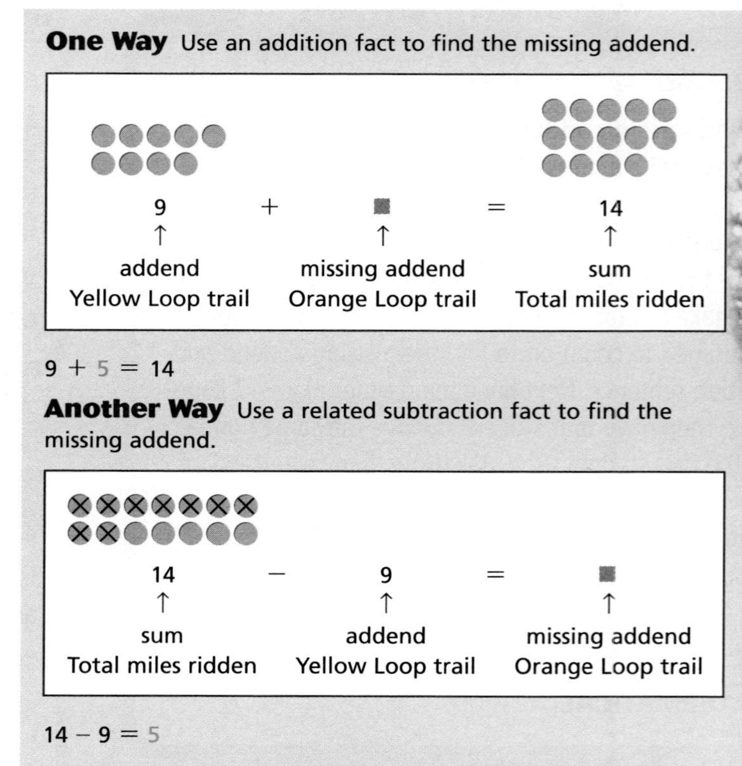

One Way Use an addition fact to find the missing addend.

9	+	■	=	14
↑		↑		↑
addend Yellow Loop trail		missing addend Orange Loop trail		sum Total miles ridden

$9 + 5 = 14$

Another Way Use a related subtraction fact to find the missing addend.

14	−	9	=	■
↑		↑		↑
sum Total miles ridden		addend Yellow Loop trail		missing addend Orange Loop trail

$14 - 9 = 5$

Since $9 + 5 = 14$ and $14 - 9 = 5$, the Orange Loop trail is 5 miles long.

MATH IDEA You can think of an addition fact or a related subtraction fact to find a missing addend.

4

Reteach 1.2

Algebra: Missing Addends

When you know the sum and one addend, you can use addition or subtraction facts to find the missing addend.

Here are two ways to find the missing addend in $5 + ? = 11$.

One way
Think about an addition fact. $5 + ? = 11$

0 1 2 3 4 5 6 7 8 9 10 11 12 — $5 + 6 = 11$

5 and 6 more is 11.

Another way
Think about a related subtraction fact. $5 + ? = 11$, so $11 - 5 = ?$

0 1 2 3 4 5 6 7 8 9 10 11 12 — $11 - 5 = 6$

5 less than 11 is 6.

Find the missing addend. Show an addition fact on the number line to help you.

1. 0 1 2 3 4 5 6 7 8 9 10 11 12 13 14 15 16 17 18 — $9 + \underline{7} = 16$

Find the missing addend. Show a subtraction fact on the number line to help you.

2. 0 1 2 3 4 5 6 7 8 9 10 11 12 13 14 15 16 17 18 — $9 + \underline{6} = 15$

Find the missing addend. Think about an addition or subtraction fact.

3. $\underline{4} + 9 = 13$ 4. $8 + \underline{0} = 8$ 5. $\underline{7} + 5 = 12$

RW2 Reteach

Practice 1.2

Algebra: Missing Addends

Find the missing addend.

1. $9 + \underline{4} = 13$ 2. $\underline{7} + 8 = 15$ 3. $\underline{4} + 7 = 11$
4. $7 + \underline{5} = 12$ 5. $9 + \underline{9} = 18$ 6. $\underline{6} + 4 = 10$
7. $0 + \underline{7} = 7$ 8. $\underline{6} + 8 = 14$ 9. $7 + \underline{9} = 16$
10. $4 + \underline{8} = 12$ 11. $8 + \underline{9} = 17$ 12. $\underline{0} + 6 = 6$
13. $\underline{8} + 6 = 14$ 14. $\underline{6} + 6 = 12$ 15. $4 + \underline{9} = 13$

Write all the possible missing pairs of addends.

16. $\underline{?} + \underline{?} = 7$
0 and 7, 1 and 6, 2 and 5, 3 and 4, 4 and 3, 5 and 2, 6 and 1, 7 and 0

17. $\underline{?} + \underline{?} = 10$
0 and 10, 1 and 9, 2 and 8, 3 and 7, 4 and 6, 5 and 5, 6 and 4, 7 and 3, 8 and 2, 9 and 1, 10 and 0

Mixed Review

Write the fact family for each set of numbers.

18. 7, 9, 16
$7 + 9 = 16$
$9 + 7 = 16$
$16 - 7 = 9$
$16 - 9 = 7$

19. 5, 6, 11
$5 + 6 = 11$
$6 + 5 = 11$
$11 - 5 = 6$
$11 - 6 = 5$

PW2 Practice

Check

1. **Explain** how you can use a related subtraction fact to find ■ + 8 = 17. **I can use 17 – 8 = 9 to find ■ + 8 = 17.**

Find the missing addend.

2. 5 + ■ = 11 **6** **3.** ■ + 3 = 12 **9** **4.** 4 + ■ = 10 **6** **5.** ■ + 5 = 13 **8**

Practice and Problem Solving

Extra Practice, page 14, Set B

Find the missing addend.

6. 8 + ■ = 15 **7** **7.** ■ + 3 = 11 **8** **8.** ■ + 6 = 13 **7** **9.** ■ + 6 = 14 **8**

10. ■ + 8 = 8 **0** **11.** 5 + ■ = 13 **8** **12.** 7 + ■ = 14 **7** **13.** ■ + 9 = 15 **6**

14. 9 + ■ = 16 **7** **15.** ■ + 7 = 13 **6** **16.** 7 + ■ = 15 **8** **17.** 8 + ■ = 17 **9**

18. James had 9 video games. He received more games as birthday gifts. Now James has 16 games. Use counters and an addition sentence to show how many games James received as gifts. **Check students' models. Possible sentence: 9 + 7 = 16; 7 games**

19. FAST FACT • SOCIAL STUDIES Indiana's Ghost Town Trail got its name from a railroad line running between old mining towns. The trail is 16 miles long. Four miles were added to the trail in 1993. How long was the trail in 1992? **12 miles**

20. REASONING How many pairs of missing addends are there for ■ + ■ = 8? List the pairs. **9 pairs; 0,8; 1,7; 2,6; 3,5; 4,4; 5,3; 6,2; 7,1; 8,0**

21. I am a number less than 50. My tens digit is 4. The sum of my digits is 4. What number am I? **40**

22. I am a number less than 100. My tens digit is 7 more than my ones digit. My ones digit is 2. What number am I? **92**

23. What's the Error? Jenna wrote 12 – 4 = 7 to help her find 4 + ■ = 12. Describe and correct her error. **She made a subtraction error. 12 – 4 = 8 is the related subtraction fact; 8 is the missing addend.**

Getting Ready for the EOG Test

24. Ellen had 2 library books. She checked out more books at the library. Now Ellen has the number of books shown at the right.

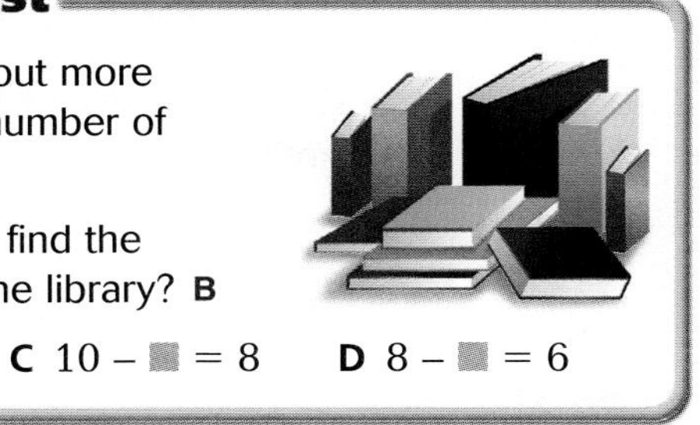

Which number sentence can you use to find the number of books Ellen checked out at the library? **B**

A 10 + ■ = 18 **B** 2 + ■ = 10 **C** 10 – ■ = 8 **D** 8 – ■ = 6

North Carolina Standards 1.02 Develop fluency with multi-digit addition and subtraction ough 9,999 using: a) Strategies for adding and subtracting numbers. *also* 5.04, 1.02c

Challenge 1.2

Missing Addend Riddle

What kind of mouse never eats cheese?

Find the missing addends.

1. 5 + <u>7</u> = 12 E	2. <u>2</u> + 8 = 10 P
3. 9 + <u>6</u> = 15 A	4. 1 + <u>15</u> = 16 T
5. <u>9</u> + 9 = 18 M	6. 8 + <u>4</u> = 12 S
7. 9 + <u>1</u> = 10 R	8. <u>10</u> + 5 = 15 C
9. <u>5</u> + 8 = 13 O	10. <u>8</u> + 9 = 17 M
11. <u>16</u> + 1 = 17 U	12. 0 + <u>14</u> = 14 O
13. <u>3</u> + 9 = 12 U	14. <u>0</u> + 9 = 9 E

Use the addition problems above to solve the riddle. Write the letter on the line that matches the addend below the line.

A		C	O	M	P	U	T	E	R
6		10	14	9	2	3	15	7	1

M	O	U	S	E
8	5	16	4	0

Problem Solving 1.2

Algebra: Missing Addends Understand → Plan → Solve → Check

Write the correct answer.

1. Amanda wants to plant 15 tulip bulbs. She planted 8 bulbs. How many bulbs does she have left to plant? **7**

2. When Tim got his cactus plant, it was 6 inches tall. Now it is 11 inches tall. How many inches has the cactus grown? **5 inches**

3. Find the missing addend. _?_ + 5 = 13 **8**

4. Greg bought 6 kites, 4 yo-yos, and 2 balls. How many toys did he buy? **12 toys**

Choose the letter of the correct answer.

5. Which operation is the inverse of subtraction?
   (A) addition
   B subtraction
   C multiplication
   D division

6. If you add 7 to a number, the sum is 12. What is the number?
   F 4
   (G) 5
   H 15
   J 19

7. Which number sentence does **not** belong to the same fact family as the other number sentences?
   A 4 + 9 = 13
   B 9 + 4 = 13
   (C) 9 – 5 = 4
   D 13 – 9 = 4

8. Which fact would **not** help you find the missing addend for _?_ + 9 = 15?
   F 15 – 9 = 6
   (G) 9 – 6 = 3
   H 9 + 6 = 15
   J 15 – 6 = 9

9. **Write About It** Explain how you found your answer to Problem 3.
   Possible answers: I thought about the addition fact 8 + 5 = 13; I thought about the related subtraction fact 13 – 5 = 8.

3 PRACTICE

Guided Practice

Do Check Exercises 1–5 with your students. Identify students who are having difficulty and choose appropriate lesson resources to provide assistance.

Independent Practice

Note that Exercise 20 is a **multistep or strategy problem.** Assign Exercises 6–23.

4 ASSESS

Summarize the lesson by having students:

DISCUSS Explain why subtraction can help you find the missing addend. Since subtraction is the inverse or opposite operation of addition, the difference in the subtraction fact becomes the missing addend.

WRITE Explain the two ways you can find missing addends. Give an example. You can use an addition fact or a related subtraction fact. 8 + ■ = 14; 14 – 8 = ■

LESSON QUIZ

Find the missing addend.

1. 9 + ■ = 17 8
2. 5 + ■ = 12 7
3. 5 + ■ = 14 9
4. ■ + 6 = 11 5
5. 9 + ■ = 18 9
6. ■ + 8 = 15 7

Lesson 1.3

Algebra: Properties

Lesson Planning

Objective To use properties of addition

NCTM Standards

1. Number and Operations
2. Algebra
6. Problem Solving
7. Reasoning and Proof
8. Communication
9. Connections
10. Representation

Math Background

These ideas will help students use properties of addition.

- The Order Property is also known as the Commutative Property and the Grouping Property is known as the Associative Property.
- The properties of addition help you find sums mentally.
- The Order and Grouping Properties of addition do not apply to subtraction.

Vocabulary

Order Property of Addition When you add two numbers in any order, you get the same sum.

Identity Property of Addition When you add zero to a number, the sum does not change.

Grouping Property of Addition When you add three or more addends in different ways, the sum stays the same.

Warm-Up Resources

Number of the Day

Transparency

The number of the day is the sum of the number of the days of the week plus the number in a dozen. Use the number to write an addition sentence. Possible answer: $7 + 12 = 19$

Daily Facts Practice

Have students practice addition facts by completing Set C of *Teacher's Resource Book*, p. TR83.

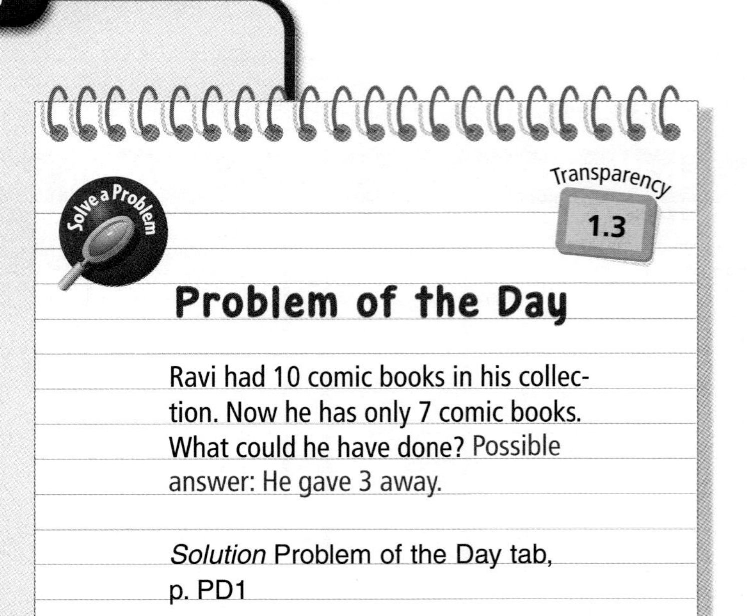

Transparency 1.3

Problem of the Day

Ravi had 10 comic books in his collection. Now he has only 7 comic books. What could he have done? Possible answer: He gave 3 away.

Solution Problem of the Day tab, p. PD1

Intervention and Extension Resources

Alternative Teaching Strategy

MATERIALS *For each pair* 18 counters

To **reinforce students' understanding of the Order and Grouping Properties,** have them model number sentences with counters. To demonstrate the Order Property, have students arrange the 18 counters into 2 groups, such as 7 and 11. Explain that whether the group of 7 is on the left or the right, the sum of the counters is 18.

To demonstrate the Grouping Property, have students arrange the counters into 3 groups, such as 3, 6, and 9. When 3 and 6 are grouped and added to 9, the sum is 18. Point out that when 6 and 9 are grouped and added to 3, the total is also 18. Check students' work.

KINESTHETIC

LOGICAL/MATHEMATICAL, INTERPERSONAL

Multistep and Strategy Problems

The following multistep or strategy problem is provided in Lesson 1.3:

Page	Item
7	17

English Language Learners

MATERIALS *For each group* poster paper, colored pencils or markers

To help students **remember the addition properties,** have students make a 3-column table with these labels: *Name of Addition Property*, *Description*, and *Drawing*. In the first column, have students identify the property. In the second column, the students should write a brief description of the property. And in the third column, have students draw a picture that illustrates the property. Have students share their posters with the class. Check students' work.

VISUAL

INTERPERSONAL, LOGICAL/MATHEMATICAL

Advanced Learners

Have students use the Grouping Property and the Order Property to find missing addends. Provide students with a few challenging problems such as the following. To help students find the missing addends, make sure the number sentences are in pairs.

$13 + (17 + \blacksquare) = 38$ 8
$(17 + 8) + \blacksquare = 38$ 13

$(15 + 7) + \blacksquare = 31$ 9
$(\blacksquare + 9) + 15 = 31$ 7

$(16 + \blacksquare) + 16 = 42$ 10
$\blacksquare + (16 + 10) = 42$ 16

$\blacksquare + (19 + 14) = 40$ 7
$(7 + 14) + \blacksquare = 40$ 19

VISUAL

LOGICAL/MATHEMATICAL

Lesson 1.3 Organizer

Objective To use properties of addition

Vocabulary Order Property of Addition, Identity Property of Addition, Grouping Property of Addition

1 INTRODUCE

QUICK REVIEW provides review of prerequisite skills.

WHY LEARN THIS? Knowing properties of addition will help you remember the sums for basic facts. *Share the lesson objective with students.*

Guided Instruction

- *Review the Order Property of Addition.*
  Why are the sums of 6 + 7 and 7 + 6 the same? When the order of the addends is changed, the sum is the same.
- *Direct students' attention to the Identity Property of Addition.*
  REASONING Does the order of the addends matter when zero is an addend? Explain. No; the sum is the same whether the zero is the first or second addend.
- *Direct students' attention to the Grouping Property of Addition.*
  REASONING Why is the term *Grouping Property* a good name for this type of addition? Group means "more than 2." In the Grouping Property, there are 3 or more addends.
  What is the purpose of the parentheses in these addition sentences? They tell you to add the group inside the parentheses first.

Algebra: Properties

Quick Review

1. 4 + 9 = ■ 13
2. 8 + 6 = ■ 14
3. 8 + 7 = ■ 15
4. 6 + 9 = ■ 15
5. 9 + 7 = ■ 16

Vocabulary

Order Property of Addition
Identity Property of Addition
Grouping Property of Addition

Learn

Special rules, called properties, can help you add.

IN THE PARK Olivia saw 6 monarch butterflies and 7 swallowtails. Courtney saw 7 monarchs and 6 swallowtails. How many butterflies did each girl see in all?

Order Property of Addition

You can add two or more numbers in any order and get the same sum.

6	+	7	=	13	7	+	6	=	13
↑		↑		↑	↑		↑		↑
addend	+	addend	=	sum	addend	+	addend	=	sum

So, 6 + 7 = 7 + 6. Olivia and Courtney each saw 13 butterflies.

Identity Property of Addition

Courtney saw 12 tulips in a garden. Olivia didn't see any. How many tulips did the girls see in all?

When you add zero to a number, the sum is that number.

12 + 0 = 12

So, the girls saw 12 tulips in all.

Grouping Property of Addition

Olivia saw 9 birds, 1 rabbit, and 4 squirrels in a meadow. How many animals did she see in all?

You can group addends in different ways and still get the same sum.

(9 + 1) + 4 = 9 + (1 + 4)
10 + 4 = 9 + 5
14 = 14

Hint: The ( ) symbols tell you which numbers to add first.

So, Olivia saw 14 animals in all.

6

Reteach 1.3

Properties

Special rules, called **properties**, can help you add.

Order Property of Addition
You can add two or more numbers in any order and get the same sum.

8 + 4 = 12   4 + 8 = 12

Identity Property of Addition
When you add zero to a number, the sum is that number.

7 + 0 = 7   0 + 7 = 7

Grouping Property of Addition
You can group addends in different ways and still get the same sum.

(2 + 6) + 5 = 2 + (6 + 5)
8 + 5 = 2 + 11
13 = 13

Find each sum. Write *Order*, *Identity*, or *Grouping* to tell what property of addition is shown.

1. 5 + 0 = 5 — Identity
2. 9 + 6 = 15, 6 + 9 = 15 — Order
3. (2 + 8) + 3 = 13, 2 + (8 + 3) = 13 — Grouping
4. 5 + 7 = 12, 7 + 5 = 12 — Order
5. 3 + (9 + 2) = 14, (3 + 9) + 2 = 14 — Grouping
6. 0 + 11 = 11 — Identity

Reteach RW3

Practice 1.3

Properties

Find each sum.

1. 9 + 4 = 13; 4 + 9 = 13
2. (2 + 8) + 6 = 16; 2 + (8 + 6) = 16
3. 14 + 0 = 14
4. 7 + 8 = 15; 8 + 7 = 15
5. 0 + 13 = 13
6. 5 + (4 + 7) = 16; (5 + 4) + 7 = 16
7. 4 + (8 + 5) = 17; (4 + 8) + 5 = 17
8. 18 + 0 = 18
9. 9 + 6 = 15; 6 + 9 = 15
10. 0 + 15 = 15
11. 5 + 7 = 12; 7 + 5 = 12
12. (3 + 7) + 8 = 18; 3 + (7 + 8) = 18
13. 8 + 3 = 11; 3 + 8 = 11
14. (1 + 5) + 7 = 13; 1 + (5 + 7) = 13
15. 9 + 0 = 9
16. (2 + 3) + 4 = 9; 2 + (3 + 4) = 9
17. 0 + 17 = 17
18. 9 + 1 = 10; 1 + 9 = 10

Mixed Review

Add or subtract.

19. 16 − 9 = 7
20. 8 + 5 = 13
21. 7 + 5 = 12
22. 11 − 5 = 6
23. 17 − 8 = 9
24. 5 + 9 = 14

Find the missing addend.

25. 5 + 9 = 14
26. 8 + 7 = 15
27. 7 + 7 = 14
28. 9 + 3 = 12
29. 6 + 5 = 11
30. 4 + 9 = 13

Practice PW3

Check

1. Explain how the Grouping Property of Addition can help you find $2 + (8 + 4)$.
   Possible answer: I can write the problem as $(2 + 8) + 4$. $2 + 8 = 10$, then add 4. $10 + 4 = 14$

Find each sum.

2. $15 + 0 = \blacksquare$ **15**
3. $8 + 6 = \blacksquare$ **14**
   $6 + 8 = \blacksquare$ **14**
4. $4 + (6 + 5) = \blacksquare$ **15**
   $(4 + 6) + 5 = \blacksquare$ **15**

Practice and Problem Solving

Extra Practice, page 14, Set C

Find each sum.

5. $7 + 4 = \blacksquare$ **11**
   $4 + 7 = \blacksquare$ **11**
6. $(3 + 7) + 8 = \blacksquare$ **18**
   $3 + (7 + 8) = \blacksquare$ **18**
7. $8 + 9 = \blacksquare$ **17**
   $9 + 8 = \blacksquare$ **17**
8. $8 + (1 + 9) = \blacksquare$ **18**
   $(8 + 1) + 9 = \blacksquare$ **18**
9. $6 + 11 = \blacksquare$ **17**
   $11 + 6 = \blacksquare$ **17**
10. $8 + (5 + 6) = \blacksquare$ **19**
    $(8 + 5) + 6 = \blacksquare$ **19**
11. $13 + 0 = \blacksquare$ **13**
12. $(6 + 8) + 3 = \blacksquare$ **17**
    $6 + (8 + 3) = \blacksquare$ **17**
13. $8 + 5 = \blacksquare$ **13**
    $5 + 8 = \blacksquare$ **13**

14. Jake has 4 cats. Matthew has 5 birds and 2 dogs. Draw a picture to show how many pets they have in all. **Check students' drawings; 11 pets**
15. The sum of two numbers is 14. One of the numbers is 5 less than the sum. What are the two numbers? **9, 5**
16. **REASONING** $3 + 9 = 12$ and $9 + 3 = 12$ shows the Order Property of Addition. Can you use the Order Property to subtract? Why or why not? **Possible answer: You cannot change the order of the numbers being subtracted because you subtract the lesser number from the greater number.**
17. Anna picked 7 roses, 7 tulips, and 3 daisies. Then she gave her mother 8 of the flowers. How many flowers did she have left? **9 flowers**

Getting Ready for the EOG Test

18. Mrs. Walters bought 12 oranges, 6 apples, and 4 pears at the farmers' market. How many pieces of fruit did she buy? **D**

A 10 C 18
B 16 D 22

North Carolina Standards 1.04 Use basic properties (identity, commutative, associative, order of operations) for addition, subtraction, multiplication, and division. *also* 1.02a, 1.06

Challenge 1.3

Colorful Matches

For each sum or set of addends in Column A, find a sum or set of addends in Column B that represents the same number. Then find a sum or set of addends in Column C that represents the same number.

Draw colored lines to connect the matching sums and addends.
- Draw a red line if the sum and addends show the Order Property of Addition.
- Draw a blue line if the sum and addends show the Identity Property of Addition.
- Draw a green line if the sum and addends show the Grouping Property of Addition.

The first one has been started for you. Trace the lines with the correct color. Red —— Blue —— Green - - -

Column A	Column B	Column C
9 + 3	11	0 + 16
16 + 0	0 + 9	8 + 9
(2 + 3) + 6	9 + 8	10
14	7 + (3 + 8)	9 + 0
4 + (7 + 4)	12	(7 + 3) + 8
9	16	2 + (3 + 6)
(2 + 8) + 3	8 + 2	13
17	5 + 9	15
2 + 8	(4 + 7) + 4	3 + 9
18	2 + (8 + 3)	9 + 5

Challenge CW3

Problem Solving 1.3

Properties

Understand → Plan → Solve → Check

Write the correct answer.

1. What addition property does the following problem represent?
   $12 + 0 = 12$
   Identity Property of Addition
2. According to the Grouping Property of Addition, how else can you group these addends?
   $(8 + 2) + 4$
   $8 + (2 + 4)$
3. When a number is added to 8, the sum is 14. What is the number?
   6
4. Beth lives 17 miles from the lake. Ben lives 9 miles from the lake. How much farther from the lake does Beth live than Ben?
   8 miles

Choose the letter of the correct answer.

5. Which shows the Order Property of Addition?
   A $9 + 4 = 13$, $5 + 8 = 13$
   B $9 + 4 = 13$, $9 - 4 = 5$
   C $9 + 4 = 13$, $13 - 9 = 4$
   (D) $9 + 4 = 13$, $4 + 9 = 13$
6. Yesterday the Hills ate 9 slices of pizza. By the end of lunch today, they had eaten all 16 slices. How many slices did they eat for lunch?
   F 6
   (G) 7
   H 8
   J 9
7. Which shows the Identity Property of Addition?
   A $5 - 0 = 5$
   B $5 + 5 = 10$
   (C) $10 + 0 = 10$
   D $10 - 10 = 0$
8. Lee has 8 goldfish and 3 guppies. Ken has 3 goldfish and 8 guppies. Which is true?
   F Ken has more fish than Lee.
   (G) Lee and Ken have the same number of fish.
   H Ken has fewer fish than Lee.
   J Lee has more fish than Ken.
9. **Write About It** Explain how to use an addition property to find your answer to Problem 8.
   Possible answer: You can add 2 numbers in any order and get the same sum.

Problem Solving PS3

3 PRACTICE

Guided Practice

Do Check Exercises 1–4 with your students. Identify students who are having difficulty and choose appropriate lesson resources to provide assistance.

Independent Practice

Note that Exercise 17 is a multistep or strategy problem. Assign Exercises 5–17.

SCAFFOLDED INSTRUCTION Use the prompts on Transparency 1 to guide instruction for the multistep or strategy problem in Exercise 17.

4 ASSESS

Summarize the lesson by having students:

DISCUSS Tell which property is shown: $6 + 8 = 14$ and $8 + 6 = 14$. Explain. This is the Order Property of Addition. You can add 2 numbers in any order and the sum is the same.

WRITE Give an example of the Order, Identity, and Grouping Properties of Addition. Answers will vary.

LESSON QUIZ

Transparency 1.3

Find each sum.

1. $9 + 5 = \blacksquare$ 14 $5 + 9 = \blacksquare$ 14
2. $0 + 10 = \blacksquare$ 10 $10 + 0 = \blacksquare$ 10
3. $7 + (3 + 9) = \blacksquare$ 19 $(7 + 3) + 9 = \blacksquare$ 19
4. $7 + 8 = \blacksquare$ 15 $8 + 7 = \blacksquare$ 15
5. $(2 + 8) + 6 = \blacksquare$ 16 $2 + (8 + 6) = \blacksquare$ 16

Lesson 1.4

Two-Digit Addition

Lesson Planning

Objective To add 2-digit numbers with and without regrouping

NCTM Standards
1. Number and Operations
6. Problem Solving
8. Communication
9. Connections

Math Background

These ideas will help students add 2-digit numbers.

- If there are ten or more ones, regroup them as tens and ones.
- Write the regrouped ten above the tens place digits.
- When adding three 2-digit numbers, first look for numbers that make a ten.

Warm-Up Resources

Number of the Day

The number of the day is the number of months in a year. 12 Add this number to your age. What is the sum? Possible answer: 20 or 21

Daily Facts Practice

Have students practice subtraction facts by completing Set D of *Teacher's Resource Book,* p. TR83.

Solve a Problem

Transparency 1.4

Problem of the Day

Pablo joined 5 red cubes and 6 blue cubes. Then he joined 4 yellow cubes and 3 green cubes. How many cubes did Pablo join in all? 18 cubes

Solution Problem of the Day tab, p. PD1

Intervention and Extension Resources

Alternative Teaching Strategy

MATERIALS *For each pair* base-ten blocks

To help students **add 2-digit numbers,** have them model the problem on page 8 with base-ten blocks and record the steps.

Step 1: Have students model 3 tens 6 ones and 4 tens 8 ones with base-ten blocks.

Step 2: The first student should add the ones: $6 + 8 = 14$, and regroup the 14 ones as 1 ten 4 ones.

Step 3: The partner should add the tens: $1 + 3 + 4 = 8$.

8 tens 4 ones = 84

Next, have students model the Check exercises. Check students' work.

KINESTHETIC

BODILY/KINESTHETIC, INTERPERSONAL

Multistep and Strategy Problems

The following multistep or strategy problem is provided in Lesson 1.4:

Page	Item
9	24

Special Needs

MATERIALS *For each student* connecting cubes

Have students **practice addition with regrouping.** Display a problem such as 43 + 29. Have students model the problem with connecting cubes. Guide them carefully through the regrouping of the ones. If necessary, pair a struggling student with one who is more proficient. Have the student who needs practice explain aloud each step as he or she works through it. Guide the "tutor" to help where needed. Check students' work.

KINESTHETIC

BODILY/KINESTHETIC, INTERPERSONAL

Early Finishers

MATERIALS *For each student* drawing paper, markers

Have students **practice two-digit addition.** Have students make copies of tables for the classroom like Exercises 12–20 on page 9. Tables should be large and should include at least five problems. Hang the tables or place them at a center where students can complete them during times when they finish early. Check students' work.

VISUAL

LOGICAL/MATHEMATICAL

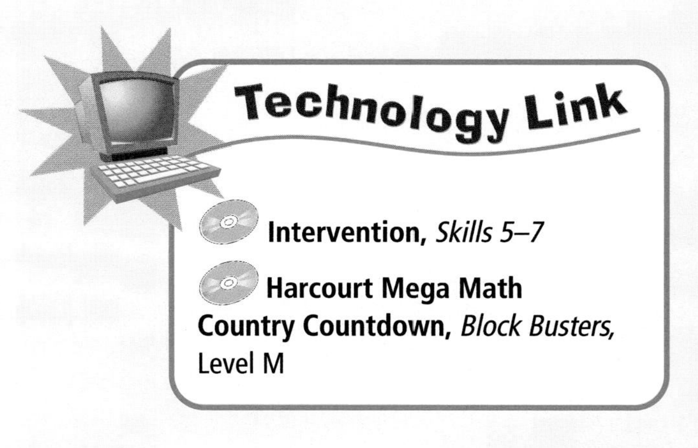

Lesson 1.4 Organizer

Objective To add 2-digit numbers with and without regrouping

1 INTRODUCE

Quick Review provides review of mental math skills.

Why Learn This? You can add many quantities of things with 2-digit numbers: pages in books you read, miles to places you drive, and so on. *Share the lesson objective with students.*

2 TEACH

Guided Instruction

- *Have students read the Learn section.*

  How do you know you need to use addition? The problem asks how many cows Zack counted in all.

  In Step 1 of Example 1, why is the small 1 written above the tens place? It is the 1 regrouped ten.

  In Step 2, why is there an 8 written in the tens place of the answer? The sum of 3 and 4 is 7, but you still have to add the 1 ten that was regrouped. So there are 8 tens in the sum.

- *Direct students' attention to Example 2.*

  Reasoning Do you have to add the column of numbers from the top down? Explain. No; you could look for numbers that make a ten first, then add the remaining numbers.

  How could you add the tens in Step 2? $1 + 4 = 5$; $5 + 5 = 10$; $10 + 3 = 13$

  Reasoning What is the greatest sum you can get by adding two 2-digit numbers? Explain. 198 is the sum of $99 + 99$.

LESSON 4

Two-Digit Addition

Quick Review

1. $9 + 7 = \blacksquare$ 16
2. $8 + 5 = \blacksquare$ 13
3. $6 + 9 = \blacksquare$ 15
4. $7 + 6 = \blacksquare$ 13
5. $3 + 8 + 7 = \blacksquare$ 18

Learn

TILL THE COWS COME HOME Zack counted 36 cows in the barn. Then he counted 48 cows grazing in the pasture. How many cows did Zack count in all?

$36 + 48 = \blacksquare$

Example 1

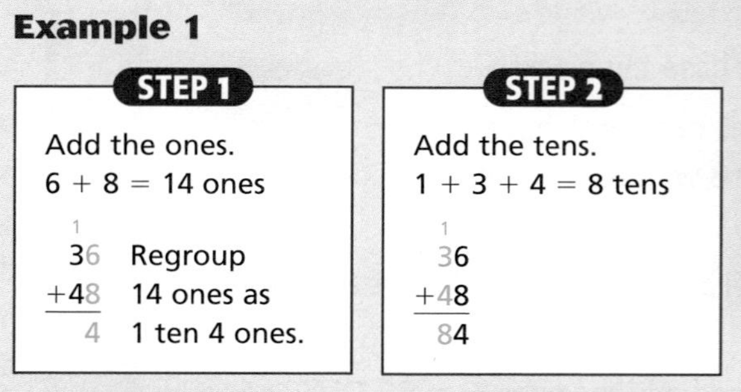

STEP 1

Add the ones.
$6 + 8 = 14$ ones

$$\begin{array}{r} {}^{1}\\ 36 \\ +48 \\ \hline 4 \end{array}$$

Regroup 14 ones as 1 ten 4 ones.

STEP 2

Add the tens.
$1 + 3 + 4 = 8$ tens

$$\begin{array}{r} {}^{1}\\ 36 \\ +48 \\ \hline 84 \end{array}$$

So, Zack counted 84 cows in all.

Technology Link

More Practice: Harcourt Mega Math Country Countdown, *Block Busters*, Level M

Example 2

One cow drank 46 gallons of water. A second cow drank 37 gallons, and a third cow drank 53 gallons. How many gallons of water did the three cows drink in all?

$46 + 37 + 53 = \blacksquare$

STEP 1

Add the ones.
$6 + 7 + 3 = 16$ ones

$$\begin{array}{r} {}^{1}\\ 46 \\ 37 \\ +53 \\ \hline 6 \end{array}$$

Make a ten.

Regroup 16 ones as 1 ten 6 ones.

STEP 2

Add the tens.
$1 + 4 + 3 + 5 = 13$ tens

$$\begin{array}{r} {}^{1}\\ 46 \\ 37 \\ +53 \\ \hline 136 \end{array}$$

Regroup 13 tens as 1 hundred 3 tens.

So, the cows drank 136 gallons of water in all.

Reteach 1.4

Two-Digit Addition

Add 86 and 37.

Step 1
Add the ones. $6 + 7 = 13$
Regroup 13 ones as 1 ten 3 ones.

Circle 10 ones when you can.

	Hundreds	Tens	Ones
		1	
		8	6
+		3	7
			3

Step 2
Add the tens and the regrouped ten.
$1 + 8 + 3 = 12$
Regroup 12 tens as 1 hundred 2 tens.

Circle 10 tens when you can.

	Hundreds	Tens	Ones
		1	
		8	6
+		3	7
	1	2	3

Use base-ten blocks to find each sum. Regroup if needed.

1.

	Hundreds	Tens	Ones
		3	9
+			8
		4	7

2.

	Hundreds	Tens	Ones
		5	6
+		4	2
		9	8

3.

	Hundreds	Tens	Ones
		6	7
+		6	5
	1	3	2

4.

	Hundreds	Tens	Ones
		9	8
+		4	7
	1	4	5

5.

	Hundreds	Tens	Ones
		3	5
+		6	8
	1	0	3

6.

	Hundreds	Tens	Ones
		7	6
+		5	9
	1	3	5

RW4 Reteach

Practice 1.4

Two-Digit Addition

Find the sum.

1. $54 + 5 = 59$
2. $26 + 73 = 99$
3. $18 + 54 = 72$
4. $23 + 38 + 7 = 68$
5. $45 + 42 = 87$
6. $37 + 6 + 84 = 127$
7. $79 + 6 = 85$
8. $47 + 89 = 136$
9. $36 + 58 = 94$
10. $41 + 9 = 50$
11. $83 + 68 = 151$
12. $65 + 39 + 85 = 189$
13. $57 + 42 = 99$
14. $63 + 17 = 80$
15. $75 + 46 = 121$
16. $55 + 31 + 26 = 112$

Complete each table.

	Add 20.	
17.	38	58
18.	6	26
19.	67	87

	Add 37.	
20.	46	83
21.	93	130
22.	77	114

	Add 52.	
23.	21	73
24.	65	117
25.	44	96

Mixed Review

Find the missing addend.

26. $6 + \underline{8} = 14$
27. $\underline{5} + 6 = 11$
28. $9 + \underline{8} = 17$
29. $4 + \underline{9} = 13$
30. $\underline{2} + 8 = 10$
31. $\underline{7} + 9 = 16$
32. $\underline{3} + 8 = 11$
33. $8 + \underline{8} = 16$
34. $6 + \underline{7} = 13$

PW4 Practice

Check

1. Explain when you need to regroup ones as tens. Give an example. **Possible answer: 18 + 25 = 43; you need to regroup 13 ones as 1 ten 3 ones because there are more than 10 ones.**

Find the sum.

2.	3.	4.	5.	6.
32	28	88	49	79
+ 6	+51	+ 7	6	64
			+12	+22
38	**79**	**95**	**67**	**165**

Practice and Problem Solving

Extra Practice, page 14, Set D

Find the sum.

7.	8.	9.	10.	11.
47	72	18	78	56
+22	+ 9	+69	+87	98
				+ 4
69	**81**	**87**	**165**	**158**

Copy and complete each table.

	Add 10.	
12.	71	**81**
13.	43	**53**
14.	**8**	18

	Add 25.	
15.	25	**50**
16.	**7**	32
17.	49	**74**

	Add 58.	
18.	30	**88**
19.	65	**123**
20.	**78**	136

21. What related subtraction fact can you write to find the missing addend for 7 + ■ = 15? **Possible answer: 15 − 7 = 8**

22. **REASONING** I am a two-digit number. My ones and tens digits are the same. The sum of my digits is 8. What number am I? **44**

23. The third-grade classes went on a field trip. One bus took 29 students. A second bus took 34 students. How many students went on the field trip? **63 students**

24. Sara and her father went fishing. Sara caught 12 fish. Her father caught 9 fish. They threw back 4 small fish. How many fish did they have left? **17 fish**

Getting Ready for the EOG Test

25. During which two months did Jon work 53 hours? **B**

A May and June
B May and July
C July and August
D June and July

HOURS JON WORKED	
Month	**Hours**
May	17
June	24
July	36
August	48

North Carolina Standards 1.02 Develop fluency with multi-digit addition and subtraction through 9,999 using: a) Strategies for adding and subtracting numbers.

3 PRACTICE

Guided Practice

Do Check Exercises 1–6 with your students. Identify students who are having difficulty and choose appropriate lesson resources to provide assistance.

COMMON ERROR ALERT

Students may forget to write the regrouped ten above the digit in the tens place.

52
+19
61

Have students draw a small box above the tens column to remind them to add the regrouped ten.

Independent Practice

Note that Exercise 24 is a **multistep or strategy problem.** Assign Exercises 7–24.

4 ASSESS

Summarize the lesson by having students:

DISCUSS How do you know when to use regrouping? Give an example. You regroup ones as tens and ones when there are ten or more ones; 46 + 37 = 83

WRITE How would you add 54 and 28? Add the ones. 4 + 8 = 12. Regroup 12 ones as 1 ten 2 ones. Add the tens and the regrouped ten. 1 + 5 + 2 = 8. 54 + 28 = 82

LESSON QUIZ

Transparency 1.4

Find the sum.

1.	2.	3.	4.	5.
58	19	42	38	36
+13	+25	+47	+22	53
				+14
71	44	89	60	103

Challenge 1.4

Addition Squares

Fill in the empty squares by adding the numbers across each row, and adding the numbers down each column.

1.

83	7	90
9	64	73
92	71	163

2.

46	34	80
31	6	37
77	40	117

3.

25	42	67
39	48	87
64	90	154

4.

65	27	92
30	25	55
95	52	147

5.

46	18	64
25	62	87
71	80	151

6.

39	39	78
53	12	65
92	51	143

7.

23	16	44	83
37	7	15	59
15	4	26	45
75	27	85	187

8.

9	31	56	96
12	6	17	35
41	23	4	68
62	60	77	199

CW4 Challenge

Problem Solving 1.4

Two-Digit Addition

Understand → Plan → Solve → Check

Write the correct answer.

1. To find the sum 56 + 84 = ?, how many times will you need to regroup? What is the sum? **2; 140**

2. Sara baked 34 gingerbread cookies and 39 chocolate chip cookies. How many cookies did she bake in all? **73 cookies**

3. What property do 3 + (9 + 2) = 14 and (3 + 9) + 2 = 14 show? **Grouping Property of Addition**

4. How many different facts are in the fact family for 7, 7, and 14? **2**

Choose the letter of the correct answer.

5. Kelly has 14 problems to solve for homework. She solved 5 problems. How many problems does she have left to solve?
A 19 (C) 9
B 11 D 8

6. The Morgans drove 49 miles before lunch and 77 miles after lunch. How far did they drive in all?
F 116 miles (H) 126 miles
G 125 miles J 181 miles

7. Matt had 25 books on the top shelf, 34 books on the middle shelf, and 5 books on the bottom shelf. How many books did he have on his book shelves?
A 54 C 60
B 59 (D) 64

8. Which operation is the inverse of addition?
F addition
(G) subtraction
H multiplication
J division

9. **Write About It** Explain how you solved Problem 6.
I added 9 ones + 7 ones and regrouped 16 ones as 1 ten 6 ones. Then I added 1 ten + 4 tens + 7 tens and regrouped 12 tens as 1 hundred 2 tens.

PS4 Problem Solving

Lesson 1.5

Two-Digit Subtraction

Lesson Planning

Objective To subtract 2-digit numbers with and without regrouping

NCTM Standards

1. Number and Operations
6. Problem Solving
7. Reasoning and Proof
8. Communication
9. Connections

Math Background

These ideas will help students subtract 2-digit numbers.

- If the number being subtracted has a greater number of ones than the number it is being subtracted from, regroup the tens.
- Write the regrouped quantities above the digits in the number being subtracted from.
- Use the inverse operation of addition to check your work with addition. The difference plus the lesser addend should equal the greater addend.

Warm-Up Resources

Number of the Day

The number of the day is the sum of the number of eggs in 2 dozen. Write a number sentence to show how to find it. 12 + 12 = 24

Have students practice subtraction facts by completing Set E of *Teacher's Resource Book,* p. TR83.

Transparency 1.5

Problem of the Day

Megan's cat climbed 6 feet up a tree. Then she climbed down 3 feet and up another 5 feet. How many feet up the tree was Megan's cat? 8 feet

Solution Problem of the Day tab, p. PD1

Intervention and Extension Resources

Alternative Teaching Strategy

MATERIALS *For each pair* base-ten blocks

To help students **subtract 2-digit numbers,** have them model the problem on page 10 with base-ten blocks and record the steps.

Step 1: Have one student show 3 tens and 2 ones.

Step 2: The partner should regroup 3 tens 2 ones as 2 tens 12 ones since there are not enough ones to subtract.

Step 3: The first student subtracts the ones. $12 - 8 = 4$

Step 4: The partner subtracts the tens. 2 tens − 1 ten = 1 ten;

1 ten 4 ones = 14

Next have students model the Check exercises. Check students' work.

KINESTHETIC

BODILY/KINESTHETIC, INTERPERSONAL

Multistep and Strategy Problems

The following multistep or strategy problem is provided in Lesson 1.5:

Page	Item
11	32

Technology Link

Intervention, *Skills 5–7, 12–13*

Harcourt Mega Math Country Countdown, *Block Busters,* Level R

Special Needs

MATERIALS *For each group* flash cards, counters

To help students **reinforce basic subtraction facts,** have them practice in small groups with flash cards. One student displays a card. The first student to give the correct answer receives a counter. When a student has five counters, it is then his or her turn to display the flash card. Check students' work.

VISUAL

LOGICAL/MATHEMATICAL, INTERPERSONAL

Science Connection

Help **reinforce 2-digit subtraction skills** by displaying the following table.

TOP LAND SPEEDS OF ANIMALS	
Animal	**Speed**
kangaroo	43 mph
human	28 mph
rabbit	35 mph
Quarterhorse	47 mph
greyhound	39 mph
gray fox	42 mph
cheetah	70 mph
squirrel	20 mph

Ask:

What is the fastest animal on land? the cheetah

How much faster can a cheetah run than a human? 42 mph faster

How much faster is a kangaroo than a rabbit? 8 mph faster

Using the table, have students make up their own questions and give to a classmate to solve.

VISUAL

LOGICAL/MATHEMATICAL

Lesson 1.5 Organizer

Objective To subtract 2-digit numbers with and without regrouping

1 INTRODUCE

Quick Review provides review of prerequisite skills.

Why Learn This? Two-digit subtraction with regrouping provides a foundation for subtracting greater numbers. *Share the lesson objective with students.*

2 TEACH

Guided Instruction

- *Have students read the Learn section.*
  How do you know you need to subtract? The question asks how many *more* fireflies Emma caught than Colin.
  In Step 2, why don't you subtract 1 ten from 3 tens? You have already regrouped 1 of the 3 tens as 10 ones. So there are only 2 tens left.
- *Direct students' attention to Examples 1 and 2.*
  If you use addition to check subtraction, how will you know if your subtraction was correct? You should have the same three numbers in both problems. The sum should match the greater number of the subtraction problem.
  Reasoning Will you have to regroup if the number you are subtracting has a zero in the ones place? Explain. No; when you subtract 0 from any number, the difference is that number.

3 PRACTICE

Guided Practice

Do Check Exercises 1–6 with your students. Identify students who are having difficulty and choose appropriate lesson resources to provide assistance.

LESSON 5

Two-Digit Subtraction

Quick Review

1. $15 - 7 = ■$ 8
2. $16 - 8 = ■$ 8
3. $14 - 9 = ■$ 5
4. $15 - 6 = ■$ 9
5. $13 - 8 = ■$ 5

Learn

GLOWING IN THE DARK Emma and her brother Colin enjoy catching fireflies. They place them in two glass jars so they can count them before letting them go. One night Emma caught 32 fireflies. Colin caught 18 fireflies. How many more fireflies did Emma catch than Colin?

$32 - 18 = ■$

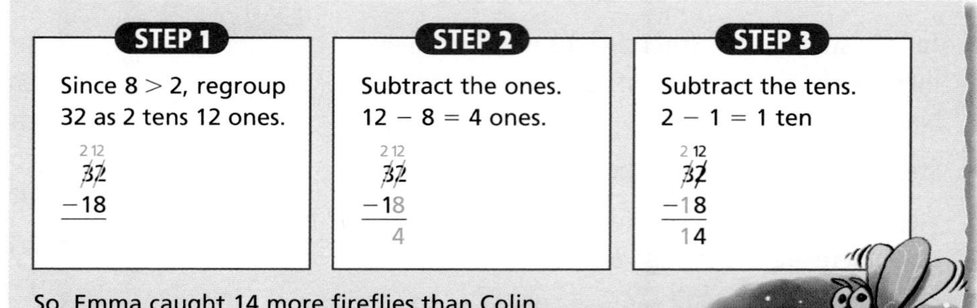

STEP 1
Since 8 > 2, regroup 32 as 2 tens 12 ones.
$$\begin{array}{r} \overset{2\,12}{\not{3}\not{2}} \\ -18 \\ \hline \end{array}$$

STEP 2
Subtract the ones. $12 - 8 = 4$ ones.
$$\begin{array}{r} \overset{2\,12}{\not{3}\not{2}} \\ -18 \\ \hline 4 \end{array}$$

STEP 3
Subtract the tens. $2 - 1 = 1$ ten
$$\begin{array}{r} \overset{2\,12}{\not{3}\not{2}} \\ -18 \\ \hline 14 \end{array}$$

So, Emma caught 14 more fireflies than Colin.

Since addition and subtraction are opposite or inverse operations, you can use addition to check subtraction.

Example 1
$$\begin{array}{r} 32 \\ -18 \\ \hline 14 \end{array} \qquad \begin{array}{r} 14 \\ +18 \\ \hline 32 \end{array}$$

Example 2
$$\begin{array}{r} 65 \\ -29 \\ \hline 36 \end{array} \qquad \begin{array}{r} 36 \\ +29 \\ \hline 65 \end{array}$$

Check

1. **Explain** how you can use an inverse operation to check $62 - 37 = 25$. **You can use addition to check subtraction. $37 + 25 = 62$**

2. $\begin{array}{r} 67 \\ -\ 3 \\ \hline 64 \end{array}$ 3. $\begin{array}{r} 82 \\ -40 \\ \hline 42 \end{array}$ 4. $\begin{array}{r} 91 \\ -23 \\ \hline 68 \end{array}$ 5. $\begin{array}{r} 74 \\ -\ 8 \\ \hline 66 \end{array}$ 6. $\begin{array}{r} 50 \\ -37 \\ \hline 13 \end{array}$

10

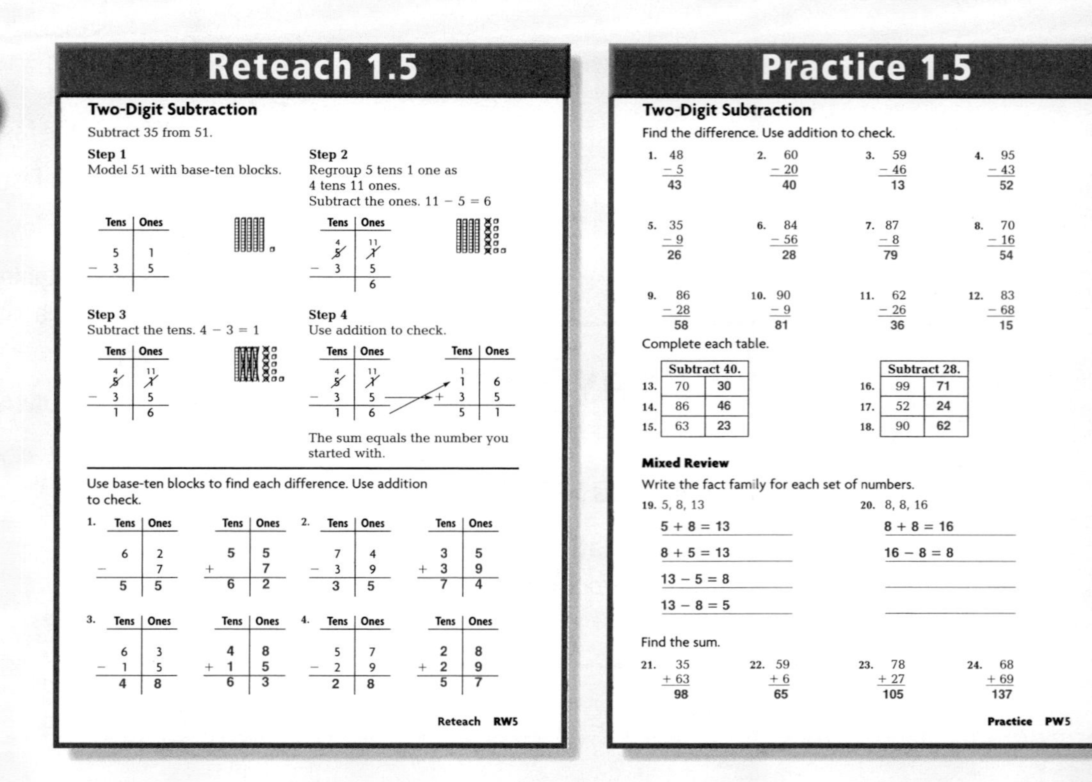

Reteach 1.5

Two-Digit Subtraction

Subtract 35 from 51.

Step 1
Model 51 with base-ten blocks.

Tens	Ones
5	1
− 3	5

Step 2
Regroup 5 tens 1 one as 4 tens 11 ones.
Subtract the ones. $11 - 5 = 6$

Tens	Ones
4 (5)	11 (1)
− 3	5
	6

Step 3
Subtract the tens. $4 - 3 = 1$

Tens	Ones
4 (5)	11 (1)
− 3	5
1	6

Step 4
Use addition to check.

Tens	Ones
4 (5)	11 (1)
− 3	5
1	6

Tens	Ones
1 1	6
+ 3	5
5	1

The sum equals the number you started with.

Use base-ten blocks to find each difference. Use addition to check.

1. $62 - 7 = 55$; $55 + 7 = 62$
2. $74 - 39 = 35$; $35 + 39 = 74$
3. $63 - 15 = 48$; $48 + 15 = 63$
4. $57 - 29 = 28$; $28 + 29 = 57$

Reteach RW5

Practice 1.5

Two-Digit Subtraction

Find the difference. Use addition to check.

1. $48 - 5 = 43$
2. $60 - 20 = 40$
3. $59 - 46 = 13$
4. $95 - 43 = 52$
5. $35 - 9 = 26$
6. $84 - 56 = 28$
7. $87 - 8 = 79$
8. $70 - 16 = 54$
9. $86 - 28 = 58$
10. $90 - 9 = 81$
11. $62 - 26 = 36$
12. $83 - 68 = 15$

Complete each table.

	Subtract 40.	
13.	70	30
14.	86	46
15.	63	23

	Subtract 28.	
16.	99	71
17.	52	24
18.	90	62

Mixed Review

Write the fact family for each set of numbers.

19. 5, 8, 13
$5 + 8 = 13$
$8 + 5 = 13$
$13 - 5 = 8$
$13 - 8 = 5$

20. 8, 8, 16
$8 + 8 = 16$
$16 - 8 = 8$

Find the sum.

21. $35 + 63 = 98$
22. $59 + 6 = 65$
23. $78 + 27 = 105$
24. $68 + 69 = 137$

Practice PW5

Practice and Problem Solving

Extra Practice, page 14, Set E

Find the difference. Use addition to check.

7. $77 - 4$ = 73
8. $96 - 51$ = 45
9. $50 - 20$ = 30
10. $48 - 16$ = 32
11. $52 - 9$ = 43
12. $23 - 14$ = 9
13. $44 - 25$ = 19
14. $71 - 38$ = 33
15. $66 - 7$ = 59
16. $80 - 53$ = 27
17. $56 - 29$ = 27
18. $60 - 8$ = 52
19. $83 - 67$ = 16
20. $95 - 78$ = 17
21. $55 - 27$ = 28

Copy and complete each table.

	Subtract 20.	
22.	54	34
23.	70	50
24.	35	15

	Subtract 35.	
25.	64	29
26.	72	37
27.	86	51

	Subtract 47.	
28.	71	24
29.	69	22
30.	94	47

USE DATA For 31–32, use the table.

FASTEST INSECT FLYERS	
Insect	**Miles per Hour**
Dragonfly	18
Bumblebee	11
West Indian butterfly	30
Hornet	13
Honeybee	7

31. The greater the number of miles per hour, the faster the insects fly. The West Indian butterfly flies how many miles per hour faster than the honeybee? **23 miles per hour faster**
32. The difference between the speed of the dragonfly and the honeybee is the same speed as which other insect? **bumblebee**

Getting Ready for the EOG Test

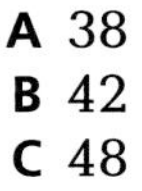

33. Two buses took 74 students to the historical museum. One bus carried 36 students. How many students were on the second bus? **A**

A 38
B 42
C 48
D 110

North Carolina Standards 1.02 Develop fluency with multi-digit addition and subtraction rough 9,999 using: a) Strategies for adding and subtracting numbers.

COMMON ERROR ALERT

Students might subtract the smaller digit from the larger, regardless of its placement in the problem.

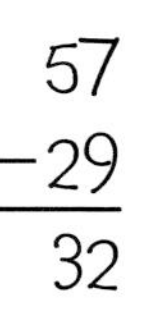

$$\begin{array}{r} 57 \\ -29 \\ \hline 32 \end{array}$$

Help students remember to always subtract the number on the bottom from the number on the top.

Independent Practice

Note that Exercise 32 is a multistep or strategy problem. Assign Exercises 7–32.

4 ASSESS

Summarize the lesson by having students:

DISCUSS How does the inverse operation help you in subtraction? Possible answer: You can use addition to check your subtraction. You could also use subtraction to check your addition.

WRITE Write and solve a subtraction problem with regrouping. Then explain the steps you used. Answers will vary.

LESSON QUIZ

Transparency 1.5

Find the difference. Use addition to check.

1. $42 - 37$ = 5
2. $56 - 18$ = 38

Complete the table.

	Subtract 35.	
3.	81	46
4.	65	30
5.	92	57

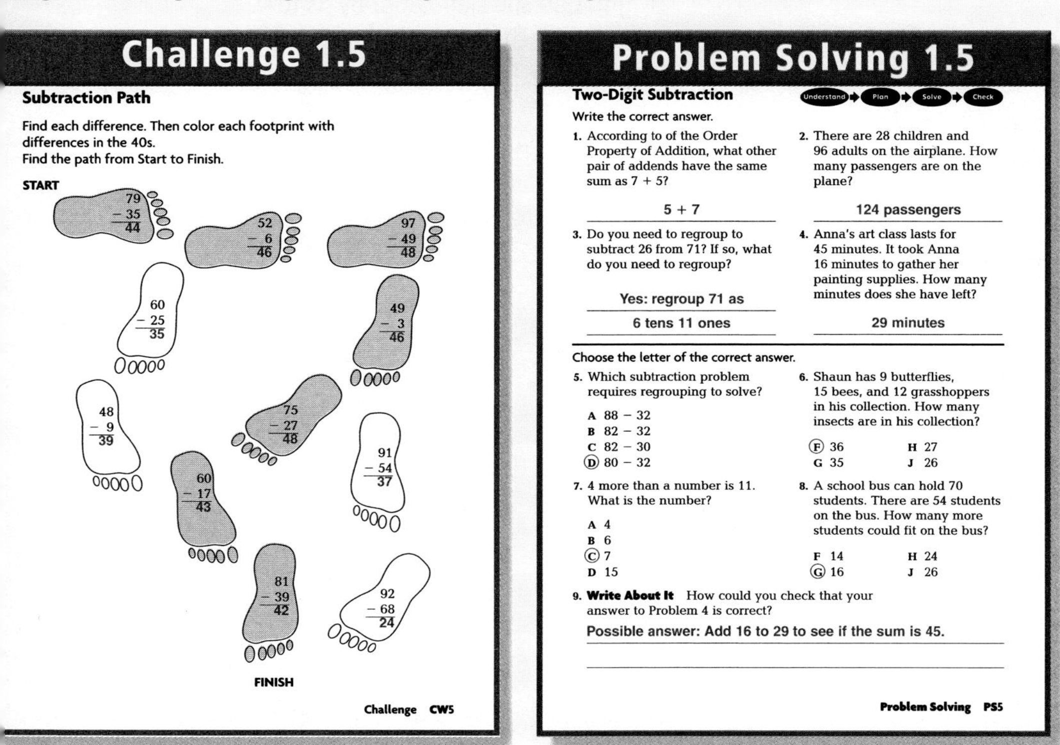

Challenge 1.5

Subtraction Path

Find each difference. Then color each footprint with differences in the 40s.
Find the path from Start to Finish.

START

- 79 − 35 = 44
- 52 − 6 = 46
- 97 − 49 = 48
- 60 − 25 = 35
- 49 − 3 = 46
- 48 − 9 = 39
- 75 − 27 = 48
- 91 − 54 = 37
- 60 − 17 = 43
- 81 − 39 = 42
- 92 − 68 = 24

FINISH

Challenge CW5

Problem Solving 1.5

Two-Digit Subtraction

Understand → Plan → Solve → Check

Write the correct answer.

1. According to of the Order Property of Addition, what other pair of addends have the same sum as 7 + 5? **5 + 7**
2. There are 28 children and 96 adults on the airplane. How many passengers are on the plane? **124 passengers**
3. Do you need to regroup to subtract 26 from 71? If so, what do you need to regroup? **Yes: regroup 71 as 6 tens 11 ones**
4. Anna's art class lasts for 45 minutes. It took Anna 16 minutes to gather her painting supplies. How many minutes does she have left? **29 minutes**

Choose the letter of the correct answer.

5. Which subtraction problem requires regrouping to solve?
A 88 − 32
B 82 − 32
C 82 − 30
D 80 − 32
6. Shaun has 9 butterflies, 15 bees, and 12 grasshoppers in his collection. How many insects are in his collection?
F 36
G 35
H 27
J 26
7. 4 more than a number is 11. What is the number?
A 4
B 6
C 7
D 15
8. A school bus can hold 70 students. There are 54 students on the bus. How many more students could fit on the bus?
F 14
G 16
H 24
J 26
9. **Write About It** How could you check that your answer to Problem 4 is correct?
Possible answer: Add 16 to 29 to see if the sum is 45.

Problem Solving PS5

Lesson 1.6

Problem Solving Skill

Choose the Operation

Lesson Planning

Objective To use the problem solving skill *choose the operation*

Lesson Resources: Reading Transparency 1; Intervention • Problem Solving, Strategy/Skill 1

NCTM Standards

1. Number and Operations
2. Algebra
6. Problem Solving
7. Reasoning and Proof
8. Communication
9. Connections

Math Background

These ideas will help students use the problem solving skill *choose the operation.*

- Addition is used to find a total or to find how many in all.
- Subtraction is used to compare numbers, to find the difference, or to find a missing part.
- You can write a number sentence with the correct operation to solve a problem.

Warm-Up Resources

Number of the Day

The number of the day is the number of days in September minus the number of girls in your class. Write a number sentence to solve. Possible answer: $30 - 14 = 16$.

Daily Facts Practice

Have students practice addition and subtraction facts by completing Set F of *Teacher's Resource Book,* p. TR83.

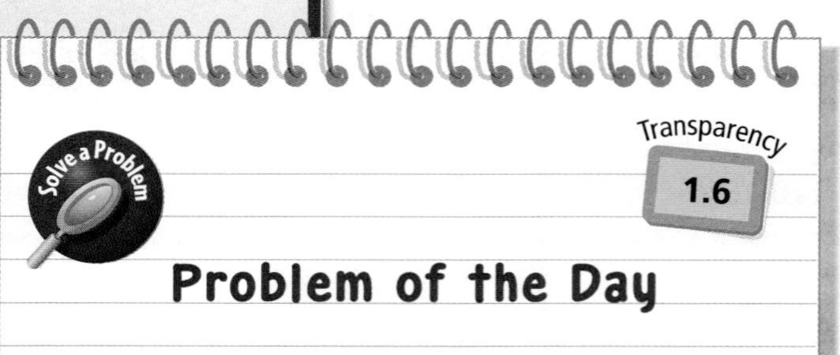

Problem of the Day

Marcella is setting up chairs for Parent Night. Can she skip-count by 5s to arrange 32 chairs in equal rows? Explain. No; possible answer: when you skip-count from 0 by 5s, the ones digit is either 0 or 5.

Solution Problem of the Day tab, p. PD1

Intervention and Extension Resources

Alternative Teaching Strategy

To help students **choose the operation,** pose this problem for discussion: For a school picnic, Judd bought 48 hot dogs and 75 hamburgers. How many more hamburgers did he buy? 27 Discuss with students what they are asked to find. Elicit that they are to compare the two quantities, so they will have to subtract.

Then pose this problem: If 45 parents and 53 children go to the picnic, how many people will there be altogether? 98 Again, discuss what students are asked to find. Explain that they need to find how many in all, so they will have to add.

AUDITORY

VERBAL/LINGUISTIC, INTERPERSONAL

English Language Learners

MATERIALS *For each student* 2 colored index cards, tape

To help students **remember the meanings of the operations,** have them prepare index cards to tape to their desks as reminders. Have students write *Addition* at the top of one card and *Subtraction* at the top of the other card. Guide them to write clues for themselves about each operation's meaning. If necessary, have a student proficient in English help them copy from page 12 the definitions for each operation.

VISUAL

VERBAL/LINGUISTIC

Reading Strategy

Draw Conclusions Explain to students that when you **draw conclusions to solve a problem,** you use information you already know to find the answer. Pose this problem: For her leaf project, Rosi found 13 different leaves on Thursday and 25 additional leaves on Saturday. So far, how many leaves has she found?

Have students list the facts provided, recall what they already know about addition, and then write a number sentence and solve the problem. Possible answer: Facts known—13 leaves and 25 leaves have been found. The question asks how many in all Rosi found, so you need to add. $13 + 25 = 38$ leaves

Transparency 1 **Reading Transparency 1**

Multistep and Strategy Problems

The following multistep or strategy problem is provided in Lesson 1.6:

Page	Item
13	7

Technology Link

Intervention • Problem Solving, *Strategy/Skill 1*

Social Studies Connection

Help students **choose the operation** by displaying the following table.

STARS ON STATE FLAGS	
State	**Number of Stars**
Alaska	8
Arkansas	29
Georgia	13
Missouri	24
Oregon	33
Rhode Island	13

Have students write number sentences to show how they solved each of the following problems.

What is the difference between the number of stars on the state flag with the fewest stars and the flag with the most stars?
$33 - 8 = 25$ stars

How many stars in all are on the Missouri and the Arkansas flags?
$24 + 29 = 53$ stars

VISUAL

LOGICAL/MATHEMATICAL

Lesson 1.6 Organizer

Objective To use the problem solving skill *choose the operation.*

Lesson Resources Reading Transparency 1; Intervention • Problem Solving, Strategy/Skill 1

1 INTRODUCE

QUICK REVIEW provides review of computational skills.

WHY LEARN THIS? You will be able to solve more complex problems if you know whether to add or subtract. *Share the lesson objective with students.*

2 TEACH

Guided Instruction

- *Read the first problem with students.*
  How do you know that you do not need to add? Addition is used to find how many in all, and you already have the total.
  What question could you ask that would require addition? There are 13 stars in the outer circle and 6 stars in the inner circle. How many stars are there in all?
- *Direct students' attention to the second problem.*
  What question could you ask about the information that would require subtraction? Possible answer: How much longer is the Two Lakes Loop than the Birdseye trail? 3 miles longer
- *Read Talk About It.*
  What operation sign will be in the first number sentence? a plus sign
  For the second question, what operation sign will you use? a minus sign

LESSON 6

Problem Solving Skill
Choose the Operation

UNDERSTAND › PLAN › SOLVE › CHECK

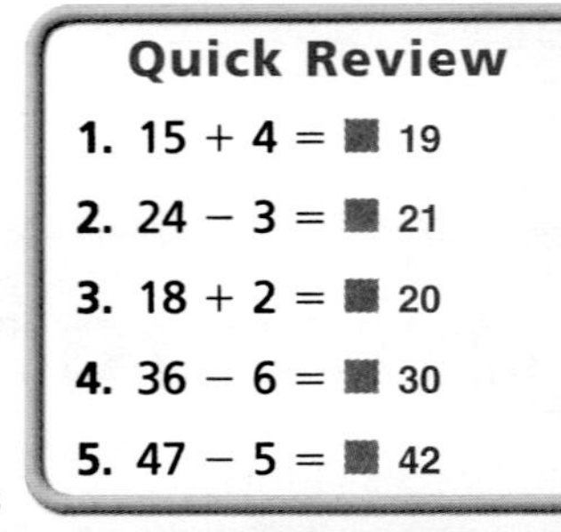

Quick Review

1. 15 + 4 = ■ 19
2. 24 − 3 = ■ 21
3. 18 + 2 = ■ 20
4. 36 − 6 = ■ 30
5. 47 − 5 = ■ 42

THE 19TH STATE The state flag of Indiana has 19 gold stars and a flaming torch. There are 13 stars in an outer circle representing the 13 original states. How many stars are in the inner circle?

Before you solve a problem, you need to decide what the problem asks you to find.

Use addition to find how many in all, or the total.	Use subtraction to find how many are left, to compare, or to find a missing part.

Since you need to find the part that is missing, you subtract.

19	−	13	=	6
↑		↑		↑
total number of stars		number of stars in outer circle		number of stars in inner circle

So, there are 6 stars in the inner circle.

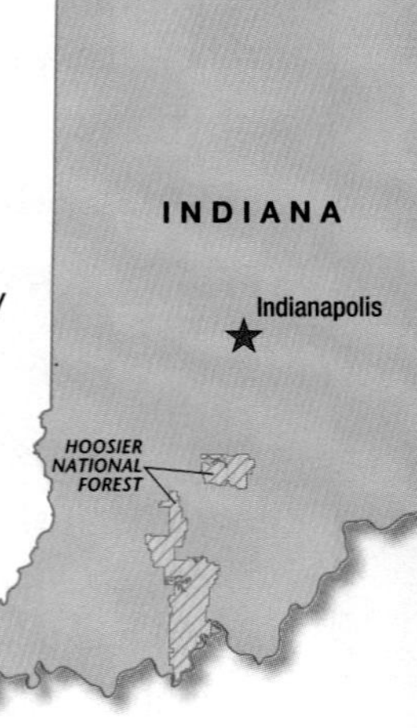

Andrew's family camped in the Hoosier National Forest. They hiked the 15-mile Two Lakes Loop and the 12-mile Birdseye trail. How many miles did they hike?

Since you need to find how many in all, you add.

15 + 12 = 27

So, they hiked 27 miles in all.

Talk About It

- Write a number sentence that shows the total number of stars on the Indiana state flag. **Possible answer: 13 + 6 = 19**
- Give an example of a problem in which you would subtract to compare. **Possible answer: James weighs 63 pounds. Paul weighs 57 pounds. Who weighs more? Explain.**

12

Reteach 1.6

Problem Solving Skill

Choose the Operation

Remember that before you solve a problem, you need to decide what the problem asks you to find. The table shows examples of problems in which you add or subtract.

Tom rode his bike 12 miles in the morning and 8 miles in the afternoon. How far did Tom ride in all?	**Add**—You are finding how many in all. 12 + 8 = 20 miles
There are 13 girls and 18 boys taking music lessons. How many children are taking music lessons?	**Add**—You are joining two groups. 13 + 18 = 31 children
The school store had 48 T-shirts. It sold 27 shirts. How many shirts were not sold?	**Subtract**—You are finding how many are left. 48 − 27 = 21 shirts
In one class there are 14 girls and 9 boys. How many more girls are there than boys?	**Subtract**—You are comparing two different amounts. 14 − 9 = 5 more girls

Choose the operation you need to use. Write *add* or *subtract*. Then write a number sentence to solve the problem.

1. Susi planted 29 pansies and 33 marigolds. How many flowers did Susi plant in all?
   add
   29 + 33 = 62 flowers
2. Ben lives 6 blocks from school, and Troy lives 11 blocks from school. How much farther from school does Troy live than Ben?
   subtract
   11 − 6 = 5 blocks
3. Mrs. Chang had 24 apples. She used 6 in a pie. How many apples does she have left?
   subtract
   24 − 6 = 18 apples
4. There are 28 adults and 78 children at the puppet show. How many people are at the show?
   add
   28 + 78 = 106 people

RW6 Reteach

Practice 1.6

Problem Solving Skill

Choose the Operation

Choose the operation. Write a number sentence. Then solve.

1. Ashley is making a patchwork quilt. She cut out 46 squares. Then she cut out 25 triangles. How many quilt pieces did she cut out?
   addition
   46 + 25 = 71
   71 quilt pieces
2. Van and Lisa were playing darts. Van scored 49 points, and Lisa scored 83 points. How many more points did Lisa score than Van?
   subtraction
   83 − 49 = 34
   34 more points

For Exercises 3–4, use the following.

On Robin's farm there are 68 cows. In the spring 54 calves were born. How many cows and calves are there altogether?

3. What number sentence can you write to solve the problem?
   A 68 + 68 = 136
   (B) 68 + 54 = 122
   C 68 − 54 = 14
   D 54 − 54 = 0
4. How many more cows than calves are there?
   F 4
   G 12
   (H) 14
   J 16

Mixed Review

Solve.

5. 34 + 13 = **47**
6. 86 + 7 = **93**
7. 59 − 36 = **23**
8. 86 − 18 = **68**
9. 59 + 41 = **100**
10. 43 − 6 = **37**
11. 94 − 38 = **56**
12. 74 + 95 = **169**

PW6 Practice

Problem Solving Practice

Choose the operation. Write a number sentence. Then solve.

▲ Indiana's state bird is the cardinal.

Problem Solving

1. There were 48 children on the playground. Then 34 children went inside. How many children were left on the playground?
subtraction; 48 − 34 = 14; 14 were left
2. Cardinals' eggs hatch in about 13 days. Baby cardinals fly about 12 days after they hatch. About how many days after the female lays her eggs do baby cardinals fly?
addition; 13 + 12 = 25; after about 25 days

From Indianapolis, Indiana, Emily's family drove 65 miles on Saturday to visit friends in Richmond. On Sunday they drove 91 miles to Fort Wayne. How many more miles did they drive on Sunday than on Saturday?

3. Which number sentence can you use to solve the problem? B

   A 65 + 91 = 156
   B 91 − 65 = 26
   C 65 − 65 = 0
   D 91 + 91 = 182

4. How many miles did Emily's family drive in the two days? H

   F 126
   G 151
   H 156
   J 165

Mixed Applications

For 5–7, use the pictograph.

THIRD-GRADE FAVORITE SPORTS

Basketball	⚽ ⚽ ⚽ ⚽
Soccer	⚽ ⚽ ⚽ ⚽ ⚽ ⚽
Football	⚽ ⚽
Baseball	⚽ ⚽ ⚽

Key: Each ⚽ = 2 students.

5. How many more third-grade students at Joel's school like soccer than basketball?
4 more students
6. How many fewer students like football than soccer?
8 fewer students
7. **What's the Question?** The answer is 6 students. How many third-grade students voted for baseball?

North Carolina Standards 1.02 Develop fluency with multi-digit addition and subtraction ough 9,999 using: a) Strategies for adding and subtracting numbers. *also* 1.06

Challenge 1.6

Solving Problems Using a Weather Map

Use the map to solve the problems below. Tell what operation you used to solve each problem.

SEATTLE 71°
PORTLAND 75°
CHICAGO 78°
OMAHA 86°
NEW YORK CITY 83°
SAN FRANCISCO 67°
HOUSTON 97°
MIAMI 91°

1. How many degrees warmer is it in Houston than in Seattle?
26 degrees
subtraction
2. How many degrees cooler is it in Portland than in Miami?
16 degrees
subtraction
3. By the end of the week, the high temperature in San Francisco is expected to rise 8 degrees. What will the temperature be then?
75 degrees
addition
4. One week ago in New York City, the high temperature was 11 degrees warmer. What was the high temperature on that day?
94 degrees
addition
5. The temperature in Omaha is expected to drop 18 degrees overnight. What will the temperature be tomorrow morning?
68 degrees
subtraction
6. Tomorrow's forecast for Chicago is an increase of 12 degrees. What will Chicago's temperature be tomorrow?
90 degrees
addition

CW6 Challenge

Reading Strategy 1.6

Draw Conclusions Understand → Plan → Solve → Check

To solve a problem, you may have to **draw conclusions** based on information you are given as well as something you already know.

Read the following problem.

Max needs to buy a container of orange juice. He bought a container of grape juice at the store for $2.89. Should Max take a $1-bill, a $5-bill, or a $10-bill to pay for the orange juice?

1. What does Max have to decide?
if he can buy orange juice for $1, for $5, or for $10
2. What does Max already know that will help him make his decision?
A container of grape juice costs $2.89.
3. Solve the problem. Explain your thinking.
A $5-bill; orange juice probably costs about the same as grape juice.

Solve. Explain your thinking. Possible explanations are given.

4. Lisa is 4 feet tall. The bookcase in her bedroom reaches from the floor to the ceiling. Should she say the bookcase is 2 feet tall, 8 feet tall, or 20 feet tall?
8 feet tall; the height of Lisa's bedroom is probably about twice Lisa's height and 4 + 4 = 8
5. Myra's large dog weighs 52 pounds. Myra is writing a story about her cat. Should she say the cat weighs 14 pounds, 40 pounds, or 80 pounds?
14 pounds; cats weigh much less than large dogs.

PS6 Reading Strategy

3 PRACTICE

Guided Practice

Do Problem Solving Practice Exercises 1–4 with students. Identify students who are having difficulty and choose appropriate lesson resources to provide assistance.

Remind students to ask themselves whether they need to find how many in all. If not, they can quickly eliminate addition.

Independent Practice

Note that Exercise 7 is a multistep or strategy problem. Assign Exercises 5–7.

4 ASSESS

Summarize the lesson by having students:

DISCUSS How do you decide whether to add or subtract to solve a problem? To find a total or how many in all, you add. To find how many are left, to compare, or to find a missing part, you subtract.

WRITE Kevin has 56 stamps. Jill has 38 stamps. Write one addition and one subtraction problem using this information. Exchange papers with a classmate and solve. Answers will vary.

LESSON QUIZ Transparency 1.6

Choose the operation. Write a number sentence. Then solve.

1. Dawn collected 36 shells on Friday. By Sunday she had collected 58 shells. How many did she collect between Friday and Sunday? subtraction; 58 − 36 = 22; 22 shells
2. Morgan had 72 stamps in his collection. He traded in 13 stamps. How many does he have left? subtraction; 72 − 13 = 59; 59 stamps

CHAPTER 1 Extra Practice

Purpose **To provide extra practice for the skills presented in this chapter**

The blue page references in each set of exercises refer to the lesson pages where each skill is taught.

Internet Resources

Visit THE LEARNING SITE at **www.harcourtschool.com** for a listing of practice activities.

Extra Practice

Set A (pp. 2–3)

Complete.

1. $14 - 5 = 9$, so $9 + \blacksquare = 14$. **5**

2. $9 + 7 = 16$, so $16 - \blacksquare = 7$. **9**

Write the fact family for each set of numbers. **See below.**

3. 5, 8, 13 **4.** 6, 8, 14 **5.** 7, 8, 15 **6.** 7, 7, 14

3. $5 + 8 = 13, 8 + 5 = 13, 13 - 5 = 8, 13 - 8 = 5$
4. $6 + 8 = 14, 8 + 6 = 14, 14 - 6 = 8, 14 - 8 = 6$
5. $7 + 8 = 15, 8 + 7 = 15, 15 - 7 = 8, 15 - 8 = 7$
6. $7 + 7 = 14, 14 - 7 = 7$

Set B (pp. 4–5)

Find the missing addend.

1. $5 + \blacksquare = 13$ **8** **2.** $\blacksquare + 6 = 15$ **9** **3.** $6 + \blacksquare = 14$ **8** **4.** $\blacksquare + 5 = 14$ **9**

5. $\blacksquare + 8 = 17$ **9** **6.** $8 + \blacksquare = 15$ **7** **7.** $7 + \blacksquare = 13$ **6** **8.** $7 + \blacksquare = 16$ **9**

Set C (pp. 6–7)

Find each sum.

1. $8 + 9 = \blacksquare$; $9 + 8 = \blacksquare$ **17, 17**

2. $9 + 5 = \blacksquare$; $5 + 9 = \blacksquare$ **14, 14**

3. $8 + (3 + 7) = \blacksquare$; $(8 + 3) + 7 = \blacksquare$ **18, 18**

4. $7 + 8 = \blacksquare$; $8 + 7 = \blacksquare$ **15, 15**

5. The pet store sold 8 hamsters, 2 guinea pigs, and 5 ferrets. How many animals did it sell in all? **15 animals**

6. Liz planted 7 daisies and 4 roses. Audrey planted 4 pansies and 7 tulips. How many flowers did each girl plant in all? **7 + 4 = 11 and 4 + 7 = 11. Each girl planted 11 flowers.**

Set D (pp. 8–9)

Find the sum.

1. $53 + 21$ **74** **2.** $72 + 8$ **80** **3.** $28 + 64$ **92** **4.** $56 + 19$ **75** **5.** $67 + 25$ **92**

Set E (pp. 10–11)

Find the difference. Use addition to check.

1. $48 - 6$ **42** **2.** $86 - 50$ **36** **3.** $75 - 38$ **37** **4.** $92 - 66$ **26** **5.** $62 - 27$ **35**

14

Review/Test

CHECK VOCABULARY

Choose the best term from the box.

1. $(6 + 4) + 7 = 6 + (4 + 7)$ is an example of the _?_. (p. 6) **Grouping Property of Addition**
2. A set of related addition and subtraction number sentences that use the same numbers is called a _?_. (p. 2) **fact family**
3. $7 + 8 = 8 + 7$ is an example of the _?_. (p. 6) **Order Property of Addition**
4. Addition and subtraction are _?_. (p. 2) **inverse operations**
5. $12 + 0 = 12$ is an example of the _?_. (p. 6) **Identity Property of Addition**

Order Property of Addition
Identity Property of Addition
Grouping Property of Addition
fact family
inverse operations
addend

CHECK SKILLS

6. 6 + 9 = 15, 9 + 6 = 15, 15 – 6 = 9, 15 – 9 = 6
7. 8 + 8 = 16, 16 – 8 = 8

Write the fact family for each set of numbers. (pp. 2–3)

6. 6, 9, 15 **See above.**
7. 8, 8, 16 **See above.**
8. 5, 7, 12 **See below.**
9. 8, 9, 17 **See below.**

8. 5 + 7 = 12, 7 + 5 = 12, 12 – 5 = 7, 12 – 7 = 5
9. 8 + 9 = 17, 9 + 8 = 17, 17 – 8 = 9, 17 – 9 = 8

Find the missing addend. (pp. 4–5)

10. $6 + ■ = 13$ **7**
11. $■ + 9 = 16$ **7**
12. $7 + ■ = 15$ **8**
13. $9 + ■ = 14$ **5**

Find the sum or difference. (pp. 8–9, 10–11)

14. $35 + 24$ **59**
15. $77 - 43$ **34**
16. $63 + 8$ **71**
17. $71 - 44$ **27**
18. $59 + 47$ **106**

CHECK PROBLEM SOLVING

Solve. (pp. 12–13)

19. Jonathan read 36 library books during the school year. His sister Kara read 48 books. How many books did the children read in all? **84 books**
20. Abby and Jack collected 72 shells in all while on vacation at the seashore. Abby collected 37 shells. How many shells did Jack collect? **35 shells**

Chapter 1 Test, page 1

Choose the correct answer.

1. 7 – 4 = 3, so 4 + 3 = ■
   A 1 B 3 C 4 (D) 7
2. 2 + 8 = 10, so 10 – 2 = ■
   F 2 (G) 8 H 10 J 12
3. 7 + 4 = 11, so 11 – ■ = 7
   (A) 4 B 10 C 11 D 18
4. What fact is part of the fact family 5, 9, and 14?
   F 9 – 4 = 5
   G 14 + 5 = 19
   H 9 – 5 = 4
   (J) 5 + 9 = 14

For 5–7, find the missing addend.

5. 6 + ■ = 12
   (A) 6 B 7 C 12 D 16
6. ■ + 4 = 13
   F 3 (G) 9 H 10 J 15
7. 8 + ■ = 11
   A 1 (B) 3 C 4 D 7
8. I am a number less than 50. My tens digit is 2 more than my ones digit. My ones digit is 1. What number am I?
   F 13 G 21 (H) 31 J 32

For 9–11, use the correct property to solve.

9. 8 + 0 = ■
   A 0 B 1 (C) 8 D 16
10. (3 + 8) + 5 = ■
   F (7 + 3) + 5
   G (5 + 3) + 5
   H 5 + (8 + 5)
   (J) 3 + (8 + 5)

Go On

Chapter 1 Test, page 2

11. 2 + 5 = 5 + ■?
   A 0 B 1 (C) 2 D 7

For 12–14, find the sum.

12. 27 + 36
   (F) 63 G 73 H 78 J 513
13. 77 + 39
   A 1,016 (B) 116 C 106 D 38
14. 95 + 56
   F 39 G 141 (H) 151 J 1,411
15. Beau has 32 stickers. His sister has 26. How many stickers do they have altogether?
   A 6 B 14 C 56 (D) 58

For 16–17, find the difference.

16. 48 – 19
   F 21 (G) 29 H 31 J 67
17. 83 – 56
   A 129 B 37 C 30 (D) 27
18. There were 64 monkeys at the zoo. Susan saw 33 monkeys climbing in the trees. The rest of the monkeys were eating. How many monkeys were eating?
   F 21 (G) 31 H 37 J 97

For 19–20, choose the operation to solve. Then solve.

19. Jamal collected 48 stamps. Peter collected 39 stamps. How many more stamps did Jamal collect than Peter?
   A addition, 87
   B addition, 77
   C subtraction, 19
   (D) subtraction, 9
20. There were 28 singers in the school chorus last year. There are 15 more singers in the chorus this year. How many singers are in the chorus this year?
   (F) addition, 43
   G addition, 53
   H subtraction, 32
   J subtraction, 13

Stop

Review/Test

Purpose To check understanding of concepts, skills, and problem solving presented in Chapter 1

Using the Page

The Chapter 1 Review/Test can be used as a **review** or a **test.**

- Items 1–5 check children's understanding of concepts and new vocabulary.
- Items 6–18 check skill proficiency.
- Items 19–20 check students' abilities to apply problem-solving strategies to real-life addition and subtraction problems.

Suggest that children place the completed Chapter 1 Review/Test in their portfolios.

Using the Assessment Guide

- Multiple-choice format of Chapter 1 Posttest—See *Assessment Guide,* pp. AG9–10.
- Free-response format of Chapter 1 Posttest—See *Assessment Guide,* pp. AG11–12.

Using Student Self-Assessment

The How Did I Do? survey helps children assess what they have learned and how they learned it. This survey is available as a copying master in *Assessment Guide,* p. AGxvii.

Getting Ready for the EOG Test
Chapter 1

Using the Pages

These pages may be used to help students get ready for the North Carolina EOG Test. The test items are written in the same style and arranged in the same format as those on the EOG Test.

The pages are cumulative. They cover the standards from the North Carolina Mathematics Standard Course of Study that have been taught up to this point in the text or in a previous grade. Each Getting Ready for the EOG Test also reviews the North Carolina mathematics strands shown below.

- Number and Operations
- Measurement
- Geometry
- Data Analysis and Probability
- Algebra

These pages can be assigned at the end of the chapter as classwork or as a homework assignment. You may want to have students use individual recording sheets presented in a multiple-choice (standardized) format. A Test Answer Sheet is available as a blackline master in the *Assessment Guide* (p. AGlii).

You may wish to have students describe how they solved each problem and share their solutions.

Getting Ready for the EOG Test

NUMBER AND OPERATIONS

1. Luke has 405 trading cards. Which word name shows the number of cards? **B**

A five hundred four
B four hundred five
C four hundred fifty
D forty-five

2. What is the value of the digit 5 in 547? **C**

A 5
B 50
C 500
D 5,000

3. Tobey found the sum of two odd addends. Neither addend is zero. What is true about this sum? **C**

A It is less than either addend.
B It is less than one addend but greater than the other addend.
C It is an even number greater than either addend.
D It is an odd number equal to one of the addends.

4. Explain It Liz has 23 stickers. Mary has 42 more stickers than Liz. Tell how to write a number sentence to find how many stickers Mary has. Then find how many stickers Mary has.
See page 17.

MEASUREMENT AND GEOMETRY

5. Carly wants to measure the length of her baby gerbil. Which would be the ***best*** unit of measure for her to use? **C**

A yard **C** inch
B foot **D** mile

6. Which temperature does the thermometer show? **C**

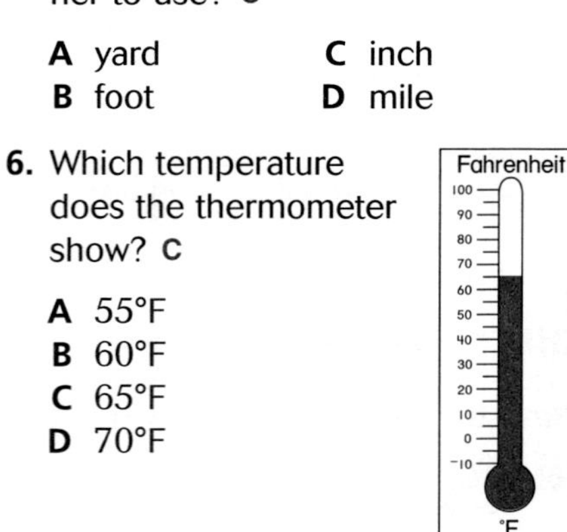

A 55°F
B 60°F
C 65°F
D 70°F

TIP **Eliminate choices.** See item 7. Find the answer choices that weigh **more or less** than 1 pound.

7. Kara names an item that weighs about 1 pound. Which item does she name? **B**

A a chair **C** a pencil
B a soccer ball **D** a bicycle

8. Explain It Dee made a sketch of her flower garden. She wants to put a fence around the garden. How can Dee decide how much fencing she should buy? **See page 17.**

4 feet
6 feet
6 feet
4 feet

16

ALGEBRA

9. How are these numbers alike? **D**

3, 9, 15

A even numbers greater than 2 but less than 15
B odd numbers greater than 3 but less than 16
C even numbers greater than 5 but less than 20
D odd numbers greater than 2 but less than 16

10. Rick practiced the piano for 10 minutes on Monday. He practiced for 20 minutes on Tuesday and for 30 minutes on Wednesday. If this pattern continues, how long will Rick practice the piano on Thursday? **B**

A 15 minutes
B 40 minutes
C 50 minutes
D 1 hour

11. Explain It How can you find a pattern rule to complete the table?

Number of bicycles	1	2	3	4	5
Number of wheels	2	4	6		

Tell the rule. Then copy and complete the table. **See below.**

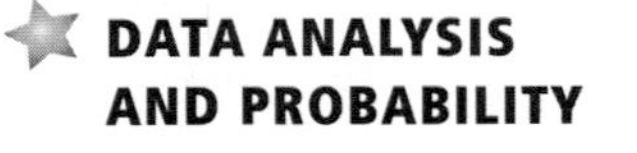

DATA ANALYSIS AND PROBABILITY

12. Jason and Amy are using this spinner to play a game. What color is Amy *most* likely to spin? **C**

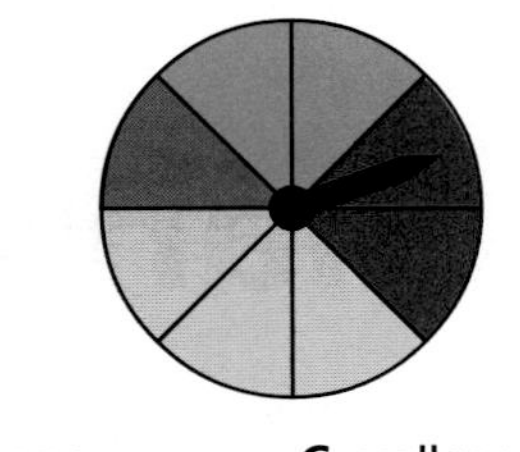

A green **C** yellow
B blue **D** red

13. The graph shows the number of animals at Frank's farm. How many ducks are at Frank's farm? **D**

ANIMALS AT FRANK'S FARM

Chickens	■■■■
Ducks	■■■■■■■■■
Cows	■■■■■■

Key: Each ■ = 2 animals.

A 8 **C** 16
B 12 **D** 18

14. Explain It Use the graph above. Tell how to order the numbers of farm animals from least to greatest. Then order the numbers of animals at Frank's farm.
See below.

Chapter 1

Item Analysis

You may wish to use the item analysis to determine which North Carolina standards need additional review.

Item	North Carolina Standard	Lesson
1	(2) 1.01	Grade 2
2	(2) 1.01	Grade 2
3	(2) Goal 1	Grade 2
4	(2) 1.04	Grade 2
5	(2) Goal 2	Grade 2
6	(2) 2.01	Grade 2
7	(2) Goal 2	Grade 2
8	(2) 2.01	Grade 2
9	(2) Goal 5	Grade 2
10	(2) 5.01	Grade 2
11	(2) Goal 5	Grade 2
12	(2) 4.02	Grade 2
13	(2) 4.01	Grade 2
14	(2) 4.01	Grade 2

SCORING RUBRIC
Explain It

2 Demonstrates a complete understanding of the problem and chooses an appropriate strategy to determine the solution

1 Demonstrates a partial understanding of the problem and chooses a strategy that does not lead to a complete and accurate solution

0 Demonstrates little understanding of the problem and shows little evidence of using any strategy to determine a solution

Explain It • Written Response

4. Possible answer: the word *more* indicates addition: $23 + 42 = 65$.

8. Possible answer: Dee can add the lengths of the 4 sides: $6 + 4 + 6 + 4 = 20$. She will need 20 feet of fencing.

11. Possible response: the number of bicycles increases by 1. The number of wheels increases by 2. The rule is count by twos. 8, 10

14. Possible response: compare the number of symbols: $4 < 6 < 9$, so the order is chickens, cows, ducks.

Place Value and Number Sense

NCTM Standards 2000

1. Number and Operations *Lessons 2.1, 2.2, 2.3, 2.5, 2.6*
2. Algebra *Lesson 2.5*
3. Geometry
4. Measurement
5. Data Analysis and Probability
6. Problem Solving *Lessons 2.1, 2.2, 2.3, 2.4, 2.5, 2.6*
7. Reasoning and Proof *Lessons 2.1, 2.2, 2.3, 2.4, 2.6*
8. Communication *Lessons 2.1, 2.2, 2.3, 2.4, 2.5, 2.6*
9. Connections *Lessons 2.1, 2.2, 2.3, 2.4, 2.6*
10. Representation *Lessons 2.1, 2.2, 2.3, 2.4, 2.5, 2.6*

Chapter Planner

Getting Ready for Chapter 2 • Assessing Prior Knowledge and INTERVENTION (See PE and TE page 19.)

LESSON	NORTH CAROLINA STANDARDS	PACING	VOCABULARY*	MATERIALS	RESOURCES AND TECHNOLOGY
2.1 Hands On: Even and Odd pp. 20–21 **Objective** To identify odd and even numbers and use a hundred chart to skip-count	maintains (2) 1.06	1 Day (For Lessons 2.1 and 2.2)	**even** **odd**	*For each student* connecting cubes, hundred chart, crayons	Reteach, Practice, Problem Solving, Challenge 2.1 Transparency 2.1 **Intervention,** *Skills 1–2* (CD or Book)
2.2 Place Value: 3-Digit Numbers pp. 22–23 **Objective** To find the value of a digit by using its place-value position	1.01a *also* 1.01b		**digits** **standard form** **expanded form** **word form**		Reteach, Practice, Problem Solving, Challenge 2.2 Transparency 2.2 **Math Jingles® CD 3–4** **Intervention,** *Skills 1–2* (CD or Book) **Harcourt Mega Math Country Countdown,** *Block Busters*
2.3 Place Value: 4-Digit Numbers pp. 24–27 **Objective** To identify place-value relationships in 4-digit numbers	1.01a *also* 1.01b	2 Days		*For each group* base-ten blocks	Reteach, Practice, Problem Solving, Challenge 2.3 Transparency 2.3 **Intervention,** *Skills 1–2* (CD or Book) **Harcourt Mega Math Country Countdown,** *Block Busters*
2.4 Problem Solving Strategy: Use Logical Reasoning pp. 28–29 **Objective** To solve problems by using the problem solving strategy *use logical reasoning*	1.01a *also* 1.01b	1 Day			Reteach, Practice, Reading Strategy, Challenge 2.4 Transparency 2.4 Reading Transparency 2 **Intervention • Problem Solving,** *Strategy/Skill 2* (CD or Book)
2.5 Algebra: Number Patterns pp. 30–31 **Objective** To describe, extend, create, and predict number patterns from numbers and models	5.01 *also* 5.02	1 Day	**pattern**		Reteach, Practice, Problem Solving, Challenge 2.5 Transparency 2.5 **Intervention,** *Skills 1–2* (CD or Book) **Harcourt Mega Math The Number Games,** *Tiny's Think Tank*
2.6 Place Value: 5- and 6-Digit Numbers pp. 32–33 **Objective** To identify the place value of digits in 5- and 6-digit numbers	1.01b	1 Day			Reteach, Practice, Problem Solving, Challenge 2.6 Transparency 2.6 **Intervention,** *Skills 1–2* (CD or Book) **Harcourt Mega Math The Number Games,** *Tiny's Think Tank*; **Fraction Action,** *Number Line Mine*

Ending Chapter 2 • **Extra Practice,** p. 34 • **Chapter 2 Review/Test,** p. 35 • **Getting Ready for the EOG Test,** pp. 36–37

* **Boldfaced** terms are the key mathematical terms for the chapter. Other terms are review vocabulary.

Voc bulary Pow r

Review Vocabulary

To be ready for Chapter 2, students should know the following vocabulary term:

- **number** (p. 19)—a word that names a quantity of something; a number is shown with a symbol, written words, or concrete models

Vocabulary Cards

Have students use the Vocabulary Cards on *Teacher's Resource Book* pages TR141–143 for the key terms in the chapter. The cards can be added to a file of mathematics terms.

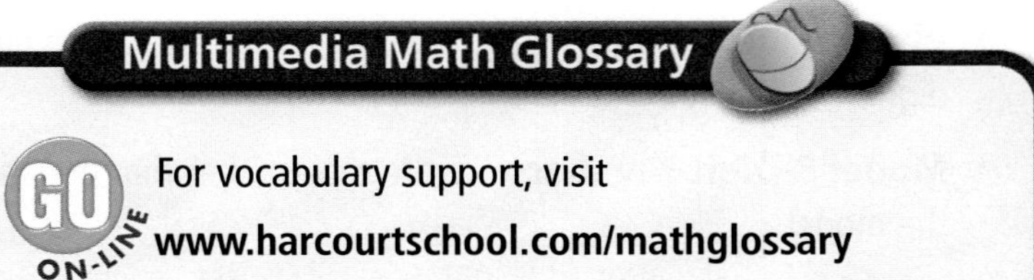

Develop Key Chapter Vocabulary

The **boldfaced** words are the key vocabulary terms in the chapter.

- **even** (p. 20)—a whole number that has a 0, 2, 4, 6, or 8 in the ones place
- **odd** (p. 20)—a whole number that has a 1, 3, 5, 7, or 9 in the ones place
- **digits** (p. 22)—any one of the ten symbols 0, 1, 2, 3, 4, 5, 6, 7, 8, or 9 used to write numbers
- **standard form** (p. 22)—a way to write numbers by using the digits 0–9, with each digit having a place value
- **expanded form** (p. 22)—a way to write numbers by showing the value of each digit
- **word form** (p. 22)—a way to write numbers by using words
- **pattern** (p. 30)—an ordered set of numbers or objects; the order helps you predict what will come next

Multimedia Math Glossary

GO ON-LINE For vocabulary support, visit **www.harcourtschool.com/mathglossary**

Math Journal

Have students define the key vocabulary terms: *even, odd, digits, standard form, expanded form, word form,* and *pattern.* Have students use their own words and give an example of each.

MATH Word Work

Objective To reinforce vocabulary concepts
Use after Lesson 2.1.

Materials *For each pair* drawing paper or construction paper, 10 counters, 10 index cards, colored pencils

Have students draw a grid similar to the one shown. Each square in the grid should be large enough to place a counter inside. Have students use counters to model the numbers 1 through 10 by filling in the grid from left to right, starting at the top.

Direct students to record each model on an index card. Have partners work together to sort the cards into stacks of odd and even numbers. Have students look for patterns in the pictures. Then have them make a poster to describe and display the patterns they found.

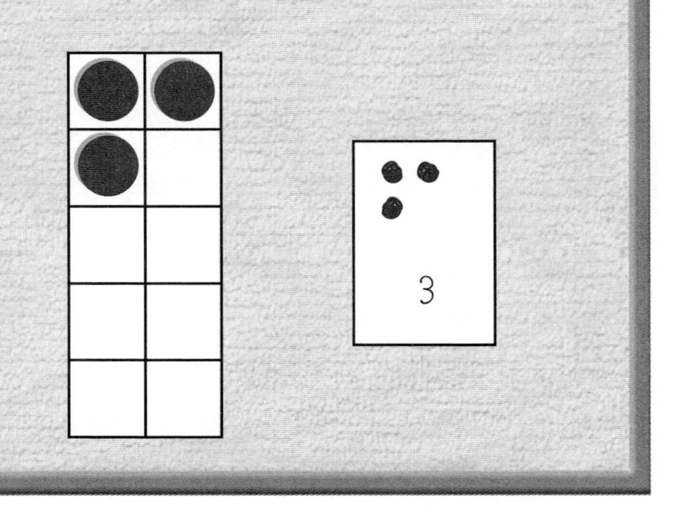

Place Value and Number Sense

Mathematics Across the Grades

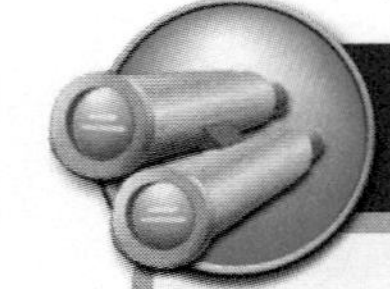

LOOKING BACK • Prerequisite Skills

To be ready for Chapter 2, students should have the following understandings and skills:

- **Place Value: 2-Digit Numbers**—write the value of a given digit
- **Model 3-Digit Numbers**—write the number that matches the model

Check What You Know

Use page 19 to determine students' knowledge of prerequisite concepts and skills.

Intervention

Help students prepare for the chapter by using the intervention resources described on TE page 19.

LOOKING AT CHAPTER 2 • Essential Skills

Students will

- identify odd and even numbers and use a hundred chart to skip-count.
- find the value of a digit by using its place-value position.
- **identify the place value of the digits in 4-, 5-, and 6-digit numbers.**
- describe, extend, create, and predict number patterns from numbers and models.
- solve problems by using logical reasoning.

Example

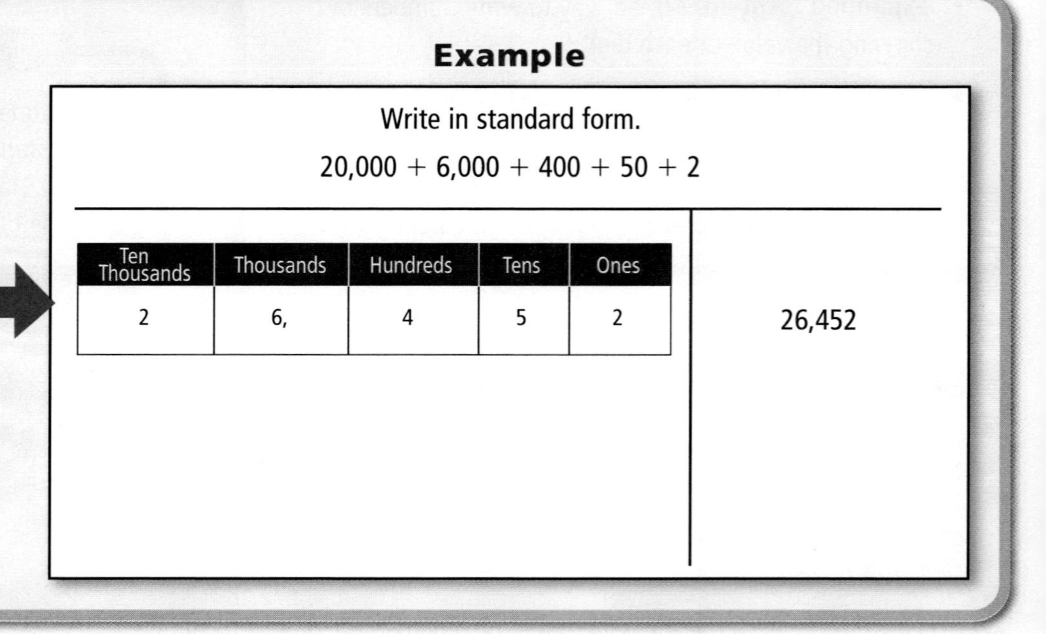

Write in standard form.

20,000 + 6,000 + 400 + 50 + 2

Ten Thousands	Thousands	Hundreds	Tens	Ones
2	6,	4	5	2

26,452

LOOKING AHEAD • Applications

Students will apply what they learn in Chapter 2 to the following new concepts:

- Addition (Chapter 4)
- Understand Multiplication (Chapter 8)
- Subtraction (Chapter 5)
- Understand Division (Chapter 12)

Differentiated Instruction

Meeting the Needs of All Learners

Extra Support	Activities for All	Enrichment
Alternative Teaching Strategy TE Lessons 2.1, 2.2, 2.3, 2.4, 2.5, 2.6 **ESOL/ESL** TE Lessons 2.1, 2.2, 2.3, 2.4, 2.5, 2.6 **Special Needs** TE Lessons 2.2, 2.6	**Cross-Curricular Connections** **Art:** TE Lesson 2.5 **Reading:** TE Lesson 2.4 **Science:** Chapter Opener **Social Studies:** TE Lesson 2.6 **Vocabulary:** TE p. 18B, PE/TE p. 19 **Writing:** TE Lesson 2.3	**Advanced Learners** TE Lessons 2.1, 2.2, 2.4 **Early Finishers** TE Lesson 2.3

Combination and Multi-age Classrooms

Grade 2	Grade 3	Grade 4
Skills Trace Across the Grades		
Read and write numbers to 1,000; identify the value of a digit in a 2-digit number; identify numbers as even or odd; skip-count using a hundred chart.	**Identify even and odd numbers; read, write, and identify the value of whole numbers through 999,999; identify, extend, develop, and use number patterns.**	Read, write, and identify the value of whole numbers through millions.
Instructional Strategies		
Students on this level may require more time to build conceptual understanding. **Assignments** **Grade 3 Pupil Edition** • Skip Lesson 2.5. • Allow students to work in pairs on Lesson 2.6. **Grade 2 Pupil Edition**—pages 1–16, 19–30, and 467–480	Students on this level should be able to complete all the lessons in the Pupil Edition and all the activities in the Teacher's Edition with minimal adjustments. **Assignment** **Grade 3 Pupil Edition**—pages 18–35	Students on this level will probably require less time to build conceptual understanding. **Assignments** **Grade 3 Pupil Edition** • Compact Lessons 2.2 and 2.3. • Challenge students to write 5- and 6-digit number patterns and have a partner extend. **Grade 4 Pupil Edition**—pages 1–15

CHAPTER 2

Place Value and Number Sense

Introducing the Chapter

Tell students that place value tells the value of each digit in a number. Have students focus on the pictograph and tell how many buckets they would draw to show how much water a horse needs to drink in two weeks. 14 buckets

Using Data

To begin the study of this chapter, have students

- Use the pictograph to tell how many gallons of water a horse needs in one day. 10 gallons
- Determine whether a horse needs more than or less than 100 gallons of water per month. more than 100
- Tell which digit in 100 is in the hundreds place. 1

Problem Solving Project

Purpose To use a pictograph to display data

Grouping partners or small groups

Background The United States is the fourth largest horse-raising country in the world, with about 6 million horses. The country with the most horses—more than 10 million—is China.

UNDERSTAND • PLAN • SOLVE • CHECK
Have students

- Redraw the pictograph so that 1 bucket equals 5 gallons of water.
- Determine how many buckets they should draw to represent the amount of water a horse needs in 1 day, 1 week, and 1 month. 2, 14, and 60 buckets
- Skip-count to check their work.

Suggest that students place the pictographs in their portfolios.

Graphing Investigations
Begin Week 2.

CHAPTER 2

Place Value and Number Sense

HOW MUCH WATER A HORSE NEEDS

Time	Water
1 day	1 bucket
1 week	7 buckets
1 month	30 buckets

Key: Each bucket = 10 gallons.

FAST FACT • SCIENCE **Horses have the largest eyes of any land mammal. Their large eyes help horses see almost directly behind themselves while facing forward. Horses need hay, oats, and fresh water to stay healthy.**

PROBLEM SOLVING **Use the pictograph. Skip-count to find how much water a horse needs each week and each month.**

Each week: 70 gallons
Each month: 300 gallons

18

WHY LEARN MATH? Horse owners and trainers need to keep track of the ages and weights of the horses on their farm. Horses are trained to race while they are young and must maintain a certain weight during the racing season. A Thoroughbred can weigh as much as 1,300 pounds. Ask: What digit is in the thousands place? the hundreds place? the tens place? the ones place? 1; 3; 0; 0

Family Involvement Activities

These activities provide:

- Letter to the Family
- Math Vocabulary
- Family Game
- Practice (Homework)

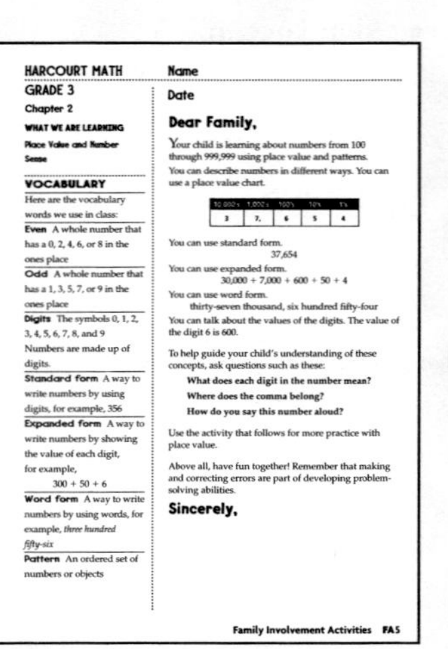

HARCOURT MATH
GRADE 3
Chapter 2
WHAT WE ARE LEARNING
Place Value and Number Sense

VOCABULARY
Here are the vocabulary words we use in class:
Even A whole number that has a 0, 2, 4, 6, or 8 in the ones place
Odd A whole number that has a 1, 3, 5, 7, or 9 in the ones place
Digits The symbols 0, 1, 2, 3, 4, 5, 6, 7, 8, and 9 Numbers are made up of digits.
Standard form A way to write numbers by using digits, for example, 356
Expanded form A way to write numbers by showing the value of each digit, for example, 300 + 50 + 6
Word form A way to write numbers by using words, for example, *three hundred fifty-six*
Pattern An ordered set of numbers or objects

Name
Date

Dear Family,

Your child is learning about numbers from 100 through 999,999 using place value and patterns. You can describe numbers in different ways. You can use a place value chart.

10,000's	1,000's	100's	10's	1's
3	7,	6	5	4

You can use standard form.
37,654
You can use expanded form.
30,000 + 7,000 + 600 + 50 + 4
You can use word form.
thirty-seven thousand, six hundred fifty-four
You can talk about the values of the digits. The value of the digit 6 is 600.

To help guide your child's understanding of these concepts, ask questions such as these:
What does each digit in the number mean?
Where does the comma belong?
How do you say this number aloud?

Use the activity that follows for more practice with place value.

Above all, have fun together! Remember that making and correcting errors are part of developing problem-solving abilities.

Sincerely,

Family Involvement Activities FA5

Family Involvement Activities, p. FA5

Use this page to help you review and remember important skills needed for Chapter 2.

PLACE VALUE: 2-DIGIT NUMBERS

Write the value of the blue digit.

1. 40 **40**
2. 73 **3**
3. 65 **60**
4. 39 **9**
5. 28 **20**
6. 19 **10**
7. 32 **30**
8. 76 **6**
9. 27 **20**
10. 84 **80**

MODEL 3-DIGIT NUMBERS

Write the number that matches the model.

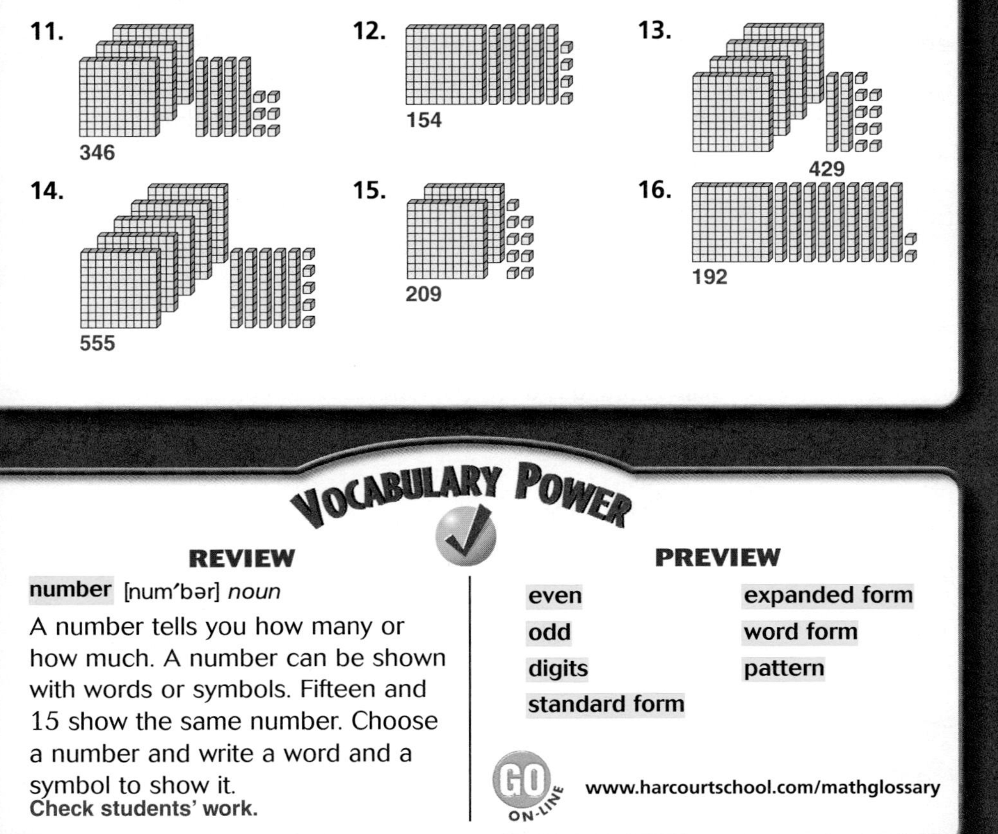

11. **346**
12. **154**
13. **429**
14. **555**
15. **209**
16. **192**

VOCABULARY POWER

REVIEW

number [num′bər] *noun*

A number tells you how many or how much. A number can be shown with words or symbols. Fifteen and 15 show the same number. Choose a number and write a word and a symbol to show it.
Check students' work.

PREVIEW

even
odd
digits
standard form
expanded form
word form
pattern

GO ON-LINE www.harcourtschool.com/mathglossary

Assessing Prior Knowledge

Use the **Check What You Know** page to determine whether your students have mastered the prerequisite skills critical for this chapter.

Intervention

- **Diagnose and Prescribe**
  Evaluate your students' performance on this page to determine whether intervention is necessary or if enrichment is appropriate. Options that provide instruction, practice, and a check are listed in the chart below.

CHECK WHAT YOU KNOW RESOURCES

Intervention Copying Masters or CD-ROMs
Enrichment Copying Masters

VOCABULARY POWER

For activities and information about the vocabulary in this chapter, see page 18B.

Were students successful with CHECK WHAT YOU KNOW?

IF . . . NO THEN . . . INTERVENE | **INTERVENTION OPTIONS** | **IF . . . YES THEN . . . ENRICH**

Skill/Items	Missed more than	Intervene with
Place Value: 2-Digit Numbers, 1–10	3	• *Intervention*, Skill 1
Model 3-Digit Numbers, 11–16	2	• *Intervention*, Skill 2

Skill/Items	Missed fewer than	Enrich with
Place Value: 2-Digit Numbers, 1–10	4	• *Intervention*, Enrichment p. IN331
Model 3-Digit Numbers, 11–16	3	• *Intervention*, Enrichment p. IN332

Lesson 2.1
Even and Odd

Lesson Planning

Objective To identify odd and even numbers and use a hundred chart to skip-count

Materials *For each student* connecting cubes; hundred chart, p. TR15; crayons

NCTM Standards
1. Number and Operations
6. Problem Solving
7. Reasoning and Proof
8. Communication
9. Connections
10. Representation

Math Background

Consider the following as you help students identify odd and even numbers and number patterns on a hundred chart.

- Connecting cubes grouped in twos enable students to visualize and understand odd and even number patterns.
- The process of skip-counting is illustrated as a pattern and made visually clear on a hundred chart.
- Skip-counting is a form of repeated addition and is a readiness activity for multiplication.

Vocabulary

even numbers that have a 0, 2, 4, 6, or 8 in the ones place

odd numbers that have a 1, 3, 5, 7, or 9 in the ones place

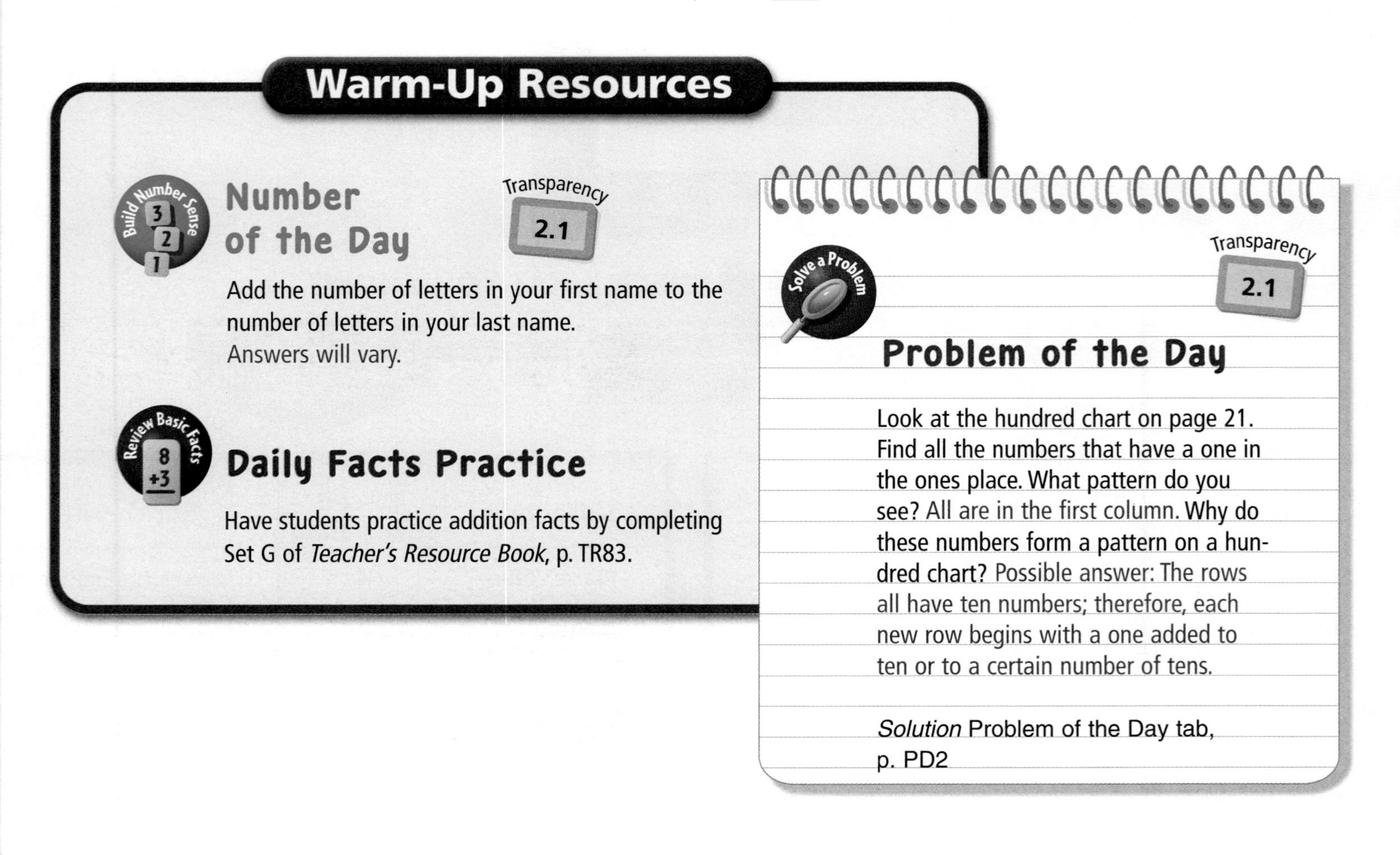

Warm-Up Resources

Number of the Day

Transparency 2.1

Add the number of letters in your first name to the number of letters in your last name.
Answers will vary.

Daily Facts Practice

Have students practice addition facts by completing Set G of *Teacher's Resource Book*, p. TR83.

Problem of the Day

Transparency 2.1

Look at the hundred chart on page 21. Find all the numbers that have a one in the ones place. What pattern do you see? All are in the first column. Why do these numbers form a pattern on a hundred chart? Possible answer: The rows all have ten numbers; therefore, each new row begins with a one added to ten or to a certain number of tens.

Solution Problem of the Day tab, p. PD2

Intervention and Extension Resources

Alternative Teaching Strategy

MATERIALS *For each student* 20 counters

Help students **understand odd and even numbers**. Have students use counters and put them into two groups. Ask: What do you observe about the groups of counters? Possible answers:

If the two groups can have the same number of objects, the number is *even.*

●● ●● (4)
●●● ●●● (6)
●●●● ●●●● (8)

If the two groups cannot have the same number of objects, the number is *odd.*

●● ● (3)
●●● ●● (5)
●●●● ●●● (7)

Have students separate additional counters and tell which groups are even and which are odd. Check students' work.

KINESTHETIC

BODILY/KINESTHETIC

ESOL/ESL

MATERIALS *For each pair* 3 sets of 10 cards, each with a number from 1 to 10

Help students **recognize odd and even numbers by playing a game.** Invite students to use the cards to play a game in which all odd numbers beat all even numbers. You may wish to have students review the definition of odd and even numbers before they play by reading a number from one of the cards and saying, "I have an odd/even number. It is ______." Make sure students thoroughly shuffle the cards before dealing.

KINESTHETIC

BODILY/KINESTHETIC

Multistep and Strategy Problems

The following multistep or strategy problems are provided in Lesson 2.1:

Page	Item
21	17–18

Advanced Learners

Challenge students to **write five or more addition problems with two addends that result in even sums.** When students are finished, ask them to generalize a rule about the addends. Possible answer: To yield an even sum, both addends must be odd or both addends must be even.

VISUAL

LOGICAL/MATHEMATICAL

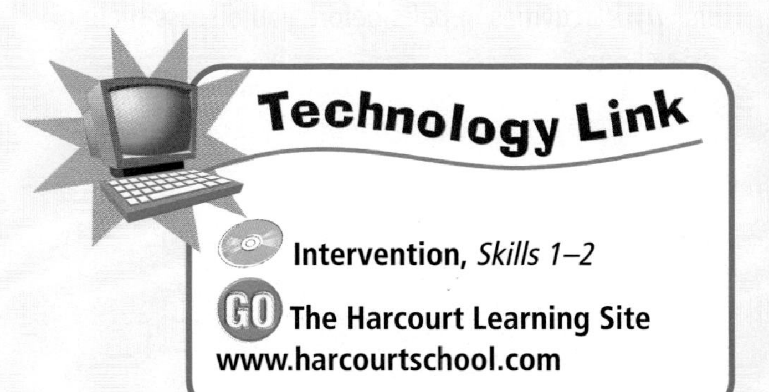

Technology Link
Intervention, Skills 1–2
GO The Harcourt Learning Site
www.harcourtschool.com

Lesson 2.1 Organizer

Objective To identify odd and even numbers and use a hundred chart to skip-count

Vocabulary even, odd

Materials *For each student* connecting cubes; hundred chart, p. TR15; crayons

1 INTRODUCE

Quick Review provides review of prerequisite skills.

Why Learn This? You will practice finding patterns and become a better problem-solver. *Share the lesson objective with students.*

Guided Instruction

- *Ask students to read the Explore section.*
  What pattern do you see in the pairs of connecting cubes in Step 2? In the odd numbers, there is one cube left over. In the even numbers, there are no cubes left over.
  Explain how the pattern you found will work with greater numbers. All greater numbers that end in 1, 3, 5, 7, or 9 are odd. If pairs of connecting cubes are made, there will be one cube left over. All greater numbers that end in 0, 2, 4, 6, or 8 are even. If pairs of connecting cubes are made, there are no cubes left over.

3 PRACTICE

Guided Practice

Complete the Try It activities with your students. Identify students who are having difficulty and choose appropriate lesson resources to provide assistance.

Modifying Instruction Students may complete the *Try It* activities in pairs before you discuss them as a class.

LESSON 1

HANDS ON

Even and Odd

Quick Review

1. 8 + 2 **10**
2. 6 + 3 **9**
3. 9 + 3 **12**
4. 10 + 5 **15**
5. 25 + 5 **30**

VOCABULARY
even odd

MATERIALS
connecting cubes, hundred chart, crayons

Explore

You can use cubes to find odd and even numbers.

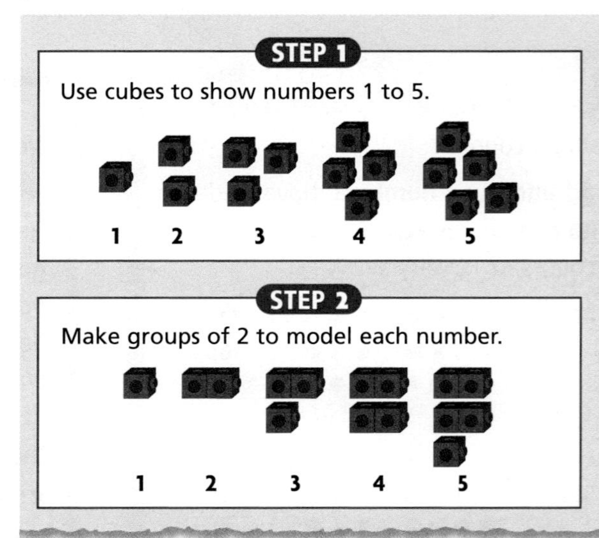

STEP 1
Use cubes to show numbers 1 to 5.
1 2 3 4 5
STEP 2
Make groups of 2 to model each number.
1 2 3 4 5

1st bulleted question: The even numbers have only pairs of cubes with no single cubes left over.
2nd bulleted question: 3 is odd; there is one cube left over when you make pairs.

a. Even numbers can be modeled in groups of 2; odd numbers always have one cube left over when you make groups of 2.

Even numbers show pairs of cubes with no cubes left over.

Odd numbers show pairs of cubes with one cube left over.

- How do you know which numbers are even? **See above.**
- Is 3 an even or odd number? Explain. **See above.**
- What pattern do you see? **The pattern is odd, even.**

Try It

a. Make models of the numbers 6 to 20. How are the models of even and odd numbers different? **See above.**

b. Choose five other numbers to model. Are they even or odd? How do you know? **Answers will vary.**

Is there one cube left over? **yes, in 7 and 9**

Reasoning The numbers 6 and 16 are even. Are 26, 36, 46, 56, and 66 even or odd? Explain. **They are even numbers because they have an even number in the ones place.**

20

Reteach 2.1

Even and Odd

Numbers can be arranged in dot patterns.

Even numbers have pairs of dots.

Odd numbers have pairs of dots, with one dot left over.

Write the number of dots in each set.
Circle the even numbers.

1. 7
2. (12)
3. (6)
4. 3
5. (10)
6. 9

Even numbers end with 0, 2, 4, 6, or 8.

7. Circle the even numbers in the chart below.

1	(2)	3	(4)	5	(6)	7	(8)	9	(10)
11	(12)	13	(14)	15	(16)	17	(18)	19	(20)
21	(22)	23	(24)	25	(26)	27	(28)	29	(30)
31	(32)	33	(34)	35	(36)	37	(38)	39	(40)

Numbers that are not even are odd.

8. Odd numbers end with **1**, **3**, **5**, **7**, or **9**.

Reteach RW7

Practice 2.1

Even and Odd

1	2	3	4	5	6	7	8	9	10
11	12	13	14	15	16	17	18	19	20
21	22	23	24	25	26	27	28	29	30
31	32	33	34	35	36	37	38	39	40
41	42	43	44	45	46	47	48	49	50
51	52	53	54	55	56	57	58	59	60
61	62	63	64	65	66	67	68	69	70
71	72	73	74	75	76	77	78	79	80
81	82	83	84	85	86	87	88	89	90
91	92	93	94	95	96	97	98	99	100

Look at each number. Tell whether the number is *odd* or *even*.

1. 34 **even**
2. 15 **odd**
3. 52 **even**
4. 23 **odd**
5. 19 **odd**
6. 35 **odd**
7. 82 **even**
8. 5 **odd**
9. 89 **odd**
10. 28 **even**

Use the hundred chart.

11. Start at 2. Skip-count by twos. Move 12 skips. What number do you land on? Is it odd or even? **26; even**
12. Start at 3. Skip-count by threes. Move 5 skips. What number do you land on? Is it odd or even? **18; even**

Mixed Review

Find each sum or difference.

13. 63 + 45 + 12 = **120**
14. 35 + 43 + 24 = **102**
15. 26 − 19 = **7**
16. 86 + 41 + 20 = **147**
17. 18 + 22 + 19 = **59**
18. 45 − 6 = **39**
19. 32 + 18 = **50**

Practice PW7

Connect

You can use a hundred chart to find odd and even numbers.

- Start at 2. Shade that box.
- Skip-count by twos and shade each box you land on.
- Look at your shaded chart. What pattern do you see?

1	2	3	4	5	6	7	8	9	10
11	12	13	14	15	16	17	18	19	20
21	22	23	24	25	26	27	28	29	30
31	32	33	34	35	36	37	38	39	40
41	42	43	44	45	46	47	48	49	50
51	52	53	54	55	56	57	58	59	60
61	62	63	64	65	66	67	68	69	70
71	72	73	74	75	76	77	78	79	80
81	82	83	84	85	86	87	88	89	90
91	92	93	94	95	96	97	98	99	100

MATH IDEA Even numbers have a 0, 2, 4, 6, or 8 in the ones place. Odd numbers have a 1, 3, 5, 7, or 9 in the ones place.

Practice and Problem Solving

Look at each number. Tell whether the number is *odd* or *even*.

1. 3 **odd**
2. 6 **even**
3. 12 **even**
4. 30 **even**
5. 27 **odd**
6. 98 **even**
7. 19 **odd**
8. 45 **odd**
9. 344 **even**
10. 281 **odd**
11. 776 **even**
12. 998 **even**
13. 173 **odd**
14. 832 **even**
15. 620 **even**
16. 411 **odd**

Use the hundred chart.

20. Possible answer: no; counting by twos from 2, he would land on even numbers.

17. Start at 5. Skip-count by fives. Move 4 skips. What number do you land on? Is it odd or even? **25; odd**
18. Start at 10. Skip-count by tens. Move 6 skips. What number do you land on? Is it odd or even? **70; even**
19. The first five houses on Quinn's street are numbered 4, 8, 12, 16, and 20. What are the next three house numbers? Explain. **24, 28, 32; I skip-counted by fours.**
20. **REASONING** Marcos skip-counted. He started at 2. He landed on 15. Could he be skip-counting by twos? Why or why not? **See above.**

Getting Ready for the EOG Test

21. Tom skip-counts: 3, 6, 9, 12. What number is he skip-counting by? **C**

    A 1
    B 2
    C 3
    D 4

22. Which list shows odd numbers? **D**

    A 0, 10, 20, 30, 40
    B 2, 4, 6, 8, 10
    C 0, 4, 8, 12, 16
    D 1, 3, 5, 7, 9

North Carolina Standards maintains (2) 1.06 Define and recognize odd and even numbers.

COMMON ERROR ALERT

Some students may confuse the terms *even* and *odd*.

47 is even

To help students remember the meanings of odd and even, remind them that *odd* has 3 letters and 3 is an odd number. *Even* has 4 letters and 4 is an even number.

Independent Practice

Note that Exercises 17 and 18 are **multistep or strategy problems.** Assign Exercises 1–20.

To help students with Exercises 1–20, have them review the steps in the Connect activity.

In Exercise 19, point out that since 20 has the same ones digit as 0, the pattern of digits in the ones place will repeat as when skip-counting from 0.

In Exercise 20, remind students that skip-counting by twos always gives an even number if you start with an even number and an odd number if you start with an odd number.

4 ASSESS

Summarize the lesson by having students:

DISCUSS Why are connecting cubes and hundred charts useful tools for understanding number patterns? Possible answers: Connecting cubes help you model odd and even numbers. A hundred chart lets you see how odd and even numbers can line up in columns and form patterns.

WRITE How can you tell odd numbers from even numbers even if you are not using connecting cubes or a hundred chart? Odd numbers have a 1, 3, 5, 7, or 9 in the ones place; even numbers have a 0, 2, 4, 6, or 8 in the ones place.

LESSON QUIZ

Transparency 2.1

Look at each number. Tell whether the number is *odd* or *even*.

1. 26 even
2. 33 odd
3. 48 even
4. 7 odd
5. 55 odd
6. 94 even
7. 392 even
8. 461 odd

Challenge 2.1

Odd-and-Even Game

Play with a partner.

Materials:

- Number chart shown below
- Number cube with numbers 1–6
- 30 game markers (15 each of two colors)

How to Play:

The object of the game is to get 5 of your markers in a row in any direction—horizontal, vertical, or diagonal.

Take turns. Roll the number cube. If the number is even, place a marker on any even number on the number chart. If the number is odd, place a marker on any odd number on the number chart.

1	2	3	4	5	6	7	8	9	10
11	12	13	14	15	16	17	18	19	20
21	22	23	24	25	26	27	28	29	30
31	32	33	34	35	36	37	38	39	40
41	42	43	44	45	46	47	48	49	50

Challenge CW7

Problem Solving 2.1

Even and Odd

Understand → Plan → Solve → Check

Write the correct answer.

1. Start at 8. Skip-count by eights. Move 3 skips. What number do you land on? Is it odd or even? **32, even**
2. If Jamal starts on 3, and skip-counts by twos, will he land on 9? **Yes**
3. Start at 7. Skip-count by sevens. Move 4 skips. What number do you land on? Is it odd or even? **35, odd**
4. Kingson had 35 math problems on his test. He answered 27 of them correctly. How many problems did he answer incorrectly? **8 problems**

Choose the letter of the correct answer.

5. Greg baked a total of 42 chocolate chip cookies on two days. If he baked 18 cookies the second day, how many cookies did he bake the first day?

   A 22
   B 23
   (C) 24
   D 25

6. Gary paid for a ball that cost \$7. He got \$3 in change. How much did he give the store clerk?

   F \$4
   G \$5
   (H) \$10
   J \$20

7. Mrs. Freeman said, "Mary, Leon, Nancy, and Vernon, please line up." Who was the third person called?

   A Mary
   B Leon
   (C) Nancy
   D Vernon

8. Beth skip-counted from zero. She landed on 18. Which number could she *not* be skip-counting by?

   F 2
   G 3
   (H) 4
   J 6

9. **Write About It** In Problem 6, how did you decide which was the correct answer?
   Possible answer: I added the cost of the ball and the change, \$7 + \$3 = \$10.

Problem Solving PS7

Lesson 2.2 Place Value: 3-Digit Numbers

Lesson Planning

Objective To find the value of a digit by using its place-value position

NCTM Standards

1. Number and Operations
6. Problem Solving
7. Reasoning and Proof
8. Communication
9. Connections
10. Representation

Math Background

Experience with base-ten blocks and expanded form helps students build understanding of place value.

- Manipulation of base-ten blocks helps students gain a visual and tactile understanding of place value.
- Using expanded form creates a bridge between base-ten blocks and standard form.
- Students gain familiarity with the relationship between the values of digits and their place-value positions.

Vocabulary

digits the ten symbols 0, 1, 2, 3, 4, 5, 6, 7, 8, and 9 used to write numbers

standard form a way to write numbers by using the digits 0–9, with each digit having a place value

expanded form a way to write numbers by showing the value of each digit

word form a way to write numbers by using words

Warm-Up Resources

Number of the Day

The number of the day is 20. Write two facts about 20. Possible answers: Twenty has 20 ones or 2 tens and no ones. Twenty is an even number.

Daily Facts Practice

Have students practice addition facts by completing Set A of *Teacher's Resource Book*, p. TR84.

Problem of the Day

On what day does this month end? Could you skip-count by twos on your calendar, beginning with the first day of the month, and land on the last day? Explain. If the month ends with a day that is an odd number (29 or 31), yes. If it ends with an even number (28 or 30), no. If you skip-count by twos and begin with an odd number, you will end with an odd number.

Solution Problem of the Day tab, p. PD2

Intervention and Extension Resources

Alternative Teaching Strategy

MATERIALS *For each group* base-ten blocks

Help students **understand the place value of a digit.** Ask students to use base-ten blocks to represent the number 123. Help students understand the connection between modeling with base-ten blocks and writing the number in expanded form. Ask what the blocks represent. _1_ hundred, _2_ tens, _3_ ones

KINESTHETIC

BODILY/KINESTHETIC

Multistep and Strategy Problems

The following multistep or strategy problem is provided in Lesson 2.2:

Page	Item
23	25

Special Needs

Help **reinforce students' understanding of expanded form.** Begin the discussion of expanded form using only tens and ones. Give students several similar examples, such as 11, 12, 13, 14, 21, 22, 23, and 24. Be sure they understand the concept of tens before moving on to hundreds. Use the same examples, with hundreds added, such as 111, 112, 113, 114, and 721, 722, 723, and 724. Then have students write the expanded form of numbers such as 525, 789, and 903. 500 + 20 + 5; 700 + 80 + 9; 900 + 3

AUDITORY, VISUAL

VISUAL/SPATIAL

Advanced Learners

MATERIALS *For each student* dictionary

Challenge students to **find two more meanings for the term *digit*.** One meaning is finger; the other is toe. Ask students how these meanings are related to the mathematical meaning. Possible answer: We have 10 toes and 10 fingers; there are 10 digits.

VISUAL

LOGICAL/MATHEMATICAL

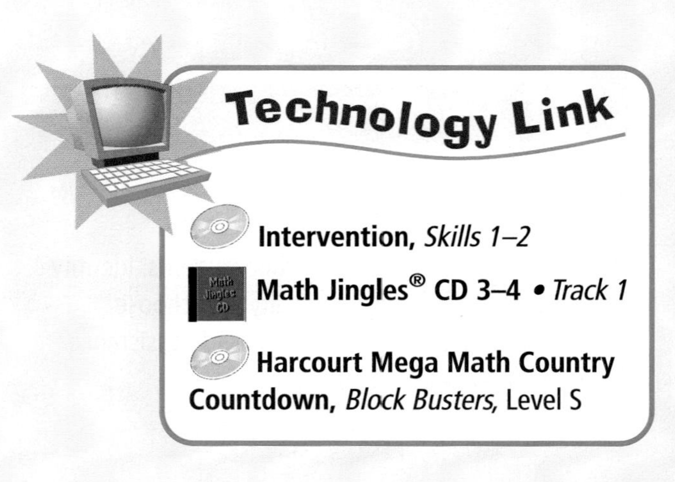

Technology Link

Intervention, *Skills 1–2*

Math Jingles® CD 3–4 • *Track 1*

Harcourt Mega Math Country Countdown, *Block Busters,* Level S

Lesson 2.2 Organizer

Objective To find the value of a digit by using its place-value position

Vocabulary digits, standard form, expanded form, word form

1 INTRODUCE

QUICK REVIEW provides review of prerequisite skills.

WHY LEARN THIS? You can understand the value of numbers you use every day. *Share the lesson objective with students.*

2 TEACH

Guided Instruction

MODIFYING INSTRUCTION After you introduce the vocabulary term *digits*, review the term, use it in context, or play word games with it, before moving on to the terms *standard form, expanded form*, and *word form.*

- *Ask students to read the Learn section.* **What digits make up the number 248?** 2, 4, 8
- *Direct students' attention to the place-value chart.* **REASONING Using base-ten blocks, how can you show the number 240 without using the hundred blocks?** 24 tens or 240 ones
- *Discuss the Math Idea.* **How would you express 249, 358, and 467 in expanded form?** 200 + 40 + 9; 300 + 50 + 8; 400 + 60 + 7.

Point out to students that when they read or write 3-digit numbers, they should not use the word *and.* For 376, it is incorrect to say *three hundred and seventy-six.*

3 PRACTICE

Guided Practice

Do Check Exercises 1–5 with your students. Identify students who are having difficulty and choose appropriate lesson resources to provide assistance.

LESSON 2

Place Value: 3-Digit Numbers

Learn

FARM FACTS The symbols 0, 1, 2, 3, 4, 5, 6, 7, 8, and 9 are **digits**. Numbers are made up of digits.

On Mr. Sam's farm there are 248 chickens. What does the number 248 mean?

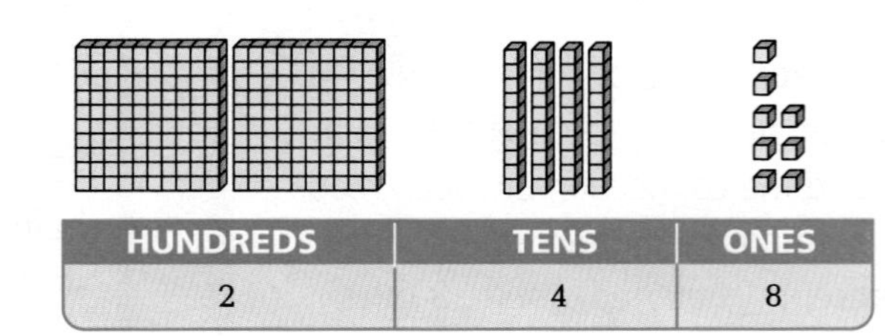

HUNDREDS	TENS	ONES
2	4	8

So, 248 means 2 hundreds + 4 tens + 8 ones or 200 + 40 + 8.

MATH IDEA You can write a number in different ways: standard form, expanded form, and word form.

Standard form: 248

Expanded form: 200 + 40 + 8

Word form: two hundred forty-eight

- In the number 408, what is the meaning of the zero in the tens place? **The zero means there are no tens.**

Check

USE DATA For 1–2, use the table.

FARM ANIMALS	
Animal	**Number**
Horses	4
Cows	376
Goats	105
Chickens	248

1. **Explain** why the value of the digit 3 is 300 in the number of cows on the farm. **The digit 3 is in the hundreds place.**
2. Write the expanded form for the number of goats on the farm. **100 + 5**

Quick Review

Write the number.

1. 5 tens 1 one **51**
2. 4 tens 3 ones **43**
3. 7 tens 0 ones **70**
4. 1 ten 9 ones **19**
5. 2 hundreds 6 tens 8 ones **268**

VOCABULARY

digits
standard form
expanded form
word form

Technology Link

Extra Practice: Harcourt Mega Math Country Countdown, *Block Busters,* Level S

Reteach 2.2

Place Value: 3-Digit Numbers

The symbols 0, 1, 2, 3, 4, 5, 6, 7, 8, and 9 are called **digits**.

Hundreds	Tens	Ones
5	2	6
500 +	20 +	6
= 526		

In the number 526 the value of the digit 5 is 5 hundreds, or 500. The value of the digit 2 is 2 tens, or 20. The value of the digit 6 is 6 ones, or 6. Read: "five hundred twenty-six"

Example 1
478
The value of the digit 4 is 4 hundreds, or 400.
Say: "four hundred seventy-eight"

Example 2
135
The value of the digit 3 is 3 tens, or 30.
Say: "one hundred thirty-five"

Example 3
629
The value of the digit 9 is 9 ones, or 9.
Say: "six hundred twenty-nine"

Example 4
401
A zero in the tens place shows that there are no tens.
Say: "four hundred one"

Write the value of the underlined digit.

1. 125 **5**
2. 658 **600**
3. 416 **10**
4. 548 **500**
5. 324 **4**
6. 906 **0**
7. 756 **50**
8. 230 **200**
9. 427 **7**
10. 643 **40**
11. 580 **0**
12. 209 **200**

RW8 Reteach

Practice 2.2

Place Value: 3-Digit Numbers

Write each number in standard form.

1. **461**
2. **302**
3. **240**
4. 300 + 40 + 9 **349**
5. 100 + 60 + 3 **163**
6. 700 + 90 + 9 **799**
7. seven hundred eighty **780**
8. six hundred thirty-two **632**
9. 5 hundreds 6 ones **506**
10. two hundreds 4 tens eight ones **248**

Write the value of the underlined digit.

11. 736 **6 ones; 6**
12. 341 **3 hundreds; 300**
13. 750 **5 tens; 50**
14. 408 **4 hundreds; 400**

Mixed Review

Add or subtract.

15. 82 − 24 = **58**
16. 34 + 56 = **90**
17. 35 + 6 = **41**
18. 71 − 42 = **29**
19. 64 − 28 = **36**
20. 32 − 7 = **25**
21. 18 + 18 = **36**
22. 88 + 15 = **103**

PW8 Practice

Write each number in standard form.

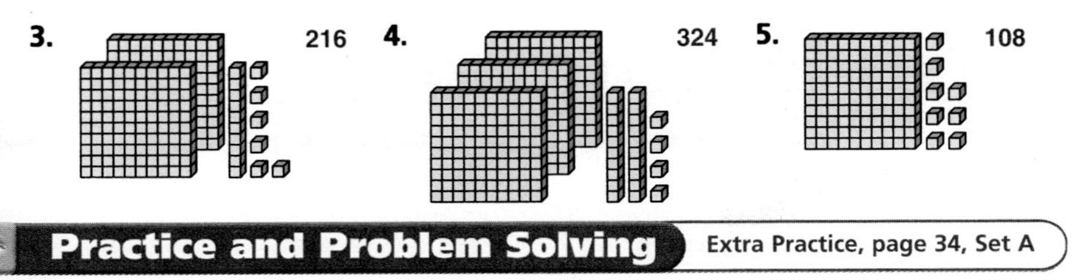

Practice and Problem Solving

Extra Practice, page 34, Set A

Write each number in standard form.

6. 100 + 50 + 3 **153**
7. 400 + 70 + 6 **476**
8. 600 + 30 + 9 **639**
9. 900 + 2 **902**
10. 4 hundreds 2 tens 1 one **421**
11. 6 hundreds 8 tens 3 ones **683**
12. 7 hundreds 2 tens 3 ones **723**
13. 4 hundreds 5 ones **405**
14. one hundred three **103**
15. three hundred forty-five **345**
16. six hundred eleven **611**
17. nine hundred seventy-one **971**

Write the value of the blue digit.

25. 3; 300 in 312, 3 in 213, 30 in 132

18. 846 **40**
19. 267 **60**
20. 493 **3**
21. 923 **900**

22. Mr. Sam put 297 bales of hay in one barn. There are still 86 bales of hay in the field. How many more bales of hay are in the barn than in the field? **211 more bales**

23. **FAST FACT** • SCIENCE There are about 210 kinds of horses in the world. What is the value of the digit 2 in the number 210? **200**

24. **Vocabulary Power** *Value* means "what something is worth." Use this meaning to describe the digit 5 in 527. **The 5 in 527 is worth 5 hundreds, or 500.**

25. **REASONING** I am a digit in each of the numbers 312, 213, and 132. My value is different in all three numbers. What digit am I? What is my value in each number? **See above.**

Getting Ready for the EOG Test

26. The table shows the visitors to a pumpkin farm one weekend. What is the value of the digit 8 in the number of visitors on Saturday? **B**

A 8 **B** 80 **C** 800 **D** 8,000

PUMPKIN FARM VISITORS	
Day	Number of Visitors
Saturday	682
Sunday	534

North Carolina Standards 1.01 Develop number sense for whole numbers through 9,999. Connect model, number word, and number using a variety of representations. b) Build understanding of place value (ones through thousands).

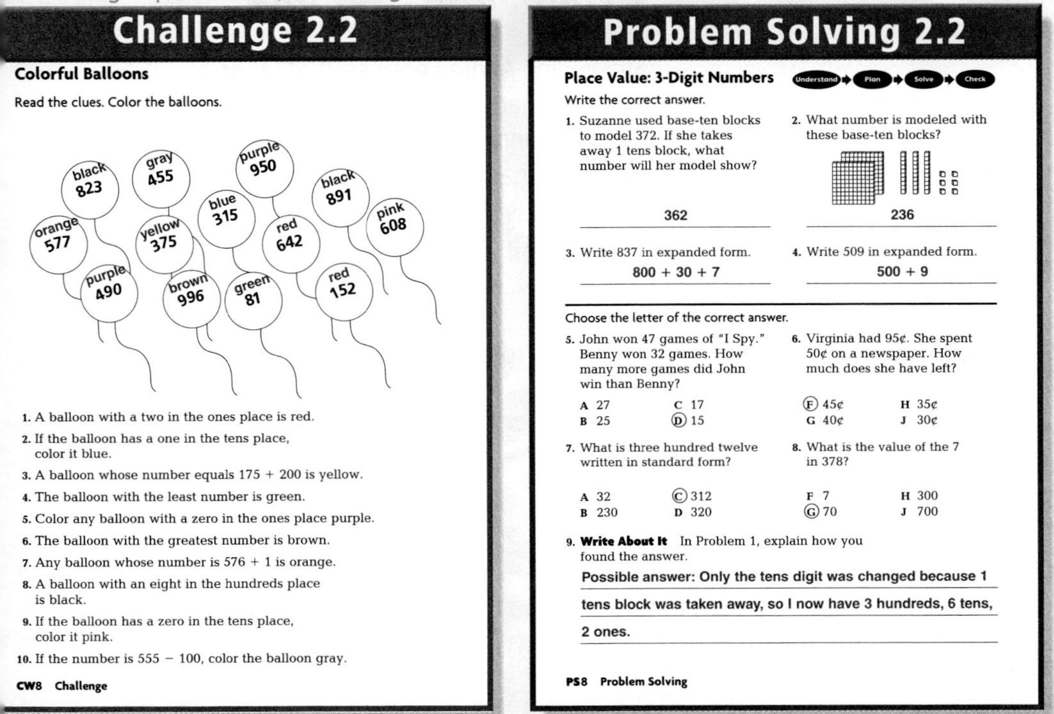

Challenge 2.2

Colorful Balloons

Read the clues. Color the balloons.

black 823, gray 455, purple 950, black 891, orange 577, blue 315, yellow 375, red 642, pink 608, purple 490, brown 996, green 81, red 152

1. A balloon with a two in the ones place is red.
2. If the balloon has a one in the tens place, color it blue.
3. A balloon whose number equals 175 + 200 is yellow.
4. The balloon with the least number is green.
5. Color any balloon with a zero in the ones place purple.
6. The balloon with the greatest number is brown.
7. Any balloon whose number is 576 + 1 is orange.
8. A balloon with an eight in the hundreds place is black.
9. If the balloon has a zero in the tens place, color it pink.
10. If the number is 555 − 100, color the balloon gray.

CW8 Challenge

Problem Solving 2.2

Place Value: 3-Digit Numbers Understand → Plan → Solve → Check

Write the correct answer.

1. Suzanne used base-ten blocks to model 372. If she takes away 1 tens block, what number will her model show? **362**
2. What number is modeled with these base-ten blocks? **236**
3. Write 837 in expanded form. **800 + 30 + 7**
4. Write 509 in expanded form. **500 + 9**

Choose the letter of the correct answer.

5. John won 47 games of "I Spy." Benny won 32 games. How many more games did John win than Benny?
   A 27 B 25 C 17 (D) 15
6. Virginia had 95¢. She spent 50¢ on a newspaper. How much does she have left?
   (F) 45¢ G 40¢ H 35¢ J 30¢
7. What is three hundred twelve written in standard form?
   A 32 B 230 (C) 312 D 320
8. What is the value of the 7 in 378?
   F 7 (G) 70 H 300 J 700
9. **Write About It** In Problem 1, explain how you found the answer.
   Possible answer: Only the tens digit was changed because 1 tens block was taken away, so I now have 3 hundreds, 6 tens, 2 ones.

PS8 Problem Solving

Independent Practice

Note that Exercise 25 is a **multistep or strategy problem.** Assign Exercises 6–25.

For Exercises 18–21, students may express the answers as numbers written in standard form or as the number of hundreds, tens, or ones.

Vocabulary Power The place-value position of the 5 in 527 is hundreds, so the *value* of the digit is 5 hundreds or 500.

For Exercise 25, suggest that students use the process of elimination to determine the digits. They can eliminate any digit that has the same place value in more than one number, such as 2 and 1.

Summarize the lesson by having students:

DISCUSS What is the value of each digit in the number nine hundred ninety-eight? 900, 90, 8

WRITE How would you show 700 + 50 + 2 on a place-value chart? Check students' work.

LESSON QUIZ

Transparency 2.2

For Exercises 1–2, write each number in standard form.

1. 500 + 30 + 9 539
2. 200 + 80 280

For Exercises 3–6, write the value of the digit 9.

3. 509 9
4. 948 900
5. 493 90
6. 619 9

Lesson 2.3

Place Value: 4-Digit Numbers

Lesson Planning

Objective To identify place-value relationships in 4-digit numbers

Materials *For each group* base-ten blocks

NCTM Standards
1. Number and Operations
6. Problem Solving
7. Reasoning and Proof
8. Communication
9. Connections
10. Representation

Math Background

Experience with base-ten blocks and place-value charts helps students build understanding of 4-digit numbers.

- Base-ten blocks help students model numbers and number relationships.
- Concrete and pictorial models help students understand the relative magnitude of numbers.
- Reading, writing, and modeling greater numbers help students build understanding of each place value as ten times more than the place to the right.
- A comma, used to separate the ones period and the thousands period when writing the standard and word form of numbers, makes the number easier to read.

Warm-Up Resources

Number of the Day

I am the number of days in a week. Use me in 3 three-digit numbers, and give me a different place-value position in each. Possible answers: 117, 472, 790

Daily Facts Practice

Have students practice addition and subtraction facts by completing Set B of *Teacher's Resource Book*, p. TR84.

Transparency 2.3

Solve a Problem

Problem of the Day

Shawn and Andrea each start at 99 on a hundred chart and count back to zero. Shawn counts back by sixes and Andrea by fives. What numbers do they both say? What is the last number each says? They both say 99, 69, 39, 9. Shawn's last number is 3; Andrea's is 4.

Solution Problem of the Day tab, p. PD2

Intervention and Extension Resources

Alternative Teaching Strategy

MATERIALS *For each pair* 14 index cards

Help students **identify place value in 4-digit numbers.** Make two sets of cards. One set should contain cards labeled with the words *ones, tens, hundreds*, and *thousands*. The other set should contain the ten digits.

Have students take turns

- shuffling the sets of cards.
- drawing one from each pile.
- writing and then stating a number that has a digit in the specified place-value position. Check students' work.

See also page 26.

KINESTHETIC

BODILY/KINESTHETIC

Multistep and Strategy Problems

The following multistep or strategy problem is provided in Lesson 2.3:

Page	Item
26	26

Writing in Mathematics

Help **reinforce students' understanding of 4-digit numbers.** Have students explain how they can use base-ten blocks to demonstrate that each place in the place-value chart is ten times the place to its right. Check students' work.

Early Finishers

Challenge students **to make up place-value riddles.** Offer this example: I have a 6 in the ones place, a 3 in the hundreds place, a 0 in the tens place, and an 8 in the thousands place. What number am I? 8,306. Partners can take turns writing and solving the riddles. Check students' work.

AUDITORY

VERBAL/LINGUISTIC

Intervention, *Skills 1–2*

Harcourt Mega Math Country Countdown, *Block Busters,* Level T

Lesson 2.3 Organizer

Objective To identify place-value relationships in 4-digit numbers

Materials *For each group* base-ten blocks

1 INTRODUCE

Quick Review provides review of prerequisite skills.

Why Learn This? You use 4-digit numbers when you use money, figure out distances, and learn about the past. *Share the lesson objective with students.*

Guided Instruction

- *Have students read the Learn section and model the Activity.*
  Reasoning How do you know how much the large cube is worth? There are 10 rows or 10 columns of 100. 10 hundreds = 1,000

Modifying Instruction This activity may be completed in small groups.

- *Discuss the place-value chart with students.*
  Which digit has the greatest value? Explain. the 3; the value is 3,000 **Which digit has the least value?** the 4
  Reasoning How does the position of the digit determine its value? The farther to the left a number is placed, the greater its value.
- *Direct students' attention to the expanded form.*
  Describe the pattern of the zeros. The number of zeros decreases by one from the thousands to the hundreds to the tens to the ones.

LESSON 3

Place Value: 4-Digit Numbers

Quick Review

Write the value of the blue digit.

1. 246 6
2. 394 300
3. 714 10
4. 502 2
5. 802 800

Learn

HORSE SENSE The largest horse on record is a Belgian that stood 18 hands—or 6 feet—tall and weighed 3,174 pounds. You can use base-ten blocks to show the number of pounds.

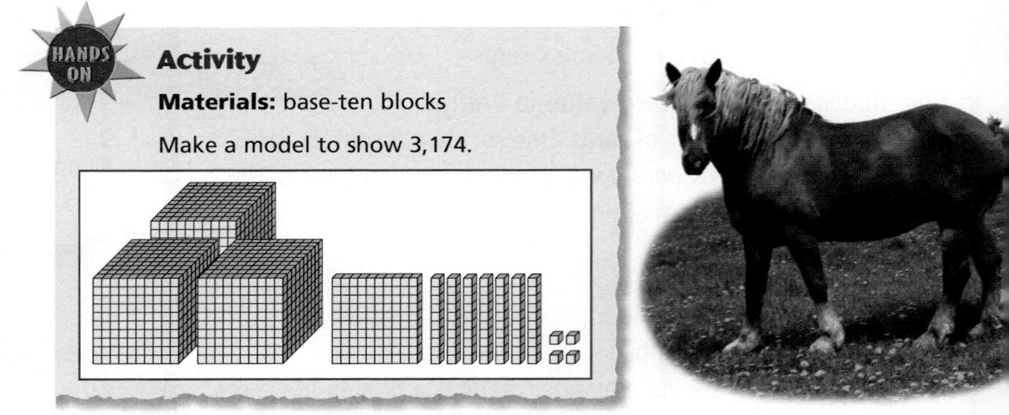

Activity

Materials: base-ten blocks

Make a model to show 3,174.

A place-value chart can help you understand the value of each digit in a number.

THOUSANDS	HUNDREDS	TENS	ONES
3,	1	7	4
↑ Value is 3,000.	↑ Value is 100.	↑ Value is 70.	↑ Value is 4.

Standard form: 3,174

A comma is used to separate the thousands and hundreds.

Expanded form: 3,000 + 100 + 70 + 4

Word form: three thousand, one hundred seventy-four

- What is the value of the digit 4 in 4,618? **4,000**

24

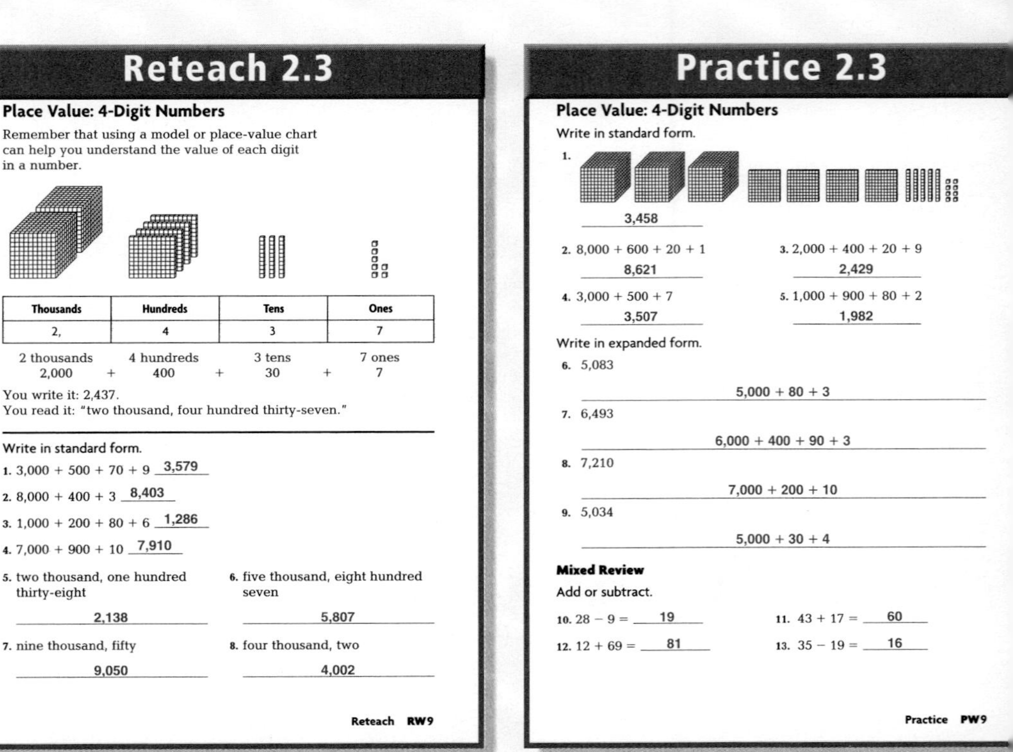

Reteach 2.3

Place Value: 4-Digit Numbers

Remember that using a model or place-value chart can help you understand the value of each digit in a number.

Thousands	Hundreds	Tens	Ones
2,	4	3	7
2 thousands 2,000 +	4 hundreds 400 +	3 tens 30 +	7 ones 7

You write it: 2,437.
You read it: "two thousand, four hundred thirty-seven."

Write in standard form.

1. 3,000 + 500 + 70 + 9 3,579
2. 8,000 + 400 + 3 8,403
3. 1,000 + 200 + 80 + 6 1,286
4. 7,000 + 900 + 10 7,910
5. two thousand, one hundred thirty-eight 2,138
6. five thousand, eight hundred seven 5,807
7. nine thousand, fifty 9,050
8. four thousand, two 4,002

Reteach RW9

Practice 2.3

Place Value: 4-Digit Numbers

Write in standard form.

1. 3,458
2. 8,000 + 600 + 20 + 1 8,621
3. 2,000 + 400 + 20 + 9 2,429
4. 3,000 + 500 + 7 3,507
5. 1,000 + 900 + 80 + 2 1,982

Write in expanded form.

6. 5,083 5,000 + 80 + 3
7. 6,493 6,000 + 400 + 90 + 3
8. 7,210 7,000 + 200 + 10
9. 5,034 5,000 + 30 + 4

Mixed Review

Add or subtract.

10. 28 − 9 = 19
11. 43 + 17 = 60
12. 12 + 69 = 81
13. 35 − 19 = 16

Practice PW9

Understanding Thousands

You can use place-value blocks to help you understand thousands.

There are 10 ones in 10.

Technology Link

More Practice:
Harcourt Mega Math Country Countdown, *Block Busters*, Level T

There are 10 tens in 100.

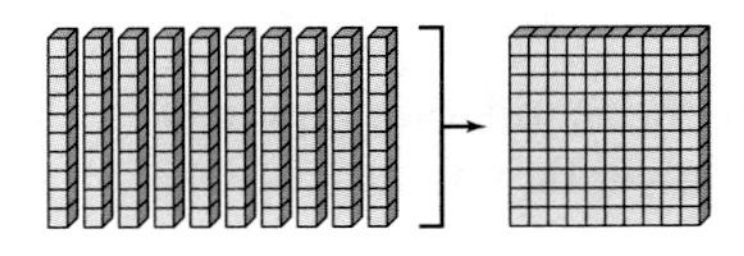

How many hundreds do you think there are in 1,000?

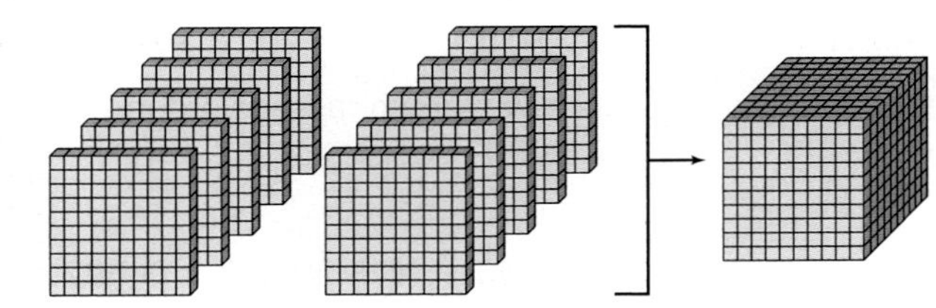

There are 10 hundreds in 1,000.

- How many hundreds do you think there are in 2,000? **20**

Check

1. **Explain** the value of each digit in 5,403. **5 = 5,000; 4 = 400; 3 = 3**

Write in standard form.

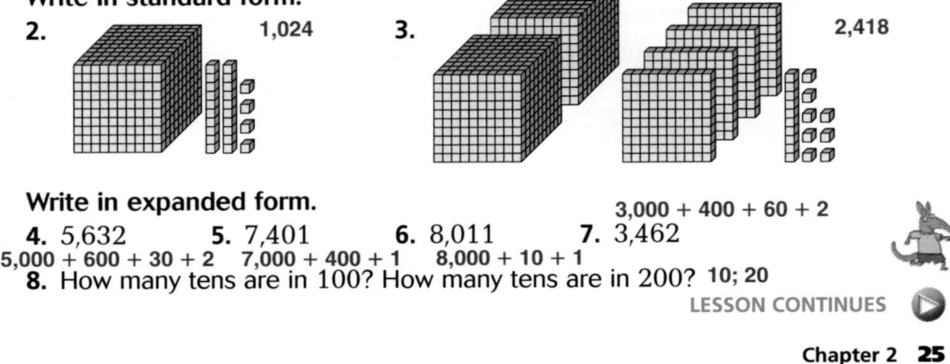

2. **1,024**
3. **2,418**

Write in expanded form.

4. 5,632 **5,000 + 600 + 30 + 2**
5. 7,401 **7,000 + 400 + 1**
6. 8,011 **8,000 + 10 + 1**
7. 3,462 **3,000 + 400 + 60 + 2**
8. How many tens are in 100? How many tens are in 200? **10; 20**

LESSON CONTINUES

- *Direct students' attention to the place-value blocks.*

Count the tens blocks in 100. Then count the columns in the hundred block. What do you notice? The number of tens blocks equals the number of columns.

REASONING Explain why you think the number of hundreds blocks in 1,000 is equal to the number of rows or columns in the thousand cube. Possible answer: Since 10 ones equals 10 and 10 tens equals 100, 10 hundreds will equal 1,000.

ALGEBRAIC THINKING Describe the pattern that these blocks show. Each place value is 10 times more. 10 is 10 ones; 100 is 10 tens; 1,000 is 10 hundreds.

3 PRACTICE

Guided Practice

Do Check Exercises 1–8 with your students. Identify students who are having difficulty and choose appropriate lesson resources to provide assistance.

North Carolina Standards 1.01 Develop number sense for whole numbers through 9,999. Connect model, number word, and number using a variety of representations. b) Build understanding of place value (ones through thousands).

Challenge 2.3

Arrays of Stars

Each sheet of stickers contains 1,000 stars. The stars are arranged in 50 rows with 20 stickers in each row. Use this information to answer each question.

1. A package of stickers contains 5,000 stars. How many sheets of stars are there? **5 sheets**
2. Each teacher at Lakota Elementary received 9 sheets of stars. How many stars did each receive? **9,000 stars**
3. If each sheet of stickers costs 50¢, how much would 12,000 stars cost? **$6**
4. Mr. Lee used 3,894 stickers during the first grading period. How many sheets was this? **4 sheets**
5. Mrs. Winslow used 2 sheets of stickers during the first grading period, 3 sheets during the second grading period and half of a sheet during the first week of the third grading period. How many stars did she use? **5,500 stars**
6. Carrie used 8 rows of stars to decorate thank-you notes for the parents that helped on the last field trip. How many stars did she use? **160 stars**
7. Martin made a design with the stars. He used one sheet of stars in the first row of his design, two sheets in the next row, three sheets in the third row, and so on. If his design had 6 rows, how many stars did he use? **21,000 stars**

Problem Solving 2.3

Place Value: 4-Digit Numbers Understand ➔ Plan ➔ Solve ➔ Check

Write the correct answer.

1. Write 3,000 + 500 + 70 + 1 in standard form. **3,571**
2. Write six thousand, three hundred eighty-five in standard form. **6,385**
3. In the number 4,967, which digit is in the hundreds place? **9**
4. Tell whether 73 is *even* or *odd*. **odd**

Choose the letter of the correct answer.

5. Manuel made a model with base-ten blocks. He used 4 thousands, 8 hundreds, and 3 ones. What number did he model?
   A 438 B 483 C 4,083 **(D) 4,803**
6. Kimberly has 845 baseball cards. Which is 845 in word form?
   F eight forty-five **(G) eight hundred forty-five** H eight thousand forty-five J eighty-four five
7. How many dimes are there in $1.00?
   A one **(B) ten** C one hundred D one thousand
8. What is the greatest possible number you can write using the digits 7, 4, 9, and 3? Use each digit only once.
   F 7,493 G 9,437 **(H) 9,743** J 9,734
9. **Write About It** How did you solve Problem 8?
   Possible answer: I knew that the greatest digit needed to be in the thousands place. The next greatest digit needed to be in the hundreds place, and so on.

COMMON ERROR ALERT

Students may have trouble translating large numbers from digits to words or words to digits. This is especially true when one or more digits are zeros.

3,09

Have students use a place-value chart to identify each digit and the place or places for zero.

Thousands	Hundreds	Tens	Ones
3,	0	0	9

Independent Practice

Note that Exercise 26 is a **multistep or strategy problem.** Assign Exercises 9–30.

REASONING For Exercise 26, encourage students to solve the problem by using a place-value chart.

MULTISTEP AND STRATEGY PROBLEM To solve Exercise 26, students can use the strategy *use logical reasoning.* They are told the ones digit is 1. Use 1 + 4 to find the tens digit: 1 + 4 = 5. Use 5 − 4 = 1 to find the thousands digit. Use 5 + 1 to find the hundreds digit: 5 + 1 = 6. Guide students to conclude they must start with the value of the ones digit in order to find the tens and hundreds digits.

Practice and Problem Solving

Extra Practice, page 34, Set B

Write in standard form.

9. 1,453

10. 1,029

11. 5,000 + 400 + 50 **5,450**

12. 4,000 + 300 + 90 + 7 **4,397**

13. 9,000 + 700 + 20 + 3 **9,723**

14. 1,000 + 10 + 8 **1,018**

15. two thousand, four hundred eighty-three **2,483**

16. six thousand, one hundred ninety-four **6,194**

For 17–20, write in expanded form.

17. 1,234 **1,000 + 200 + 30 + 4**

18. 4,321 **4,000 + 300 + 20 + 1**

19. 3,016 **3,000 + 10 + 6**

20. 8,367 **8,000 + 300 + 60 + 7**

21. How many tens are in 400? **40**

22. How many hundreds are in 3,000? **30**

Complete.

23. 1,000 + 500 + ■ + 8 = 1,548 **40**

24. 3,000 + ■ + 90 + 7 = 3,897 **800**

25. **USE DATA** The pictograph shows what Molly saw at the farm. How many animals did Molly see in all? **120 animals**

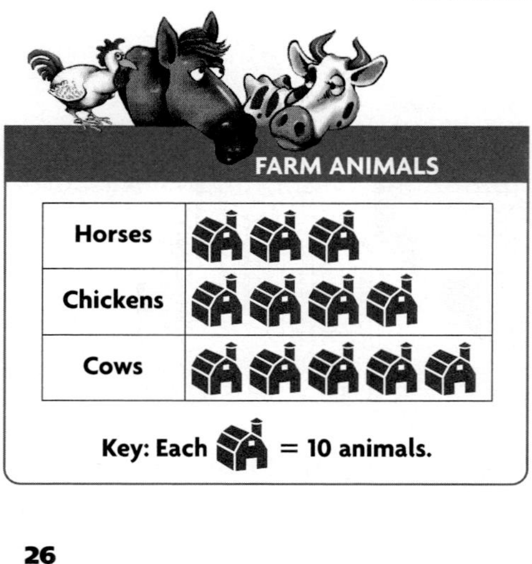

26. **REASONING** I am a 4-digit number. My thousands digit is 4 less than my tens digit. My hundreds digit equals the sum of my tens digit and my ones digit. My tens digit is 4 more than my ones digit. My ones digit is 1. What number am I? **1,651**

27. What is the least possible number you can write with the digits 2, 9, 4, and 7? Use each digit only once. **2,479**

28. **Write About It** Why do you have to use a zero when you write one thousand, six hundred four in standard form? **Possible answer: I have to write a zero in the tens place to show that there are no tens: 1,604.**

26

Alternative Teaching Strategy

Scaffolded Instruction

PURPOSE Students apply what they have learned about place value in 3-digit numbers to place value in 4-digit numbers.

MATERIALS *For each group* base-ten blocks, 10-by-10 grid paper, construction paper, paste, stapler

Have students model 100 with a base-ten hundreds block. Next, have students model 1,000 with hundreds blocks. Ask: How many hundreds blocks did you stack to build a cube of 1,000? 10

Then have students make a book of 1,000 squares.

- Have students paste 10-by-10 paper grids onto pieces of paper, using one grid per piece of paper.
- Next, have students number each page at the bottom.
- Then have students staple the pages together.
- Students should take turns numbering the squares of the grid from 1–100, 101–200, etc. Check students' work.

Ask: How many 10-by-10 grids did it take to make the 1,000 book? 10 If you put three books of 1,000 together, how many squares would you have in all? 3,000

29. The number 124 is an even number. Write 5 more even numbers including one with 4 digits. **Check students' answers.**

30. Show that each of the even numbers 6, 8, 10, and 12 can be written as the sum of a group of twos.
6 = 2 + 2 + 2
8 = 2 + 2 + 2 + 2
10 = 2 + 2 + 2 + 2 + 2
12 = 2 + 2 + 2 + 2 + 2 + 2

Getting Ready for the EOG Test

31. What is the *greatest* number you can make using all the digits shown on the cards? **A**

A 9,521 **C** 9,251
B 9,512 **D** 9,125

32. What is the *least* number you can make using all the digits shown on the cards? **D**

A 1,952
B 1,529
C 1,295
D 1,259

Problem Solving Thinker's Corner

NAMES FOR NUMBERS You can name any number in different ways. Here are different names for 78 and 152.

78	152
70 + 8	100 + 50 + 2
25 + 25 + 25 + 3	50 + 50 + 52
80 − 2	155 − 3
100 − 22	200 − 48

Write two other names for each number. **Possible answers below.**

1. 45 **40 + 5; 100 − 55**
2. 215 **100 + 100 + 15; 220 − 5**
3. 698 **600 + 90 + 8; 700 − 2**
4. 1,523 **1,000 + 523; 1,525 − 2**

Problem Solving Thinker's Corner

- *Direct students' attention to the different ways to name 78 and 152.*

REASONING What odd number, added to itself, is another name for 78? 39

REASONING What even number, added to itself, is another name for 152? 76

Summarize the lesson by having students:

DISCUSS What are two ways you can use your base-ten blocks to build 1,000? Possible answers: 10 hundreds blocks; 100 tens blocks; 1,000 ones blocks

WRITE Make up a 4-digit number. Write the number in expanded form, standard form, and word form. Answers will vary.

LESSON QUIZ

Write in standard form.

1. five thousand, eight hundred sixty-two 5,862
2. nine thousand, two hundred four 9,204

Write in expanded form.

3. 9,027 9,000 + 20 + 7
4. 6,135 6,000 + 100 + 30 + 5

Lesson 2.4

Problem Solving Strategy

Use Logical Reasoning

Lesson Planning

PROFESSIONAL DEVELOPMENT

Objective To solve problems by using the problem solving strategy *use logical reasoning*

Lesson Resources Reading Transparency 2; Intervention • Problem Solving, Strategy/Skill 2

NCTM Standards

6. Problem Solving
7. Reasoning and Proof
8. Communication
9. Connections
10. Representation

Math Background

Consider the following when you introduce logical reasoning.

- Logical reasoning is one of several strategies students use for solving problems.
- Identifying information needed to solve a given problem and determining the best way to begin to solve it are key steps in finding solutions.
- Include "if . . . then" and "what if" sentences as a way to introduce logical reasoning.

Warm-Up Resources

Build Number Sense

Number of the Day

Take the age you will be in 10 years. Find the sum of the two digits. Answers will vary.

Daily Facts Practice

Have students practice subtraction facts by completing Set C of *Teacher's Resource Book*, p. TR84.

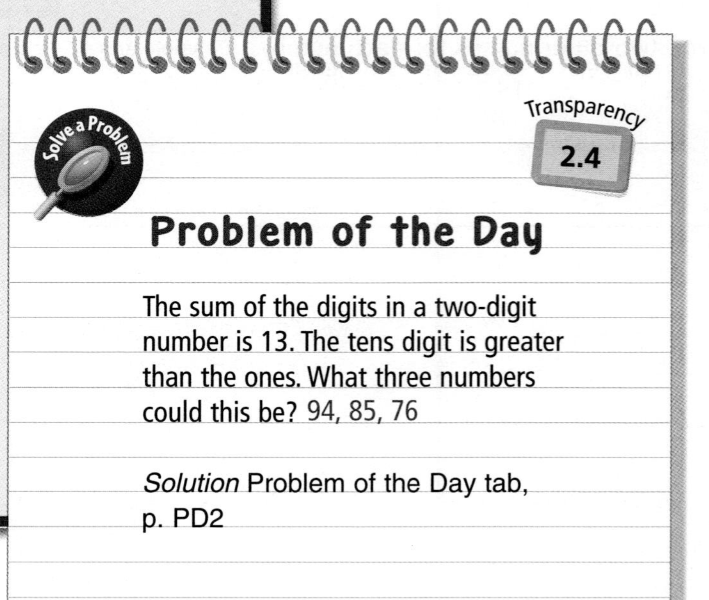

Transparency 2.4

Solve a Problem

Problem of the Day

The sum of the digits in a two-digit number is 13. The tens digit is greater than the ones. What three numbers could this be? 94, 85, 76

Solution Problem of the Day tab, p. PD2

Intervention and Extension Resources

Alternative Teaching Strategy

Help students **practice identifying key information and breaking the problem into manageable parts**. Copy the Problem on page 28 and share with students. Have students draw lines under key words or phrases. base-ten blocks; 243; 2 hundreds, 4 tens, 3 ones; what other way Have students list steps for solving the problem. Set up blocks to show Todd's model; begin regrouping either tens or hundreds; write a description of your model.

KINESTHETIC/VISUAL

VISUAL/SPATIAL

ESOL/ESL

MATERIALS *For each pair* base-ten blocks

Help students **practice using logical reasoning** to solve Exercise 1 on page 29. Review the term *trading*. Then review trading hundreds for tens and tens for ones. Have students work with a partner to model Exercise 1. Since there are no tens, students should trade 4 tens for 40 ones and add the 3 ones. Check students' work.

KINESTHETIC

BODILY/KINESTHETIC

Reading Strategy

Cause and Effect Tell students a cause is the reason something happens. The effect is what happens as a result of the cause. Have students identify the cause and effect of each scenario:

- Christopher wants to model 167 with base-ten blocks. He has no hundreds blocks. He uses 16 tens, 7 ones. cause: he has no hundreds blocks; effect: he uses 16 tens, 7 ones
- Jade wants to model 439 with base-ten blocks. She has no tens blocks. She uses 4 hundreds, 39 ones. cause: she has no tens blocks; effect: she uses 4 hundreds, 39 ones.

Transparency 2 **Reading Transparency 2**

Advanced Learners

Challenge students to **extend their logical reasoning skills by writing problems** that are similar to Exercises 1–4 on page 29. Have students exchange with a partner and solve. Check students' work.

VISUAL

LOGICAL/MATHEMATICAL

Multistep and Strategy Problems

The following multistep or strategy problems are provided in Lesson 2.4:

Page	Item
29	1–8

Intervention • Problem Solving, *Strategy/Skill 2*

Lesson 2.4 Organizer

Objective To solve problems by using the problem solving strategy *use logical reasoning*

Lesson Resources Reading Transparency 2; Intervention • Problem Solving, Strategy/Skill 2

1 INTRODUCE

QUICK REVIEW provides review of prerequisite skills.

WHY LEARN THIS? You can use logical reasoning to make decisions in everyday life, such as deciding which train or bus to take, or which item to buy. *Share the lesson objective with students.*

2 TEACH

Guided Instruction

- *Ask students to read the Problem.*
  Why is it important to read the problem more than once? Possible answer: There is a lot of information. You have to be sure of what the problem is asking.
- *Refer to the Understand, Plan, and Solve steps.*
  REASONING Do you think you would always need to look for unnecessary information? Explain. Possible answer: Yes. It is a good way to make sure you have located the important numbers.
- *Direct students' attention to the Check step.*
  REASONING How could you model 243 if you had no hundreds blocks? Possible answer: You could trade 2 hundreds for 20 tens and then add 4 tens, 3 ones.
  What if you checked and found that your answer did not make sense? What could you do? Possible answer: You could model the problem a different way.

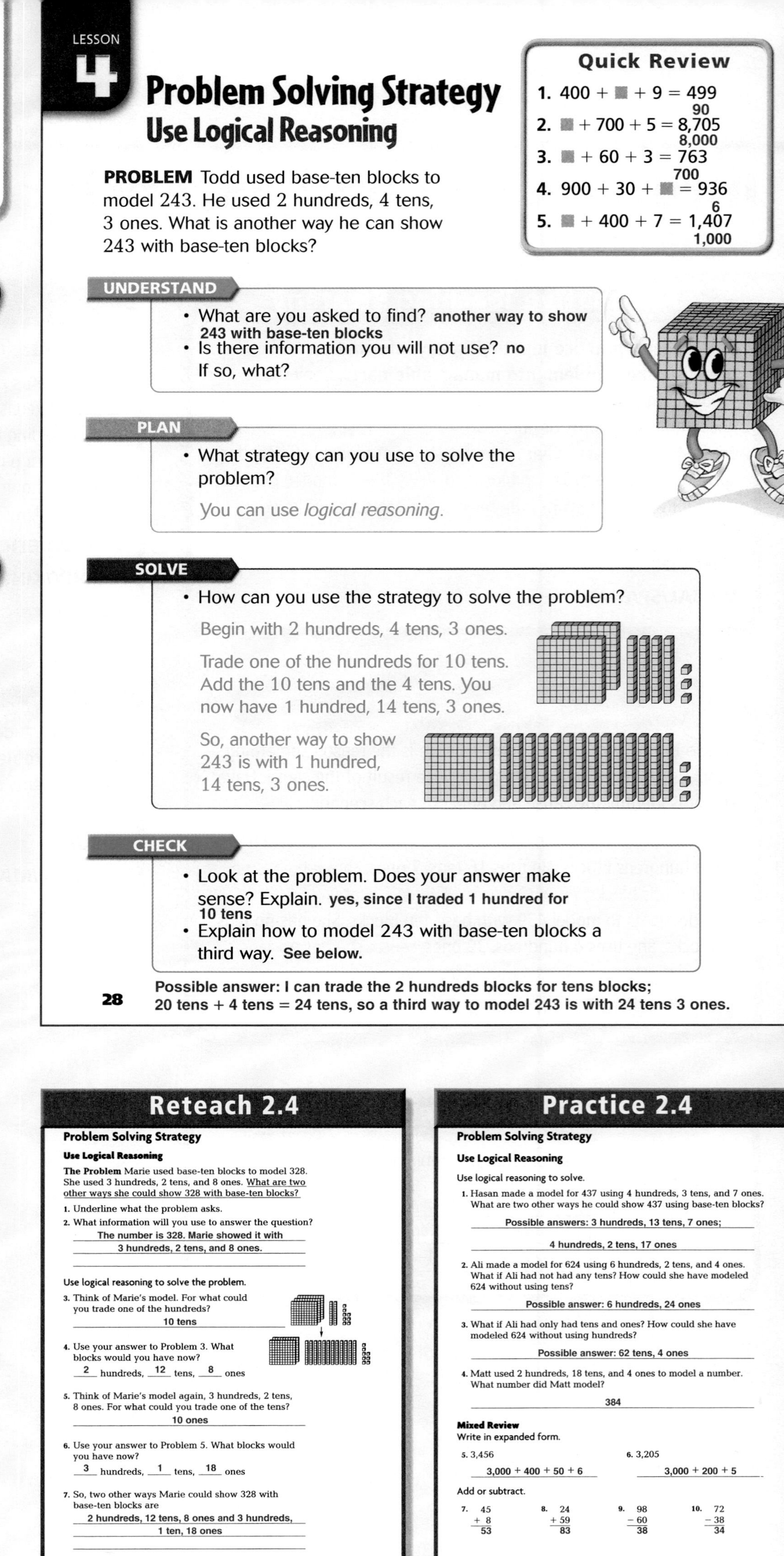

LESSON 4

Problem Solving Strategy
Use Logical Reasoning

Quick Review

1. 400 + ■ + 9 = 499 **90**
2. ■ + 700 + 5 = 8,705 **8,000**
3. ■ + 60 + 3 = 763 **700**
4. 900 + 30 + ■ = 936 **6**
5. ■ + 400 + 7 = 1,407 **1,000**

PROBLEM Todd used base-ten blocks to model 243. He used 2 hundreds, 4 tens, 3 ones. What is another way he can show 243 with base-ten blocks?

UNDERSTAND

- What are you asked to find? **another way to show 243 with base-ten blocks**
- Is there information you will not use? **no** If so, what?

PLAN

- What strategy can you use to solve the problem?

You can use *logical reasoning*.

SOLVE

- How can you use the strategy to solve the problem?

Begin with 2 hundreds, 4 tens, 3 ones.

Trade one of the hundreds for 10 tens. Add the 10 tens and the 4 tens. You now have 1 hundred, 14 tens, 3 ones.

So, another way to show 243 is with 1 hundred, 14 tens, 3 ones.

CHECK

- Look at the problem. Does your answer make sense? Explain. **yes, since I traded 1 hundred for 10 tens**
- Explain how to model 243 with base-ten blocks a third way. **See below.**

28

Possible answer: I can trade the 2 hundreds blocks for tens blocks; 20 tens + 4 tens = 24 tens, so a third way to model 243 is with 24 tens 3 ones.

Reteach 2.4

Problem Solving Strategy

Use Logical Reasoning

The Problem Marie used base-ten blocks to model 328. She used 3 hundreds, 2 tens, and 8 ones. What are two other ways she could show 328 with base-ten blocks?

1. Underline what the problem asks.
2. What information will you use to answer the question? **The number is 328. Marie showed it with 3 hundreds, 2 tens, and 8 ones.**

Use logical reasoning to solve the problem.

3. Think of Marie's model. For what could you trade one of the hundreds? **10 tens**
4. Use your answer to Problem 3. What blocks would you have now? **2** hundreds, **12** tens, **8** ones
5. Think of Marie's model again, 3 hundreds, 2 tens, 8 ones. For what could you trade one of the tens? **10 ones**
6. Use your answer to Problem 5. What blocks would you have now? **3** hundreds, **1** tens, **18** ones
7. So, two other ways Marie could show 328 with base-ten blocks are **2 hundreds, 12 tens, 8 ones and 3 hundreds, 1 ten, 18 ones**

RW10 Reteach

Practice 2.4

Problem Solving Strategy

Use Logical Reasoning

Use logical reasoning to solve.

1. Hasan made a model for 437 using 4 hundreds, 3 tens, and 7 ones. What are two other ways he could show 437 using base-ten blocks? **Possible answers: 3 hundreds, 13 tens, 7 ones; 4 hundreds, 2 tens, 17 ones**
2. Ali made a model for 624 using 6 hundreds, 2 tens, and 4 ones. What if Ali had not had any tens? How could she have modeled 624 without using tens? **Possible answer: 6 hundreds, 24 ones**
3. What if Ali had only had tens and ones? How could she have modeled 624 without using hundreds? **Possible answer: 62 tens, 4 ones**
4. Matt used 2 hundreds, 18 tens, and 4 ones to model a number. What number did Matt model? **384**

Mixed Review

Write in expanded form.

5. 3,456 **3,000 + 400 + 50 + 6**
6. 3,205 **3,000 + 200 + 5**

Add or subtract.

7. 45 + 8 = **53**
8. 24 + 59 = **83**
9. 98 − 60 = **38**
10. 72 − 38 = **34**

PW10 Practice

Problem Solving Practice

Use logical reasoning and solve.

1. **What if** Todd doesn't have any tens? How can he model 243 without using any tens? **Possible answer: 2 hundreds, 43 ones**
2. Emily made a model for 156 using 1 hundred, 5 tens, 6 ones. What are two other ways she can show 156 using base-ten blocks? **15 tens, 6 ones; 156 ones**
3. Sage used 34 tens, 2 ones to model a number. What other way can she model the same number? **D**
   A 3 hundreds, 4 tens
   B 3 tens, 2 ones
   C 3 hundreds, 2 ones
   D 3 hundreds, 4 tens, 2 ones
4. Louis used 1 thousand, 2 hundreds, 4 tens, 3 ones to model a number. What number did he model? **G**
   F 143　　**H** 1,423
   G 1,243　　**J** 2,143

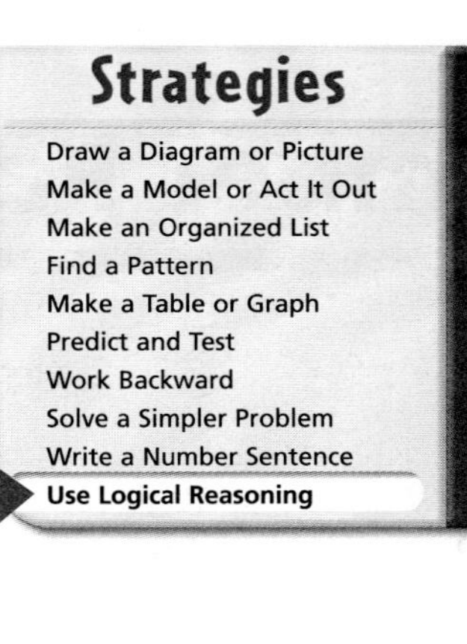

Strategies

- Draw a Diagram or Picture
- Make a Model or Act It Out
- Make an Organized List
- Find a Pattern
- Make a Table or Graph
- Predict and Test
- Work Backward
- Solve a Simpler Problem
- Write a Number Sentence
- **Use Logical Reasoning**

Problem Solving

Mixed Strategy Practice

5. Write the greatest possible 4-digit number using the digits 3, 4, 5, and 6. Write the least possible 4-digit number. **6,543; 3,456**
6. **REASONING** A 3-digit number has the same number of ones, tens, and hundreds. If the sum of the digits is 9, what is the number? **333**
7. **USE DATA** The pictograph shows farm animals. How many more sheep than horses are there? How many animals are there in all? **70 more sheep; 95 animals**
8. **Write a problem** about 8 hundreds, 4 tens, 6 ones. Tell how to solve the problem. **Check students' problems.**

FARM ANIMALS

Horses	
Cows	
Sheep	

Key: Each [symbol] = 5 animals.

3 PRACTICE

Guided Practice

Do Problem Solving Practice Exercises 1–4 with your students. Identify students who are having difficulty and choose appropriate lesson resources to provide assistance. Note that Exercises 1–4 are **multistep or strategy problems.**

Independent Practice

Note that Exercises 5–8 are **multistep or strategy problems.** Assign Exercises 5–8.

4 ASSESS

Summarize the lesson by having students:

DISCUSS One way to model 356 with base-ten blocks is 3 hundreds, 5 tens, 6 ones. What is another way to model 356? Possible answer: You can trade one of the hundreds for 10 tens. Add 10 tens and 5 tens. You now have 2 hundreds, 15 tens, 6 ones.

WRITE How would you tell other students to solve Exercise 3 in the Practice section? Possible answer: You can use base-ten blocks to model 34 tens, 2 ones. Since 10 tens = 1 hundred, you can trade 30 tens for 3 hundreds. 34 tens, 2 ones = 3 hundreds, 4 tens, 2 ones.

LESSON QUIZ

Transparency 2.4

Use logical reasoning and solve.

1. What are two ways to model 746 with base-ten blocks? Possible answers: 7 hundreds, 4 tens, 6 ones; 6 hundreds, 14 tens, 6 ones
2. How can you model 327 without using any tens? Possible answer: 3 hundreds, 27 ones

North Carolina Standards 1.01 Develop number sense for whole numbers through 9,999. Connect model, number word, and number using a variety of representations. b) Build understanding of place value (ones through thousands).

Challenge 2.4

Problem Solving Strategy
Use Logical Reasoning

Read the clues. Color the squares on the hundred chart.

1	2	3	4	5	6	7	8	9	10
11	12	13	14	15	16	17	18	19	20
21	22	23	24	25	26	27	28	29	30
31	32	33	34	35	36	37	38	39	40
41	42	43	44	45	46	47	48	49	50
51	52	53	54	55	56	57	58	59	60
61	62	63	64	65	66	67	68	69	70
71	72	73	74	75	76	77	78	79	80
81	82	83	84	85	86	87	88	89	90
91	92	93	94	95	96	97	98	99	100

1. A 2-digit number the sum of whose digits is 1. **10**
2. The last number on the hundred chart. **100**
3. The number that is 99 less than the greatest number on the hundred chart. **1**
4. Both digits are odd. The tens digit minus the ones digit is 4. Their sum is 10. **73**
5. The digits are equal. The sum of the digits is 10. **55**
6. The number that is 1 less than the number whose digits have a sum of 12 and whose tens digit is greater than 4 but less than 6. **56**
7. The number whose digits have a sum of 15 and a difference of 1. This number is not 8 less than 95. **78**
8. If you subtract 6 from the ones digit, you get the tens digit. Skip-count by 2 four times to get the ones digit. **28**
9. The number that is 5 less than the answer to Problem 8. **23**
10. The number whose ones digit is 8 less than its tens digit. The sum of the digits is a 2-digit number. **91**
11. The number whose digits have a sum the same as the digits in 36. This number is less than 50 and greater than 36. **45**
12. The number in the sixth column, fifth row. **46**

CW10 Challenge

Reading Strategy 2.4

Cause and Effect　Understand → Plan → Solve → Check

A **cause** is the reason something happens. An **effect** is what happens as a result of the cause. Read the problem below carefully.

Mrs. Cheng had a chart for her students to write down the titles of books that they read each month. She told her students that they would have a popcorn party each month that they read at least 45 books altogether. On the chart, there were 39 titles for October, 53 titles for November, and 46 titles for December. Did Mrs. Cheng's class have any popcorn parties?

1. Complete the table. **Possible answers are given.**

Cause	Effect
The students read 39 books altogether in October.	They will not have a popcorn party.
The students read 53 books altogether in November.	They will have a popcorn party.
The students read 46 books altogether in December.	They will have a popcorn party.

2. Solve the problem.
   They will have a popcorn party in November and in December.
3. Describe the strategy you used.
   Possible answer: I compared each month's number of titles to 45. 39 < 45; 53 > 45; 46 > 45.

PS10 Reading Strategy

Algebra: Number Patterns

Lesson Planning

Objective To describe, extend, create, and predict number patterns from numbers and models

NCTM Standards

1. Number and Operations
2. Algebra
6. Problem Solving
8. Communication
10. Representation

Math Background

These ideas will help students understand how to describe and analyze patterns.

- A pattern is an ordered set of numbers or objects.
- The order helps you identify missing parts and predict what will come next.
- Patterns help students understand number relationships, a key element in algebra.

Vocabulary

pattern an ordered set of numbers or objects whose elements can be predicted

Warm-Up Resources

Number of the Day

I am the number of pennies in one dollar. Skip-count by that number to tell how many pennies are in ten dollars. There are 1,000 pennies in ten dollars.

Daily Facts Practice

Have students practice addition and subtraction facts by completing Set D of *Teacher's Resource Book*, p. TR84.

Solve a Problem

Transparency 2.5

Problem of the Day

Katie signed up for a karate class. It lasts for five weeks and meets two times each week. Use skip-counting to find out how many classes she will have in all. She will have 10 classes.

Solution Problem of the Day tab, p. PD2

Intervention and Extension Resources

Alternative Teaching Strategy

MATERIALS *For each group* base-ten blocks

Help students **make a pattern.** Tell them to model the numbers 21, 31, 41, and 51. Then have them line up the models in order.

Have students

- describe the pattern. The tens digits increase by 1, so the numbers increase by 1 ten each time.
- predict the next two numbers in the pattern. 61, 71
- make a model and count by 10s to see if their prediction is right.

If time allows, have students make up their own pattern with three-digit numbers.

KINESTHETIC

VISUAL/SPATIAL, INTERPERSONAL

Multistep and Strategy Problems

The following multistep or strategy problem is provided in Lesson 2.5:

Page	Item
31	16

Technology • Calculator

MATERIALS *For each student* TI-108 calculator

Help students **find number patterns on a calculator**. Have students skip-count by tens to 100.

- Have students press the plus key, 10, and the equal sign. 10 will appear. The students have counted 1 ten.
- To count another ten, students press the equal sign again. 20 will appear.
- Students continue pressing the equal sign until they reach 100. If time permits, have students skip-count by 25s, 100s, and 1,000s.

VISUAL

LOGICAL/MATHEMATICAL

Art Connection

Help students **understand patterns**. Display the following pattern:

○ △ □ ○ △ □ ○ △ □

Divide the class into small groups. Ask each group to draw a picture that illustrates a pattern. Have groups share their patterns with the class. Ask volunteers to name the order of the objects in the patterns that students share.

VISUAL

LOGICAL/MATHEMATICAL

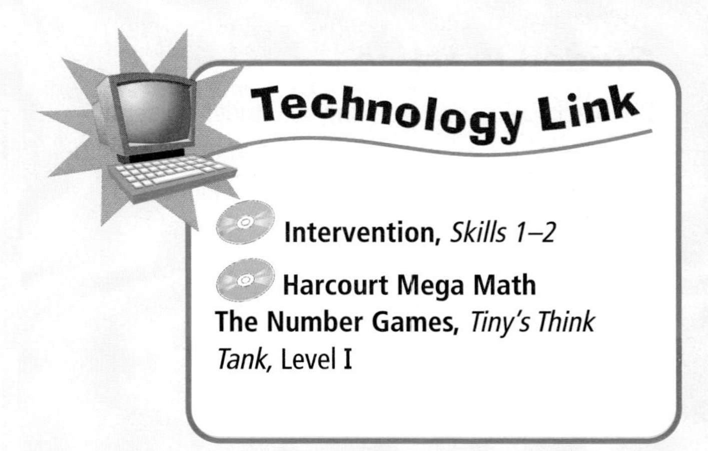

Technology Link
Intervention, *Skills 1–2*
Harcourt Mega Math
The Number Games, *Tiny's Think Tank,* Level I

Lesson 2.5 Organizer

Objective To describe, extend, create, and predict number patterns from numbers and models

Vocabulary pattern

1 INTRODUCE

QUICK REVIEW provides a review of computational skills.

WHY LEARN THIS? You will be able to identify number patterns in addition and multiplication. *Share the lesson objective with students.*

2 TEACH

Guided Instruction

- *Discuss the vocabulary term* pattern *with students.* **Give an example of a number pattern you have learned.** Possible answer: Odd numbers end in 1, 3, 5, 7, or 9.
- *Direct students' attention to the Examples.* **What is another name for what you are doing in Example A?** skip-counting by 2 **in Example B?** skip-counting by 10 **in Example C?** skip-counting by 100
  In Example C, can you hear what the pattern is by saying the numbers the models represent out loud? Explain. Yes; possible answer: by saying the numbers out loud, you can hear that only the hundreds digit changes. It increases by 1 hundred each time.
  Name a 3-digit number pattern where the digit in the tens place decreases. Possible answer: 290, 280, 270, 260, 250, and so on.

3 PRACTICE

Guided Practice

Do Check Exercises 1–6 with your students. Identify students who are having difficulty and choose appropriate lesson resources to provide assistance.

LESSON 5

Algebra: Number Patterns

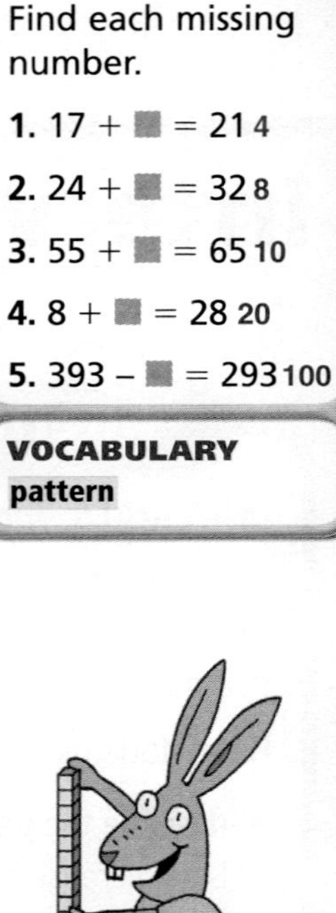

Quick Review

Find each missing number.

1. 17 + ■ = 21 4
2. 24 + ■ = 32 8
3. 55 + ■ = 65 10
4. 8 + ■ = 28 20
5. 393 − ■ = 293 100

VOCABULARY
pattern

Learn

WHAT'S NEXT? A **pattern** is an ordered set of numbers or objects. The order helps you predict what will come next.

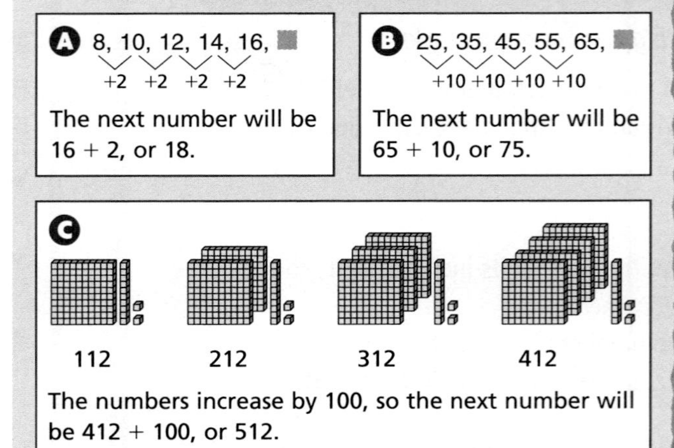

Examples

Predict the next number in each pattern.

A 8, 10, 12, 14, 16, ■
+2 +2 +2 +2
The next number will be 16 + 2, or 18.

B 25, 35, 45, 55, 65, ■
+10 +10 +10 +10
The next number will be 65 + 10, or 75.

C
112 212 312 412
The numbers increase by 100, so the next number will be 412 + 100, or 512.

- **REASONING** What is the next number in the pattern 923, 823, 723, 623? Explain.
  523; Possible answer: the numbers decrease by 100.

Check

1. Explain what base-ten blocks are needed for the sixth number of the pattern in Example C. **Possible answer: 6 hundreds, 1 ten, 2 ones are needed to show 100 more than 512.**

Predict the next number in each pattern. Explain.

2. **60; add 10 to each number**
3. **10; subtract 5 from each number**
4. 30, 35, 40, 45, ■ **50; add 5 to each number**
5. 58, 68, 78, 88, ■ **98; add 10 to each number**
6. 13, 17, 21, 25, ■ **29; add 4 to each number**

30

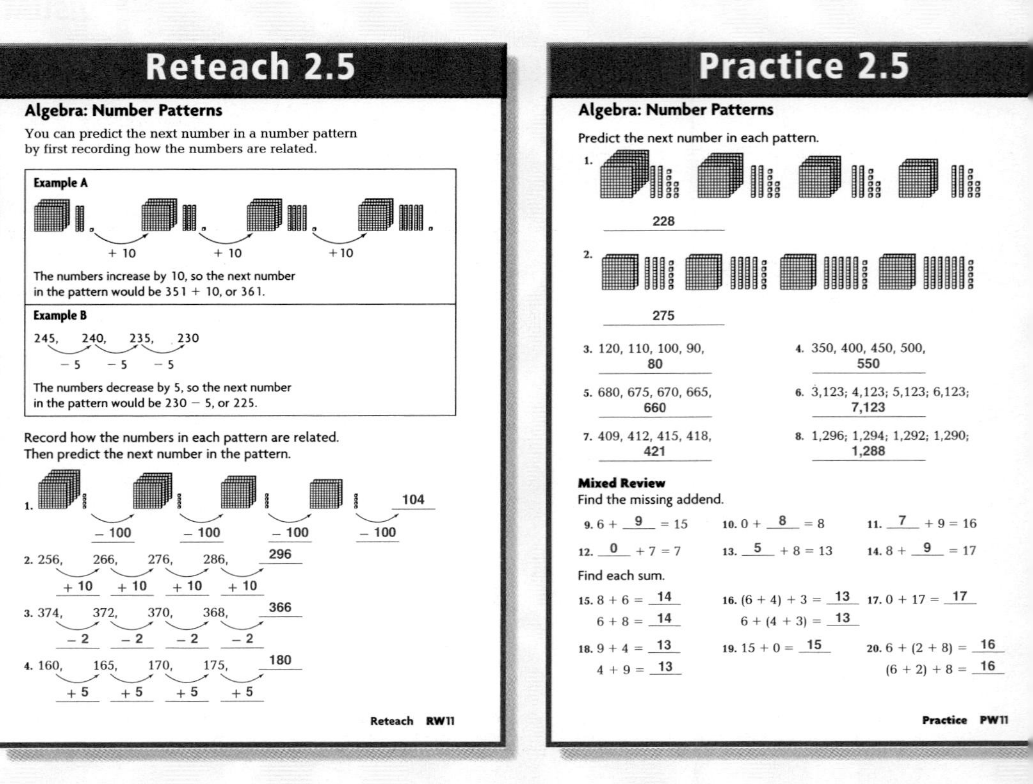

Reteach 2.5

Algebra: Number Patterns

You can predict the next number in a number pattern by first recording how the numbers are related.

Example A

+ 10 + 10 +10

The numbers increase by 10, so the next number in the pattern would be 351 + 10, or 361.

Example B

245, 240, 235, 230
− 5 − 5 − 5

The numbers decrease by 5, so the next number in the pattern would be 230 − 5, or 225.

Record how the numbers in each pattern are related. Then predict the next number in the pattern.

1. − 100 − 100 − 100 − 100 **104**
2. 256, 266, 276, 286, **296**
   + 10 + 10 + 10 + 10
3. 374, 372, 370, 368, **366**
   − 2 − 2 − 2 − 2
4. 160, 165, 170, 175, **180**
   + 5 + 5 + 5 + 5

Reteach RW11

Practice 2.5

Algebra: Number Patterns

Predict the next number in each pattern.

1. **228**
2. **275**
3. 120, 110, 100, 90, **80**
4. 350, 400, 450, 500, **550**
5. 680, 675, 670, 665, **660**
6. 3,123; 4,123; 5,123; 6,123; **7,123**
7. 409, 412, 415, 418, **421**
8. 1,296; 1,294; 1,292; 1,290; **1,288**

Mixed Review

Find the missing addend.

9. 6 + **9** = 15
10. 0 + **8** = 8
11. **7** + 9 = 16
12. **0** + 7 = 7
13. **5** + 8 = 13
14. 8 + **9** = 17

Find each sum.

15. 8 + 6 = **14**; 6 + 8 = **14**
16. (6 + 4) + 3 = **13**; 6 + (4 + 3) = **13**
17. 0 + 17 = **17**
18. 9 + 4 = **13**; 4 + 9 = **13**
19. 15 + 0 = **15**
20. 6 + (2 + 8) = **16**; (6 + 2) + 8 = **16**

Practice PW11

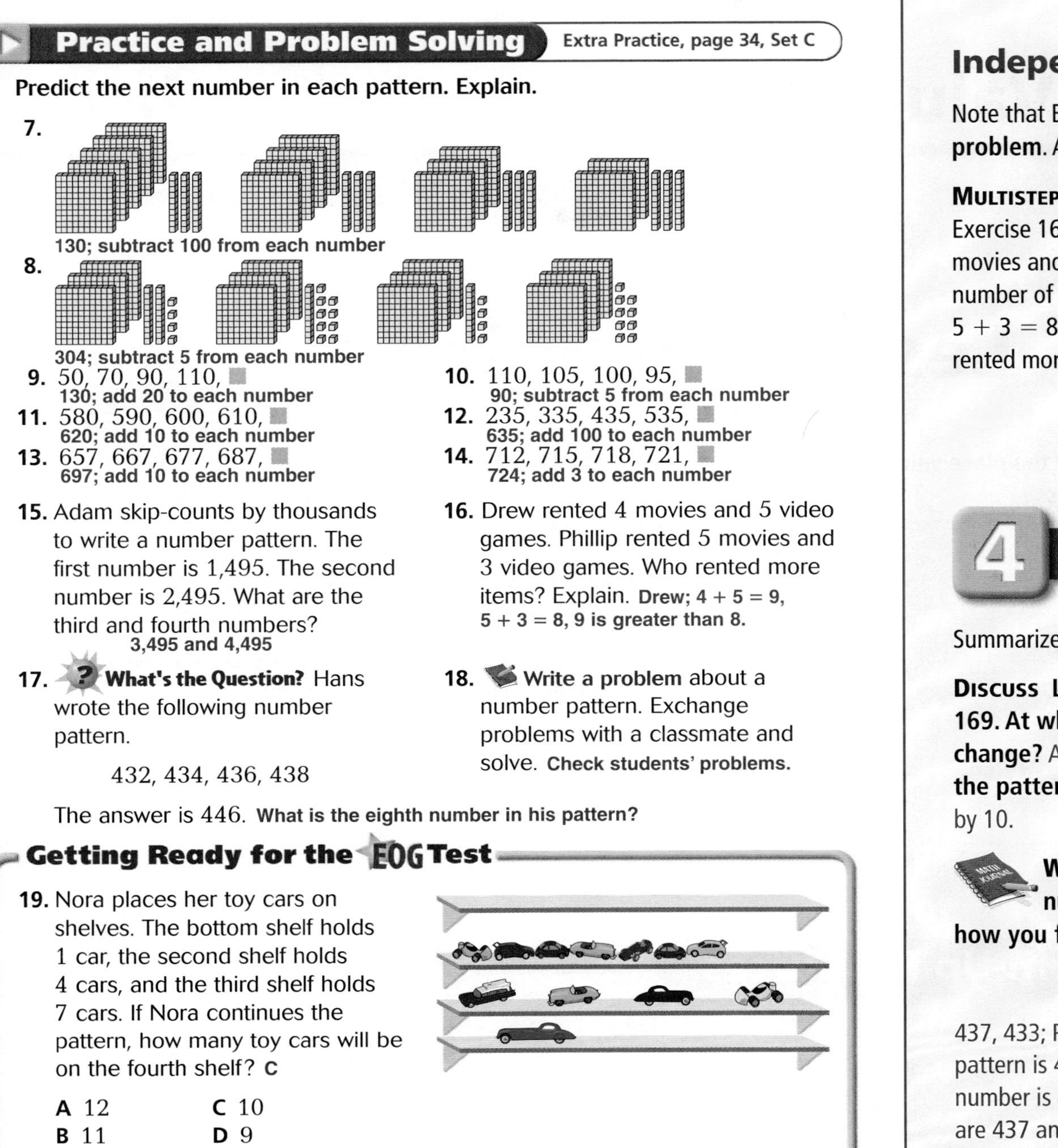

Practice and Problem Solving

Extra Practice, page 34, Set C

Predict the next number in each pattern. Explain.

7. 130; subtract 100 from each number

8. 304; subtract 5 from each number

9. 50, 70, 90, 110, ■ **130; add 20 to each number**

10. 110, 105, 100, 95, ■ **90; subtract 5 from each number**

11. 580, 590, 600, 610, ■ **620; add 10 to each number**

12. 235, 335, 435, 535, ■ **635; add 100 to each number**

13. 657, 667, 677, 687, ■ **697; add 10 to each number**

14. 712, 715, 718, 721, ■ **724; add 3 to each number**

15. Adam skip-counts by thousands to write a number pattern. The first number is 1,495. The second number is 2,495. What are the third and fourth numbers? **3,495 and 4,495**

16. Drew rented 4 movies and 5 video games. Phillip rented 5 movies and 3 video games. Who rented more items? Explain. **Drew; 4 + 5 = 9, 5 + 3 = 8, 9 is greater than 8.**

17. **What's the Question?** Hans wrote the following number pattern.

    432, 434, 436, 438

    The answer is 446. **What is the eighth number in his pattern?**

18. **Write a problem** about a number pattern. Exchange problems with a classmate and solve. **Check students' problems.**

Getting Ready for the EOG Test

19. Nora places her toy cars on shelves. The bottom shelf holds 1 car, the second shelf holds 4 cars, and the third shelf holds 7 cars. If Nora continues the pattern, how many toy cars will be on the fourth shelf? **C**

    A 12 C 10
    B 11 D 9

North Carolina Standards 5.01 Describe and extend numeric and geometric patterns. *also* 5.02

Independent Practice

Note that Exercise 16 is a **multistep or strategy problem**. Assign Exercises 7–18.

MULTISTEP OR STRATEGY PROBLEM To solve Exercise 16, students should add the number of movies and games Drew rented, $4 + 5 = 9$, and the number of movies and games that Phillip rented, $5 + 3 = 8$. Next, they need to compare to find who rented more. $9 > 8$, so Drew rented more.

4 ASSESS

Summarize the lesson by having students:

DISCUSS Look at the pattern: 139, 149, 159, 169. At what point will more than 1 digit change? At 199 to 209, two digits will change. **Is the pattern the same?** Yes. It is still only increasing by 10.

WRITE What will the sixth and seventh numbers of this pattern be? Explain how you found the pattern.

457, 453, 449, 445

437, 433; Possible answer: Each number in the pattern is 4 less than the previous number. The fifth number is 445 – 4 or 441, so the next two numbers are 437 and 433.

LESSON QUIZ

Predict the next number in each pattern. Explain.

1. 97, 87, 77, 67, 57; subtract 10
2. 15, 25, 35, 45, 55; add 10
3. 272, 372, 472, 572; add 100
4. 43, 38, 33, 28, 23; subtract 5

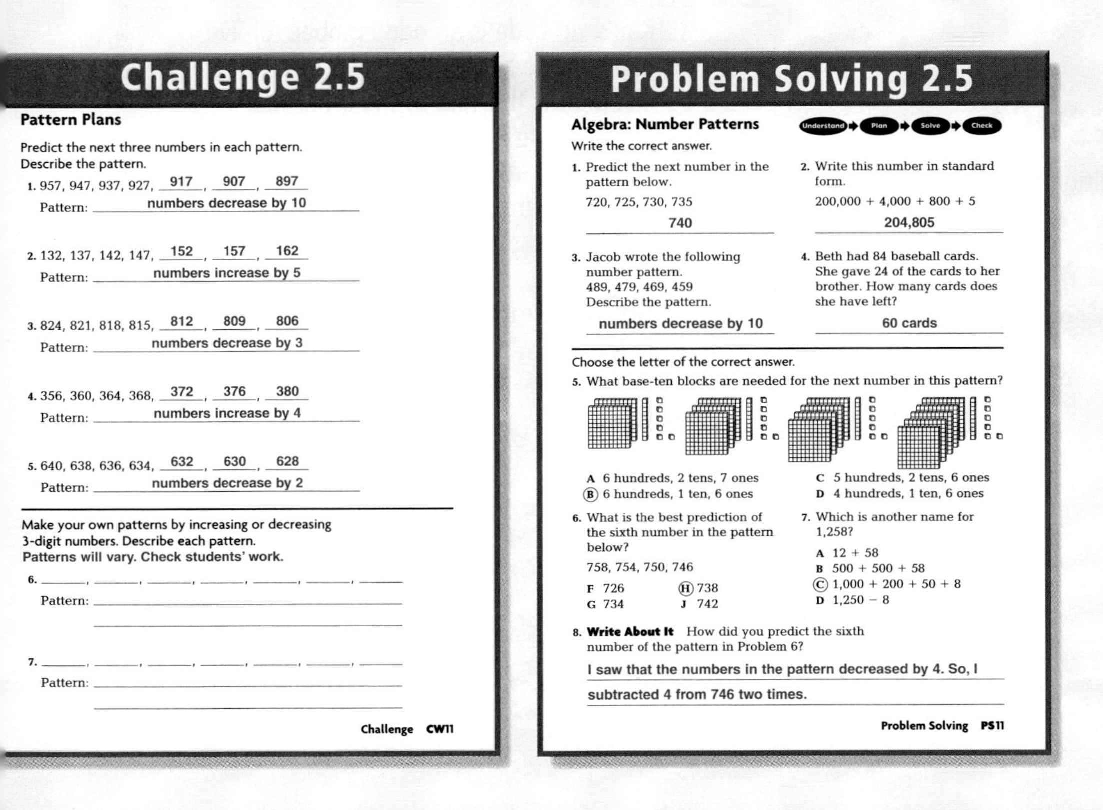

Challenge 2.5

Pattern Plans

Predict the next three numbers in each pattern. Describe the pattern.

1. 957, 947, 937, 927, 917, 907, 897
   Pattern: numbers decrease by 10
2. 132, 137, 142, 147, 152, 157, 162
   Pattern: numbers increase by 5
3. 824, 821, 818, 815, 812, 809, 806
   Pattern: numbers decrease by 3
4. 356, 360, 364, 368, 372, 376, 380
   Pattern: numbers increase by 4
5. 640, 638, 636, 634, 632, 630, 628
   Pattern: numbers decrease by 2

Make your own patterns by increasing or decreasing 3-digit numbers. Describe each pattern.
Patterns will vary. Check students' work.

6. ____, ____, ____, ____, ____, ____, ____
   Pattern: ____
7. ____, ____, ____, ____, ____, ____, ____
   Pattern: ____

Challenge CW11

Problem Solving 2.5

Algebra: Number Patterns

Understand → Plan → Solve → Check

Write the correct answer.

1. Predict the next number in the pattern below.
   720, 725, 730, 735
   740
2. Write this number in standard form.
   200,000 + 4,000 + 800 + 5
   204,805
3. Jacob wrote the following number pattern.
   489, 479, 469, 459
   Describe the pattern.
   numbers decrease by 10
4. Beth had 84 baseball cards. She gave 24 of the cards to her brother. How many cards does she have left?
   60 cards

Choose the letter of the correct answer.

5. What base-ten blocks are needed for the next number in this pattern?
   A 6 hundreds, 2 tens, 7 ones
   (B) 6 hundreds, 1 ten, 6 ones
   C 5 hundreds, 2 tens, 6 ones
   D 4 hundreds, 1 ten, 6 ones
6. What is the best prediction of the sixth number in the pattern below?
   758, 754, 750, 746
   F 726
   G 734
   (H) 738
   J 742
7. Which is another name for 1,258?
   A 12 + 58
   B 500 + 500 + 58
   (C) 1,000 + 200 + 50 + 8
   D 1,250 – 8
8. **Write About It** How did you predict the sixth number of the pattern in Problem 6?
   I saw that the numbers in the pattern decreased by 4. So, I subtracted 4 from 746 two times.

Problem Solving PS11

Lesson 2.6

Place Value: 5- and 6-Digit Numbers

Lesson Planning

Objective To identify the place value of digits in 5- and 6-digit numbers

NCTM Standards
1. Number and Operations
6. Problem Solving
7. Reasoning and Proof
8. Communication
9. Connections
10. Representation

Math Background

The following experiences will help students build understanding of greater numbers.

- Place-value charts and expanded form will help students understand numbers written in standard form.
- Numbers used in real life contexts help students understand the magnitude of larger quantities.
- A comma is used to separate the ones period and the thousands period when writing the standard and word form of numbers.

Warm-Up Resources

Number of the Day

There are 5,280 feet in a mile. Write this number in standard form, in expanded form, and in word form. 5,280; 5,000 + 200 + 80; five thousand, two hundred eighty

Daily Facts Practice

Have students practice addition facts by completing Set E of *Teacher's Resource Book*, p. TR84.

Solve a Problem

Transparency 2.6

Problem of the Day

Kim's zip code is an odd number. All five digits in the zip code are different. The last digit is the sum of the other four digits. The first digit is one more than the second, and the second is one more than the third. What is Kim's zip code? 43209

Solution Problem of the Day tab, p. PD2

Intervention and Extension Resources

Alternative Teaching Strategy

MATERIALS *For each group* 5–6 books

Help students **understand 1,000,10,000, and 100,000.** Bring in several books with more than 1,000 pages. Divide the class into small groups and give a book to each.

- Have each group use a self-stick note to mark page 1,000 and consider it to be the end of the book.
- Ask students to use the book and nine more self-stick notes to prove that there are ten hundreds in 1,000. Students should mark pages 100, 200, and so on.
- Ask students what pages they would mark in a book with 10,000 pages to show that there are 10 thousands in 10,000. 1,000, 2,000, and so on
- Then ask students what pages they would mark in a book with 100,000 pages to show that there are 10 ten thousands in 100,000 10,000; 20,000; and so on

KINESTHETIC

LOGICAL/MATHEMATICAL

Multistep and Strategy Problems

The following multistep or strategy problem is provided in Lesson 2.6:

Page	Item
33	21

Special Needs

ESOL/ESL

Help students **practice reading and writing numbers to 10,000**. Display two place-value charts. Dictate these numbers in order: 7; 87; 487; 3,487; 53,487; 653,487. Have students take turns writing each number in one of the charts and then reading it aloud. Check students' work.

VISUAL

VERBAL/LINGUISTIC

Social Studies Connection

Help **reinforce students' understanding of 10,000**. The population of a community helps tell about the community and its needs. Share with students the following changes in a community's population: 1970, 1,200; 1980, 3,800; 1990, 7,000; 2000, 12,200.

Invite students to

- display the information in a table that shows years in one column and population in a second column. Check students' work.
- write a statement that tells how the population is changing. Possible answer: The population is growing.

VISUAL

LOGICAL/MATHEMATICAL

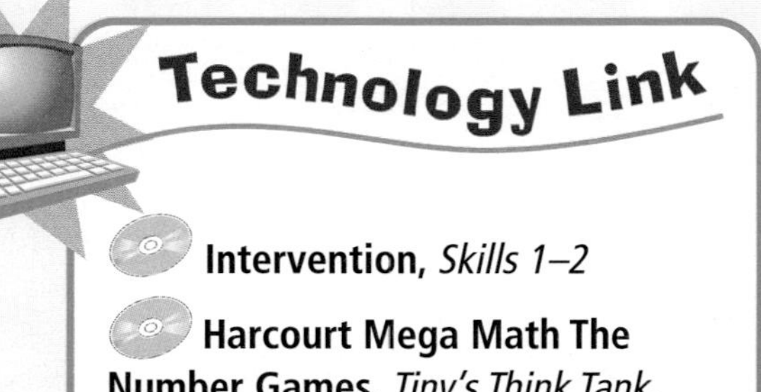

Technology Link

Intervention, *Skills 1–2*

Harcourt Mega Math The Number Games, *Tiny's Think Tank,* Level A; **Fraction Action,** *Number Line Mine,* Level A

Lesson 2.6 Organizer

Objective To identify the place value of digits in 5- and 6-digit numbers

1 INTRODUCE

QUICK REVIEW provides review of prerequisite skills.

WHY LEARN THIS? You will use greater numbers to understand many things in the world, including distances to other countries, lengths and heights of natural formations, and populations of cities and states. *Share the lesson objective with students.*

Guided Instruction

- *Direct students' attention to the place-value charts.*

  What is the difference between the first and second place-value chart? The second chart has a column for hundred thousands. **What place value has no value in 506,132?** the ten thousands

  REASONING Why is the position of a digit important? It tells the value of the number. The farther to the left a number is placed, the greater its value.

MODIFYING INSTRUCTION Spend some time on comma placement, asking students where it appears in the place-value chart and providing several practice examples for correctly inserting the comma.

Remind students not to use the word *and* when reading 3–6 digit numbers. *And* will be used later with mixed numbers and decimals.

LESSON 6

Place Value: 5- and 6-Digit Numbers

Quick Review

Write in expanded form.

1. 384 — 300 + 80 + 4
2. 51 — 50 + 1
3. 677 — 600 + 70 + 7
4. 9,240 — 9,000 + 200 + 40
5. 3,818 — 3,000 + 800 + 10 + 8

Learn

THE SOONER STATE Oklahoma has an area of 69,903 square miles. You can use a place-value chart to help you understand each digit in the number.

TEN THOUSANDS	THOUSANDS	HUNDREDS	TENS	ONES
6	9,	9	0	3

Remember

Put a comma between the thousands place and the hundreds place.

69,903
↑
comma

You can write this number in three ways:

Standard form: 69,903

Expanded form: 60,000 + 9,000 + 900 + 3

Word form: sixty-nine thousand, nine hundred three

- How many ten thousands are in 69,903? **6**

In 2000, there were 506,132 residents in Oklahoma City, the state capital. Look at this number in the place-value chart.

HUNDRED THOUSANDS	TEN THOUSANDS	THOUSANDS	HUNDREDS	TENS	ONES
5	0	6,	1	3	2

You can write this number in three ways:

Standard form: 506,132

Expanded form: 500,000 + 6,000 + 100 + 30 + 2

Word form: five hundred six thousand, one hundred thirty-two

OKLAHOMA
Oklahoma City

- What is the value of the digit 5 in 506,132? **500,000**

Reteach 2.6

Place Value: 5- and 6-Digit Numbers

Ten Thousands	Thousands	Hundreds	Tens	Ones
2	3,	6	4	7

2 ten thousands, 3 thousands, 6 hundreds, 4 tens, 7 ones

20,000 + 3,000 + 600 + 40 + 7

You write it: 23,647.
You read it: "twenty-three thousand, six hundred forty-seven."

Hundred Thousands	Ten Thousands	Thousands	Hundreds	Tens	Ones
4	8	0,	2	7	6

4 hundred thousands, 8 ten thousands, 0 thousands, 2 hundreds, 7 tens, 6 ones

400,000 + 80,000 + 200 + 70 + 6

You write it: 480,276.
You read it: "four hundred eighty thousand, two hundred seventy-six."

Write in standard form.

1. 60,000 + 4,000 + 500 + 90 + 4 **64,594**
2. 200,000 + 30,000 + 5,000 + 200 + 4 **235,204**
3. fifty-five thousand, three hundred eighty-seven **55,387**
4. thirty-six thousand, two hundred twenty **36,220**
5. ninety thousand, forty **90,040**
6. thirty-four thousand, five hundred forty-three **34,543**
7. one hundred eleven thousand, six hundred **111,600**
8. two hundred five thousand, thirty-eight **205,038**

RW12 Reteach

Practice 2.6

Place Value: 5- and 6-Digit Numbers

Write in standard form.

1. 30,000 + 5,000 + 300 + 20 + 1 **35,321**
2. 40,000 + 9,000 + 400 + 70 + 2 **49,472**
3. 700,000 + 20,000 + 3,000 **723,000**
4. 80,000 + 800 + 8 **80,808**
5. 70,000 + 200 + 80 + 9 **70,289**
6. 300,000 + 10,000 + 90 + 4 **310,094**
7. two hundred sixty-one thousand, eight hundred thirty-one **261,831**
8. forty-three thousand, five hundred forty-five **43,545**

Write the value of the underlined digit.

9. 91,643 **1 thousand; 1,000**
10. 536,955 **3 ten thousands; 30,000**
11. 72,561 **5 hundreds; 500**
12. 15,406 **6 ones; 6**
13. 21,789 **2 ten thousands; 20,000**
14. 445,632 **5 thousands; 5,000**

Mixed Review

Solve.

15. 16 + 15 = **31**
16. 20 − 17 = **3**
17. 22 − **8** = 14
18. 17 + 58 = **75**
19. 38 + 62 = **100**
20. 40 − 36 = **4**
21. 24 − 18 = **6**
22. 16 + 16 = **32**

PW12 Practice

Check

1. Explain the value of each digit in 21,694.
2 = 20,000; 1 = 1,000; 6 = 600; 9 = 90; 4 = 4

Write in standard form.

2. 500,000 + 20,000 + 6,000 + 700 + 30 + 4
526,734
3. thirty-five thousand, nine hundred forty-seven
35,947

Write in expanded form.

4. 16,723
10,000 + 6,000 + 700 + 20 + 3
5. 52,019
50,000 + 2,000 + 10 + 9
6. 238,605
200,000 + 30,000 + 8,000 + 600 + 5

Practice and Problem Solving

Extra Practice, page 34, Set D

Write in standard form.

7. 20,000 + 6,000 + 700 + 30 + 4
26,734
8. 400,000 + 10,000 + 400 + 8
410,408
9. forty-two thousand, three hundred fifteen 42,315
10. six hundred eighteen thousand, nine hundred 618,900

Write in expanded form.

11. 316,723
300,000 + 10,000 + 6,000 + 700 + 20 + 3
12. 55,119
50,000 + 5,000 + 100 + 10 + 9
13. 11,012
10,000 + 1,000 + 10 + 2
14. 749,207
700,000 + 40,000 + 9,000 + 200 + 7

Write the value of the blue digit.

15. 81,465
400
16. 262,817
200,000
17. 843,912
3,000
18. 19,273
10,000

Complete.

19. 100,000 + ■ + 2,000 + 600 + 50 + 1 = 112,651
10,000
20. 60,000 + ■ + 300 + 10 + 9 = 62,319
2,000

21. **REASONING** I am an even number between 51,680 and 51,700. The sum of my digits is 23. What number am I? 51,692

22. **What's the Error?** Karla wrote eleven thousand, forty-five as 1,145. Explain her error. Write the number correctly in standard form. Karla forgot to write a zero in the hundreds place; 11,045.

Getting Ready for the EOG Test

23. What is the number of cans written in standard form? B

A 26,050
B 20,650
C 20,605
D 2,650

DAILY NEWS
Third graders collect twenty thousand, six hundred fifty cans!

North Carolina Standards 1.01 Develop number sense for whole numbers through 9,999. Build understanding of place value (ones through thousands).

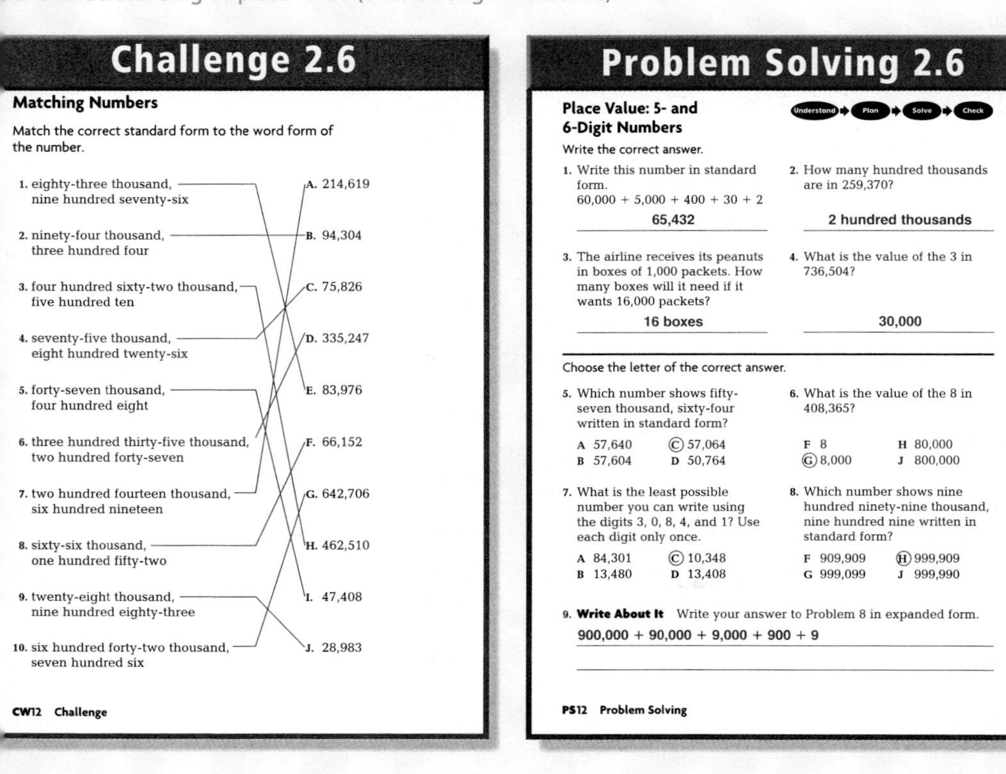

Challenge 2.6

Matching Numbers

Match the correct standard form to the word form of the number.

1. eighty-three thousand, nine hundred seventy-six — A. 214,619
2. ninety-four thousand, three hundred four — B. 94,304
3. four hundred sixty-two thousand, five hundred ten — C. 75,826
4. seventy-five thousand, eight hundred twenty-six — D. 335,247
5. forty-seven thousand, four hundred eight — E. 83,976
6. three hundred thirty-five thousand, two hundred forty-seven — F. 66,152
7. two hundred fourteen thousand, six hundred nineteen — G. 642,706
8. sixty-six thousand, one hundred fifty-two — H. 462,510
9. twenty-eight thousand, nine hundred eighty-three — I. 47,408
10. six hundred forty-two thousand, seven hundred six — J. 28,983

CW12 Challenge

Problem Solving 2.6

Place Value: 5- and 6-Digit Numbers

Understand → Plan → Solve → Check

Write the correct answer.

1. Write this number in standard form.
60,000 + 5,000 + 400 + 30 + 2
65,432
2. How many hundred thousands are in 259,370?
2 hundred thousands
3. The airline receives its peanuts in boxes of 1,000 packets. How many boxes will it need if it wants 16,000 packets?
16 boxes
4. What is the value of the 3 in 736,504?
30,000

Choose the letter of the correct answer.

5. Which number shows fifty-seven thousand, sixty-four written in standard form?
A 57,640 (C) 57,064
B 57,604 D 50,764
6. What is the value of the 8 in 408,365?
F 8 H 80,000
(G) 8,000 J 800,000
7. What is the least possible number you can write using the digits 3, 0, 8, 4, and 1? Use each digit only once.
A 84,301 (C) 10,348
B 13,480 D 13,408
8. Which number shows nine hundred ninety-nine thousand, nine hundred nine written in standard form?
F 909,909 (H) 999,909
G 999,099 J 999,990
9. **Write About It** Write your answer to Problem 8 in expanded form.
900,000 + 90,000 + 9,000 + 900 + 9

PS12 Problem Solving

3 PRACTICE

Guided Practice

Do Check Exercises 1–6 with your students. Identify students who are having difficulty and choose appropriate lesson resources to provide assistance.

COMMON ERROR ALERT

Many students have difficulty reading greater numbers. Display a number such as 523,214. Remind students that the comma separates the thousands from the hundreds. Cover the 214 and have students read 523 thousand. Then cover the 523 and the comma and have students read 214. Have students read the entire number.

Independent Practice

Note that Exercise 21 is a **multistep or strategy problem.** Assign Exercises 7–22.

For items 15–18, students may express the answers as numbers written in standard form or as the number of thousands, hundreds, tens, or ones.

SCAFFOLDED INSTRUCTION Use the prompts on Transparency 2 to guide instruction for the multistep or strategy problem in Exercise 21.

Summarize the lesson by having students:

DISCUSS What is the difference between the way you would write 900,000, the way you would write 90,000, and the way you would write 9,000 in standard form? 9,000 is a 4-digit number with 3 zeros; 90,000 is a 5-digit number with 4 zeros; and 900,000 is a 6-digit number with 5 zeros.

WRITE In what place-value positions are the zeros in the number 70,010?
thousands, hundreds, ones

LESSON QUIZ

Transparency 2.6

Write in standard form.

1. eighty thousand
80,000
2. three thousand
3,000
3. 300,000 + 90
300,090
4. fifty-one thousand
51,000

Extra Practice

Purpose To provide extra practice for the skills presented in this chapter

The blue page references in each set of exercises refer to the lesson pages where each skill is taught.

Internet Resources

Visit THE LEARNING SITE at **www.harcourtschool.com** for a listing of practice activities.

Extra Practice

Set A (pp. 22–23)

Write each number in standard form.

1. 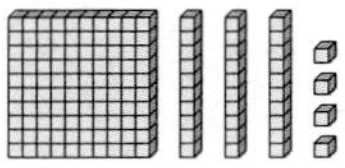 [base-ten blocks] 134
2. 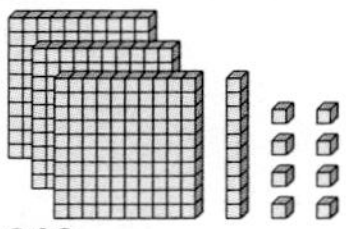 [base-ten blocks] 318
3. 500 + 60 + 6 **566**
4. 700 + 4 **704**
5. four hundred seventy-six **476**
6. nine hundred ninety-one **991**

Write the value of the blue digit.

7. 346 **40**
8. 872 **2**
9. 13 **10**
10. 554 **500**

Set B (pp. 24–27)

Write in standard form.

1. 1,000 + 900 + 40 + 2 **1,942**
2. 5,000 + 700 + 80 + 3 **5,783**
3. two thousand, four hundred sixty-seven **2,467**
4. eight thousand, eighteen **8,018**

Write in expanded form.

5. 5,487 **5,000 + 400 + 80 + 7**
6. 6,055 **6,000 + 50 + 5**
7. 6,170 **6,000 + 100 + 70**
8. 7,796 **7,000 + 700 + 90 + 6**

Set C (pp. 30–31)

Predict the next number in each pattern. Explain.

1. 310, 410, 510, 610, ■ **710; add 100 to each number**
2. 75, 70, 65, 60, ■ **55; subtract 5 from each number**
3. 503, 506, 509, 512, ■ **515; add 3 to each number**
4. 8,324, 7,324, 6,324, 5,324, ■ **4,324; subtract 1,000 from each number**

Set D (pp. 32–33)

Write in standard form.

1. 10,000 + 6,000 + 900 + 60 + 5 **16,965**
2. 600,000 + 50,000 + 3,000 + 6 **653,006**
3. fifty-one thousand, four hundred **51,400**
4. twenty-two thousand, eighteen **22,018**

Write in expanded form.

5. 65,487
6. 376,055
7. 536,173
8. 47,796

5. 60,000 + 5,000 + 400 + 80 + 7
6. 300,000 + 70,000 + 6,000 + 50 + 5
7. 500,000 + 30,000 + 6,000 + 100 + 70 + 3
8. 40,000 + 7,000 + 700 + 90 + 6

34

CHAPTER 2

Review/Test

CHECK VOCABULARY

Choose the best term from the box.

odd
even
digits
expanded form

1. A number with a 0, 2, 4, 6, or 8 in the ones place is an _?_ number. (p. 20) **even**
2. The symbols 0, 1, 2, 3, 4, 5, 6, 7, 8, and 9 are called _?_. (p. 22) **digits**

CHECK SKILLS

Write whether the number is *odd* or *even*. (pp. 20–21)

3. 31 **odd**
4. 74 **even**
5. 348 **even**
6. 929 **odd**

Write in standard form. (pp. 22–27, 32–33)

7. 800 + 60 + 9 **869**
8. 3,000 + 700 + 10 + 1 **3,711**
9. 8,000 + 500 + 20 + 2 **8,522**
10. 30,000 + 4,000 + 700 + 5 **34,705**
11. 200,000 + 90,000 + 4,000 + 600 + 50 + 5 **294,655**
12. fifty-three thousand, eight hundred nineteen **53,819**

Predict the next number in each pattern. (pp. 30–31)

13. 135, 235, 335, 435, ■ **535**
14. 250, 230, 210, 190, ■ **170**

Write the value of the blue digit. (pp. 22–27, 32–33)

15. 863 **800**
16. 9,845 **9,000**
17. 12,053 **50**
18. 372,859 **300,000**

CHECK PROBLEM SOLVING

Solve. (pp. 28–29)

19. Katie made a model using base-ten blocks. She used 3 hundreds, 12 tens, 8 ones. What number did she model? **428**
20. Randy modeled 257 with base-ten blocks. He used 2 hundreds, 4 tens. How many ones did he use? **17 ones**

Review/Test

Purpose To check understanding of concepts, skills, and problem solving presented in Chapter 2

Using the Page

The Chapter 2 Review/Test can be used as a **review** or a **test**.

- Items 1–2 check understanding of concepts and new vocabulary.
- Items 3–18 check skill proficiency.
- Items 19–20 check students' abilities to choose and apply problem solving strategies to real-life number sense problems.

Suggest that students place the completed Chapter 2 Review/Test in their portfolios.

Using the Assessment Guide

- Multiple-choice format of Chapter 2 Posttest—See *Assessment Guide*, pp. AG13–14.
- Free-response format of Chapter 2 Posttest—See *Assessment Guide*, pp. AG15–16.

Using Student Self-Assessment

The How Did I Do? survey helps students assess what they have learned and how they learned it. This survey is available as a copying master in *Assessment Guide*, p. AGxvii.

Chapter 2 Test, page 1

Choose the correct answer.

1. What number is **odd**?
   A 18 (B) 47 C 66 D 94
2. What is the value of the 5 in 4,572?
   F 5 G 50 (H) 500 J 5,000
3. What is 345 written in expanded form?
   (A) 300 + 40 + 5
   B 30 + 45
   C 34 + 5
   D 3 + 4 + 5
4. What number is **even**?
   F 133 G 247 (H) 358 J 581
5. What is the value of the 8 in 683,472?
   A 800
   B 8,000
   (C) 80,000
   D 800,000
6. Predict the next number in the pattern.
   33, 37, 41, 45, ____
   F 47 (G) 49 H 51 J 59
7. What is 700 + 50 + 8 written in standard form?
   A 7,508 B 7,058 (C) 758 D 20
8. Jesse modeled 133 with base-ten blocks. He used 1 hundred and 2 tens. How many ones did he use?
   F 33 G 23 (H) 13 J 3
9. What is 8,734 written in expanded form?
   A 87 + 34
   B 800 + 734
   C 800 + 70 + 34
   (D) 8,000 + 700 + 30 + 4
10. Which number is **odd**?
    F 244 (G) 401 H 658 J 972

Go On

Chapter 2 Test, page 2

11. What is 18,329 written in expanded form?
    (A) 10,000 + 8,000 + 300 + 20 + 9
    B 18,000 + 3,000 + 29
    C 1,800 + 300 + 20 + 9
    D 1 + 8 + 3 + 2 + 9
12. What is four thousand, six hundred five written in standard form?
    F 4,065 (G) 4,605 H 4,650 J 46,005
13. What is eight hundred seventy-two written in standard form?
    A 80,072 B 8,702 C 8,072 (D) 872
14. What number completes the number sentence?
    8,000 + 400 + ■ + 5 = 8,425
    F 2,000 G 25 (H) 20 J 2
15. Jenny skip-counts by threes. She says, "3, 6, 9, 12." What numbers should Jenny say next?
    (A) 15, 18, 21 B 16, 17, 18 C 16, 18, 21 D 20, 25, 30
16. The code to a safe is a number pattern that skip-counts by hundreds. The first number is 432. The second number is 532. The third number is 632. What is the fourth number of the code?
    (F) 732 G 782 H 832 J 1,632
17. What is two hundred fifty-five thousand, four hundred eight written in standard form?
    (A) 255,408 B 255,084 C 255,048 D 25,548
18. What is the greatest 4-digit number that can be written using 3,8,5, and 6?
    (F) 8,653 G 8,635 H 8,563 J 8,536
19. What is the greatest 3-digit number that can be written using 5, 7, and 2?
    A 257 B 572 C 725 (D) 752
20. Brittany made a model using base-ten blocks. She used 4 hundreds, 17 tens, and 6 ones. What number did she model?
    F 476 G 486 H 516 (J) 576

Stop

Getting Ready for the EOG Test

Chapters 1–2

Using the Pages

These pages may be used to help students get ready for the North Carolina EOG Test. The test items are written in the same style and arranged in the same format as those on the EOG Test.

The pages are cumulative. They cover the standards from the North Carolina Mathematics Standard Course of Study that have been taught up to this point in the text or in a previous grade. Each Getting Ready for the EOG Test also reviews the North Carolina mathematics strands shown below.

- Number and Operations
- Measurement
- Geometry
- Data Analysis and Probability
- Algebra

These pages can be assigned at the end of the chapter as classwork or as a homework assignment. You may want to have students use individual recording sheets presented in a multiple-choice (standardized) format. A Test Answer Sheet is available as a blackline master in the *Assessment Guide* (p. AGlii).

You may wish to have students describe how they solved each problem and share their solutions.

Getting Ready for the EOG Test

NUMBER AND OPERATIONS

1. Rosa is taller than Jed. Jed is taller than Mark. Rosa is 46 inches tall. Mark is 43 inches tall. How tall could Jed be? **C**

A 49 inches
B 47 inches
C 44 inches
D 42 inches

2. Which number makes the number sentence true? **B**

$7{,}000 + 300 + \blacksquare + 6 = 7{,}396$

A 9 **C** 900
B 90 **D** 9,000

3. You are playing a game with numbered tiles. In order to play, you draw three tiles from the pile.

6 4 7

The winner is the player who makes the ***greatest*** odd 3-digit number from the tiles. What number should you make? **C**

A 764 **C** 647
B 746 **D** 467

4. **Explain It** A 3-digit number has the same number of ones, tens, and hundreds. If the sum of the digits is 6, what is the number? Explain how you know.
See page 37.

MEASUREMENT AND GEOMETRY

5. According to the clock, what could Juan be watching on television? **B**

TELEVISION PROGRAMS	
Time	**Show**
3:30	*Rocket Blasters*
4:00	*All Star Sports*
4:30	*Western Trails*
5:00	*Thriller Time*

A *All Star Sports*
B *Western Trails*
C *Thriller Time*
D *Rocket Blasters*

6. Shannon has some yarn. Which is the ***best*** unit to measure the length of the yarn? **C**

A cup
B pound
C inch
D gallon

7. **Explain It** Jon has 4 quarters, 3 dimes, 2 nickels, and 6 pennies. What is another way you can show this amount of money?
See page 37.

ALGEBRA

TIP **Eliminate choices.** See item 8. Since the digit in the hundreds place decreases by 1 in each number, eliminate all choices that do not have 5 in the hundreds place.

8. What is the next number in the pattern? B

858, 758, 658, ■

- **A** 458
- **B** 558
- **C** 648
- **D** 657

9. Beth is making a quilt. On Monday, she cut 2 triangles and 4 squares. On Tuesday, she cut 3 triangles and 6 squares. On Wednesday, she cut 4 triangles and 8 squares. If this pattern continues, how many shapes in all will Beth cut on Thursday? D

- **A** 5
- **B** 10
- **C** 12
- **D** 15

10. Explain It Rico wrote this number pattern.

400, 403, 406, 409

What rule did Rico use to make his pattern? Explain how you know. What are the next three numbers in the pattern?
See below.

DATA ANALYSIS AND PROBABILITY

11. Which color cube are you *most likely* to pull from the bag? A

- **A** yellow
- **B** green
- **C** red
- **D** blue

12. Which statement is true about the pointer on the spinner? C

- **A** It will most likely land on 1.
- **B** It will most likely land on 2.
- **C** It will most likely land on 3.
- **D** It will least likely land on 3.

13. Explain It Adam made a pictograph of these data.

FAVORITE JUICE	
Apple	4 symbols
Grape	2 symbols
Orange	5 symbols
Key: Each symbol = 5 votes.	

How many more votes did orange juice get than grape juice? Explain your answer. See below.

Chapters 1–2

Item Analysis

You may wish to use the item analysis to determine which North Carolina standards need additional review.

Item	North Carolina Standard	Lesson
1	(2) 1.01	Grade 2
2	1.01	2.3
3	(2) 1.01	Grade 2
4	1.01	2.2
5	(2) 2.02	Grade 2
6	(2) Goal 2	Grade 2
7	(2) Goal 2	Grade 2
8	5.01	2.5
9	(2) 5.01	Grade 2
10	(2) 5.01	Grade 2
11	(2) 4.02	Grade 2
12	(2) 4.02	Grade 2
13	(2) 4.01	Grade 2

SCORING RUBRIC
Explain It

2 Demonstrates a complete understanding of the problem and chooses an appropriate strategy to determine the solution

1 Demonstrates a partial understanding of the problem and chooses a strategy that does not lead to a complete and accurate solution

0 Demonstrates little understanding of the problem and shows little evidence of using any strategy to determine a solution

Explain It • Written Response

4. 222; the sum of 2 + 2 + 2 is 6.

7. Possible answer: Jon has $1.46. You can use one $1 bill, 1 quarter, 2 dimes, and 1 penny.

10. Add 3; possible answer: the difference between 403 and 400 is 3. The difference between 403 and 406 is 3, and so on. 412, 415, 418

13. 15 more votes; possible answer: since each symbol = 5 votes, skip-count by 5 five times to find the number of votes for orange juice. Skip-count by 5 two times to find the number of votes for grape juice. Then subtract. 25 − 10 = 15

Compare, Order, and Round Numbers

NCTM Standards 2000

1. Number and Operations
Lessons 3.1, 3.2, 3.3, 3.4, 3.5, 3.6
2. Algebra
Lesson 3.2
3. Geometry
4. Measurement
5. Data Analysis and Probability
Lessons 3.2, 3.4, 3.5, 3.6
6. Problem Solving
Lessons 3.1, 3.2, 3.3, 3.4, 3.5, 3.6
7. Reasoning and Proof
Lessons 3.1, 3.2, 3.3, 3.4, 3.5, 3.6
8. Communication
Lessons 3.1, 3.2, 3.3, 3.4, 3.5, 3.6
9. Connections
Lessons 3.1, 3.2, 3.3, 3.4, 3.5, 3.6
10. Representation
Lessons 3.5, 3.6

Chapter Planner

Getting Ready for Chapter 3 • Assessing Prior Knowledge and INTERVENTION (See PE and TE page 39.)

LESSON	NORTH CAROLINA STANDARDS	PACING	VOCABULARY*	MATERIALS	RESOURCES AND TECHNOLOGY
3.1 Benchmark Numbers pp. 40–41 **Objective** To use benchmarks to understand the relative magnitude of numbers	1.01	1 Day	**benchmark numbers**		Reteach, Practice, Problem Solving, Challenge 3.1 Transparency 3.1 **Intervention,** *Skills 3, 60* (CD or Book)
3.2 Algebra: Compare Numbers pp. 42–45 **Objective** To use models, place value, and number lines to compare numbers	1.01c	1 Day	**compare** **greater than** $>$ **less than** $<$ **equal to** $=$		Reteach, Practice, Problem Solving, Challenge 3.2 Transparency 3.2 **Intervention,** *Skills 3, 60* (CD or Book)
3.3 Order Numbers pp. 46–47 **Objective** To use models, number lines, and place value to order numbers	1.01c	1 Day			Reteach, Practice, Problem Solving, Challenge 3.3 Transparency 3.3 **Intervention,** *Skills 3, 60* (CD or Book)
3.4 Problem Solving Skill: Use a Bar Graph pp. 48–49 **Objective** To use the problem solving skill *use a bar graph* to solve problems	1.01c	1 Day			Reteach, Practice, Reading Strategy, Challenge 3.4 Transparency 3.4 Reading Transparency 3 **Intervention • Problem Solving,** *Strategy/Skill 3* (CD or Book)
3.5 Round to Nearest 10 and 100 pp. 50–51 **Objective** To use rounding rules to round numbers to the nearest 10 and 100	1.01	1 Day	**rounding**		Reteach, Practice, Problem Solving, Challenge 3.5 Transparency 3.5 **Intervention,** *Skills 3, 60* (CD or Book) **Harcourt Mega Math Fraction Action,** *Number Line Mine*
3.6 Round to Nearest 1,000 pp. 52–53 **Objective** To use rounding rules to round to the nearest 1,000	1.01	1 Day			Reteach, Practice, Problem Solving, Challenge 3.6 Transparency 3.6 Scaffolded Instruction Transparency 3 **Intervention,** *Skills 3, 60* (CD or Book) **Math Jingles® CD 3–4**

Ending Chapter 3 • **Extra Practice,** p. 54 • **Chapter 3 Review/Test,** p. 55 • **Getting Ready for the EOG Test,** pp. 56–57

Ending Unit 1 • **It's in the Bag,** p. 58; **Challenge,** p. 59; **Study Guide and Review,** pp. 60–61; **Performance Assessment,** p. 62; **Technology Linkup,** p. 63; **Problem Solving in North Carolina,** pp. 64–65

* **Boldfaced** terms are the key mathematical terms for the chapter.

Vocabulary Power

Review Vocabulary

To be ready for Chapter 3, students should know the following vocabulary term:

- **hundred** (p. 39)—the value of 10 groups of 10

Develop Key Chapter Vocabulary

The **boldfaced** words are the key vocabulary terms in the chapter.

- **benchmark numbers** (p. 40)—numbers that help you estimate the number of objects without counting them, such as 25, 50, 100, 1,000
- **compare** (p. 42)—to describe whether numbers are equal to, less than, or greater than each other
- **greater than (>)** (p. 42)—a relation symbol used to compare two numbers, with the greater number given first
- **less than (<)** (p. 42)—a relation symbol used to compare two numbers, with the lesser number given first
- **equal to (=)** (p. 42)—a relation symbol used to show that two numbers have the same value
- **rounding** (p. 50)—to increase or decrease a number to the nearest 10, 100, or 1,000

Vocabulary Cards

Have students use the Vocabulary Cards on *Teacher's Resource Book* pages TR143–145 for the key terms in the chapter. The cards can be added to a file of mathematics terms.

benchmark numbers

Multimedia Math Glossary

GO ON-LINE For vocabulary support, visit **www.harcourtschool.com/mathglossary**

Math Journal

Have students define the key vocabulary terms: *benchmark numbers, compare, greater than* (>), *less than* (<), *equal to* (=), and *rounding.* Have students use their own words and give an example of each.

MATH Word Work

Objective To reinforce vocabulary concepts
Use after Lesson 3.3.

Materials *For each pair* base-ten blocks, paper, pencil

Review the vocabulary terms *greater than* (>), *less than* (<), and *equal to* (=).

Have one student model two 3-digit numbers with base-ten blocks. Have the partner find the value of each number and tell which is greater. Direct partners to reverse roles and repeat the activity. Discuss how to arrange piles that have the same number of base-ten blocks.

Then have partners do a similar activity with 3 piles of base-ten blocks. Students should order the amounts from least to greatest and then from greatest to least. Again, ask partners to reverse roles and repeat the activity.

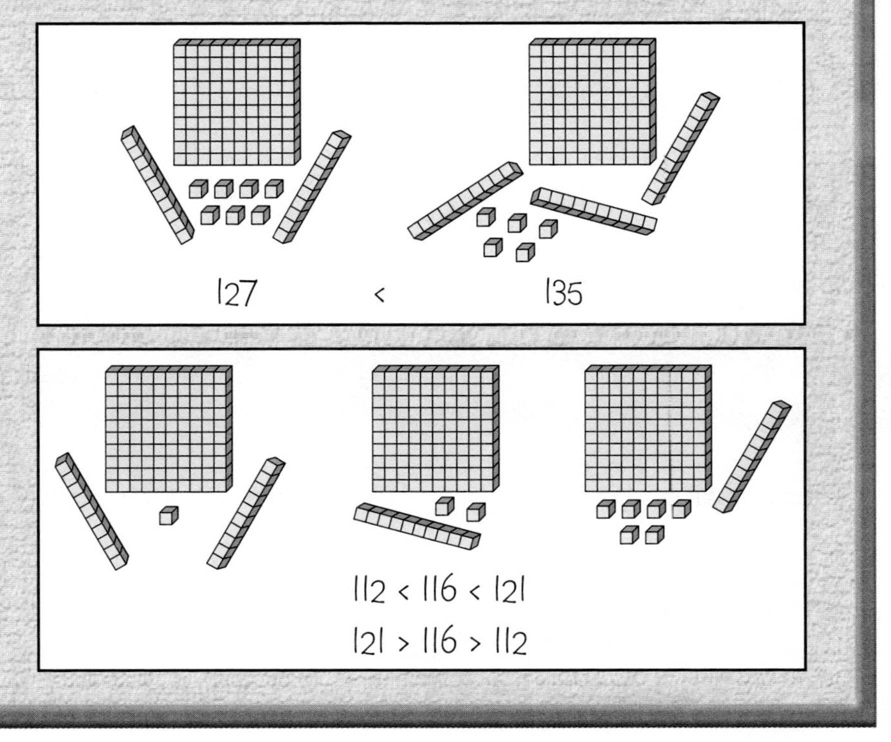

Compare, Order, and Round Numbers

Mathematics Across the Grades

LOOKING BACK • Prerequisite Skills

To be ready for Chapter 3, students should have the following understandings and skills:

- **Compare 2- and 3-Digit Numbers**—review basic comparison of 2- and 3-digit numbers
- **Order Numbers**—write 3-digit numbers in order from least to greatest

Check What You Know

Use page 39 to determine students' knowledge of prerequisite concepts and skills.

Intervention

Help students prepare for the chapter by using the intervention resources described on TE page 39.

LOOKING AT CHAPTER 3 • Essential Skills

Students will

- use benchmark numbers to estimate quantities.
- use number lines and place value to compare and order numbers to 999,999.
- solve problems by using a bar graph.
- **use rounding rules to round numbers to the nearest 10, 100, and 1,000.**

Example

Round 3,704 to the nearest thousand.

Thousands	Hundreds	Tens	Ones
3,	7	0	4

Look at the hundreds digit. Since 7 > 5, the 3 thousands round to 4 thousands.

So, 3,704 rounds to 4,000.

LOOKING AHEAD • Applications

Students will apply what they learn in Chapter 3 to the following new concepts:

- Add 3- and 4-Digit Numbers (Chapter 4)
- Subtract 3- and 4-Digit Numbers (Chapter 5)
- Compare and Order Fractions (Chapter 25)
- Compare and Order Decimals (Chapter 27)

Differentiated Instruction

Meeting the Needs of All Learners

Extra Support	Activities for All	Enrichment
Alternative Teaching Strategy TE Lessons 3.1, 3.2, 3.3, 3.4, 3.5, 3.6 **ESOL/ESL** TE Lessons 3.1, 3.2, 3.3, 3.4, 3.5, 3.6 **Special Needs** TE Lesson 3.6	**Cross-Curricular Connections** **Language Arts:** TE Lesson 3.1 **Reading:** TE Lesson 3.4 **Science:** TE Lesson 3.4 **Social Studies:** Chapter Opener **Vocabulary:** TE p. 38B; TE Lessons 3.1, 3.5; PE p. 39 **Writing:** TE Lesson 3.3	**Advanced Learners** TE Lessons 3.2, 3.5 **Early Finishers** TE Lessons 3.3, 3.6

Combination and Multi-age Classrooms

Grade 2	Grade 3	Grade 4
Skills Trace Across the Grades		
Identify ordinal numbers; compare and order 2-digit numbers; round numbers to the nearest 10.	**Use benchmark numbers to estimate; compare and order numbers to 999,999; round numbers to the nearest 10, 100, and 1,000.**	Find a reasonable number for an amount by using benchmarks; compare and order whole numbers through millions; round whole numbers to the nearest 1,000; 10,000; 100,000; or 1,000,000.
Instructional Strategies		
Students on this level may require more time to build conceptual understanding. **Assignments** **Grade 3 Pupil Edition** • Have students work in pairs on Lessons 3.2 and 3.3, as well as 3.5 and 3.6. **Grade 2 Pupil Edition**—pages 33–46, 483–498	Students on this level should be able to complete all the lessons in the Pupil Edition and all the activities in the Teacher's Edition with minimal adjustments. **Assignment** **Grade 3 Pupil Edition**—pages 38–55	Students on this level will probably require less time to build conceptual understanding. **Assignments** **Grade 3 Pupil Edition** • Compact Lessons 3.2 and 3.3, as well as 3.5 and 3.6. **Grade 4 Pupil Edition**—pages 18–35

CHAPTER 3

Compare, Order, and Round Numbers

Introducing the Chapter

Learning to compare, order, and round numbers helps students gain a better understanding of whole numbers. Have students look at the length of the bars and tell which bar is the longest. the bar for Lake Superior

Using Data

To begin the study of this chapter, have students

- Use the lengths of the bars to list the lakes in order from shallowest to deepest. Erie, Huron, Ontario, Michigan, Superior
- Describe the pattern of the numbers along the bottom of the graph. They increase by 200.
- The depth of Lake Erie is 210 feet. Tell which hundreds 210 is between. Which is closer? 200 and 300; 200 is closer.

Problem Solving Project

Purpose To compare the lengths of rivers

Background The Great Lakes are the largest system of fresh water on Earth. Only the polar ice caps contain more fresh water.

UNDERSTAND • PLAN • SOLVE • CHECK

Have students

- Research the depths of 5 lakes or the lengths of 5 rivers in your state.
- Round each number to the nearest hundred.
- Order the depths or lengths from least to greatest. Check students' work.

Portfolio Have students place their lists in their portfolios.

DATA ***Graphing Investigations*** Begin Week 3.

CHAPTER 3 Compare, Order, and Round Numbers

FAST FACT • SOCIAL STUDIES **The five Great Lakes are on or near the border between the United States and Canada. Lake Superior is the largest and the deepest of the five lakes.**

PROBLEM SOLVING **The graph shows the depths of the Great Lakes. Which lakes have depths that round to 800 feet?**

Lake Ontario, Lake Huron

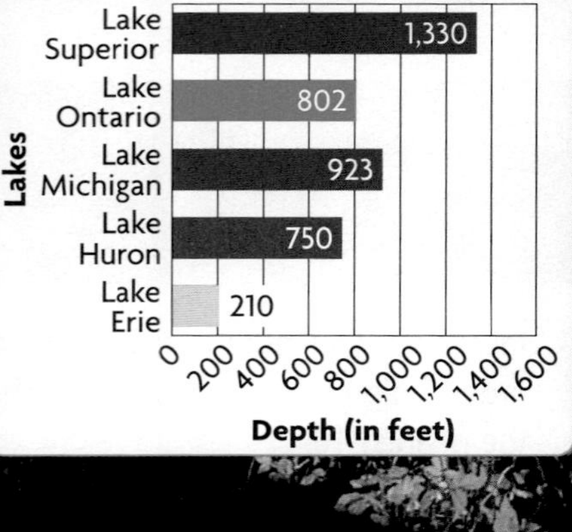

38

WHY LEARN MATH? Mapmakers, also called cartographers, accurately present the sizes and shapes of continents and countries. They use math to record the depths of oceans and seas and the lengths of borders and rivers. Use a map to compare the length of your street to a classmate's street. Which one is longer or shorter? Explain. Answers will vary.

Family Involvement Activities

These activities provide:

- Letter to the Family
- Math Vocabulary
- Family Game
- Practice (Homework)

Family Involvement Activities, p. FA9

HARCOURT MATH
GRADE 3
Chapter 3
WHAT WE ARE LEARNING
Compare, Order, and Round Numbers

VOCABULARY
Here are the vocabulary words we use in class:
Benchmark numbers Numbers such as 10, 25, 50, and 100 that are useful for estimating another amount without counting
Compare To describe numbers as greater than, less than, or equal to other numbers
Rounding A way to estimate by replacing numbers with numbers that tell *about* how many or how much
Less than (<) A symbol used to compare two numbers, with the lesser number given first
Greater than (>) A symbol used to compare two numbers, with the greater number given first
Equal to (=) A symbol used to show that two numbers have the same value

Name
Date

Dear Family,

Your child is learning to compare, order, and round numbers. One way we order numbers is by using a number line. Your child is also learning to round a number. We often do this when we want to estimate costs.

This is how your child has learned to round numbers:
Find the digit in the place to which you want to round.
Look at the digit to its right.
If the digit is less than 5, the digit in the rounding place stays the same.
If the digit is 5 or more, the digit in the rounding place increases by 1.
Then the digits to the right of the rounded digit are replaced with zeros.

To help guide your child's thinking, ask questions such as these:
To which place do you want to round?
What place is to the right?
Is the digit in the place to the right less than 5?
How do you know when to increase the digit in the rounding place?

Use the real-life activity to practice rounding. Compare vehicles to "buy."
Remember, seeing mathematics as useful helps motivate your child!

Sincerely,

Family Involvement Activities FA9

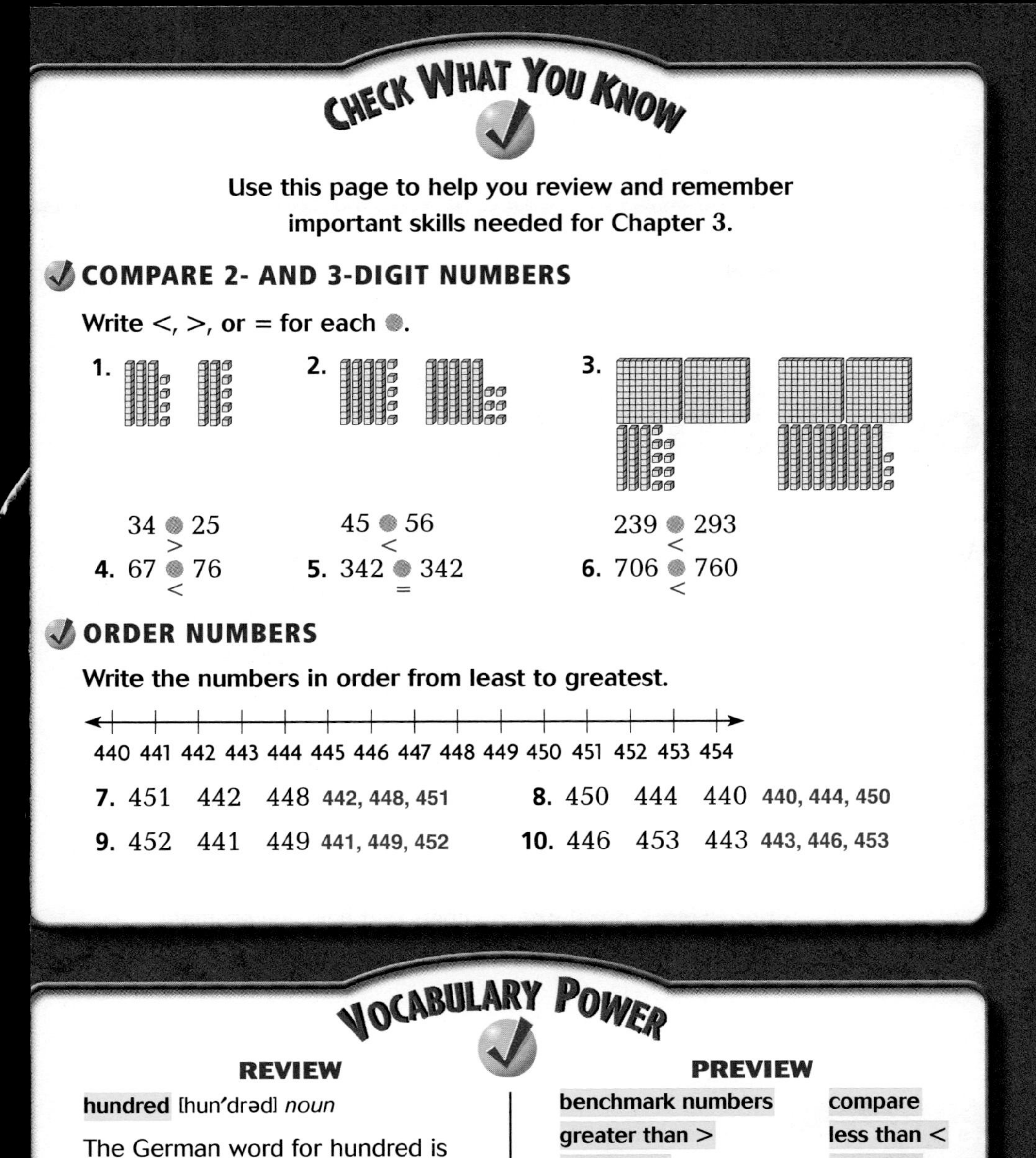

CHECK WHAT YOU KNOW

Use this page to help you review and remember important skills needed for Chapter 3.

COMPARE 2- AND 3-DIGIT NUMBERS

Write <, >, or = for each ●.

1. 34 ● 25 >
2. 45 ● 56 <
3. 239 ● 293 <
4. 67 ● 76 <
5. 342 ● 342 =
6. 706 ● 760 <

ORDER NUMBERS

Write the numbers in order from least to greatest.

440 441 442 443 444 445 446 447 448 449 450 451 452 453 454

7. 451 442 448 **442, 448, 451**
8. 450 444 440 **440, 444, 450**
9. 452 441 449 **441, 449, 452**
10. 446 453 443 **443, 446, 453**

VOCABULARY POWER

REVIEW

hundred [hun′drəd] *noun*

The German word for hundred is *hundert*. Its value and meaning have changed over time. Its value is now 100. How many hundreds are in 672? **6 hundreds**

PREVIEW

benchmark numbers
compare
greater than >
less than <
equal to =
rounding

GO ON-LINE www.harcourtschool.com/mathglossary

Chapter 3 39

Assessing Prior Knowledge

Use the **Check What You Know** page to determine whether your students have mastered the prerequisite skills critical for this chapter.

Intervention

- **Diagnose and Prescribe**
  Evaluate your students' performance on this page to determine whether intervention is necessary or if enrichment is appropriate. Options that provide instruction, practice, and a check are listed in the chart below.

CHECK WHAT YOU KNOW RESOURCES

Intervention Copying Masters or CD-ROMs

Enrichment Copying Masters

VOCABULARY POWER

For activities and information about the vocabulary in this chapter, see page 38B.

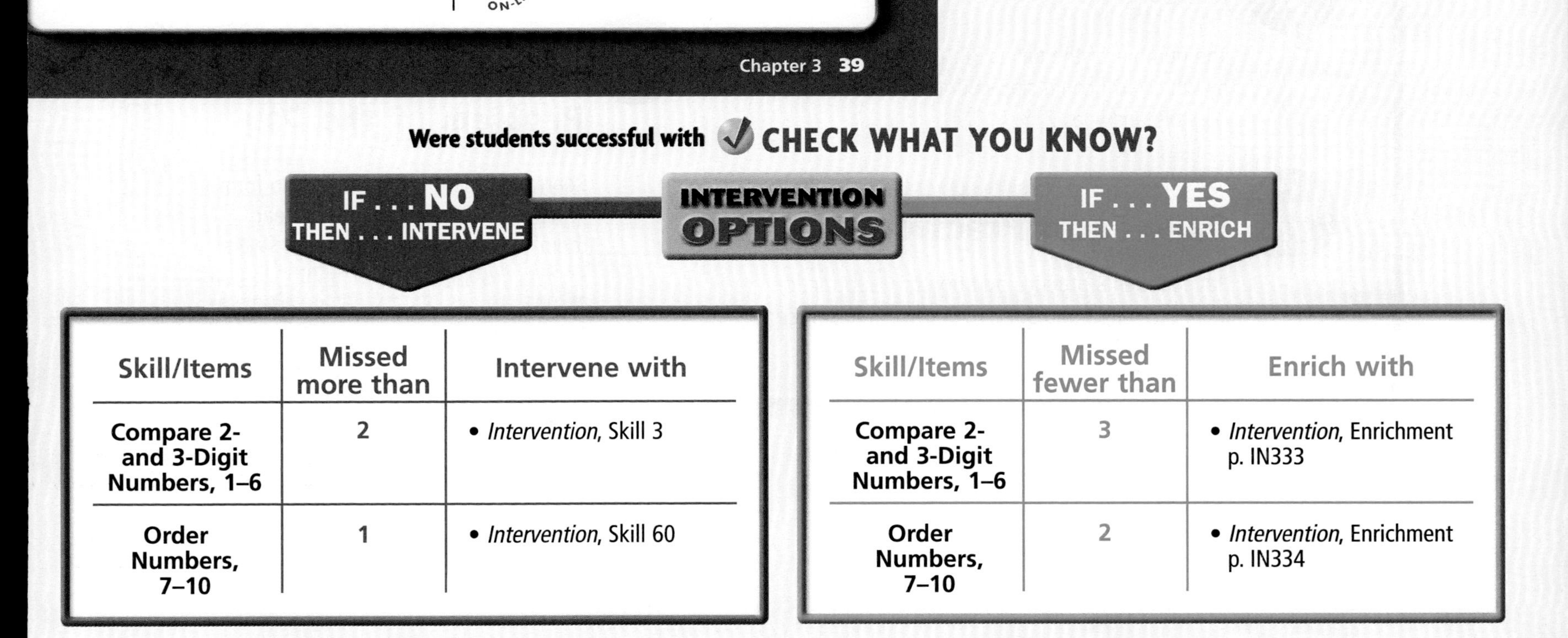

Were students successful with CHECK WHAT YOU KNOW?

IF . . . NO THEN . . . INTERVENE

INTERVENTION OPTIONS

IF . . . YES THEN . . . ENRICH

Skill/Items	Missed more than	Intervene with
Compare 2- and 3-Digit Numbers, 1–6	2	• *Intervention*, Skill 3
Order Numbers, 7–10	1	• *Intervention*, Skill 60

Skill/Items	Missed fewer than	Enrich with
Compare 2- and 3-Digit Numbers, 1–6	3	• *Intervention*, Enrichment p. IN333
Order Numbers, 7–10	2	• *Intervention*, Enrichment p. IN334

Lesson 3.1

Benchmark Numbers

Lesson Planning

Objective To use benchmarks to understand the relative magnitude of numbers

NCTM Standards

1. Number and Operations
6. Problem Solving
7. Reasoning and Proof
8. Communication
9. Connections

Math Background

Benchmark numbers help students develop their estimation skills.

- Benchmark numbers help students estimate a part of a quantity or multiples of a quantity.
- Estimation helps students build understanding of number sense.

Vocabulary

benchmark numbers numbers that help you estimate the number of objects without counting them

Warm-Up Resources

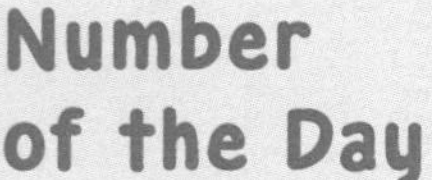

Number of the Day

The number of the day is 30. Think of four numbers by which you could skip-count to 30.
Possible answers: 2, 3, 5, 6, 10

Daily Facts Practice

Have students practice addition and subtraction facts by completing Set F of *Teacher's Resource Book*, p. TR84.

Solve a Problem

Transparency 3.1

Problem of the Day

Rearrange the digits in 57,070 to form at least 12 different numbers. Read them to a classmate. Possible answers: 77,500; 77,050; 77,005; 75,700; 75,070; 75,007; 70,075; 57,700, 57,007; 50,770; 50,707; 50,077

Solution Problem of the Day tab, p. PD3

Intervention and Extension Resources

Alternative Teaching Strategy

MATERIALS *For each group* jar of coins or buttons

Help students **understand benchmark numbers.** Introduce the concept of benchmark numbers by using hands-on materials, such as coins or buttons in a jar. Have students count a small number to use as a benchmark. Then present amounts that are approximately two, three, four, and ten times as great as the benchmark number for students to estimate. Check students' work.

KINESTHETIC

BODILY/KINESTHETIC

Vocabulary Strategy

Help **reinforce students' understanding of benchmark numbers**. Explore the meaning of the term *benchmark number* by displaying a word map. Ask students to volunteer ideas for these categories:

- What is it? a useful number; a number used to estimate
- What are some examples? 10, 25, 100, 1,000
- When would you use it? when the number of things is too large to count, or when you don't need to know the exact number of things

VISUAL

VISUAL/SPATIAL

Multistep and Strategy Problems

The following multistep or strategy problem is provided in Lesson 3.1:

Page	Item
41	10

Language Arts Connection

Have students **relate benchmark numbers to real-world scenarios**. Challenge students to write a news story about a child who won a jelly bean-counting contest. Remind them that a news story tells *who, what, when, where, why,* and *how*. For the *how* part of the story, have students explain how the winner used a benchmark number to estimate. Check students' work.

VISUAL

VERBAL/LINGUISTIC

Intervention, *Skills 3, 60*

The Harcourt Learning Site
www.harcourtschool.com

Lesson 3.1 Organizer

Objective To use benchmarks to understand the relative magnitude of numbers

Vocabulary benchmark numbers

QUICK REVIEW provides review of prerequisite skills.

Why Learn This? You can estimate the number of objects in a container or package, such as pennies, marbles, or beans. *Share the lesson objective with students.*

2 TEACH

Guided Instruction

- *Direct students' attention to the Learn section. Be sure all students are familiar with the term* esti-mate.
  What is an estimate? When might you use an estimate? a way to find out about how many; to tell the number of books you have read
- *Have students compare Jar A and Jar B.*
  Why might you estimate the number of jelly-beans in Jar B instead of counting them? Possible answers: Some large groups are too time-consuming to count; you don't need to know the exact number of jellybeans.
- *Point out the table with benchmark numbers.*
  REASONING Why might you use a different benchmark to estimate the number of books in the school library than you would use to estimate the number of students in your classroom? Possible answer: You have to choose a useful number as a benchmark. To estimate books in a library, you might use 500 as a bench-mark number. For the number of students, you might use 25 as a benchmark number.

MODIFYING INSTRUCTION You might want to mod-ify the two-column table by writing benchmarks that are appropriate for your school.

LESSON 1

Benchmark Numbers

Quick Review

Which is greater?

1. 29 or 92 **92**
2. 101 or 1,001 **1,001**
3. 523 or 498 **523**
4. 7 or 70 **70**
5. 64 or 65 **65**

VOCABULARY

benchmark numbers

Learn

HOW MANY? Numbers that help you estimate the number of objects without counting them are called **benchmark numbers**. Any useful number can be a benchmark.

About how many jellybeans are in Jar B? You can use 25 as a benchmark to estimate.

There are 25 jellybeans in Jar A.

There are about ■ jellybeans in Jar B.

There are about twice as many jellybeans in Jar B.

So, there are about 50 jellybeans in Jar B.

Think about the number of students in your class, your grade, and your school. Which has about 25 students? Which has about 100 students? Which has about 500 students?

BENCHMARK	NUMBER TO BE ESTIMATED
25	students in your class
100	students in your grade
500	students in your school

- Suppose all the third and fourth-grade classes went on a field trip. About how many students went? What benchmark can you use?
  about 200 students; benchmark of 100

40

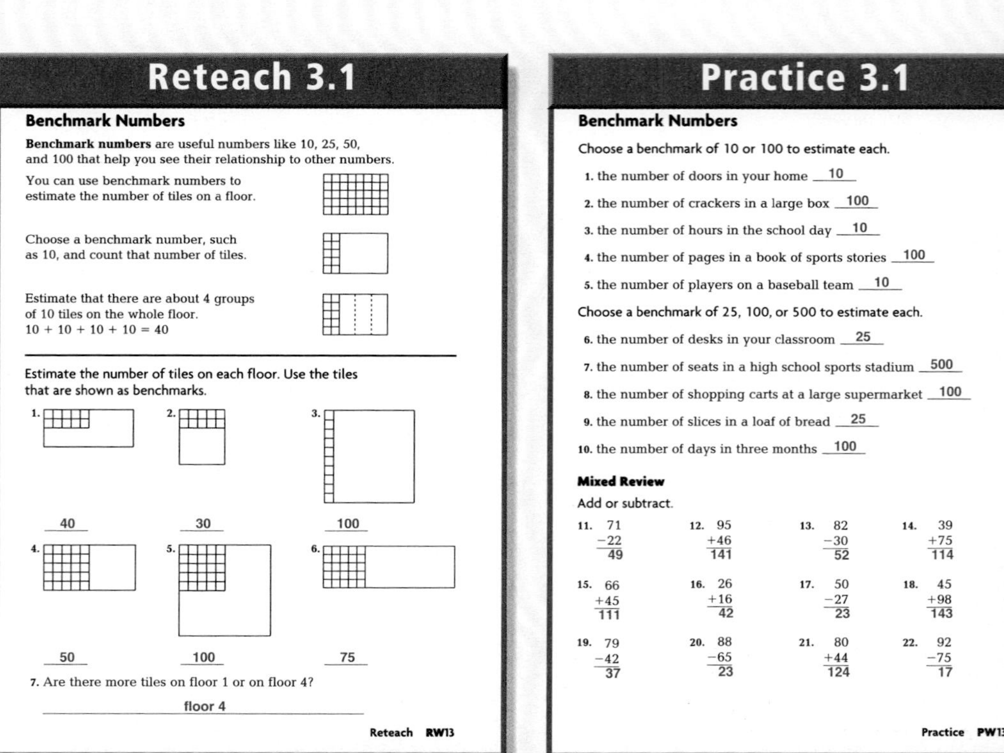

Reteach 3.1

Benchmark Numbers

Benchmark numbers are useful numbers like 10, 25, 50, and 100 that help you see their relationship to other numbers.

You can use benchmark numbers to estimate the number of tiles on a floor.

Choose a benchmark number, such as 10, and count that number of tiles.

Estimate that there are about 4 groups of 10 tiles on the whole floor.
10 + 10 + 10 + 10 = 40

Estimate the number of tiles on each floor. Use the tiles that are shown as benchmarks.

1. 40
2. 30
3. 100
4. 50
5. 100
6. 75

7. Are there more tiles on floor 1 or on floor 4? floor 4

Reteach RW13

Practice 3.1

Benchmark Numbers

Choose a benchmark of 10 or 100 to estimate each.

1. the number of doors in your home 10
2. the number of crackers in a large box 100
3. the number of hours in the school day 10
4. the number of pages in a book of sports stories 100
5. the number of players on a baseball team 10

Choose a benchmark of 25, 100, or 500 to estimate each.

6. the number of desks in your classroom 25
7. the number of seats in a high school sports stadium 500
8. the number of shopping carts at a large supermarket 100
9. the number of slices in a loaf of bread 25
10. the number of days in three months 100

Mixed Review

Add or subtract.

11. 71 − 22 = 49
12. 95 + 46 = 141
13. 82 − 30 = 52
14. 39 + 75 = 114
15. 66 + 45 = 111
16. 26 + 16 = 42
17. 50 − 27 = 23
18. 45 + 98 = 143
19. 79 − 42 = 37
20. 88 − 65 = 23
21. 80 + 44 = 124
22. 92 − 75 = 17

Practice PW13

Check

1. **Explain** how a benchmark could help you estimate the number of girls in your grade. **Possible answer: if you know the numbers of girls in your class, you can use addition to find the number in your grade.**

Estimate the number of jellybeans in each jar. Use Jars A and B as benchmarks.

Jar A has 10 jellybeans. (A)

Jar B has about 50 jellybeans. (B)

2. 10 or 50? **10**
3. 25 or 50? **25**
4. 100 or 200? **200**

Practice and Problem Solving

Extra Practice, page 54, Set A

5. Estimate the number of jellybeans in the jar at the right. Use Jars A and B above as benchmarks. **Possible answer: 100**

For 6–9, choose a benchmark of 10, 100, or 500 to estimate.

6. the number of players on a soccer team **10**
7. the number of pretzels in a large bag **100**
8. the number of sheets in a package of notebook paper **100**
9. the number of leaves on a tree in summer **500**
10. Juan had 30 blocks. He gave 18 to Rick but got 14 from Ron. How many blocks does Juan have now? **26**
11. **Write a problem** in which a benchmark is used to estimate. Solve. **Check students' problems.**

Getting Ready for the EOG Test

12. Napkin A has 10 ants on it. *About* how many ants are on Napkin B? **C**

A 10 **B** 15 **C** 20 **D** 30

Napkin A Napkin B

North Carolina Standards 1.01 Develop number sense for whole numbers through 9,999.

3 PRACTICE

Guided Practice

Do Check Exercises 1–4 with your students. Identify students who are having difficulty and choose appropriate lesson resources to provide assistance.

Independent Practice

Note that Exercise 10 is a **multistep or strategy problem.** Assign Exercises 5–11.

If students have difficulty with Exercise 11, suggest they refer to the Check section to see how a benchmark number was used there.

4 ASSESS

Summarize the lesson by having students:

DISCUSS Casey has a large bag of potato chips. How could she use a benchmark to estimate the total number of chips? Possible answer: She could count 25 chips and then use those to decide about how many are in the bag.

WRITE How would you estimate the number of sheets of paper in a big stack of paper? Possible answer: by making a small stack of paper, using the number of sheets it contains as a benchmark number, and then deciding how the small stack compares with the whole stack

LESSON QUIZ

Transparency 3.1

Choose a benchmark of 10, 100, or 500 to estimate each.

1. people on a bus 10
2. kernels of popped popcorn in a large bag 100
3. pages in your math book 500
4. plates in the school cafeteria 100
5. number of words in a chapter 500

Challenge 3.1

Missing Numbers

Detective Casey needs to find some missing numbers. Can you help her? When you find them, circle the numbers so she knows where to look. The numbers can be found going up, across, down, backward, and diagonally.

1	2	8	6	7	4	3	0	5
5	0	1	9	4	2	1	8	9
2	2	7	8	0	1	3	6	4
4	8	7	5	2	6	0	4	3
7	5	1	4	6	2	1	0	8
4	6	9	8	2	0	3	4	7
9	8	5	2	4	3	0	1	6
2	9	3	7	4	6	5	0	9
1	7	2	8	3	9	6	4	5

1. 17,283
2. 50,194
3. 3,756
4. 27,423
5. 44,104
6. 4,301
7. 9,820
8. 5,469
9. 94,387
10. 9,132
11. 6,150
12. 7,402
13. 31,301
14. 28,674
15. 5,820

Detective Casey thanks you for all your hard work in helping her find the missing numbers.

Challenge CW13

Problem Solving 3.1

Benchmark Numbers

Understand → Plan → Solve → Check

Write the correct answer.

For Problems 1 and 2, use the 25 beans in this jar as a benchmark.

1. About how many beans are in this jar? **Accept answers from 10 to 15.**
2. About how many beans are in this jar? **Accept answers from 40 to 50.**

Choose the letter of the correct answer.

3. A benchmark of 20 would be best to estimate which number?
   - A the number of cars in a large city
   - B the number of cars in a driveway
   - C the number of cars made each year
   - (D) the number of cars parked at a supermarket
4. Hanah is 60 inches tall. Hanah is 1 inch taller than Eli, who is 4 inches shorter than Carrie. How tall is Carrie?
   - (F) 63 inches
   - G 62 inches
   - H 59 inches
   - J 58 inches
5. **Write About It** Explain what benchmark you would use to estimate the number of people that can ride on a bus. **Possible answer: I would use 10 as a benchmark because it would be easy to compare the number of people on a bus to a group of ten.**

Problem Solving PS13

Algebra: Compare Numbers

Lesson Planning

Objective To use models, place value, and number lines to compare numbers

NCTM Standards

1. Number and Operations
2. Algebra
5. Data Analysis and Probability
6. Problem Solving
7. Reasoning and Proof
8. Communication
9. Connections

Math Background

Experience with comparing numbers helps students improve their number sense.

- When comparing numbers, only three possibilities exist: one number is greater than, is less than, or is equal to the other.
- Base-ten blocks, number lines, and place-value charts show concrete and pictorial models of comparisons.
- Place-value charts are useful for comparing greater numbers.

Vocabulary

compare describe whether two numbers are equal to, less than, or greater than each other

greater than > a symbol used to compare two numbers, with the greater number given first

less than < a symbol to compare two numbers, with the lesser number given first

equal to = a symbol used to show that two numbers have the same value

Warm-Up Resources

Number of the Day

I am an even number that is less than the number of pennies in a nickel and greater than the number of nickels in a dime. What number am I? 4

Daily Facts Practice

Have students practice addition facts by completing Set G of *Teacher's Resource Book*, p. TR84.

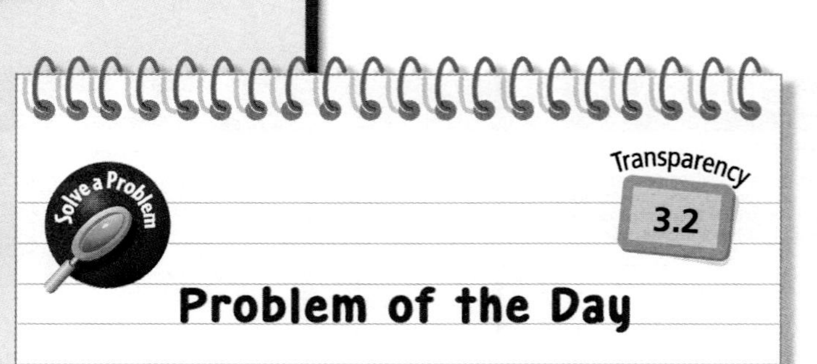

Problem of the Day

Samantha is swimming across a lake to reach a diving platform that is 18 yards away. Every time she swims 6 yards, the waves push her back 2 yards. At this rate, how many times must she swim foward 6 yards to reach the platform? 4 times

Solution Problem of the Day tab, p. PD3

Intervention and Extension Resources

Alternative Teaching Strategy

MATERIALS *For each student* number line, p. TR6

Help students **compare numbers on a number line**. For the number-line explanation on page 42, supply students with number lines from 100 to 300 that are marked in increments of 10. Have students mark the line to show where 245 and 262 would appear. Supply this mnemonic: **l**eft, **l**esser; ri**g**ht, **g**reater. If you wish, have students record the two parts of this mnemonic on the left and right sides of their number lines. Check students' work.

See also page 44.

VISUAL

VISUAL/SPATIAL

ESOL/ESL

MATERIALS *For each pair* 2 sets of cards numbered 1–20, 3 cards labeled $<$, $>$, $=$

Have students **practice comparing numbers by playing a game**. Students shuffle the number cards and place them face down. Then they place the cards with the less than, greater than, and equal to signs face up. Have students take turns choosing two numbers and a symbol to form a comparison and then reading their comparisons to each other. Have students play the same game using 3- to 6-digit numbers. Check students' work.

KINESTHETIC

BODILY/KINESTHETIC

Multistep and Strategy Problems

The following multistep or strategy problem is provided in lesson 3.2:

Page	Item
45	32

Advanced Learners

MATERIALS *For each pair* number cube

Challenge students to **compare and order 6-digit numbers**. Have each student roll a number cube three times and record the numbers. Then have students work together to form as many 6-digit numbers as possible from the numbers rolled, and to write the numbers in order from least to greatest. Have students repeat this process several times, alternating between writing the numbers from least to greatest and from greatest to least. Check students' work.

KINESTHETIC

BODILY/KINESTHETIC

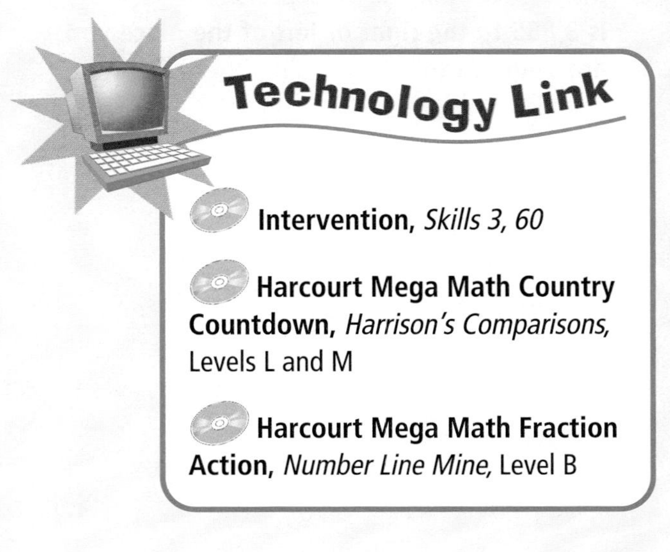

Intervention, *Skills 3, 60*

Harcourt Mega Math Country Countdown, *Harrison's Comparisons,* Levels L and M

Harcourt Mega Math Fraction Action, *Number Line Mine,* Level B

Lesson 3.2 Organizer

Objective To use models, place value, and number lines to compare numbers

Vocabulary compare, greater than >, less than <, equal to =

1 INTRODUCE

QUICK REVIEW provides review of prerequisite skills.

WHY LEARN THIS? Comparing numbers helps you find the shortest distance or the lowest price. *Share the lesson objective with students.*

2 TEACH

Guided Instruction

- *Display the word* compare *and ask students for a definition.*
  What are three ways that you can use words to compare numbers? *greater than, less than,* and *equal to*
- *Discuss the symbols with the class.*
  When do you use the greater than (>) symbol? when the greater number is written first
  When do you use the less than (<) symbol? when the lesser number is written first
- *Review One Way and Another Way.*
  REASONING Why do you compare the number of hundreds before you compare the number of tens? Possible answer: If the number of hundreds is greater, the number is greater. You don't need to compare the number of tens.
- *Ask students to look at the number line in Example A. Suggest that they place a finger on the point at which 3,710 appears.*
  Is 3,855 to the right or left of the place you are pointing to? to the right

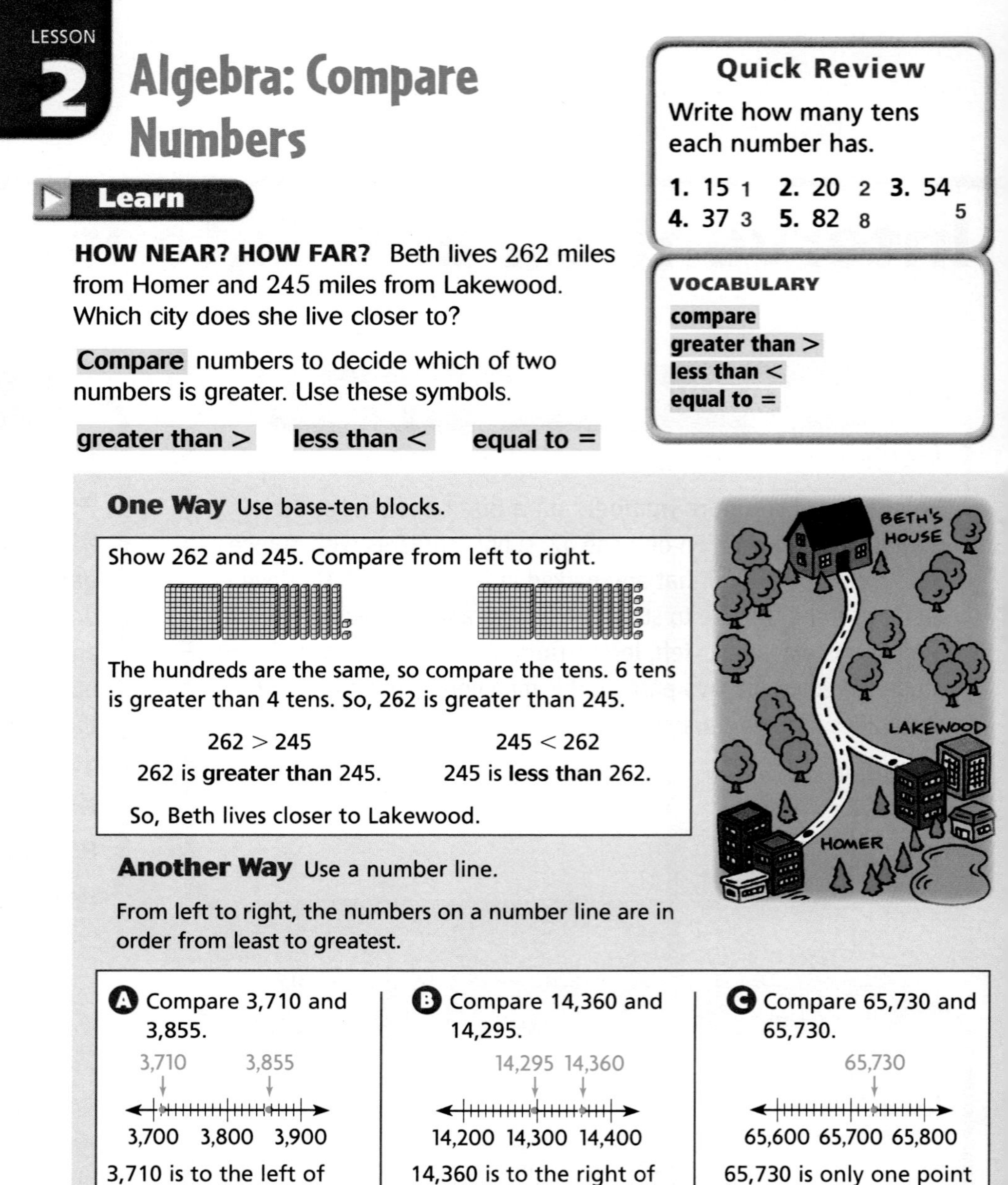

LESSON 2

Algebra: Compare Numbers

Quick Review

Write how many tens each number has.

1. 15 1
2. 20 2
3. 54 5
4. 37 3
5. 82 8

VOCABULARY
compare
greater than >
less than <
equal to =

Learn

HOW NEAR? HOW FAR? Beth lives 262 miles from Homer and 245 miles from Lakewood. Which city does she live closer to?

Compare numbers to decide which of two numbers is greater. Use these symbols.

greater than > **less than <** **equal to =**

One Way Use base-ten blocks.

Show 262 and 245. Compare from left to right.

The hundreds are the same, so compare the tens. 6 tens is greater than 4 tens. So, 262 is greater than 245.

262 > 245 — 262 is **greater than** 245.
245 < 262 — 245 is **less than** 262.

So, Beth lives closer to Lakewood.

Another Way Use a number line.

From left to right, the numbers on a number line are in order from least to greatest.

A Compare 3,710 and 3,855.

3,710 is to the left of 3,855, so it is less than 3,855.

3,710 < 3,855

B Compare 14,360 and 14,295.

14,360 is to the right of 14,295, so it is greater than 14,295.

14,360 > 14,295

C Compare 65,730 and 65,730.

65,730 is only one point on the number line, so it is equal to 65,730.

65,730 = 65,730

42

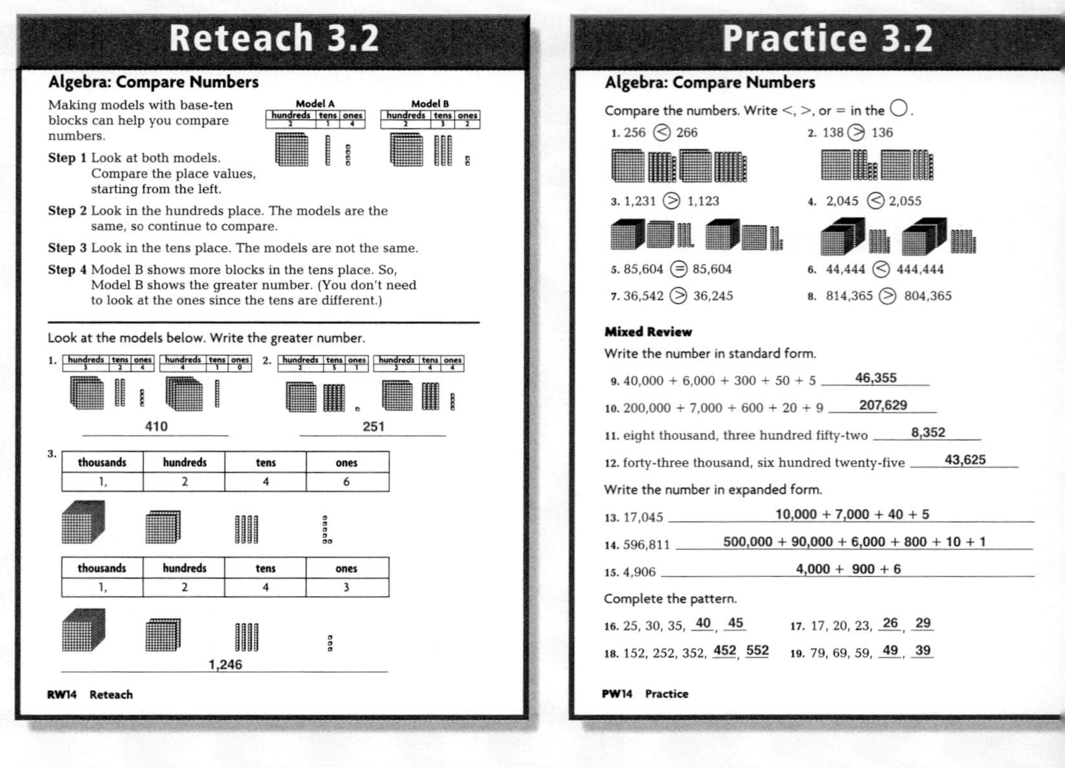

Reteach 3.2

Algebra: Compare Numbers

Making models with base-ten blocks can help you compare numbers.

Model A

hundreds	tens	ones
2	1	4

Model B

hundreds	tens	ones
2	3	2

Step 1 Look at both models. Compare the place values, starting from the left.

Step 2 Look in the hundreds place. The models are the same, so continue to compare.

Step 3 Look in the tens place. The models are not the same.

Step 4 Model B shows more blocks in the tens place. So, Model B shows the greater number. (You don't need to look at the ones since the tens are different.)

Look at the models below. Write the greater number.

1.

hundreds	tens	ones
3	2	4

hundreds	tens	ones
4	1	0

410

2.

hundreds	tens	ones
2	5	1

hundreds	tens	ones
2	4	4

251

3.

thousands	hundreds	tens	ones
1,	2	4	6

thousands	hundreds	tens	ones
1,	2	4	3

1,246

RW14 Reteach

Practice 3.2

Algebra: Compare Numbers

Compare the numbers. Write <, >, or = in the ○.

1. 256 (<) 266
2. 138 (>) 136
3. 1,231 (>) 1,123
4. 2,045 (<) 2,055
5. 85,604 (=) 85,604
6. 44,444 (<) 444,444
7. 36,542 (>) 36,245
8. 814,365 (>) 804,365

Mixed Review

Write the number in standard form.

9. 40,000 + 6,000 + 300 + 50 + 5 **46,355**
10. 200,000 + 7,000 + 600 + 20 + 9 **207,629**
11. eight thousand, three hundred fifty-two **8,352**
12. forty-three thousand, six hundred twenty-five **43,625**

Write the number in expanded form.

13. 17,045 **10,000 + 7,000 + 40 + 5**
14. 596,811 **500,000 + 90,000 + 6,000 + 800 + 10 + 1**
15. 4,906 **4,000 + 900 + 6**

Complete the pattern.

16. 25, 30, 35, **40**, **45**
17. 17, 20, 23, **26**, **29**
18. 152, 252, 352, **452**, **552**
19. 79, 69, 59, **49**, **39**

PW14 Practice

Use a Place-Value Chart

A place-value chart can help you compare greater numbers.

Compare 413,165 and 413,271, starting from the left.

HUNDRED THOUSANDS	TEN THOUSANDS	THOUSANDS	HUNDREDS	TENS	ONES
4	1	3,	1	6	5
4	1	3,	2	7	1
↑ Hundred thousands are the same.	↑ Ten thousands are the same.	↑ Thousands are the same.	↑ 200 > 100		

So, 413,271 > 413,165 and 413,165 < 413,271.

MATH IDEA Compare numbers by using base-ten blocks, a number line, or a place-value chart.

Technology Link

More Practice: Harcourt Mega Math Country Countdown, *Harrison's Comparisons,* Levels L and M; *Fraction Action,* Number Line Mine, Level B

Check

1. Explain how to use base-ten blocks to compare 341 and 300 + 40 + 1. What do you notice? **Model 341 and 300 + 40 + 1 with 3 hundreds, 4 tens, and 1 one. The two are equal. They each have the same number of blocks.**
2. Use the number line in Example A on page 42 to compare 3,820 and 3,780. Which number is greater? Explain. **3,820 is greater. It is to the right of 3,780 on the number line.**

Compare the numbers. Write <, >, or = for each ●.

3.

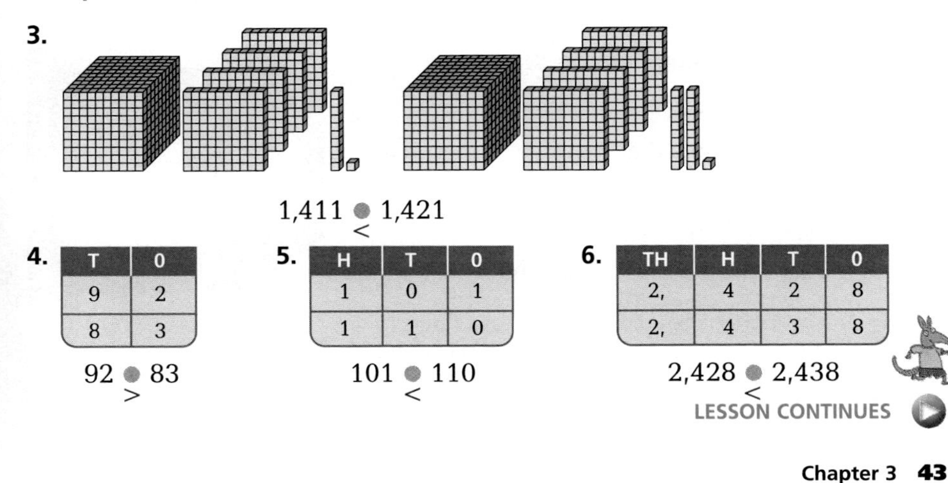

1,411 ● 1,421
<

4.

T	O
9	2
8	3

92 ● 83
>

5.

H	T	O
1	0	1
1	1	0

101 ● 110
<

6.

TH	H	T	O
2,	4	2	8
2,	4	3	8

2,428 ● 2,438
<

LESSON CONTINUES

- *Conduct a discussion of the place-value chart.*
  Why should you read the chart starting from the left? If you read from left to right, you start with the greatest place. If one of these digits is greater than the other, then you know which number is greater without comparing any of the other digits.
  What is an advantage of using a place-value chart rather than base-ten blocks or a number line to compare 13,165 and 13,271? Possible answer: You may not always have enough base-ten blocks or a number line available.

3 PRACTICE

Guided Practice

Do Check Exercises 1–6 with your students. Identify students who are having difficulty and choose appropriate lesson resources to provide assistance.

North Carolina Standards 1.01 Develop number sense for whole numbers through 9,999. Compare and order.

Challenge 3.2

Model Numbers

Look at the models below. Under each, write the number that the model represents. When you finish, follow the directions at the bottom of the page.

○ = hundreds ☆ = tens □ = ones

1. ☆ ☆ ☆ ☆ □ □ □ □ — 44
2. ☆ ☆ ☆ □ □ — 32
3. ☆ ☆ ☆ □ — 31
4. ☆ ☆ ☆ ☆ ☆ □ □ □ — 53
5. ☆ ☆ ☆ ☆ □ □ □ □ □ □ — 46
6. ☆ ☆ □ □ — 22 (squared)
7. ○ ○ ○ ☆ ☆ □ □ □ — 323
8. ○ ○ ○ ☆ ☆ ☆ — 330
9. ○ ○ ○ ☆ ☆ ☆ □ □ — 332 (circled)
10. In Exercises 1–9, circle the answer that is the greatest number.
11. In Exercises 1–9, what is the number that is closest in size to the greatest number? **330**
12. In Exercises 1–9, put a square around the answer that is the least number.
13. In Exercises 1–9, what is the number that is closest in size to the least number? **31**
14. Choose your own number. Write what that number is, and model it by using circles, stars, and squares. **Check students' answers.**

CW14 Challenge

Problem Solving 3.2

Algebra: Compare Numbers Understand → Plan → Solve → Check

Write the correct answer.

1. Look at the place-value chart. Compare 5,684 and 5,679. Which place-value position tells you which number is greater? **tens**

Thousands	Hundreds	Tens	Ones
5,	6	8	4
5,	6	7	9

2. Use the number line to compare 135 and 178. Which number is greater? **178**
   100 110 120 130 140 150 160 170 180 190 200
3. There are 94 third-graders at Zack's school. Of these, 48 are girls. How many are boys? **46**
4. How could you use base-ten blocks to model 527 if you did not have any hundreds? **Possible answer: 52 tens, 7 ones**

Choose the letter of the correct answer.

5. Which number line has a star on a number less than 473?
   A 462 464 466 468 470 472 474 476 478
   (B) 462 464 466 468 470 472 474 476 478
   C 462 464 466 468 470 472 474 476 478
   D 462 464 466 468 470 472 474 476 478
6. Which number shows sixty-three thousand, thirty in standard form?
   F 630
   (G) 63,030
   H 63,300
   J 60,030
7. Which number is greater than 2,478?
   A 1,479 C 2,439
   B 2,399 (D) 2,487
8. Which benchmark would you use to estimate the number of students in your classroom?
   F 1 H 50
   (G) 25 J 100
9. **Write About It** How did you find the answer to Problem 2? **Possible answer: 178 is to the right of 135 on the number line.**

PS14 Problem Solving

COMMON ERROR ALERT

Students may confuse the symbols for *greater than* and *less than*. Help them develop their own memory devices for remembering which is which. Some students benefit by remembering that the *less than* sign looks a bit like a tilted L. Students might also remember that the *less than* sign starts small and points to something big, or that the greater quantity is on the side where the opening is.

lesser → < ← greater
greater → > ← lesser

Independent Practice

Note that Exercise 32 is a **multistep or strategy problem.** Assign Exercises 7–32.

ALGEBRAIC THINKING As students compare numbers, they develop their understanding of the concept of equivalence. For the numbers being compared in Exercises 24–25, have students identify which digits, if any, have equal values.

Practice and Problem Solving

Extra Practice, page 54, Set B

Compare the numbers. Write <, >, or = for each ●.

7. 203 ● 165 >

8. 1,058 ● 1,205 <

9.

H	T	O
6	2	1
6	2	1

621 ● 621 =

10.

H	T	O
8	1	6
8	2	3

816 ● 823 <

11.

TH	H	T	O
4,	8	0	5
4,	8	1	9

4,805 ● 4,819 <

12. 629 ● 631 <
13. 5,712 ● 5,412 >
14. 102,412 ● 102,421 <
15. 1,894 ● 2,139 <
16. 10,348 ● 10,348 =
17. 437,393 ● 473,396 <
18. 151 + 200 ● 350 >
19. 696 − 418 ● 296 <
20. 475 + 72 ● 537 >

ALGEBRA **Write the missing number that makes the number sentence true.**

21. 341 = 34■ 1
22. 887 < 8■4 9
23. 1,196 > 1,■98 0

24. What is the greatest place-value position in which the digits of 5,831 and 5,819 are different? Compare the numbers. **tens place; 5,831 > 5,819, or 5,819 < 5,831**

25. Compare the numbers 5,361 and 3,974. Which number is less? Draw a picture to show how you know. **3,974 is less. Check students' drawings.**

For 26–28, use the numbers on the box.

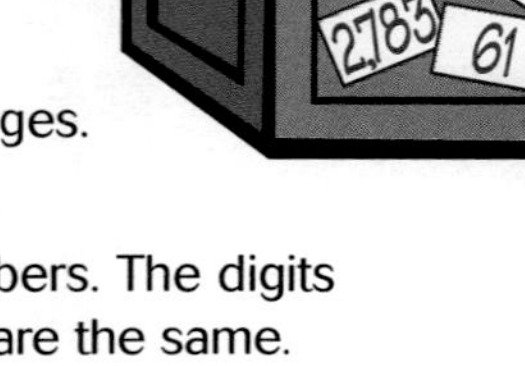

26. List all the numbers that are less than 575. **61, 98, 145, 429**
27. List all the numbers that are greater than 830. **837; 915; 1,736; 2,783**
28. List all the numbers that are greater than 326 and less than 748. **429**
29. **What's the Question?** Louis read 125 pages. Tom read 137 pages. The answer is 12. **How many more pages did Tom read than Louis?**
30. **Write About It** You have 3 four-digit numbers. The digits in the thousands, hundreds, and ones places are the same. Which digits would you use to compare the numbers? Explain. **the digits in the tens place because those are the only digits that are different**

Alternative Teaching Strategy

Scaffolded Instruction

PURPOSE Students compare numbers by beginning with the greatest place-value position.

Step 1

Compare 5,867 and 5,986. Display the numbers:

5,867
5,986

Step 2

Ask students to begin by comparing thousands. Draw arrows as shown. Ask: Which is greater? Both are the same.

5,867
↕
5,986

Step 3

Ask students what they do next to compare these numbers. Compare the hundreds. Draw arrows to connect these positions. Then ask which digit is greater. the 9

5,867
↕
5,986

Step 4

Ask: Is it necessary to compare the tens or ones to determine which of these numbers is greater? Explain. No; 900 is greater than 800, so you know that 5,986 is greater than 5,867.

Repeat the same steps with these pairs of numbers:

- 5,978 and 5,940
- 2,003 and 2,006

If you wish, have students use this method to compare the numbers on page 44 in Exercises 12–17.

31. The numbers 456 and 564 have the same digits in a different order. Do they both have the same value? Explain. **Possible answer: no; 456 has 4 hundreds and 564 has 5 hundreds. $564 > 456$**

32. The sum of three addends is 24. One addend is 5. Another addend is 3 more than 7. What is the missing addend? **9**

Getting Ready for the EOG Test

33. Claire is 4,300 days old. Selena is 4,225 days old. Use the number line to compare their ages. Which of the following shows how the ages compare? **A**

4,225 ↓ 4,300 ↓
4,200 4,220 4,240 4,260 4,280 4,300 4,320

A $4{,}300 > 4{,}225$

B $4{,}300 < 4{,}225$

C $4{,}300 = 4{,}225$

D $4{,}225 > 4{,}300$

Possible answers given. 1.a. 65 inches tall; 5 shirts 1.b. 1st in line; 5th house on the block 1.c. 127 Main Street; July 23

Problem Solving Thinker's Corner

MANY USES OF NUMBERS Numbers tell how much or how many. They also tell the order of things. Numbers are even used to name things.

1. Give at least two examples for each.
   a. a number used to tell how much or how many **See above.**
   b. a number used to tell the order of things **See above.**
   c. a number used to name things **See above.**
2. **REASONING** Give an example of numbers you would compare. Give an example of numbers that it wouldn't make sense to compare. Explain. **Possible answers: compare the number of feet 2 students jumped; do not compare height of 1 dog and weight of 1 dog.**

Reading Strategy

K-W-L CHART Before having students read the Thinker's Corner, have them look at the art. Ask them to predict what the Thinker's Corner will be about. Then have students make a three-column chart headed *What I Know, What I Want to Know,* and *What I Learned.* Ask them to fill in the first two columns. Have them fill in the third column after they discuss uses of numbers.

What I Know	What I Want to Know	What I Learned

MULTISTEP OR STRATEGY PROBLEM To solve Exercise 32, students can add $3 + 7 = 10$, $10 + 5 = 15$. They may then subtract $24 - 15 = 9$.

Problem Solving Thinker's Corner

Have students read and discuss the many uses of numbers.

- *Name some ways you might use numbers before you get to school in the morning.* Possible answers: numbers on an alarm clock, on a microwave oven, on a television; address on a friend's house
- *How might you use numbers to help you get in touch with a classmate?* Possible answers: telephone numbers, e-mail address, house address
- *How can you use numbers to tell your birthday?* Possible answer: number of month, day, year

4 ASSESS

Summarize the lesson by having students:

DISCUSS How would you compare 786 and 787 to find the greater number? Possible answer: Since the hundreds digits and the tens digits are the same, compare the ones digits. $7 > 6$, so $787 > 786$.

WRITE Show the steps you would follow to compare the numbers 319,234 and 319,239. Possible answer: Since the hundred thousands, ten thousands, thousands, hundreds, and tens digits are the same, compare the ones digits. $9 > 4$, so $319{,}239 > 319{,}234$.

LESSON QUIZ Transparency 3.2

Compare the numbers. Write $<$, $>$, or $=$ for each ●.

1. 60 ● 32 $>$
2. 3,861 ● 3,861 $=$
3. 304 ● 314 $<$
4. 91,027 ● 19,072 $>$

Lesson 3.3

Order Numbers

Lesson Planning

Objective To use models, number lines, and place value to order numbers

NCTM Standards

1. Number and Operations
6. Problem Solving
7. Reasoning and Proof
8. Communication
9. Connections

Math Background

These ideas will help students build understanding of ordering numbers.

- You can order numbers by comparing digits in the same place-value positions, working from left to right.
- Place-value position of the digit with the greatest value and location of the number on a number line are related.

Warm-Up Resources

Build Number Sense

Number of the Day

A number is found between 58 and 65 on a number line. It is less than the number of minutes in an hour. What number is it? 59

Daily Facts Practice

Have students practice addition facts by completing Set A of *Teacher's Resource Book*, p. TR85.

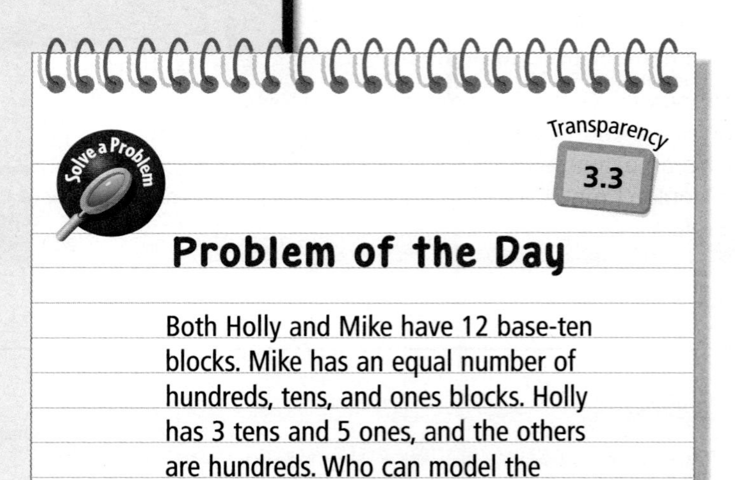

Problem of the Day

Both Holly and Mike have 12 base-ten blocks. Mike has an equal number of hundreds, tens, and ones blocks. Holly has 3 tens and 5 ones, and the others are hundreds. Who can model the greater number? Mike

Solution Problem of the Day tab, p. PD3

Intervention and Extension Resources

Alternative Teaching Strategy

MATERIALS *For each group* base-ten blocks, pp. TR8–9

Help students **compare and order 4-digit numbers**. Have students model three 4-digit numbers by using base-ten blocks. Remind students to first compare the number of thousands represented, then the number of hundreds, then the number of tens, and then the number of ones. Then relate the precise numbers represented with base-ten blocks, first to their representations on a place-value chart and then to their relative positions on a number line. Check students' work.

KINESTHETIC

BODILY/KINESTHETIC

Multistep and Strategy Problems

The following multistep or strategy problem is provided in Lesson 3.3:

Page	Item
47	13

Writing in Mathematics

Challenge students to **compare and contrast a ruler with a number line.** Have students draw a number line that begins at 0, has marks at 3, 6, and 9, and ends at 12. You may want to encourage them to use a Venn diagram or a compare-contrast chart as a prewriting activity. Check students' work.

Early Finishers

Invite small groups of students to **write a word problem that compares and orders the numbers 100, 200, and 250.** To show their answers, have students construct a number line and write the numbers using the symbol $<$ or $>$. Possible answer: Rosa has three boxes of pencils. The yellow box has 100 pencils, the blue box has 200, and the red box has 250. Which box has the greatest number of pencils? $250 > 200 > 100$, so the red box has the greatest number of pencils.

Have students who finish early write word problems for 4- and 5-digit numbers.

VISUAL

VERBAL/LINGUISTIC

Intervention, *Skills 3, 60*

Lesson 3.3 Organizer

Objective **To use models, number lines, and place value to order numbers**

QUICK REVIEW provides review of prerequisite skills.

WHY LEARN THIS? You can order numbers such as the heights of mountains. *Share the lesson objective with students.*

2 TEACH

Guided Instruction

- *Ask students to read the Learn section.*
  Do you need a number line with the exact points shown to order 4-digit numbers? Explain. Possible answer: No; you can see about where each number would be placed.
  Where would zero be on this number line, and why doesn't it appear? Possible answer: It would be to the left of 3,000; the number line isn't long enough.
  How do you know where to place 3,718 on the number line? Possible answer: Each tick mark on the number line stands for 1,000. 3,718 would be a little to the right of the mark for 3,700.
- *Direct students' attention to Steps 1–3.*
  Why do you begin ordering with the ten-thousands digits? They have the greatest value. If these digits are not the same, it is not necessary to compare the other digits.
  If the ten-thousands digits and the thousands digits were the same, what would you do next? Compare the hundreds digits.

MODIFYING INSTRUCTION For Steps 1–3, have students put the numbers in a place-value chart.

3 PRACTICE

Guided Practice

Do Check Exercises 1–3 with your students. Identify students who are having difficulty and choose appropriate lesson resources to provide assistance.

LESSON 3

Order Numbers

Quick Review

Tell which number is greater.

1. 37 or 29 37
2. 21 or 32 32
3. 58 or 65 65
4. 120 or 99 120
5. 235 or 253 253

Learn

MOUNTAIN HIGH The table lists the heights of three mountains in the United States. Which is the tallest?

Use a number line to order the numbers.

4,039 — 5,729 — 6,643

3,000 4,000 5,000 6,000 7,000

4,039 < 5,729 < 6,643

So, Clingmans Dome is the tallest.

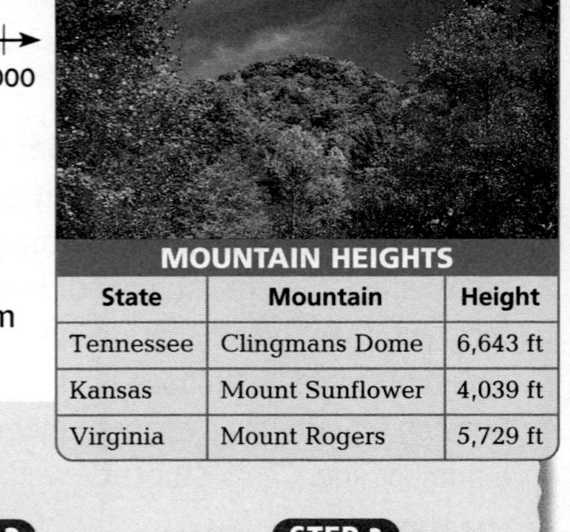

MOUNTAIN HEIGHTS

State	Mountain	Height
Tennessee	Clingmans Dome	6,643 ft
Kansas	Mount Sunflower	4,039 ft
Virginia	Mount Rogers	5,729 ft

You can order numbers by comparing the digits in the same place-value position from left to right.

Example

Order 47,613; 45,435; and 46,551.

STEP 1
Compare ten thousands.
47,613
45,435
46,551
The digits are the same.

STEP 2
Compare thousands.
47,613
45,435
46,551
They are not the same.
7 > 6 > 5

STEP 3
Write the numbers in order from greatest to least.
47,613 > 46,551 > 45,435

Check

1. **Explain** how you can order the numbers 251,432; 251,438; and 251,463 from greatest to least.
Possible answer: Since the hundred thousands, ten thousands, thousands, and hundreds digits are the same, compare the tens digits: 6 > 3. Compare the ones digits: 8 > 2, so 251,463 > 251,438 > 251,432.

Reteach 3.3

Order Numbers

When you put more than two numbers in order, you compare the digits, starting with the place value farthest to the left. Set the numbers vertically to help you compare.

Put 351, 352, and 251 in order from least to greatest.

351 352 251

Step 1 Compare the hundreds of all three numbers. 351 352 251 — 251 has the fewest hundreds, so it has the least value.

Step 2 Compare the tens of the other two numbers. 351 352 — There is no difference, so look at the place value to the right.

Step 3 Now compare the ones. 351 352 — 1 < 2, so 351 < 352.

The numbers from least to greatest: 251, 351, 352

Write the numbers from least to greatest. Look at the numbers in the box to help you compare.

1. 450, 458, 397 [450 / 458 / 397] **397, 450, 458**
2. 6,519; 8,917; 6,425 [6,519 / 8,917 / 6,425] **6,425; 6,519; 8,917**

Write the numbers from greatest to least. Look at the numbers in the box to help you compare.

3. 265, 387, 254 [265 / 387 / 254] **387, 265, 254**
4. 1,268; 6,540; 3,495 [1,268 / 6,540 / 3,495] **6,540; 3,495; 1,268**
5. 45,823; 45,546; 46,515 [45,823 / 45,546 / 46,515] **46,515; 45,823; 45,546**
6. 781,123; 842,120; 782,132 [781,123 / 842,120 / 782,132] **842,120; 782,132; 781,123**

Reteach RW15

Practice 3.3

Order Numbers

Write the numbers in order from *least* to *greatest*.

1,000 2,000 3,000 4,000 5,000 6,000 7,000 8,000 9,000

1. 2,221; 2,210; 2,235 **2,210; 2,221; 2,235**
2. 4,305; 3,275; 3,255 **3,255; 3,275; 4,305**
3. 7,246; 7,232; 7,310 **7,232; 7,246; 7,310**
4. 2,326; 1,503; 3,235 **1,503; 2,326; 3,235**
5. 5,609; 5,950; 4,999 **4,999; 5,609; 5,950**
6. 9,000; 7,607; 4,439 **4,439; 7,607; 9,000**
7. 8,256; 6,208; 7,065 **6,208; 7,065; 8,256**
8. 4,135; 2,857; 4,351 **2,857; 4,135; 4,351**
9. 2,904; 2,499; 1,894 **1,894; 2,499; 2,904**

Write the numbers in order from *greatest* to *least*.

10. 1,652; 1,328; 1,691 **1,691; 1,652; 1,328**
11. 87,114; 88,205; 79,343 **88,205; 87,114; 79,343**
12. 254,357; 124,899; 304,506 **304,506; 254,357; 124,899**

Mixed Review

Solve.

13. 29 + 10 + 4 = **43**
14. 71 + 12 + 8 = **91**
15. 53 + 11 + 14 = **78**
16. 72 + 8 + 0 = **80**
17. 13 + 58 + 29 = **100**
18. 49 + 49 + 10 = **108**
19. 71 − 39 = **32**
20. 97 − 38 = **59**
21. 91 − 84 = **7**
22. 60 − 25 = **35**

Practice PW15

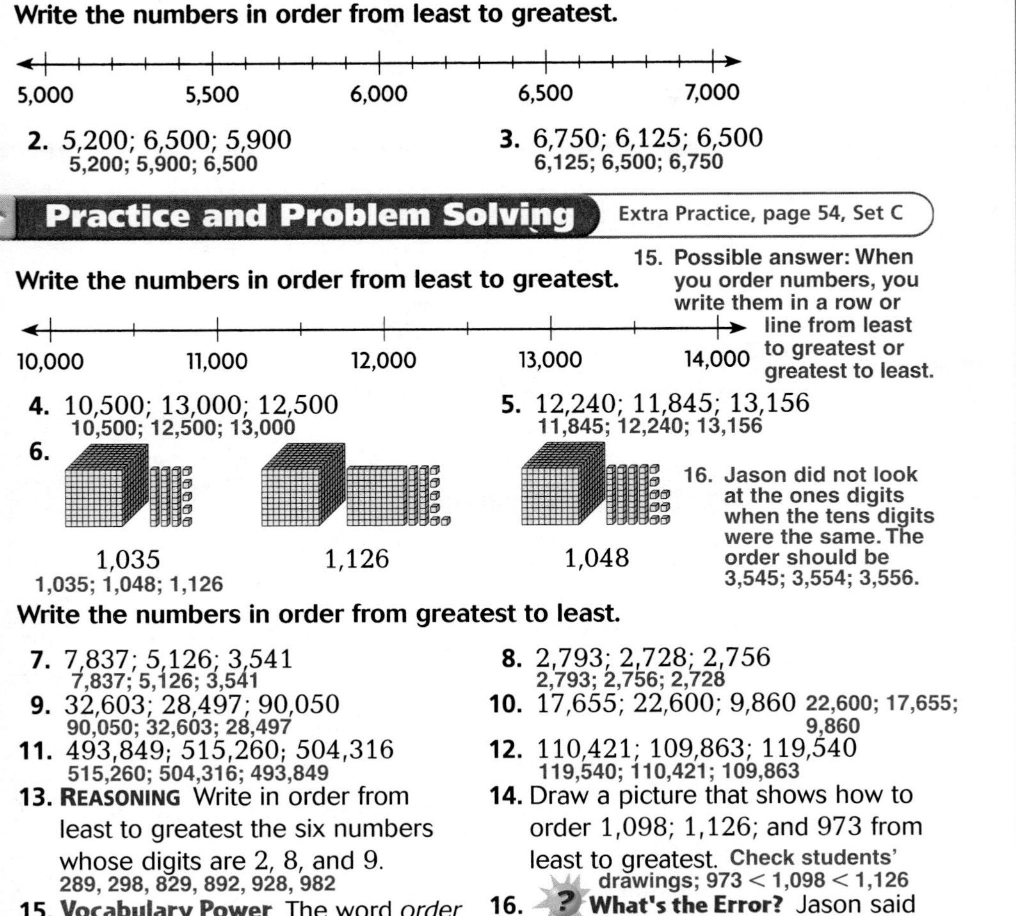

Write the numbers in order from least to greatest.

5,000 5,500 6,000 6,500 7,000

2. 5,200; 6,500; 5,900
5,200; 5,900; 6,500

3. 6,750; 6,125; 6,500
6,125; 6,500; 6,750

Practice and Problem Solving

Extra Practice, page 54, Set C

Write the numbers in order from least to greatest.

10,000 11,000 12,000 13,000 14,000

15. Possible answer: When you order numbers, you write them in a row or line from least to greatest or greatest to least.

4. 10,500; 13,000; 12,500
10,500; 12,500; 13,000

5. 12,240; 11,845; 13,156
11,845; 12,240; 13,156

6.
1,035 1,126 1,048
1,035; 1,048; 1,126

16. Jason did not look at the ones digits when the tens digits were the same. The order should be 3,545; 3,554; 3,556.

Write the numbers in order from greatest to least.

7. 7,837; 5,126; 3,541
7,837; 5,126; 3,541

8. 2,793; 2,728; 2,756
2,793; 2,756; 2,728

9. 32,603; 28,497; 90,050
90,050; 32,603; 28,497

10. 17,655; 22,600; 9,860 22,600; 17,655; 9,860

11. 493,849; 515,260; 504,316
515,260; 504,316; 493,849

12. 110,421; 109,863; 119,540
119,540; 110,421; 109,863

13. **REASONING** Write in order from least to greatest the six numbers whose digits are 2, 8, and 9.
289, 298, 829, 892, 928, 982

14. Draw a picture that shows how to order 1,098; 1,126; and 973 from least to greatest. Check students' drawings; $973 < 1,098 < 1,126$

15. **Vocabulary Power** The word *order* comes from the Latin word *ordo*, which means "a row or a line." How does this meaning relate to ordering numbers? See above.

16. **What's the Error?** Jason said that the numbers 3,545; 3,556; and 3,554 were in order from least to greatest. What is his error? See above.

Getting Ready for the EOG Test

17. Order these numbers from *greatest* to *least*.
7,224; 8,224; 7,596 C

A 7,224; 7,596; 8,224
B 7,596; 7,224; 8,224
C 8,224; 7,596; 7,224
D 8,224; 7,224; 7,596

North Carolina Standards 1.01 Develop number sense for whole numbers through 9,999. Compare and order.

Independent Practice

Note that Exercise 13 is a **multistep or strategy problem.** Assign Exercises 4–16.

For Exercise 13, suggest that students break the problem into steps. For example, write all the numbers formed from the digits 2, 8, and 9. Then order the numbers by using a number line or by comparing the digits in the same place-value position from left to right.

Vocabulary Power Remind students that ordering numbers from least to greatest is similar to putting spelling words in alphabetical order.

4 ASSESS

Summarize the lesson by having students:

DISCUSS Suppose you want to choose two numbers to the right of 12,025 on the number line. What numbers might you choose? Possible answers: 12,050; 12,075

WRITE Describe and draw the number line you would use to order the following numbers: 113, 127, 74. Possible answer: Draw a number line beginning at 70 and ending at 130, with intervals of 10. Place the numbers. $74 < 113 < 127$; 127 is the greatest number.

LESSON QUIZ

Write the numbers in order from least to greatest.

1. 765, 983, 503 503, 765, 983
2. 71,117; 17,707; 10,700 10,700; 17,707; 71,117

Write the numbers in order from greatest to least.

3. 7,321; 7,359; 7,366 7,366; 7,359; 7,321
4. 45,174; 45,192; 43,165 45,192; 45,174; 43,165

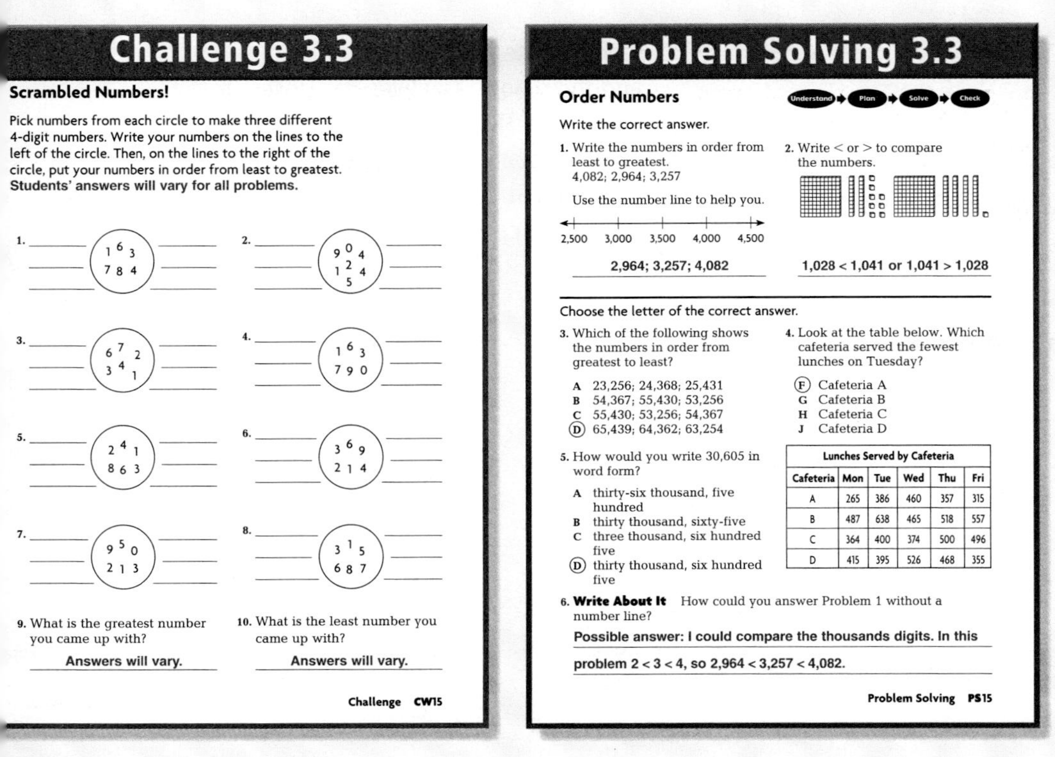

Challenge 3.3

Scrambled Numbers!

Pick numbers from each circle to make three different 4-digit numbers. Write your numbers on the lines to the left of the circle. Then, on the lines to the right of the circle, put your numbers in order from least to greatest. Students' answers will vary for all problems.

1. 1 6 3 7 8 4
2. 9 0 4 1 2 4 5
3. 6 7 2 3 4 1
4. 1 6 3 7 9 0
5. 2 4 1 8 6 3
6. 3 6 9 2 1 4
7. 9 5 0 2 1 3
8. 3 1 5 6 8 7

9. What is the greatest number you came up with? Answers will vary.

10. What is the least number you came up with? Answers will vary.

Challenge CW15

Problem Solving 3.3

Order Numbers

Understand → Plan → Solve → Check

Write the correct answer.

1. Write the numbers in order from least to greatest.
4,082; 2,964; 3,257
Use the number line to help you.
2,500 3,000 3,500 4,000 4,500
2,964; 3,257; 4,082

2. Write < or > to compare the numbers.
$1,028 < 1,041$ or $1,041 > 1,028$

Choose the letter of the correct answer.

3. Which of the following shows the numbers in order from greatest to least?
A 23,256; 24,368; 25,431
B 54,367; 55,430; 53,256
C 55,430; 53,256; 54,367
(D) 65,439; 64,362; 63,254

4. Look at the table below. Which cafeteria served the fewest lunches on Tuesday?
(F) Cafeteria A
G Cafeteria B
H Cafeteria C
J Cafeteria D

5. How would you write 30,605 in word form?
A thirty-six thousand, five hundred
B thirty thousand, sixty-five
C three thousand, six hundred five
(D) thirty thousand, six hundred five

Lunches Served by Cafeteria

Cafeteria	Mon	Tue	Wed	Thu	Fri
A	265	386	460	357	315
B	487	638	465	518	557
C	364	400	374	500	496
D	415	395	526	468	355

6. **Write About It** How could you answer Problem 1 without a number line?
Possible answer: I could compare the thousands digits. In this problem $2 < 3 < 4$, so $2,964 < 3,257 < 4,082$.

Problem Solving PS15

Lesson 3.4

Problem Solving Skill

Use a Bar Graph

Lesson Planning

Objective To use the problem solving skill *use a bar graph* to solve problems

Lesson Resources Reading Transparency 3; Intervention • Problem Solving, Strategy/Skill 3

NCTM Standards

1. Number and Operations
5. Data Analysis and Probability
6. Problem Solving
7. Reasoning and Proof
8. Communication
9. Connections

Math Background

These ideas will help students understand how to use a bar graph:

- A bar graph is a visual tool for displaying many pieces of data.
- The information in the bar graph can be stated in a rule or written as a pattern.
- Once the relationship between two quantities is understood, the bar graph can be extended to show greater quantities.

Warm-Up Resources

Number of the Day

The number of the day is 100. Compare 100 with two other numbers, once showing *less than* and once showing *greater than.* Possible answers: 100 < 200; 100 > 99

Daily Facts Practice

Have students practice addition and subtraction facts by completing Set B of *Teacher's Resource Book*, p. TR85.

Solve a Problem

Transparency 3.4

Problem of the Day

Josh's house is between Fran's house and the school. Kay lives the closest to the school. Their houses are at 846, 862, and 822 Main Street. The school is at 826 Main Street. What is the house number of each student? Kay, 822; Josh, 846; Fran, 862

Solution Problem of the Day tab, p. PD3

Intervention and Extension Resources

Alternative Teaching Strategy

Help students **understand how comparing numbers on a bar graph is like comparing numbers in a place-value chart.** Ask students to read the problem on page 48. Instead of following Step 1, have students work with a partner to list the mountain heights in a place-value chart. Check students' work. Ask:

- The digits in what places are equal? the 1 in the ten thousands place and the 0 in the thousands place
- What is the highest mountain? Mount Hood
- What mountain height is greater than 10,095 feet but less than 11,235 feet? Mount Jefferson

VISUAL

VISUAL/SPATIAL

ESOL/ESL

Help students **understand that comparing numbers on a bar graph is like comparing numbers on a number line.** Draw a number line and have students copy it. Use the same numbers as the bar graph on page 48. Explain that since the height of Mount Hood is 11,235 feet, they would place the dot on the number line about halfway between the lines for 11,000 and 11,500. Have students work with a partner to locate the heights of the other mountains on the number line. Suggest that they put the mountain heights in order from least to greatest. Then have them find the mountain height that is greater than that of North Sister but less than that of Mount Hood. Check students' work.

VISUAL

VISUAL/SPATIAL

Reading Strategy

Use Graphic Aids Explain that a bar graph can help you compare and order numbers. Draw a horizontal bar graph with a scale from 1,000 to 5,000. Illustrate the following problem by completing the bar graph.

The students at Mayfair School collected pennies for a school picnic. The second grade collected 1,600 pennies. The third grade collected 3,800 pennies, and the fourth grade collected 3,200 pennies. Ask:

- Which grade collected the most pennies? third grade

By comparing the lengths of the bars, students can solve the problem.

Transparency 3 **Reading Transparency 3**

Science Connection

Have students **apply their comparing and ordering skills to solve a real-world problem.** Ask students to study the information showing water use for one person during one month.

Washing clothes	450 gallons
Washing dishes	40 gallons
Showering	360 gallons
Watering the grass	1,500 gallons

Have students put the number of gallons used for each activity in order from least to greatest. 40, 360, 450, 1,500 Have students identify the relationship between the numbers that show gallons used for washing dishes and gallons used for washing clothes. $40 < 450$

VISUAL

LOGICAL/MATHEMATICAL

Multistep and Strategy Problems

The following multistep or strategy problem is provided in Lesson 3.4:

Page	Item
49	6

Intervention • Problem Solving, *Strategy/Skill 3*

Lesson 3.4 Organizer

Objective To use the problem solving skill *use a bar graph* to solve problems

Lesson Resources Reading Transparency 3; Intervention • Problem Solving, Strategy/Skill 3

1 INTRODUCE

Quick Review provides review of prerequisite skills.

Why Learn This? You can use this skill to understand bar graphs in your textbooks and in the newspaper. *Share the lesson objective with students.*

Guided Instruction

- *Introduce the skill by asking students to study the graph.*
  What information do you get from the title and labels? The graph shows the heights and names of some Oregon mountains.
- *Ask students to read the problem.*
  What are you being asked to do? Find the mountain that is higher than North Sister but not as high as Mount Hood.
- *Ask students to think about the steps.*
  In Step 1, how can you determine how the numbers are related? You can compare them by studying the bars in the bar graph.
  If a fifth mountain, Mount Baker, with a height of 10,778 ft, were added to the graph, where would the bar extend? to between 10,500 and 11,000 ft
  How does the graph help you solve the problem? Possible answer: The bars on the graph help you see how the heights of the mountains are related.

Guided Practice

Do Problem Solving Practice Exercises 1–5 with your students. Identify students who are having difficulty and choose appropriate lesson resources to provide assistance.

LESSON 4

Problem Solving Skill
Use a Bar Graph

UNDERSTAND | PLAN | SOLVE | CHECK

FOLLOW THE TRAIL Nancy and Emilio are studying the Oregon Cascade Mountains. They want to hike to the mountain that is higher than North Sister but not as high as Mount Hood. Which one should they choose?

Sometimes a bar graph can help you solve a problem.

Quick Review

Compare. Write <, >, or = for each ●.

1. 124 ● 118 >
2. 229 ● 232 <
3. 244 ● 244 =
4. 3,156 ● 3,165 <
5. 4,371 ● 4,372 <

Example

STEP 1

Look at the lengths of the bars in the graph. List the 4 mountains from highest to lowest.

Mount Hood, Mount Jefferson, North Sister, and Broken Top

STEP 2

Find all the mountains that are higher than North Sister.

Mount Jefferson and Mount Hood

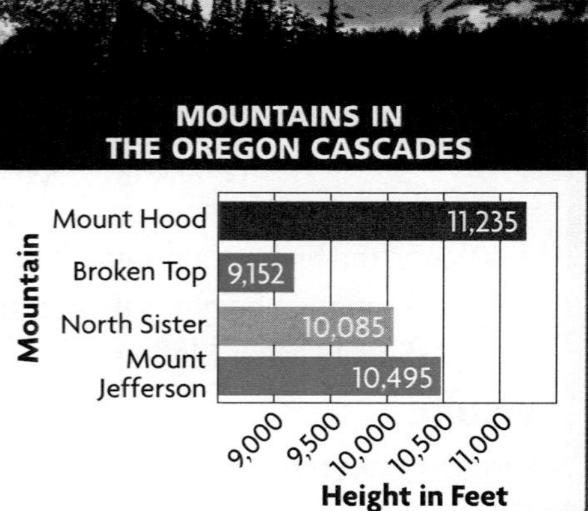

STEP 3

Find all the mountains that are not as high as Mount Hood.

Mount Jefferson, North Sister, and Broken Top

STEP 4

Find the mountain that is listed in both Step 2 and Step 3.

Mount Jefferson is the only mountain listed in both steps.

So, Nancy and Emilio chose Mount Jefferson.

Talk About It

- How does the height of Broken Top compare to that of North Sister? **Broken Top is not as high as North Sister.**

48

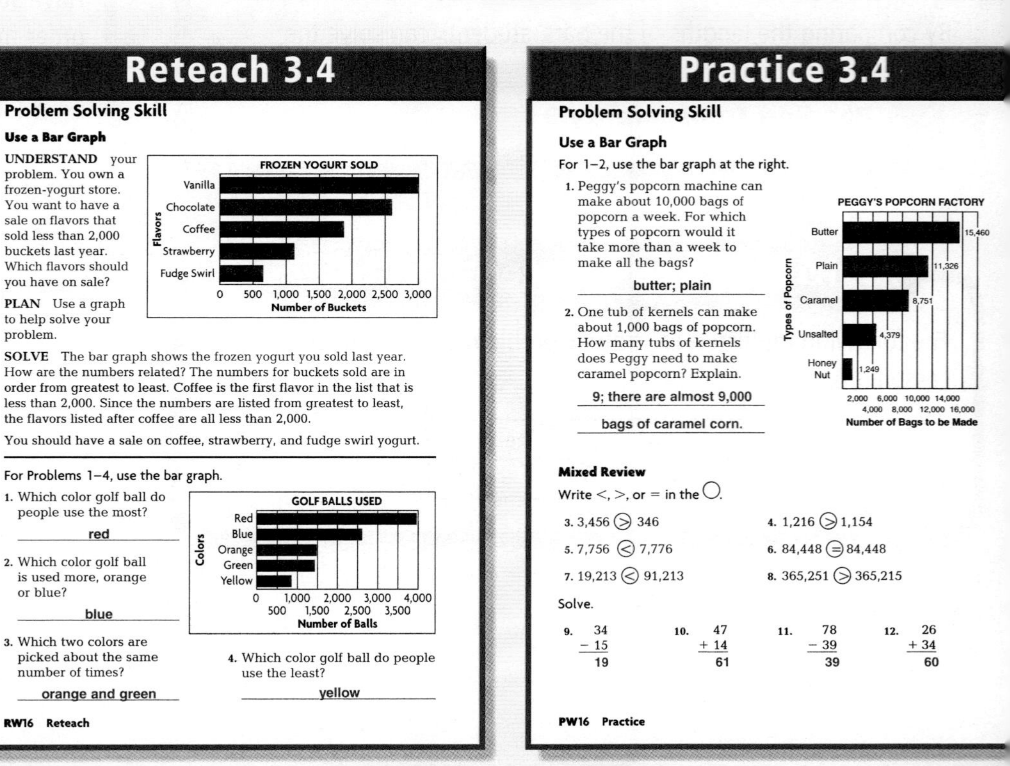

Reteach 3.4

Problem Solving Skill

Use a Bar Graph

UNDERSTAND your problem. You own a frozen-yogurt store. You want to have a sale on flavors that sold less than 2,000 buckets last year. Which flavors should you have on sale?

PLAN Use a graph to help solve your problem.

SOLVE The bar graph shows the frozen yogurt you sold last year. How are the numbers related? The numbers for buckets sold are in order from greatest to least. Coffee is the first flavor in the list that is less than 2,000. Since the numbers are listed from greatest to least, the flavors listed after coffee are all less than 2,000.

You should have a sale on coffee, strawberry, and fudge swirl yogurt.

For Problems 1–4, use the bar graph.

1. Which color golf ball do people use the most? **red**
2. Which color golf ball is used more, orange or blue? **blue**
3. Which two colors are picked about the same number of times? **orange and green**
4. Which color golf ball do people use the least? **yellow**

RW16 Reteach

Practice 3.4

Problem Solving Skill

Use a Bar Graph

For 1–2, use the bar graph at the right.

1. Peggy's popcorn machine can make about 10,000 bags of popcorn a week. For which types of popcorn would it take more than a week to make all the bags? **butter; plain**
2. One tub of kernels can make about 1,000 bags of popcorn. How many tubs of kernels does Peggy need to make caramel popcorn? Explain. **9; there are almost 9,000 bags of caramel corn.**

Mixed Review

Write <, >, or = in the ○.

3. 3,456 (>) 346
4. 1,216 (>) 1,154
5. 7,756 (<) 7,776
6. 84,448 (=) 84,448
7. 19,213 (<) 91,213
8. 365,251 (>) 365,215

Solve.

9. $34 - 15 = $ **19**
10. $47 + 14 = $ **61**
11. $78 - 39 = $ **39**
12. $26 + 34 = $ **60**

PW16 Practice

Problem Solving Practice

1. **What if** Emilio and Nancy hiked to the mountain that is higher than Broken Top but not as high as Mount Jefferson? To which mountain did they hike? **North Sister**
2. What is the highest mountain under 11,000 feet that Emilio and Nancy studied? **Mount Jefferson**
3. **What if** the mountains were listed in order of height from least to greatest? What would be the order of the mountains? **Broken Top, North Sister, Mount Jefferson, and Mount Hood**

USE DATA For 4–5, use the bar graph at the right.

SMALLEST STATES IN THE U.S.

State	Size in Square Miles
Connecticut	5,006
New Jersey	7,790
Rhode Island	1,213
Hawaii	6,459
Delaware	2,026

4. Which state is larger than Connecticut but smaller than New Jersey? **A**
   - A Hawaii
   - B Rhode Island
   - C New Jersey
   - D Delaware
5. Name the three smallest states. **J**
   - F Delaware, Rhode Island, Hawaii
   - G New Jersey, Hawaii, Connecticut
   - H Hawaii, Rhode Island, New Jersey
   - J Rhode Island, Delaware, Connecticut

Mixed Applications

6. Louis had base-ten blocks that showed 6 hundreds, 7 tens, 3 ones. Tom gave him 2 hundreds, 1 ten, 5 ones. Using standard form, write the number that shows the value of Louis's blocks now. **888**
7. Celia lives in a town with a population of 12,346. Last year there were 1,000 fewer people living in the town. How many people lived in the town last year? **11,346 people**
8. Tony had 128 postcards. Arlo gave him some more postcards. Now Tony has 152 postcards. How many postcards did Arlo give to Tony? **24 postcards**
9. There were 253 students that went to the Science Museum. Of them, 127 were girls. How many were boys? **126 boys**
10. **Write About It** Explain how you would compare 4,291; 4,921; and 4,129 to put them in order from greatest to least. **Possible answer: Since the thousands digits are the same, compare the hundreds: 9 > 2 > 1. The order is 4,921; 4,291; and 4,129.**

Problem Solving

North Carolina Standards 1.01 Develop number sense for whole numbers through 9,999. Compare and order.

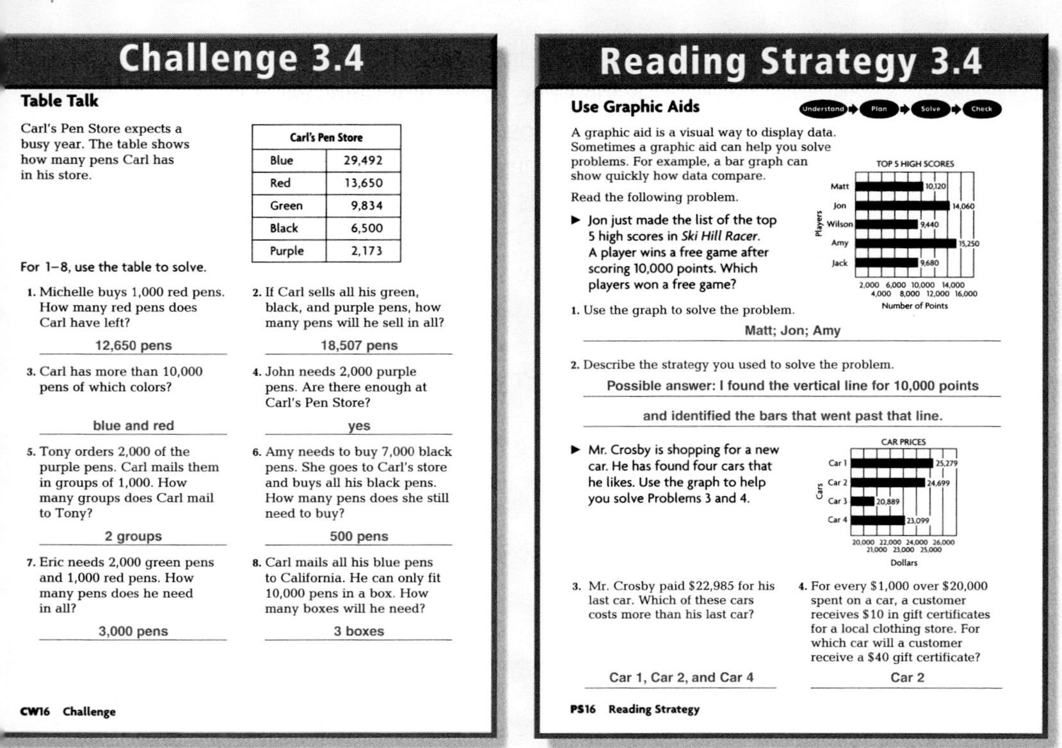

Challenge 3.4

Table Talk

Carl's Pen Store expects a busy year. The table shows how many pens Carl has in his store.

Carl's Pen Store	
Blue	29,492
Red	13,650
Green	9,834
Black	6,500
Purple	2,173

For 1–8, use the table to solve.

1. Michelle buys 1,000 red pens. How many red pens does Carl have left? 12,650 pens
2. If Carl sells all his green, black, and purple pens, how many pens will he sell in all? 18,507 pens
3. Carl has more than 10,000 pens of which colors? blue and red
4. John needs 2,000 purple pens. Are there enough at Carl's Pen Store? yes
5. Tony orders 2,000 of the purple pens. Carl mails them in groups of 1,000. How many groups does Carl mail to Tony? 2 groups
6. Amy needs to buy 7,000 black pens. She goes to Carl's store and buys all his black pens. How many pens does she still need to buy? 500 pens
7. Eric needs 2,000 green pens and 1,000 red pens. How many pens does he need in all? 3,000 pens
8. Carl mails all his blue pens to California. He can only fit 10,000 pens in a box. How many boxes will he need? 3 boxes

CW16 Challenge

Reading Strategy 3.4

Use Graphic Aids Understand → Plan → Solve → Check

A graphic aid is a visual way to display data. Sometimes a graphic aid can help you solve problems. For example, a bar graph can show quickly how data compare.

Read the following problem.

▶ Jon just made the list of the top 5 high scores in *Ski Hill Racer*. A player wins a free game after scoring 10,000 points. Which players won a free game?

TOP 5 HIGH SCORES

Players	Number of Points
Matt	10,120
Jon	14,060
Wilson	9,440
Amy	15,250
Jack	9,680

1. Use the graph to solve the problem. Matt; Jon; Amy
2. Describe the strategy you used to solve the problem. Possible answer: I found the vertical line for 10,000 points and identified the bars that went past that line.

▶ Mr. Crosby is shopping for a new car. He has found four cars that he likes. Use the graph to help you solve Problems 3 and 4.

CAR PRICES

Cars	Dollars
Car 1	25,279
Car 2	24,699
Car 3	20,889
Car 4	23,099

3. Mr. Crosby paid $22,985 for his last car. Which of these cars costs more than his last car? Car 1, Car 2, and Car 4
4. For every $1,000 over $20,000 spent on a car, a customer receives $10 in gift certificates for a local clothing store. For which car will a customer receive a $40 gift certificate? Car 2

PS16 Reading Strategy

Independent Practice

Note that Exercise 6 is a **multistep or strategy problem.** Assign Exercises 6–10.

You may want pairs of students to discuss Exercise 10 before they explain it.

4 ASSESS

Summarize the lesson by having students:

DISCUSS Order from smallest to largest the sizes in square miles of the five states in the graph on page 49. 1,213; 2,026; 5,006; 6,459; 7,790

WRITE Three 4-digit numbers have the same digit in the thousands place and different digits in the hundreds place. How do you order them from least to greatest? Possible answer: Compare the digits in the hundreds place. The number with the least digit in the hundreds place comes first, the number with the next-to-least digit comes second, and the number with the greatest digit comes last.

Transparency 3.4

LESSON QUIZ

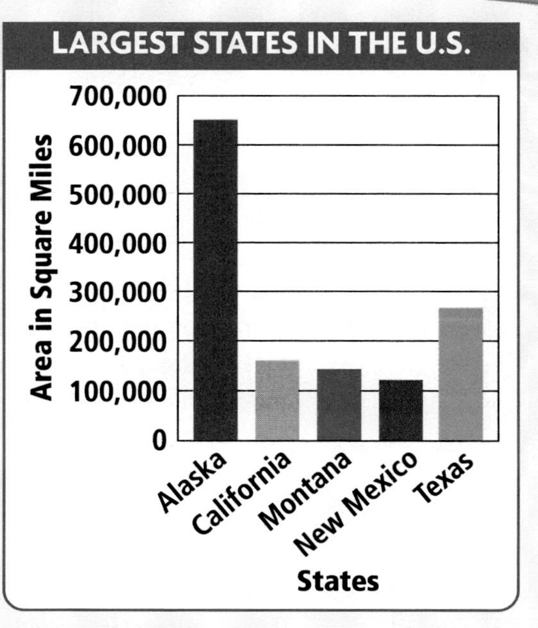

For 1–2, use the graph.

1. Put the states in order from greatest to least area. Alaska, Texas, California, Montana, New Mexico
2. What state is larger than Montana but smaller than Texas? California

Lesson 3.5

Round to Nearest 10 and 100

Lesson Planning

Objective To use rounding rules to round numbers to the nearest 10 and 100

NCTM Standards

1. Number and Operations
5. Data Analysis and Probability
6. Problem Solving
7. Reasoning and Proof
8. Communication
9. Connections
10. Representation

Math Background

These ideas will help students understand rounding to the nearest 10 and 100.

- 2- and 3-digit numbers can be rounded to the nearest 10 or 100.
- When rounding to the nearest 10, look at the ones digit; when rounding to the nearest 100, look at the tens digit.
- Rounding is one estimation strategy.

Vocabulary

rounding one way to estimate

Warm-Up Resources

Number of the Day

Transparency 3.5

The number of the day is 2,001. Include this number as part of two 3-number sets. In the first set, make it the greatest number. In the second set, make it the least number. Possible answers: 100, 454, 2,001; 2,001, 3,000, 9,999

Daily Facts Practice

Have students practice addition and subtraction facts by completing Set C of *Teacher's Resource Book*, p. TR85.

Solve a Problem

Transparency 3.5

Problem of the Day

Find the number whose thousands value is the same as the thousands value in 4,106; whose hundreds value is the same as the hundreds value in 2,039; whose tens value is the same as the tens value in 4,303; and whose ones value is the same as the ones value in 6,288. 4,008

Solution Problem of the Day tab, p. PD3

Intervention and Extension Resources

Alternative Teaching Strategy

Help students **practice rounding to the nearest 10**. Display the following reminder:

- If the ones digit is less than 5, the tens digit stays the same.
- If the ones digit is 5 or more, the tens digit increases by one.

Have students round these numbers to the nearest ten by using the reminder: 44, 55, 71, 83, 39, 26, 12. 40, 60, 70, 80, 40, 30, 10

VISUAL

VISUAL/SPATIAL

Multistep and Strategy Problems

The following multistep or strategy problem is provided in Lesson 3.5:

Page	Item
51	28

Vocabulary Strategy

Help students **understand rounding**. Ask students to complete a semantic map for the verb *round*. Categories might be:

- What can I help you do? Possible answer: decide about how many
- What is another name for me? estimate
- What are some examples? Possible answers: rounding to the nearest ten: 6 to 10 or 83 to 80; rounding to the nearest hundred: 156 to 200 or 849 to 800.

VISUAL

VISUAL/SPATIAL

Advanced Learners

Challenge students to **write and solve rounding riddles**. Have students write, exchange, and solve riddles like this sample:

I am a number between 345 and 360. When I am rounded to the nearest 100, I am 300. What numbers could I be? 346, 347, 348, 349; Check students' work.

VISUAL

VERBAL/LINGUISTIC

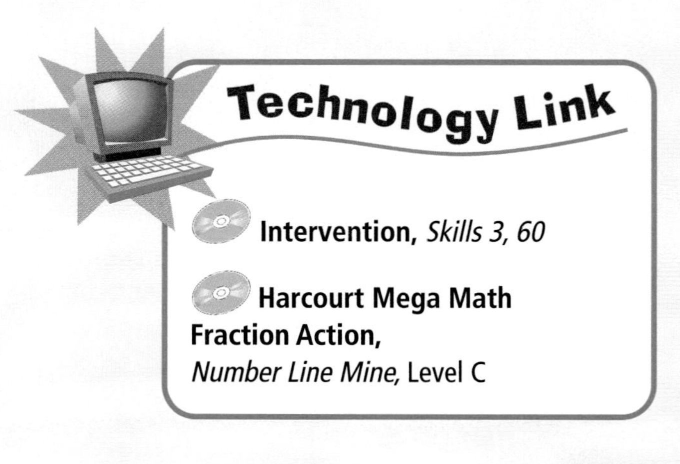

Technology Link
Intervention, *Skills 3, 60*
Harcourt Mega Math Fraction Action, *Number Line Mine,* Level C

Lesson 3.5 Organizer

Objective To use rounding rules to round numbers to the nearest 10 and 100

Vocabulary rounding

1 INTRODUCE

Quick Review provides review of prerequisite skills.

Why Learn This? You can use rounding to estimate an amount, such as the number of students on a bus. *Share the lesson objective with students.*

2 TEACH

Guided Instruction

- *Have students read the Learn section.*
  Which digit helps you find the closest ten? the digit in the ones place
  Reasoning What 2-digit numbers rounded to the nearest ten are 3-digit numbers? 95, 96, 97, 98, 99

Modifying Instruction Provide additional examples for rounding to tens before moving on to rounding to hundreds.

- *Direct students' attention to the 3-digit numbers in Example 2.*
  Which digit helps you find the closest hundred? the digit in the tens place
  Reasoning How is rounding to the nearest hundred like rounding to the nearest 10? Possible answer: If the number you are rounding is at least halfway between the tens or the hundreds, round to the greater number; if the number is less than halfway between the tens or hundreds, round to the lesser number.

LESSON 5

Round to Nearest 10 and 100

Quick Review

Write the numbers in order from least to greatest.

1. 23, 19, 16 **16, 19, 23**
2. 37, 31, 23 **23, 31, 37**
3. 29, 33, 32 **29, 32, 33**
4. 59, 57, 58 **57, 58, 59**
5. 218, 287, 278 **218, 278, 287**

VOCABULARY
rounding

Learn

HOW CLOSE? There are 43 third graders and 47 fourth graders going on a field trip to the zoo. About how many students in each grade are going to the zoo?

Rounding is one way to estimate when you want to know *about how many*.

A number line can help you.

Example 1

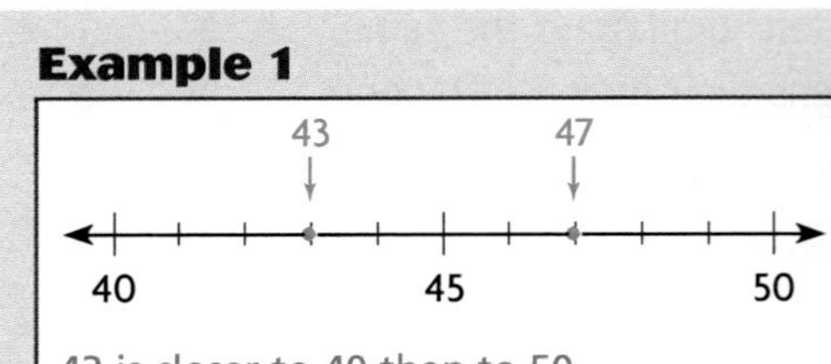

43 is closer to 40 than to 50.
43 rounds to 40.

47 is closer to 50 than to 40.
47 rounds to 50.

45 is halfway between 40 and 50. If a number is halfway between two tens, round to the greater ten. 45 rounds to 50.

So, about 40 third graders and about 50 fourth graders are going to the zoo.

Example 2

Round 3-digit numbers to the nearest ten and the nearest hundred.

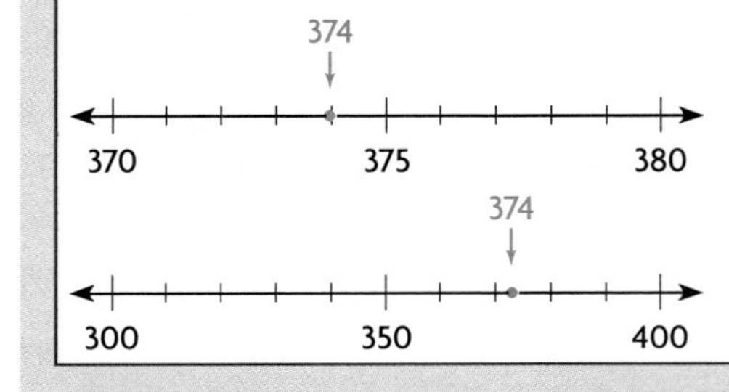

Round to the nearest ten.
374 is closer to 370 than to 380.
374 rounds to 370.

Round to the nearest hundred.
374 is closer to 400 than to 300.
374 rounds to 400.

50

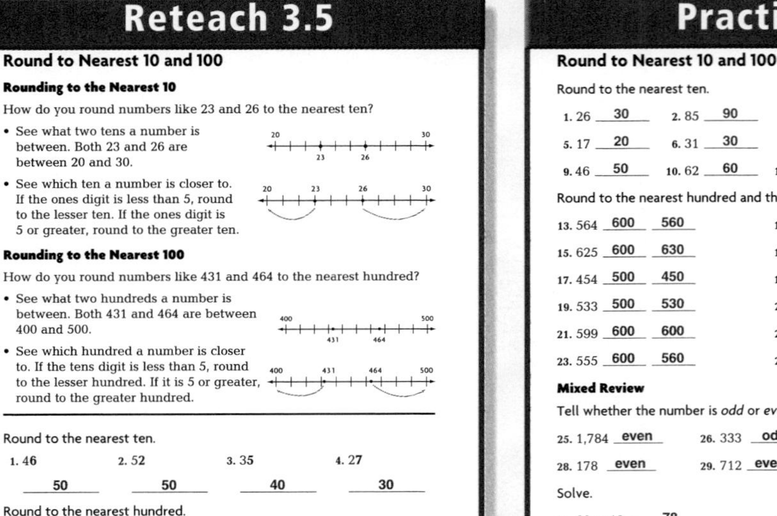

Reteach 3.5

Round to Nearest 10 and 100

Rounding to the Nearest 10

How do you round numbers like 23 and 26 to the nearest ten?

- See what two tens a number is between. Both 23 and 26 are between 20 and 30.
- See which ten a number is closer to. If the ones digit is less than 5, round to the lesser ten. If the ones digit is 5 or greater, round to the greater ten.

Rounding to the Nearest 100

How do you round numbers like 431 and 464 to the nearest hundred?

- See what two hundreds a number is between. Both 431 and 464 are between 400 and 500.
- See which hundred a number is closer to. If the tens digit is less than 5, round to the lesser hundred. If it is 5 or greater, round to the greater hundred.

Round to the nearest ten.

1. 46 **50**
2. 52 **50**
3. 35 **40**
4. 27 **30**

Round to the nearest hundred.

5. 134 **100**
6. 782 **800**
7. 893 **900**
8. 615 **600**
9. 125 **100**
10. 675 **700**
11. 832 **800**
12. 550 **600**

Reteach RW17

Practice 3.5

Round to Nearest 10 and 100

Round to the nearest ten.

1. 26 **30**
2. 85 **90**
3. 72 **70**
4. 55 **60**
5. 17 **20**
6. 31 **30**
7. 88 **90**
8. 97 **100**
9. 46 **50**
10. 62 **60**
11. 8 **10**
12. 29 **30**

Round to the nearest hundred and the nearest ten.

13. 564 **600** **560**
14. 412 **400** **410**
15. 625 **600** **630**
16. 445 **400** **450**
17. 454 **500** **450**
18. 621 **600** **620**
19. 533 **500** **530**
20. 689 **700** **690**
21. 599 **600** **600**
22. 327 **300** **330**
23. 555 **600** **560**
24. 649 **600** **650**

Mixed Review

Tell whether the number is *odd* or *even*.

25. 1,784 **even**
26. 333 **odd**
27. 95 **odd**
28. 178 **even**
29. 712 **even**
30. 619 **odd**

Solve.

31. 90 − 12 = **78**
32. 39 + 21 = **60**
33. 47 + 54 = **101**
34. 60 − 23 = **37**
35. 93 − 78 = **15**
36. 56 − 48 = **8**
37. 57 + 63 = **120**
38. 82 − 39 = **43**

Practice PW17

Check

1. **Explain** how you can round 350 to the nearest hundred using the number line below. **350 is halfway between 300 and 400, so to the nearest hundred, 350 rounds to 400.**

Round to the nearest hundred and the nearest ten.

300 350 400 450 500 550 600 650 700 750 800

2. 643 **600; 640** 3. 377 **400; 380** 4. 445 **400; 450** 5. 518 **500; 520** 6. 750 **800; 750**

Practice and Problem Solving

Extra Practice, page 54, Set D

Round to the nearest ten.

7. 16 **20** 8. 72 **70** 9. 53 **50** 10. 5 **10** 11. 78 **80**

12. 37 **40** 13. 44 **40** 14. 66 **70** 15. 94 **90** 16. 95 **100**

Round to the nearest hundred and the nearest ten.

17. 363 **400; 360** 18. 405 **400; 410** 19. 115 **100; 120** 20. 165 **200; 170** 21. 952 **1,000; 950**

22. 698 **700; 700** 23. 917 **900; 920** 24. 385 **400; 390** 25. 456 **500; 460** 26. 883 **900; 880**

USE DATA For 27–28, use the table.

ZOO ANIMALS	
Type	Number
Mammals	214
Birds	428
Reptiles	174

27. To the nearest hundred, about how many kinds of birds does the zoo have? **about 400 birds**

28. **REASONING** The number of _?_ + the number of _?_ < the number of _?_. **mammals; reptiles; birds**

29. Kim rounded 348 to the nearest ten and said it was 350. She rounded 348 to the nearest hundred and said it was 400. Was this correct? Explain. **No, 350 rounds to 400, but 348 rounds to 300.**

30. **Write a problem** about animals. Use rounding to the nearest ten or to the nearest hundred in your problem. **Check students' problems.**

Getting Ready for the EOG Test

31. *About* how many miles long is the Blue Ridge Parkway? **B**

A 600 miles C 400 miles
B 500 miles D 50 miles

BLUE RIDGE PARKWAY IN NORTH CAROLINA	
Length	469 miles
Speed Limit	45 miles per hour

North Carolina Standards 1.01 Develop number sense for whole numbers through 9,999.

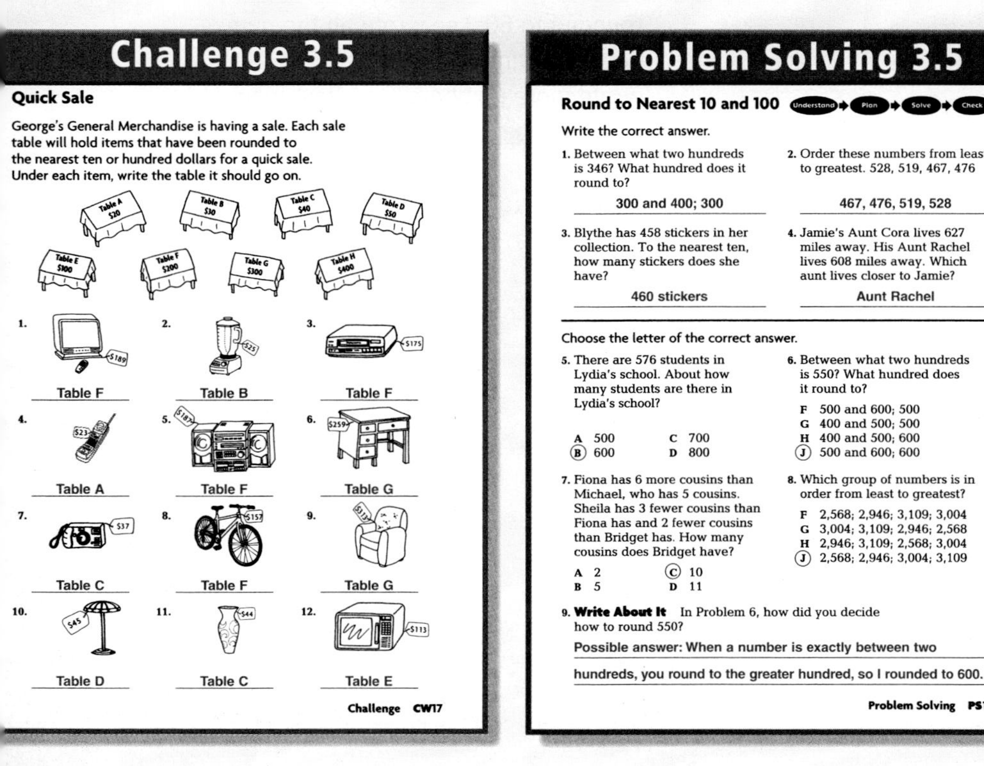

Challenge 3.5

Quick Sale

George's General Merchandise is having a sale. Each sale table will hold items that have been rounded to the nearest ten or hundred dollars for a quick sale. Under each item, write the table it should go on.

Table A $20; Table B $30; Table C $40; Table D $50; Table E $100; Table F $200; Table G $300; Table H $400

1. $189 **Table F** 2. $25 **Table B** 3. $175 **Table F**
4. $23 **Table A** 5. $187 **Table F** 6. $259 **Table G**
7. $37 **Table C** 8. $157 **Table F** 9. $313 **Table G**
10. $45 **Table D** 11. $44 **Table C** 12. $113 **Table E**

Challenge CW17

Problem Solving 3.5

Round to Nearest 10 and 100 Understand ➔ Plan ➔ Solve ➔ Check

Write the correct answer.

1. Between what two hundreds is 346? What hundred does it round to? **300 and 400; 300**
2. Order these numbers from least to greatest. 528, 519, 467, 476 **467, 476, 519, 528**
3. Blythe has 458 stickers in her collection. To the nearest ten, how many stickers does she have? **460 stickers**
4. Jamie's Aunt Cora lives 627 miles away. His Aunt Rachel lives 608 miles away. Which aunt lives closer to Jamie? **Aunt Rachel**

Choose the letter of the correct answer.

5. There are 576 students in Lydia's school. About how many students are there in Lydia's school?
A 500 (B) 600 C 700 D 800
6. Between what two hundreds is 550? What hundred does it round to?
F 500 and 600; 500
G 400 and 500; 500
H 400 and 500; 600
(J) 500 and 600; 600
7. Fiona has 6 more cousins than Michael, who has 5 cousins. Sheila has 3 fewer cousins than Fiona has and 2 fewer cousins than Bridget has. How many cousins does Bridget have?
A 2 B 5 (C) 10 D 11
8. Which group of numbers is in order from least to greatest?
F 2,568; 2,946; 3,109; 3,004
G 3,004; 3,109; 2,946; 2,568
H 2,946; 3,109; 2,568; 3,004
(J) 2,568; 2,946; 3,004; 3,109
9. **Write About It** In Problem 6, how did you decide how to round 550?
Possible answer: When a number is exactly between two hundreds, you round to the greater hundred, so I rounded to 600.

Problem Solving PS17

3 PRACTICE

Guided Practice

Do Check Exercises 1–6 with your students. Identify students who are having difficulty and choose appropriate lesson resources to provide assistance.

COMMON ERROR ALERT

If students are having difficulty visualizing numbers without a number line, have them practice writing the number they are rounding and the tens it is between before moving on to the hundreds it is between.

Independent Practice

Note that Exercise 28 is a **multistep or strategy problem.** Assign Exercises 7–30.

ALGEBRAIC THINKING Encourage students to solve Exercise 28 by comparing the values in the hundreds place for each type of animal. Then ask them to decide which two digits, when added, are less than the remaining digit.

4 ASSESS

Summarize the lesson by having students:

DISCUSS What happens when you round 964 to the nearest hundred? Explain. 964 rounds to 10 hundreds, or 1,000.

WRITE Describe how you would decide whether to round $661 to $600 or to $700. $661 is more than halfway to $700, so round to $700.

LESSON QUIZ

Transparency 3.5

Round to the nearest hundred and the nearest ten.

1. 108 100, 110 2. 684 700, 680
3. 251 300, 250 4. 345 300, 350

Lesson 3.6

Round to Nearest 1,000

Lesson Planning

Objective To use rounding rules to round to the nearest 1,000

NCTM Standards

1. Number and Operations
5. Data Analysis and Probability
6. Problem Solving
7. Reasoning and Proof
8. Communication
9. Connections
10. Representation

Math Background

These ideas will help students understand rounding to the nearest 1,000.

- 3- and 4-digit numbers can be rounded to the nearest 10, 100, or 1,000.
- When rounding to the nearest 1,000, look at the digit in the hundreds place. If the digit is less than 5, the digit in the thousands place stays the same. If the digit in the hundreds place is 5 or more, the thousands place increases by 1.

Warm-Up Resources

Number of the Day

The number of the day is 365, the number of days in a year. Round it to the nearest ten and the nearest hundred. 370, 400

Daily Facts Practice

Have students practice subtraction facts by completing Set D of *Teacher's Resource Book*, p. TR85.

Transparency 3.6

Problem of the Day

Sue wrote all the numbers that can be rounded to 60. Lee wrote all the numbers that can be rounded to 600. Who wrote more numbers? Lee How many more numbers? 90

Solution Problem of the Day tab, p. PD3

Intervention and Extension Resources

Alternative Teaching Strategy

ESOL/ESL

Help students **understand rounding to the nearest 1,000**. Students may round 2,548 to 2,000 because they focus on the tens place instead of the hundreds place. Help students focus on the hundreds digit when rounding to the nearest thousand by having them underline the digit in the hundreds place. Then review rounding with these numbers: 2,4̲90; 6,5̲03; 8,0̲99; 5,5̲42; 3,4̲87. 2,000; 7,000; 8,000; 6,000; 3,000

VISUAL

VISUAL/SPATIAL

Multistep and Strategy Problems

The following multistep or strategy problem is provided in Lesson 3.6:

Page	Item
53	22

Special Needs

MATERIALS *For each pair* 9 cards

Have students **round 2-digit numbers with 5 ones, 3-digit numbers with 5 tens, and 4-digit numbers with 5 hundreds.**

Provide students with cards with these numbers: 15, 35, 75; 254, 659, 853; 1,500, 6,594, 3,501.

Have partners take turns

- drawing numbers.
- finding the 5 ones, 5 tens, or 5 hundreds.
- rounding each number to the nearest 10, 100, or 1,000.

Check students' work.

VISUAL

BODILY/KINESTHETIC

Early Finishers

MATERIALS *For each group* poster board

Invite students to **make a poster showing the rounding rules**. Have students illustrate examples of applying the rules when rounding to the nearest 10, 100, and 1,000. Challenge students to make their posters helpful, clear, and interesting. Check students' work.

VISUAL

BODILY/KINESTHETIC

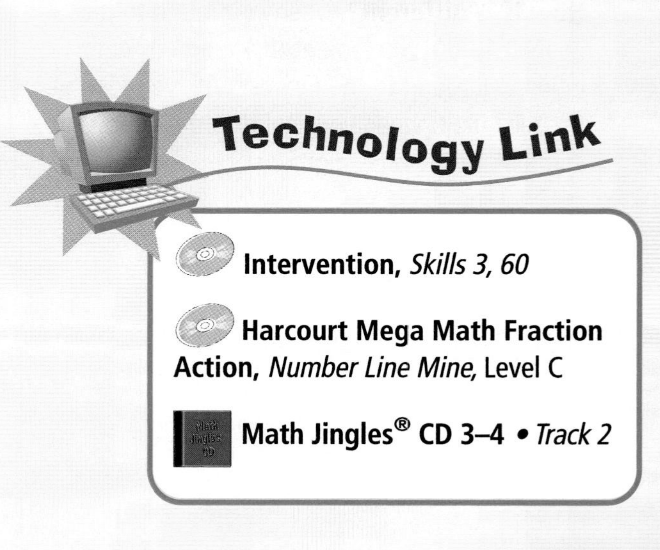

Technology Link

Intervention, *Skills 3, 60*

Harcourt Mega Math Fraction Action, *Number Line Mine,* Level C

Math Jingles® CD 3–4 • *Track 2*

Lesson 3.6 Organizer

Objective To use rounding rules to round to the nearest 1,000

1 INTRODUCE

Quick Review provides review of prerequisite skills.

Why Learn This? You can use rounding to 1,000 to estimate the number of people attending concerts or sporting events. *Share the lesson objective with students.*

2 TEACH

Guided Instruction

- *Direct students' attention to the number line in the Learn section.*
  Reasoning Why does the number line use thousands and not other values, such as hundreds and tens? Possible answers: You need to find an answer that is expressed in thousands.
  Name three ways you can round 4,405. to the nearest ten; to the nearest hundred; to the nearest thousand
- *Check students' understanding of Examples A and B.*
  How are 4,405 and 2,641 different when rounded to the nearest 1,000? In 4,405, the thousands digit, 4, stays the same. In 2,641 the thousands digit, 2, increases to 3.
  How is rounding to the nearest 1,000 like rounding to the nearest 100 or 10? Possible answer: You look at the digit to the right of the place you are rounding. If it is less than 5, the digit in the rounding place stays the same. If it is 5 or more, the digit increases by 1.
  How is it different? When you round to the nearest 1,000, you look at the hundreds digit; when you round to the nearest 100, you look at the tens digit; when you round to the nearest 10, you look at the ones digit.

LESSON 6

Round to Nearest 1,000

Quick Review

Round to the nearest ten.

1. 52 — 50
2. 15 — 20
3. 27 — 30
4. 68 — 70
5. 76 — 80

Learn

ABOUT HOW MANY? When the Bronx Zoo in New York City first opened in 1899, it had 843 animals. In the spring of 2002, the Bronx Zoo had 4,405 animals.

To the nearest thousand, how many animals are in the zoo?

4,405

4,000 — 4,500 — 5,000

4,405 is closer to 4,000 than to 5,000.
4,405 rounds to 4,000.

So, there are about 4,000 animals in the zoo.

You can use rounding rules to round numbers.

Examples

A Round 2,641 to the nearest *thousand*.

2,641
↑

Look at the hundreds digit. Since $6 > 5$, the 2 thousands digit rounds to 3 thousands. So, 2,641 rounds to 3,000.

B Round 2,641 to the nearest *hundred*.

2,641
↑

Look at the tens digit. Since $4 < 5$, the 6 hundreds digit stays the same. So, 2,641 rounds to 2,600.

Rounding Rules

- Find the place to which you want to round.
- Look at the digit to its right.
- If the digit is less than 5, the digit in the rounding place stays the same.
- If the digit is 5 or more, the digit in the rounding place increases by 1.

52

Reteach 3.6

Round to Nearest 1,000

Rounding to the nearest thousand is just like rounding to the nearest ten and hundred.

The population of Cassandra's town is 6,643.
Is the population about 6,000 or 7,000?

Pop.
6,643

You are rounding to thousands, so look at the hundreds digit. Is it less than or greater than 5?
Greater; so, you would round 6,643 to 7,000.
The population is about 7,000.

Akira's town has a population of 5,237. How can you round that number to the nearest hundred?

Pop.
5,237

You are rounding to hundreds, so look at the tens digit. Is it less than or greater than 5?
Less; so, you would round 5,237 to 5,200.
The population is about 5,200.

Round to the nearest hundred. Underline the digit that helps you know which way to round.

1. 369 400
2. 135 100
3. 2,187 2,200
4. 3,746 3,700
5. 9,260 9,300
6. 1,742 1,700
7. 7,309 7,300
8. 5,691 5,700

Round to the nearest thousand. Underline the digit that helps you know which way to round.

9. 6,809 7,000
10. 3,579 4,000
11. 2,469 2,000
12. 1,333 1,000
13. 7,168 7,000
14. 5,702 6,000
15. 9,088 9,000
16. 4,625 5,000

RW18 Reteach

Practice 3.6

Round to Nearest 1,000

Round to the nearest thousand.

1. 2,345 2,000
2. 1,765 2,000
3. 8,821 9,000
4. 6,109 6,000
5. 3,001 3,000
6. 3,679 4,000
7. 9,134 9,000
8. 4,556 5,000
9. 7,733 8,000

Round to the nearest thousand, the nearest hundred, and the nearest ten.

10. 3,490 3,000 3,500 3,490
11. 7,509 8,000 7,500 7,510
12. 2,565 3,000 2,600 2,570
13. 3,115 3,000 3,100 3,120
14. 1,350 1,000 1,400 1,350
15. 8,999 9,000 9,000 9,000
16. 6,784 7,000 6,800 6,780
17. 2,288 2,000 2,300 2,290
18. 5,501 6,000 5,500 5,500

Mixed Review

Write the value of the underlined digit.

19. 4,523 20
20. 13,886 10,000
21. 60,600 600
22. 327 300
23. 687,235 7,000
24. 22,789 20,000

Solve.

25. $65 - 48 = 17$
26. $86 - 58 = 28$
27. $49 + 13 = 62$
28. $92 - 34 = 58$

PW18 Practice

Check

1. Explain how you would use the rounding rules to round 3,728 to the nearest thousand. Look at the hundreds digit. Since 7 > 5, 3 thousands rounds to 4 thousands. 3,728 rounds to 4,000.

Round to the nearest thousand.

2. 6,427 6,000
3. 2,500 3,000
4. 4,526 5,000
5. 1,670 2,000

Practice and Problem Solving

Extra Practice, page 54, Set E

Round to the nearest thousand.

6. 8,312 8,000
7. 4,500 5,000
8. 674 1,000
9. 9,478 9,000
10. 1,611 2,000
11. 5,920 6,000
12. 2,543 3,000
13. 4,444 4,000

Round each to the nearest thousand, the nearest hundred, and the nearest ten.

14. 3,581 4,000; 3,600; 3,580
15. 6,318 6,000; 6,300; 6,320
16. 2,350 2,000; 2,400; 2,350
17. 8,914 9,000; 8,900; 8,910
18. 4,624 5,000; 4,600; 4,620
19. 5,337 5,000; 5,300; 5,340
20. 1,273 1,000; 1,300; 1,270
21. 2,845 3,000; 2,800; 2,850

USE DATA For 22–23, use the table.

22. Round the weights of the giraffe and rhinoceros to the nearest thousand pounds. About how many giraffes would it take to equal the weight of the rhinoceros? 3,000 lb; 9,000 lb; about 3 giraffes
23. **Write About It** Tell how to round the weight of the hippopotamus to the nearest thousand, hundred, and ten. Check students' explanations; 4,000 lb; 4,400 lb; 4,410 lb
24. **FAST FACT** • SCIENCE Asian elephants weigh less than African elephants. One Asian elephant weighed 7,586 pounds. What is 7,586 rounded to the nearest thousand? 8,000

HEAVIEST LAND MAMMALS

Animal	Weight in Pounds
African elephant	11,023
Indian rhinoceros	8,818
Hippopotamus	4,409
Giraffe	2,646

Getting Ready for the EOG Test

25. Marla's dresser is 46 inches tall. Her desk is 28 inches tall. How tall could her bookcase be? C

A 20 inches
B 24 inches
C 34 inches
D 54 inches

Dresser   Bookcase   Desk

North Carolina Standards 1.01 Develop number sense for whole numbers through 9,999.

Challenge 3.6

Round and Round We Go!

Look at the table at the bottom of the page. Round the three-digit numbers to the nearest hundred and the four-digit numbers to the nearest thousand. Then find the heart that has the rounded number. Use the code in the table to color it.

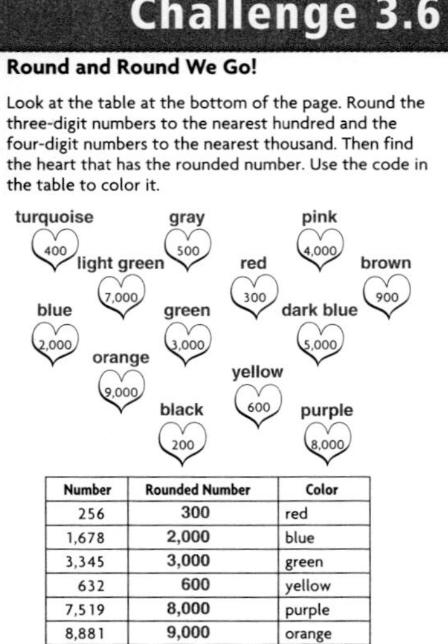

Number	Rounded Number	Color
256	300	red
1,678	2,000	blue
3,345	3,000	green
632	600	yellow
7,519	8,000	purple
8,881	9,000	orange
853	900	brown
3,780	4,000	pink
472	500	gray
187	200	black
4,574	5,000	dark blue
6,961	7,000	light green
390	400	turquoise

CW18 Challenge

Problem Solving 3.6

Round to Nearest 1,000

Understand ▸ Plan ▸ Solve ▸ Check

Write the correct answer.

1. What two hundreds is 650 between? 600 and 700
2. Round 4,348 to the nearest thousand. 4,000
3. There are 6,780 books in the school library. About how many books are there? 7,000 or 6,800
4. The four best spelling scores in Max's class were 212, 202, 226, and 222. Put the scores in order from greatest to least. 226, 222, 212, 202

Choose the letter of the correct answer. Use the table for 5–6.

CANDIDATE	NUMBER OF VOTES
Burns	3,445
McCarty	3,742
Watters	4,656
Volante	4,389

5. How many votes did McCarty get, rounded to the nearest hundred?
A 3,000 (C) 3,700
B 3,500 D 3,800
6. Which two candidates received over 4,000 votes?
F Watters, Burns
G Burns, Volante
(H) Watters, Volante
J McCarty, Volante
7. Which number can be rounded to 7,000?
A 6,445 C 7,597
(B) 7,034 D 7,612
8. **Write About It** In Problem 2, which digit helps you find the closer thousand?
Possible answer: The thousands digit tells me the number is between 4,000 and 5,000; the hundreds digit tells me that the thousands digit stays the same.

PS18 Problem Solving

3 PRACTICE

Guided Practice

Do Check Exercises 1–5 with your students. Identify students who are having difficulty and choose appropriate lesson resources to provide assistance.

Independent Practice

Note that Exercise 23 is a **multistep or strategy problem.** Assign Exercises 6–24.

SCAFFOLDED INSTRUCTION Use the prompts on Transparency 3 to guide instruction for the multistep or strategy problem in Exercise 23.

Transparency 3

For Exercises 14–21, encourage students to do all the thousands first, then all the hundreds, and then all the tens. Remind them that when they are finished, they need to have three answers for each item.

4 ASSESS

Summarize the lesson by having students:

DISCUSS What steps do you follow when rounding a number to the nearest thousand? Find the thousands place. Then look at the digit in the hundreds place. If this digit is less than 5, the thousands digit stays the same. If this digit is 5 or more, the digit in the thousands place increases by 1.

WRITE Describe and draw a number line to show how you round 5,432 to the nearest thousand. Check students' work.

LESSON QUIZ

Round each to the nearest thousand, the nearest hundred, and the nearest ten.

1. 8,119 8,000; 8,100; 8,120
2. 6,932 7,000; 6,900; 6,930
3. 3,549 4,000; 3,500; 3,550
4. 5,504 6,000; 5,500; 5,500

CHAPTER 3 Extra Practice

Purpose To provide extra practice for the skills presented in this chapter

The blue page references in each set of exercises refer to the lesson pages where each skill is taught.

Internet Resources

Visit THE LEARNING SITE at **www.harcourtschool.com** for a listing of practice activities.

Extra Practice

Set A (pp. 40–41)

For 1–2, choose a benchmark of 10, 100, or 500 to estimate.

1. the number of pieces in a small bag of dog food **500**
2. the number of teeth in your mouth **10**
3. There are 25 students in Ken's third-grade class. There are 4 third-grade classes. About how many students are in the third grade? **about 100 students**

Set B (pp. 42–45)

Compare the numbers. Write <, >, or = for each ●.

1. 400 ● 12 >
2. 646 ● 600 >
3. 741 ● 741 =
4. 57 ● 75 <
5. 4,701 ● 4,071 >
6. 10,313 ● 10,515 <

Set C (pp. 46–47)

Write the numbers in order from least to greatest.

1. 124; 562; 347 **124; 347; 562**
2. 102; 89; 157 **89; 102; 157**
3. 1,466; 1,365; 1,988 **1,365; 1,466; 1,988**

Write the numbers in order from greatest to least.

4. 42,218; 43,010; 42,115 **43,010; 42,218; 42,115**
5. 610,100; 615,010; 605,310 **615,010; 610,100; 605,310**

Set D (pp. 50–51)

Round to the nearest hundred and the nearest ten.

1. 414 **400; 410**
2. 888 **900; 890**
3. 502 **500; 500**
4. 635 **600; 640**
5. 157 **200; 160**
6. 733 **700; 730**
7. 374 **400; 370**
8. 498 **500; 500**

Set E (pp. 52–53)

Round to the nearest thousand.

1. 3,345 **3,000**
2. 8,866 **9,000**
3. 5,533 **6,000**
4. 6,500 **7,000**
5. 9,457 **9,000**
6. 1,168 **1,000**
7. 7,662 **8,000**
8. 2,220 **2,000**

Review/Test

✓ CHECK VOCABULARY AND CONCEPTS

Choose the best term from the box.

greatest to least
compare
round

1. You can use <, >, or = to __?__ numbers. (p. 42) **compare**
2. One way to estimate is to __?__ numbers. (p. 50) **round**

Suppose you want to round 371 to the nearest hundred. (pp. 50–51)

3. Which hundreds is 371 between? **300 and 400**
4. Which hundred is 371 closer to? **400**

✓ CHECK SKILLS

Compare the numbers. Write <, >, or = for each ●. (pp. 42–45)

5. 532 ● 523 **>**
6. 23,246 ● 32,325 **<**
7. 7,583 ● 7,583 **=**

Write the numbers in order from least to greatest. (pp. 46–47)

8. 143, 438, 92 **92, 143, 438**
9. 7,304; 7,890; 7,141 **7,141; 7,304; 7,890**
10. 23,256; 23,161; 23,470 **23,161; 23,256; 23,470**
11. Round 85 to the nearest ten. (pp. 50–51) **90**
12. Round 824 to the nearest hundred. (pp. 50–51) **800**
13. Round 3,721 to the nearest thousand and hundred. (pp. 52–53) **4,000; 3,700**

✓ CHECK PROBLEM SOLVING

USE DATA For 14–15, use the bar graph. (pp. 48–49)

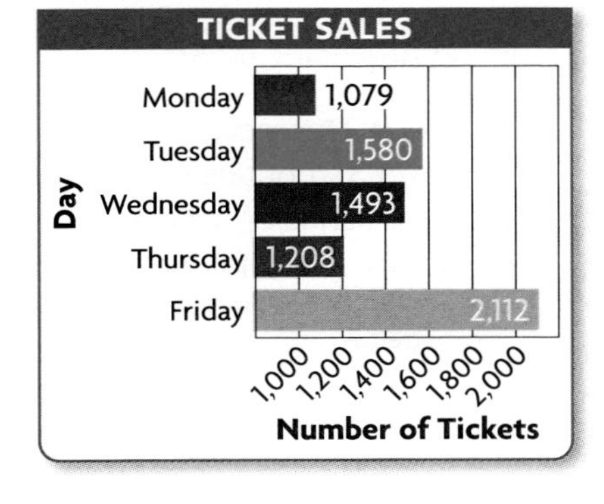

14. On which night was the number of tickets sold greater than the number sold on Monday but less than the number sold on Wednesday? **Thursday**
15. On which night was the number of tickets sold less than the number sold on Friday but greater than the number sold on Wednesday? **Tuesday**

Review/Test

Purpose To check understanding of concepts, skills, and problem solving presented in Chapter 3

Using the Page

The Chapter 3 Review/Test can be used as a **review** or a **test**.

- Items 1–4 check understanding of concepts and new vocabulary.
- Items 5–13 check skill proficiency.
- Items 14–15 check students' abilities to choose and apply problem solving strategies to real-life comparing or ordering problems.

Suggest that students place the completed Chapter 3 Review/Test in their portfolios.

Using the Assessment Guide

- Multiple-choice format of Chapter 3 Posttest—See *Assessment Guide*, pp. AG17–18.
- Free-response format of Chapter 3 Posttest—See *Assessment Guide*, pp. AG19–20.

Using Student Self-Assessment

The How Did I Do? survey helps students assess what they have learned and how they learned it. This survey is available as a copying master in *Assessment Guide*, p. AGxvii.

Chapter 3 Test, page 1

Choose the correct answer.

1. What is 585 rounded to the nearest hundred?
   (A) 600 C 580
   B 590 D 500
2. Choose a benchmark of 10, 100, 500, or 1,000 to ESTIMATE the number of players on a hockey team.
   F 1,000 H 100
   G 500 (J) 10
3. Which group of numbers is in order from **least** to **greatest**?
   A 5,592; 5,583; 4,785
   B 5,583; 5,592; 4,785
   C 4,785; 5,592; 5,583
   (D) 4,785; 5,583; 5,592
4. Which number is **greater than** 7,560?
   F 7,559 H 7,000
   G 7,060 (J) 7,801
5. What is 14,781 rounded to the nearest thousand?
   (A) 15,000 C 14,000
   B 14,700 D 10,000
6. Choose a benchmark of 10, 50, 100, or 1,000 to ESTIMATE the number of peanuts in a large bag.
   F 10 (H) 100
   G 50 J 1,000
7. Which group of numbers is in order from **least** to **greatest**?
   A 737,869; 733,457; 825,789
   B 737,869; 825,789; 733,457
   C 825,789; 733,457; 737,869
   (D) 733,457; 737,869; 825,789
8. Which group of numbers is in order from **greatest** to **least**?
   F 38,621; 38,479; 38,512
   (G) 38,621; 38,512; 38,479
   H 38,512; 38,479; 38,621
   J 38,479; 38,512; 38,621
9. What is 7,356 rounded to the nearest thousand?
   A 8,000 C 7,300
   B 7,400 (D) 7,000
10. What is the **greatest** place-value position in which the digits of 8,451 and 8,579 are different?
    F ones (H) hundreds
    G tens J thousands
11. What is 355 rounded to the nearest ten?
    A 300 (C) 360
    B 350 D 400
12. The height of Grand Teton is 13,766 ft. What is this number rounded to the nearest thousand?
    (F) 14,000 H 13,600
    G 13,700 J 10,000

Go On

Chapter 3 Test, page 2

13. What is 7,642 rounded to the nearest hundred?
    A 8,000 C 7,640
    B 7,700 (D) 7,600
14. Which is a true statement?
    (F) 4,895 > 4,871
    G 4,356 < 3,789
    H 389 > 398
    J 861 < 816

For 15–17, use the bar graph.

U.S. NATIONAL PARKS
Badlands 244,000
Big Cypress 729,000
Craters of the Moon 714,000
Dismal Swamp 107,000
Shenandoah 199,000
Parks
0 100,000 200,000 300,000 400,000 500,000 600,000 700,000 800,000
Size in Acres

15. Which two national parks are **smaller** than Badlands?
    A Big Cypress and Shenandoah
    B Dismal Swamp and Big Cypress
    C Craters of the Moon and Shenandoah
    (D) Shenandoah and Dismal Swamp
16. Which two parks have areas **greater than** 300,000 acres?
    F Big Cypress and Badlands
    G Dismal Swamp and Big Cypress
    (H) Big Cypress and Craters of the Moon
    J Badlands and Dismal Swamp
17. Which lists these parks in order from **least** to **greatest**?
    (A) Dismal Swamp, Shenandoah, Badlands
    B Big Cypress, Craters of the Moon, Badlands
    C Shenandoah, Dismal Swamp, Badlands
    D Badlands, Shenandoah, Dismal Swamp
18. Which number is **less than** 383,064?
    F 383,064 H 384,000
    G 383,100 (J) 383,060

For 19–20, use the table.

BASEBALL GAME ATTENDANCE	
Day	Number of People
Friday	8,749
Saturday	9,322
Sunday	4,886

19. To the nearest hundred, how many people attended the baseball game on Friday?
    A 9,000 (C) 8,700
    B 8,750 D 8,000
20. To the nearest thousand, how many people attended the games on Saturday and Sunday altogether?
    F 10,000 (H) 14,000
    G 13,000 J 15,000

Stop

Getting Ready for the EOG Test

Chapters 1–3

Using the Pages

These pages may be used to help students get ready for the North Carolina EOG Test. The test items are written in the same style and arranged in the same format as those on the EOG Test.

The pages are cumulative. They cover the standards from the North Carolina Mathematics Standard Course of Study that have been taught up to this point in the text or in a previous grade. Each Getting Ready for the EOG Test also reviews the North Carolina mathematics strands shown below.

- Number and Operations
- Measurement
- Geometry
- Data Analysis and Probability
- Algebra

These pages can be assigned at the end of the chapter as classwork or as a homework assignment. You may want to have students use individual recording sheets presented in a multiple-choice (standardized) format. A Test Answer Sheet is available as a blackline master in the *Assessment Guide* (p. AGlii).

You may wish to have students describe how they solved each problem and share their solutions.

Getting Ready for the EOG Test

NUMBER AND OPERATIONS

1. Springfield has three schools. The table shows how many students go to each school. Which list shows the number of students in order from **greatest** to **least**? C

SPRINGFIELD STUDENTS	
School	Number of Students
Central	824
Eastgate	931
Westville	796

A $931 > 796 > 824$
B $796 > 824 > 931$
C $931 > 824 > 796$
D $824 > 796 > 931$

2. When Michael Jordan retired in 2003, he had scored 32,292 points. What is the value of the digit 9 in 32,292? A

A 90
B 900
C 9,000
D 90,000

3. **Explain It** The recycling club collected 37 pounds of newspaper and 14 pounds of aluminum cans. ***About*** how many pounds did the club collect? Explain your estimate.
See page 57.

MEASUREMENT AND GEOMETRY

4. Lilly wants to find how much water a bathtub holds. Which unit of measure should she use? A

A gallon C foot
B pound D mile

5. Mrs. Lang wants to put a fence around her square flower garden. Each side of the garden is 4 feet long. How many feet of fencing does she need? D

A 4 feet C 12 feet
B 8 feet D 16 feet

6. This is Ellie's cat.

About how much does Ellie's cat weigh? C

A 900 pounds
B 90 pounds
C 9 pounds
D 9 ounces

7. **Explain It** Marco found a seashell on the beach. Explain which of these measurements best describes the length of the shell: 3 yards, 3 feet, or 3 inches.
See page 57.

ALGEBRA

TIP **Get the information you need.** See item 8. You need to find the difference between 24 and 27, 27 and 30, and so on to solve this problem.

8. Jacob counts 24, 27, 30, 33, 36, 39. What is a rule for the pattern? **B**

A Count by twos.
B Count by threes.
C Count by fives.
D Count by tens.

9. Anna baked 36 cookies in the morning. In the afternoon, she baked more cookies. When Anna finished, she had a total of 60 cookies. Which number sentence shows how many cookies Anna baked? **B**

A ■ − 36 = 60
B 36 + ■ = 60
C 60 + 36 = ■
D 6 + ■ = 36

10. Explain It Describe a rule that could have been used to form the pattern shown below. Then use the same rule to make a similar pattern. **See below.**

1, 8, 15, 22, 29

DATA ANALYSIS AND PROBABILITY

11. The bar graph below shows the favorite season of some third-grade students.

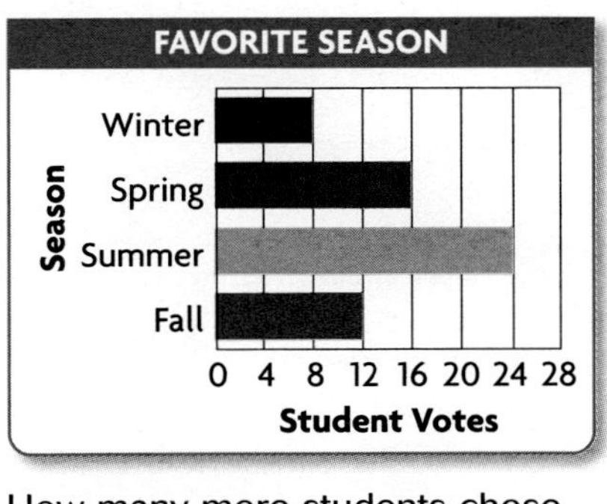

How many more students chose Summer than Fall? **C**

A 4
B 8
C 12
D 14

12. Ethan made this table.

FAVORITE AFTER-SCHOOL ACTIVITY

Activity	Number of Students
Bike Riding	25
In-line Skating	10
Playing Computer Games	15

How many students in all voted? **D**

A 25
B 35
C 40
D 50

13. Explain It If Ethan made a pictograph using the above data, what key could he use? Explain. **See below.**

Chapters 1–3

Item Analysis

You may wish to use the item analysis to determine which North Carolina standards need additional review.

Item	North Carolina Standard	Lesson
1	1.01	3.1
2	1.01	2.6
3	(2) 1.04	Grade 2
4	(2) Goal 2	Grade 2
5	(2) Goal 2	Grade 2
6	(2) Goal 2	Grade 2
7	(2) Goal 2	Grade 2
8	(2) 5.01	Grade 2
9	5.03	1.6
10	(2) Goal 5	Grade 2
11	(2) 4.01	Grade 2
12	(2) 4.01	Grade 2
13	(2) 4.01	Grade 2

SCORING RUBRIC
Explain It

2 Demonstrates a complete understanding of the problem and chooses an appropriate strategy to determine the solution

1 Demonstrates a partial understanding of the problem and chooses a strategy that does not lead to a complete and accurate solution

0 Demonstrates little understanding of the problem and shows little evidence of using any strategy to determine a solution

Explain It • Written Response

3. About 50 pounds; Possible answer: you can use rounding to find the total. 37 rounds to 40, and 14 rounds to 10. 40 + 10 = 50

7. 3 inches; Possible answer: yards and feet are used to measure length, but they are too long to use for a seashell.

10. Add 7; Possible answer: 5, 12, 19, 26, 33

13. Possible answer: each symbol could stand for 5 votes. You can skip-count by fives to 10, 15, and 25.

UNIT 1

It's in the Bag

Pocket Place Value

Purpose To make a place-value game
Materials 20-pocket plastic slide pages, 5 colors of construction paper, square pattern, p. TR184, markers, scissors

Using the Page

Preparing the Materials

- Assemble the materials needed for each student. Plastic slide pages can be found at camera stores or at stores selling office and school supplies. You may wish to cut out the squares for students or provide students with construction paper prepared with cutting lines.

Making the Project

- Make sure students cut 10 squares out of each color of construction paper, since they will be making 5 sets of digit cards. Direct students to write each of the digits 0–9 on each set of squares.

Extending the Project

- Have students work with a partner and use the place-value pockets to compare and order 3-, 4-, and 5-digit numbers. Have one student call out two numbers to compare or three numbers to order from least to greatest or from greatest to least. The partner uses the digit cards and the place-value pocket to compare or order the numbers. Have partners reverse roles. Provide students materials to make additional digit cards as needed.

IT'S IN THE BAG

Pocket Place Value

PROJECT Make and play a place-value game.

Materials
• 1 20-pocket plastic slide page
• 5 colors of construction paper
• Square pattern
• Markers
• Scissors

Directions

1. Use the square pattern. Cut ten $1\frac{1}{2}$-inch squares out of each piece of construction paper. *(Picture A)*

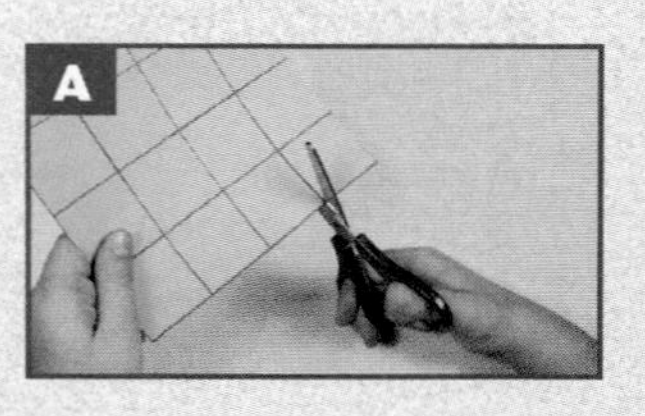

2. Choose one square of each color. Write *Ones, Tens, Hundreds, Thousands,* or *Ten Thousands.* Insert these place-value labels into the pockets in the top row of the slide page. Write a number 1 through 9 on each of the remaining colored squares. With a marker, write a comma between the hundreds and thousands columns in each row. *(Picture B)*

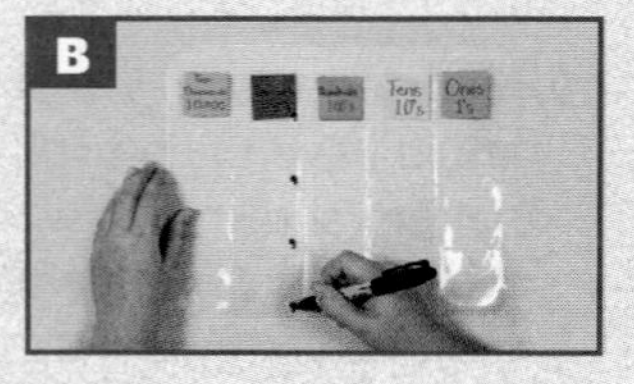

3. Work with a partner. The first student names a place value and a number. The partner finds the card for that number and slides it into the proper pocket. Players take turns naming place values and numbers and finding cards until all pockets are filled. One student reads the numbers aloud. *(Picture C)*

4. Now play the game without the place-value labels.

58 Unit 1 • It's in the Bag

Challenge

Roman Numerals

The ancient Romans used only seven letters to name numbers. These Roman numerals are still used today. You may see them on clocks and buildings.

I	V	X	L	C	D	M
1	5	10	50	100	500	1,000

Place value is not used with Roman numerals. The values of the letters are added or subtracted to find the total value of the numeral.

Here are some rules for finding the value of Roman numerals.

When a letter is repeated, add the value of each letter.

III → 1 + 1 + 1 = 3

When a letter with a lesser value follows a letter with a greater value, add the values of the letters.

XVI → 10 + 5 + 1 = 16

When a letter with a greater value follows a letter with a lesser value, subtract the values of the letters.

XL → 50 − 10 = 40

Talk About It

- Explain how to find the value of XXI.
  The X's repeat, so add the values. 10 + 10 = 20; the I has a lesser value than the X before it, so add the values. 20 + 1 = 21

Try It

Write the value of each Roman numeral.

1. VIII **8** **2.** CX **110** **3.** IX **9** **4.** MMM **3,000**

5. CD **400** **6.** DCLXV **665** **7.** XXXVII **37** **8.** XLV **45**

Challenge

Roman Numerals

Objective **To extend the concepts and skills of Chapters 1–3**

Using the Page

- *Direct students' attention to the table.*
  What do you notice about the Roman numerals? Possible answer: they look like letters of the alphabet rather than numbers.
  Reasoning **What can you do to remember the values of the Roman numerals?** Possible answers: the word *five* contains the letter *V*, whose value is 5. The *C* is similar to the symbol for *cents.* Since 100 cents = 1 dollar, *C* = 100. The slanted line in a tally mark is used to mark off 5. So, you can think of the 2 slanted lines in *X* as 2 fives, or 10.

Try It Before assigning Try It Exercies 1–8, explain that students can use scrap paper to add or subtract the values.

Portfolio Have students record the value of each Roman numeral in their journals. Challenge students to describe a place where they might have seen Roman numerals.

Intervention and Extension Resources

Advanced Learners

Help students **practice finding the value of Roman numerals** by writing the current year using Roman numerals. Explain that Roman numerals are often used to record the year. For example, the copyright date at the end of a movie usually uses Roman numerals. The cornerstone of many buildings contains Roman numerals to tell when the building was completed. After students write the year in Roman numerals, have them write the next two years. Check students' work. Possible answers: MMV, MMVI

LOGICAL/MATHEMATICAL

UNIT 1

Study Guide and Review

Purpose To help students review concepts and skills presented in Chapters 1–3

Using the Pages

✓ Assessment Checkpoint

The Study Guide and Review includes content from Chapters 1–3.

Chapter 1

- **1.1** Algebra: Fact Families
- **1.2** Algebra: Missing Addends
- **1.3** Algebra: Properties
- **1.4** Two-Digit Addition
- **1.5** Two-Digit Subtraction
- **1.6** Problem Solving Skill: *Choose the Operation*

Chapter 2

- **2.1** Hands On: Even and Odd
- **2.2** Place Value: 3-Digit Numbers
- **2.3** Place Value: 4-Digit Numbers
- **2.4** Problem Solving Strategy: *Use Logical Reasoning*
- **2.5** Algebra: Number Patterns
- **2.6** Place Value: 5- and 6-Digit Numbers

Chapter 3

- **3.1** Benchmark Numbers
- **3.2** Algebra: Compare Numbers
- **3.3** Order Numbers
- **3.4** Problem Solving Skill: *Use a Bar Graph*
- **3.5** Round to Nearest 10 and 100
- **3.6** Round to Nearest 1,000

The blue page numbers in parentheses provided with each group of exercises indicate the pages on which the concept or skill was presented.

UNIT 1

Study Guide and Review

VOCABULARY

Choose the best term from the box.

fact family
digits
pattern
inverse operations
benchmark numbers

1. Addition and subtraction are examples of _?_. (p. 2) **inverse operations**
2. The symbols 0, 1, 2, 3, 4, 5, 6, 7, 8, and 9 are called _?_. (p. 22) **digits**
3. An ordered set of numbers or objects is a _?_. (p. 30) **pattern**

STUDY AND SOLVE

Chapter 1

Make fact families.

9 + 5 = 14	5 + 9 = 14
14 − 5 = 9	14 − 9 = 5

Complete. (pp. 2–3)

4. 5 + 8 = 13, so 13 − ■ = 5 **8**
5. 17 − 9 = 8, so ■ + 9 = 17 **8**

Add 2-digit numbers.

$$\begin{array}{r} {}^{1} \\ 27 \\ +34 \\ \hline 61 \end{array}$$

Add the ones. 7 + 4 = 11 Regroup 11 ones as 1 ten, 1 one. Add the tens.

Find the sum. (pp. 8–9)

6. $72 + 18$ = **90**
7. $56 + 29$ = **85**
8. $17 + 43 + 24$ = **84**

Subtract 2-digit numbers.

$$\begin{array}{r} {}^{4\,13} \\ 53 \\ -26 \\ \hline 27 \end{array}$$

Since 6 > 3, regroup 53 as 4 tens 13 ones. Subtract the ones. Subtract the tens.

Find the difference. (pp. 10–11)

9. $63 - 8$ = **55**
10. $77 - 19$ = **58**
11. $50 - 33$ = **17**

Chapter 2

Identify odd and even numbers.

Even numbers have a 0, 2, 4, 6, or 8 in the ones place.
Odd numbers have a 1, 3, 5, 7, or 9 in the ones place.

Tell whether the number is *odd* or *even*. (pp. 20–21)

12. 9 **odd**
13. 23 **odd**
14. 40 **even**

Understand place value.

Ten Thousands	Thousands	Hundreds	Tens	Ones
4	2,	1	0	5

Standard form: 42,105
Expanded form:
40,000 + 2,000 + 100 + 5
Word form:
forty-two thousand, one hundred five

Write in standard form. (pp. 22–27, 32–33)

15. seven hundred twenty-eight **728**

16. two hundred eighty **280**

17. 10,000 + 2,000 + 500 + 20 + 2 **12,522**

18. 300,000 + 2,000 + 20 + 5 **302,025**

Write in expanded form. (pp. 22–27, 32–33)

19. 4,542 **4,000 + 500 + 40 + 2**

20. 571,061 **500,000 + 70,000 + 1,000 + 60 + 1**

Chapter 3

Compare and order numbers.

Write in order from greatest to least.
2,761; 1,793; 5,219

Compare the thousands.
5 > 2 > 1

5,219; 2,761; 1,793

Write <, >, or = for each ●. (pp. 42–45)

21. 739 ● 728 **>**

22. 461 ● 461 **=**

23. 3,125 ● 452 **>**

24. 1,203 ● 1,209 **<**

Write in order from greatest to least. (pp. 46–47)

25. 9,005; 5,009; 5,010 **9,005; 5,010; 5,009**

26. 27,423; 28,432; 29,417 **29,417; 28,432; 27,423**

Round numbers.

Round 4,483 to the nearest thousand.
4,483 is between 4,000 and 5,000.
It is closer to 4,000.
So, 4,483 rounded to the nearest thousand is 4,000.

Round to the nearest hundred. (pp. 50–51)

27. 184 **200**

28. 653 **700**

29. 247 **200**

Round to the nearest thousand. (pp. 52–53)

30. 3,609 **4,000**

31. 1,289 **1,000**

PROBLEM SOLVING PRACTICE

Solve. (pp. 12–13, 28–29)

32. Dan's mother cut out 23 coupons from the newspaper. She used 9 at the grocery store. How many does she have left? **14**

33. Tamara modeled 368 with base-ten blocks. She used 3 hundreds and 18 ones. How many tens did she use? **5 tens**

✓ Assessment Checkpoint

Portfolio

Portfolio Suggestions The portfolio represents the growth, talents, achievements, and reflections of the mathematics learner. Students might spend a short time selecting work samples for their portfolios and completing A Guide to My Math Portfolio from *Assessment Guide*, page AGxix.

You may want to have students respond to the following questions:

- **What new understanding of math have I developed in the past several weeks?**
- **What growth in understanding or skills can I see in my work?**
- **What can I do to improve my understanding of math ideas?**
- **What would I like to learn more about?**

For information on how to organize, share, and evaluate portfolios, see *Assessment Guide*, page AGxviii.

Use the item analysis in the **Intervention** chart to diagnose students' errors. You may wish to reinforce content or remediate misunderstandings by using the text pages or lesson resources.

Unit Test

- Multiple-choice format of Unit 1 Posttest–See *Assessment Guide*, pp. AG21–24.
- Free-Response format of Unit 1 Posttest–See *Assessment Guide*, pp. AG25–28.

Study Guide and Review Intervention • How to Help Options

Items	Text Pages	Reteach and Practice Resources
4–5	2–3	Worksheets for Lesson 1.1
6–8	8–9	Worksheets for Lesson 1.4
9–11	10–11	Worksheets for Lesson 1.5
12–14	20–21	Worksheets for Lesson 2.1
15–20	22–27, 32–33	Worksheets for Lessons 2.2, 2.3, 2.6
21–26	42–47	Worksheets for Lessons 3.2, 3.3
27–31	50–53	Worksheets for Lessons 3.5, 3.6
32–33	12–13, 28–29	Worksheets for Lessons 1.6, 2.4

UNIT 1

Performance Assessment

Purpose To provide performance assessment tasks for Chapters 1–3

Using the Page

- *Have students work individually or in pairs as an alternative to formal assessment.*
- *Use the performance indicators and work samples below to evaluate Tasks A–B.*

See *Performance Assessment* for

- a complete scoring rubric, p. PAx, for this unit.
- additional student work samples for this unit.
- copying masters for this unit.

Portfolio You may suggest that students place completed Performance Assessment tasks in their portfolios.

PERFORMANCE ASSESSMENT

TASK A • TRIP TO THE BEACH

Jeremy and his family are driving from their home to the beach. The map shows the roads they can take and the distances in miles.

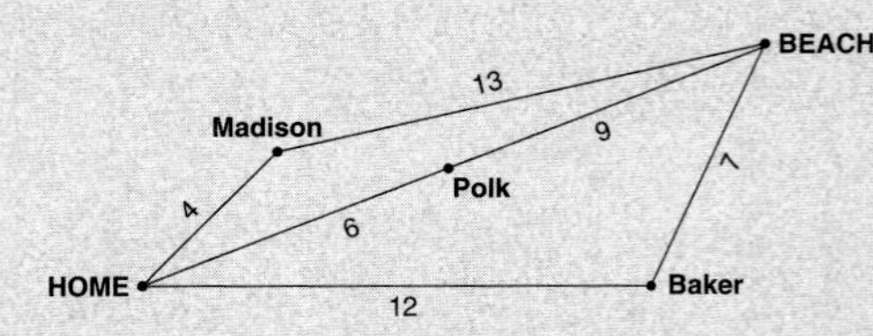

a. Write the name of one city they could drive through. Then find the total distance they will drive if they choose this road. **Possible answer: Madison; 17 miles**

b. Which route is the longest? Which route is the shortest? Explain. **Longest route: through Baker, 19 mi; shortest route: through Polk, 15 mi; To go through Madison is 17 mi, and 19 > 17 > 15.**

TASK B • MAKE A GOOD GUESS

Jar A has 250 jelly beans in it. Abe, Beth, Carla, and Devon guessed the number of jelly beans in Jar B. Beth guessed that there were 1,459. Abe, Carla, and Devon gave clues for their guesses.

a. Copy and complete the table. Use the clues to write possible numbers for the other three guesses. **Possible answers are given.**

JELLYBEAN GUESSES	
Abe	**1,470**
Beth	1,459
Carla	**1,370**
Devon	**1,025**

Abe's clue: My guess is less than 1,500 but greater than Beth's guess.

Carla's clue: My guess is 100 less than Abe's guess.

Devon's clue: My guess rounded to the nearest hundred is 1,000.

b. Write the guesses in order from least to greatest. **Possible answer: 1,025; 1,370; 1,459; 1,470**

62 Unit 1 • Performance Assessment

Performance Indicators

Task A

A student with a Level 3 paper

- ✓ Finds the sum of two numbers.
- ✓ Determines the distance between two locations on a map.
- ✓ Compares numbers to identify the longest and shortest routes.

Task B

A student with a Level 3 paper

- ✓ Completes the table with guesses that match the clues given.
- ✓ Writes the guesses in order from least to greatest.

Work Samples for Task A and Task B

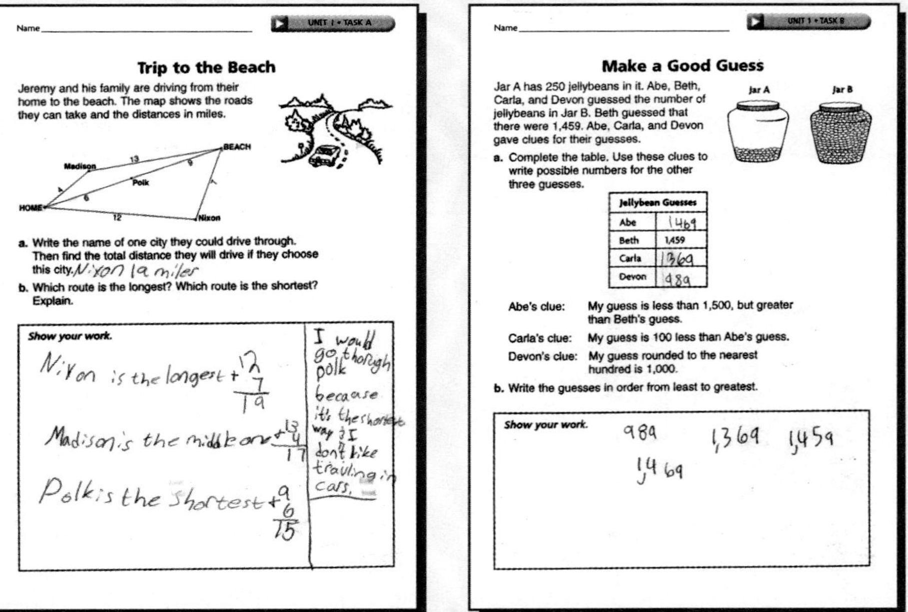
Name ______ UNIT 1 • TASK A

Trip to the Beach

Jeremy and his family are driving from their home to the beach. The map shows the roads they can take and the distances in miles.

a. Write the name of one city they could drive through. Then find the total distance they will drive if they choose this city. Nixon 19 miles

b. Which route is the longest? Which route is the shortest? Explain.

Show your work.

Nixon is the longest 12 + 7 = 19

Madison's the middle one 13 + 4 = 17

Polk is the shortest 9 + 6 = 15

I would go through polk because it's the shortest way & I don't like traveling in cars.

Name ______ UNIT 1 • TASK B

Make a Good Guess

Jar A has 250 jellybeans in it. Abe, Beth, Carla, and Devon guessed the number of jellybeans in Jar B. Beth guessed that there were 1,459. Abe, Carla, and Devon gave clues for their guesses.

a. Complete the table. Use these clues to write possible numbers for the other three guesses.

Jellybean Guesses	
Abe	1469
Beth	1,459
Carla	1369
Devon	989

Abe's clue: My guess is less than 1,500, but greater than Beth's guess.

Carla's clue: My guess is 100 less than Abe's guess.

Devon's clue: My guess rounded to the nearest hundred is 1,000.

b. Write the guesses in order from least to greatest.

Show your work.

989 1,369 1,459 1,469

Level 3 Student shows understanding of the task. All steps are addressed. Computations are correct.

Level 3 Student's work is complete and accurate. Responses show a good understanding of the task. Guesses are listed in order from least to greatest.

Technology Linkup

Number Patterns

Jung started with the number 8 and added 4 a total of 10 times. What patterns do you notice in the ones digits of the sums?

ones digits: 2, 6, 0, 4, 8, 2, 6, 0, 4, 8

All of the digits are even numbers. The digits 2, 6, 0, 4, and 8 repeat.

Start with 8. Add 4.	
12	32
16	36
20	40
24	44
28	48

A calculator can help you explore number patterns. Start with 8 and add 5 at least 10 times. What patterns do you notice in the ones digits of the sums?

STEP 1

Enter the starting number, 8, and add 5.

ON/C 8 + 5 =

STEP 2

Press the equal key 10 times. Record each sum.

Start with 8. Add 5.	
13	23
18	28

STEP 3

Look for a pattern.

Start with 8. Add 5.				
13	23	33	43	53
18	28	38	48	58

The digits 3 and 8 repeat. They follow this pattern: odd, even.

Practice and Problem Solving

Use a calculator to find the number patterns.

1. Start with 7 and add 6 at least 10 times. What patterns do you notice in the ones digits of the sums?
   Possible answer: The digits 3, 9, 5, 1, and 7 repeat.
2. **Write About It** Start with a number from 1–9. Choose a number from 1–9 to add at least 10 times. Record each sum, and describe the patterns you find in the ones digits.
   Possible answer: $6 + 5 = 11$, 16, 21, 26, 31, 36, 41, 46, 51, 56; the numbers 1 and 6 repeat in the ones column.

GO ON-LINE **Multimedia Math Glossary** www.harcourtschool.com/mathglossary

Vocabulary Power Look up *digit* in the Multimedia Math Glossary. Choose a two-digit number. Add a number from 1–9 to it at least 10 times. Record each sum. Describe the pattern.

Possible answer: $21 + 8 = 29$; 37, 45, 53, 61, 69, 77, 85, 93, 101; the numbers 9, 7, 5, 3, and 1 repeat in the ones column.

Technology Linkup

Objective To use a calculator to explore number patterns

Using the Page

- *Direct students' attention to the pattern of even numbers in the ones digits.*
  What do you think the ones digits of the next 10 numbers in the pattern will be? Possible answer: 2, 6, 0, 4, 8, 2, 6, 0, 4, 8

Using the Calculator

Remind students that the calculator they use may not match the one in the lesson. Have students experiment with their calculators to determine the correct key sequence for showing the pattern.

Practice and Problem Solving

For Exercise 1, students will need to add 6 at least 10 times in order for the pattern to appear. Ask: **How many items make up the pattern unit?** 5 items

For Exercise 2, encourage students to look for a pattern when adding odd numbers.

Multimedia Math Glossary

Digits, even, odd, pattern, and all other vocabulary words in this unit can be found in the Harcourt Multimedia Math Glossary.
www.harcourtschool.com/mathglossary

UNIT 1

Problem Solving
in North Carolina

Purpose To provide additional practice for concepts and skills in Chapters 1–3

Using the Page

LIGHTHOUSES

- *Direct students' attention to the table.* **Which lighthouse has a height that has an even number of tens and an even number of ones?** Currituck Beach
- *Direct students' attention to Exercise 1.* **Write in expanded form the height of the tallest lighthouse.** 100 + 90 + 8

Extension Have students research the heights of other lighthouses in the U.S. and write problems based on these data. Have them exchange problems with a classmate and solve. Check students' work.

LIGHTHOUSES

Lighthouses were designed to warn ships of danger where the ocean meets the coastline. A beam of light is magnified through powerful lenses and can be seen from 20 miles away. Some lighthouses send fog warnings by using bells, horns, or whistles.

North Carolina Lighthouses

Lighthouse	Year Built	Height
Bodie Island	1872	156 feet
Cape Hatteras	1870	198 feet
Cape Lookout	1859	169 feet
Currituck Beach	1875	162 feet
Oak Island	1958	169 feet

3. Bodie Island: 160 feet; Cape Hatteras: 200 feet; Cape Lookout: 170 feet; Currituck Beach: 160 feet; Oak Island: 170 feet

USE DATA For 1–3, use the table.

1. Which lighthouse is the shortest? Which is the tallest? **Bodie Island; Cape Hatteras**
2. List the lighthouses in order from newest to oldest. **Oak Island, Currituck Beach, Bodie Island, Cape Hatteras, Cape Lookout**
3. Round the height of each lighthouse to the nearest ten. **See above.**
4. There are 268 steps in the Cape Hatteras Lighthouse. Round the number of steps to the nearest ten. Round to the nearest hundred. **270 steps; 300 steps**

◀ **Oak Island Lighthouse has the most intense beam of light of all lighthouses in the United States.**

OUTER BANKS

The Outer Banks of North Carolina is a chain of islands more than 90 miles long. The islands are called barrier islands because they protect the state's coast from strong Atlantic Ocean waves.

1. Visitors to Cape Hatteras National Seashore saw 267 pilot whales. Round this number to the nearest 100. **300**
2. Wilbur and Orville Wright flew the world's first powered airplane near Kitty Hawk in 1903. Use these clues to find out how far the plane flew. **852 feet**
   - The number of feet is between 850 and 860.
   - The number of feet is less than 855.
   - The ones digit is greater than 0 and less than 3.
   - It is an even number.
3. **REASONING** Four friends collected seashells on Hatteras Island. Use the clues below to find how many shells each friend collected. Copy and complete the table. **Ron: 43; Alex: 70; Janeen: 15**
   - Ron collected 20 more than Shanna.
   - Alex collected 27 more than Ron.
   - Janeen collected 28 fewer than Ron.

▲ **Wilbur and Orville Wright made the first successful powered flight near Kitty Hawk, North Carolina, on December 17, 1903.**

Seashells Collected

Person	Number of Shells
Shanna	23
Ron	■
Alex	■
Janeen	■

Using the Page

OUTER BANKS

- *Direct students' attention to the introductory paragraph.*
  If you flew from one end of the Outer Banks to the other, and then back, about how many miles would you have flown? more than 180 miles
- *Direct students' attention to Exercise 3.*
  Arrange the students in order from the one who collected the most seashells to the one who collected the fewest seashells on Hatteras Island. Alex, Ron, Shanna, and Janeen

Modifying Instruction You may wish to have students use base-ten blocks to model the number of seashells each friend collected in Exercise 3.

Extension Challenge students to research other facts about the Kitty Hawk flight, such as the total distance of the flight, the number of people who witnessed the flight, or the length and weight of the plane. Then have the students write 3 to 4 problems, exchange them with a classmate, and solve. Check students' work.

Teaching Notes

Additional Ideas:

Good Questions to Ask:

Additional Resources:

Notes for Next Time:

UNIT 2

Addition, Subtraction, Money, and Time

Unit at a Glance

EXCERPTS FROM THE RESEARCH

"Algorithms are important in school mathematics because they can help students understand better the fundamental operations of arithmetic and important concepts such as place value and also because they pave the way for learning more advanced topics." (Kilpatrick, Swafford, and Bradford, 2001)

Assessment Options

Assessing Prior Knowledge

Determine whether students have the required prerequisite concepts and skills.

Check What You Know, PE pp. 67, 87, 109, 127

Test Preparation

Provide review and practice for chapter and standardized tests.

Getting Ready for the EOG Test, PE pp. 69, 71, 73, 79, 81, 84–85, 89, 91, 95, 97, 101, 106–107, 113, 117, 119, 121, 124–125, 131, 133, 135, 137, 141, 146–147

Study Guide and Review, PE pp. 150–151

Formal Assessment

Assess students' mastery of chapter concepts and skills.

Chapter Review/Test, PE pp. 83, 105, 123, 145

Pretest and Posttest Options

Chapter Test, Form A

pp. AG29–30, 33–34, 37–38, 41–42

Chapter Test, Form B

pp. AG31–32, 35–36, 39–40, 43–44

Unit 2 Test • Chapters 4–7

Form A, pp. AG45–48

Form B, pp. AG49–52

Daily Assessment

Obtain daily feedback on students' understanding of concepts.

Quick Review, See the first page of each PE lesson.

Getting Ready for the EOG Test

See the last page of each PE skill lesson.

Number of the Day

See the first page of each TE lesson.

Problem of the Day

See the first page of each TE lesson.

Lesson Quiz

See the *Assess* section of each TE lesson.

Performance Assessment

Assess students' understanding of concepts applied to real-world situations.

Performance Assessment (Tasks A–B), PE p. 152; pp. PA12–13

Student Self-Assessment

Have students evaluate their own work.

How Did I Do?, p. AGxvii

A Guide to My Math Portfolio, p. AGxix

Math Journal

See *Write* in the *Assess* section of each TE lesson and TE pages 68B, 98B, 114B, 118B, 120B, 136B.

Harcourt Assessment System

Make and grade chapter tests electronically.

This software includes:

- **multiple-choice items**
- **free-response items**
- **customizable tests**
- **the means to build your own tests from available items**
- **customizable student and class reports**

Portfolio

Portfolio opportunities appear throughout the Pupil and Teacher's Editions.

Suggested work samples:

Problem Solving Project, TE pp. 108, 126

Write About It, PE pp. 115, 135, 137

Chapter Review/Test, PE pp. 83, 105, 123, 145

AG Assessment Guide **TE** Teacher's Edition **PA** Performance Assessment **PE** Pupil Edition

Correlation to STANDARDIZED TESTS

	LEARNING GOAL	TAUGHT IN LESSONS	CAT/ TERRA NOVA	CTBS/ TERRA NOVA	ITBS FORM A	MAT 8	STANFORD 10	NORTH CAROLINA STANDARDS
4A	To write estimates and sums of two- to four-digit numbers with and without regrouping	4.1. 4.2, 4.3, 4.5	•	•	•	•	•	1.02 1.06
4B	To solve problems by using an appropriate strategy such as *predict and test*	4.4	•	•		•	•	1.06
4C	To write expressions and complete number sentences using addition or subtraction	4.6	•	•	•	•	•	5.04
5A	To write estimates and differences of two- to four-digit numbers with and without regrouping	5.1, 5.2, 5.3, 5.4, 5.5	•	•	•	•	•	1.02 1.06
5B	To solve problems using an appropriate skill such as *estimate or exact answer*	5.6	•	•	•	•	•	1.02
6A	To count amounts of coins and bills and to write equivalent or greater amounts	6.1, 6.3	•	•	•	•	•	1.01, 2.01
6B	To write sums and differences of amounts of money and to make change by counting on	6.4, 6.5	•	•	•	•	•	1.02 and maintains (2) 1.05
6C	To solve problems by using an appropriate strategy such as *make a table*	6.2	•	•		•	•	2.01
7A	To identify the time of day	7.1, 7.2	•	•	•	•	•	Goal 2
7B	To write elapsed times	7.3	•	•	•	•	•	2.01
7C	To use a schedule and a calendar	7.4, 7.5	•	•	•		•	2.01
7D	To solve problems by using an appropriate skill such as *sequence events*	7.6	•	•			•	Goal 2

Technology Links

Harcourt Mega Math CD-ROM Series

The learning activities in this exciting new comprehensive math software series complement, enrich, and enhance the Pupil Edition lessons.

Harcourt Mega Math Correlation

Lesson	Activity/Level	Skill
4.2 & 5.2	Country Countdown, Block Busters, Levels V and W, Y and Z	Addition and Subtraction with Regrouping
4.5 & 5.4	The Number Games, Tiny's Think Tank, Levels B and C	Add and Subtract 3- and 4-Digit Numbers
4.6	Ice Station Exploration, Arctic Algebra, Level B	Algebra: Expressions and Number Sentences
6.1	The Number Games, Buggy Bargains, Levels A and B	Count Bills and Coins
6.4	The Number Games, Buggy Bargains, Level D	Make Change
6.5	The Number Games, Buggy Bargains, Levels E and H	Add and Subtract Money
7.1 & 7.5	Country Countdown, Clock-a-Doodle-Doo, Levels F, I, and J	Use a Calendar, Tell Time
7.3	Country Countdown, Clock-a-Doodle-Doo, Level K; The Number Games, Tiny's Think Tank, Level D	Elapsed Time

The Harcourt Learning Site

www.harcourtschool.com

Visit THE LEARNING SITE at **www.harcourtschool.com** for a variety of activities and resources that can be used to explore, reinforce, practice, and extend the learning of the chapter.

- Multimedia Math Glossary
- Activities and instructional resources
- E-Lab Activities
- Show Me math models

Intervention CD-ROMs

These CD-ROMs help you

- assess prerequisite concepts and skills for each chapter and assess problem-solving at point of use.
- diagnose to determine whether intervention is necessary or if enrichment is appropriate for a concept or skill.
- diagnose to determine whether intervention is necessary for a specific problem-solving strategy or skill.
- prescribe intervention for concepts, skills, and problem-solving strategies and skills.
- provide enrichment for students who mastered the prerequisite concepts and skills.

For the Student

The following technology can be used with students that need more instruction with skills or problem solving, and with students that will benefit from reinforcement, practice, and extension of skills from this chapter.

Intervention CD-ROMs

- Support and enrichment for prerequisite skills
- Support for problem solving

Harcourt Mega Math CD-ROMs

- Reinforcement, practice and extension

Clock-a-Doodle-Doo
Skill Level K

The Harcourt Learning Site
www.harcourtschool.com

- Multimedia Math Glossary
- E-Lab activities
- Show Me math models
- Games and activities

For the Teacher

Intervention CD-ROMs

- Diagnose and prescribe intervention for prerequisite skills.
- Provide enrichment for prerequisite skills.
- Diagnose and prescribe intervention for problem-solving strategies and skills.

Harcourt Mega Math CD-ROMs

- Customize additional practice for each student in your class.
- The leveled activities increase in difficulty as students progress.

The Harcourt Learning Site
www.harcourtschool.com

- Find activities and other resources.

Harcourt Assessment System

This software includes:

- Online test taking and automatic scoring
- A bank of items from which to build tests
- Immediate feedback on students' performance
- Correlation of items to textbook and state standards
- Comprehensive program management and class reporting
- Prescriptive reports

ePlanner

This on-line resource allows you to:

- Customize planning and pacing.
- Select resources for daily instruction.
- Reorder content to meet your state, district, or local needs.

For the Parent

The Harcourt Learning Site
www.harcourtschool.com

Encourage parents to visit the Math section of the Harcourt Learning Site to help them reinforce mathematics vocabulary, concepts, and skills with their children.

- Multimedia Math Glossary
- E-Lab interactive learning experiences
- Show Me math models
- Family Involvement tips and activities

Cross-Curricular Connections

Use these topics to help integrate mathematics into your daily planning.
See the pages indicated to find out more about each topic.

Literature

- ***If You Made a Million*** by David M. Schwartz (Lothrop, Lee and Shepard, 1989), TE p. 66G
- ***Math Counts: Time*** by Henry Pluckrose (Children's Press, 1995), TE p. 66G

Writing

- **Describe a situation,** TE p. 68B
- **Describe subtraction across zeroes,** TE p. 98B
- **Write dictionary entries,** TE p. 102B
- **Describe tables,** TE p. 114B
- **Write word problems,** TE pp. 118B, 120B
- **Write a short story using time vocabulary,** TE p. 132B
- **Write problems about schedules,** TE p. 136B

Science

- **Sea turtles,** PE p. 95

Language Arts/Reading

- **Paraphrase,** TE p. 74B
- **Restate vocabulary definitions,** TE p. 76B
- **Identify number sentences and expressions,** TE p. 80B
- **Compare and contrast number sentences with word sentences,** TE p. 80B
- **Choose important information,** TE p. 102B
- **Use graphic aids,** TE p. 114B
- **Put things in sequence,** TE p. 142B

Social Studies

- **Canine Companions,** PE/TE p. 66
- **Appalachian Trail,** PE/TE p. 86
- **Estimate or find exact mileage,** TE p. 102B
- **Currency production,** PE/TE p. 108
- **Golden dollar coin,** PE/TE p. 113
- **International currency,** TE p. 118B
- **Wrigley Building,** PE/TE p. 126
- **Telling time throughout history,** TE p. 128B
- **Explore world calendars,** TE p. 138B

Reaching All Learners

Differentiated Instruction

PURPOSE To write and identify times as A.M. or P.M.

USING THE ACTIVITY WHEEL Have each student choose one activity to complete independently. *Use after Lesson 7.2.*

*The Activity Wheel provides each student with a choice, according to learning style, for practicing an important skill.

Check students' work.

ACTIVITY WHEEL*

Write 3 times without A.M. or P.M. Then name an activity for each time. Have a classmate match the times to the activities using A.M. or P.M.

Explain the meaning of the abbreviations A.M. and P.M. Look up the meanings in a dictionary or an encyclopedia.

Write a poem describing A.M. and P.M. using the rhythm of the nursery rhyme *Hickory Dickory Dock*. Begin with the same line and change the last word to make a new rhyme: Hickory dickory dilly (or diddly, dolly, tack, and so on).

Literature Connections

These books provide students with ways to explore time and money.

Math Counts: Time by Henry Pluckrose (Children's Press, 1995). Concepts of time, from hours and minutes to weeks and years, are discussed in this colorful book.

- Have students write the times pictured in the book. *Use with Lesson 7.1.*

If You Made a Million by David M. Schwartz (Lothrop, Lee and Shepard, 1989) explores the fascinating world of money.

- Have students use play coins and bills to make equivalent sets for amounts of money mentioned in the book. *Use with Lessons 6.1 and 6.3.*

PRACTICE GAME

Beat the Clock

PURPOSE To read schedules and measure time

MATERIALS *For each group* activity cards, p. TR72; watch or timer with a second hand

ABOUT THE GAME

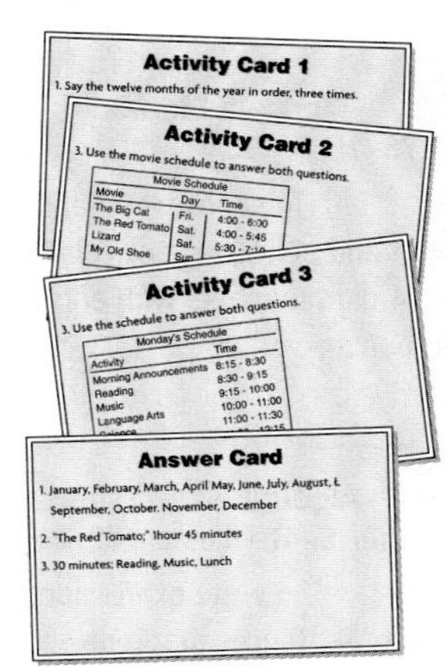

- The game is played by 2 teams with 2 or 3 players each.
- Team A draws a card and performs the activity on the card.
- Team B times the activity and records the elapsed time.
- The two teams reverse roles.
- Teams compare their times after both teams have performed the two activities. The team with the lesser time wins the game. *Use with Lessons 7.4–7.5.*

VISUAL; VISUAL/SPATIAL

Addition

NCTM Standards 2000

1. Number and Operations
Lessons 4.1, 4.2, 4.3, 4.4, 4.5, 4.6
2. Algebra
Lessons 4.3, 4.4, 4.5, 4.6
3. Geometry
4. Measurement
5. Data Analysis and Probability
6. Problem Solving
Lessons 4.1, 4.2, 4.3, 4.4, 4.5, 4.6
7. Reasoning and Proof
Lessons 4.1, 4.2, 4.3, 4.4, 4.6
8. Communication
Lessons 4.1, 4.2, 4.3, 4.4, 4.5, 4.6
9. Connections
Lessons 4.2, 4.3, 4.4
10. Representation
Lessons 4.2, 4.3, 4.4, 4.5, 4.6

Chapter Planner

Getting Ready for Chapter 4 • Assessing Prior Knowledge and INTERVENTION (See PE and TE page 67.)

LESSON	NORTH CAROLINA STANDARDS	PACING	VOCABULARY*	MATERIALS	RESOURCES AND TECHNOLOGY
4.1 Estimate Sums pp. 68–69 **Objective** To estimate sums of 2-, 3-, and 4-digit numbers using rounding and front-end estimation	1.02b *also* 1.06	1 Day	**estimate** **front-end estimation**		Reteach, Practice, Problem Solving, Challenge 4.1 Worksheets Transparency 4.1 **Intervention,** *Skills 5–7, 9–10* (CD or Book)
4.2 Hands On: Addition with Regrouping pp. 70–71 **Objective** To explore adding 3-digit numbers with and without regrouping	1.02a	1 Day (For Lessons 4.2 and 4.3)		*For each group* base-ten blocks	Reteach, Practice, Problem Solving, Challenge 4.2 Worksheets Transparency 4.2 **Intervention,** *Skills 5–7, 9–10* (CD or Book) **Harcourt Mega Math Country Countdown,** *Block Busters*
4.3 Add 3- and 4-Digit Numbers pp. 72–73 **Objective** To add 3-digit and 4-digit numbers with and without regrouping	1.02a				Reteach, Practice, Problem Solving, Challenge 4.3 Worksheets Transparency 4.3 **Intervention,** *Skills 5–7, 9–10* (CD or Book)
4.4 Problem Solving Strategy: Predict and Test pp. 74–75 **Objective** To solve problems using the strategy *predict and test*	1.06	1 Day			Reteach, Practice, Reading Strategy, Challenge 4.4 Worksheets Transparency 4.4 Scaffolded Instruction Transparency 4 Reading Transparency 4 **Intervention • Problem Solving,** *Strategy/Skill 4* (CD or Book)
4.5 Choose a Method pp. 76–79 **Objective** To choose mental math, paper and pencil, or a calculator to add 4-digit numbers with and without regrouping	1.06	2 Days		*For Thinker's Corner* index cards numbered 0–9	Reteach, Practice, Problem Solving, Challenge 4.5 Worksheets Transparency 4.5 **Intervention,** *Skills 5–10* (CD or Book) **Harcourt Mega Math The Number Games,** *Tiny's Think Tank*
4.6 Algebra: Expressions and Number Sentences pp. 80–81 **Objective** To write expressions and number sentences that represent situations and to select operational symbols to make number sentences true	5.04 *also* 1.02	1 Day	**expression** **not equal to ≠**		Reteach, Practice, Problem Solving, Challenge 4.6 Worksheets Transparency 4.6 **Intervention,** *Skills 5–10* (CD or Book) **Harcourt Mega Math Ice Station Exploration,** *Arctic Algebra*

Ending Chapter 4 • **Extra Practice,** p. 82 • **Chapter 4 Review/Test,** p. 83 • **Getting Ready for the EOG Test,** pp. 84–85

* **Boldfaced** terms are the key mathematical terms for the chapter.

Vocabulary Power

Review Vocabulary

To be ready for Chapter 4, students should know the following vocabulary term:

- **sum** (p. 67)—the result of adding numbers

Vocabulary Cards

Have students use the Vocabulary Cards on *Teacher's Resource Book* page TR145 for the key terms in the chapter. The cards can be added to a file of mathematics terms.

front-end estimation

Develop Key Chapter Vocabulary

The **boldfaced** words are the key vocabulary terms in the chapter.

- **estimate** (p. 68)—to find about how much or how many
- **front-end estimation** (p. 68)—a method of estimating in which only the front digits are used
- **expression** (p. 80)—the part of a number sentence that combines numbers and operation signs
- **not equal to ≠** (p. 80)—a relation symbol used to show that two numbers are not equal to each other

Multimedia Math Glossary

GO ON-LINE For vocabulary support, visit **www.harcourtschool.com/mathglossary**

Math Journal

Have students define the key vocabulary terms: *estimate, front-end estimation, expression,* and *not equal to ≠*. Have students use their own words and give an example of each.

MATH Word Work

Objective To reinforce vocabulary concepts
Use after Lesson 4.1.

Materials *For each pair* base-ten blocks

Display a problem on the board and ask students to estimate the sum. Have one student explain how to estimate the sum by using front-end estimation. Have another student explain how to estimate the sum by rounding. Have students use base-ten blocks to find the sum. Then have students compare the estimates to the sum and discuss what they notice.

Front-End Estimation	Rounding	Sum
481 → 400 +309 → +300 700	481 → 500 +309 → +300 800	481 +309 790

Have students repeat the activity with a different addition problem.

Addition

Mathematics Across the Grades

LOOKING BACK • Prerequisite Skills

To be ready for Chapter 4, students should have the following understandings and skills:

- **Addition Facts**—addition of 1-digit numbers
- **Column Addition**—addition of 3 addends
- **2-Digit Addition**—addition of 2-digit numbers

Check What You Know

Use page 67 to determine students' knowledge of prerequisite concepts and skills.

Intervention

Help students prepare for the chapter by using the intervention resources described on TE page 67.

LOOKING AT CHAPTER 4 • Essential Skills

Students will

- estimate sums of 2-, 3-, and 4-digit numbers using rounding and front-end estimation.
- **add 2-, 3-, and 4-digit numbers with and without regrouping.**
- solve problems using the strategy *predict and test.*
- choose an appropriate calculation method to add 3- and 4-digit numbers.
- write expressions that represent situations and select operational symbols to make number sentences true.

Example

Sarah has 492 stickers. Raymond has 697 stickers. How many stickers do Sarah and Raymond have together?

Model	Algorithm
Regrouping in Tens Place	$\begin{array}{r} {}^{1} \\ 492 \\ +697 \\ \hline 1{,}189 \end{array}$ So, together, Sarah and Raymond have 1,189 stickers.

LOOKING AHEAD • Applications

Students will apply what they learn in Chapter 4 to the following new concepts:

- Add and Subtract Money (Chapter 6)
- Add and Subtract Decimals and Money (Chapter 28)
- Connect Addition and Multiplication (Chapter 8)
- Add Fractions (Chapter 26)

Differentiated Instruction

Meeting the Needs of All Learners

Extra Support	Activities for All	Enrichment
Alternative Teaching Strategy TE Lessons 4.1, 4.2, 4.3, 4.4, 4.5, 4.6 **ESOL/ESL** TE Lessons 4.1, 4.2, 4.3, 4.4, 4.5, 4.6 **Special Needs** TE Lessons 4.2, 4.3	**Cross-Curricular Connections** **Language Arts:** TE Lessons 4.5, 4.6 **Reading:** TE Lesson 4.4 **Social Studies:** Chapter Opener **Vocabulary:** TE p. 66I, TE Lesson 4.6, PE/TE p. 67 **Writing:** TE Lesson 4.1	**Advanced Learners** TE Lessons 4.1, 4.2 **Early Finishers** TE Lessons 4.3, 4.4

Combination and Multi-age Classrooms

Grade 2	Grade 3	Grade 4
Skills Trace Across the Grades		
Use the strategies counting on, doubles, doubles plus 1, and make a ten to solve addition sentences; estimate sums; add 2-digit numbers; add 1- and 2-digit numbers using models; identify number expressions.	**Write estimates and sums of 2- to 4-digit numbers with and without regrouping; write expressions and complete number sentences using addition or subtraction.**	Write estimates and sums of 4- to 6-digit numbers; use mental math strategies; use properties of addition; write, evaluate, and interpret addition expressions that contain parentheses.
Instructional Strategies		
Students on this level may require more time to build conceptual understanding. **Assignments** **Grade 3 Pupil Edition** • Have students work in pairs on Lessons 4.2, 4.3, and 4.5. • Have students skip Lessons 4.4 and 4.6. **Grade 2 Pupil Edition**—pages 65–78, 105–118, 121–138, 177–184, and 501–508	Students on this level should be able to complete all the lessons in the Pupil Edition and all the activities in the Teacher's Edition with minimal adjustments. **Assignment** **Grade 3 Pupil Edition**—pages 66–83	Students on this level will probably require less time to build conceptual understanding. **Assignments** **Grade 3 Pupil Edition** • Compact Lessons 4.2 and 4.3. **Grade 4 Pupil Edition**—pages 38–59, 62–83

CHAPTER 4

Addition

Introducing the Chapter

Tell students that addition joins groups. Have students focus on the chart. To estimate the total number of companion dogs that graduated in 2000 and 2001, ask them to round each number to the nearest ten and add. 250 graduates

Using Data

To begin the study of this chapter, have students

- Determine the year in which there were the most canine companion graduates. 2001
- Round the number of total graduates of each year to the nearest ten. 1998: 130; 1999: 110; 2000: 110; 2001: 140

Problem Solving Project

Purpose To use addition to solve a problem

Grouping small groups

Background The American Kennel Club classifies dogs into seven major groups: sporting, hounds, working, terriers, toys, nonsporting, and herding. The Labrador retriever in the photo is a breed in the sporting dog group.

UNDERSTAND • PLAN • SOLVE • CHECK

Share this information:

GROUP	NUMBER OF BREEDS
sporting	24
hounds	22
working	19
herding	15

Have students

- Find the total of sporting and working breeds. 43
- Find the total number of hounds and herding breeds. 37
- Decide which total is greater. 43

Graphing Investigations
Begin Week 4.

CHAPTER 4

Addition

FAST FACT • SOCIAL STUDIES **Dogs were first used as watchdogs, herding dogs, and hunting dogs. Now, more dogs are pets than workers. Some dogs are still trained to help disabled people.**

PROBLEM SOLVING **Look at the chart. How many dogs in all graduated in 2000 and 2001?**

252 dogs

NUMBER OF CANINE COMPANION GRADUATES

66

WHY LEARN MATH? Volunteers in animal shelters need to know how much exercise to give dogs each day. If a dog is walked 30 minutes in the morning, 1 hour at noon, and 30 minutes in the evening, how much exercise does the dog get every day? 2 hours Ask: What other professions are concerned with animal welfare? Possible answers: veterinarian, breeder, zookeeper, pet store worker

Family Involvement Activities

These activities provide:

- Letter to the Family
- Math Vocabulary
- Family Game
- Practice (Homework)

Family Involvement Activities, p. FA13

Check What You Know

Use this page to help you review and remember important skills needed for Chapter 4.

ADDITION FACTS

Add.

1. $2 + 7$ = 9
2. $9 + 4$ = 13
3. $7 + 9$ = 16
4. $3 + 8$ = 11
5. $8 + 7$ = 15

COLUMN ADDITION

Find the sum.

6. $1 + 4 + 6$ = 11
7. $2 + 1 + 9$ = 12
8. $6 + 6 + 6$ = 18
9. $5 + 4 + 7$ = 16
10. $8 + 5 + 2$ = 15

2-DIGIT ADDITION

Add.

11. $21 + 48$ = 69
12. $43 + 35$ = 78
13. $14 + 79$ = 93
14. $53 + 18$ = 71
15. $15 + 45$ = 60

Vocabulary Power

REVIEW

sum [sum] *noun*

The word *sum* comes from the Latin word *summus*, which means "highest." When early Romans added columns of numbers, they wrote the answer at the top. What word for the top of a mountain comes from *summus*? ***summit***

PREVIEW

estimate
front-end estimation
expression
not equal to ≠

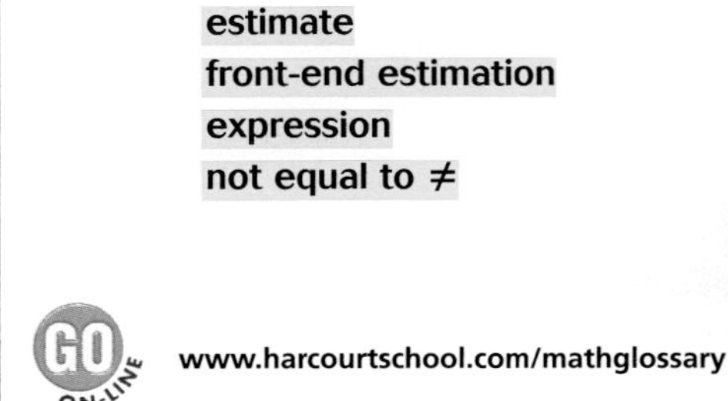

GO ON-LINE www.harcourtschool.com/mathglossary

Assessing Prior Knowledge

Use the **Check What You Know** page to determine whether your students have mastered the prerequisite skills critical for this chapter.

Intervention

- **Diagnose and Prescribe**
  Evaluate your students' performance on this page to determine whether intervention is necessary or if enrichment is appropriate. Options that provide instruction, practice, and a check are listed in the chart below.

CHECK WHAT YOU KNOW RESOURCES

Intervention Copying Masters or CD-ROMs
Enrichment Copying Masters

VOCABULARY POWER

For activities and information about the vocabulary in this chapter, see page 66I.

Were students successful with CHECK WHAT YOU KNOW?

IF . . . NO THEN . . . INTERVENE | **INTERVENTION OPTIONS** | **IF . . . YES THEN . . . ENRICH**

Skill/Items	Missed more than	Intervene with
Addition Facts, 1–5	1	• *Intervention*, Skills 5, 6, 7
Column Addition, 6–10	1	• *Intervention*, Skill 9
2-Digit Addition, 11–15	1	• *Intervention*, Skill 10

Skill/Items	Missed fewer than	Enrich with
Addition Facts, 1–5	2	• *Intervention*, Enrichment p. IN335
Column Addition, 6–10	2	• *Intervention*, Enrichment p. IN336
2-Digit Addition, 11–15	2	• *Intervention*, Enrichment p. IN336

Estimate Sums

Lesson Planning

Objective To estimate sums of 2-, 3-, and 4-digit numbers using rounding and front-end estimation

NCTM Standards

1. Number and Operations
6. Problem Solving
7. Reasoning and Proof
8. Communication

Math Background

Tell students to consider the following when estimating sums of 2-, 3-, and 4-digit numbers.

- There are many estimation strategies. Rounding and front-end estimation are two strategies that are useful for addition.
- Estimating has value in real-life situations and is useful when you don't need to find an exact answer.

Vocabulary

estimate to find about how much

front-end estimation an estimation method that uses only the value of the front digit in each number

Warm-Up Resources

Number of the Day

Julio went to the park at 10 A.M. every day for three days. On the first day, he left the park at 4 P.M.; on the second, at 5 P.M.; and on the third, at 6 P.M. How many hours did Julio spend at the park? 21 hours

Daily Facts Practice

Have students practice subtraction facts by completing Set E of *Teacher's Resource Book*, p. TR85.

Solve a Problem

Problem of the Day

To find the sum of a 2-addend number sentence, Josh thinks of 5 + 5 + 1. For the same number sentence, Augie thinks of 6 + 6 − 1. What is the 2-addend number sentence?
6 + 5 = 11 or 5 + 6 = 11

Solution Problem of the Day tab, p. PD4

Intervention and Extension Resources

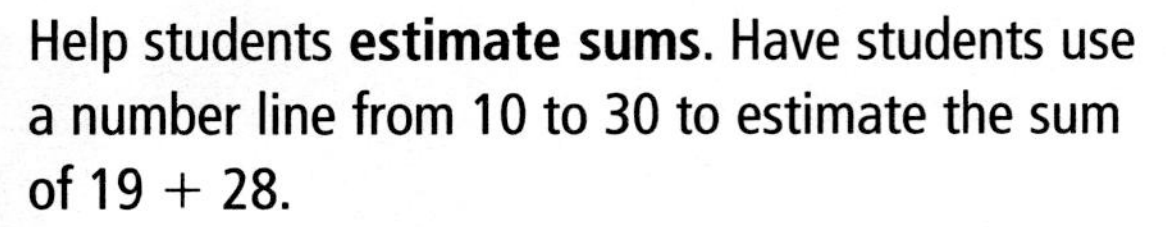

Alternative Teaching Strategy

MATERIALS *For each student* number line, p. TR5

ESOL/ESL

Help students **estimate sums.** Have students use a number line from 10 to 30 to estimate the sum of 19 + 28.

- Have students first find 19 on the number line and then find the nearest ten. 20
- Then have students find 28 on the number line and find the nearest ten. 30
- Ask students to add 20 and 30 to estimate the sum of 19 and 28. 50

VISUAL, KINESTHETIC

VISUAL/SPATIAL

Multistep and Strategy Problems

The following multistep or strategy problem is provided in Lesson 4.1:

Page	Item
69	15

Writing in Mathematics

Have students **write about a situation in their own lives when it would be better to estimate a sum** than to find an exact sum. Answers will vary. Students might suggest estimating the amount of school supplies, such as paper and pencils, that they will need for the school year.

Advanced Learners

Challenge students to work in pairs to **estimate sums.**

- Each student thinks of a number from 1 to 9,999 and writes it on a shared sheet of paper.
- Using front-end estimation, they each mentally add the numbers.
- Then they each record their estimates and compare answers.
- Continue with two or three more problems. Check students' work.

VISUAL

LOGICAL/MATHEMATICAL

Technology Link

Intervention, *Skills 5–7, 9–10*

GO The Harcourt Learning Site www.harcourtschool.com

Lesson 4.1 Organizer

Objective To estimate sums of 2-, 3-, and 4-digit numbers using rounding and front-end estimation

Vocabulary estimate, front-end estimation

1 INTRODUCE

QUICK REVIEW provides review of prerequisite skills.

WHY LEARN THIS? You can use an estimate when you don't need to know an exact number. *Share the lesson objective with students.*

2 TEACH

Guided Instruction

- *Ask students to read the Learn section.*

Give an example of when an exact answer is needed and when an estimate is needed. Possible answer: Exact: when you are buying groceries; Estimate: how long it will take to do homework.

REASONING If you rounded 329 and 174 to the nearest ten, would the sum be the same as when you rounded to the nearest hundred? Explain. Yes; 329 rounds to 330 and 174 rounds to 170. 330 + 170 = 500.

In the rounding example, why is 174 rounded to 200? 7 is more than 5, so the hundreds digit increases to 2.

In the front-end estimation example, why is 174 estimated as 100? You use the front digit and write zeros for the other digits.

Which method gives a closer estimate? Explain. The sum of 174 + 329 is 503, so rounding gives a closer estimate.

Is estimating the money amount in Example A different from estimating the sum in Example B? Explain. Possible answer: Yes; In Example A, you are rounding. In Example B, you are using front-end estimation.

3 PRACTICE

Guided Practice

Do Check Exercises 1–5 with your students. Identify students who are having difficulty and choose appropriate lesson resources to provide assistance.

LESSON 1

Estimate Sums

Quick Review

1. 5 + 25 30
2. 30 + 20 50
3. 70 + 20 90
4. \$4 + \$6 \$10
5. 20 + 55 75

VOCABULARY
estimate
front-end estimation

Learn

MANATEE WINTER HOME Wildlife officers counted 329 manatees living in the warm waters of Florida's Gulf Coast. Along Florida's Atlantic Coast, officers counted 174 manatees. About how many manatees did the wildlife officers count in all?

To find *about* how many, you can estimate.

Example

One Way Use rounding. Round each number to the nearest hundred.

329 → 300
+174 → +200
500

Another Way Use front-end estimation. Add the front digit of each addend. Write zeros for the other digits.

329 → 300
+174 → +100
400

So, both 400 and 500 are reasonable estimates of how many manatees were counted.

More Examples

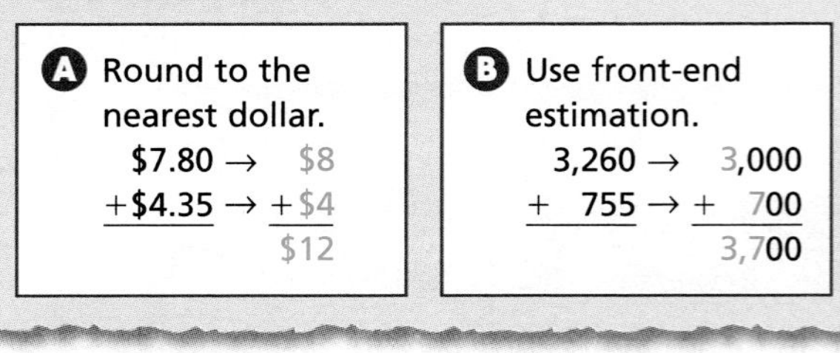

A Round to the nearest dollar.

\$7.80 → \$8
+\$4.35 → +\$4
\$12

B Use front-end estimation.

3,260 → 3,000
+ 755 → + 700
3,700

▲ A manatee spends 5 to 8 hours per day feeding on plants in the water and alo[ng] the shoreline.

MATH IDEA When you do not need an exact answer, you can estimate by using rounding or front-end estimation.

- When you use front-end estimation, will your estimate be greater than or less than the actual sum? When you use rounding? Explain. **Less than; because you add only the front digit of each addend, the estimate will be less than the actual sum. If the digit you are rounding is 5 or greater, your estimate will be greater than the actual sum. If the digit you are rounding is less than 5, your estimate will be less than the actual sum.**

Reteach 4.1

Estimate Sums

You can use rounding or front-end estimation to estimate the sum.

634
+ 691

A. Use rounding.
You are rounding to the nearest hundred, so look at the tens digit of each addend.
Write the rounded addend. Then add.

634 Think: 3 < 5, so round 634 to 600. → 600
+ 691 Think: 9 > 5, so round 691 to 700. → + 700
Estimate → 1,300

B. Use front-end estimation.
You are adding the front digit of each addend.
Write the front digit of each addend. Write zeros for the other digits. Then add.

634 → 600
+ 691 → + 600
Estimate → 1,200

Estimate the sum using rounding and front-end estimation.

	ROUNDING	FRONT-END ESTIMATION
1. 392 + 451	400 + 500 = 900	300 + 400 = 700
2. \$3.12 + \$5.88	\$3.00 + \$6.00 = \$9.00	\$3.00 + \$5.00 = \$8.00
3. 4,278 + 1,190	4,000 + 1,000 = 5,000	4,000 + 1,000 = 5,000

Practice 4.1

Estimate Sums

Use rounding to estimate the sum. **Possible estimates are given.**

1. 236 + 710 **900**
2. \$4.84 + \$2.63 **\$8.00**
3. 6,927 + 1,280 **8,000**
4. \$42.98 + \$25.79 **\$70.00**

Use front-end estimation to estimate the sum.

5. 436 + 517 **900**
6. \$1.82 + \$2.64 **\$3.00**
7. 3,467 + 7,517 **10,000**
8. \$12.52 + \$28.34 **\$30.00**

For 9–11, use the numbers at the right.

533, 38, 1,092, 41, 229, 3,481

9. Choose two numbers whose sum is about 80. **38 and 41**
10. Choose two numbers whose sum is about 4,000. **533 and 3,481, or 1,092 and 3,481**
11. Choose two numbers whose sum is about 700. **533 and 229**

Mixed Review

Write <, >, or = for each ○.

12. 334 (<) 443
13. 4,980 (>) 4,098
14. 814 (=) 814
15. 39,215 (>) 31,872

Write each number in standard form.

16. 60,000 + 2,000 + 500 + 50 **62,550**
17. forty-three thousand, nine hundred sixty-six **43,966**
18. 2,000 + 900 + 40 + 3 **2,943**
19. eight hundred thousand, two hundred eleven **800,211**
20. 700,000 + 3,000 + 200 + 70 + 9 = **703,279**

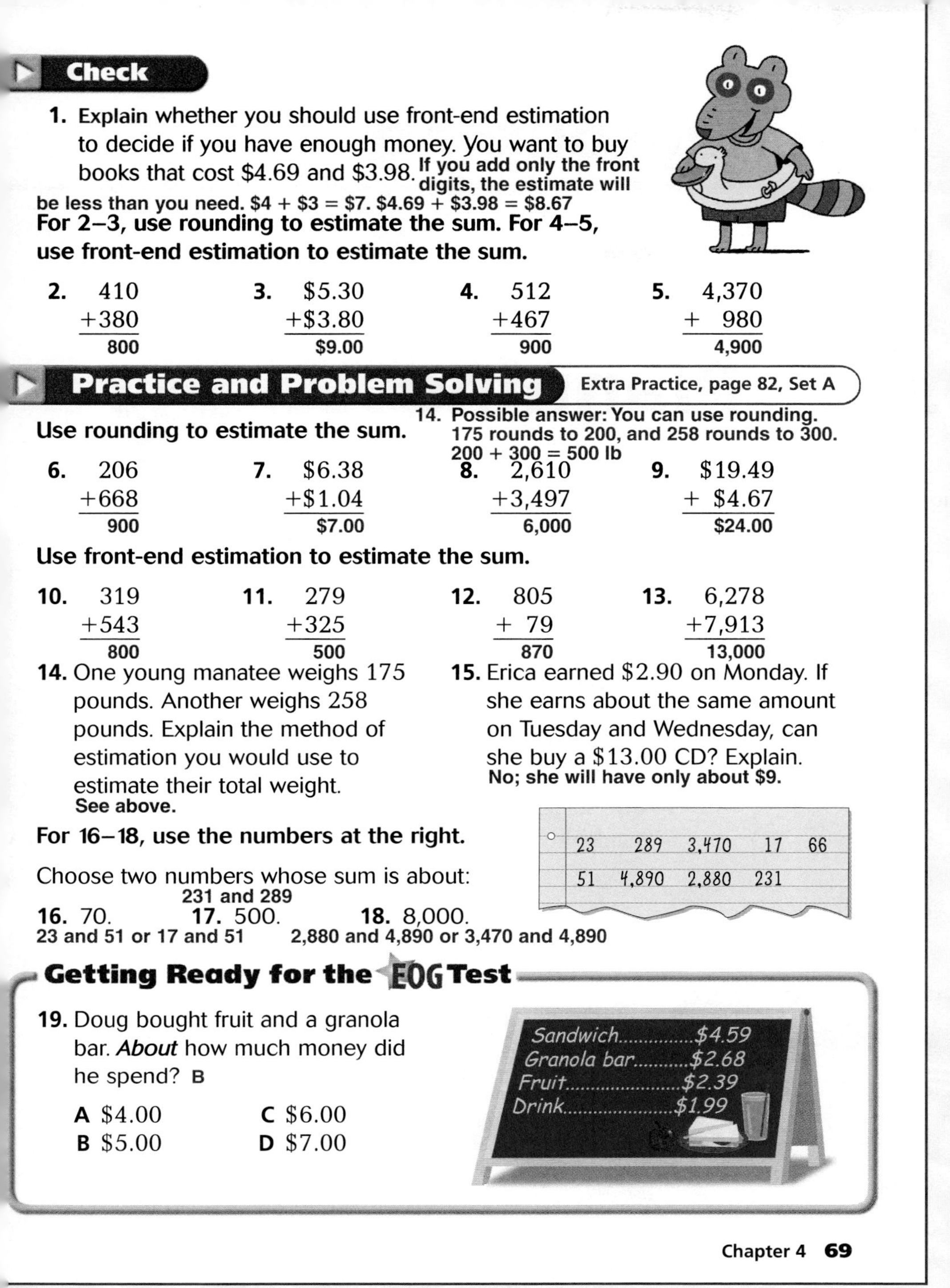

Check

1. Explain whether you should use front-end estimation to decide if you have enough money. You want to buy books that cost $4.69 and $3.98. **If you add only the front digits, the estimate will be less than you need. $4 + $3 = $7. $4.69 + $3.98 = $8.67**

For 2–3, use rounding to estimate the sum. For 4–5, use front-end estimation to estimate the sum.

2. 410 + 380 **800**
3. $5.30 + $3.80 **$9.00**
4. 512 + 467 **900**
5. 4,370 + 980 **4,900**

Practice and Problem Solving

Extra Practice, page 82, Set A

Use rounding to estimate the sum.

6. 206 + 668 **900**
7. $6.38 + $1.04 **$7.00**
8. 2,610 + 3,497 **6,000**
9. $19.49 + $4.67 **$24.00**

Use front-end estimation to estimate the sum.

10. 319 + 543 **800**
11. 279 + 325 **500**
12. 805 + 79 **870**
13. 6,278 + 7,913 **13,000**

14. One young manatee weighs 175 pounds. Another weighs 258 pounds. Explain the method of estimation you would use to estimate their total weight. **See above.**
    14. Possible answer: You can use rounding. 175 rounds to 200, and 258 rounds to 300. 200 + 300 = 500 lb
15. Erica earned $2.90 on Monday. If she earns about the same amount on Tuesday and Wednesday, can she buy a $13.00 CD? Explain. **No; she will have only about $9.**

For 16–18, use the numbers at the right.

23	289	3,470	17	66
51	4,890	2,880	231	

Choose two numbers whose sum is about:

16. 70. **23 and 51 or 17 and 51**
17. 500. **231 and 289**
18. 8,000. **2,880 and 4,890 or 3,470 and 4,890**

Getting Ready for the EOG Test

19. Doug bought fruit and a granola bar. *About* how much money did he spend? **B**

    A $4.00 C $6.00
    B $5.00 D $7.00

North Carolina Standards 1.02 Develop fluency with multi-digit addition and subtraction through 9,999 using: b) Estimation of sums and differences in appropriate situations. *also* 1.06

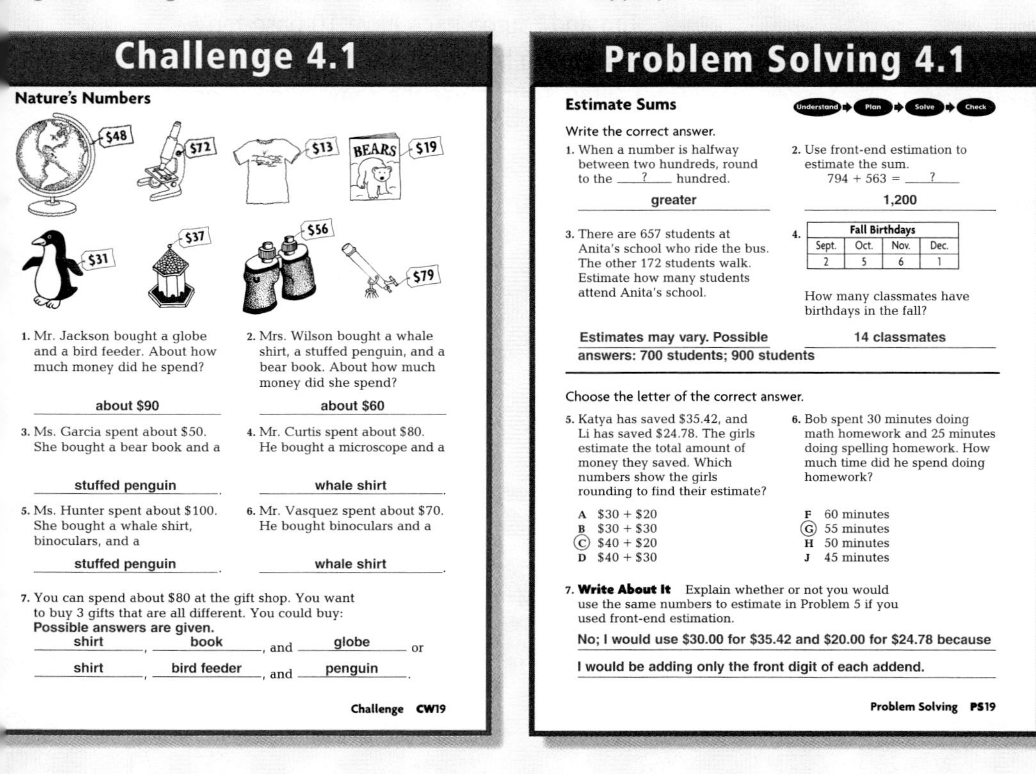

Challenge 4.1

Nature's Numbers

1. Mr. Jackson bought a globe and a bird feeder. About how much money did he spend? **about $90**
2. Mrs. Wilson bought a whale shirt, a stuffed penguin, and a bear book. About how much money did she spend? **about $60**
3. Ms. Garcia spent about $50. She bought a bear book and a **stuffed penguin**.
4. Mr. Curtis spent about $80. He bought a microscope and a **whale shirt**.
5. Ms. Hunter spent about $100. She bought a whale shirt, binoculars, and a **stuffed penguin**.
6. Mr. Vasquez spent about $70. He bought binoculars and a **whale shirt**.
7. You can spend about $80 at the gift shop. You want to buy 3 gifts that are all different. You could buy: **Possible answers are given.**
   shirt, **book**, and **globe** or
   shirt, **bird feeder**, and **penguin**.

Challenge CW19

Problem Solving 4.1

Estimate Sums

Understand → Plan → Solve → Check

Write the correct answer.

1. When a number is halfway between two hundreds, round to the ___?___ hundred. **greater**
2. Use front-end estimation to estimate the sum. 794 + 563 = ___?___ **1,200**
3. There are 657 students at Anita's school who ride the bus. The other 172 students walk. Estimate how many students attend Anita's school. **Estimates may vary. Possible answers: 700 students; 900 students**
4.

Fall Birthdays			
Sept.	Oct.	Nov.	Dec.
2	5	6	1

How many classmates have birthdays in the fall? **14 classmates**

Choose the letter of the correct answer.

5. Katya has saved $35.42, and Li has saved $24.78. The girls estimate the total amount of money they saved. Which numbers show the girls rounding to find their estimate?
   A $30 + $20
   B $30 + $30
   (C) $40 + $20
   D $40 + $30
6. Bob spent 30 minutes doing math homework and 25 minutes doing spelling homework. How much time did he spend doing homework?
   F 60 minutes
   (G) 55 minutes
   H 50 minutes
   J 45 minutes
7. **Write About It** Explain whether or not you would use the same numbers to estimate in Problem 5 if you used front-end estimation. **No; I would use $30.00 for $35.42 and $20.00 for $24.78 because I would be adding only the front digit of each addend.**

Problem Solving PS19

COMMON ERROR ALERT

Students may round to find a sum by finding an exact answer first and then rounding. Explain that the point of estimating sums is to work with simpler numbers. When estimating by rounding, students should first round the addends and then add to find the sum.

Independent Practice

Note that Exercise 15 is a **multistep or strategy problem.** Assign Exercises 6–18.

Point out to students that in Exercise 12 the number of digits in each addend is not the same. They should still use the front digit of each addend and write zeros for the other digits.

Reasoning Have students explore the concept of obtaining a closer estimate. In money amounts, if both addends have cents amounts that are just over half a dollar, you can get a closer estimate by rounding one addend up and one down. Have students provide problems that demonstrate getting a closer estimate.

4 ASSESS

Summarize the lesson by having students:

Discuss How do you estimate a sum? You can round the addends, and then add the rounded numbers. Or you can use front-end estimation and add the front digit of each addend.

Write Jenna spent $3.79 for markers and $4.95 for a notebook. Explain how to estimate to find how much she spent in all. Possible answer: Round each addend to the nearest dollar: $4, $5; add the rounded numbers to find the sum: $9.

LESSON QUIZ

Transparency 4.1

Use rounding to estimate the sum.

1. 185 + 237 = 400
2. 290 + 275 = 600
3. $3.80 + $2.98 = $7

Use front-end estimation to estimate the sum.

4. 471 + 198 = 500
5. 904 + 156 = 1,000
6. 6,379 + 2,146 = 8,000

Lesson 4.2

Addition with Regrouping

Lesson Planning

Objective To explore adding 3-digit numbers with and without regrouping

Materials *For each group* base-ten blocks

NCTM Standards

1. Number and Operations
6. Problem Solving
7. Reasoning and Proof
8. Communication
9. Connections
10. Representation

Math Background

These ideas will help students understand place value and regrouping.

- Using manipulatives helps students develop a concrete understanding of addition, especially as it requires regrouping.
- Using base-ten blocks helps students connect manipulatives with symbolic procedures.
- Give students experiences with regrouping to make hundreds with tens.

Warm-Up Resources

Build Number Sense

Number of the Day

Transparency

Estimate the total number of days in February, March, and April. about 90 days

Review Basic Facts

Daily Facts Practice

Have students practice subtraction facts by completing Set F of *Teacher's Resource Book*, p. TR85.

Solve a Problem

Transparency 4.2

Problem of the Day

Tim and Lauren each have 10 base-ten blocks. Tim has 1 more tens block than Lauren. Lauren has the same number of tens as ones. What is the sum of their numbers? 64 (Tim) + 55 (Lauren) = 119

Solution Problem of the Day tab, p. PD4

Intervention and Extension Resources

Alternative Teaching Strategy

ESOL/ESL

Demonstrate the following alternative way to **add 3-digit numbers**:

$$\begin{array}{r} 159 \\ +324 \\ \hline \end{array} \quad \begin{array}{l} 100 + 50 + 9 \\ \underline{+300 + 20 + 4} \\ 400 + 70 + 13 = 483 \end{array}$$

Provide several examples for students to practice with. Check students' work.

VISUAL

LOGICAL/MATHEMATICAL

Special Needs

MATERIALS *For each pair* base-ten blocks

Help **reinforce the concept of regrouping** by having students model addition using base-ten blocks. Each student takes a handful of tens and a handful of ones. Students regroup as needed to show each amount using the fewest possible blocks. Students then record each amount and work together to find the sum.

KINESTHETIC

BODILY/KINESTHETIC, INTERPERSONAL/SOCIAL

Multistep and Strategy Problems

The following multistep or strategy problem is provided in Lesson 4.2:

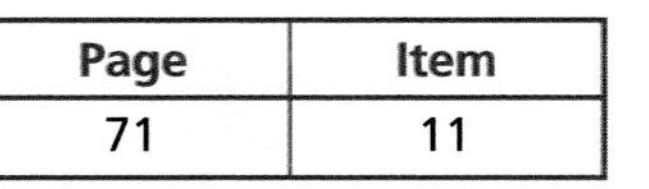

Page	Item
71	11

Advanced Learners

Challenge students to **find sums of 2- and 3-digit numbers.** Have pairs of students work together to find the greatest sum possible when adding three different 2-digit numbers and three different 3-digit numbers. 99 + 98 + 97 = 294; 999 + 998 + 997 = 2,994

VISUAL

INTERPERSONAL/SOCIAL

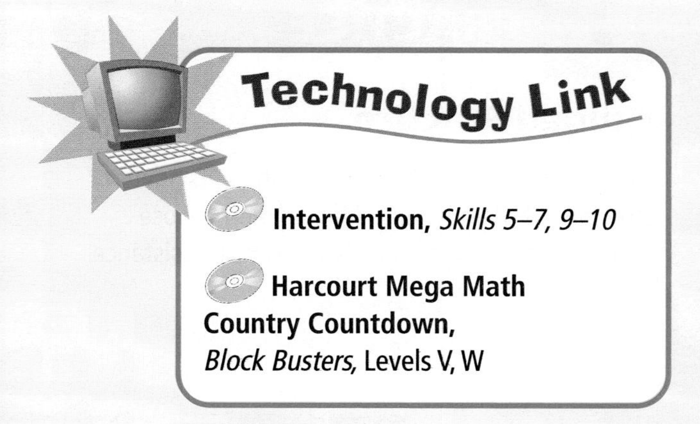

Lesson 4.2 Organizer

Objective To explore adding 3-digit numbers with and without regrouping

Materials *For each group* base-ten blocks

1 INTRODUCE

QUICK REVIEW provides review of prerequisite skills.

WHY LEARN THIS? You may need to add 3-digit numbers to find sums of measurements, money amounts, and data from tables and graphs. *Share the lesson objective with students.*

2 TEACH

Guided Instruction

- *Lead students through Steps 1–3.*
  In Step 1, why do you have to regroup the ones? The sum of the digits in the ones place is greater than 9.
  If you were adding only 3 tens and 7 tens, would you have to regroup the tens? Explain. Yes; there would be 10 tens, which would have to be regrouped as 1 hundred.
  REASONING For a problem with 3-digit addends, why do you add the hundreds last? Possible answer: If the tens were regrouped, there might be an extra hundred to add. If you had already added the hundreds, you would have to add again.

- *Challenge students to apply what they learned.*
  How do you know whether you have to regroup? When the sum of the digits is more than 9, you have to regroup.

MODIFYING INSTRUCTION Students may benefit from completing Steps 1–3 individually or in pairs.

3 PRACTICE

Guided Practice

Do Try It Exercises a–b with your students. Identify students who are having difficulty and choose appropriate lesson resources to provide assistance.

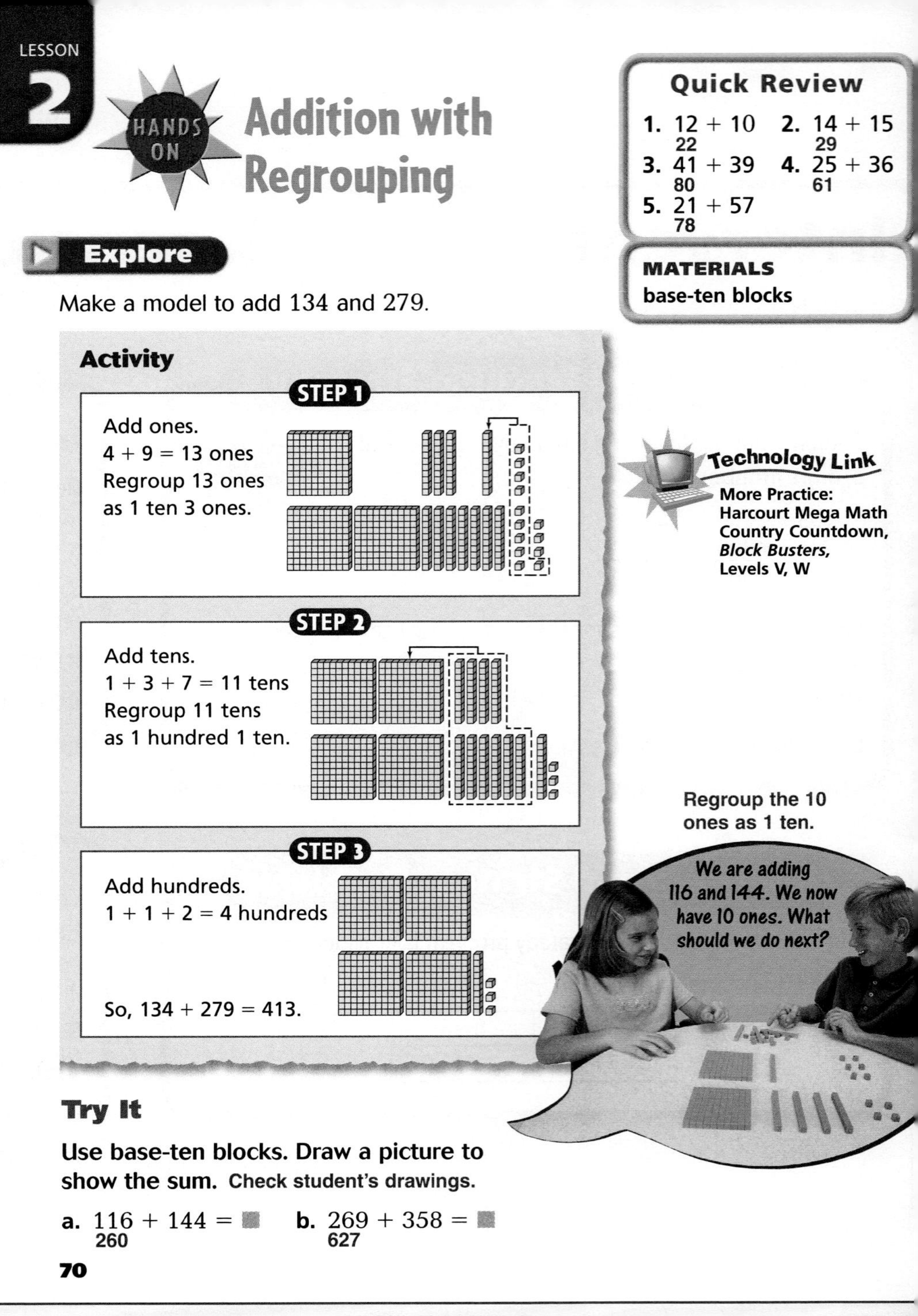

LESSON 2 HANDS ON

Addition with Regrouping

Quick Review

1. 12 + 10 — 22
2. 14 + 15 — 29
3. 41 + 39 — 80
4. 25 + 36 — 61
5. 21 + 57 — 78

MATERIALS
base-ten blocks

Explore

Make a model to add 134 and 279.

Activity

STEP 1
Add ones.
4 + 9 = 13 ones
Regroup 13 ones as 1 ten 3 ones.

STEP 2
Add tens.
1 + 3 + 7 = 11 tens
Regroup 11 tens as 1 hundred 1 ten.

STEP 3
Add hundreds.
1 + 1 + 2 = 4 hundreds

So, 134 + 279 = 413.

Technology Link
More Practice: Harcourt Mega Math Country Countdown, *Block Busters,* Levels V, W

Regroup the 10 ones as 1 ten.

We are adding 116 and 144. We now have 10 ones. What should we do next?

Try It

Use base-ten blocks. Draw a picture to show the sum. Check student's drawings.

a. 116 + 144 = ■ 260 **b.** 269 + 358 = ■ 627

70

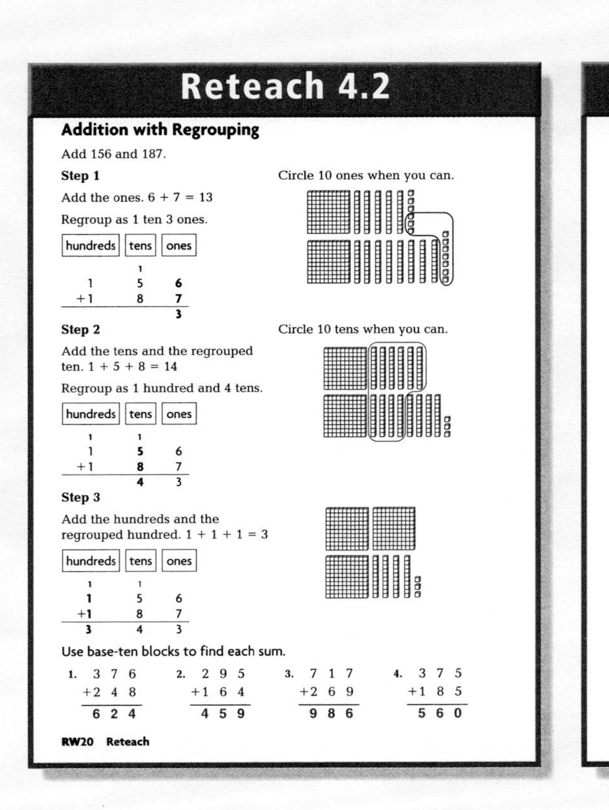

Reteach 4.2

Addition with Regrouping

Add 156 and 187.

Step 1
Add the ones. 6 + 7 = 13
Regroup as 1 ten 3 ones.

Circle 10 ones when you can.

hundreds	tens	ones
	1	
1	5	6
+1	8	7
		3

Step 2
Add the tens and the regrouped ten. 1 + 5 + 8 = 14
Regroup as 1 hundred and 4 tens.

Circle 10 tens when you can.

hundreds	tens	ones
1	1	
1	5	6
+1	8	7
	4	3

Step 3
Add the hundreds and the regrouped hundred. 1 + 1 + 1 = 3

hundreds	tens	ones
1	1	
1	5	6
+1	8	7
3	4	3

Use base-ten blocks to find each sum.

1. 376 + 248 = 624
2. 295 + 164 = 459
3. 717 + 269 = 986
4. 375 + 185 = 560

RW20 Reteach

Practice 4.2

Addition with Regrouping

Find each sum.

1. 341 + 237 = 578
2. 832 + 138 = 970
3. 426 + 427 = 853
4. 359 + 196 = 555
5. 532 + 389 = 921
6. 644 + 317 = 961
7. 277 + 235 = 512
8. 442 + 469 = 911
9. 353 + 588 = 941
10. 527 + 197 = 724
11. 438 + 279 = 717
12. 377 + 195 = 572
13. 159 + 262 = 421
14. 349 + 464 = 813
15. 618 + 329 = 947
16. 627 + 326 = 953
17. 378 + 577 = 955
18. 819 + 153 = 972
19. 377 + 188 = 565
20. 429 + 469 = 898

Mixed Review

Add.

21. 57 + 36 = 93
22. 88 + 97 = 185
23. 49 + 57 = 106
24. 67 + 38 = 105
25. 49 + 89 = 138

Subtract.

26. 71 − 32 = 39
27. 98 − 84 = 14
28. 83 − 57 = 26
29. 56 − 38 = 18
30. 99 − 81 = 18
31. 92 − 18 = 74
32. 14 − 8 = 6
33. 76 − 54 = 22
34. 29 − 14 = 15
35. 75 − 26 = 49

PW20 Practice

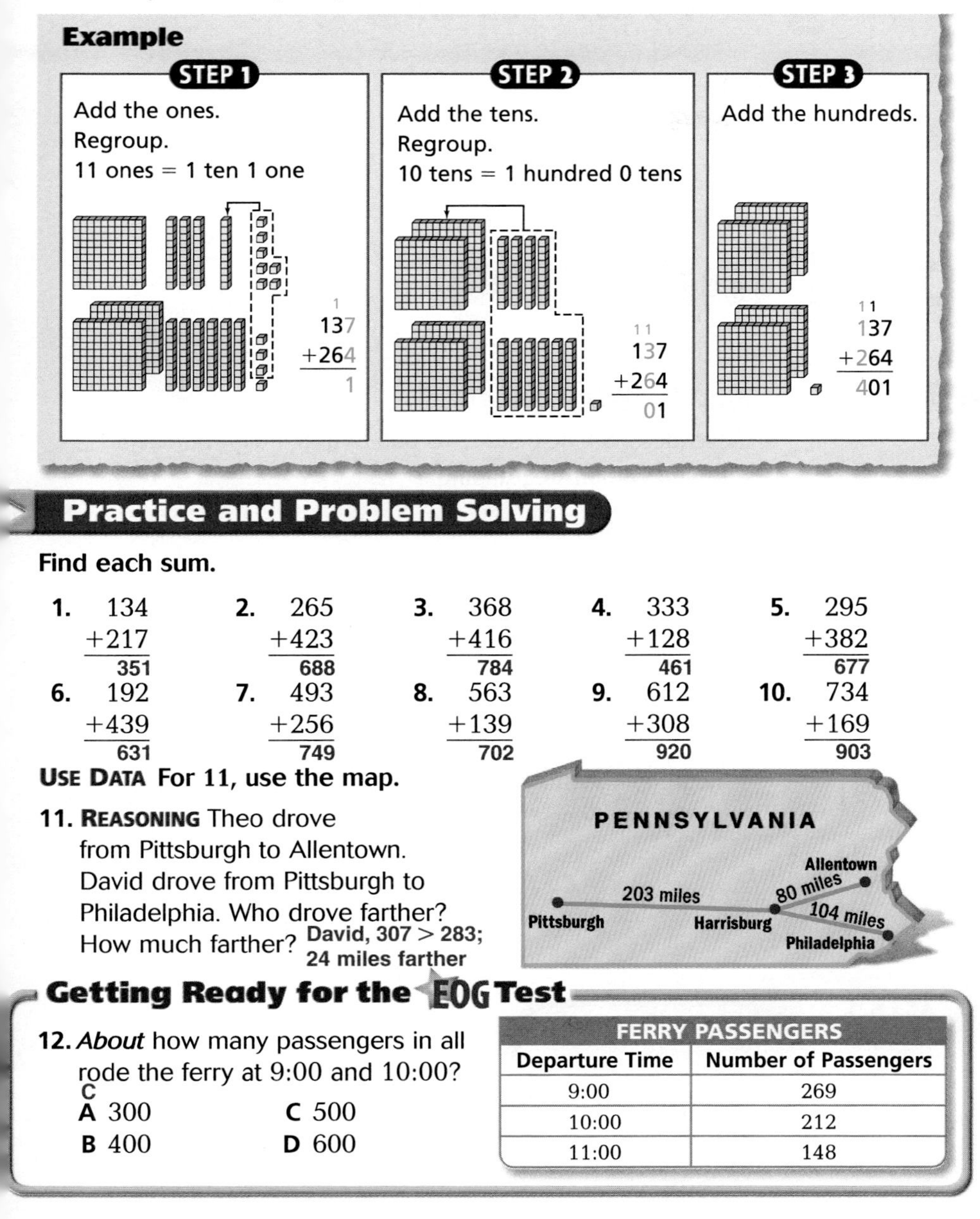

Connect

Here is a way to record addition. To add 137 and 264, first line up hundreds, tens, and ones.

Example

STEP 1
Add the ones.
Regroup.
11 ones = 1 ten 1 one

```
   1
  137
+264
    1
```

STEP 2
Add the tens.
Regroup.
10 tens = 1 hundred 0 tens

```
  11
  137
+264
   01
```

STEP 3
Add the hundreds.

```
  11
  137
+264
  401
```

Practice and Problem Solving

Find each sum.

1. 134 + 217 = 351
2. 265 + 423 = 688
3. 368 + 416 = 784
4. 333 + 128 = 461
5. 295 + 382 = 677
6. 192 + 439 = 631
7. 493 + 256 = 749
8. 563 + 139 = 702
9. 612 + 308 = 920
10. 734 + 169 = 903

USE DATA For 11, use the map.

11. **REASONING** Theo drove from Pittsburgh to Allentown. David drove from Pittsburgh to Philadelphia. Who drove farther? How much farther? **David, 307 > 283; 24 miles farther**

Getting Ready for the EOG Test

12. *About* how many passengers in all rode the ferry at 9:00 and 10:00? **C**
A 300
B 400
C 500
D 600

FERRY PASSENGERS

Departure Time	Number of Passengers
9:00	269
10:00	212
11:00	148

Independent Practice

Note that Exercise 11 is a **multistep or strategy problem.** Assign Exercises 1–11.

Remind students to add the regrouped ten or hundred as they find each sum in Exercises 1–11.

REASONING Point out that students regroup once in some exercises and twice in others. Have students change Exercise 5 so they regroup twice instead of once.

4 ASSESS

Summarize the lesson by having students:

DISCUSS How do you record addition when you regroup? Possible answer: When there is more than 9 in a place-value position, write the regrouped number above the digits in the next column and add it to the other digits in that place-value position. Write the remaining number in the column that was added.

WRITE How would you regroup to find the sum of 375 and 125? What is the sum? Regroup the ones as 1 ten and 0 ones; regroup the 7 tens and 2 tens and 1 ten as 1 hundred and 0 tens; add the hundreds; 500

LESSON QUIZ
Find each sum.

1. 146 + 327 = ■ 473
2. 251 + 418 = ■ 669
3. 690 + 299 = ■ 989
4. 555 + 246 = ■ 801

North Carolina Standards 1.02 Develop fluency with multi-digit addition and subtraction ough 9,999 using: a) Strategies for adding and subtracting numbers.

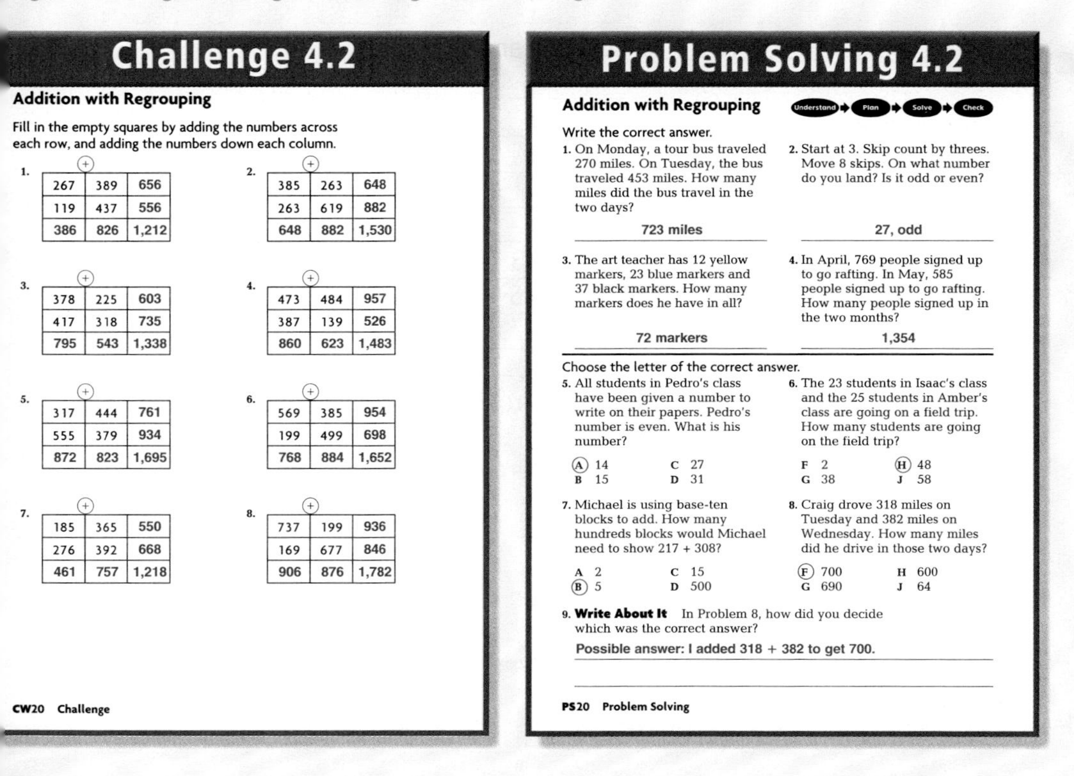

Challenge 4.2

Addition with Regrouping

Fill in the empty squares by adding the numbers across each row, and adding the numbers down each column.

1.

267	389	656
119	437	556
386	826	1,212

2.

385	263	648
263	619	882
648	882	1,530

3.

378	225	603
417	318	735
795	543	1,338

4.

473	484	957
387	139	526
860	623	1,483

5.

317	444	761
555	379	934
872	823	1,695

6.

569	385	954
199	499	698
768	884	1,652

7.

185	365	550
276	392	668
461	757	1,218

8.

737	199	936
169	677	846
906	876	1,782

CW20 Challenge

Problem Solving 4.2

Addition with Regrouping Understand → Plan → Solve → Check

Write the correct answer.

1. On Monday, a tour bus traveled 270 miles. On Tuesday, the bus traveled 453 miles. How many miles did the bus travel in the two days? **723 miles**
2. Start at 3. Skip count by threes. Move 8 skips. On what number do you land? Is it odd or even? **27, odd**
3. The art teacher has 12 yellow markers, 23 blue markers and 37 black markers. How many markers does he have in all? **72 markers**
4. In April, 769 people signed up to go rafting. In May, 585 people signed up to go rafting. How many people signed up in the two months? **1,354**

Choose the letter of the correct answer.

5. All students in Pedro's class have been given a number to write on their papers. Pedro's number is even. What is his number?
   (A) 14 C 27
   B 15 D 31
6. The 23 students in Isaac's class and the 25 students in Amber's class are going on a field trip. How many students are going on the field trip?
   F 2 (H) 48
   G 38 J 58
7. Michael is using base-ten blocks to add. How many hundreds blocks would Michael need to show 217 + 308?
   A 2 C 15
   (B) 5 D 500
8. Craig drove 318 miles on Tuesday and 382 miles on Wednesday. How many miles did he drive in those two days?
   (F) 700 H 600
   G 690 J 64
9. **Write About It** In Problem 8, how did you decide which was the correct answer?
   Possible answer: I added 318 + 382 to get 700.

PS20 Problem Solving

Lesson 4.3

Add 3- and 4-Digit Numbers

Lesson Planning

Objective To add 3- and 4-digit numbers with and without regrouping

NCTM Standards

1. Number and Operations
2. Algebra
6. Problem Solving
7. Reasoning and Proof
8. Communication
9. Connections
10. Representation

Math Background

These ideas will help students add 3- and 4-digit numbers with and without regrouping.

- An estimate can be used to check the reasonableness of an answer.
- An amount of money is often expressed as a 3-digit or 4-digit number and is added like whole numbers, with the additional steps of including a dollar sign and a decimal point to separate dollars and cents.
- Regrouping with money involves regrouping pennies to dimes and dimes to dollars.

Warm-Up Resources

Number of the Day

Add the number of days in July, September, and December. What is the sum? 92

Daily Facts Practice

Have students practice addition and subtraction facts by completing Set G of *Teacher's Resource Book*, p. TR85.

Solve a Problem

Transparency 4.3

Problem of the Day

Add down and across.

2	9	7	?18
4	6	1	?11
? 6	?15	? 8	?29

35	43	?78
29	36	?65
?64	?79	?143

Solution Problem of the Day tab, p. PD4

Intervention and Extension Resources

Alternative Teaching Strategy

Have students try an alternative way to **add with regrouping** where the regrouped numbers are placed below the addends instead of above. Work through the examples below with students. Demonstrate placing the regrouped number below the addends and the sum beneath the regroupings as shown here.

```
                 137          245
                +264         +276
regroupings→      11           11  ←regroupings
        sum→     401          521  ←sum
```

Have students practice solving exercises 6–15 on page 73 using this method.

VISUAL

VISUAL/SPATIAL

Multistep and Strategy Problems

The following multistep or strategy problems are provided in Lesson 4.3:

Page	Item
73	27–28

Special Needs

MATERIALS *For each group* base-ten blocks

ESOL/ESL

Have students **review place value of 3- and 4-digit numbers**. Write the digits 0–9. Review that each number is called a digit.

- Provide examples of 1-digit, 2-digit, 3-digit, and 4-digit numbers and have students tell how many digits are in each number.
- Have students write examples of a 3-digit number and a 4-digit number.
- Give students an opportunity to model each number with base-ten blocks and then read the number, identifying the value of each place, for example: 325 is 3 hundreds, 2 tens, and 5 ones. Check students' work.

AUDITORY

VERBAL/LINGUISTIC, BODILY/KINESTHETIC

Early Finishers

Have students **make visual aids for adding 3- and 4-digit numbers**. Have early finishers work in pairs to make posters to display in the classroom. Have them show the steps for adding 3- and 4-digit numbers, or make a reminder to place the dollar sign and decimal point when adding money. Check students' work.

VISUAL

VISUAL/SPATIAL, INTERPERSONAL/SOCIAL

Lesson 4.3 Organizer

Objective To add 3- and 4-digit numbers with and without regrouping

INTRODUCE

QUICK REVIEW provides review of prerequisite skills.

WHY LEARN THIS? In the future, you can solve problems in which you add greater numbers. *Share the lesson objective with students.*

2 TEACH

Guided Instruction

- *Discuss the problem presented in the Learn section.*
  Why should you estimate? Estimating helps you determine if your answer is reasonable.
- *Point out Step 1.*
  How do you know when to regroup ones? when there are more than 9 ones
- *Ask students to read Step 2.*
  Why is there a 0 in the tens place in the answer? 10 tens are regrouped as 1 hundred 0 tens.
- *Discuss Examples A, B, and C.*
  How is adding money like adding whole numbers? How is it different? Possible answer: Like: Add digits in each place value starting at the right. Different: Use a decimal point and dollar sign when adding money amounts.
- *Point out the Math Idea.*
  How does the estimated sum help you know if the answer is reasonable? If your answer is close to the estimated sum, the answer is reasonable.

MODIFYING INSTRUCTION Students may benefit from modeling Steps 1–4 with base-ten blocks, individually or in pairs.

LESSON 3

Add 3- and 4-Digit Numbers

Quick Review

1. 7 + ■ = 13 6
2. ■ + 9 = 18 9
3. 5 + 6 11
4. 8 + 7 15
5. 6 + 8 14

Learn

THOUSANDS OF BOOKS How many books did Grade 3 and Grade 4 read in all?

1,467 + 1,638 = ■

Estimate. 1,467 → 1,000
+1,638 → +2,000
3,000

READ-A-THON RESULTS	
Grade 2	1,265 books
Grade 3	1,467 books
Grade 4	1,638 books

Example

STEP 1 Add the ones. Regroup. 15 ones = 1 ten 5 ones

```
    1
 1,467
+1,638
     5
```

STEP 2 Add the tens. Regroup. 10 tens = 1 hundred 0 tens

```
   11
 1,467
+1,638
    05
```

STEP 3 Add the hundreds. Regroup. 11 hundreds = 1 thousand 1 hundred

```
  1 11
 1,467
+1,638
   105
```

STEP 4 Add the thousands.

```
  1 11
 1,467
+1,638
 3,105
```

So, the two grades read 3,105 books in all. Since 3,105 is close to the estimate of 3,000, the answer is reasonable.

More Examples

A

```
  1  1
 4,325
+  867
 5,192
```

B

```
  2
 591
 173
+290
1,054
```

C

```
dollar sign
 ↓11
 $24.83
+$45.74
 $70.57
    ↑
decimal point
```

- Add money like whole numbers.
- Include a dollar sign, and use a decimal point to separate dollars and cents.

MATH IDEA Estimate to see if your answer is reasonable.

72

Reteach 4.3

Add 3- and 4-Digit Numbers

You can regroup: 10 ones as 1 ten
10 tens as 1 hundred
10 hundreds as 1 thousand

Add 2,483 + 3,959.

Step 1
Add the ones.
3 + 9 = 12 ones
12 ones = 1 ten 2 ones

	thousands	hundreds	tens	ones
			1	
	2,	4	8	3
+	3,	9	5	9
				2

Step 2
Add the tens.
1 + 8 + 5 = 14 tens
14 tens = 1 hundred 4 tens

	thousands	hundreds	tens	ones
		1	1	
	2,	4	8	3
+	3,	9	5	9
			4	2

Step 3
Add the hundreds.
1 + 4 + 9 = 14 hundreds
14 hundreds = 1 thousand 4 hundreds

	thousands	hundreds	tens	ones
	1	1	1	
	2,	4	8	3
+	3,	9	5	9
		4	4	2

Step 4
Add the thousands.
1 + 2 + 3 = 6 thousands

	thousands	hundreds	tens	ones
	1	1	1	
	2,	4	8	3
+	3,	9	5	9
	6,	4	4	2

Find the sum. Estimate to check.

1.

H	T	O
3	5	6
+1	2	8
4	8	4

2.

H	T	O
2	4	6
+6	7	8
9	2	4

3.

TH	H	T	O
3,	5	6	4
+4,	9	1	2
8,	4	7	6

4.

TH	H	T	O
1,	9	4	3
+1,	8	9	8
3,	8	4	1

Reteach RW21

Practice 4.3

Add 3- and 4-Digit Numbers

Find the sum. Estimate to check.

1. 356 + 228 = 584
2. $14.95 + $22.78 = $37.73
3. 657 + 155 = 812
4. 1,494 + 9,369 = 10,863
5. 4,364 + 2,465 = 6,829
6. 7,648 + 5,173 = 12,821
7. $64.93 + $34.82 = $99.75
8. 146 + 594 = 740
9. $52.47 + $34.53 = $87.00
10. 152 + 688 = 840
11. $38.46 + $16.59 = $55.05
12. 473 + 437 = 910
13. 3,349 + 8,449 = 11,798
14. 147 + 366 = 513
15. 528 + 869 + 131 = 1,528

Mixed Review

Write the value of the underlined digit.

16. 25,781 — 5,000
17. 13,499 — 10,000
18. 245,006 — 200,000
19. 77,712 — 70,000
20. 576 — 500
21. 92,440 — 40
22. 11,299 — 9
23. 4,810 — 800

Round to the nearest ten.

24. 566 — 570
25. 717 — 720
26. 32 — 30
27. 673 — 670
28. 1,854 — 1,850
29. 392 — 390
30. 428 — 430
31. 4,668 — 4,670

Practice PW21

Check

1. You would have to regroup 12 ones as 1 ten 2 ones and regroup 13 tens as 1 hundred 3 tens.

1. **Explain** whether you would regroup to find how many books Grades 2 and 3 read in all. **See above.**

Find the sum. Estimate to check.

2. 224 + 511 **735**
3. $9.07 + $1.25 **$10.32**
4. 1,298 + 1,872 **3,170**
5. 214 + 468 + 89 **771**

Practice and Problem Solving

Extra Practice, page 82, Set B

Find the sum. Estimate to check.

26. Possible answer: greater than; 458 > 450 and 83 > 50. 450 + 50 = 500, so 458 + 83 must be greater than 500.

6. 321 + 268 **589**
7. 4,505 + 1,828 **6,333**
8. 268 + 173 + 368 **809**
9. 415 + 561 + 246 **1,222**
10. 309 + 299 + 66 **674**
11. 2,984 + 325 **3,309**
12. $7.44 + $5.02 **$12.46**
13. 629 + 67 **696**
14. $31.42 + $48.61 **$80.03**
15. 152 + 339 **491**

Copy and complete each table.

25. How many pages are in the book in all?

	Add 152.		
16.	174	■	326
17.	319	■	471
18.	457	■	609

	Add 306.		
19.	565	■	871
20.	798	■	1,104
21.	824	■	1,130

	Add 2,547.		
22.	1,149	■	3,696
23.	2,845	■	5,392
24.	5,854	■	8,401

25. **What's the Question?** Eva read to page 112 in her book. There are 67 more pages in the book. The answer is 179 pages. **See above.**

26. Sharon added 458 and 83. Was her answer greater than or less than 500? Explain how you know. **See above.**

27. **ALGEBRA** Write the missing addend. 230 + ■ + 40 = 282 **12**

28. **ALGEBRA** Write the missing addend. 1,475 + ■ + 95 = 1,745 **175**

Getting Ready for the EOG Test

29. *About* how many muffins were sold on Monday and Thursday? **C**

A 400 B 500 C 700 D 800

MUFFINS SOLD	
Day	**Number Sold**
Monday	316
Tuesday	298
Wednesday	430
Thursday	350

North Carolina Standards 1.02 Develop fluency with multi-digit addition and subtraction ough 9,999 using: a) Strategies for adding and subtracting numbers.

3 PRACTICE

Guided Practice

Do Check Exercises 1–5 with your students. Identify students who are having difficulty and choose appropriate lesson resources to provide assistance.

For Exercise 5, students may need help in estimating to check. Have them round all addends to the nearest hundred.

Independent Practice

Note that Exercises 27–28 are **multistep or strategy problems.** Assign Exercises 6–28.

For Exercises 6–15, you may want to have students explain their method of estimation.

ALGEBRAIC THINKING For Exercises 27–28, have students explain how to find the missing addends.

4 ASSESS

Summarize the lesson by having students:

DISCUSS How do you find the sum of two 4-digit numbers when the sum of the tens is more than 9 and the sum of the hundreds is more than 9? Possible answer: regroup twice; regroup the tens first and then the hundreds.

WRITE Explain how to find the sum 1,387 + 4,265. Add 7 and 5; regroup the 12 ones as 1 ten and 2 ones; record the 2 ones in the sum. Add 8, 6, and 1; regroup the 15 tens as 1 hundred and 5 tens; record the 5 tens in the sum; Add the 3, 2, and 1 hundreds and record the 6 hundreds in the sum. Add 1 and 4 thousands and record the 5 thousands in the sum.

LESSON QUIZ

Transparency 4.3

Find the sum. Estimate to check.

1. 386 + 299 **685**
2. 2,438 + 397 **2,835**
3. 3,509 + 4,398 **7,907**
4. 3,642 + 1,499 + 109 **5,250**

Challenge 4.3

Palindromes

A *palindrome* is a word or phrase that reads the same forward and backward. Some examples are *Otto, Ada,* and *Madam, I'm Adam.*

Numbers can also be palindromes. Some examples are 88, 151, and 34,143. You can make your own number palindromes using addition. Look at the boxes.

Choose any 2- or 3-digit number. Reverse the digits. 14 + 41. Add. 55. 55 is a palindrome. It reads the same forward and backward.

Choose any 2- or 3-digit number. Reverse the digits. 48 + 84. Add. 132. Reverse the digits of the sum. 132 + 231. Add. 363. The number 363 is a palindrome.

Reverse and add until you get a palindrome.

1. 57 + 75 = 132; 132 + 231 = 363
2. 153 + 351 = 504; 504 + 405 = 909
3. 29 + 92 = 121
4. 261 + 162 = 423; 423 + 324 = 747

Try this out with your own 2- or 3-digit numbers. For some numbers, you need to reverse and add many times before you get a palindrome. You may need an extra piece of paper. **Check students' work. Answers will vary.**

5. 6. 7. 8. **A 3-digit combination of 7, 8, & 9 will not work.**

Challenge CW21

Problem Solving 4.3

Add 3- and 4-Digit Numbers Understand → Plan → Solve → Check

Write the correct answer.

1. To solve 347 + 469 = __?__, how many times will you need to regroup? What is the sum? **2; 816**
2. To solve 4,527 + 5,839 = __?__, how many times will you need to regroup? What is the sum? **2; 10,366**
3. Valerie has 227 stickers in her sticker book. Heather has 198 in hers. Estimate how many stickers are in the girls' books in all. **about 400 stickers**
4. Evette could read 14 words by the time she was four years old. During the next year, she learned 58 more words. How many words did she learn to read by her fifth birthday? **72 words**

Choose the letter of the correct answer.

5. How should the tens be regrouped to find this sum? 248 + 161
   - A 1 ten 0 ones
   - B 0 hundreds 10 tens
   - (C) 1 hundred 0 tens
   - D 10 hundreds
6. Beth rode her bicycle 4 blocks to Robin's house. Robin and Beth rode 5 blocks to Susan's house for lunch. Beth, Robin, and Susan rode back to Robin's house. How many blocks did Beth ride altogether?
   - F 4 blocks
   - G 5 blocks
   - H 9 blocks
   - (J) 14 blocks
7. **Write About It** In Problem 3, how did you decide whether to add or subtract? **Possible answer: I decided to add because I had to find out how many in all.**

Problem Solving PS21

Problem Solving Strategy
Predict and Test

Lesson Planning

Objective To solve problems using the strategy *predict and test*

Lesson Resources Reading Transparency 4; Intervention • Problem Solving, Strategy/Skill 4

NCTM Standards
1. Number and Operations
2. Algebra
6. Problem Solving
7. Reasoning and Proof
8. Communication
9. Connections
10. Representation

Math Background

These ideas will help students solve problems by using the strategy *predict and test*.

- Making predictions is an important step in problem solving.
- The strategy *predict and test* involves analyzing a problem, making a prediction, and testing that prediction.
- The process of solving problems may include adjusting predictions. Use each prediction to get closer to the actual answer.

Warm-Up Resources

Number of the Day

Write 2 addition sentences with three addends. Use the number of minutes in one hour in each number sentence. Possible answers: 60 + 5 + 10 = 75; 12 + 22 + 26 = 60

Daily Facts Practice

Have students practice addition and subtraction facts by completing Set A of *Teacher's Resource Book*, p. TR86.

Solve a Problem

Transparency 4.4

Problem of the Day

The digits 0–9 are used only once in either an addend or the sum. Write the missing digits. Possible arrangements:

■8■	784	289
+■■■	+269	+764
1,053	1,053,	1,053,
	789	284
	+264 or	+769
	1,053	1,053

Solution Problem of the Day tab, p. PD4

Intervention and Extension Resources

Alternative Teaching Strategy

Help students **use the strategy *predict and test*.**

- Point out that the problem on page 74 is like an addition problem with missing addends. Have students draw rectangles to illustrate the quantities and see the part-whole relationship.

? cans	15
? bags	

Total is 75.
■ + ■ + 15 = 75 30; 30

- Have students use this method to solve other problems in the lesson.

VISUAL

VISUAL/SPATIAL

Reading Strategy

Paraphrase To paraphrase means to restate a problem in your own words. Have students use this strategy to help them understand and solve the problem on page 74. Possible answer: The third graders bought 75 cans and bags in all. They had 15 more cans than bags. How many cans and bags did they buy?

Transparency 4 **Reading Transparency 4**

Multistep and Strategy Problems

The following multistep or strategy problems are provided in Lesson 4.4:

Page	Item
75	1–8

ESOL/ESL

Have students work in small groups to **review the sequence used in predicting and testing** to solve a problem like the one on page 74. Write the steps they identify on sentence strips, cut them apart, and have groups order, read, and review them. Check students' work.

ESOL/ESL

AUDITORY, KINESTHETIC

VERBAL/LINGUISTIC, INTERPERSONAL/SOCIAL, LOGICAL/MATHEMATICAL

Early Finishers

MATERIALS *For each group* small items, containers

Have students **practice using the strategy *predict and test*.** Fill several containers with small items, such as marbles. Tell students the total number of items in all the containers. Have them predict the number of items in each container and test their predictions by counting. Have students add the number of items in all the containers and check their sum against the given total. Check students' work.

VISUAL

VISUAL/SPATIAL, LOGICAL/MATHEMATICAL

Technology Link

Intervention • Problem Solving, *Strategy/Skill 4*

Lesson 4.4 Organizer

Objective To solve problems using the strategy *predict and test*

Lesson Resources Reading Transparency 4; Intervention • Problem Solving, Strategy/Skill 4

QUICK REVIEW provides review of prerequisite skills.

WHY LEARN THIS? You can predict and test to determine an unknown number. *Share the lesson objective with students.*

2 TEACH

Guided Instruction

- *Ask students to read the Problem and the Understand section.*

  REASONING Is this a simple addition problem in which you are finding the sum? Explain. Possible answer: No; you already know the sum. You have to find the unknown addends.

- *Direct students' attention to the table.*

  How is the first prediction tested? Fifteen is added to find the number of cans. The total of 55 is compared to the sum of 75.

  REASONING When do you use a greater number as your next prediction? when the test with your first number gives an answer that is too low

  Why is the strategy called *predict and test*? Possible answer: You have to test each prediction you make to see if it is too high, too low, or just right.

Problem Solving Strategy
Predict and Test

Quick Review

1. 21 + 6 27
2. 45 + 15 60
3. 9 + 36 45
4. 72 + 8 80
5. 12 + 13 25

PROBLEM The third-grade classes bought 75 containers of food for the animal shelter. They had 15 more cans than bags of food. How many bags and cans did the classes buy?

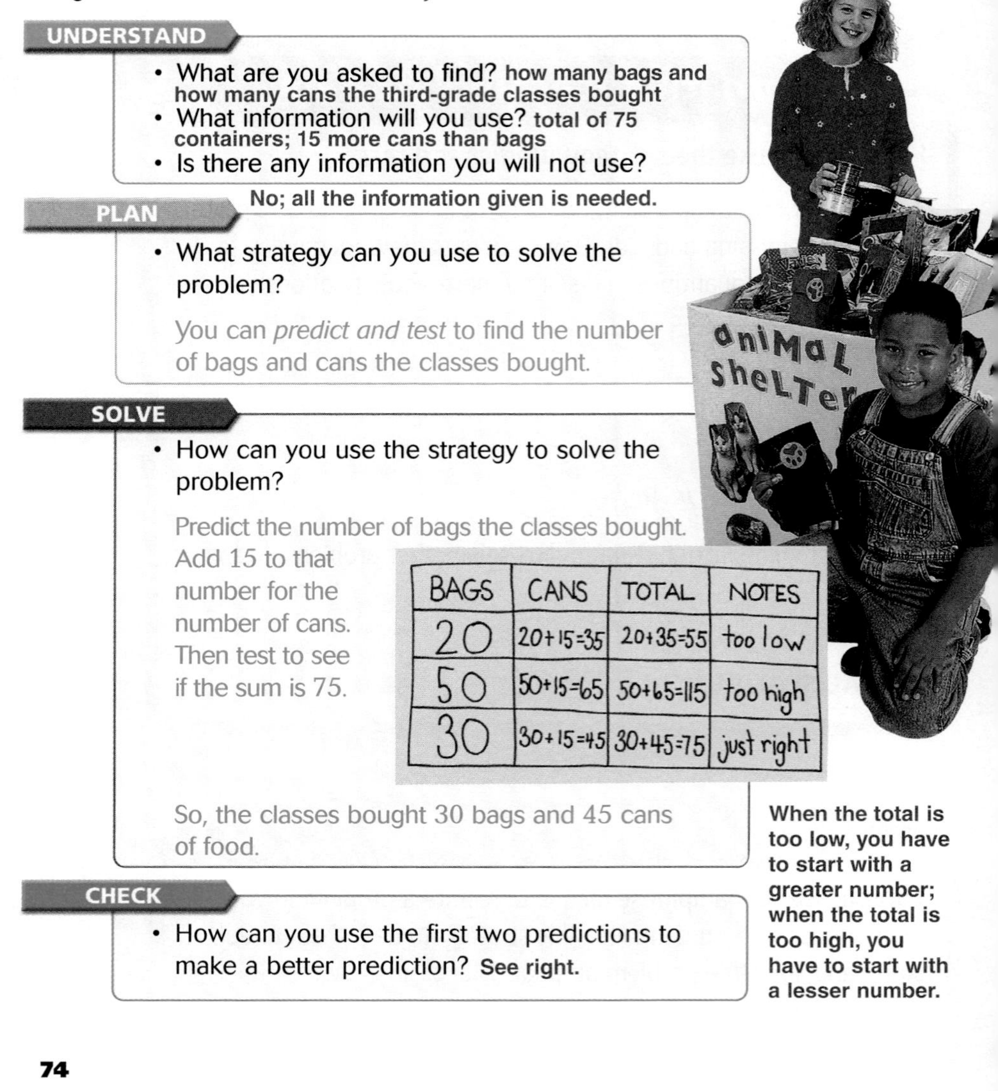

UNDERSTAND

- What are you asked to find? **how many bags and how many cans the third-grade classes bought**
- What information will you use? **total of 75 containers; 15 more cans than bags**
- Is there any information you will not use? **No; all the information given is needed.**

PLAN

- What strategy can you use to solve the problem?

  You can *predict and test* to find the number of bags and cans the classes bought.

SOLVE

- How can you use the strategy to solve the problem?

  Predict the number of bags the classes bought. Add 15 to that number for the number of cans. Then test to see if the sum is 75.

BAGS	CANS	TOTAL	NOTES
20	20+15=35	20+35=55	too low
50	50+15=65	50+65=115	too high
30	30+15=45	30+45=75	just right

So, the classes bought 30 bags and 45 cans of food.

CHECK

- How can you use the first two predictions to make a better prediction? **See right.**

When the total is too low, you have to start with a greater number; when the total is too high, you have to start with a lesser number.

74

Reteach 4.4

Problem Solving Strategy

Predict and Test

Sometimes you can find an answer by first predicting and then testing your answer.

Mary has 20 red and blue balloons at her party. She has 4 more red balloons than blue balloons. How many balloons of each color does she have?

	Blue	Red	Total	Notes
Prediction 1	5	5 + 4 = 9	5 + 9 = 14	too low
Prediction 2	10	10 + 4 = 14	10 + 14 = 24	too high
Prediction 3	8	8 + 4 = 12	8 + 12 = 20	just right

Mary has 8 blue balloons and 12 red balloons.

Use *predict and test* to solve. You may wish to make your own tables.

1. Peter delivers 110 newspapers on the weekend. He delivers 20 more newspapers on Sunday than on Saturday. How many newspapers does he deliver each day?

   45 newspapers on Saturday;

   65 newspapers on Sunday

2. Paul is 5 years older than Lisa. The sum of their ages is 19. How old is each person?

   Lisa is 7; Paul is 12.

3. Jesse has earned $40 more by washing cars than Tyrone has by raking leaves. Together they have $140. How much has each boy earned?

   Jesse has earned $90;

   Tyrone has earned $50.

RW22 Reteach

Practice 4.4

Problem-Solving Strategy

Predict and Test

Use *predict and test* to solve.

1. Two numbers have a sum of 39. Their difference is 11. What are the two numbers? **14 and 25**
2. Two numbers have a sum of 22. Their difference is 4. What are the two numbers? **9 and 13**
3. Gina traveled 450 miles to her grandmother's house in two days. She traveled 50 more miles on Saturday than on Sunday. How many miles did she travel on Saturday? on Sunday? **250 mi; 200 mi**
4. Maria practiced the recorder for 40 minutes on Saturday. She practiced 10 minutes less in the afternoon than in the morning. How many minutes did Maria practice in the morning? in the afternoon? **25 min; 15 min**

Mixed Review

Solve.

5. 17 + 22 + 56 = **95**
6. $42.80 + $23.90 + $6.00 = **$72.70**
7. 134 + 326 + 422 = **882**
8. 79 + 18 + 27 = **124**

Write <, >, or = in the ◯.

9. 25 + 25 (=) 50
10. 721 + 322 (>) 1,000
11. $3.50 + $2.25 (>) $4.25
12. 582 + 241 (<) 1,200
13. 276 + 524 (=) 800
14. $19.83 + $4.99 (<) $25.00

Solve.

15. 19 + 59 = **78**
16. 276 + 347 = **623**
17. 365 + 485 = **850**
18. 63 + 29 + 15 = **107**
19. 54 + 48 + 39 = **141**

PW22 Practice

Problem Solving Practice

Use *predict and test* to solve.

1. **What if** the classes bought 120 containers and had 30 more cans than bags? How many bags and how many cans did they buy? **45 bags and 75 cans**
2. Pilar has 170 stamps in her collection. Her first book of stamps has 30 more stamps in it than her second book. How many stamps are in each book? **first: 100 stamps; second: 70 stamps**

Two numbers have a sum of 27. Their difference is 3. What are the two numbers?

3. Which is a reasonable prediction for one of the numbers? **B**
   A 3 B 10 C 27 D 30
4. What solution answers the question? **J**
   F 3 and 27 G 10 and 13 H 10 and 17 J 12 and 15

Strategies

Draw a Diagram or Picture
Make a Model or Act It Out
Make an Organized List
Find a Pattern
Make a Table or Graph
Predict and Test
Work Backward
Solve a Simpler Problem
Write a Number Sentence
Use Logical Reasoning

Problem Solving

Mixed Strategy Practice

USE DATA For 5–6, use the table.

5. The number of pounds used in Week 2 was greater than in Week 1, but less than in Week 3. The number of pounds used in Week 2 is an odd number that does not end in 5. How many pounds were used in Week 2? **77 lb**
6. **Write a problem** about the dog food used at the shelter in which the difference is greater than 5. **Check students' problems.**

DOG FOOD USED AT SHELTER

February	Pounds
Week 1	73
Week 2	■
Week 3	79
Week 4	81

7. The sum of two numbers is 55. Their difference is 7. What are the numbers? **24 and 31**
8. There are 4 students in line. Max is before Keiko but after Liz. Adam is fourth. Who is first? **Liz**

North Carolina Standards 1.06 Develop flexibility in solving problems by selecting strategies and using mental computation, estimation, calculators or computers, and paper and pencil.

Challenge 4.4

Get in Shape

For each pair of number sentences, each shape represents a single number. You may use the strategy *predict and test* to figure out the number that each shape represents. Write the number inside the shape.

Example: (7) + [5] = 12; (7) − [5] = 2

1. (9) + △6 = 15; (9) − △6 = 3
2. (15) + [5] = 20; (15) − [5] = 10
3. (80) + [20] = 100; (80) − [20] = 60
4. (9) + △4 = 13; (9) − △4 = 5
5. △4 + [3] = 7; △4 − 1 = [3]
6. (9) + △7 = 16; (9) − 2 = △7

Answers will vary.

For Problems 7–8, there is more than one possible solution.

7. △ + □ = 10; 10 − □ = △
8. 8 − △ = ○; 8 − ○ = △

CW22 Challenge

Reading Strategy 4.4

Make and Confirm Predictions Understand → Plan → Solve → Check

As you read a story, you probably find yourself thinking ahead to what might happen next. This is making a **prediction**. When you estimate before finding the exact answer to a word problem, this is also a prediction. After you make a prediction, you need to test it.

Read the following problem.

▶ Tony and Katie picked corn. On Wednesday, they picked 126 ears of corn. Katie picked 20 more ears of corn than Tony. How many ears did they each pick?

1. What does the problem ask you to find? **how many ears Tony and Katie each picked**
2. What are the important facts in the problem? **They picked 126 ears. Katie picked 20 more than Tony.**
3. Copy the table onto notebook paper. Use it to make your predictions. Test each prediction. One prediction has been made for you.

Prediction (Tony)	Katie	Total	Notes
30	30 + 20 = 50	30 + 50 = 80	too low

Check students' tables. Tony: 53 ears; Katie: 73 ears

Make a table for each problem. Use important facts in the problem to help you predict the solution. Solve. **Check students' tables.**

4. Ed and Mark built towers with connecting cubes. They used 220 connecting cubes. Mark used 40 more than Ed. How many cubes did each use? **Ed: 90 cubes; Mark: 130 cubes**
5. Myoshi collected 200 stamps from Mexico and Japan. She has 20 more from Mexico than from Japan. How many does she have from each country? **Mexico: 110 stamps; Japan: 90 stamps**

PS22 Reading Strategy

3 PRACTICE

Guided Practice

Do Problem Solving Practice Exercises 1–4 with your students. Identify students who are having difficulty and choose appropriate lesson resources to provide assistance. Note that Exercises 1–4 are **multistep or strategy problems.**

Independent Practice

Note that Exercises 5–8 are **multistep or strategy problems.** Assign Exercises 5–8.

SCAFFOLDED INSTRUCTION Use the prompts on Transparency 4 to guide instruction for the multistep problem in Exercise 2.

ALGEBRAIC THINKING For Exercise 7, students must look for a relationship between the numbers to determine two unknown numbers.

4 ASSESS

Summarize the lesson by having students:

DISCUSS How do you know whether a prediction you made is correct or incorrect? Test the prediction by trying it out in the problem.

WRITE The sum of two numbers is 21. Their difference is 3. Explain how to use the strategy *predict and test* to find the two numbers. Possible answer: Make a prediction with two numbers. Test the prediction by finding the sum and difference. If needed, make a better prediction until the sum is 21 and the difference is 3; 12 and 9.

LESSON QUIZ

Use *predict and test* to solve.

1. Two numbers have a difference of 5. Their sum is 145. What are the two numbers? 70 and 75
2. The class collected 100 containers for art supplies. They had 30 more boxes than cans. How many boxes and cans did they have? 65 boxes, 35 cans

Lesson 4.5

Choose a Method

Lesson Planning

Objective To choose mental math, paper and pencil, or a calculator to add 4-digit numbers with and without regrouping

Materials calculator; *For Thinker's Corner* index cards numbered 0–9

NCTM Standards
1. Number and Operations
2. Algebra
6. Problem Solving
8. Communication
10. Representation

Math Background

These ideas will help students add 4-digit numbers with and without regrouping.

- To add 4-digit numbers, follow the same steps as for adding 3-digit numbers, and continue to the thousands place.
- Estimating can be used to check the reasonableness of an answer.
- Money is often expressed as a 4-digit number and is added like whole numbers, with the additional step of including a dollar sign and a decimal point to separate dollars and cents.
- When adding money amounts, pennies are regrouped as dimes, dimes are regrouped as dollars, and dollars are regrouped as ten dollars.

Warm-Up Resources

Number of the Day

When added to a number that is ten more than I am, our sum is 124. What number am I? 57

Review Basic Facts

Daily Facts Practice

Have students practice subtraction facts by completing Set B of *Teacher's Resource Book*, p. TR86.

Solve a Problem

Transparency 4.5

Problem of the Day

To find this secret number, add the greatest whole number that rounds to 50 and the least number that rounds to 80. What is the secret number?

54 + 75 = 129

Make up a secret number of your own for a classmate to solve.

Solution Problem of the Day tab, p. PD4

Intervention and Extension Resources

Alternative Teaching Strategy

MATERIALS *For each pair* base-ten blocks

Have students **use base-ten blocks to add two 4-digit numbers**.

- Ask one student to write a 4-digit number for the first addend and then model it.
- Ask the other student to write another 4-digit number for the second addend.
- Then have partners work together to model the addition of the two numbers, regrouping as needed. Check students' work.

See also page 78.

KINESTHETIC

BODILY/KINESTHETIC, INTERPERSONAL/SOCIAL

Multistep and Strategy Problems

The following multistep or strategy problem is provided in Lesson 4.5:

Page	Item
78	36

ESOL/ESL

Help students **understand a reasoning game**. Have pairs of students work together to read the steps of the *Thinker's Corner* game in the lesson and take turns restating them in their own words or demonstrating them to each other by using number cards, writing, gestures, and words. After students play the game, invite them to discuss the strategy they used.

AUDITORY

VERBAL/LINGUISTIC, INTERPERSONAL/SOCIAL

Language Arts Connection

Have students **explore the meanings of the terms *vertical* and *horizontal*.** Have them look up the definitions and restate them in their own words. Have them draw and label an example of something horizontal and something vertical, such as a bed and a door. Ask students to look at Exercises 11–31 on page 78 and identify those that are written vertically and those that are written horizontally. vertically: 11–26; horizontally: 27–31 Have students discuss which way they prefer to work and why.

VISUAL, AUDITORY

VISUAL/SPATIAL, VERBAL/LINGUISTIC

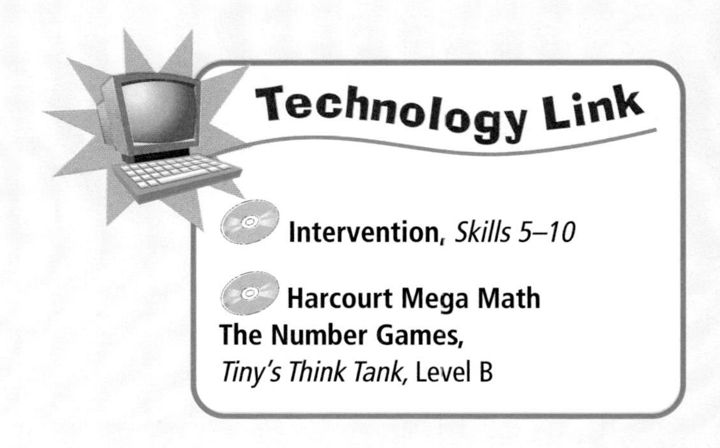

Technology Link

Intervention, *Skills 5–10*

Harcourt Mega Math The Number Games, *Tiny's Think Tank,* Level B

Lesson 4.5 Organizer

Objective To choose mental math, paper and pencil, or a calculator to add 4-digit numbers with and without regrouping

Materials calculator; *For Thinker's Corner* index cards numbered 0–9

1 INTRODUCE

QUICK REVIEW provides review of prerequisite skills.

WHY LEARN THIS? You can add distances. *Share the lesson objective with students.*

2 TEACH

Guided Instruction

- *Ask students to read the Learn section.*
  Why was the estimate of 4,000 selected for both addends? Possible answer: The digit in the hundreds place in 4,365 is 3, so the number was rounded to 4,000. The digit in the hundreds place in 3,852 is 8, so the number was rounded to 4,000.
- *Ask students to read Steps 1–4.*
  How is the process shown in these steps the same as the process for adding 3-digit numbers? How is it different? Possible answers: Steps 1–3 are the same and are completed in the same order. Step 4 has been added since you are adding 4 digits.
  How does using estimation help you check your answer? Possible answer: You can use the estimate to tell whether your answer is a reasonable one.

LESSON 5

Choose a Method

Quick Review

1. 350 + 40 **390**
2. 150 + 212 **362**
3. 560 + 161 **721**
4. 205 + 52 **257**
5. 90 + 215 **305**

Learn

You can find a sum by using paper and pencil, a calculator, or mental math.

PADDLE POWER Tom and Eli paddled from White Rock to Bear Corner to Raccoon Falls. How many yards did they paddle in all?

$4,365 + 3,852 = \blacksquare$

Estimate. $4,000 + 4,000 = 8,000$

Use Paper and Pencil The numbers are large. The problem involves regrouping. So, paper and pencil is a good choice.

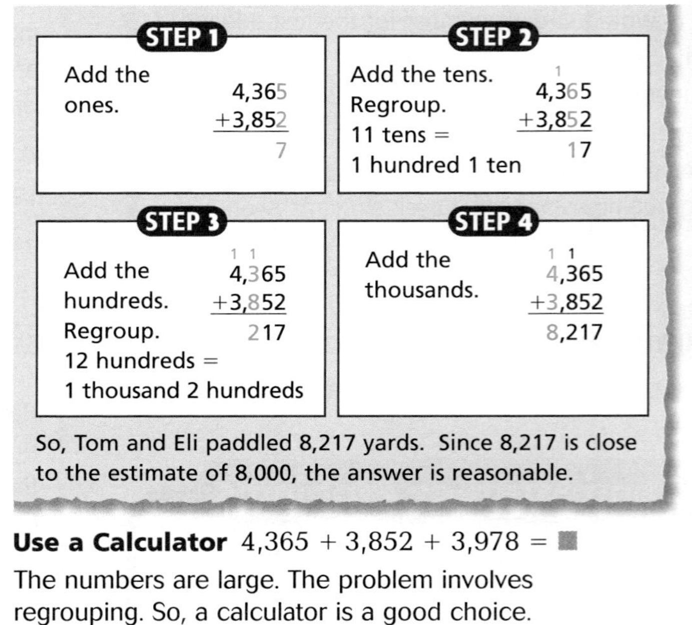

STEP 1

Add the ones.

```
  4,365
 +3,852
      7
```

STEP 2

Add the tens. Regroup. 11 tens = 1 hundred 1 ten

```
     1
  4,365
 +3,852
     17
```

STEP 3

Add the hundreds. Regroup. 12 hundreds = 1 thousand 2 hundreds

```
   1 1
  4,365
 +3,852
    217
```

STEP 4

Add the thousands.

```
   1 1
  4,365
 +3,852
  8,217
```

So, Tom and Eli paddled 8,217 yards. Since 8,217 is close to the estimate of 8,000, the answer is reasonable.

Use a Calculator $4,365 + 3,852 + 3,978 = \blacksquare$

The numbers are large. The problem involves regrouping. So, a calculator is a good choice.

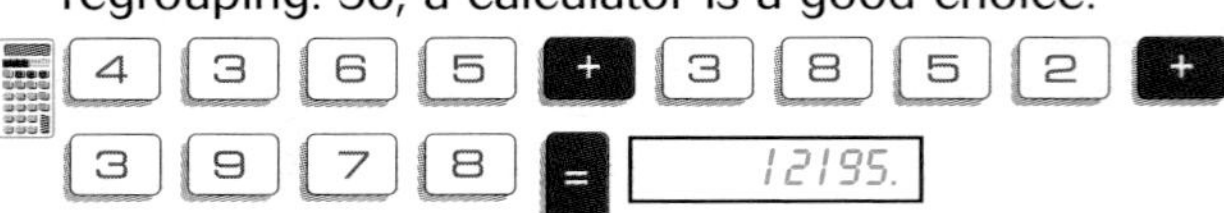

REASONING How can you estimate to check? **4,000 + 4,000 + 4,000 = 12,000 Since 12,195 is close to 12,000, the answer is reasonable.**

76

Reteach 4.5

Choose a Method

Add 1,968 and 4,327.

Step 1 Estimate.

1,968 → 2,000
+ 4,327 → + 4,000
6,000

Step 2 Add the ones. Regroup. 15 ones = 1 ten 5 ones

```
     1
  1,968
+ 4,327
      5
```

Step 3 Add the tens and the regrouped ten.

```
     1
  1,968
+ 4,327
     95
```

Step 4 Add the hundreds. Regroup. 12 hundreds = 1 thousand 2 hundreds

```
   1 1
  1,968
+ 4,327
    295
```

Step 5 Add the thousands and the regrouped thousand.

```
   1 1
  1,968
+ 4,327
  6,295
```

Step 6 Compare your answer to your estimate.

Since 6,295 is close to 6,000, the answer is reasonable.

Find the sum.

1. 3,758 + 2,169 = **5,927**
2. 4,738 + 5,167 = **9,905**
3. 1,426 + 5,939 = **7,365**
4. 8,119 + 1,586 = **9,705**

Find the sum. Tell what method you used. **Methods will vary.**

5. 2,403 + 1,212 = **3,615**
6. 1,397 + 1,455 = **2,852**
7. 1,718 + 3,658 = **5,376**
8. 4,610 + 5,320 = **9,930**

Reteach RW23

Practice 4.5

Choose a Method

Find the sum. Tell what method you used. **Methods will vary.**

1. 2,341 + 6,237 = **8,578**
2. 861 + 733 = **1,594**
3. 800 + 300 = **1,100**
4. 1,776 + 1,954 = **3,730**
5. 1,952 + 1,980 = **3,932**
6. 988 + 982 = **1,970**
7. 1,113 + 5,988 = **7,101**
8. $7.82 + $9.39 = **$17.21**
9. 4,000 + 3,000 = **7,000**
10. 6,318 + 4,916 = **11,234**
11. 7,657 + 1,284 = **8,941**
12. 5,000 + 8,000 = **13,000**
13. 588 + 455 = **1,043**
14. 5,387 + 8,347 = **13,734**
15. $4.25 + $5.56 = **$9.81**
16. 6,859 + 1,346 = **8,205**

Mixed Review

Write the numbers in order from *least* to *greatest*.

17. 245, 253, 232 **232, 245, 253**
18. 7,924; 7,429; 7,249 **7,249; 7,429; 7,924**
19. 632, 599, 900 **599, 632, 900**

Add.

20. 47 + 69 + 81 = **197**
21. 75 + 83 + 52 = **210**
22. 94 + 18 + 60 = **172**
23. 26 + 99 + 34 = **159**
24. 221 + 876 = **1,097**
25. 595 + 111 = **706**
26. 469 + 568 = **1,037**
27. 670 + 710 = **1,380**

Practice PW23

Use Mental Math

$9.30 + $5.60 = ■

There is no regrouping. You can add the dollar and cents amounts in your head. So, mental math is a good choice.

Think: Add the dollar amounts. $9.00 + $5.00 = $14.00
Then add the cents. $0.30 + $0.60 = $0.90
Find the sum. $14.00 + $0.90 = $14.90

So, $9.30 + $5.60 = $14.90.

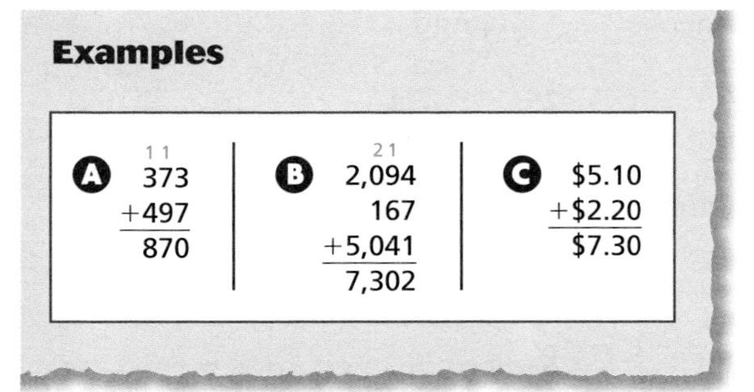

Examples

A	B	C
373 + 497 = 870	2,094 + 167 + 5,041 = 7,302	$5.10 + $2.20 = $7.30

Technology Link
More Practice: Harcourt Mega Math The Number Games, *Tiny's Think Tank*, Level B

- Which example can you solve by using mental math? Explain. **Possible answer: C; there is no regrouping.**
- Which method would you choose to solve Example B? Explain. **Possible answer: calculator; there are 3 numbers to add and there is regrouping.**

MATH IDEA You can find a sum by using paper and pencil, a calculator, or mental math. Choose the method that works best with the numbers in the problem.

Check

1. **Explain** how you can use mental math to add 747 and 242. **Possible answer: Add the hundreds, 7 + 2 = 9. Add the tens, 4 + 4 = 8. Add the ones, 7 + 2 = 9. So, 747 + 242 = 989.**

Find the sum. Tell what method you used. **Methods will vary.**

2. 347 + 91 = **438**
3. 1,348 + 1,231 = **2,579**
4. 919 + 489 = **1,408**
5. 1,625 + 350 = **1,975**
6. $5.80 + $5.25 = **$11.05**
7. 1,032 + 5,198 = ■ **6,230**
8. $69.81 + $23.11 = ■ **$92.92**
9. 3,035 + 989 + 4,918 = ■ **8,942**
10. 2,354 + 4,526 + 831 = ■ **7,711**

LESSON CONTINUES

North Carolina Standards 1.06 Develop flexibility in solving problems by selecting strategies and using mental computation, estimation, calculators or computers, and paper and pencil.

- *Have students look at Example A.*

What method is best for solving Example A? Possible answer: Example A can be solved using paper and pencil. The numbers are not so large that I need to use a calculator, but I do need to regroup. So, using mental math might be too hard.

How could you use mental math to solve Example A? Possible answer: You can think of 497 as 500 − 3. 373 + 500 = 873, and 873 − 3 = 870.

REASONING When adding 4-digit numbers, is it possible to regroup 3 times? Give an example. Yes; Possible answer: 1,875 + 1,986 = 3,861

3 PRACTICE

Guided Practice

Do Check Exercises 1–10 with your students. Identify the students who are having difficulty and choose appropriate lesson resources to provide assistance.

Challenge 4.5

Add Greater Numbers

Fill in the missing digits. Possible answers are given for Exercises 4, 10, and 20.

1. 3,477 + 4,176 = 7,653
2. 2,935 + 3,782 = 6,717
3. 1,638 + 6,284 = 7,922
4. 4,021 + 4,193 = 8,214
5. 8,516 + 1,398 = 9,914
6. 2,828 + 5,353 = 8,181
7. 6,402 + 4,976 = 11,378
8. 4,588 + 3,219 = 7,807
9. 5,189 + 2,303 = 7,492
10. 3,737 + 4,646 = 8,383
11. 2,791 + 4,171 = 6,962
12. 5,729 + 4,173 = 9,902
13. 3,235 + 6,371 = 9,606
14. 1,357 + 2,468 = 3,825
15. 8,885 + 4,444 = 13,329
16. 5,258 + 2,848 = 8,106
17. 7,802 + 1,556 = 9,358
18. 3,824 + 2,176 = 6,000
19. 2,093 + 5,376 = 7,469
20. 4,175 + 3,478 = 7,653
21. 5,479 + 4,181 = 9,660

Challenge CW23

Problem Solving 4.5

Choose a Method

Understand → Plan → Solve → Check

Write the correct answer.

1. To solve 1,568 + 4,384 = ___?___ how many times will you need to regroup? What is the sum? **2; 5,952**
2. The population of Jaime's town is 3,572. Ryan's town has 7,859 more people than Jaime's town. What is the population of Ryan's town? **11,431**
3. Lee says the sum of 589 + 838 is close to 1,400. Olivia says the sum is closer to 1,300. Who is correct? **Lee**
4. Pedro charges $14 to mow a lawn and $6 to do the edging. If Pedro mowed 2 lawns and edged 1 lawn, how much did he earn? **$34**

Choose the letter of the correct answer.

5. How should the hundreds be regrouped to find this sum?
6,824 + 1,735
A 1 hundred 5 tens
B 0 thousands 15 hundreds
(C) 1 thousand 5 hundreds
D 5 thousands 1 hundred

6. Greg left for school at 8:00. His sister Liza had a meeting before school. She left one hour before Greg. What time did Liza leave for school?
(F) 7:00
G 7:30
H 8:00
J 9:00

7. A helicopter flew 1,568 feet above a radio tower that is 1,269 feet tall. How high did the helicopter fly?
A 299 feet
B 2,727 feet
C 2,737 feet
(D) 2,837 feet

8. There are 8,499 students enrolled in the Tylersville school system. Round 8,499 to the nearest thousand.
F 9,000
G 8,500
H 8,400
(J) 8,000

9. **Write About It** Is an estimate enough for the answer to Problem 2? Why or why not? **Possible answer: No. The question asks for the population of the town, so an exact answer is necessary.**

Problem Solving PS23

Independent Practice

Note that Exercise 36 is a **multistep or strategy problem.** Assign Exercises 11–39.

Point out that students may use more than one method to solve a given problem. Encourage volunteers to explain how they might use paper and pencil and mental math to solve one of the exercises.

VOCABULARY POWER Explain to students that *-or* is a suffix that, when added to the end of a noun, means "a person or thing that." What is the meaning of the word *invent* with the suffix *-or*? Possible answer: a person that makes something new

Remind students to estimate to check their answers in Exercises 30–31.

ALGEBRAIC THINKING Suggest that students use the *predict and test* strategy to help them solve Exercise 33.

MULTISTEP OR STRATEGY PROBLEM To solve Exercise 36, students can add \$7.50 and \$7.50 to find the price for mowing two lawns, and then add \$4.50 and \$4.50 to find the price for raking two lawns. Then they can add \$15.00 and \$9.00 to find how much Craig earned and compare. \$15.00 + \$9.00 = \$24.00. Since 24 > 20, Craig earned more than \$20.

Practice and Problem Solving

Extra Practice, page 82, Set C

Find the sum. Tell what method you used. Methods will vary.

11. 709 + 226 — 935
12. \$2.78 + \$5.01 — \$7.79
13. 821 + 744 — 1,565
14. \$3.58 + \$2.65 — \$6.23
15. 259 + 74 — 333
16. 458 + 221 — 679
17. \$7.35 + \$2.44 — \$9.79
18. 624 + 347 — 971
19. 769 + 347 — 1,116
20. \$4.11 + \$3.48 — \$7.59
21. 641 + 989 — 1,630
22. 329 + 110 — 439
23. 5,492 + 1,205 — 6,697
24. 1,895 + 1,700 — 3,595
25. 9,294 + 2,104 — 11,398
26. 2,164 + 6,235 — 8,399

Find the sum. Explain your method. Accept reasonable explanations.

27. 429 + 640 = ■ 1,069
28. 565 + 424 = ■ 989
29. \$14.40 + \$10.20 = ■ \$24.60

Use a calculator. Find the sum. 35. He forgot to add the regrouped ten. Sum is 9,221.

30. 1,647 + 897 + 3,467 = ■ 6,011
31. \$12.79 + \$3.49 + \$6.98 = ■ \$23.26

32. **NUMBER SENSE** Write a number less than 3,425 + 8,630 but greater than 7,614 + 4,429. any number from 12,044 to 12,054

33. **ALGEBRA** Write the missing addend. 4,020 + ■ = 4,222 202

34. **ESTIMATION** Allie estimates that 5,109 + 4,995 is about 1,000. Do you agree or disagree? Explain. Disagree; the answer is close to 10,000, not 1,000.

35. **What's the Error?** Sergio used paper and pencil to find this sum. Describe his error. Find the sum. See above.

```
  1 11
  8,235
+   986
  9,211
```

36. **USE DATA** Use the price list. If Craig mows and rakes 2 lawns, has he earned more than \$20? Explain how you know. Yes, since \$7.50 + \$4.50 = \$12.00, Craig has earned \$24.00

CRAIG'S PRICE LIST
Weed Garden $5.00
Mow Lawn $7.50
Rake Lawn $4.50

37. **Vocabulary Power** The root of the word *calculator* is the Greek word *kalyx,* which means "pebble or small stone." Small stones were once counted to find sums. When do you use a calculator to find sums? Possible answer: when you are ad[ding] greater numbers and there is regrouping

38. **FAST FACT** • SOCIAL STUDIES Volunteers raise Canine Companion puppies until they are about 18 months old. Use a calculator to find how many weeks this is. 72 weeks

39. Can you add two 3-digit numbers and get a sum greater than 2,000? Explain. No, the greatest 3-digit number is 999; 999 + 999 = 1,998. This is less than 2,000.

78

Alternative Teaching Strategy

Scaffolded Instruction

PURPOSE Students add 4-digit numbers using manipulatives.

MATERIALS *For each group* base-ten blocks for thousands, hundreds, tens, and ones

Step 1

Ask volunteers to make 2 groups of base-ten blocks representing 1,459 and 1,563.

Step 2

Have students line up the thousands, hundreds, tens, and ones blocks for each number.

Step 3

Have students add their thousands, hundreds, tens, and ones beginning with the ones. Have them regroup their ones by trading in ten of them for a tens block, leaving the two ones and adding the tens block to the tens.

Step 4

Have students add the tens. Have them regroup their tens by trading in ten of them for a hundreds block, leaving the two tens and adding the hundreds block to the hundreds.

Step 5

PROFESSIONAL DEVELOPMENT

Have students add the hundreds. Have them regroup their hundreds by trading in all ten of them for a thousands block, leaving none in the hundreds, and adding the thousands block to the thousands.

Step 6

Have students count the thousands. Then have them find the sum. 3,022

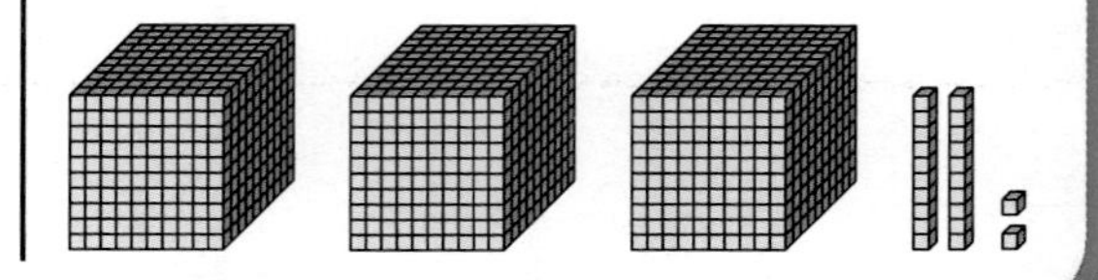

Getting Ready for the EOG Test

40. The Flower Shop ordered 3,225 carnations and 1,080 roses for a wedding. *About* how many flowers did the shop order altogether? C

A 1,000 **C** 4,000
B 3,000 **D** 5,000

41. Michael drove 84 miles from Charlotte to Winston-Salem, 146 miles from Winston-Salem to Asheville, and then 130 miles from Asheville to Charlotte. How many miles did he drive in all? A

A 360 miles **C** 276 miles
B 350 miles **D** 230 miles

42. During which two weeks did Sara save a total of $7.00? D

SARA'S APRIL SAVINGS	
Week 1	$3.00
Week 2	$4.75
Week 3	$2.50
Week 4	$2.25

A Weeks 1 and 2
B Weeks 2 and 3
C Weeks 3 and 4
D Weeks 2 and 4

Problem Solving Thinker's Corner

Try to make a greater sum than your partner's.

MATERIALS: index cards numbered 0–9

- Player 1 chooses 4 cards and uses the digits to write two different 4-digit addends. Each digit should be used twice. Player 1 replaces the cards.
- Player 2 repeats the first step.
- Both players find the sum. The player with the greater sum wins. Play this game several times. See if you can find a winning strategy.
- Repeat this game. Try to make the lesser sum.

1. When making the greater sum, where is the best place to put a 9?
in the thousands place
2. When making the lesser sum, where is the best place to put a 9?
in the ones place

Problem Solving Thinker's Corner

- *Have students follow the bulleted directions.*

Where is the best position to place any zero you might draw? If you are trying to make the greater sum, the zero should be in the ones place. If you are trying to make the lesser sum, the zero cannot go in the thousands place, because you would not have a 4-digit number. It should be placed in the hundreds place.

Reasoning Explain whether the strategy you use for making the greater sum would change if you were using 3-digit numbers. No, the strategy would be the same. Place the least number drawn in the ones place and the greatest number drawn in the hundreds place.

Summarize the lesson by having students:

Discuss Explain the steps you use to add 4-digit numbers that require regrouping. Add the ones and regroup, if needed; add the tens and regroup, if needed; add the hundreds and regroup, if needed; add the thousands.

Write Why should you estimate when adding 4-digit numbers? Give an example. It helps you determine whether the sum is reasonable. Examples will vary.

LESSON QUIZ

Find the sum. Estimate to check.

1. $3{,}268 + 4{,}107 = 7{,}375$
2. $5{,}894 + 7{,}346 = 13{,}240$
3. $8{,}062 + 2{,}598 = 10{,}660$
4. $4{,}999 + 4{,}999 = 9{,}998$

Algebra: Expressions and Number Sentences

Lesson Planning

Objective To write expressions and number sentences that represent situations and to select operation symbols to make number sentences true

NCTM Standards

1. Number and Operations
2. Algebra
6. Problem Solving
7. Reasoning and Proof
8. Communication
10. Representation

Math Background

These ideas will help students write expressions and number sentences and select operation symbols that make number sentences true.

- Expressions combine numbers and operation symbols, but do not have equal symbols.
- An expression is part of a number sentence.
- A number sentence can be true or false.

Vocabulary

expression the part of a number sentence that combines numbers and operation signs

not equal to ≠ a symbol used in a number sentence to show that two amounts are unequal

Warm-Up Resources

Number of the Day

Use the number of days in a leap year to write an addition problem that requires regrouping. Solve the problem. Possible answer: 366 + 189 = 555

Daily Facts Practice

Have students practice addition and subtraction facts by completing Set C of *Teacher's Resource Book*, p. TR86.

Solve a Problem

Transparency 4.6

Problem of the Day

Pedro's number has as many tens as Sandra's number has ones and as many ones as Sandra's number has tens. If Pedro subtracts 9 from his number and Sandra adds 9 to her number, they will each have the same number, 22. What are their numbers? Pedro, 31; Sandra, 13

Solution Problem of the Day tab, p. PD4

Intervention and Extension Resources

Alternative Teaching Strategy

To **practice writing expressions**, have students identify the possible missing element(s) in the following expressions: Possible answers are given:

1 + ■ 6   7 − ■ 3

19 ■ 1 −   6 ■ 5 ■ 1 +, +

7 ■ 18 +   63 + ■ + ■ 35, 42

350 ■ 150 −   ■ − 21 30

VISUAL

LOGICAL/MATHEMATICAL

Multistep and Strategy Problems

The following multistep or strategy problem is provided in Lesson 4.6:

Page	Item
81	21

Vocabulary Strategy

ESOL/ESL

Have students **practice identifying number sentences and expressions** by writing *expression* or *number sentence* to describe the following:

$55 - 33 \neq 30$ number sentence

$17 + 12 + 9$ expression

$100 - 34$ expression

$14 + 27 = 41$ number sentence

Then have students write one expression and one number sentence of their own. Check students' work.

VISUAL

VERBAL/LINGUISTIC

Language Arts Connection

Have students **compare and contrast a number sentence with a sentence** that they might write in a report, letter, or story. Invite students to think about what each one consists of; what each one needs in order to be complete; and whether a sentence with words can be, like a number sentence, true or false. Ask students to organize their ideas into one or more paragraphs and include information on how a number sentence and a sentence are alike and how they are different. Possible answer: A number sentence must have an operation sign and an equal sign. A sentence needs a subject, a verb, and punctuation at the end of the sentence.

VISUAL

VERBAL/LINGUISTIC

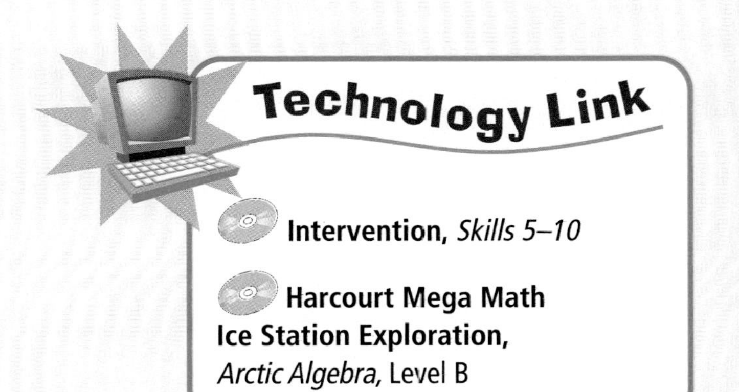

Technology Link
Intervention, *Skills 5–10*
Harcourt Mega Math Ice Station Exploration, *Arctic Algebra,* Level B

Lesson 4.6 Organizer

Objective To write expressions and number sentences that represent situations and to select operation symbols to make number sentences true

Vocabulary expression, not equal to ≠

1 INTRODUCE

QUICK REVIEW provides review of prerequisite skills.

WHY LEARN THIS? Knowing how to write expressions and number sentences will help you solve problems. *Share the lesson objective with students.*

2 TEACH

Guided Instruction

- *Have students read the Learn section.*
  What does an expression include? numbers and operation signs
  What would you need to add to an expression to make it a number sentence? Possible answer: an equal or a not equal sign plus another value, such as a sum or a difference

- *Have students apply what they learn about true number sentences.*
  Give an example of a *true* number sentence and a number sentence that is false. Possible answer: 5 + 5 = 10; 20 + 6 = 14
  Give an example of a number sentence using 27 and 45 and the ≠ symbol. Possible answer: 45 − 27 ≠ 28
  REASONING What are four ways of changing only one thing to make the number sentence 8 − 2 = 10 true? Possible answers: 8 + 2 = 10; 12 − 2 = 10; 8 − 2 = 6; 8 − 2 ≠ 10

LESSON 6

Algebra: Expressions and Number Sentences

Quick Review

1. 14 + 14 **28**
2. 12 + 21 **33**
3. 42 + 25 **67**
4. 90 + 18 **108**
5. 25 + 49 **74**

VOCABULARY
expression
not equal to ≠

Learn

LUNCH LINE In the morning, visitors bought 34 packets of food for the animals in the petting zoo. In the afternoon, visitors bought 58 packets. How many food packets were bought in all?

You can write an expression for this problem. An **expression** is part of a number sentence. It combines numbers and operation signs. It does not have an equal sign.

34 + 58 is the expression that models the problem.

34 + 58 = 92 is a number sentence.

Visitors bought 92 food packets in all.

MATH IDEA A number sentence can be true or false.
4 + 3 = 7 is true. 4 − 3 = 7 is false.

Another way to show that 4 − 3 does not equal 7 is to write 4 − 3 ≠ 7.

The ≠ is a symbol that means "**not equal to**."

Mike spent $12 for a cap and $18 for a shirt at the petting zoo. How much more did the shirt cost?

$18 ● $12 = $6

Which symbol will make the sentence *true*?

Try +. $18 + $12 = $6 False or $18 + $12 ≠ $6.
Try −. $18 − $12 = $6 **True**.

So, the correct symbol is −.

80

Reteach 4.6

Algebra: Expressions and Number Sentences

Number sentences contain numbers, operations, and an equal sign.
Examples: 4 + 5 = 9 9 − 4 = 5

Some number sentences are *true*.
Examples: 3 + 5 = 8 True 9 − 7 = 2 True

Some number sentences are *false*.
Examples: 3 + 2 = 9 False 7 − 5 = 6 False

An **expression** is part of a number sentence. It contains numbers and operations. It does not contain an equal sign.
Examples: 3 + 2 3 + 5 9 − 7 7 − 5 9 − 4 4 + 5

Write an expression for each. Then write a number sentence and solve.

1. Ron has 13 yellow apples and 25 red apples. How many apples does he have altogether? **13 + 25; 13 + 25 = 38**
2. Marsha bought 24 eggs. She used 8 for breakfast. How many eggs does she have now? **24 − 8; 24 − 8 = 16**
3. Kyle has 15 more pages to read than Linda. Linda has 12 pages to read. How many pages does Kyle have to read? **15 + 12; 15 + 12 = 27**
4. Jill bought 2 oranges, 3 apples, and 9 bananas. How many more bananas than oranges did she buy? **9 − 2; 9 − 2 = 7**

Write + or − to complete the number sentence.

5. 8 (+) 4 = 12
6. 7 = 16 (−) 9
7. 12 (−) 3 = 9
8. 18 − 6 = 7 (+) 5
9. 19 (+) 3 = 22
10. 16 (+) 11 = 27
11. 12 (−) 7 = 3 + 2
12. 2 + 9 = 17 (−) 6
13. 8 (+) 8 = 16

RW24 Reteach

Practice 4.6

Algebra: Expressions and Number Sentences

Write an expression. Then write a number sentence to solve.

1. Garnet bought 16 red buttons, 8 blue buttons, and 25 green buttons. How many blue and red buttons did she buy? **8 + 16; 8 + 16 = 24**
2. Kay has 13 more sheets of lined paper than unlined paper. She has 26 sheets of unlined paper. How many sheets of lined paper does she have? **26 + 13; 26 + 13 = 39**
3. Lyle had 152 pages to read in his library book. He read 65 pages. How many pages does he have left? **152 − 65; 152 − 65 = 87**
4. Neil had 35 cookies. He gave 26 cookies to his classmates. How many cookies does he have left? **35 − 26; 35 − 26 = 9**

Write + or − to complete the number sentence.

5. 4 (−) 2 = 2
6. 27 = 18 (+) 9
7. 32 (+) 3 = 35
8. 67 = 7 (+) 60
9. 39 (+) 16 = 55
10. 16 (−) 11 = 5
11. 15 (−) 7 = 8
12. 50 = 61 (−) 11
13. 71 = 43 (+) 28

Write the missing number.

14. 9 + **12** = 21
15. 8 = **17** − 9
16. **12** + 81 = 93
17. 160 = 50 + **110**
18. **139** − 123 = 16
19. 36 − **31** = 5
20. 57 + 18 = **75**
21. 115 − 113 = **2**
22. 237 − **42** = 195

Mixed Review

Find each sum.

23. 25 + 70 + 97 = **192**
24. 38 + 63 + 81 = **182**
25. 52 + 49 + 74 = **175**
26. 86 + 85 + 38 = **209**

PW24 Practice

Check

For 1–2, write an expression. Then write a number sentence to solve.

1. Takeo had 273 cards. He gave away 35. How many cards does he have left? **$273 - 35$; $273 - 35 = 238$ cards**
2. Mia had 13 apples. She bought 7 more. How many does she have in all? **$13 + 7$; $13 + 7 = 20$ apples**

Write + or – to complete the number sentence.

3. $12 \bullet 2 = 10$ **–**
4. $37 \bullet 11 \neq 40$ **+ or –**
5. $126 \bullet 79 = 47$ **–**
6. $367 \bullet 43 = 410$ **+**

Practice and Problem Solving

Extra Practice, page 82, Set D

For 7–8, write an expression. Then write a number sentence to solve.

22. Possible answer: $5 + 9 = 14$; $5 + 14 \neq 9$

7. Gwen bought 12 red pencils, 2 blue pencils, and 22 yellow pencils. How many blue and red pencils did she buy? **$2 + 12$; $2 + 12 = 14$**
8. Ned has 17 crayons. He has 15 pens. How many more crayons than pens does he have? **$17 - 15$; $17 - 15 = 2$**

Write + or – to complete the number sentence.

9. $4 \bullet 3 = 1$ **–**
10. $28 \bullet 9 = 37$ **+**
11. $329 \bullet 87 = 222 + 20$ **–**
12. $559 \bullet 50 = 609$ **+**
13. $74 \bullet 47 = 17 + 10$ **–**
14. $444 \bullet 6 \neq 460 - 10$ **–**

Write the missing number.

15. $\blacksquare + 3 = 14$ **11**
16. $140 + 5 = \blacksquare$ **145**
17. $45 - \blacksquare = 25$ **20**
18. $309 - \blacksquare = 209$ **100**
19. $215 - \blacksquare = 120$ **95**
20. $\blacksquare - 125 = 318$ **443**
21. **REASONING** Blair says, "$12 + 3 + 1 = 19 - 3$ is a true number sentence." Do you agree or disagree? Explain. **agree; $16 = 16$**
22. **REASONING** Use the numbers 5, 9, and 14. Write two true number sentences—one using the equal sign and one using the not equal sign. **See above.**

Getting Ready for the EOG Test

23. Dustin has about the same number of quarters as dimes in his collection. *About* how many coins does he have altogether? **C**

A 500 **B** 600 **C** 800 **D** 900

DUSTIN'S COIN COLLECTION

Coin	Number
Pennies	318
Nickels	118
Dimes	195
Quarters	?

North Carolina Standards 5.04 Find the value of the unknown in a whole number sentence.
o 1.02

Challenge 4.6

Write Expressions and Number Sentences

Write the missing number that completes the sentence. Find the code letter for each answer in the code box below. Write the code letter under each answer. Your answers will solve a riddle.

$18 + \square = 44$	$15 = \square - 12$	$\square + 48 = 62$	$120 = 20 + \square$
26	27	14	100
P	L	E	A
$\square - 45 = 45$	$56 - \square = 42$	$33 + 44 = \square$	$162 - 135 = \square$
90	14	77	27
S	E		L
$\square - 9 = 5$	$16 + 123 = \square$	$\square - 32 = 107$	$\square - 123 = 15$
14	139	139	138
E	T	T	U
$\square - 15 = 4$	$\square + 53 = 67$	$\square - 14 = 63$	$123 - \square = 23$
19	14	77	100
C	E		A
$\square - 17 = 10$	$\square + 77 = 99$	$353 = \square - 16$	$\square + 124 = 138$
27	22	369	14
L	O	N	E

100 = A	337 = B	19 = C	77 = (space)
14 = E	22 = O	138 = U	283 = H
75 = J	139 = T	27 = L	108 = M
369 = N	26 = P	80 = R	90 = S

What did the rabbits say when the farmer caught them in his garden?

Please lettuce alone.

CW24 Challenge

Problem Solving 4.6

Algebra: Expressions and Number Sentences

Understand → Plan → Solve → Check

Write the correct answer.

1. Mr. Lee is 53 years older than his 8-year-old grandson. How old is Mr. Lee? Write the operation sign that makes the number sentence true.

   $53 \oplus 8 = 61$ years old

2. Justin has 8 fewer videos than Jeff. Jeff has 24 videos. How many videos does Justin have? Write the operation sign that makes the number sentence true.

   $24 \ominus 8 = 16$

3. Ryan bought melons for a picnic. He gave the clerk \$10. He got \$3 in change. How much did the melons cost?

   $7

4. I am an odd number that rounds to 50. The sum of my digits is 11. What number am I?

   47

Choose the letter of the correct answer.

5. There were 15 boys and 16 girls at the meeting. Each person brought 2 stamps. How many stamps were brought in all?

   A 30 B 31 C 46 (D) 62

6. Gail has \$55.23. She spends \$15.35 on a video tape. Which expression shows this?

   (F) \$55.23 – \$15.35
   G \$15.35 – \$55.23
   H \$55.23 + \$15.35
   J \$55.23 > \$15.35

7. Which number completes this number sentence?
   $30 - \blacksquare = 13$

   A 28 B 27 C 23 (D) 17

8. Pat rode 2,358 feet on his bicycle. Matt rode 3,673 feet on his bicycle. How many more feet did Matt ride than Pat?

   F 6,031 feet G 1,375 feet H 1,325 feet (J) 1,315 feet

9. **Write About It** How did you solve Problem 7?

   Possible answer: I subtracted each of the choices from 30 to see which gave the answer of 13.

PS24 Problem Solving

3 PRACTICE

Guided Practice

Do Check Exercises 1–6 with your students. Identify students who are having difficulty and choose appropriate lesson resources to provide assistance.

Independent Practice

Note that Exercise 21 is a **multistep or strategy problem.** Assign Exercises 7–22.

ALGEBRAIC THINKING Have students explain how they would solve for the missing number in Exercises 15–20.

4 ASSESS

Summarize the lesson by having students:

DISCUSS What is an expression? Give an example. a part of a number sentence that contains numbers and operation signs; Possible answer: $32 - 14$

WRITE Use the expression 15 + 8 to write a word problem. Possible answer: Carly saw 15 sheep and 8 goats at the petting zoo. How many animals did she see?

LESSON QUIZ

Write an expression. Then write a number sentence to solve.

1. Jesse had 175 stickers. She gave 50 to her sister Lisa as a birthday present. How many stickers does Jesse have left? $175 - 50$; $175 - 50 = 125$; 125 stickers
2. Lisa had 60 stickers and received 50 more from her sister. How many stickers does Lisa have now? $60 + 50$; $60 + 50 = 110$; 110 stickers

Extra Practice

Purpose **To provide extra practice for the skills presented in this chapter**

The blue page references in each set of exercises refer to the lesson pages where each skill is taught.

Internet Resources

Visit THE LEARNING SITE at **www.harcourtschool.com** for a listing of practice activities.

Extra Practice

Set A (pp. 68–69)

Use rounding to estimate the sum.

1.	2.	3.	4.	5.
611	248	$5.63	1,659	2,798
+323	+174	+$4.27	+2,205	+4,568
900	**400**	**$10.00**	**4,000**	**8,000**

Use front-end estimation to estimate the sum.

6.	7.	8.	9.	10.
645	584	560	2,375	6,757
+594	+248	+439	+4,082	+4,446
1,100	**700**	**900**	**6,000**	**10,000**

Set B (pp. 72–73)

Find the sum. Estimate to check.

1.	2.	3.	4.	5.
365	789	4,978	$3.29	368
+521	+123	+2,234	+$5.75	919
886	**912**	**7,212**	**$9.04**	+453
				1,740

Set C (pp. 76–79)

Find the sum. Tell what method you used. **Methods will vary.**

1.	2.	3.	4.	5.
310	$8.40	618	6,247	3,485
+470	+$5.80	+143	+2,319	+9,856
780	**$14.20**	**761**	**8,566**	**13,341**

6. Estimate to decide if the sum 1,874 + 3,205 is greater than 4,000. Explain your answer. **2,000 + 3,000 = 5,000, so the answer is greater than 4,000.**

7. ALGEBRA Write the missing addend. 4,000 + ■ = 5,100 **1,100**

Set D (pp. 80–81)

Write + or – to complete the number sentence.

1. 8 ■ 15 = 23 **+**
2. 95 ■ 16 = 79 **–**
3. 517 ■ 483 = 1,000 **+**
4. 35 = 29 ■ 6 **+**
5. 42 ■ 9 = 51 **+**
6. 27 ■ 4 = 23 **–**
7. Shelby had $18.50. She spent $7.25 at the car wash. Write an expression that shows how much she spent. **$18.50 – $7.25**

82

CHAPTER 4

Review/Test

✓ CHECK VOCABULARY AND CONCEPTS

Choose the best term from the box.

regroup
estimate
front-end estimation

1. To find *about* how many, you can __?__. (p. 68) estimate
2. When you estimate a sum by adding the front digit of each addend, you are using __?__. (p. 68) front-end estimation

For 3, think of how to model 129 + 138. (pp. 70–71)

3. Do you need to regroup to find the sum 129 + 138? Explain. Yes, 9 + 8 = 17 ones. Regroup as 1 ten 7 ones.

✓ CHECK SKILLS

For 4–5, use rounding to estimate the sum. For 6–7, use front-end estimation to estimate the sum. (pp. 68–69)

4. 267 + 193 — 500
5. \$5.92 + \$3.25 — \$9.00
6. 420 + 589 — 900
7. 6,528 + 1,347 — 7,000

Find the sum. Estimate to check. (pp. 72–73, 76–79)

8. 419 + 451 = ■ 870
9. 321 + 683 = ■ 1,004
10. 127 + 315 + 299 = ■ 741
11. \$6.33 + \$2.98 — \$9.31
12. 5,436 + 7,695 — 13,131
13. 4,782 + 3,917 — 8,699
14. 3,764 + 8,109 — 11,873

Write + or – to complete the number sentence. (pp. 80–81)

15. 58 ● 12 = 46 –
16. 42 ● 67 = 109 +
17. 845 ● 369 = 476 –
18. 92 = 165 ● 73 –

✓ CHECK PROBLEM SOLVING

19. Mr. Samuel has 150 pennies in two jars. There are 40 more pennies in one jar than in the other. How many pennies are in each jar? (pp. 74–75) 55 in one, 95 in the other
20. Two numbers have a sum of 47. Their difference is 5. What are the two numbers? (pp. 74–75) 21, 26

Chapter 4 **83**

Review/Test

Purpose To check understanding of concepts, skills, and problem solving presented in Chapter 4

Using the Page

The Chapter 4 Review/Test can be used as a **review** or a **test**.

- Items 1–3 check understanding of concepts and new vocabulary.
- Items 4–18 check skill proficiency.
- Items 19–20 check students' abilities to choose and apply problem solving strategies to real-life addition problems.

Portfolio

Suggest that students place the completed Chapter 4 Review/Test in their portfolios.

Using the Assessment Guide

- Multiple-choice format of Chapter 4 Posttest— See *Assessment Guide*, pp. AG29–30.
- Free-response format of Chapter 4 Posttest— See *Assessment Guide*, pp. AG31–32.

Using Student Self-Assessment

The How Did I Do? survey helps students assess what they have learned and how they learned it. This survey is available as a copying master in *Assessment Guide*, p. AGxvii.

Chapter 4 Test, page 1

Choose the correct answer.

1. **Round to the nearest ten** to ESTIMATE the sum.
   235 + 552
   A 700 B 780 (C) 790 D 800
2. Which two numbers have a sum that is about 800?
   F 243 and 489 G 243 and 702 (H) 325 and 489 J 325 and 243
3. Which two numbers have a sum that is about 6,000?
   (A) 4,289 and 1,802 B 3,457 and 3,821 C 2,056 and 4,902 D 1,723 and 5,625
4. Use **front-end estimation** to ESTIMATE the sum.
   408 + 354
   F 600 (G) 700 H 800 J 900
5. 3,524 + 106
   A 3,520 B 3,620 (C) 3,630 D 3,720
6. 315 + 576
   F 881 (G) 891 H 981 J 8,811
7. \$3.50 + \$5.75
   A \$8.25 B \$8.45 C \$8.55 (D) \$9.25
8. 229 + 148 + 356
   F 913 (G) 733 H 725 J 713
9. 4,623 + 2,947
   A 7,581 B 7,580 (C) 7,570 D 7,560
10. The sum of two numbers is 35. Their difference is 9. What are the numbers?
    F 15 and 20 G 15 and 24 (H) 22 and 13 J 18 and 17

Go On

Chapter 4 Test, page 2

11. Joel has 210 baseball and football cards. He has 50 more baseball cards than football cards. How many of each does he have?
    (A) 130 baseball and 80 football B 120 baseball and 70 football C 110 baseball and 60 football D 80 baseball and 130 football
12. A parking lot has 85 cars and trucks in it. There are 17 more trucks than cars. How many of each are there?
    F 17 cars and 68 trucks G 23 cars and 62 trucks (H) 34 cars and 51 trucks J 40 cars and 45 trucks
13. 5,629 + 3,782 = ■
    (A) 9,411 B 9,402 C 8,311 D 8,301
14. \$25.83 + \$65.27 = ■
    (F) \$91.10 G \$90.10 H \$80.10 J \$80.00
15. Gina has \$34.75. She earns \$15.95. How much money does she have in all?
    A \$40.70 B \$49.60 C \$49.70 (D) \$50.70
16. 5,781 + 2,653 = ■
    F 7,334 G 7,434 H 8,334 (J) 8,434
17. A high school has 1,523 students. Another high school has 2,079 students. How many students are there in the two schools altogether?
    A 3,692 (B) 3,602 C 3,593 D 3,592
18. José has 85 more colored pencils than pens. He has 49 pens. Which expression shows how many colored pencils he has?
    F 85 – 49 (G) 49 + 85 H 85 + 85 J 49 + 49
19. A store has 24 blue, 49 white, 18 red, and 33 black shirts. Which expression can be used to find how many more white than red shirts there are?
    A 49 + 18 (B) 49 – 18 C 33 – 18 D 49 – 24
20. What is the missing number?
    205 + ■ = 430
    F 635 G 235 (H) 225 J 175

Stop

Getting Ready for the EOG Test
Chapters 1–4

Using the Pages

These pages may be used to help students get ready for the North Carolina EOG Test. The test items are written in the same style and arranged in the same format as those on the EOG Test.

The pages are cumulative. They cover the standards from the North Carolina Mathematics Standard Course of Study that have been taught up to this point in the text or in a previous grade. Each Getting Ready for the EOG Test also reviews the North Carolina mathematics strands shown below.

- Number and Operations
- Measurement
- Geometry
- Data Analysis and Probability
- Algebra

These pages can be assigned at the end of the chapter as classwork or as a homework assignment. You may want to have students use individual recording sheets presented in a multiple-choice (standardized) format. A Test Answer Sheet is available as a blackline master in the *Assessment Guide* (p. AGlii).

You may wish to have students describe how they solved each problem and share their solutions.

Getting Ready for the EOG Test

NUMBER AND OPERATIONS

TIP **Eliminate choices.** See item 1. Look at the thousands place first. Eliminate any choices whose digits are greatest.

1. Ted wants to order these numbers from *least* to *greatest*.

   2,879; 3,798; 2,897

   What should he write? **C**

   A 3,798; 2,897; 2,879
   B 2,897; 2,879; 3,798
   C 2,879; 2,897; 3,798
   D 2,879; 3,798; 2,897

2. Which number can be written as $400 + 10 + 3$? **B**

   A 431 C 314
   B 413 D 143

3. Which is fifty thousand three written in standard form? **A**

   A 50,003 C 50,033
   B 53,000 D 50,300

4. **Explain It** The Oakdale Band has to sell 1,500 raffle tickets to buy new uniforms. Last week, band members sold 768 raffle tickets. They sold 622 tickets this week. Explain how you can estimate whether the band has sold enough tickets to buy the uniforms. **See page 85.**

MEASUREMENT AND GEOMETRY

5. The Earth is close to the shape of which solid figure? **B**

   A cube
   B sphere
   C cylinder
   D cone

6. What unit of measure would be most appropriate to determine the length of a crayon? **A**

   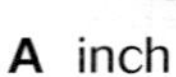

   A inch
   B cup
   C pound
   D gallon

7. What unit of measure would be most appropriate to determine the weight of a pencil? **C**

   A meter C gram
   B liter D kilogram

8. **Explain It** Fernando said this figure has 2 lines of symmetry. Explain whether you agree or disagree. **See page 85.**

   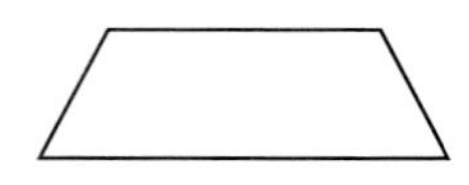

ALGEBRA

9. Which are the next two figures in this pattern? **A**

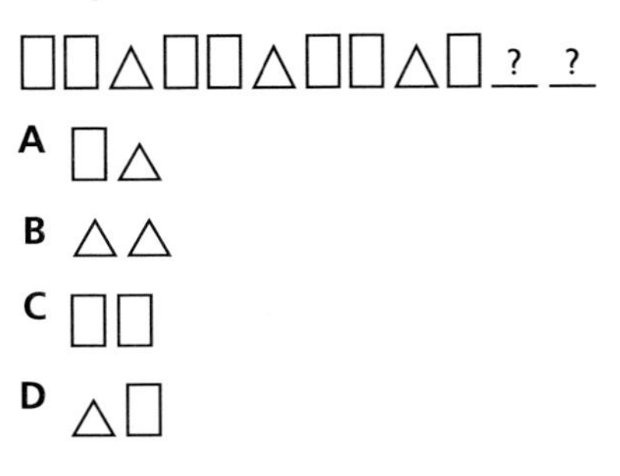

10. On Monday, Griffin's class sold 6 tickets for the fall festival. On Tuesday, the students sold 12 tickets. On Wednesday, 18 tickets were sold. If this pattern continues, how many tickets will be sold on Friday? **D**

A 20
B 22
C 24
D 30

11. Explain It Laura wants to know how much it will cost to buy four tickets to the fall festival. Explain how she can find the cost.

FALL FESTIVAL TICKETS	
Number of Tickets	**Cost**
1	$7.00
2	$14.00
3	$21.00
4	■

See below.

DATA ANALYSIS AND PROBABILITY

12. Kareem listed the ages of people attending a concert in this tally table.

AGES OF PEOPLE	
Age	**Tally**
19	|||
20	卌 |
21	||||
22	卌 ||

How many people in all attended the concert? **C**

A 12 **C** 20
B 17 **D** 22

13. Use the table above. What age was listed most often? **D**

A 19 **C** 21
B 20 **D** 22

14. Explain It The bar graph below shows the favorite winter sports of Tamara's classmates. How many more students voted for snowboarding than skiing? Explain how you found your answer.

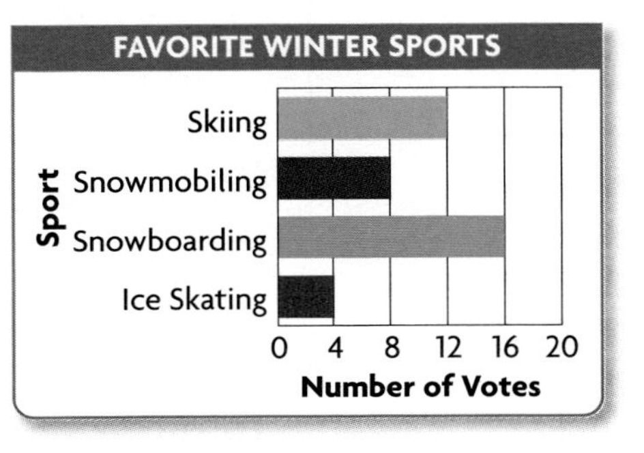

Chapters 1–4

Item Analysis

You may wish to use the item analysis to determine which North Carolina standards need additional review.

Item	North Carolina Standard	Lesson
1	1.01	3.3
2	1.01	2.2
3	1.01	2.6
4	1.02	4.1
5	(1) 3.02	Grade 1
6	(2) Goal 2	Grade 2
7	(2) Goal 2	Grade 2
8	(2) 3.03	Grade 2
9	(2) 5.01	Grade 2
10	(2) 5.01	Grade 2
11	(2) 5.01	Grade 2
12	(2) Goal 4	Grade 2
13	(2) Goal 4	Grade 2
14	(2) Goal 4	Grade 2

SCORING RUBRIC
Explain It

2 Demonstrates a complete understanding of the problem and chooses an appropriate strategy to determine the solution

1 Demonstrates a partial understanding of the problem and chooses a strategy that does not lead to a complete and accurate solution

0 Demonstrates little understanding of the problem and shows little evidence of using any strategy to determine a solution

Explain It • Written Response

4. Possible answer: you can use front-end estimation. 700 + 600 = 1,300; 1,300 < 1,500. The band has not sold enough tickets.

8. Disagree; there is only 1 line of symmetry.

11. Possible answer: find a pattern in the table. Add $7.00 for each ticket. Four tickets will cost $28.00. $21.00 + $7.00 = $28.00

14. 4 more students; possible answer: subtract the number of votes for skiing from the votes for snowboarding.

Subtraction

NCTM Standards 2000

1. Number and Operations
Lessons 5.1, 5.2, 5.3, 5.4, 5.5, 5.6
2. Algebra
Lessons 5.3, 5.4, 5.5
3. Geometry
4. Measurement
5. Data Analysis and Probability
6. Problem Solving
Lessons 5.1, 5.2, 5.3, 5.4, 5.5, 5.6
7. Reasoning and Proof
Lessons 5.2, 5.3, 5.4, 5.5, 5.6
8. Communication
Lessons 5.2, 5.3, 5.4, 5.5, 5.6
9. Connections
Lessons 5.1, 5.3, 5.4, 5.5
10. Representation
Lessons 5.2, 5.3, 5.6

Chapter Planner

Getting Ready for Chapter 5 • Assessing Prior Knowledge and INTERVENTION (See PE and TE page 87.)

LESSON	NORTH CAROLINA STANDARDS	PACING	VOCABULARY*	MATERIALS	RESOURCES AND TECHNOLOGY
5.1 Estimate Differences pp. 88–89 **Objective** To estimate differences of 2- to 4-digit numbers	1.02b *also* 1.06	1 Day			Reteach, Practice, Problem Solving, Challenge 5.1 Worksheets Transparency 5.1 **Intervention,** *Skills 12–13, 15* (CD or Book)
5.2 Hands On: Subtraction with Regrouping pp. 90–91 **Objective** To explore subtracting 3-digit numbers with regrouping	1.02a	2 Days (For Lessons 5.2 and 5.3)		*For each group* base-ten blocks	Reteach, Practice, Problem Solving, Challenge 5.2 Worksheets Transparency 5.2 **Intervention,** *Skills 12–13, 15* (CD or Book) **Harcourt Mega Math Country Countdown,** *Block Busters*
5.3 Subtract Across Zeros pp. 92–95 **Objective** To subtract 3-digit numbers with and without regrouping, including numbers with zeros in the minuend	1.02a				Reteach, Practice, Problem Solving, Challenge 5.3 Worksheets Transparency 5.3 **Intervention,** *Skills 12–13, 15* (CD or Book)
5.4 Subtract 3- and 4-Digit Numbers pp. 96–97 **Objective** To subtract 3- and 4-digit numbers with and without regrouping	1.02a	1 Day			Reteach, Practice, Problem Solving, Challenge 5.4 Worksheets Transparency 5.4 **Intervention,** *Skills 12–13, 15* (CD or Book) **Harcourt Mega Math The Number Games,** *Tiny's Think Tank*
5.5 Choose a Method pp. 98–101 **Objective** To choose paper and pencil, a calculator, or mental math to subtract 4-digit numbers	1.06 *also* 1.02	2 Days			Reteach, Practice, Problem Solving, Challenge 5.5 Worksheets Transparency 5.5 **Intervention,** *Skills 12–13, 15* (CD or Book)
5.6 Problem Solving Skill: Estimate or Exact Answer pp. 102–103 **Objective** To identify whether an estimate or an exact answer is needed to solve a problem	1.02b	1 Day			Reteach, Practice, Reading Strategy, Challenge 5.6 Worksheets Transparency 5.6 Scaffolded Instruction Transparency 5 Reading Transparency 5 **Intervention • Problem Solving,** *Strategy/Skill 5* (CD or Book)

Ending Chapter 5 • **Extra Practice,** p. 104 • **Chapter 5 Review/Test,** p. 105 • **Getting Ready for the EOG Test,** pp. 106–107

Vocabulary Power

Review Vocabulary

To be ready for Chapter 5, students should know the following vocabulary terms:

- **subtract** (p. 87)—to find the difference between two quantities
- **estimate** (p. 88)—*verb:* to find about how much or how many; *noun:* an approximate amount
- **rounding** (p. 88)—a method of estimating by substituting a number that is close
- **front-end estimation** (p. 88)—a method of estimating in which only the front digits are used
- **regrouping** (p. 90)—exchanging amounts of equal value to rename a number

Vocabulary Cards

There are no key words in this chapter, but mathematics vocabulary is reinforced visually and verbally. Encourage students to review the mathematics vocabulary in their journals.

Multimedia Math Glossary

For vocabulary support, visit **www.harcourtschool.com/mathglossary**

Math Journal

Have students list each review vocabulary term. Then have them use each vocabulary term in a sentence.

MATH Word Work

Objective To reinforce vocabulary concepts
Use after Lesson 5.2.

Materials *For each student* Regrouping Workmat, *Teacher's Resource Book*, p. TR21; base-ten blocks

Have students write 316 − 257 on a workmat. Ask students to estimate the difference and to record the estimate on the workmat. Then have students model the problem using base-ten blocks. Students should begin by using base-ten blocks to show the greatest number. Direct them to find the difference, regrouping when necessary.

Have students take turns describing their solutions to the class. Ask students to describe the method they used to estimate, how they regrouped the base-ten blocks to find the difference, and how the difference compares to the estimate. As time allows, have students write a new subtraction problem to model with base-ten blocks.

Workmat 6

Hundreds	Tens	Ones
316 − 257 Estimate: 100		

Subtraction

Mathematics Across the Grades

LOOKING BACK • Prerequisite Skills

To be ready for Chapter 5, students should have the following understandings and skills:

- **Subtraction Facts**—automatic recall of basic facts
- **2-Digit Subtraction**—application of basic facts and regrouping with tens and ones

Check What You Know

Use page 87 to determine students' knowledge of prerequisite concepts and skills.

Intervention

Help students prepare for the chapter by using the intervention resources described on TE page 87.

LOOKING AT CHAPTER 5 • Essential Skills

Students will

- estimate differences of 2- to 4-digit numbers.
- **subtract 2-, 3-, and 4-digit numbers with and without regrouping, including numbers with zeros in the minuend.**
- choose paper and pencil, a calculator, or mental math to subtract 4-digit numbers.
- identify whether an estimate or an exact answer is needed to solve a problem.

Example

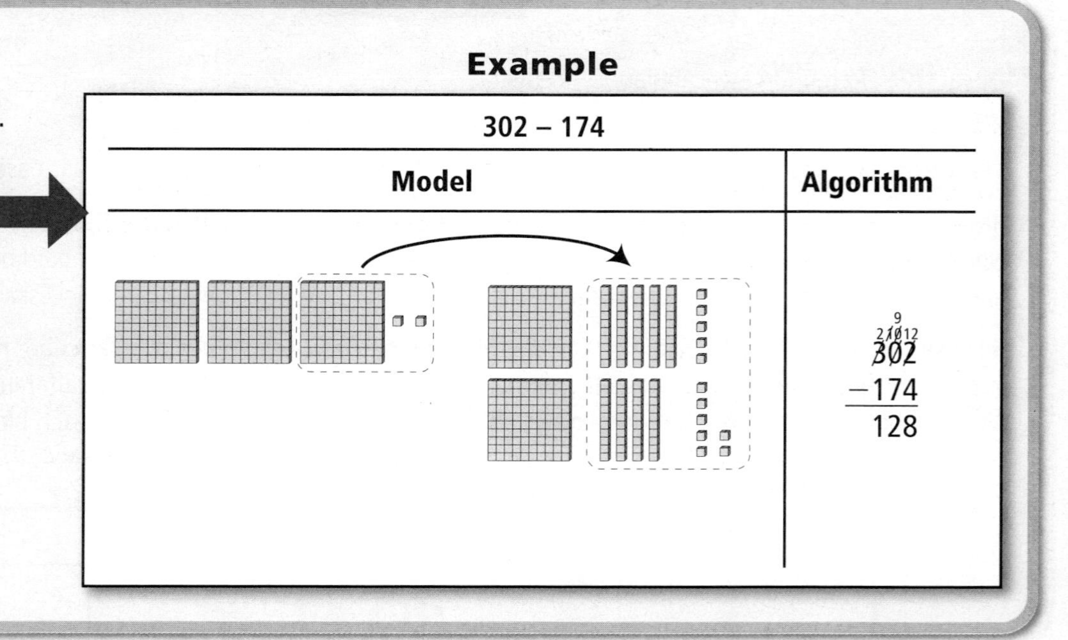

LOOKING AHEAD • Applications

Students will apply what they learn in Chapter 5 to the following new concepts:

- Subtract Money (Chapter 6)
- Write Number Sentences (Chapter 12)
- Relate Subtraction and Division (Chapter 12)
- Write Expressions and Equations (Chapter 13)

Differentiated Instruction

Meeting the Needs of All Learners

Extra Support	Activities for All	Enrichment
Alternative Teaching Strategy TE Lessons 5.1, 5.2, 5.3, 5.4, 5.5, 5.6 **ESOL/ESL** TE Lessons 5.1, 5.2, 5.3, 5.4, 5.5, 5.6 **Special Needs** TE Lesson 5.3	**Cross-Curricular Connections** **Math:** TE Lesson 5.3 **Reading:** TE Lesson 5.6 **Social Studies:** Chapter Opener, TE Lesson 5.6 **Vocabulary:** TE p. 86B, TE Lesson 5.6, PE/TE p. 87 **Writing:** TE Lesson 5.5	**Advanced Learners** TE Lessons 5.2, 5.5 **Early Finishers** TE Lessons 5.1, 5.2, 5.4

Combination and Multi-age Classrooms

Grade 2	Grade 3	Grade 4
Skills Trace Across the Grades		
Estimate differences; subtract 1- and 2-digit numbers with and without regrouping; use addition to check subtraction.	**Estimate and find differences of 2- to 4-digit numbers with and without regrouping.**	Estimate and find differences of 4- to 6-digit numbers; use mental math strategies; write, evaluate, and interpret subtraction expressions that contain parentheses.
Instructional Strategies		
Students on this level may require more time to build conceptual understanding. **Assignments** **Grade 3 Pupil Edition** • Have students work in pairs on Lessons 5.1, 5.2, 5.3, 5.4, and 5.5. **Grade 2 Pupil Edition**—pages 81–95, 141–174, 185–190, and 509–514	Students on this level should be able to complete all the lessons in the Pupil Edition and all the activities in the Teacher's Edition with minimal adjustments. **Assignment** **Grade 3 Pupil Edition**—pages 86–105	Students on this level will probably require less time to build conceptual understanding. **Assignments** **Grade 3 Pupil Edition** • Compact Lessons 5.2, 5.3, and 5.4. **Grade 4 Pupil Edition**—pages 38–59, 62–83

CHAPTER 5

Subtraction

Introducing the Chapter

Students will use the same concepts and skills to regroup numbers in subtraction as they did in the previous addition chapter. What is the difference in the number of miles of the Trail in Maine and the number of miles in New Hampshire? 120 miles

Using Data

To begin the study of this chapter, have students

- Subtract the number of miles of the Trail in New Jersey from the number of miles of the Trail in New York. 14 miles
- Which two states have the least number of miles of the Trail? Maryland and West Virginia How many more miles of Trail does Maryland have than West Virginia has? 41 − 2 = 39 more miles
- Which two states have the greatest number of miles of the Trail? Virginia and North Carolina How many more miles of Trail does Virginia have than North Carolina? 544 − 292 = 252 more miles

Problem Solving Project

Purpose To compare the lengths of hiking trails to other trails in your state

Grouping Small groups

Background One end of the Appalachian Trail is Mt. Katahdin in Maine. The other end is Springer Mountain in Georgia.

UNDERSTAND • PLAN • SOLVE • CHECK

Have students

- Research, on the website for your state, the total mileage of hiking trails in your state or in a state park.
- Compare that mileage to the total lengths of other types of trails in your state, such as those for skiing, biking, horseback riding, and so on.
- Use the data to write and solve subtraction problems.

Graphing Investigations
Begin Week 5.

CHAPTER 5 Subtraction

FAST FACT • SOCIAL STUDIES The Appalachian Trail is over 2,100 miles long. It goes through 14 states from Maine to Georgia. It would take an experienced hiker about 180 days to travel from one end to the other.

PROBLEM SOLVING The table shows how many miles of the Trail are in each state. How many more miles are in Virginia than in Vermont?

398 miles

APPALACHIAN TRAIL

State	Number of Miles
Maine	281
New Hampshire	161
Vermont	146
Massachusetts	90
Connecticut	52
New York	88
New Jersey	74
Pennsylvania	232
Maryland	41
West Virginia	2
Virginia	544
Tennessee	88
North Carolina	292
Georgia	75

86

WHY LEARN MATH? Field biologists often count animal species to find out whether a species is surviving. When they compare the data, they can tell if the number is increasing or decreasing. Ask: If 150 cardinals were counted one year and 154 cardinals were counted the following year, what conclusion could you draw about the health of the species? Possible answer: that it was relatively stable

Family Involvement Activities

These activities provide:

- Letter to the Family
- Math Vocabulary
- Family Game
- Practice (Homework)

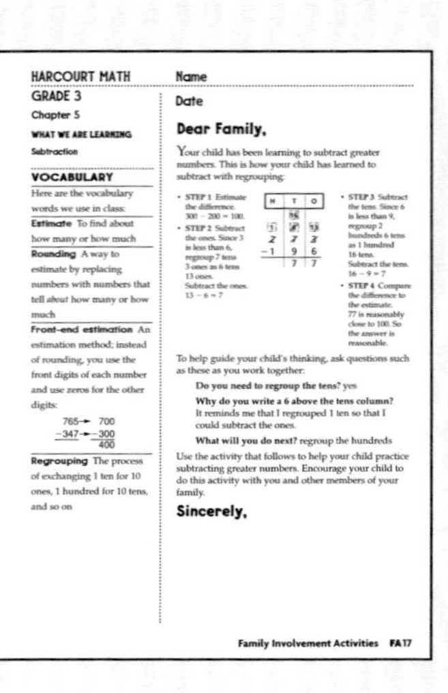
HARCOURT MATH
GRADE 3
Chapter 5
WHAT WE ARE LEARNING
Subtraction

Name
Date

Dear Family,

Your child has been learning to subtract greater numbers. This is how your child has learned to subtract with regrouping.

VOCABULARY

Sincerely,

Family Involvement Activities FA17

Family Involvement Activities, p. FA17

Use this page to help you review and remember important skills needed for Chapter 5.

SUBTRACTION FACTS

1. 12 − 9 = 3	2. 15 − 7 = 8	3. 12 − 8 = 4	4. 14 − 6 = 8	5. 13 − 5 = 8
6. 13 − 7 = 6	7. 14 − 9 = 5	8. 12 − 7 = 5	9. 13 − 4 = 9	10. 16 − 7 = 9
11. 15 − 6 = 9	12. 18 − 9 = 9	13. 17 − 8 = 9	14. 16 − 9 = 7	15. 14 − 7 = 7

2-DIGIT SUBTRACTION

Subtract.

16. 56 − 4 = 52	17. 49 − 36 = 13	18. 67 − 15 = 52	19. 95 − 50 = 45	20. 38 − 9 = 29
21. 33 − 18 = 15	22. 90 − 48 = 42	23. 98 − 17 = 81	24. 57 − 27 = 30	25. 25 − 19 = 6

REVIEW

subtract [səb•trakt′] *verb*

The word *subtract* begins with *sub*, which means "under" or "below." The second part of the word, *tract*, means "to pull" or "to carry away." What word beginning with the word part *tract* names a machine that is used to pull or to carry?
tractor

GO ON-LINE www.harcourtschool.com/mathglossary

Assessing Prior Knowledge

Use the **Check What You Know** page to determine whether your students have mastered the prerequisite skills critical for this chapter.

Intervention

- **Diagnose and Prescribe**
  Evaluate your students' performance on this page to determine whether intervention is necessary or if enrichment is appropriate. Options that provide instruction, practice, and a check are listed in the chart below.

CHECK WHAT YOU KNOW RESOURCES

Intervention Copying Masters or CD-ROMs

Enrichment Copying Masters

VOCABULARY POWER

For activities and information about the vocabulary in this chapter, see page 86B.

Were students successful with CHECK WHAT YOU KNOW?

IF . . . NO THEN . . . INTERVENE — INTERVENTION OPTIONS — IF . . . YES THEN . . . ENRICH

Skill/Items	Missed more than	Intervene with
Subtraction Facts, 1–15	4	• *Intervention*, Skills 12–13
2-Digit Subtraction, 16–25	3	• *Intervention*, Skill 15

Skill/Items	Missed fewer than	Enrich with
Subtraction Facts, 1–15	5	• *Intervention*, Enrichment p. IN337
2-Digit Subtraction, 16–25	4	• *Intervention*, Enrichment p. IN338

Lesson 5.1

Estimate Differences

Lesson Planning

Objective To estimate differences of 2- to 4-digit numbers

NCTM Standards

1. Number and Operations
6. Problem Solving
9. Connections

Math Background

Consider these ideas when introducing estimating differences with 2- to 4-digit numbers.

- Rounding is one way to estimate differences. To round numbers, determine the digit to be rounded. Look at the digit to its right. If it is 0–4, the digit in the rounding place stays the same. If it is 5 or more, the digit in the rounding place increases by 1.
- Front-end estimation is another way to estimate differences. To use front-end estimation, subtract the front digit of each number. Write zeros for the other digits.
- Unless students are told to estimate to a specific place, estimates may vary. Accept reasonable estimates.
- Estimating has value in real-life situations and may be preferred to finding the exact difference in certain situations.

Warm-Up Resources

Number of the Day

Transparency 5.1

Use a calendar to find the number of days you have been in school so far this year. Check students' work.

Review Basic Facts

Daily Facts Practice

Have students practice addition and subtraction facts by completing Set D of *Teacher's Resource Book*, p. TR86.

Solve a Problem

Transparency 5.1

Problem of the Day

The sum of the digits in a 3-digit number is 6. If the digits are rearranged to make the new number, 321, the difference between the two numbers is 198. What is the number? 123

Solution Problem of the Day tab, p. PD5

Intervention and Extension Resources

Alternative Teaching Strategy

MATERIALS *For each group* number lines, p. TR6

Have students use a number line to **estimate differences**.

- Give them a number line from 0 to 1,000 with increments of 100. Have them place a mark between hundreds to show 50 (halfway) as a benchmark.
- Have students estimate the difference of 489 and 607 by rounding. To do so, have students find the nearest hundreds for 489 and 607. 500, 600
- Have students find the difference between 600 and 500. 100

VISUAL

VISUAL/SPATIAL

Multistep and Strategy Problems

The following multistep or strategy problem is provided in Lesson 5.1:

Page	Item
89	20

ESOL/ESL

MATERIALS *For each group* number lines, p. TR5

Help pairs of students **practice identifying rounded numbers** by having them play "Guess the Number."

- Label the number line from 0 to 20.
- Have one student give a clue such as: I am thinking of a number that rounds to 10. It is 2 greater than 7. What is the number? 9
- The partner repeats the clue, names the number, and finds it on the number line. The student may tap the number on the desk after identifying it.
- Then use a number line to 100. Have students repeat the steps above, finding numbers that round to the nearest ten. Check students' work.

AUDITORY, KINESTHETIC

VERBAL/LINGUISTIC

Early Finishers

Have students **estimate differences**.

Provide the following numbers: 43, 154, 57, 239, 592, 91, 811, and 167.

- Have students find two numbers whose difference is about 30; about 50; about 400; and about 600. Encourage students to use either rounding or front-end estimation. 91, 57; 91, 43; 592, 239; 811, 239
- Have them work with a partner to write and solve similar problems using the numbers above. Check students' work.

VISUAL

INTERPERSONAL/SOCIAL

Intervention, *Skills 12–13, 15*

The Harcourt Learning Site
www.harcourtschool.com

Lesson 5.1 Organizer

Objective To estimate differences of 2- to 4-digit numbers

Vocabulary *Review* estimate

1 INTRODUCE

QUICK REVIEW provides review of prerequisite skills.

WHY LEARN THIS? You can estimate a difference to find about how many more. *Share the lesson objective with students.*

2 TEACH

Guided Instruction

- *Discuss the Learn section.*
  In the rounding example, why do you round to the nearest hundred? Possible answer: you are working with 3-digit numbers.
  In the front-end estimation example, explain why it is not difficult to estimate the difference. Possible answer: You only have to subtract the digits in the hundreds place.
- *Check students' understanding of the additional examples.*
  In Example A, why do you round $8.95 to $9.00? The digit in the tens place is 9; when the digit to the right of a place you are rounding is 5 or more, the digit in the rounding place increases by 1.
  REASONING In Example B, would the estimate be different if you used rounding? Explain. No; The numbers would round to 7,000 and 5,000. The difference would still be 2,000.
  REASONING Rounded to the nearest ten, how many more nests were counted on Charlotte County beaches than on Manatee County beaches? 470

LESSON 1

Estimate Differences

Quick Review

1. 50 − 30 20
2. 40 − 10 30
3. 35 − 10 25
4. 60 − 20 40
5. 50 − 40 10

Learn

TRACKING TURTLES Scientists counted the number of loggerhead sea turtle nests found on southwest Florida beaches in 2001. About how many more nests were counted on Charlotte County beaches than on Manatee County beaches?

To find *about* how many more, you can estimate.

LOGGERHEAD SEA TURTLE NESTS

County	Nests Found
Charlotte	775
Collier	954
Lee	660
Manatee	306

Example

One Way Use rounding. Round each number to the nearest hundred. Subtract.

775 → 800
−306 → −300
500

Another Way Use front-end estimation. Subtract, using the front digit of each number. Write zeros for the other digits.

775 → 700
−306 → −300
400

So, both 500 and 400 are reasonable estimates of how many more nests were counted.

More Examples

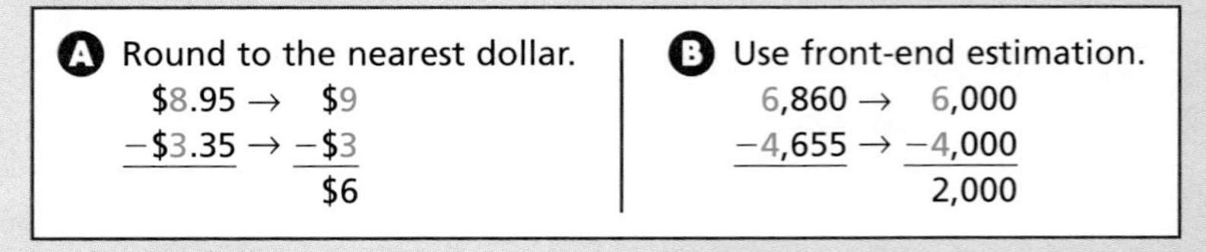

A Round to the nearest dollar.

$8.95 → $9
−$3.35 → −$3
$6

B Use front-end estimation.

6,860 → 6,000
−4,655 → −4,000
2,000

Sometimes it makes sense to round to a different place. Try estimating 341 − 265 to the nearest hundred.

341 → 300
−265 → −300
0

Then round to the nearest ten to get a closer estimate.

341 → 340
−265 → −270
70

88

Reteach 5.1

Estimate Differences

You can use **rounding** or **front-end estimation** to estimate this difference. 345 − 166

A. Use rounding.
You are rounding to the nearest hundred, so look at the tens digit of each number. Write the rounded numbers. Then subtract.

345 Think: 4 < 5, so round 345 to 300. → 300
− 166 Think: 6 > 5, so round 166 to 200. → − 200
Estimate → 100

B. Use front-end estimation.
You are subtracting the front digits of the numbers. Write the front digit of each number. Write zeros for the other digits. Then subtract.

345 → 300
− 166 → − 100
Estimate → 200

Estimate the difference by using rounding and front-end estimation.

	ROUNDING	FRONT-END ESTIMATION
1. 631 − 258	600 − 300 = 300	600 − 200 = 400
2. $7.95 − $3.12	$8 − $3 = $5	$7 − $3 = $4
3. 6,671 − 1,725	7,000 − 2,000 = 5,000	6,000 − 1,000 = 5,000

Reteach RW25

Practice 5.1

Estimate Differences

Use rounding to estimate the difference.

1. 59 → 60; − 16 → − 20; 40
2. $8.17 → $8; − $5.51 → − $6; $2
3. 8,909 → 9,000; − 2,408 → − 2,000; 7,000

Use front-end estimation to estimate the difference.

4. 83 → 80; − 38 → − 30; 50
5. 5,501 → 5,000; − 3,288 → − 3,000; 2,000
6. $8.15 → $8; − $4.37 → − $4; $4

Estimate the difference. Round to the place that makes sense.

7. 728 → 730; − 684 → − 680; 50
8. 504 → 500; − 467 → − 470; 30
9. 8,316 → 8,300; − 7,923 → − 7,900; 400

Mixed Review

Write the missing number.

10. 8, 13, 18, 23, 28
11. 16, 23, 30, 37, 44
12. 11, 20, 29, 38, 47

Write the value of the underlined digit.

13. 53,980 50,000
14. 46,831 30
15. $367.15 $300

Add.

16. 3,483 + 547 = 4,030
17. 1,209 + 593 = 1,802
18. 1,756 + 8,394 = 10,150
19. 7,674 + 3,421 = 11,095
20. 54 + 24 + 17 = 95
21. 31 + 31 + 39 = 101
22. 35 + 26 + 13 = 74
23. 42 + 63 + 12 = 117

Practice PW25

Check

1. Explain how you would estimate 201 − 181. Tell which method you chose and why. See above.

1. Possible answer: round each number to the nearest ten. 200 − 180 = 20. I rounded to the place that makes sense. If I round to the nearest hundred, the estimated difference is 0.

20. Possible answer: about 4 loggerhead turtles; a loggerhead weighs about 200 pounds. A leatherback weighs about 800 pounds. 200 + 200 + 200 + 200 = 800.

For 2–4, use rounding to estimate the difference. For 5–6, use front-end estimation to estimate the difference.
For 2–4, possible estimates are given.

2. 87 − 32 → 60
3. 478 − 115 → 400
4. \$9.01 − \$2.60 → \$6
5. 813 − 491 → 400
6. 5,020 − 1,750 → 4,000

Practice and Problem Solving

Extra Practice, page 104, Set A

Use rounding to estimate the difference. For 7–11, possible estimates are given.

7. 42 − 19 → 20
8. 613 − 371 → 200
9. \$7.08 − \$3.80 → \$3
10. 625 − 489 → 100
11. 4,819 − 1,966 → 3,000

Use front-end estimation to estimate the difference.

12. 84 − 23 → 60
13. 880 − 114 → 700
14. 322 − 199 → 200
15. \$5.17 − \$1.01 → \$4
16. 3,288 − 1,255 → 2,000

Estimate the difference. Round to the place that makes sense. Possible estimates are given.

17. 422 − 394 → 30
18. 302 − 277 → 20
19. 4,411 − 3,509 → 900

20. Look at the table. How many loggerhead turtles weigh about the same as one leatherback turtle? Explain. See above.

21. **Write a problem** using estimation and subtraction. Use the table at the right. Tell which method you would use to estimate the difference. Explain your choice. Check students' problems.

ADULT SEA TURTLE WEIGHTS

Sea Turtle	Weight in Pounds
Loggerhead	185
Hawksbill	125
Leatherback	779

Getting Ready for the EOG Test

22. Nick bought tuna salad. Jana bought cheese sticks. *About* how much more did Nick spend than Jana? C

A \$5.00 B \$4.00 C \$3.00 D \$2.00

MENU
Tuna Salad........\$4.75
Egg Salad.........\$3.50
Burger Plate......\$6.99
Cheese Sticks....\$1.79

North Carolina Standards 1.02 Develop fluency with multi-digit addition and subtraction through 9,999 using: b) Estimation of sums and differences in appropriate situations. *also* 1.06

3 PRACTICE

Guided Practice

Do Check Exercises 1–6 with your students. Identify students who are having difficulty and choose appropriate lesson resources to provide assistance.

Independent Practice

Note that Exercise 20 is a **multistep or strategy problem.** Assign Exercises 7–21.

4 ASSESS

Summarize the lesson by having students:

Discuss Explain how you would estimate to find about how many more. You can round both numbers to the place value that makes sense and subtract the rounded numbers or you can subtract the front-end digits.

Write List two numbers that would round to 50 and two that would round to 200. Explain. Possible answer: 49, 51; 175, 249; Check students' explanations.

LESSON QUIZ Transparency 5.1

Use rounding to estimate the difference. Possible estimates are given.

1. 467 − 375 → 100
2. 7,640 − 5,500 → 2,000

Use front-end estimation to estimate the difference.

3. \$4.89 − \$1.75 → \$3.00
4. 5,736 − 4,281 → 1,000

Challenge 5.1

Estimate Differences

Work with a partner.

Materials:
- one number cube, with numbers 0–5
- one number cube, with numbers 1–6
- one number cube, with numbers 4–9

How to Play:
The object of the game is to get the greatest number of points.

Step 1 The first player rolls the three number cubes. This person arranges the cubes to make a 3-digit number. This person also rounds the number to the nearest hundred and writes it down.

Step 2 The second player rolls the three number cubes. This person arranges the cubes to make a 3-digit number that can be subtracted from the number the first player wrote down.

Step 3 The first player rounds that 3-digit number to the nearest hundred and subtracts it from the number that was written down.

Step 4 The answer to the estimated difference is the number of points the first player gets.

Take turns repeating Steps 1–4.

After playing the game, answer these questions.

1. What strategies did you use?
Possible answer: When I was the first player, I tried to make my 3-digit number the greatest number possible. When I was the second player, I tried to make the number subtracted the greatest number possible.

What was the most difficult part of playing this game?
Possible answer: It was hard to decide which 3-digit number to make for my partner to subtract. I had to be sure my partner would get the least number of points possible.

Challenge CW25

Problem Solving 5.1

Estimate Differences

Understand → Plan → Solve → Check

Write the correct answer.

1. The left side of the auditorium seats 865. The right side seats 783. How many seats are there altogether?
1,648 seats

2. There are 1,376 people seated in a stadium that can seat 2,950. About how many more people can be seated in the stadium?
Possible answer: about 2,000 more people

3. Tom had 56¢. He spent 35¢ on a pencil. How much does he have left?
21¢

4. Paula has \$495. She spends \$219 on airline tickets to Florida. About how much does she have left?
about \$300

Choose the letter of the correct answer.

5. A number is greater than 423 + 378 and less than 159 + 644. What is the number?
A 797 Ⓒ 802
B 801 D 803

6. Which number shows four thousand, six hundred eight written in standard form?
F 468 H 4,680
Ⓖ 4,608 J 46,008

7. Use rounding to estimate the difference between 4,126 and 8,970.
A 3,000 Ⓒ 5,000
B 4,000 D 13,000

8. The difference between two numbers is about 200. One number is 691. Which number could be the other number?
F 953 H 567
G 819 Ⓙ 515

9. **Write About It** In Problem 4, how did you decide what to round the numbers to?
Possible answer: \$495 is closer to \$500 than to \$400. \$219 is closer to \$200 than to \$300.

Problem Solving PS25

Lesson 5.2

Subtraction with Regrouping

Lesson Planning

Objective To explore subtracting 3-digit numbers with regrouping

Materials *For each group* base-ten blocks

NCTM Standards
1. Number and Operations
6. Problem Solving
7. Reasoning and Proof
8. Communication
10. Representation

Math Background

Consider the following when having students explore subtraction of 3-digit numbers with and without regrouping.

- The process of regrouping can be modeled with base-ten blocks.
- Each place value should be evaluated to determine whether regrouping is needed.
- The steps in the process of regrouping should be recorded in the correct place-value position.

Warm-Up Resources

Number of the Day

Transparency 5.2

The number of the day is 15. Write five subtraction sentences that use this number. Possible answer: $20 - 15 = 5$; $15 - 5 = 10$; $15 - 14 = 1$; $25 - 15 = 10$; $15 - 8 = 7$

Daily Facts Practice

Have students practice addition facts by completing Set E of *Teacher's Resource Book*, p. TR86.

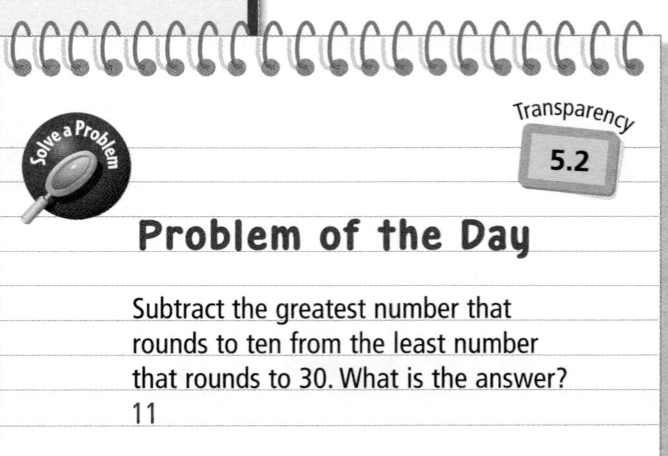

Problem of the Day

Subtract the greatest number that rounds to ten from the least number that rounds to 30. What is the answer? 11

Solution Problem of the Day tab, p. PD5

Intervention and Extension Resources

Alternative Teaching Strategy

MATERIALS *For each group* base-ten blocks, place-value workmat, p. TR12

Have students **model subtracting 3-digit numbers with regrouping**. Have them represent the steps of the subtraction process by keeping the correct numbers of blocks within the correct columns on the place-value workmat. As students work through the steps, reinforce that they are renaming values, such as renaming 1 hundred as 10 tens, in order to regroup them. Check students' work.

KINESTHETIC

BODILY/KINESTHETIC

Multistep and Strategy Problems

The following multistep or strategy problem is provided in Lesson 5.2:

Page	Item
91	7

Advanced Learners

Challenge students to **solve 4-digit subtraction problems with regrouping**. Have them write five subtraction problems with 4-digit numbers that require regrouping more than once. Then have students exchange problems with a partner and solve. Check students' work.

VISUAL

INTRAPERSONAL/INTROSPECTIVE

Early Finishers

MATERIALS *For each pair* number cubes

Have students who finish early **write and solve 3-digit subtraction problems**. Have each student roll a number cube 3 times to make a 3-digit number. Have each pair compare their numbers. Then have one student set up a subtraction problem and subtract the lesser number from the greater number. The other student estimates to see if the answer is reasonable. Have students roll the cubes again and reverse roles. Check students' work.

KINESTHETIC

LOGICAL/MATHEMATICAL

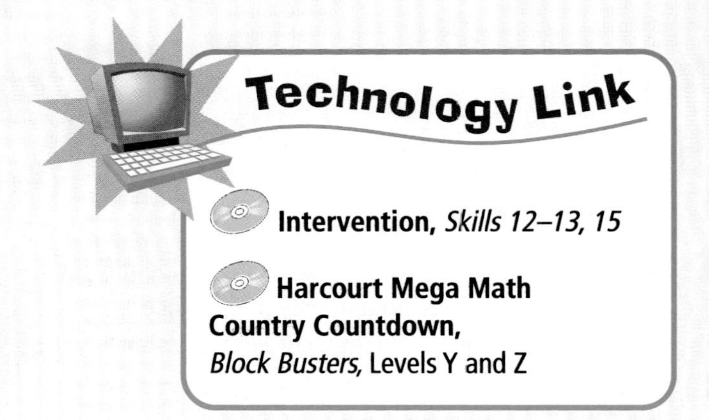

Technology Link
Intervention, Skills 12–13, 15
Harcourt Mega Math Country Countdown, Block Busters, Levels Y and Z

Lesson 5.2 Organizer

Objective To explore subtracting 3-digit numbers with regrouping

Materials *For each group* base-ten blocks

1 INTRODUCE

QUICK REVIEW provides review of prerequisite skills.

WHY LEARN THIS? You can use this skill to solve real-life problems such as how much farther one distance is than another. *Share the lesson objective with students.*

Guided Instruction

MODIFYING INSTRUCTION You may wish to begin the lesson by using base-ten blocks to subtract 2-digit numbers, such as 31 − 19, so that students can review regrouping with only tens and ones.

- *Discuss the Explore section.*

  In Step 2, why do you have to regroup? You cannot subtract 5 ones from 4 ones.

  How many tens do you have left after you regroup to get 10 ones? 1 ten

  After you complete Step 3, how many hundreds do you have left? Explain. 2 hundreds; You regroup 1 hundred to make 10 tens.

  REASONING How could you use the base-ten blocks to check your difference of 129? Put all the blocks (the 195 you subtracted and the 129 you got as the difference) together again to make 324.

  REASONING How is regrouping in subtraction different than regrouping in addition? Possible answer: In addition, you make a 10 or 100 and add it to the place value position to the left. In subtraction, you break apart a 10 or 100 and add it to the place value position to the right.

Guided Practice

Do Try It Exercises a–b with your students. Identify students who are having difficulty and choose appropriate lesson resources to provide assistance.

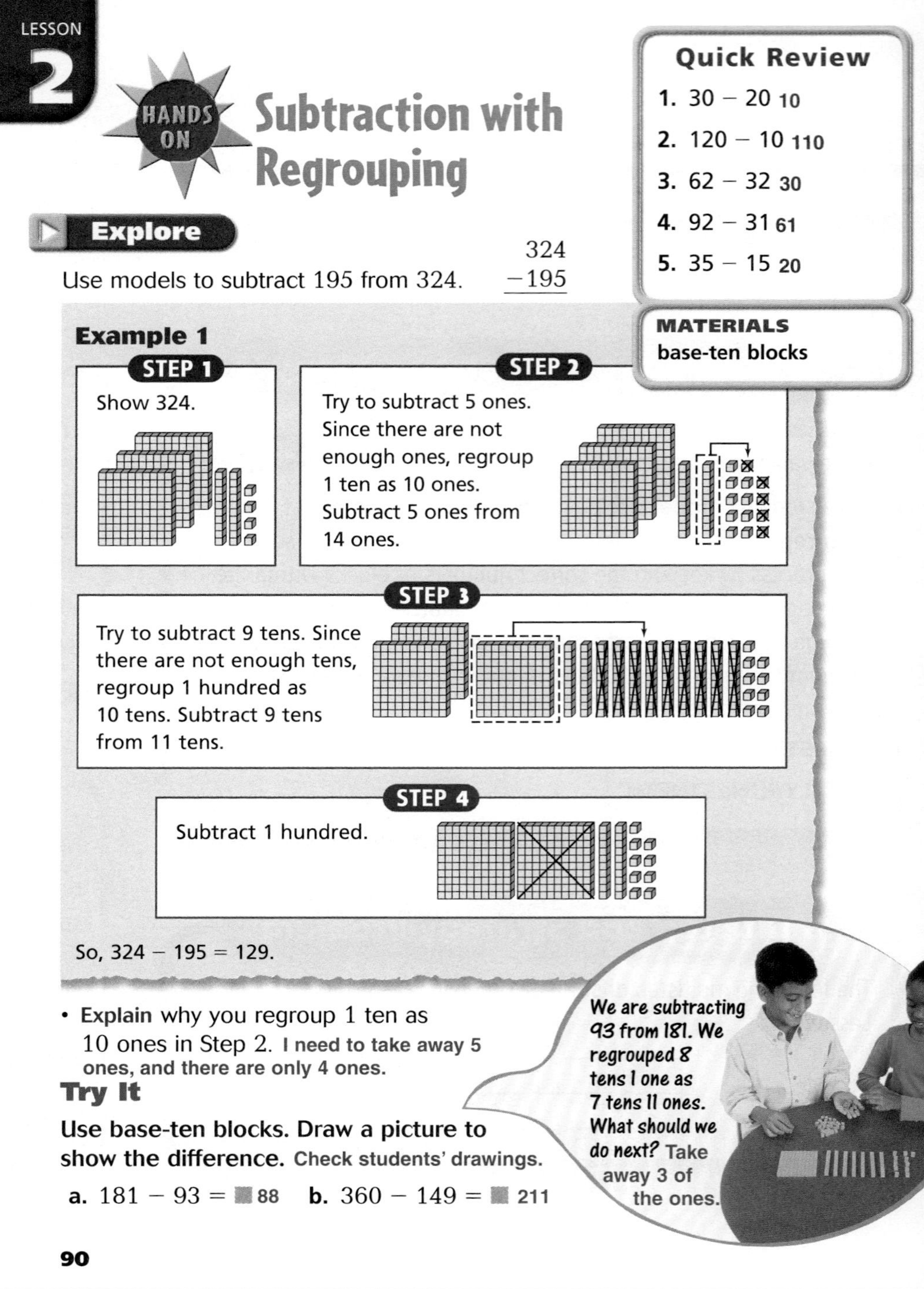

LESSON 2

HANDS ON

Subtraction with Regrouping

Quick Review

1. 30 − 20 10
2. 120 − 10 110
3. 62 − 32 30
4. 92 − 31 61
5. 35 − 15 20

Explore

Use models to subtract 195 from 324.

$$\begin{array}{r} 324 \\ -195 \\ \hline \end{array}$$

MATERIALS base-ten blocks

Example 1

STEP 1 Show 324.

STEP 2 Try to subtract 5 ones. Since there are not enough ones, regroup 1 ten as 10 ones. Subtract 5 ones from 14 ones.

STEP 3 Try to subtract 9 tens. Since there are not enough tens, regroup 1 hundred as 10 tens. Subtract 9 tens from 11 tens.

STEP 4 Subtract 1 hundred.

So, 324 − 195 = 129.

- **Explain** why you regroup 1 ten as 10 ones in Step 2. I need to take away 5 ones, and there are only 4 ones.

We are subtracting 93 from 181. We regrouped 8 tens 1 one as 7 tens 11 ones. What should we do next? Take away 3 of the ones.

Try It

Use base-ten blocks. Draw a picture to show the difference. Check students' drawings.

a. 181 − 93 = ■ 88 **b.** 360 − 149 = ■ 211

90

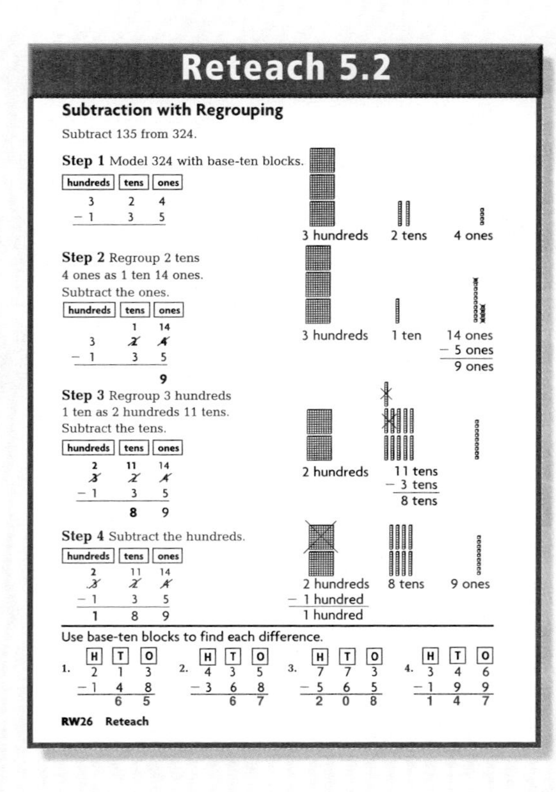

Reteach 5.2

Subtraction with Regrouping

Subtract 135 from 324.

Step 1 Model 324 with base-ten blocks.

hundreds	tens	ones
3	2	4
− 1	3	5

3 hundreds 2 tens 4 ones

Step 2 Regroup 2 tens 4 ones as 1 ten 14 ones. Subtract the ones.

hundreds	tens	ones
	1	14
3	~~2~~	~~4~~
− 1	3	5
		9

3 hundreds 1 ten 14 ones − 5 ones = 9 ones

Step 3 Regroup 3 hundreds 1 ten as 2 hundreds 11 tens. Subtract the tens.

hundreds	tens	ones
2	11	14
~~3~~	~~2~~	~~4~~
− 1	3	5
	8	9

2 hundreds 11 tens − 3 tens = 8 tens

Step 4 Subtract the hundreds.

hundreds	tens	ones
2	11	14
~~3~~	~~2~~	~~4~~
− 1	3	5
1	8	9

2 hundreds − 1 hundred = 1 hundred; 8 tens 9 ones

Use base-ten blocks to find each difference.

1. 213 − 148 = 65
2. 435 − 368 = 67
3. 773 − 565 = 208
4. 346 − 199 = 147

RW26 Reteach

Practice 5.2

Subtraction with Regrouping

Use base-ten blocks. Draw a picture to show the difference.

1. 352 − 236 = 116
2. 532 − 248 = 284
3. 436 − 127 = 309
4. 457 − 285 = 172
5. 512 − 369 = 143
6. 327 − 127 = 200
7. 438 − 249 = 189
8. 367 − 175 = 192
9. 452 − 259 = 193
10. 414 − 126 = 288
11. 378 − 187 = 191
12. 333 − 155 = 178

Mixed Review

Add.

13. 150 + 30 = 180
14. 60 + 90 = 150
15. 72 + 35 = 107
16. 56 + 28 = 84
17. 165 + 67 = 232

Subtract.

18. 80 − 30 = 50
19. 90 − 50 = 40
20. 79 − 24 = 55
21. 84 − 57 = 27
22. 91 − 37 = 54
23. 73 − 35 = 38
24. 65 − 16 = 49
25. 34 − 17 = 17
26. 62 − 28 = 34
27. 71 − 14 = 57

PW26 Practice

Connect

Here is a way to record subtraction. To subtract 126 from 215, first line up the hundreds, tens, and ones.

Technology Link
More Practice: Harcourt Mega Math Country Countdown, *Block Busters*, Levels Y and Z

Example 2

STEP 1

Subtract the ones. 6 > 5
Regroup.
1 ten 5 ones =
0 tens 15 ones

$$\begin{array}{r} {\scriptstyle 0\ 15} \\ 2\,\not{1}\,\not{5} \\ -1\,2\,6 \\ \hline 9 \end{array}$$

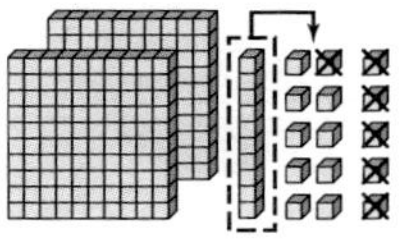

STEP 2

Subtract the tens. 2 > 0
Regroup.
2 hundreds 0 tens =
1 hundred 10 tens

$$\begin{array}{r} {\scriptstyle 10} \\ {\scriptstyle 1\ \not{0}\ 15} \\ \not{2}\,\not{1}\,\not{5} \\ -1\,2\,6 \\ \hline 8\,9 \end{array}$$

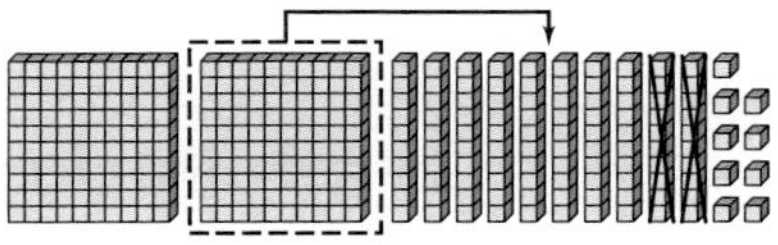

STEP 3

Subtract the hundreds.

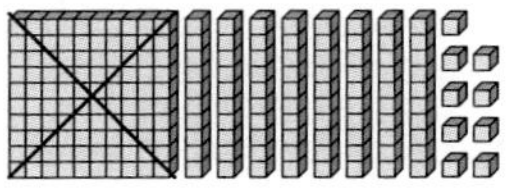

$$\begin{array}{r} {\scriptstyle 10} \\ {\scriptstyle 1\ \not{0}\ 15} \\ \not{2}\,\not{1}\,\not{5} \\ -1\,2\,6 \\ \hline 8\,9 \end{array}$$

Practice and Problem Solving

Use base-ten blocks. Draw a picture to show the difference.
Check students' drawings.

1. 94 − 28 = ■ **66**
2. 212 − 123 = ■ **89**
3. 437 − 243 = ■ **194**
4. 183 − 159 = ■ **24**
5. 329 − 87 = ■ **242**
6. 223 − 135 = ■ **88**
7. **REASONING** There are 32 more apples than oranges at a fruit stand. How many apples and oranges could there be? **Accept any answer with 32 more apples than oranges, e.g., 33 apples, 1 orange.**

Getting Ready for the EOG Test

8. How many more pizzas did Antonio's sell in September than in August? **A**

A 466 **B** 486 **C** 586 **D** 970

PIZZA SOLD
August.........252
September...718

- *Direct students' attention to the Connect section.* **In Step 2, explain why 2 hundreds 0 tens were regrouped instead of 2 hundreds 1 ten.** The 1 ten was regrouped in Step 1 so there are 0 tens in Step 2.

Independent Practice

Note that Exercise 7 is a **multistep or strategy problem.** Assign Exercises 1–7.

4 ASSESS

Summarize the lesson by having students:

DISCUSS When do you have to regroup to subtract a 3-digit number? when the number you are subtracting from does not have enough ones or tens

WRITE In addition to the difference, what do you record when you regroup to subtract 345 from 627? the regrouped 6 hundreds and 2 tens as 5 hundreds and 12 tens

LESSON QUIZ

Transparency 5.2

Use base-ten blocks. Draw a picture to show the difference. Check students' drawings.

1. $\begin{array}{r} 385 \\ -149 \\ \hline 236 \end{array}$ 2. $\begin{array}{r} 260 \\ -\ \ 95 \\ \hline 165 \end{array}$ 3. $\begin{array}{r} 635 \\ -427 \\ \hline 208 \end{array}$

North Carolina Standards 1.02 Develop fluency with multi-digit addition and subtraction through 9,999 using: a) Strategies for adding and subtracting numbers.

Challenge 5.2

Subtraction Puzzles

Fill in the empty squares by subtracting the numbers across each row and subtracting the numbers down each column.

1. (−)

467	289	178
119	68	51
348	221	127

2. (−)

585	299	286
263	159	104
322	140	182

3. (−)

476	288	188
318	169	149
158	119	39

4. (−)

463	184	279
287	39	248
176	145	31

5. (−)

617	344	273
355	179	176
262	165	97

6. (−)

569	285	284
311	196	115
258	89	169

7. (−)

485	167	318
272	163	109
213	4	209

8. (−)

733	377	356
466	179	287
267	198	69

CW26 Challenge

Problem Solving 5.2

Subtraction with Regrouping Understand ➔ Plan ➔ Solve ➔ Check

Write the correct answer.

1. Aaron wants to know *about* how many people live in the United States. He does not want to know an exact number. What kind of number does he want?
 an estimate
2. Olivia has two puzzles. A balloon picture has 525 pieces. A boat picture has 350. How many more pieces does the balloon picture have than the boat picture?
 175
3. Logan had 76¢. She spent 59¢ on an ink pen. How much does she have left?
 17¢
4. In one week Samuel read 135 pages. Wes read 161 pages. How many more pages did Wes read?
 26

Choose the letter of the correct answer.

5. A number is greater than 423 − 378 and less than 87 − 38. What is this number?
 A 43 Ⓒ 47
 B 45 D 49
6. Which number shows 30,000 + 6,000 + 50 + 4 written in standard form?
 F 30,654 H 36,504
 Ⓖ 36,054 J 36,540
7. What is the value of the 5 in the number 85,671?
 A 5
 B 50
 C 500
 Ⓓ 5,000
8. An Internet site had 724 visitors this month. Last month it had 599 fewer visitors. How many visitors did it have last month?
 F 1,323 H 175
 G 275 Ⓙ 125
9. **Write About It** In Problem 8, how did you decide whether to add or subtract?
 Possible answer: Last month had fewer visitors than this month.
 To find how many fewer, I need to subtract.

PS26 Problem Solving

Subtract Across Zeros

Lesson Planning

PROFESSIONAL DEVELOPMENT

Objective To subtract 3-digit numbers with and without regrouping, including numbers with zeros in the minuend

NCTM Standards

1. Number and Operations
2. Algebra
6. Problem Solving
7. Reasoning and Proof
8. Communication
9. Connections
10. Representation

Math Background

Consider the following when introducing subtraction of 3-digit numbers with zeros in the minuend.

- Estimating helps determine whether an answer is reasonable.
- Regrouping may be recorded in each place-value position to ensure accuracy.
- Regrouping may need to be done more than once in a given problem, especially in a problem with zeros in the minuend.
- Regrouping sometimes requires starting with the greatest place value (hundreds) and then regrouping from hundreds to tens and from tens to ones.

Warm-Up Resources

Number of the Day

Write and solve five subtraction sentences that use the number of hours in one day. Possible answer: 44 − 24 = 20; 24 − 20 = 4; 24 − 4 = 20; 24 − 6 = 18; 24 − 12 = 12

Daily Facts Practice

Have students practice addition and subtraction facts by completing Set F of *Teacher's Resource Book*, p. TR86.

Solve a Problem

Transparency 5.3

Problem of the Day

Lee, Brandon, and Kate each picked the same number of apples. Lee picked 8 yellow apples, and Brandon picked 3 yellow apples. Kate picked 5 yellow apples and 7 red apples. How many red apples did Lee pick? 4 red apples How many red apples did Brandon pick? 9 red apples

Solution Problem of the Day tab, p. PD5

Intervention and Extension Resources

Alternative Teaching Strategy

Have students **use the Associative Property to solve subtraction problems with regrouping**.

Work through the following example with students:

404 − 75 =

(300 + 104) − 75 =

(300 + 100 + 4) − 75 =

300 + (4 + 100 − 75) =

300 + 29 = 329

Have students practice this method with exercises from the lesson. You may wish to have students use base-ten blocks to help. Check students' work.

See also page 94.

VISUAL

LOGICAL/MATHEMATICAL

Multistep and Strategy Problems

The following multistep or strategy problem is provided in Lesson 5.3:

Page	Item
94	38

Special Needs

MATERIALS *For each group* base-ten blocks

Have students **model equivalent sets of 3-digit numbers** with a combination of base-ten blocks including ten or more ones. Have them model 506, 200, and 302. Possible answer: 49 tens and 16 ones; 19 tens and 10 ones; 2 hundreds, 9 tens, and 12 ones. Then have students model each number by using the fewest possible base-ten blocks. Discuss why the two representations for each number are equivalent.

KINESTHETIC

BODILY/KINESTHETIC

Math Connection • Measurement

MATERIALS *For each group* yardstick or tape measure

Have students measure and **compare distances** from the classroom door to several objects or points in the classroom. Have students make a table of their findings. Then ask them to write problems by using data from their tables, such as "How much farther is it from the door to the ______ than from the door to the ______?" Check students' work.

KINESTHETIC

VISUAL/SPATIAL

Intervention, *Skills 12–13, 15*

Lesson 5.3 Organizer

Objective To subtract 3-digit numbers with and without regrouping, including numbers with zeros in the minuend

1 INTRODUCE

QUICK REVIEW provides review of prerequisite skills.

WHY LEARN THIS? You can subtract 3-digit numbers to solve real-life problems such as to compare the weights of large animals or objects. *Share the lesson objective with students.*

2 TEACH

Guided Instruction

- *Have students look at the lesson title.*
  What do you think "subtract across zeros" means? Possible answer: There are zeros in the number I am subtracting from.
- *Introduce the Learn section.*
  Why do you estimate? so you will know if your answer is reasonable
- *Have students read Steps 1–3.*
  In Step 1, why do you regroup hundreds as tens before you regroup tens as ones? You have to subtract 6 ones from 0 ones. There are not enough ones and there are not enough tens.
  In Step 2 why is there a 9 over the crossed-out 10 in the tens column? Since there aren't enough ones to subtract, 1 ten of the 10 tens is regrouped as 10 ones, leaving 9 tens in the tens column.
  REASONING What is another name for 2 hundreds 9 tens 10 ones? 300

LESSON 3

Subtract Across Zeros

Quick Review

1. 12 − 5 7
2. 16 − 9 7
3. 11 − 7 4
4. 15 − 6 9
5. 15 − 8 7

Learn

TURTLE TALK After Hurricane Michelle, many green sea turtles that had escaped from the Cayman Turtle Farm were recaptured. One male weighed 300 pounds. One female weighed 226 pounds. How much more did the male weigh than the female?

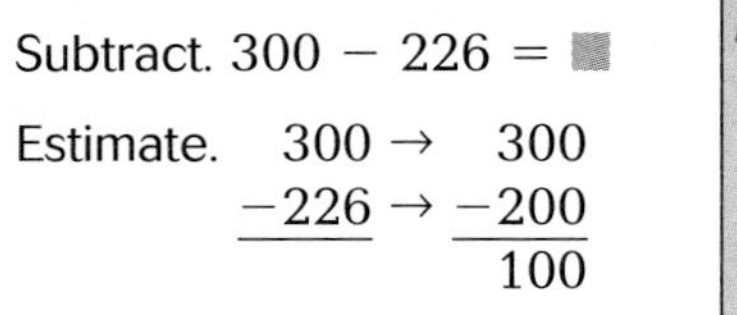

Subtract. 300 − 226 = ■

Estimate. 300 → 300
−226 → −200
100

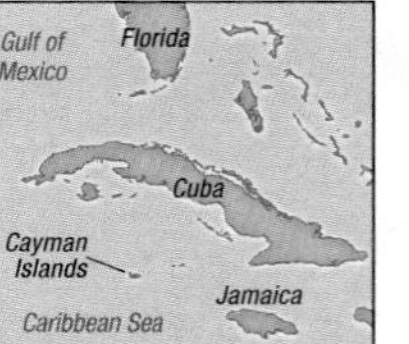

▲ About 15,000 turtles live at the Cayman Turtle Farm.

Example 1

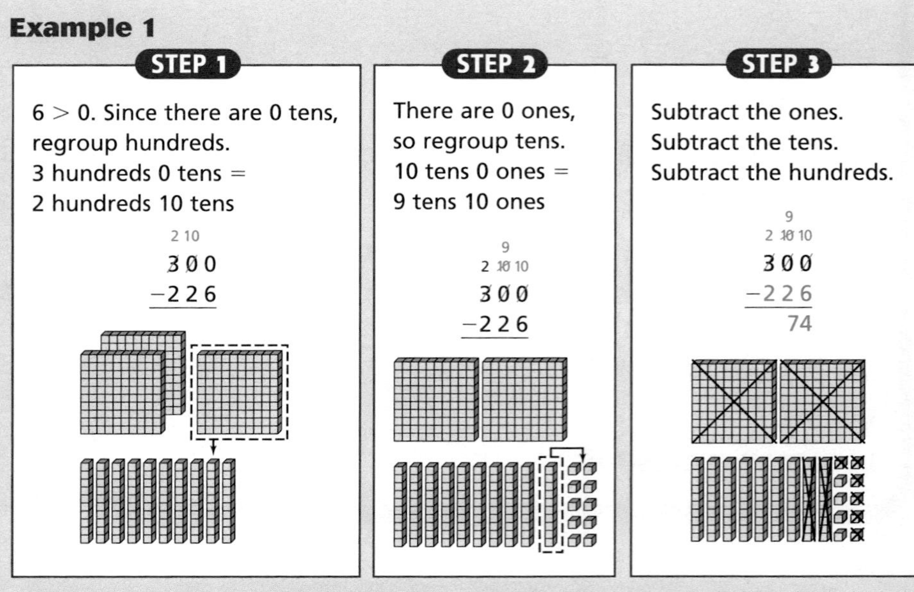

STEP 1
6 > 0. Since there are 0 tens, regroup hundreds.
3 hundreds 0 tens = 2 hundreds 10 tens

2 10
300
−226

STEP 2
There are 0 ones, so regroup tens.
10 tens 0 ones = 9 tens 10 ones

9
2 10 10
300
−226

STEP 3
Subtract the ones.
Subtract the tens.
Subtract the hundreds.

9
2 10 10
300
−226
74

So, the male weighed 74 pounds more than the female. Since 74 is close to the estimate 100, the answer is reasonable.

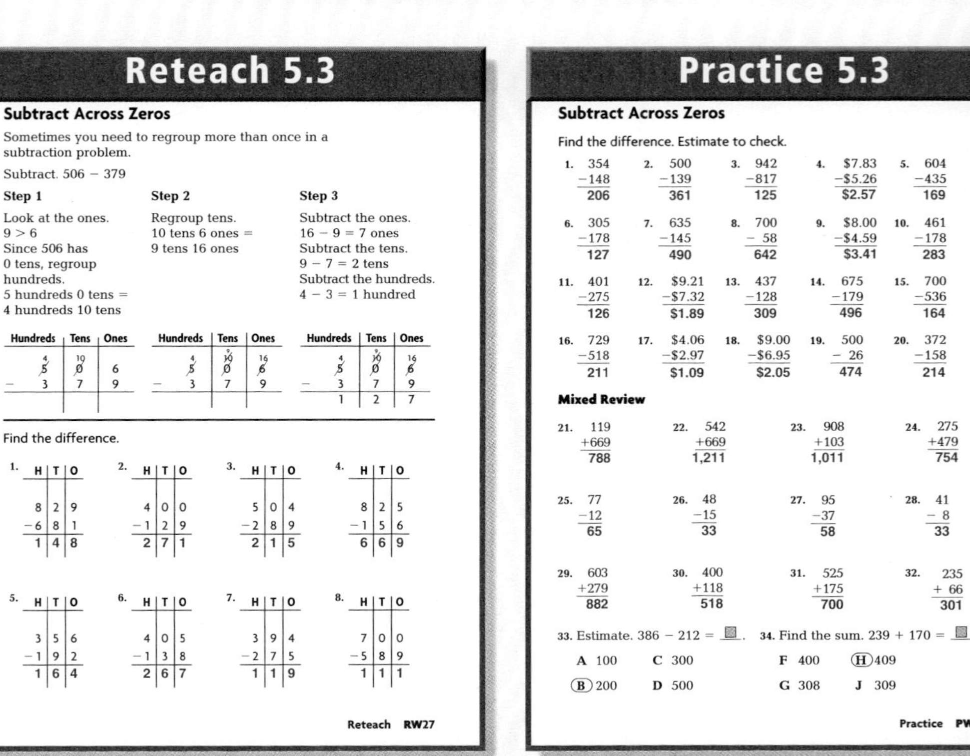

Reteach 5.3

Subtract Across Zeros

Sometimes you need to regroup more than once in a subtraction problem.

Subtract. 506 − 379

Step 1
Look at the ones.
9 > 6
Since 506 has 0 tens, regroup hundreds.
5 hundreds 0 tens = 4 hundreds 10 tens

Hundreds	Tens	Ones
4 (5 crossed out)	10 (0 crossed out)	6
− 3	7	9

Step 2
Regroup tens.
10 tens 6 ones = 9 tens 16 ones

Hundreds	Tens	Ones
4 (5 crossed out)	9 (10 crossed out, 0 crossed out)	16 (6 crossed out)
− 3	7	9

Step 3
Subtract the ones.
16 − 9 = 7 ones
Subtract the tens.
9 − 7 = 2 tens
Subtract the hundreds.
4 − 3 = 1 hundred

Hundreds	Tens	Ones
4 (5 crossed out)	9 (10 crossed out, 0 crossed out)	16 (6 crossed out)
− 3	7	9
1	2	7

Find the difference.

1. 829 − 681 = 148
2. 400 − 129 = 271
3. 504 − 289 = 215
4. 825 − 156 = 669
5. 356 − 192 = 164
6. 405 − 138 = 267
7. 394 − 275 = 119
8. 700 − 589 = 111

Reteach RW27

Practice 5.3

Subtract Across Zeros

Find the difference. Estimate to check.

1. 354 − 148 = 206
2. 500 − 139 = 361
3. 942 − 817 = 125
4. \$7.83 − \$5.26 = \$2.57
5. 604 − 435 = 169
6. 305 − 178 = 127
7. 635 − 145 = 490
8. 700 − 58 = 642
9. \$8.00 − \$4.59 = \$3.41
10. 461 − 178 = 283
11. 401 − 275 = 126
12. \$9.21 − \$7.32 = \$1.89
13. 437 − 128 = 309
14. 675 − 179 = 496
15. 700 − 536 = 164
16. 729 − 518 = 211
17. \$4.06 − \$2.97 = \$1.09
18. \$9.00 − \$6.95 = \$2.05
19. 500 − 26 = 474
20. 372 − 158 = 214

Mixed Review

21. 119 + 669 = 788
22. 542 + 669 = 1,211
23. 908 + 103 = 1,011
24. 275 + 479 = 754
25. 77 − 12 = 65
26. 48 − 15 = 33
27. 95 − 37 = 58
28. 41 − 8 = 33
29. 603 + 279 = 882
30. 400 + 118 = 518
31. 525 + 175 = 700
32. 235 + 66 = 301
33. Estimate. 386 − 212 = ■.
A 100 (B) 200 C 300 D 500
34. Find the sum. 239 + 170 = ■.
F 400 G 308 (H) 409 J 309

Practice PW27

More 3-Digit Subtraction

Another captured female green sea turtle weighed 332 pounds. Another captured male weighed 198 pounds. How much more did the female turtle weigh?

Subtract. 332 − 198 = ■

Estimate.
$$\begin{array}{rcr} 332 & \rightarrow & 330 \\ -198 & \rightarrow & -200 \\ \hline & & 130 \end{array}$$

Example 2

STEP 1	STEP 2	STEP 3
Subtract the ones. 8 > 2 Regroup. 3 tens 2 ones = 2 tens 12 ones	Subtract the tens. 9 > 2 Regroup. 3 hundreds 2 tens = 2 hundreds 12 tens	Subtract the hundreds.
$\begin{array}{r} \scriptstyle 2\ 12 \\ 332 \\ -198 \\ \hline 4 \end{array}$	$\begin{array}{r} \scriptstyle 12 \\ \scriptstyle 2\ 2\ 12 \\ 332 \\ -198 \\ \hline 34 \end{array}$	$\begin{array}{r} \scriptstyle 12 \\ \scriptstyle 2\ 2\ 12 \\ 332 \\ -198 \\ \hline 134 \end{array}$

So, the female weighed 134 pounds more than the male. Since 134 is close to 130, the answer is reasonable.

More Examples

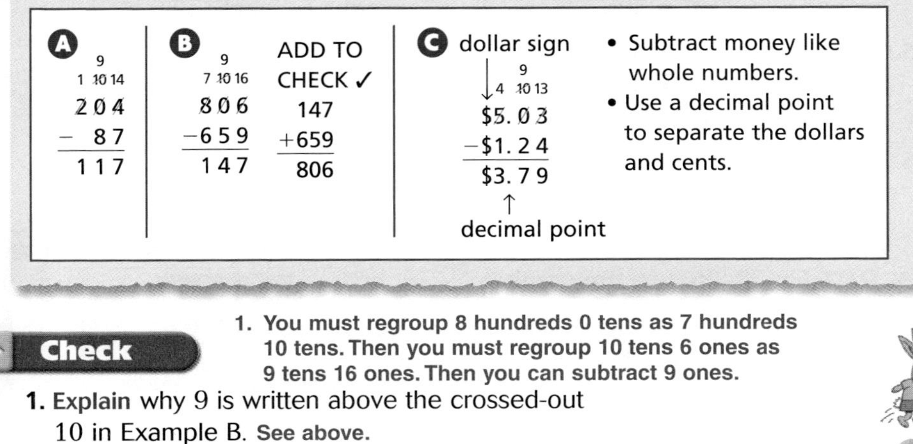

A
9
1 10 14
204
− 87
117
B
9
7 10 16
806
−659
147
ADD TO CHECK ✓
147
+659
806
C
dollar sign
9
4 10 13
$5.03
−$1.24
$3.79
decimal point
• Subtract money like whole numbers.
• Use a decimal point to separate the dollars and cents.

Check

1. Explain why 9 is written above the crossed-out 10 in Example B. **See above.**

1. You must regroup 8 hundreds 0 tens as 7 hundreds 10 tens. Then you must regroup 10 tens 6 ones as 9 tens 16 ones. Then you can subtract 9 ones.

LESSON CONTINUES

- *Direct students' attention to the problem and the steps.*

REASONING How are Examples 1 and 2 alike? They are both 3-digit numbers that need regrouping in the tens and hundreds columns.

How are they different? In Example 1, you regroup hundreds as tens and tens as ones before you subtract. In Example 2, you regroup tens as ones, subtract, and then regroup hundreds as tens.

In Step 2, why are the 3 hundreds regrouped? There are not enough tens to subtract. 3 hundreds need to be regrouped as 2 hundreds 12 tens.

REASONING What numbers can you subtract from 400 without regrouping? 0, 100, 200, 300, and 400

Guided Practice

Do Check Exercises 1–6 with your students. Identify the students who are having difficulty and choose appropriate lesson resources to provide assistance.

North Carolina Standards 1.02 Develop fluency with multi-digit addition and subtraction through 9,999 using: a) Strategies for adding and subtracting numbers.

Challenge 5.3

Riddle Ride

Find each difference. Then look at the rows of boxes at the bottom of the page. Find the two numbers that the difference falls between. In the box between those two numbers, write the letter that is next to the difference.

Example: 566 − 199 = 367 G

956 − 280 = 676 T	424 − 218 = 206 Y	613 − 272 = 341 N	430 − 385 = 45 A
613 − 438 = 175 L	756 − 255 = 501 R	900 − 261 = 639 E	425 − 126 = 299 I
525 − 68 = 457 A	802 − 242 = 560 P	720 − 285 = 435 C	456 − 344 = 112 F

What kind of pet can you take a ride on?

0–50	50–100	100–150	150–200	200–250	250–300	300–350	350–400
A		F	L	Y	I	N	G

400–450	450–500	500–550	550–600	600–650	650–700
C	A	R	P	E	T

Problem Solving 5.3

Subtract Across Zeros Understand → Plan → Solve → Check

Write the correct answer.

1. Irving saved his allowance until he had $5.00. He spent $3.97 on folders and pencils. How much change should Irving receive? **$1.03**
2. Write *ones*, *tens*, or *hundreds* to show where you will regroup when you add to find the sum. 341 + 262 + 110 **tens**
3. The Recreation Department ordered 350 baseballs and 175 bats. How many more baseballs than bats were ordered? **175 more**
4. Sue earned $9.75 babysitting last week and $5.50 the week before. How much did she earn in all? **$15.25**

Choose the letter of the correct answer.

5.

Muffin Sale	
Grade	Muffins Sold
1	215
2	186
3	259

How many more muffins were sold by Grade 3 than by Grade 2?
A 29 B 44 **(C) 73** D 133

6. Michael has 125 stamps in his stamp collection. Brice collected 20 more stamps than Michael. Keith has 164 stamps. How many stamps do the boys have altogether?
(F) 434 stamps G 309 stamps H 270 stamps J 184 stamps

7. **Write About It** In Problem 5, why aren't any of the tens regrouped to subtract the ones? **The tens don't need to be regrouped because there are enough ones to subtract from.**

COMMON ERROR ALERT

When subtracting across zeros, if students try regrouping tens and ones before regrouping hundreds, have them use base-ten blocks to work through some of the exercises.

Independent Practice

Note that Exercise 38 is a **multistep or strategy problem.** Assign Exercises 7–38.

ALGEBRAIC THINKING Have students explain what operation they could use to find the answer to Exercise 33. Subtraction; the sum minus one of the addends equals the other addend.

MULTISTEP OR STRATEGY PROBLEM To solve Exercise 38, students can add 75 to Tyson's weight, 150 pounds, and then subtract 200 (Sparky's weight) from this sum. Emphasize to students the importance of reading the bar graph correctly.

Find the difference. Estimate to check.

2. 300 − 84 = **216**
3. $4.00 − $2.83 = **$1.17**
4. 595 − 242 = **353**
5. 336 − 191 = **145**
6. 607 − 349 = **258**

Practice and Problem Solving

Extra Practice, page 104, Set B

Find the difference. Estimate to check.

7. 574 − 412 = **162**
8. 504 − 250 = **254**
9. 438 − 119 = **319**
10. 600 − 68 = **532**
11. $9.63 − $4.05 = **$5.58**
12. 294 − 137 = **157**
13. 891 − 86 = **805**
14. $6.57 − $4.98 = **$1.59**
15. 372 − 196 = **176**
16. 703 − 217 = **486**
17. 800 − 585 = **215**
18. 548 − 439 = **109**
19. $7.00 − $2.11 = **$4.89**
20. 805 − 99 = **706**
21. $9.06 − $4.08 = **$4.98**
22. 354 − 88 = **266**
23. 942 − 817 = **125**
24. 647 − 435 = **212**
25. 461 − 178 = **283**
26. 704 − 536 = **168**

Subtract. Use addition to check.

27. 900 − 312 = ■ **588**
28. 308 − 149 = ■ **159**
29. 604 − 485 = ■ **119**
30. 401 − 173 = ■ **228**
31. 304 − 255 = ■ **49**
32. 300 − 92 = ■ **208**

33. ALGEBRA Write the missing addend. 255 + ■ = 305 **50**

34. **What's the Error?** Michael wrote a subtraction problem like this. Describe his error. Find the difference.

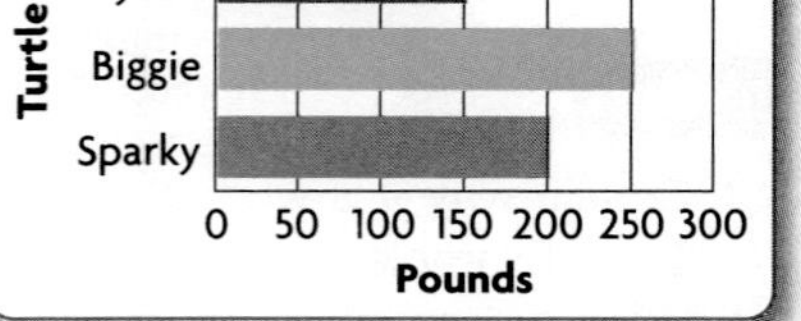

He forgot to cross out the 2 and write a 1 after he regrouped 2 hundreds; 91.

35. Sherrie is thinking of a number. It is 128 less than 509. What number is she thinking of? **381**

36. **REASONING** Do you have to regroup to find 204 − 125? Explain. **Yes; 5 > 4, so regroup 2 hundreds 4 ones as 1 hundred 9 tens 14 ones.**

USE DATA For 37–38, use the graph.

37. How much do Tyson, Biggie, and Sparky weigh altogether? **600 lb**

38. If Tyson gained 75 pounds, how much more would he weigh than Sparky? **25 pounds more**

WEIGHTS OF TURTLES

94

Alternative Teaching Strategy

Scaffolded Instruction

PURPOSE Students practice modeling 3-digit numbers by using base-ten blocks for tens and ones and then by using base-ten blocks to subtract across zeros.

MATERIALS base-ten blocks for tens and ones

Step 1

Have students model 100 by using the tens blocks, and then have them model 100 again by using tens and ones.

Step 2

Ask students to model 200 by using tens blocks.

Step 3

Display this problem: 200 − 23 = 177

Have students describe different ways of changing their models so that they can find the difference.

PROFESSIONAL DEVELOPMENT

Step 4

Have students complete the subtraction problem by using their models.

Step 5

Students can use models and write problems to find the difference when subtracting 23 from 100, 202, and 207. Encourage students to talk about the variation in steps from one problem to another. Check students' work.

Getting Ready for the EOG Test

39. How much farther is the drive from Raleigh to Asheville than from Raleigh to Boone? D

A 430 miles
B 152 miles
C 62 miles
D 52 miles

40. When Susan's family arrived in Charlotte, the car's odometer read 403 miles. If the car's odometer read 279 miles before they left, how many miles did they travel? A

A 124 miles
B 134 miles
C 224 miles
D 682 miles

MILEAGE FROM RALEIGH	
Boone	189
Greensboro	78
Charlotte	143
Asheville	241

Problem Solving LINKUP . . . to Science

Turtles are the only reptiles with shells. A turtle can pull its head, legs, and tail into its shell. The female turtle digs a hole on land, lays her eggs, and covers them. The heat from the sun hatches the eggs.

1. There are about 250 kinds of turtles. About 60 kinds live in the United States and in Canada. About how many kinds don't live in the United States and Canada? **about 200 kinds**
2. One of the largest green sea turtles ever measured weighed 871 pounds. If a green sea turtle weighs 395 pounds, how much heavier is the largest green sea turtle? **476 lb**
3. If a flatback sea turtle swam 752 miles in the spring and 374 miles in the summer, how much farther did the turtle swim in the spring? **378 mi**
4. If a leatherback sea turtle traveled 989 miles one year and 873 miles the next year, how far did it travel in the two years? **1,862 mi**

Reading Strategy

K-W-L CHART Before having students read the Link Up, have them look at the photo. Ask them to predict what the Link Up is about. Then have students make a three-column chart headed *What I Know, What I Want to Know,* and *What I Learned.* Ask them to fill in the first two columns. Have them fill in the third column as they read the paragraph.

K-W-L Chart

What I Know	What I Want to Know	What I Learned

Problem Solving LINKUP . . . to Science

- *Have students read about turtles.*
  In Exercise 3, how far did the flatback sea turtle swim in spring and summer combined? 1,126 miles

4 ASSESS

Summarize the lesson by having students:

DISCUSS How many times do you have to regroup to find 300 − 156? Explain. 2 times; you regroup 1 hundred as 10 tens; then you regroup 1 ten as 10 ones.

WRITE How is subtracting dollars and cents like subtracting 3-digit numbers? How is it different? Alike: You regroup and subtract like whole numbers; Different: you use a decimal point to separate dollars and cents.

LESSON QUIZ

Transparency 5.3

Find the difference. Estimate to check.

1. $700 - 543 = 157$
2. $452 - 376 = 76$
3. $\$7.25 - \$3.79 = \$3.46$

Lesson 5.4

Subtract 3- and 4-Digit Numbers

Lesson Planning

Objective To subtract 3- and 4-digit numbers with and without regrouping

NCTM Standards

1. Number and Operations
2. Algebra
6. Problem Solving
7. Reasoning and Proof
8. Communication
9. Connections

Math Background

These ideas will help students subtract 3- and 4-digit numbers.

- Students follow the same steps to regroup 4-digit numbers as with 2- and 3-digit numbers.
- Regrouping may need to be done twice in the same place-value position.
- Estimating helps determine the reasonableness of the answer.

Warm-Up Resources

Number of the Day

The number of the day is $10 + 10 + 10 - 6$. Solve to find the number of the day. 24

Daily Facts Practice

Have students practice addition and subtraction facts by completing Set G of *Teacher's Resource Book,* p. TR86.

Transparency 5.4

Problem of the Day

Tasha planned to read 100 pages over the weekend. She read 33 pages on Friday and 45 pages on Saturday. How many pages will she have to read on Sunday to meet her goal? 22 pages

Solution Problem of the Day tab, p. PD5

Intervention and Extension Resources

Alternative Teaching Strategy

MATERIALS *For each group* base-ten blocks

To help students **subtract 3- and 4-digit numbers**, pose this problem: Cammi lives in Fort Lauderdale, Florida. One set of her grandparents lives in Oakland, California, 3,041 miles away. Her other set of grandparents lives 1,219 miles away in Youngstown, Ohio. Ask: How much farther is Oakland than Youngstown? Have students use base-ten blocks to solve the problem.

- Have students estimate the difference by rounding. 3,041 rounds to 3,000. 1,219 rounds to 1,000. $3,000 - 1,000 = 2,000$
- Have students model $3,041 - 1,219$. Ask: Why do you need to regroup? $9 > 1$. There are not enough ones or tens. You need to regroup: 4 tens 1 one = 3 tens 11 ones.
- Ask a volunteer to record the subtraction and find the difference. 1,822 miles

KINESTHETIC

BODILY/KINESTHETIC, VERBAL/LINGUISTIC

Multistep and Strategy Problems

The following multistep or strategy problem is provided in Lesson 5.4:

Page	Item
97	23

ESOL/ESL

MATERIALS *For each pair* number cube, place-value chart

Help students **practice 3- and 4-digit subtraction.** Have each partner roll a number cube 3 times and write a 3-digit number. Then have students record their numbers in a place-value chart and subtract. Ask: How do you know which number to write on top? Possible answer: You have to subtract the lesser number from the greater number. Have partners repeat the activity by rolling a number cube 4 times.

KINESTHETIC

LOGICAL/MATHEMATICAL

Early Finishers

Have students **write a word problem that involves the subtraction of money**. Then have them exchange problems with a partner and solve. Check students' problems.

VISUAL

LOGICAL/MATHEMATICAL

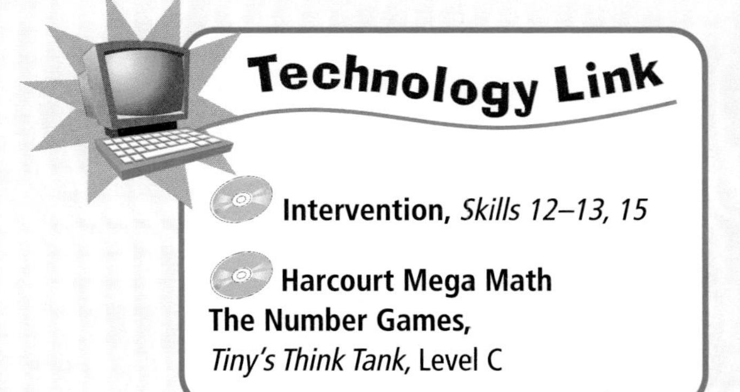

Intervention, *Skills 12–13, 15*

Harcourt Mega Math The Number Games, *Tiny's Think Tank,* Level C

Lesson 5.4 Organizer

Objective To subtract 3- and 4-digit numbers with and without regrouping

1 INTRODUCE

QUICK REVIEW provides review of prerequisite skills.

WHY LEARN THIS? You'll be able to find answers to questions that involve larger numbers, like mileage or population.

2 TEACH

Guided Instruction

- *Direct students' attention to the estimate.*
  REASONING Explain how the numbers were rounded. 1 is less than 5, so 2,167 rounds to 2,000. 3 is less than 5, so 1,377 rounds to 1,000.
- *Direct students' attention to the steps in the Example.*
  In Step 1, why is there no regrouping? 7 = 7
  In Step 3, why are there a 0 and a 10 over the hundreds column? To subtract the tens, you have to regroup 1 hundred 6 tens as 16 tens. To subtract hundreds, you have to regroup 2 thousands as 1 thousand 10 hundreds.
  MODIFYING INSTRUCTION Use base-ten blocks to model the problem for students who might benefit from concrete instruction.
- *Direct students' attention to Examples A and C.*
  How are Examples A and C different and how are they alike? Different: Example A uses commas to separate thousands from hundreds. Example C uses a decimal point to separate dollars from cents, and a dollar sign to indicate dollars. Alike: Money amounts are subtracted like whole numbers. The ones, tens, hundreds, and thousands are regrouped.

LESSON 4

Subtract 3- and 4-Digit Numbers

Quick Review

Use rounding to estimate the difference. Possible estimates are given

1. 363 − 140 300
2. 515 − 272 200
3. 704 − 451 200
4. 281 − 165 100
5. 492 − 384 100

Learn

WALK OR RIDE? If you hiked the Appalachian National Scenic Trail, you would hike 2,167 miles. The driving distance from one end to the other along roads and highways is 1,377 miles. How many more miles is it to hike than to drive?

Subtract. 2,167 − 1,377 = ■

Estimate.
2,167 → 2,000
−1,377 → −1,000
1,000

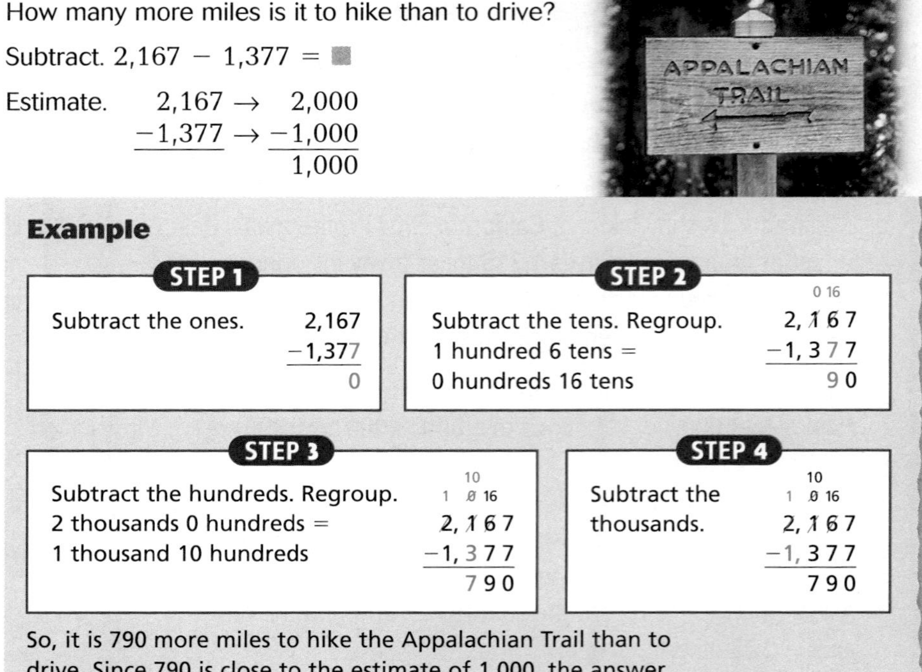

Example

STEP 1
Subtract the ones.
2,167
−1,377
0

STEP 2
Subtract the tens. Regroup.
1 hundred 6 tens =
0 hundreds 16 tens
0 16
2,1̸6̸7
−1,377
90

STEP 3
Subtract the hundreds. Regroup.
2 thousands 0 hundreds =
1 thousand 10 hundreds
10
1 0̸ 16
2̸,1̸6̸7
−1,377
790

STEP 4
Subtract the thousands.
10
1 0̸ 16
2̸,1̸6̸7
−1,377
790

So, it is 790 more miles to hike the Appalachian Trail than to drive. Since 790 is close to the estimate of 1,000, the answer is reasonable.

More Examples

A
13 15
2 3 5 13
3,463
−1,867
1,596

B
9 11
3 10 1 17
4,027
− 598
3,429

C
11 10
3 1 0 15
$42.15
−$27.36
$14.79

D
9 9
4 10 10 10
5,000
−3,574
1,426

96

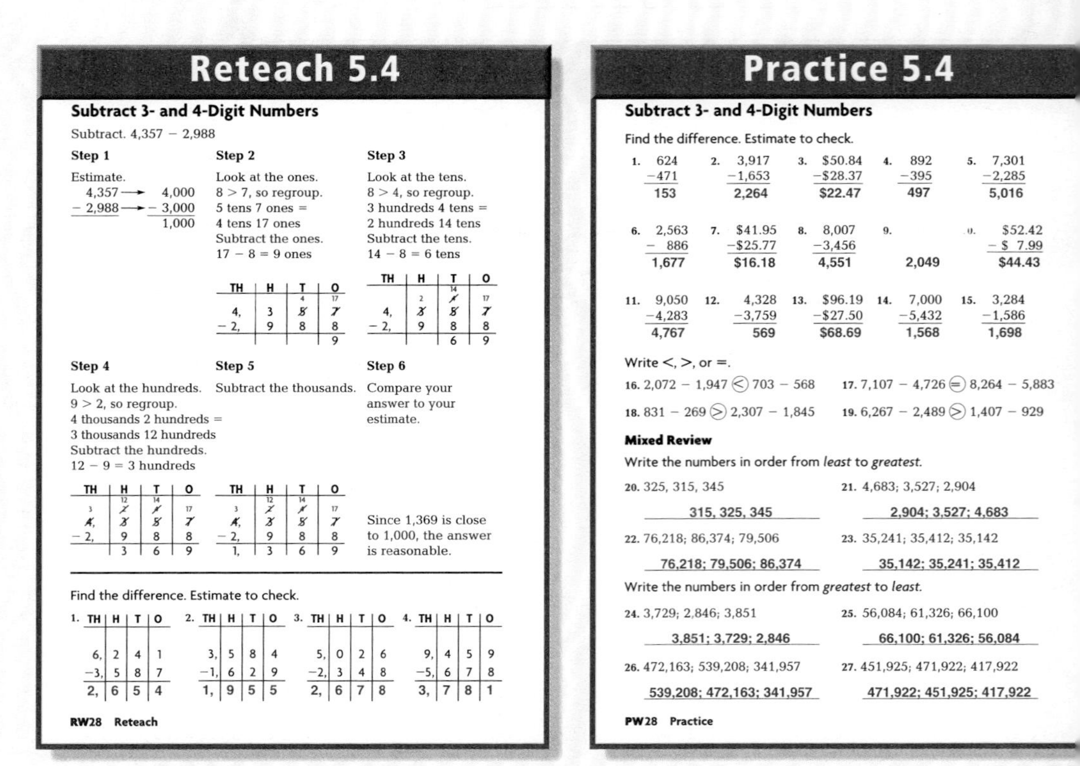

Reteach 5.4

Subtract 3- and 4-Digit Numbers

Subtract. 4,357 − 2,988

Step 1
Estimate.
4,357 → 4,000
− 2,988 → − 3,000
1,000

Step 2
Look at the ones.
8 > 7, so regroup.
5 tens 7 ones =
4 tens 17 ones
Subtract the ones.
17 − 8 = 9 ones

TH	H	T	O
		4	17
4,	3	5̸	7̸
− 2,	9	8	8
			9

Step 3
Look at the tens.
8 > 4, so regroup.
3 hundreds 4 tens =
2 hundreds 14 tens
Subtract the tens.
14 − 8 = 6 tens

TH	H	T	O
		14	
	2	4̸	17
4,	3̸	5̸	7̸
− 2,	9	8	8
		6	9

Step 4
Look at the hundreds.
9 > 2, so regroup.
4 thousands 2 hundreds =
3 thousands 12 hundreds
Subtract the hundreds.
12 − 9 = 3 hundreds

TH	H	T	O
3	12 2̸	14 4̸	17
4̸,	3̸	5̸	7̸
− 2,	9	8	8
	3	6	9

Step 5
Subtract the thousands.

TH	H	T	O
3	12 2̸	14 4̸	17
4̸,	3̸	5̸	7̸
− 2,	9	8	8
1,	3	6	9

Step 6
Compare your answer to your estimate.

Since 1,369 is close to 1,000, the answer is reasonable.

Find the difference. Estimate to check.

1.

TH	H	T	O
6,	2	4	1
−3,	5	8	7
2,	6	5	4

2.

TH	H	T	O
3,	5	8	4
−1,	6	2	9
1,	9	5	5

3.

TH	H	T	O
5,	0	2	6
−2,	3	4	8
2,	6	7	8

4.

TH	H	T	O
9,	4	5	9
−5,	6	7	8
3,	7	8	1

RW28 Reteach

Practice 5.4

Subtract 3- and 4-Digit Numbers

Find the difference. Estimate to check.

1. 624 − 471 = 153
2. 3,917 − 1,653 = 2,264
3. $50.84 − $28.37 = $22.47
4. 892 − 395 = 497
5. 7,301 − 2,285 = 5,016
6. 2,563 − 886 = 1,677
7. $41.95 − $25.77 = $16.18
8. 8,007 − 3,456 = 4,551
9. 2,049
10. $52.42 − $ 7.99 = $44.43
11. 9,050 − 4,283 = 4,767
12. 4,328 − 3,759 = 569
13. $96.19 − $27.50 = $68.69
14. 7,000 − 5,432 = 1,568
15. 3,284 − 1,586 = 1,698

Write <, >, or =.

16. 2,072 − 1,947 (<) 703 − 568
17. 7,107 − 4,726 (=) 8,264 − 5,883
18. 831 − 269 (>) 2,307 − 1,845
19. 6,267 − 2,489 (>) 1,407 − 929

Mixed Review

Write the numbers in order from *least* to *greatest*.

20. 325, 315, 345 — 315, 325, 345
21. 4,683; 3,527; 2,904 — 2,904; 3,527; 4,683
22. 76,218; 86,374; 79,506 — 76,218; 79,506; 86,374
23. 35,241; 35,412; 35,142 — 35,142; 35,241; 35,412

Write the numbers in order from *greatest* to *least*.

24. 3,729; 2,846; 3,851 — 3,851; 3,729; 2,846
25. 56,084; 61,326; 66,100 — 66,100; 61,326; 56,084
26. 472,163; 539,208; 341,957 — 539,208; 472,163; 341,957
27. 451,925; 471,922; 417,922 — 471,922; 451,925; 417,922

PW28 Practice

Check

23. Possible answer: Jada forgot to regroup 1 hundred 5 tens as 0 hundreds 15 tens. The correct difference is 291.

1. **Explain** how subtracting 4-digit numbers is like subtracting 3-digit numbers. How is it different? **Possible answers: alike: you subtract from right to left. You regroup when there aren't enough to subtract from. Different: You subtract across 4 places instead of 3.**

Find the difference. Estimate to check.

2. 4,137 − 1,562 = **2,575**
3. 2,421 − 865 = **1,556**
4. $26.03 − $19.54 = **$6.49**
5. 734 − 588 = **146**
6. 5,085 − 2,629 = **2,456**

Practice and Problem Solving

Extra Practice, page 104, Set C

Find the difference. Estimate to check.

7. 2,624 − 1,832 = **792**
8. 8,716 − 5,940 = **2,776**
9. 317 − 198 = **119**
10. $51.93 − $37.06 = **$14.87**
11. 6,102 − 581 = **5,521**
12. 951 − 674 = **277**
13. $10.46 − $ 8.58 = **$1.88**
14. 5,932 − 3,187 = **2,745**
15. 3,005 − 1,643 = **1,362**
16. $32.98 − $18.59 = **$14.39**

ALGEBRA Write <, >, or = for each ●.

17. 964 − 825 ● 1,029 − 893 **>**
18. 2,516 − 1,728 ● 1,964 − 1,139 **<**
19. 5,013 − 4,862 ● 785 − 634 **=**
20. 504 − 186 ● 3,380 − 3,061 **<**

21. **ESTIMATION** Estimate the difference between 1,836 and 1,754. Round each number to the place that makes sense. **Possible answer: 90**

22. The Appalachian Trail opened in 1937. Write a number sentence that shows how long the trail has been open. **Possible answer: 2004 − 1937 = 67; 67 years**

23. **What's the Error?** Jada says that the difference between 4,152 and 3,861 is greater than the sum of 196 and 95. Explain her error and find the correct difference. **See above.**

24. **FAST FACT • SOCIAL STUDIES** Mount Katahdin, in Maine, is 5,267 feet high. Springer Mountain, in Georgia, is 3,282 feet high. How much higher is Mount Katahdin? **Mount Katahdin is 1,985 feet higher.**

Getting Ready for the EOG Test

25. The nine planets in our solar system revolve around the sun. How many more days does it take Mars than Earth to revolve around the sun? **D**

A 1,052 B 599 C 462 D 322

Days to Revolve Around Sun

Planet	Days
Earth	365
Mars	687

North Carolina Standards 1.02 Develop fluency with multi-digit addition and subtraction ough 9,999 using: a) Strategies for adding and subtracting numbers.

Challenge 5.4

Subtract 3- and 4-Digit Numbers

Subtract. Connect the dots in order from the least difference to the greatest difference.

6,002 − 2,315 = **3,687**
9,280 − 6,347 = **2,933**
6,283 − 1,756 = **4,527**
8,459 − 2,763 = **5,696**
5,174 − 1,896 = **3,278**
2,825 − 767 = **2,058**
9,215 − 2,806 = **6,409**
901 − 165 = **736**
936 − 248 = **688**
7,394 − 6,852 = **542**
8,050 − 1,393 = **6,657**
7,000 − 1,284 = **5,716**

CW28 Challenge

Problem Solving 5.4

Subtract 3- and 4-Digit Numbers

Understand → Plan → Solve → Check

Write the correct answer.

1. Students at Spring Lake School want to collect 8,000 cans for recycling. So far, they have collected 5,286 cans. How many more cans must they collect to reach their goal? **2,714 cans**

2. In what places will you regroup when you subtract to find the difference? 7,357 − 2,495 **tens and hundreds**

3. Marie's family drove 1,357 miles to Yellowstone Park. On the way home they drove 1,489 miles. How far did they drive in all? **2,846 miles**

4. Ben saved 76 quarters and dimes. He has 30 dimes. How many quarters does he have? **46 quarters**

Choose the letter of the correct answer.

5. How many books did Grades 3 and 4 read altogether?
   A 1,384 books
   B 2,168 books
   C 2,268 books
   (D) 3,268 books

Reading Marathon

Grade	Books Read
3	942
4	2,326
5	1,419

6. How many more books did Grade 4 read than Grade 5?
   F 3,745 books H 1,113 books
   G 3,735 books **(J)** 907 books

7. **Write About It** How do you know that your answer to Problem 6 is reasonable? **Possible answer: I rounded 2,326 to 2,300 and 1,419 to 1,400 and estimated the difference to be 900; since 907 is close to the estimate of 900, the answer is reasonable.**

PS28 Problem Solving

3 PRACTICE

Guided Practice

Do Check Exercises 1–6 with your students. Identify students who are having difficulty and choose appropriate lesson resources to provide assistance.

Independent Practice

Note that Exercise 23 is a **multistep or strategy problem.** Assign Exercises 7–24.

ALGEBRAIC THINKING For Exercises 17–20, remind students to find the difference between each set of numbers before they compare the expressions.

4 ASSESS

Summarize the lesson by having students:

Discuss Explain the steps you use to subtract 4-digit numbers. Possible answer: Subtract the ones and regroup, if needed. Subtract the tens and regroup, if needed. Subtract the hundreds and regroup, if needed. Subtract the thousands.

WRITE How is subtracting 3- and 4-digit numbers different from subtracting 2-digit numbers? How is it the same? Possible answer: The regrouping process is the same. But for 3- and 4-digit numbers, you may need to regroup 1 or 2 more times.

LESSON QUIZ

Transparency 5.4

Find the difference. Estimate to check.

1. 4,021 − 680 = 3,341
2. 7,500 − 3,488 = 4,012
3. $49.17 − $25.68 = $23.49

Choose a Method

Lesson Planning

Objective To choose paper and pencil, a calculator, or mental math to subtract 4-digit numbers

Materials Calculator

NCTM Standards
1. Number and Operations
2. Algebra
6. Problem Solving
7. Reasoning and Proof
8. Communication
9. Connections

Math Background

Consider the following when choosing a method to find differences of 4-digit numbers.

- Estimation can be used to determine the reasonableness of an answer.
- Mental math can be used when there is no regrouping and you can find the difference in your head.
- Paper and pencil or a calculator can be used when the numbers are large and there is regrouping.

Warm-Up Resources

Number of the Day

I am a 4-digit number. My thousands digit is one more than my hundreds digit, which is one more than my tens digit, which is one more than my ones digit. My ones digit is 3. What number am I ? 6,543

Daily Facts Practice

Have students practice addition facts by completing Set A of *Teacher's Resource Book*, p. TR87.

Problem of the Day

Subtract down and across.

900	340	? 560
503	108	? 395
? 397	? 232	? 165

Solution Problem of the Day tab, p. PD5

Intervention and Extension Resources

Alternative Teaching Strategy

ESOL/ESL

Have students **find differences** using an alternative method. Demonstrate the following method of subtraction when using paper and pencil: To subtract 1,522 from 4,000, rewrite 4,000 as 3,999 + 1. Find 3,999 − 1,522 = 2,477. Add 1. The answer is 2,478. Then ask: What are two ways to find out if this answer is correct? Regroup and then subtract; add the difference and the number you subtracted to see if it equals the number you subtracted from plus 1.

Have students practice using this method with the following:

- 3,000 − 1,431 = ■ 1,569
- 5,000 − 3,654 = ■ 1,346

See also page 100.

VISUAL

VISUAL/SPATIAL

Writing in Mathematics

Have students write in their math journals how to **find the difference** of 1,000 − 175. Possible answer: Regroup the thousands to make 9 hundreds, 9 tens, and 10 ones. Then subtract the ones, tens, and hundreds to find 825.

Advanced Learners

Challenge students to use the data in the Lengths of Rivers table on page 100 to **write word problems that require subtraction and addition** to solve. Students can challenge classmates to solve their problems. Check students' work.

VISUAL

LOGICAL/MATHEMATICAL

Multistep and Strategy Problems

The following multistep or strategy problem is provided in Lesson 5.5:

Page	Item
101	39

Lesson 5.5 Organizer

Objective To choose paper and pencil, a calculator, or mental math to subtract 4-digit numbers

Materials Calculators

QUICK REVIEW provides review of prerequisite skills.

WHY LEARN THIS? In the future, you will be able to subtract even greater numbers using similar steps. *Share the lesson objective with students.*

2 TEACH

Guided Instruction

- *Introduce the Learn section.*
  What do you need to find? the difference between 1,920 feet and 1,025 feet
- *Call attention to each of the steps.*
  In Step 1, why is there a 10 over the crossed-out 0 in the ones column? You cannot subtract 5 from zero, so a ten had to be regrouped as 10 ones.
  In Step 2, a 9 appears in the tens place in the difference. Why? The 2 in the tens place had become 1 when the tens were regrouped. Then 1 hundred was regrouped as 10 tens and added to the 1 remaining ten. Two tens were then subtracted from 11 tens to make 9 tens.
  In Step 3, why aren't the thousands regrouped? 0 hundreds is less than 8 hundreds, so no thousands need to be regrouped.
- *Call attention to the Calculator method.*
  If you are using a calculator, why do you need to estimate? Possible answer: You may press an incorrect number or an incorrect operation key.

LESSON 5

Choose a Method

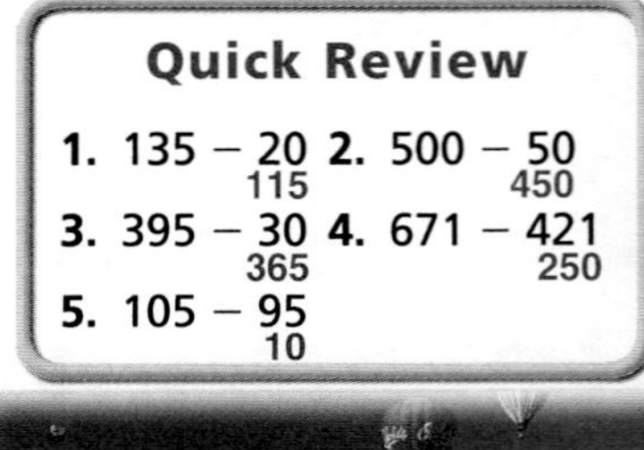

Quick Review
1. 135 − 20 115
2. 500 − 50 450
3. 395 − 30 365
4. 671 − 421 250
5. 105 − 95 10

Learn

You can find a difference by using paper and pencil, a calculator, or mental math.

UP, UP AND AWAY A hot-air balloon rose to 1,025 feet above the ground. Then it rose to 1,920 feet above the ground. How much higher was it then?

Subtract. $1,920 - 1,025 = \blacksquare$

Estimate. $2,000 - 1,000 = 1,000$

Use Paper and Pencil The numbers are large. The problem involves regrouping. So, paper and pencil is a good choice.

STEP 1

Subtract the ones. $5 > 0$
Regroup.
2 tens 0 ones =
1 ten 10 ones

$$\begin{array}{r} 1,9\overset{1}{\cancel{2}}\overset{10}{\cancel{0}} \\ -1,025 \\ \hline 5 \end{array}$$

STEP 2

Subtract the tens. $2 > 1$
Regroup.
9 hundreds 1 ten =
8 hundreds 11 tens

$$\begin{array}{r} 1,\overset{8}{\cancel{9}}\overset{11}{\cancel{2}}\overset{10}{\cancel{0}} \\ -1,025 \\ \hline 95 \end{array}$$

STEP 3

Subtract the hundreds.
Subtract the thousands.

$$\begin{array}{r} 1,\overset{8}{\cancel{9}}\overset{11}{\cancel{2}}\overset{10}{\cancel{0}} \\ -1,025 \\ \hline 895 \end{array}$$

So, the hot-air balloon was 895 feet higher. Since 895 is close to 1,000, the answer is reasonable.

REASONING How can you add to check your answer? **895 + 1,025 = 1,920**

Use a Calculator $3,894 - 2,596 = \blacksquare$

The amounts are large. The problem involves regrouping. So, a calculator is a good choice.

REASONING How can you estimate to check your answer?
4,000 − 3,000 = 1,000; Since 1,000 is close to 1,298, the answer is reasonable.

Reteach 5.5

Choose a Method

$$\begin{array}{r} 3,000 \\ -1,260 \\ \hline ? \end{array}$$

How can you subtract 1,260 from 3,000? You can't subtract from 0 tens or 0 hundreds, so regroup the thousands.

3 thousands = Regroup 3 thousands as 2 thousands 10 hundreds = Regroup 2 thousands 10 hundreds as 2 thousands 9 hundreds 10 tens

$$\begin{array}{r} 3,000 \\ -1,260 \\ \hline \end{array} \qquad \begin{array}{r} \overset{2}{\cancel{3}},\overset{10}{\cancel{0}}00 \\ -1,260 \\ \hline \end{array} \qquad \begin{array}{r} \overset{2}{\cancel{3}},\overset{9}{\cancel{10}}\overset{10}{\cancel{0}}0 \\ -1,260 \\ \hline 1,740 \end{array}$$

Show how you would regroup before subtracting.

1.

TH	H	T	O
~~6~~ 5	~~0~~ 10 ~~10~~ 9	~~0~~ 10	0
−2,	5	7	0
3,	4	3	0

2.

TH	H	T	O
~~5~~ 4,	~~0~~ ~~10~~ 9	~~0~~ ~~10~~ 9	~~0~~ 10
−1,	5	1	1
3,	4	8	9

3.

TH	H	T	O
~~8~~ 7,	~~0~~ ~~10~~ 9	~~0~~ 10	0
−4,	3	7	0
3,	6	3	0

Find the difference. Tell what method you used. **Methods will vary.**

4. 3,675 − 2,430 = **1,245**
5. 5,062 − 3,355 = **1,707**
6. 8,304 − 4,202 = **4,102**
7. 7,200 − 3,821 = **3,379**

Reteach RW29

Practice 5.5

Choose a Method

Find the difference. Tell what method you used. **Methods will vary.**

1. 1,500 − 1,132 = **368**
2. 406 − 258 = **148**
3. 1,600 − 1,198 = **402**
4. 2,902 − 2,435 = **467**
5. 700 − 137 = **563**
6. 3,408 − 2,135 = **1,273**
7. 800 − 600 = **200**
8. 3,306 − 3,108 = **198**
9. 6,300 − 2,229 = **4,071**
10. 8,000 − 5,000 = **3,000**

11. 7,005 − 3,605 = **3,400**
12. 8,588 − 5,666 = **2,922**
13. 2,175 − 1,987 = **188**
14. 921 − 108 = **813**

Mixed Review

Find each sum or difference.

15. 19 + 6 = **25**
16. 78 − 49 = **29**
17. 84 − 27 = **57**
18. 29 + 54 = **83**

Find the missing addend.

19. 24 + **36** = 60
20. 35 + **36** = 71
21. 17 + **41** = 58
22. 42 + **37** = 79

Find each sum.

23. 996 + 132 = **1,128**
24. 4,597 + 1,950 = **6,547**
25. 3,956 + 2,007 = **5,963**
26. 774 + 2,981 = **3,755**

27. Which number is between 4,888 and 6,123?
(A) 5,030 C 1,325
B 7,548 D 3,987

28. Which symbol completes the following:
4,620 ◯ 4,062
(F) > G < H =

Practice PW29

Use Mental Math

$6.80 − $3.10 = ■

There is no regrouping. You can subtract the dollar and cents amounts in your head. So, using mental math is a good choice.

Think: Subtract the dollar amounts. $6.00 − $3.00 = $3.00
Subtract the cents amounts. $0.80 − $0.10 = $0.70
The difference is $3.00 + $0.70, or $3.70.

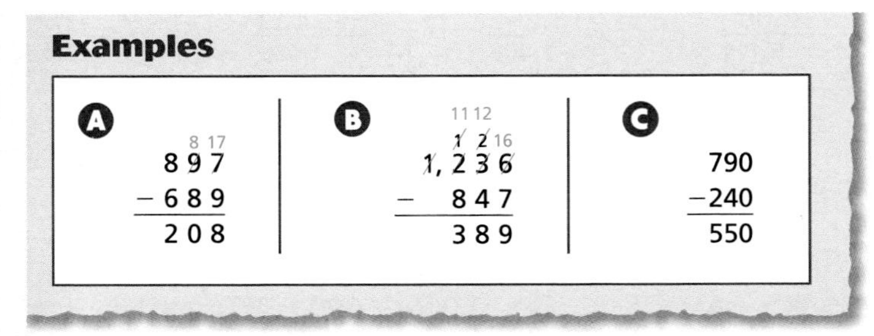

Examples

A	B	C
8 17 897 − 689 208	11 12 1 2 16 1,236 − 847 389	790 −240 550

- Which problem can you solve using mental math? Explain.
  Possible answer: Example C; there is no regrouping.
- Which method would you use to solve Example A? Explain.
  Possible answer: paper and pencil; there is some regrouping.

MATH IDEA You can find a difference by using paper and pencil, a calculator, or mental math. Choose the method that works best with the numbers in the problem.

Check

1. **Explain** how you can use mental math to subtract 656 from 987. **Possible answer: subtract the hundreds, 9 − 6 = 3; subtract the tens, 8 − 5 = 3; subtract the ones, 7 − 6 = 1. So, 987 − 656 = 331.**

Find the difference. Tell what method you used. **Methods will vary.**

2.	3.	4.	5.	6.
287 −178 **109**	$7.98 −$3.56 **$4.42**	127 − 94 **33**	2,165 −1,084 **1,081**	$35.98 − $15.46 **$20.52**

LESSON CONTINUES

North Carolina Standards 1.06 Develop flexibility in solving problems by selecting strategies and using mental computation, estimation, calculators or computers, and paper and pencil. *also* 1.02

- *Have students look at the Mental Math method.* **What difference do you notice in the steps to record subtraction when you use mental math?** Possible answer: You can subtract from left to right when you use mental math.
- *Have students read the Math Idea.* **Before solving a problem, how do you decide how much regrouping will need to be done?** by comparing the digits in each of the place-value positions

3 PRACTICE

Guided Practice

Do Check Exercises 1–6 with your students. Identify students who are having difficulty and choose appropriate lesson resources to provide assistance.

Challenge 5.5

Missing Digits

Fill in the missing digits.

1.	2.	3.
1,30[0] − 125 1,1[7]5	1,500 − 32[7] 1,[1]73	3,[9]00 − 3,6[3]4 266

4.	5.	6.
5,50[3] − 198 5,3[0]5	2,6[0]1 − 284 2,31[7]	6,707 − 1,1[4]9 5,55[8]

7.	8.	9.
2,40[0] − [2],195 [2]05	7,[7]00 − 5,33[2] [2],368	[1],040 − 3[9]0 65[0]

Find the difference. Then check by adding.

5,006 − 1,251 [3],[7][5]5	1,251 + [3],[7][5]5 5,006	7,004 − 3,59[3] [3],[4][1]1	3,59[3] + [3],[4][1]1 7,004
[3],407 − 129 3,[2][7][8]	3,[2][7][8] + 129 [3],407	9,029 − 1,35[2] [7],[6][7][7]	[7],[6][7][7] + 1,35[2] 9,029

Possible answers given.

Challenge CW29

Problem Solving 5.5

Choose a Method

Understand → Plan → Solve → Check

Write the correct answer.

1. To solve 4,384 − 1,568 = ■, how many times will you need to regroup? What is the difference?
   2; 2,816
2. Mr. Cheng has 25 new tires and 19 used tires. If the answer is 44 tires, what is the question?
   How many tires does he have in all?
3. Bill says the difference of 3,000 − 838 is close to 2,000. Sandy says the difference is closer to 1,000. Who is correct?
   Bill
4. Last week Mrs. Cabot drove 518 miles and Mr. Wills drove 325 miles. How much farther did Mrs. Cabot drive than Mr. Wills?
   193 miles

Choose the letter of the correct answer.

5. Joyce has 1,365 pennies. Alan has 546 nickels. How many more coins does Joyce have than Alan?
   (A) 819 C 1,901
   B 821 D 1,911
6. Find the missing addend.
   3,116 + ■ = 3,218
   F 122 H 108
   G 120 (J) 102
7. Reggie wants to buy a pair of shoes for $46 and a hat for $19. Which sentence shows his estimated cost?
   A $40 + $10 = $50
   (B) $50 + $20 = $70
   C $50 + $10 = $60
   D $46 + $14 = $60
8. A number has the same number of ones, tens, and hundreds. If the sum of the digits is 15, what is the number?
   (F) 555 H 5,550
   G 5,505 J 55,000
9. **Write About It** How did you solve Problem 7?
   Possible answer: I estimated the sum of 46 and 19 by rounding 46 to 50 and 19 to 20.

Problem Solving PS29

COMMON ERROR ALERT

Students may not place the numbers for regrouping in the correct columns or add the regrouped number to the number in the correct place-value column.

$$\begin{array}{r} 7{,}032 \\ -4{,}381 \\ \hline 2{,}713 \end{array}$$

Students may benefit from using grid paper to practice the proper positioning and alignment of the numerals.

Independent Practice

Note that Exercise 39 is a **multistep or strategy problem.** Assign Exercises 7–40.

Vocabulary Power You have discussed the suffix *-or*. There are many other suffixes which, when added to the ends of words, change the meanings of those words. The suffix *-ion* means "the result of an act." An example is *donation*. The suffix *-ly* means "like in appearance or manner." An example is *fatherly*. The suffix *-ist* means "one who plays or performs." An example is *violinist*.

Point out that students may use more than one method to solve a given problem. Encourage volunteers to explain how they might use paper and pencil and mental math to solve one of the exercises.

For Exercises 32 and 33, you may wish to tell students that addition could be used to find the missing numbers.

Practice and Problem Solving

Extra Practice, page 104, Set D

Find the difference. Tell what method you used. Methods will vary.

7. 365 − 104 = **261**
8. 884 − 282 = **602**
9. 951 − 148 = **803**
10. 821 − 631 = **190**
11. 930 − 821 = **109**
12. 211 − 120 = **91**
13. 545 − 438 = **107**
14. 900 − 642 = **258**
15. 760 − 479 = **281**
16. 397 − 254 = **143**
17. 5,000 − 1,294 = **3,706**
18. 7,116 − 2,005 = **5,111**
19. 4,690 − 3,282 = **1,408**
20. 3,050 − 1,422 = **1,628**
21. 2,860 − 750 = **2,110**
22. 8,907 − 5,605 = **3,302**
23. 9,437 − 6,420 = **3,017**
24. 7,884 − 3,802 = **4,082**
25. 8,932 − 4,613 = **4,319**
26. 4,507 − 1,602 = **2,905**

Find the difference. Explain your method. Accept reasonable explanations.

27. 8,000 − 5,000 = ■ **3,000**
28. 650 − 290 = ■ **360**
29. 5,850 − 4,420 = ■ **1,430**
30. 2,000 − 900 = ■ **1,100**

Use a calculator to solve.

31. 4,665 − ■ = 3,962 **703**
32. ■ − 978 = 396 **1,374**
33. ■ − 1,324 = 687 **2,011**

USE DATA For 34–37, use the table.

LENGTHS OF RIVERS	
Mississippi River	2,348 miles
Yukon River	1,979 miles
Rio Grande	1,885 miles
Ohio River	981 miles

34. What is the difference between the lengths of the Ohio River and the Rio Grande? **904 miles**
35. The Ohio River is 998 miles shorter than which one of these rivers? **Yukon River**
36. How much longer is the Mississippi River than the Ohio River? **1,367 miles**
37. **Write a problem** about the difference between river lengths. Exchange with a partner. Solve. **Check students' problems.**
38. **Vocabulary Power** When you add the suffix *–or* to a word, it can mean "someone or something that does." How does adding this suffix change the meaning of the word *calculate?* **Possible response: a calculator is a tool that does calculations, or solves math problems.**

100

Alternative Teaching Strategy — Scaffolded Instruction

PROFESSIONAL DEVELOPMENT

PURPOSE Students use play money to regroup when subtracting greater numbers.

MATERIALS play bills and coins, pp. TR51–53 (fives, ones, dimes, and pennies)

Step 1

Give small groups amounts of money representing $14.20. Make additional dollars, dimes, and pennies available at a "bank" where students can cash in five-dollar bills for one-dollar bills, dollar bills for dimes, and dimes for pennies. Put one or two students in charge of this "bank."

Step 2

Tell students their job is to subtract $10.25 from the money they have. They must do so by beginning with the pennies.

Step 3

Ask students whether they have enough pennies to subtract 5 pennies. No. Then have them cash in one dime to get enough pennies and tell how many dimes and pennies they have now. 1 dime and 10 pennies

Step 4

Have students subtract the pennies and then decide whether they can subtract the dimes. Again, students can cash in their money; this time they will need to cash in a one-dollar bill to get ten dimes. Ask them how many dimes and one-dollar bills they have now. 3 one-dollar bills and 11 dimes

Step 5

Have students subtract the dimes and the dollars. Ask: How much money do you have left? 3 dollars, 9 dimes, and 5 pennies, or $3.95

39. Sheli's mother was born 25 years before 1987. How old was Sheli's mother in 2004? **42 years old**

40. Write a 3-digit number you could subtract from 274 without regrouping. **Check students' answers.**

Getting Ready for the EOG Test

41. Crestview School collected pennies for computer software. How many more pennies did Grade 2 collect than Grade 3? **C**

A 47 **C** 149
B 147 **D** 159

PENNIES COLLECTED	
Grade	**Number of Pennies**
Grade 1	509
Grade 2	778
Grade 3	629

42. Grade 4 collected 49 fewer pennies than Grade 1. How many pennies did Grade 4 collect? **A**

A 460 **C** 560
B 470 **D** 570

Problem Solving Thinker's Corner

SOLVE IT!

Find the sum or difference.

51 − 23 **O** 28	36 + 49 **N** 85	70 − 53 **H** 17		
64 − 15 **Y** 49	91 + 59 **P** 150	647 + 178 **A** 825	313 + 448 **U** 761	500 − 195 **E** 305
200 − 77 **C** 123	464 + 446 **T** 910	384 + 165 **J** 549	675 − 179 **S** 496	853 − 194 **M** 659

To answer the riddle, match the letters from the sums and differences above to the numbers below. **Anyone. A house can't jump!**

Who can jump higher than a house? __ __ __ __ __ __.
825 85 49 28 85 305

__ __ __ __ __ __ __ __ __'__ __ __ __ __!
825 17 28 761 496 305 123 825 85 910 549 761 659 150

MULTISTEP OR STRATEGY PROBLEM To solve Exercise 39, students can subtract 1987 from 2004, and then add 25 to this difference to find Sheli's mother's age.

Problem Solving Thinker's Corner

- *Have students look at the puzzle.*
  How can you tell, without solving, if a subtraction exercise requires regrouping? Possible answer: if a digit you are subtracting is greater than the digit you are subtracting from
  How many of the subtraction exercises require regrouping to solve? 7 exercises

4 ASSESS

Summarize the lesson by having students:

DISCUSS How can you check to make sure you have regrouped correctly when subtracting? Add the difference and the number you subtracted to see if the sum equals the number you subtracted from, or look at your estimate to see if your answer is reasonable.

WRITE How would you regroup to subtract 1,986 from 4,035? by regrouping 4,035 as 3 thousands, 9 hundreds, 12 tens, and 15 ones

LESSON QUIZ

Transparency 5.5

Find the difference. Tell what method you used. Methods will vary.

1. 3,056 − 798 = 2,258
2. 2,050 − 685 = 1,365
3. 7,000 − 4,009 = 2,991

Problem Solving Skill
Estimate or Exact Answer

Lesson Planning

Objective To identify whether an estimate or an exact answer is needed to solve a problem

Lesson Resources Reading Transparency 5; Intervention • Problem Solving, Strategy/Skill 5

NCTM Standards

1. Number and Operations
6. Problem Solving
7. Reasoning and Proof
8. Communication
10. Representation

Math Background

Consider these ideas when introducing the problem solving skill *estimate or exact answer.*

- Estimates are often used to solve real-life problems. Accept a range of reasonable estimates. Ask students to justify the reasonableness of their estimates.
- Sometimes only an estimate is necessary; sometimes an estimate is preferred to an exact answer.
- In some situations, only an exact answer is useful and acceptable.

Warm-Up Resources

Build Number Sense

Number of the Day

The number of the day is your age in months. Use this number to estimate the combined age in months for the members of the class. Answers will vary.

Daily Facts Practice

Have students practice subtraction facts by completing Set B of *Teacher's Resource Book*, p. TR87.

Solve a Problem

Transparency 5.6

Problem of the Day

Craig has 3 dimes and 4 pennies in one pocket and 5 dimes and 8 pennies in the other pocket. If he exchanges 10 pennies for 1 dime, how many dimes and pennies does he have? 9 dimes and 2 pennies What is the value of the coins? 92¢

Solution Problem of the Day tab, p. PD5

Intervention and Extension Resources

Alternative Teaching Strategy

Help students **use data to estimate or find exact answers** by posing the following problem: The members of an outdoor club are planning a backpacking trip. To decide where to go, they need to know how much higher Mt. Katahdin is than Mt. Greylock.

- Have students work with a partner to study the table of high points along the Appalachian Trail.
- Ask a volunteer to explain if an estimate or an exact answer is needed to solve the problem. an exact answer because the question is "how much higher?"
- Have students solve the problem. Mt. Katahdin is 1,776 feet higher.
- Ask a volunteer to explain if the answer is reasonable. Possible answer: 5,276 rounds to 5,000 and 3,491 rounds to 3,000. $5,000 - 3,000 = 2,000$, which is close to 1,776.

VISUAL

VISUAL/SPATIAL, INTERPERSONAL

Reading Strategy

Choose Important Information Remind students that some word problems have more information than is needed. Students need to find the facts that are relevant, or important, to solve the problem. Have students reread the problem on page 92 about the Cayman Turtle Farm. Ask: What are the relevant facts you need to solve the problem? One turtle weighed 300 pounds and one female weighed 226 pounds. Tell what information you will not need. After Hurricane Michelle, many green sea turtles that had escaped from the Cayman Turtle Farm were recaptured. Suggest to students that it is often helpful to write or list the relevant information.

Transparency 5 **Reading Transparency 5**

Multistep and Strategy Problems

The following multistep and strategy problems are provided in Lesson 5.6:

Page	Item
103	1, 5, 7, 8

Vocabulary Strategy

Have students **make dictionary entries for the words *estimate* and *exact*.** Have them include some of the following information:

- a meaning for the word
- a labeled number sentence or problem illustrating the term
- an illustration, graphic organizer, or mnemonic device that might be helpful for remembering the term
- their own guide to pronouncing the terms

Check students' work.

VISUAL

VERBAL/LINGUISTIC

Social Studies Connection

Have students **use data and determine whether an estimate or exact answer is needed to solve a problem.** Read the following problem and display the data:

Erica's family is on vacation. Erica wanted to know when they had driven about 1,000 miles. She recorded the miles they drove each day in a table.

Day	Miles Driven
Monday	350
Wednesday	317
Saturday	423

- Ask: After Saturday, had they driven 1,000 miles? yes
- Ask: Do you need an estimate or an exact answer to solve the problem? Explain. an estimate; you can estimate the sum by using rounding. 350 rounds to 400, 317 rounds to 300, and 423 rounds to 400. $400 + 300 + 400 = 1,100$

VISUAL

LOGICAL/MATHEMATICAL

Intervention • Problem Solving, *Strategy/Skill 5*

Lesson 5.6 Organizer

Objective To identify whether an estimate or an exact answer is needed to solve a problem

Lesson Resources Reading Transparency 5; Intervention • Problem Solving, Strategy/Skill 5

1 INTRODUCE

QUICK REVIEW provides review of prerequisite skills.

WHY LEARN THIS? In real-life situations, you'll be able to determine if an exact answer or estimate is needed. *Share the lesson objective with students.*

2 TEACH

Guided Instruction

- *Direct students' attention to Example A.*
  REASONING Where was regrouping used in this problem? Both the tens and ones were regrouped.
- *Direct students' attention to Example B.*
  How do you know to estimate the sum and not the difference by rounding? Possible answer: You need to find the height of the airplane and the mountain. You are joining, not comparing or finding the difference, in heights.

3 PRACTICE

Guided Practice

Do Problem Solving Practice Exercises 1–4 with your students. Identify students who are having difficulty and choose appropriate lesson resources to provide assistance.

LESSON 6

Problem Solving Skill
Estimate or Exact Answer

UNDERSTAND › PLAN › SOLVE › CHECK

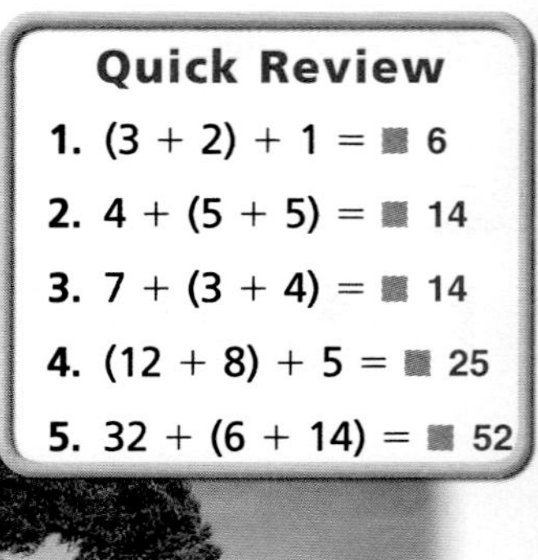

Quick Review

1. (3 + 2) + 1 = ■ 6
2. 4 + (5 + 5) = ■ 14
3. 7 + (3 + 4) = ■ 14
4. (12 + 8) + 5 = ■ 25
5. 32 + (6 + 14) = ■ 52

VIEW FROM THE TOP The table shows some of the highest points along the Appalachian Trail, which stretches from Maine to Georgia.

HIGH POINTS ALONG THE APPALACHIAN TRAIL		
High Point	**State**	**Height in Feet**
Mount Katahdin	Maine	5,267
Mount Washington	New Hampshire	6,288
Mount Greylock	Massachusetts	3,491
Mount Rogers	Virginia	5,729
Clingmans Dome	Tennessee	6,643

MATH IDEA Sometimes you need an exact or actual answer. Sometimes an estimate is all you need.

Examples

A How many feet higher is Clingmans Dome than Mount Washington?

Since the problem asks *how many feet higher,* subtract to find the actual answer.

$$\begin{array}{r} 6{,}643 \\ -6{,}288 \\ \hline 355 \end{array}$$

So, Clingmans Dome is 355 feet higher than Mount Washington.

B Suppose an airplane is flying 2,390 feet above Mount Rogers. Estimate the height of the airplane.

Since the problem asks for an *estimate,* you can use rounding to find the height.

$$\begin{array}{rcr} 2{,}390 & \rightarrow & 2{,}000 \\ +5{,}729 & \rightarrow & +6{,}000 \\ \hline & & 8{,}000 \end{array}$$

So, the height of the airplane is about 8,000 feet.

102

Reteach 5.6

Problem Solving Skill

Estimate or Exact Answer

Estimate to find the answer when you need to know *about* how many or *about* how much.

Find an exact answer when you need to know *exactly* how many or how much.

Here are some examples.

U.S. RIVERS	
River	**Length in Miles**
Mississippi	2,348
Missouri	2,315
Columbia	1,243

Estimate to find the answer

Problem About how much longer is the Mississippi River than the Columbia River?

Estimate the difference in the lengths of the rivers.

Mississippi 2,348 → 2,000
Columbia − 1,243 → − 1,000
1,000

The Mississippi River is about 1,000 miles longer than the Columbia River.

Exact answer

Problem How long are the Mississippi and Missouri Rivers altogether?

Find an exact answer.

Mississippi 2,348
Missouri + 2,315
4,663

The Mississippi and Missouri Rivers are 4,663 miles long in all.

Write whether you need an exact answer or an estimate. Then solve.

1. There are 84 children, 275 adults, and 138 senior citizens with tickets for a riverboat ride. About how many people will be taking the ride?
   Estimate;
   100 + 300 + 100 = 500 people
2. A life preserver is needed for each passenger on the riverboat. How many life preservers are needed?
   Exact answer; 84 + 275 +
   138 = 497 life preservers

RW30 Reteach

Practice 5.6

Problem Solving Skill

Estimate or Exact Answer

Use the table for 1–2. Write whether you need an exact answer or an estimate. Then solve.

Camping Supplies	
Item	**Price**
Cooler	$36.29
Lantern	$23.88
Sleeping bag	$74.99

1. Justin has $100. Can he buy a cooler and a sleeping bag? Explain.
   Estimate; no, because
   $40 + $70 = $110, which is more than $100.
2. Roxana pays for a lantern with $30. How much change will she get?
   Exact answer; $6.12

There will be 258 adults and 362 children at the Lazy River Campground this weekend. The campground will give one trail map to each camper. How many maps are needed in all?

3. Which number sentence can you use to solve the problem?
   (A) 258 + 362 = ____
   B 300 + 400 = ____
   C 300 + 362 = ____
   D 362 − 258 = ____
4. How many maps does the campground need in all?
   F 104 maps
   G 610 maps
   (H) 620 maps
   J 700 maps

Mixed Review

Solve.

5. 3,641 − 2,915 = 726
6. 1,094 + 6,378 = 7,472
7. 5,183 − 4,692 = 491
8. 2,796 + 5,847 = 8,643

PW30 Practice

Problem Solving Practice

Tell whether you need an exact answer or an estimate. Then solve.

1. Kayla's class went to a water park. Kayla took $35.00. She paid $24.95 for the ticket and $7.39 for a T-shirt. Does she have enough money to buy a bottle of juice that costs $2.50? **exact answer; yes; $24.95 + $7.39 = $32.34, $35.00 − $32.34 = $2.66, $2.66 > $2.50**
2. Records showed there were 783 students at the water park. There were 496 girls. About how many students were boys? **estimate; about 300 were boys**

Eve has 439 stickers in her collection. Her sister Ellen has 674 stickers. How many stickers do the sisters have in all?

3. Which number sentence can you use to solve the problem? **B**
   - A 439 + 439 = ▪
   - B 439 + 674 = ▪
   - C 674 − 439 = ▪
   - D 674 + 674 = ▪
4. How many stickers do Eve and Ellen have in all? **H**
   - F 235
   - G 439
   - H 1,113
   - J 1,348

Problem Solving

Mixed Applications

For 5-6, use the table.

TALLEST BUILDINGS IN CHICAGO, ILLINOIS	
Name	**Height in Feet**
Amoco Building	1,136
Sears Tower	1,454
John Hancock Center	1,127

5. **Write About It** Explain how you would compare the building heights, and put them in order from greatest to least. **Check students' explanations. 1,454 > 1,136 > 1,127**
6. How much taller is the Sears Tower than the John Hancock Center? **327 feet taller**
7. I am a 2-digit number. My tens digit is two more than my ones digit. My ones digit is between 4 and 6. What number am I? **75**
8. Wesley has 4 more hockey cards than baseball cards. If he has 28 cards in all, how many hockey cards does he have? **16**
9. **What's the Question?** Last week Luann ran 50 miles and Patrick ran 15 miles. The answer is 35 miles. **How many more miles did Luann run than Patrick?**
10. **REASONING** Joel had 48 inches of rope. He cut 15 inches off each end of the rope. What is the length of the rope he has left? **18 inches**

North Carolina Standards 1.02 Develop fluency with multi-digit addition and subtraction [th]rough 9,999 using: b) Estimation of sums and differences in appropriate situations.

Independent Practice

Note that Exercises 1, 5, 7, and 8 are **multistep or strategy problems.** Assign Exercises 5–10.

SCAFFOLDED INSTRUCTION Use the prompts on Transparency 5 to guide instruction for the multistep problem in Exercise 1.

Summarize the lesson by having students:

DISCUSS When might you use an estimate instead of an exact answer? Possible answer: when you need to know if you have enough money to buy something

WRITE Explain the difference between an estimate and an exact answer. An estimate determines about how many; an exact answer is a specific number.

LESSON QUIZ

Tell whether you need an exact answer or an estimate. Then solve.

1. Gina has saved $20. She wants to buy a CD that costs $14.99 (including tax) and a brush that costs $4.39. Does she have enough money? estimate; yes
2. Rico needs to make a total of 22 home runs to beat his team's season record. So far he has 16 home runs. How many more home runs does he need? exact answer; 6 home runs

Challenge 5.6

Planning a Party

Mrs. Laff is catering a party for 14 girls and 14 boys. Use the chart to help her plan the party.

Cupcakes	16 in a box
Pizza	1 pizza has 8 slices
Lemonade	1 bottle fills 10 glasses
Chips	9 servings in a bag
Balloons	12 in a bag

1. Each person will get 1 cupcake. How many boxes of cupcakes are needed? **2 boxes**
2. How many cupcakes will be left if each person eats one cupcake? **4**
3. How many pizzas would give each person 2 slices? **7 pizzas**
4. How many bottles of lemonade would give each person 2 glasses of lemonade? **6 bottles of lemonade**
5. Mrs. Laff bought 3 bags of chips. About how many servings per person is this? **about 1 serving**
6. Mrs. Laff plans to make a name card for each person. How many name cards must she make? **28**
7. Mrs. Laff plans to decorate the party room with balloons. She wants to use at least 50 balloons. How many bags should she buy? **5 bags**
8. A package of party napkins costs $8.85. Mrs. Laff pays for the napkins with $10. How much change will she get? **$1.15**
9. Mrs. Laff has $120 to spend on food for this party. The cupcakes will cost $32.85. The pizza will cost $48.00. The lemonade will cost $8.19. The chips will cost $10.94. Will she need more money for the food? Explain. **No; because $30 + $50 + $10 + $10 = $100, which is less than $120.**
10. Mrs. Laff can arrange the tables in 3 different ways. Each way seats a different number of people. She is able to seat 20, 25, or 36. Which way should she arrange her tables? Explain. **Since she needs seats for 28, she will have to arrange the tables to seat 36.**

CW30 Challenge

Reading Strategy 5.6

Choose Important Information

Understand ➔ Plan ➔ Solve ➔ Check

A word problem may contain more information than is needed to solve it. You must decide what information is important to use when solving a problem.

Read the following problem.

▶ There are 14 boys and 12 girls in Mrs. Menker's class. Each student needs a pair of scissors and 2 feet of string. Mrs. Menker must decide how many pairs of scissors to get.

1. Underline the important information.
2. Solve the problem. Describe the strategy you used. **Possible answer: I added to find the answer: 14 + 12 = 26; 26 pairs of scissors.**

Underline the important information. Solve. Describe your strategy.

3. Mrs. Menker's class is making beaded bracelets. Mrs. Menker must pay $5.79 for every 100 beads she buys. Altogether the students need 624 red beads, 780 yellow beads, and 572 blue beads. How many beads are needed in all? **Possible answer: I added: 624 + 780 + 572 = 1,976 beads**
4. Mrs. Menker also bought a set of paints for another project. The set had 5 colors. The paint cost $3.59. She paid for the paint with $5. How much change did she get? **Possible answer: I subtracted: $5 − $3.59 = $1.41. She got $1.41 in change.**

PS30 Reading Strategy

CHAPTER 5 Extra Practice

Purpose To provide extra practice for the skills presented in this chapter

The blue page references in each set of exercises refer to the lesson pages where each skill is taught.

Internet Resources

Visit THE LEARNING SITE at **www.harcourtschool.com** for a listing of practice activities.

Extra Practice

Set A (pp. 88–89)

Use rounding to estimate the difference. Estimates may vary.

1.	2.	3.	4.	5.
63	547	\$9.65	595	8,732
−49	−164	−\$5.48	−227	−4,759
10	300	\$5	400	4,000

Use front-end estimation to estimate the difference.

6.	7.	8.	9.	10.
795	7,850	8,026	\$55.75	2,521
−309	−2,187	−4,826	−\$47.46	−1,779
400	5,000	4,000	\$10	1,000

Set B (pp. 92–95)

Find the difference. Estimate to check.

1.	2.	3.	4.	5.
205	608	500	900	402
− 67	−409	−165	−198	−317
138	199	335	702	85

6. ALGEBRA The sum of 885 and another number is 901. What is the other number? 16

7. **MENTAL MATH** How might you use mental math to find 500 − 199? 500 − 200 = 300, so 500 − 199 = 301.

Set C (pp. 96–97)

Find the difference. Estimate to check.

1.	2.	3.	4.	5.
475	373	6,032	3,744	\$51.46
−283	−197	− 748	−1,495	−\$33.28
192	176	5,284	2,249	\$18.18

Set D (pp. 98–101)

Find the difference. Tell what method you used. Accept reasonable explanations.

1.	2.	3.	4.	5.
\$4.80	8,135	7,608	4,005	8,922
−\$2.30	−3,645	−5,810	−3,318	− 902
\$2.50	4,490	1,798	687	8,020

6. Lindsey paddled 4,033 feet in her canoe. Ronald paddled 2,077 feet in his. How much farther did Lindsey paddle than Ronald? 1,956 feet

7. **REASONING** The library was built 6 years before the post office was built. The post office was built in 1971. How old was the library in 1988? 23 years old

104

Review/Test

CHECK VOCABULARY AND CONCEPTS

Choose the correct term from the box.

estimate
regroup

1. To find *about* how many more, you can ?. (p. 88)
   estimate

Tell whether you need to regroup to find each difference. Explain. (pp. 90–91)

2. 342 − 214 = ■
   Yes, regroup 4 tens.
3. 312 − 181 = ■
   Yes, regroup 3 hundreds.
4. 162 − 51 = ■
   No regrouping needed; 2 > 1; 6 > 5

CHECK SKILLS

For 5–7, use rounding to estimate the difference. For 8–9, use front-end estimation to estimate the difference. (pp. 88–89) Estimates may vary.

5. 67 − 29 = 40
6. 967 − 283 = 700
7. 748 − 599 = 100
8. 4,175 − 1,832 = 3,000
9. 8,596 − 3,714 = 5,000

Find the difference. Estimate to check. (pp. 92–101)

10. 341 − 133 = ■ 208
11. 837 − 247 = ■ 590
12. \$3.73 − \$2.08 = ■ \$1.65
13. 645 − 347 = ■ 298
14. 800 − 364 = 436
15. \$4.02 − \$2.56 = \$1.46
16. 1,728 − 339 = 1,389
17. 2,073 − 1,895 = 178
18. \$48.56 − \$35.77 = \$12.79
19. 4,250 − 2,872 = 1,378
20. 970 − 560 = 410
21. 8,029 − 6,047 = 1,982
22. 7,300 − 1,074 = 6,226
23. 5,789 − 898 = 4,891

CHECK PROBLEM SOLVING

24. Abe wants each person at his party to have about 1 cup of punch. If he invites 18 children and 9 adults, about how many cups of punch should he make? (pp. 102–103)
    about 30 cups
25. Danielle wants to buy a favor for each child who attends her birthday party. She invited 16 girls and 15 boys. How many favors should she buy? (pp. 102–103)
    31 favors

Review/Test

Purpose To check understanding of concepts, skills, and problem solving presented in Chapter 5

Using the Page

The Chapter 5 Review/Test can be used as a **review** or a **test**.

- Items 1–4 check understanding of concepts and new vocabulary.
- Items 5–23 check skill proficiency.
- Items 24–25 check students' abilities to choose and apply problem solving strategies to real-life problems.

Suggest that students place the completed Chapter 5 Review/Test in their portfolios.

Using the Assessment Guide

- Multiple-choice format of Chapter 5 Posttest—See *Assessment Guide*, pp. AG33–34.
- Free-response format of Chapter 5 Posttest—See *Assessment Guide*, pp. AG35–36.

Using Student Self-Assessment

The How Did I Do? survey helps students assess what they have learned and how they learned it. This survey is available as a copying master in *Assessment Guide*, p. AGxvii.

Chapter 5 Test, page 1

Choose the correct answer.

1. Which two numbers have a difference that is about 300?
   A 871 and 495
   B 839 and 272
   C 710 and 482
   (D) 792 and 546
2. **Round to the nearest hundred** to ESTIMATE the difference.
   5,679 − 4,458
   F 200 (H) 1,200
   G 1,100 J 1,300
3. Laura watched 618 minutes of TV in May and 389 minutes in June. About how many more minutes of TV did she watch in May than in June?
   A 600 (C) 200
   B 400 D 100
4. Use **front-end estimation** to ESTIMATE the difference.
   4,727 − 1,283
   F 6,000 H 4,000
   G 5,000 (J) 3,000
5. **Round to the nearest ten** to ESTIMATE the sum.
   329 + 544
   A 800 (C) 870
   B 850 D 880
6. **Round to the nearest dollar** to ESTIMATE the difference.
   \$7.28 − \$4.80
   (F) \$2.00 H \$3.00
   G \$2.50 J \$12.00
7. 562 − 288
   (A) 274 C 386
   B 326 D 850
8. 606 − 311 = ■
   F 315 (H) 295
   G 305 J 285
9. \$8.74 − \$2.75
   (A) \$5.99 C \$6.09
   B \$6.01 D \$6.79
10. 900 − 126
    F 764 H 864
    (G) 774 J 884

Go On

Chapter 5 Test, page 2

11. Joe has 24 CDs, 208 stickers, and 134 trading cards. How many more stickers than trading cards does he have?
    A 342 C 110
    B 184 (D) 74
12. 6,000 − 3,859
    F 2,140
    (G) 2,141
    H 3,251
    J 3,859
13. 5,246 − 789 = ■
    (A) 4,457
    B 4,547
    C 5,447
    D 5,543
14. 5,668 − 792
    (F) 4,876
    G 4,966
    H 5,876
    J 5,976
15. Mr. Gomez traveled 5,389 miles last year. Mr. Burton traveled 7,912 miles. How many more miles did Mr. Burton travel than Mr. Gomez?
    A 2,517 C 2,673
    (B) 2,523 D 2,677
16. Kayla lives 2,379 miles away from her grandparents. Marcus lives 1,480 miles away from his grandparents. How much farther from her grandparents does Kayla live than Marcus?
    F 1,299 miles (H) 899 miles
    G 1,119 miles J 859 miles
17. A restaurant will serve pancakes to 25 adults and 13 children. Each person will eat 2 pancakes. About how many pancakes should the cook make?
    A 50 (C) 80
    B 60 D 100
18. A store sells pens for \$1.29 and paper for \$1.49. Margo has \$5.00. How much money will she have left if she buys paper?
    (F) \$3.51 H \$4.81
    G \$4.61 J \$6.49

For 19–20, use this information.
Tasha's dad spent \$35.06 at the grocery store. Tasha's mom spent \$47.50 at the hardware store.

19. Which expression can you use to show how much money Tasha's mom and dad spent in all?
    A \$35.06 + \$35.06
    (B) \$35.06 + \$47.50
    C \$47.50 − \$35.06
    D \$47.50 + \$47.50
20. How much money did Tasha's mom and dad spend in all?
    F \$12.44 (H) \$82.56
    G \$70.12 J \$95.00

Stop

Getting Ready for the EOG Test

Chapters 1–5

Using the Pages

These pages may be used to help students get ready for the North Carolina EOG Test. The test items are written in the same style and arranged in the same format as those on the EOG Test.

The pages are cumulative. They cover the standards from the North Carolina Mathematics Standard Course of Study that have been taught up to this point in the text or in a previous grade. Each Getting Ready for the EOG Test also reviews the North Carolina mathematics strands shown below.

- Number and Operations
- Measurement
- Geometry
- Data Analysis and Probability
- Algebra

These pages can be assigned at the end of the chapter as classwork or as a homework assignment. You may want to have students use individual recording sheets presented in a multiple-choice (standardized) format. A Test Answer Sheet is available as a black-line master in the *Assessment Guide* (p. AGlii).

You may wish to have students describe how they solved each problem and share their solutions.

Getting Ready for the EOG Test

NUMBER AND OPERATIONS

1. Shelli picked 4 number cards and made this number. How many hundreds are there? A

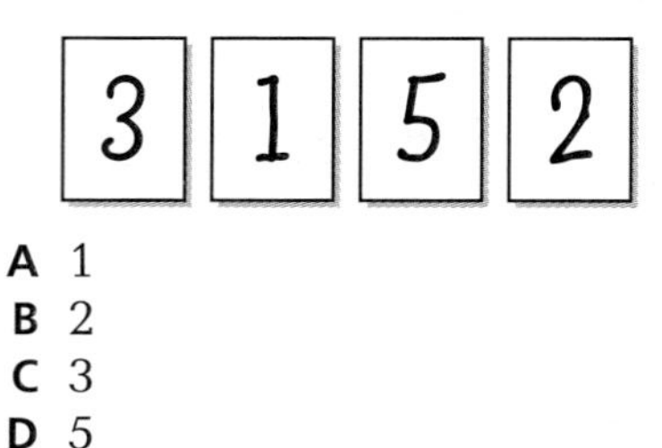

A 1
B 2
C 3
D 5

TIP **Eliminate choices.** See item 2. Look at the last two numbers in each answer choice. If the second number is greater than the third number, eliminate that choice.

2. Which group of numbers is ordered from *least* to *greatest*? D

A 4,593; 3,549; 3,459
B 8,095; 9,058; 5,980
C 3,855; 5,853; 5,358
D 4,178; 7,418; 8,741

3. **Explain It** Rob has 538 trading cards. Seth has 252 trading cards. Rob says that he has *about* 300 more cards than Seth. Do you agree? Explain. See page 107.

MEASUREMENT AND GEOMETRY

4. The clock shows the time Dennis began to read. He read for one hour. At what time did Dennis stop reading? D

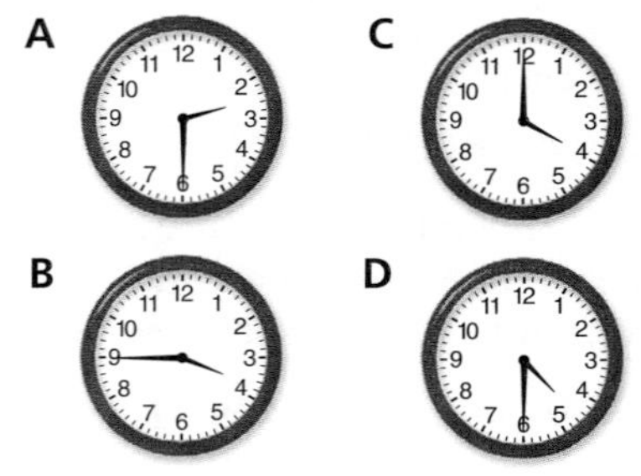

A C

B D

5. What is the length of Julia's hair clip to the nearest inch? B

inches 1 2

A 1 inch
B 2 inches
C 3 inches
D 4 inches

6. Which item weighs *about* one pound? A

A football
B pen
C car
D eyeglasses

7. **Explain It** Skye has 20 inches of ribbon. She needs to cut 3 pieces of ribbon that are each 6 inches long to make bows. Should Skye estimate or measure with a ruler to cut each piece of ribbon? Explain. See page 107.

ALGEBRA

8. Which figure is missing from this pattern? **A**

○▭△ ○▭△ ○▭△ ○ ? △

A ▭
B □
C ○
D △

9. What are the next two letters in this pattern? **B**

AAA AAB AAC AAD A ? ?

A E A
B A E
C E F
D F A

10. Which is the missing addend? **C**

8 + ■ = 14

A 8
B 7
C 6
D 5

11. Explain It What are the next two numbers in Jonathan's pattern? Explain how you know.

1, 6, 11, 16, ? , ?
See below.

DATA ANALYSIS AND PROBABILITY

12. The pictograph shows the number of hours some animals sleep in one day.

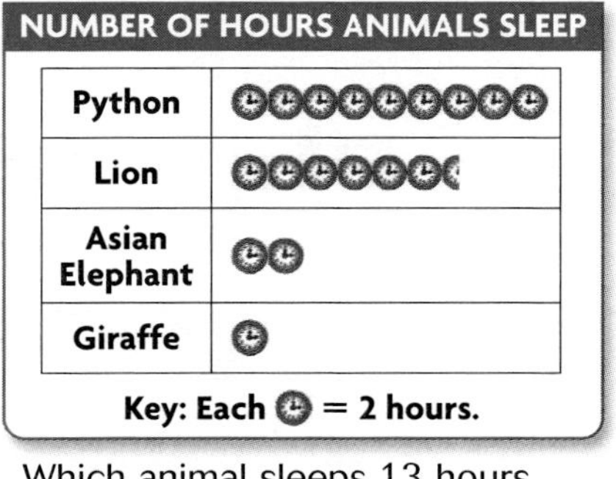

NUMBER OF HOURS ANIMALS SLEEP
Python
Lion
Asian Elephant
Giraffe
Key: Each = 2 hours.

Which animal sleeps 13 hours each day? **B**

A python **C** Asian elephant
B lion **D** giraffe

13. Guy writes the numbers 2, 4, 6, 8, and 10 on five cards. He puts the cards in a box. Without looking, he pulls a card from the box. Which of these statements is true? **A**

A The number is even.
B The number is odd.
C The number is less than 2.
D The number is greater than 10.

14. Explain It Kerri put 3 red marbles and 3 blue marbles in a bag. Is Kerri *more* likely to draw a red marble or a blue marble from the bag? Explain your answer.
See below.

Chapters 1–5

Item Analysis

You may wish to use the item analysis to determine which North Carolina standards need additional review.

Item	North Carolina Standard	Lesson
1	1.01	2.2
2	1.01	3.3
3	1.02	5.1
4	(2) 2.02	Grade 2
5	(2) 2.01	Grade 2
6	(2) Goal 2	Grade 2
7	2.01	5.6
8	(2) Goal 5	Grade 2
9	(2) Goal 5	Grade 2
10	5.04	1.2
11	5.01	2.5
12	(2) 4.01	Grade 2
13	(2) 4.02	Grade 2
14	(2) 4.02	Grade 2

SCORING RUBRIC
Explain It

2 Demonstrates a complete understanding of the problem and chooses an appropriate strategy to determine the solution

1 Demonstrates a partial understanding of the problem and chooses a strategy that does not lead to a complete and accurate solution

0 Demonstrates little understanding of the problem and shows little evidence of using any strategy to determine a solution

Explain It • Written Response

3. Possible answer: yes; you can use front-end estimation: $500 - 200 = 300$.

7. Possible answer: Skye should measure with a ruler since each piece must be 6 inches long.

11. 21, 26; Possible answer: each number is 5 more than the number before it. Since each number increases by 5, the next numbers would be $16 + 5$, or 21, and $21 + 5$, or 26.

14. Kerri is equally likely to draw red or blue because the same number of each color is in the bag.

Use Money

NCTM Standards 2000

1. Number and Operations
Lessons 6.1, 6.2, 6.3, 6.4, 6.5
2. Algebra
Lessons 6.3, 6.5
3. Geometry
4. Measurement
5. Data Analysis and Probability
Lesson 6.2
6. Problem Solving
Lessons 6.1, 6.2, 6.3, 6.4, 6.5
7. Reasoning and Proof
Lessons 6.1, 6.2, 6.3, 6.4
8. Communication
Lessons 6.1, 6.2, 6.3, 6.4, 6.5
9. Connections
Lesson 6.1
10. Representation
Lessons 6.1, 6.2, 6.3, 6.4, 6.5

Chapter Planner

Getting Ready for Chapter 6 • Assessing Prior Knowledge and INTERVENTION (See PE and TE page 109.)

LESSON	NORTH CAROLINA STANDARDS	PACING	VOCABULARY*	MATERIALS	RESOURCES AND TECHNOLOGY
6.1 Count Bills and Coins pp. 110–113 Objective To count sets of bills and coins and to make equivalent sets of money	2.01b	1 Day	**decimal point** **equivalent**		Reteach, Practice, Problem Solving, Challenge 6.1 Worksheets; Transparency 6.1; **Intervention,** *Skills 16, 17* (CD or Book); **Harcourt Mega Math The Number Games,** *Buggy Bargains*
6.2 Problem Solving Strategy Make a Table pp. 114–115 Objective To use the problem solving strategy *make a table* to solve a problem	2.01b	1 Day			Reteach, Practice, Reading Strategy, Challenge 6.2 Worksheets; Transparency 6.2; Scaffolded Instruction Transparency 6; Reading Transparency 6; **Intervention • Problem Solving,** *Strategy/Skill 6* (CD or Book)
6.3 Compare Money Amounts pp. 116–117 Objective To compare money amounts	1.01c	1 Day			Reteach, Practice, Problem Solving, Challenge 6.3 Worksheets; Transparency 6.3; **Intervention,** *Skills 16, 17* (CD or Book)
6.4 Hands On: Make Change pp. 118–119 Objective To use the strategy *counting on* to make change	maintains (2) 1.05	1 Day		*For each group* play bills and coins	Reteach, Practice, Problem Solving, Challenge 6.4 Worksheets; Transparency 6.4; **Intervention,** *Skills 16, 17* (CD or Book); **Harcourt Mega Math The Number Games,** *Buggy Bargains*; **Math Jingles® CD 3–4**
6.5 Add and Subtract Money pp. 120–121 Objective To add and subtract money amounts	1.02a	1 Day			Reteach, Practice, Problem Solving, Challenge 6.5 Worksheets; Transparency 6.5; **Intervention,** *Skills 16, 17* (CD or Book); **Harcourt Mega Math The Number Games,** *Buggy Bargains*

Ending Chapter 6 • **Extra Practice,** p. 122 • **Chapter 6 Review/Test,** p. 123 • **Getting Ready for the EOG Test,** pp. 124–125

* **Boldfaced** terms are the key mathematical terms for the chapter.

Voc bulary Pow r

Review Vocabulary

To be ready for Chapter 6, students should know the following vocabulary term:

- **dollar sign** (p. 109)—a symbol used to indicate dollars that looks like a capital S with one or two vertical lines through it

Vocabulary Cards

Have students use the Vocabulary Cards on *Teacher's Resource Book*, page TR145 for the key terms in the chapter. The cards can be added to a file of mathematics terms.

decimal point

Multimedia Math Glossary

GO ON-LINE For vocabulary support, visit **www.harcourtschool.com/mathglossary**

Develop Key Chapter Vocabulary

The **boldfaced** words are the key vocabulary terms in the chapter.

- **decimal point** (p. 110)—the symbol used to separate the dollars and cents in money and to separate the ones place from the tenths place in decimals
- **equivalent** (p. 111)—two or more sets that name the same amount

Math Journal

Have students define the key vocabulary terms: *decimal point* and *equivalent*. Have students use their own words and give an example of each.

MATH Word Work

Objective To reinforce vocabulary concepts
Use after Lesson 6.1.

Materials *For each student* play coins and bills, *Teacher's Resource Book,* pp. TR51–53, poster board or drawing paper, markers or crayons, glue or paste

Name an amount of money. Have students use the play coins and bills to make two equivalent sets. Then have them make a poster to show the equivalent amounts. First, ask students to cut out and paste the play coins and bills on poster board or drawing paper. Then, have them title their poster *Equivalent Sets of Money.* Underneath each set, have students write the amount and label the dollar sign and the decimal point.

When the posters are finished, students should have used all the review and key vocabulary terms for the chapter. You may want to display the posters around the classroom.

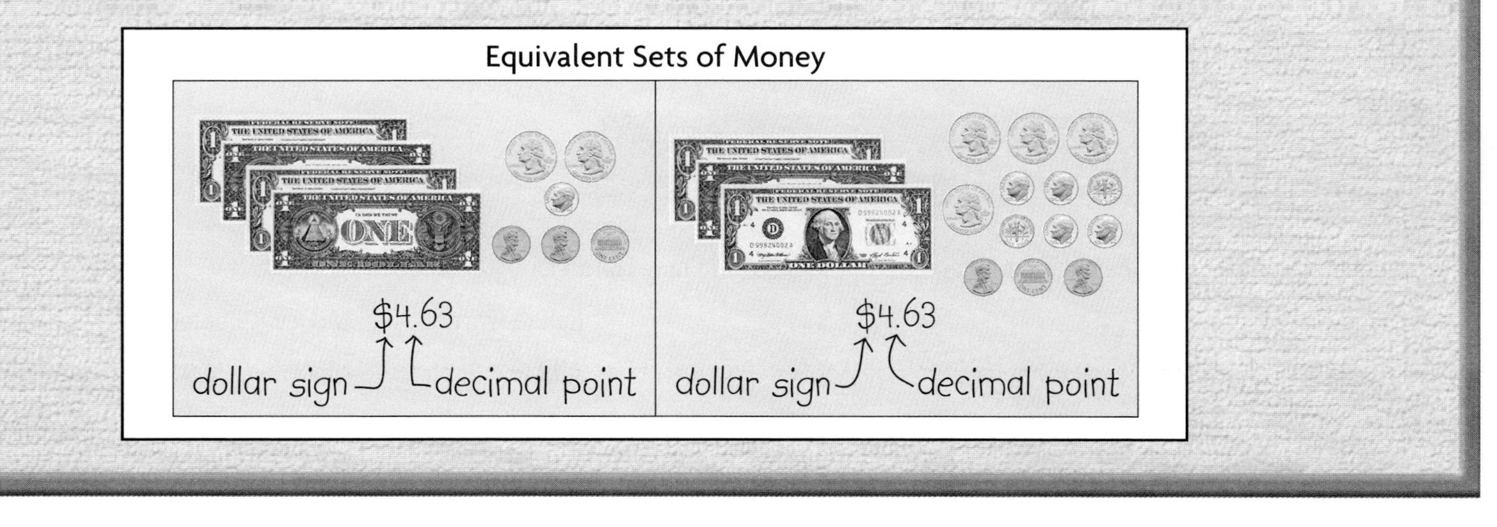

Use Money

Mathematics Across the Grades

LOOKING BACK • Prerequisite Skills

To be ready for Chapter 6, students should have the following understandings and skills:

- **Count Coins**—review counting and writing coin amounts
- **Same Amounts**—make different sets of coins with the same value

Check What You Know

Use page 109 to determine students' knowledge of prerequisite concepts and skills.

Intervention

Help students prepare for the chapter by using the intervention resources described on TE page 109.

LOOKING AT CHAPTER 6 • Essential Skills

Students will

- count sets of bills and coins and make equivalent sets of money.
- use the problem solving strategy *make a table* to solve problems.
- **add, subtract, and compare money amounts.**
- use the strategy *counting on* to make change.

Example

$2.27 + $1.32	
Model	**Algorithm**
	$2.27 +$1.32 $3.59

LOOKING AHEAD • Applications

Students will apply what they learn in Chapter 6 to the following new concepts:

- Find the Cost (Chapter 14)
- Relate Decimals and Money (Chapter 28)
- Relate Fractions and Money (Chapter 28)
- Add and Subtract Decimals and Money (Chapter 28)

Differentiated Instruction

Meeting the Needs of All Learners

Extra Support	Activities for All	Enrichment
Alternative Teaching Strategy TE Lessons 6.1, 6.2, 6.3, 6.4, 6.5 **ESOL/ESL** TE Lessons 6.1, 6.2, 6.3, 6.4, 6.5 **Special Needs** TE Lesson 6.3	**Cross-Curricular Connections** **Health:** TE Lesson 6.2 **Math:** TE Lesson 6.3 **Reading:** TE Lesson 6.2 **Social Studies:** Chapter Opener, TE Lesson 6.4 **Vocabulary:** TE p. 108B, PE/TE p. 109 **Writing:** TE Lessons 6.2, 6.4, 6.5	**Advanced Learners** TE Lessons 6.1, 6.5

Combination and Multi-age Classrooms

Grade 2	Grade 3	Grade 4
Skills Trace Across the Grades		
Count mixed collections of coins; use the decimal notation and the dollar symbol for money; use the cents sign when adding and subtracting money amounts; identify different ways to make the same amount; count on to make change.	**Count sets of bills and coins and write equivalent amounts; count on to make change; write sums and differences of money amounts.**	Write sums and differences of money amounts.
Instructional Strategies		
Students on this level may require more time to build conceptual understanding. **Assignments** **Grade 3 Pupil Edition** • Have students work in pairs on Lessons 6.1 and 6.4. • Have students skip Lesson 6.2. **Grade 2 Pupil Edition**—pages 203–218 and 221–238	Students on this level should be able to complete all the lessons in the Pupil Edition and all the activities in the Teacher's Edition with minimal adjustments. **Assignment** **Grade 3 Pupil Edition**—pages 108–123	Students on this level will probably require less time to build conceptual understanding. **Assignments** **Grade 3 Pupil Edition** • Compact Lessons 6.1 and 6.3. **Grade 4 Pupil Edition**—pages 592–595

CHAPTER 6

Use Money

Introducing the Chapter

Tell students that equal amounts of money can be represented in a variety of ways.

Using Data

To begin the study of this chapter, have students

- Round the total amount on one sheet of five-dollar bills to the nearest hundred. $200
- Determine how many sheets of one-dollar bills are needed to equal one sheet of five-dollar bills. 5 sheets
- Subtract the amount of money on a sheet of one-dollar bills from the amount on a sheet of ten-dollar bills. $128

Problem Solving Project

Purpose To add money amounts

Grouping partners

Background U.S. currency is printed on special paper and with special inks that keep it from being easily copied. Bills have been made with a thread that glows when put under a certain type of light.

UNDERSTAND • PLAN • SOLVE • CHECK
Have students

- Decide on a group of items to sell, such as snacks or school supplies.
- Draw several items and label them with a price in cents.
- Choose three items to buy from their partner.
- Record each price and find the sum. Check students' work.

Suggest that students place the drawings and the other information they gathered in their portfolios.

Graphing Investigations
Begin Week 6.

CHAPTER 6

Use Money

FAST FACT • SOCIAL STUDIES In one hour, presses at the Bureau of Engraving and Printing can print 8,000 sheets of currency. Each sheet of $1 and $5 bills contains 32 bills. That means that 256,000 $1 and $5 bills are printed every hour.

VALUE OF 1 SHEET OF PRINTED CURRENCY

Bill	Dollars
$1 bill	$32
$5 bill	$160
$10 bill	$160
$20 bill	$

Dollars: 0 40 80 120 160 200 240 28

PROBLEM SOLVING The graph shows how much one sheet of each type of bill is worth. How much are two sheets of $20 bills worth?

108 $640

WHY LEARN MATH? A bank teller cashes checks, gives customers money from their bank accounts, and receives money from customers to deposit into their accounts. A bank teller needs to know the value of money, how to count money, and how to add and subtract money amounts. Ask: Why is it important for bank tellers to be able to add and subtract money accurately? Possible answer: A mistake could cause the bank or a customer to lose money.

Family Involvement Activities

These activities provide:

- Letter to the Family
- Math Vocabulary
- Family Game
- Practice (Homework)

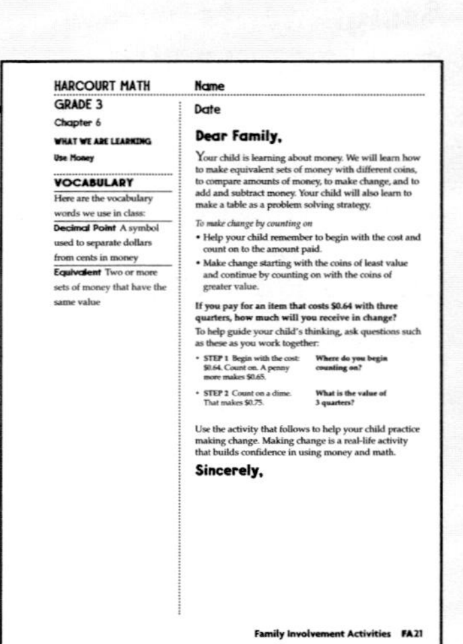

HARCOURT MATH
GRADE 3
Chapter 6
WHAT WE ARE LEARNING
Use Money

VOCABULARY
Here are the vocabulary words we use in class:
Decimal Point A symbol used to separate dollars from cents in money
Equivalent Two or more sets of money that have the same value

Name
Date

Dear Family,

Your child is learning about money. We will learn how to make equivalent sets of money with different coins, to compare amounts of money, to make change, and to add and subtract money. Your child will also learn to make a table as a problem solving strategy.

To make change by counting on
- Help your child remember to begin with the cost and count on to the amount paid.
- Make change starting with the coins of least value and continue by counting on with the coins of greater value.

If you pay for an item that costs $0.64 with three quarters, how much will you receive in change?
To help guide your child's thinking, ask questions such as these as you work together:

- STEP 1 Begin with the cost: $0.64. Count on. A penny more makes $0.65. **Where do you begin counting on?**
- STEP 2 Count on a dime. That makes $0.75. **What is the value of 3 quarters?**

Use the activity that follows to help your child practice making change. Making change is a real-life activity that builds confidence in using money and math.

Sincerely,

Family Involvement Activities FA21

Family Involvement Activities, p. FA21

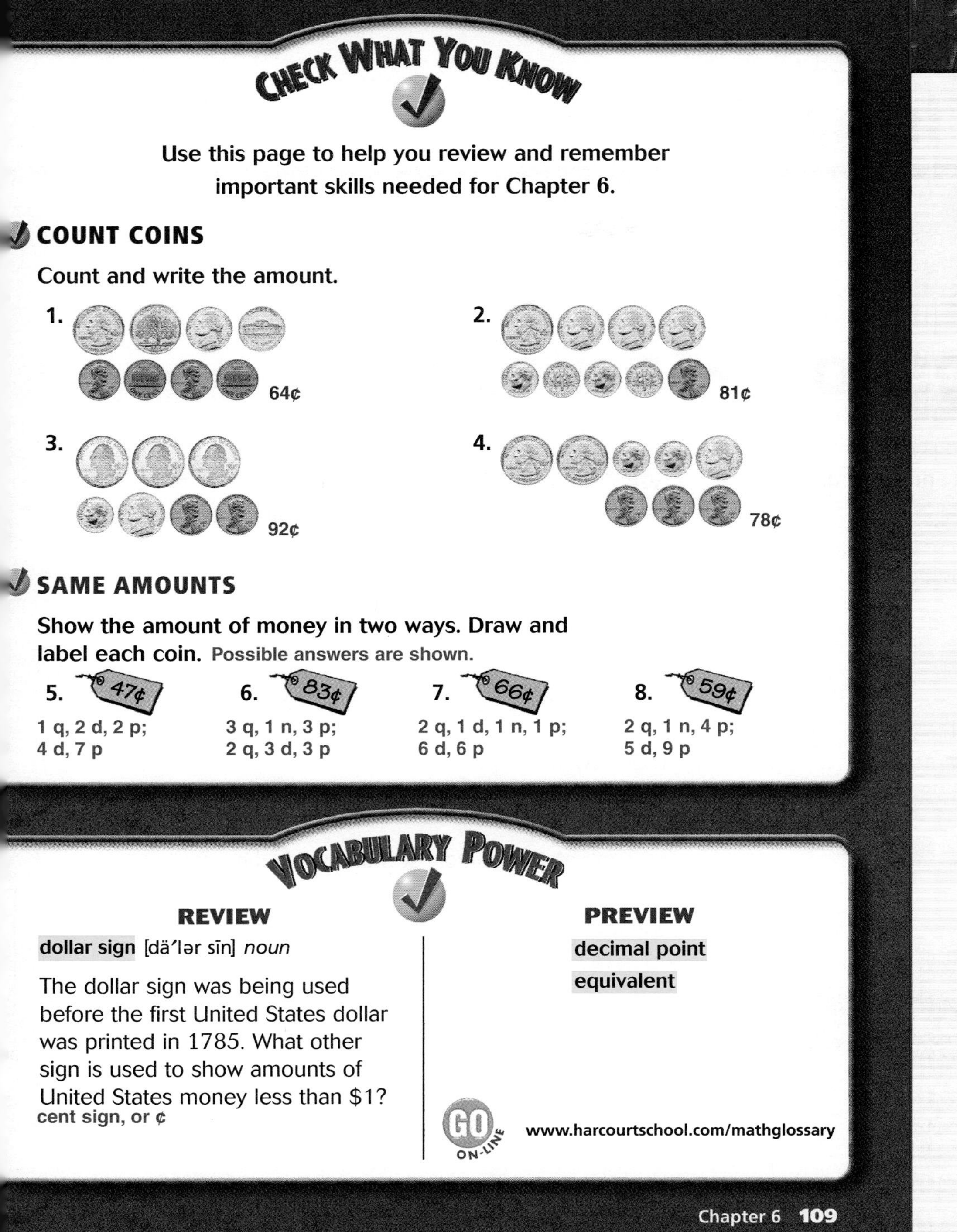

CHECK WHAT YOU KNOW

Use this page to help you review and remember important skills needed for Chapter 6.

COUNT COINS

Count and write the amount.

1. 64¢
2. 81¢
3. 92¢
4. 78¢

SAME AMOUNTS

Show the amount of money in two ways. Draw and label each coin. Possible answers are shown.

5. 47¢ — 1 q, 2 d, 2 p; 4 d, 7 p
6. 83¢ — 3 q, 1 n, 3 p; 2 q, 3 d, 3 p
7. 66¢ — 2 q, 1 d, 1 n, 1 p; 6 d, 6 p
8. 59¢ — 2 q, 1 n, 4 p; 5 d, 9 p

VOCABULARY POWER

REVIEW

dollar sign [dä′lər sīn] *noun*

The dollar sign was being used before the first United States dollar was printed in 1785. What other sign is used to show amounts of United States money less than $1?
cent sign, or ¢

PREVIEW

decimal point
equivalent

GO ON-LINE www.harcourtschool.com/mathglossary

Chapter 6 109

Assessing Prior Knowledge

Use the **Check What You Know** page to determine whether your students have mastered the prerequisite skills critical for this chapter.

Intervention

- **Diagnose and Prescribe**
  Evaluate your students' performance on this page to determine whether intervention is necessary or if enrichment is appropriate. Options that provide instruction, practice, and a check are listed below.

CHECK WHAT YOU KNOW RESOURCES

Intervention Copying Masters or CD-ROMs
Enrichment Copying Masters

VOCABULARY POWER

For activities and information about the vocabulary in this chapter, see page 108B.

Were students successful with CHECK WHAT YOU KNOW?

IF . . . NO THEN . . . INTERVENE — **INTERVENTION OPTIONS** — **IF . . . YES THEN . . . ENRICH**

Skill/Items	Missed more than	Intervene with
Count Coins 1–4	1	• *Intervention*, Skill 16
Same Amounts 5–8	1	• *Intervention*, Skill 17

Skill/Items	Missed fewer than	Enrich with
Count Coins 1–4	2	• *Intervention*, Enrichment p. IN339
Same Amounts 5–8	2	• *Intervention*, Enrichment p. IN340

Lesson 6.1

Count Bills and Coins

Lesson Planning

Objective To count sets of bills and coins and to make equivalent sets of money

NCTM Standards

1. Number and Operations
6. Problem Solving
7. Reasoning and Proof
8. Communication
9. Connections
10. Representation

Math Background

Keep these ideas in mind when helping students understand how to count money.

- When counting money, it is easiest to begin with the coin or bill of greatest value, but you can count coins and bills in any order.
- Sets of money that have the same value are equivalent.

Vocabulary

decimal point a symbol used to separate dollars from cents in money

equivalent two or more sets that name the same amount

Warm-Up Resources

Number of the Day

The number of the day is the number of cents in a quarter. Write and solve an addition sentence using the number. Possible answer: 25 + 5 = 30

Daily Facts Practice

Have students practice addition and subtraction facts by completing Set C of *Teacher's Resource Book,* p. TR87.

Solve a Problem

Transparency 6.1

Problem of the Day

Use a dollar sign, a decimal point, and the digits 0, 4, and 8. Write as many different amounts of money as you can. List the coins and bills that would equal each amount. $0.48, $0.84, $4.08, $4.80, $8.04, $8.40; Answers will vary.

Solution Problem of the Day tab, p. PD6

Intervention and Extension Resources

Alternative Teaching Strategy

MATERIALS *For each pair* play bills and coins, pp. TR51–53

Have students **make equivalent sets of money.** Have them use the fewest coins to make a specified amount of money. After they show the model with their coins, have them draw pictures or make a table to record their answers. Check students' work.

KINESTHETIC, VISUAL

LOGICAL/MATHEMATICAL, INTERPERSONAL

Multistep and Strategy Problems

The following multistep or strategy problem is provided in Lesson 6.1:

Page	Item
112	32

ESOL/ESL

MATERIALS *For each pair* play bills and coins, pp. TR51–53

To help students **practice counting money,** have them "buy" classroom items. Affix self-adhesive price tags to items such as a book, a globe, a game, a puzzle, and a box of crayons. Have students take turns using a combination of bills and coins to "buy" the items. Have them count aloud. Check students' work.

KINESTHETIC, VISUAL

LOGICAL/MATHEMATICAL, INTERPERSONAL

Advanced Learners

Have students **solve problems using money.**

- Kenneth has 4 coins in his pocket. The value of the coins is \$0.37. Two of the coins are pennies. What are the other two coins? 1 quarter and 1 dime
- Alice has 8 coins totaling \$0.40. What are her coins? 1 quarter, 2 nickels, and 5 pennies, or 8 nickels

Discuss the solutions and ask students to write a similar problem for classmates to solve.

VISUAL

LOGICAL/MATHEMATICAL

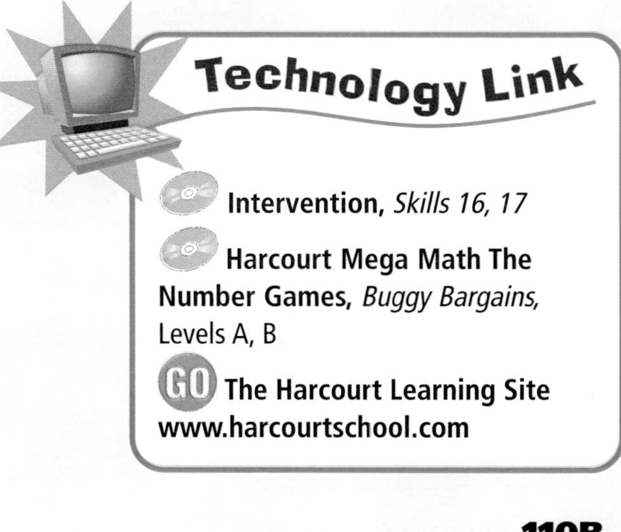

Technology Link

Intervention, *Skills 16, 17*

Harcourt Mega Math The Number Games, *Buggy Bargains,* Levels A, B

The Harcourt Learning Site www.harcourtschool.com

Lesson 6.1 Organizer

Objective To count sets of bills and coins and to make equivalent sets of money

Vocabulary decimal point, equivalent

QUICK REVIEW provides review of prerequisite skills.

WHY LEARN THIS? You can pay for something with different combinations of bills and coins. *Share the lesson objective with students.*

2 TEACH

Guided Instruction

- *Ask students to look at Example A.*
  REASONING How did Jolene order the coins? She ordered the coins from greatest to least value.
  What operation are you using when you are counting bills and coins? addition
  Why is it helpful to begin counting with the bill or coin with the greatest value? Possible answer: When you begin with the greatest value, the addition is easier than if you begin with the least value. You can use mental math.
- *Direct students' attention to Example B.*
  What coins would you need to add to Andrew's money to make $2.65? 3 pennies

MODIFYING INSTRUCTION Provide students with the bills and coins to match Example B. Have a volunteer demonstrate counting the money in front of the class, handling each bill and coin as it is counted.

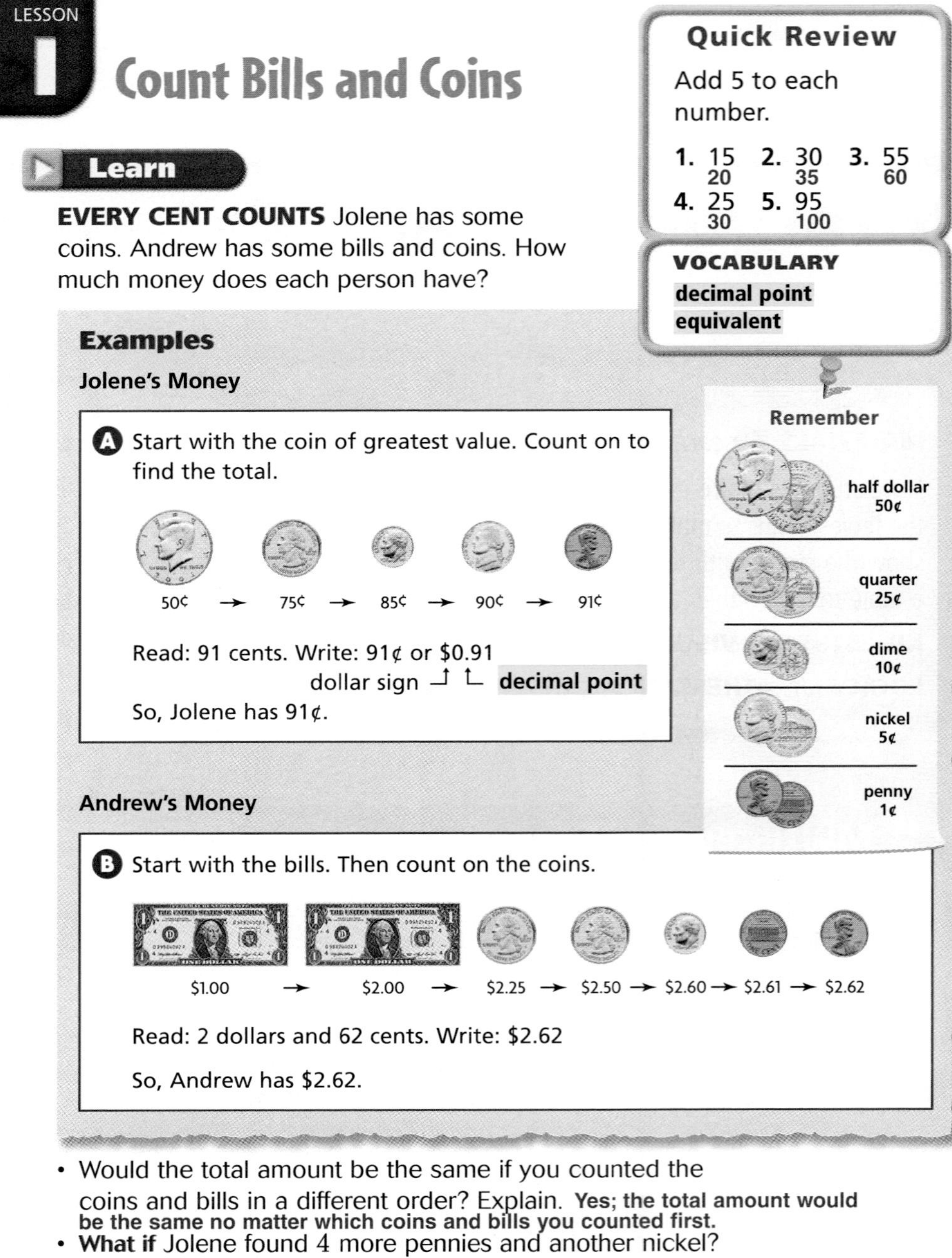
LESSON 1

Count Bills and Coins

Quick Review

Add 5 to each number.

1. 15 (20) 2. 30 (35) 3. 55 (60)
4. 25 (30) 5. 95 (100)

VOCABULARY
decimal point
equivalent

Learn

EVERY CENT COUNTS Jolene has some coins. Andrew has some bills and coins. How much money does each person have?

Examples

Jolene's Money

A Start with the coin of greatest value. Count on to find the total.

50¢ → 75¢ → 85¢ → 90¢ → 91¢

Read: 91 cents. Write: 91¢ or $0.91
dollar sign, decimal point

So, Jolene has 91¢.

Remember
half dollar 50¢
quarter 25¢
dime 10¢
nickel 5¢
penny 1¢

Andrew's Money

B Start with the bills. Then count on the coins.

$1.00 → $2.00 → $2.25 → $2.50 → $2.60 → $2.61 → $2.62

Read: 2 dollars and 62 cents. Write: $2.62

So, Andrew has $2.62.

- Would the total amount be the same if you counted the coins and bills in a different order? Explain. **Yes; the total amount would be the same no matter which coins and bills you counted first.**
- **What if** Jolene found 4 more pennies and another nickel? How much money would she then have in all? **100¢, 1 dollar, or $1.00**

110

Reteach 6.1

Count Bills and Coins

When counting money, start with the bill or coin that is worth the most. Then, count on.

Count: 25¢ 50¢ 60¢ 61¢ 62¢	**Count:** $5.00 $5.50 $5.51 $5.52 $5.53

Sets of money that are worth the same amount are **equivalent**.

The two sets of coins shown below are equivalent.
Each set of coins has a value of $5.50.

Count: $5.00 $5.25 $5.50	**Count:** $5.00 $5.25 $5.35 $5.45 $5.50

Write the value of each set of coins, using a dollar sign and decimal point. Then draw a picture of an equivalent set. Remember to start with the bill or coin that is worth the most. **Check students' drawings. Possible answers are given.**

1. $0.26
2. $2.35
3. $3.80

Reteach RW31

Practice 6.1

Count Bills and Coins

Write the amount.

1. $0.73
2. $2.65

Find two equivalent sets for each. List the c... ...s.
Check students' lists. Possible answers are given.

3. $1.60 **one $1 bill, 2 quarters, 1 dime**
6 quarters, 2 nickels
4. $6.53 **one $5 bill, one $1 bill, 2 quarters, 3 pennies**
six $1 bills, 5 dimes, 3 pennies

Write the missing number.

5. 1 nickel = **5** pennies
6. 10 pennies = **2** nickel(s)
7. 1 dollar = **10** dime(s)
8. 5 nickels = **1** quarter(s)

List the fewest bills and coins you can use to make each amount.

9. $1.89 **one $1 bill, one half dollar, 1 quarter, 1 dime, 4 pennies**
10. $7.32 **one $5 bill, two $1 dollar bills, 1 quarter, 1 nickel, 2 pennies**

Mixed Review

Round to the nearest hundred.

11. 84 **100**
12. 319 **300**
13. 4,866 **4,900**
14. 91 **100**
15. 449 **400**
16. 7,601 **7,600**
17. Which digit is in the hundreds place of 8,310? **3**
18. Which digit is in the thousands place of 19,036? **9**

Practice PW31

Equivalent Sets

Sets of money that have the same value are **equivalent**. You can make two equivalent sets of money with a value of \$6.13 by using different combinations of bills and coins.

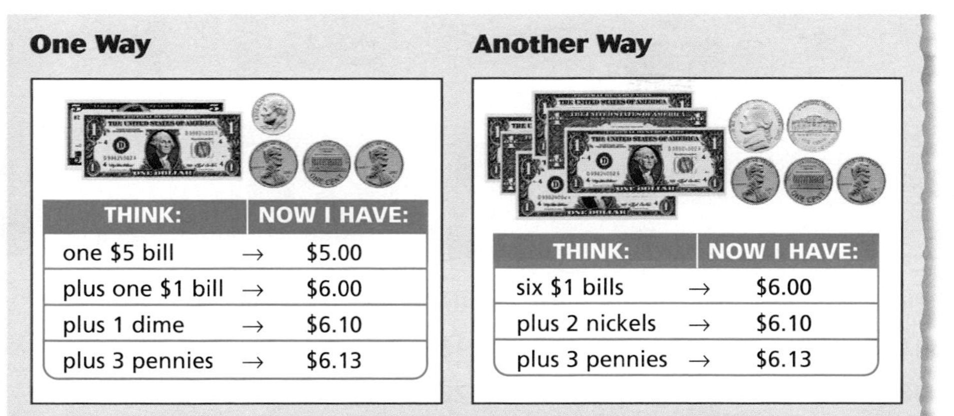

One Way

THINK:	NOW I HAVE:
one \$5 bill →	\$5.00
plus one \$1 bill →	\$6.00
plus 1 dime →	\$6.10
plus 3 pennies →	\$6.13

Another Way

THINK:	NOW I HAVE:
six \$1 bills →	\$6.00
plus 2 nickels →	\$6.10
plus 3 pennies →	\$6.13

- Which set uses the fewest bills and coins?
  the set on the left
- Name two sets of coins that are equivalent to one dollar.
  Possible answers: 2 q, 5 d; 10 d
- What are three ways to show 50¢?
  Possible answers: 2 q; 5 d; 1 q, 2 d, 1 n

Technology Link

More Practice: Harcourt Mega Math The Number Games, *Buggy Bargains*, Levels A, B

Check

1. **Explain** three different ways to make \$2.26. **Possible answers: two \$1 bills, 1 q, 1 p; two \$1 bills, 2 d, 6 p; one \$1 bill, 5 q, 1 p**

Write the amount.

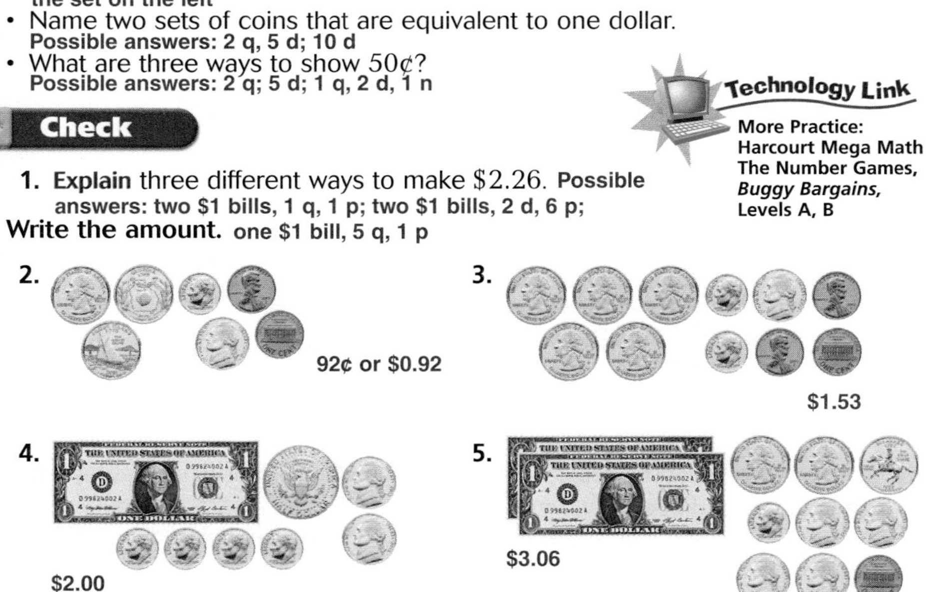

2. **92¢ or \$0.92**
3. **\$1.53**
4. **\$2.00**
5. **\$3.06**

Find two equivalent sets for each. List the coins and bills.
Check students' lists.

6. \$0.35
7. \$5.50
8. \$2.46
9. \$6.92

LESSON CONTINUES

North Carolina Standards 2.01 Solve problems using measurement concepts and procedures olving: b) Equivalent measures within the same measurement system.

- *Discuss One Way and Another Way.*
  How can you make equivalent sets of money? Make sets with the same value using different bills and coins. Then count to check the value of each set.
  REASONING If you wanted to make an equivalent set with the greatest number of coins, which coins would you use? pennies

  ALGEBRAIC THINKING Have students look at One Way. Ask: **What coins could you substitute for the dollar bill and still keep the set equivalent to \$6.13?** Possible answers: 4 quarters, 10 dimes, or 20 nickels

3 PRACTICE

Guided Practice

Complete Check Exercises 1–9 with your students. Identify students who are having difficulty and choose appropriate lesson resources to provide assistance.

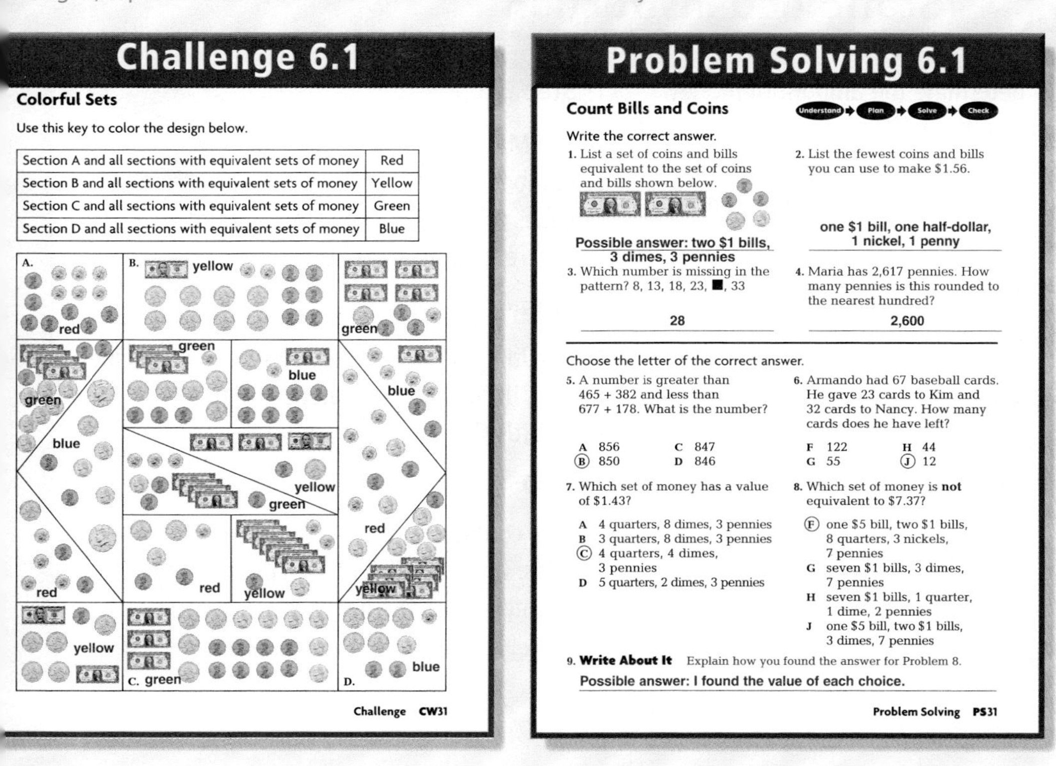

Challenge 6.1

Colorful Sets

Use this key to color the design below.

Section A and all sections with equivalent sets of money	Red
Section B and all sections with equivalent sets of money	Yellow
Section C and all sections with equivalent sets of money	Green
Section D and all sections with equivalent sets of money	Blue

Challenge CW31

Problem Solving 6.1

Count Bills and Coins

Understand → Plan → Solve → Check

Write the correct answer.

1. List a set of coins and bills equivalent to the set of coins and bills shown below.
   Possible answer: two \$1 bills, 3 dimes, 3 pennies
2. List the fewest coins and bills you can use to make \$1.56.
   one \$1 bill, one half-dollar, 1 nickel, 1 penny
3. Which number is missing in the pattern? 8, 13, 18, 23, ■, 33
   28
4. Maria has 2,617 pennies. How many pennies is this rounded to the nearest hundred?
   2,600

Choose the letter of the correct answer.

5. A number is greater than 465 + 382 and less than 677 + 178. What is the number?
   A 856 (B) 850 C 847 D 846
6. Armando had 67 baseball cards. He gave 23 cards to Kim and 32 cards to Nancy. How many cards does he have left?
   F 122 G 55 H 44 (J) 12
7. Which set of money has a value of \$1.43?
   A 4 quarters, 8 dimes, 3 pennies
   B 3 quarters, 8 dimes, 3 pennies
   (C) 4 quarters, 4 dimes, 3 pennies
   D 5 quarters, 2 dimes, 3 pennies
8. Which set of money is **not** equivalent to \$7.37?
   (F) one \$5 bill, two \$1 bills, 8 quarters, 3 nickels, 7 pennies
   G seven \$1 bills, 3 dimes, 7 pennies
   H seven \$1 bills, 1 quarter, 1 dime, 2 pennies
   J one \$5 bill, two \$1 bills, 3 dimes, 7 pennies
9. **Write About It** Explain how you found the answer for Problem 8.
   Possible answer: I found the value of each choice.

Problem Solving PS31

COMMON ERROR ALERT

Some students might omit coins as they count.

68¢

Have students touch each coin as they count it. Then, before counting the coin with the next value (such as dimes to nickels), have them record the value of the coin(s) just counted.

Independent Practice

Note that Exercise 32 is a **multistep or strategy problem.** Assign Exercises 10–36.

MULTISTEP OR STRATEGY PROBLEM For Exercise 32, students should first add the coins that Tom has left. Two dimes, 1 nickel, and 2 pennies = 27¢. He has 27¢ left. Subtract 27¢ from 43¢. 43¢ − 27¢ = 16¢. So, 16¢ fell out of his pocket. Then students can tell what 3 coins make 16¢: 1 dime, 1 nickel, and 1 penny.

For Exercises 14–21, it might be helpful for some students to draw pictures.

Vocabulary Power Some other U.S. coins no longer in circulation include half cent, two cent, three cent, half dime, twenty cent, quarter eagle, and three dollars.

Practice and Problem Solving

Extra Practice, page 122, Set A

Write the amount.

10. 68¢ or $0.68

11. $1.00

12. $5.65

13. $4.52

Find two equivalent sets for each. List the coins and bills. Check students' lists.

14. $0.67	15. $5.03	16. $2.25	17. $3.75
18. $1.40	19. $2.15	20. $4.35	21. $8.04

Write the missing number.

22. 1 dime = ■ nickels 2

23. 5 pennies = ■ nickel 1

24. 2 quarters = ■ dimes 5

25. 1 quarter = ■ nickels 5

26. 1 half dollar = ■ quarters 2

27. 1 dollar = ■ quarters 4

For 28–31, list the fewest bills and coins you can use to make each amount.

28. $0.48 1 q, 2 d, 3 p

29. $1.79 one $1 bill, 3 q, 4 p

30. $2.37 two $1 bills, 1 q, 1 d, 2 p

31. $8.86 one $5 bill, three $1 bills, 3 q, 1 d, 1 p

32. Tom had $0.43 in his pocket. Three coins fell out of a hole in the pocket. Tom still has the coins shown at the right. What coins fell out of his pocket? 1 d, 1 n, 1 p

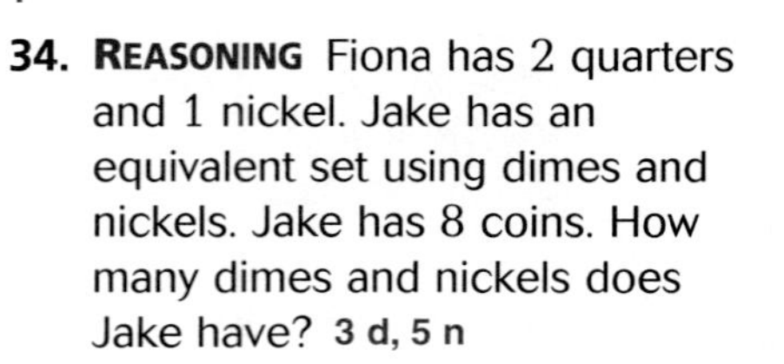

33. **Vocabulary Power** Colonial Americans used Spanish silver dollar coins. The dollar was cut into 8 bits called pieces of eight. If 2 bits equaled 25¢, what did 4 bits equal? 50¢

34. **REASONING** Fiona has 2 quarters and 1 nickel. Jake has an equivalent set using dimes and nickels. Jake has 8 coins. How many dimes and nickels does Jake have? 3 d, 5 n

112

Alternative Teaching Strategy

Scaffolded Instruction

PURPOSE Students play a game to practice counting bills and coins and finding equivalent sets.

MATERIALS play bills and coins, pp. TR51–53; 3 number cubes numbered 1–6, p. TR65; 5 counters

Step 1

A "bank" is set up with a variety of bills and coins. Three players take turns being "Player," "Matcher," and "Judge."

Step 2

Each student begins with $1.00. The first Player tosses three number cubes, one at a time, to determine the amount of money. The first number tells the number of dollars. The second number tells the number of dimes. The third number tells the number of pennies.

For example, if a student tosses a 2, a 6, and a 3, the student collects $2.63 from the bank and adds it to his or her money.

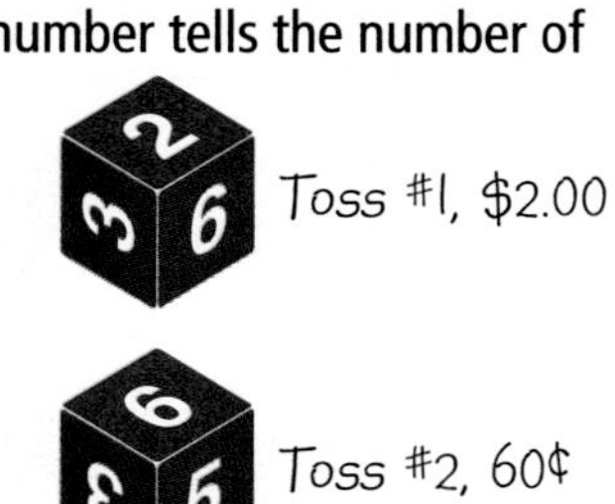

Step 3

The Matcher looks at the number on the number cubes and makes the same amount, using different coins and bills.

Step 4

The Judge looks at the two sets of coins and bills. If they are equivalent, the Judge awards the Matcher a counter.

Step 5

Play continues. At each turn, players switch roles. The first player to accumulate five counters wins the game.

35. **FAST FACT** • SOCIAL STUDIES The United States Mint was established in 1792. How many years ago was this? **Check students' answers. In 2004, it was 212 years ago.**

36. Abraham Lincoln's likeness was first used on the penny in 1909. This was 100 years after Lincoln's birth. In what year was Abraham Lincoln born? **1809**

Getting Ready for the EOG Test

37. Kate has one $1 bill, 3 quarters, 1 dime, 1 nickel, and 2 pennies. How much money does she have? **C**

A $1.67 **C** $1.92

B $1.82 **D** $2.17

38. Jesse has exactly $1.85. He has one $1 bill. What set of coins could Jesse have? **B**

A 8 dimes

B 3 quarters, 1 dime

C 4 quarters

D 8 dimes, 3 nickels

Problem Solving LINKUP . . . to Social Studies

NEW GOLDEN COIN In 2000 the golden dollar coin took the place of the Susan B. Anthony dollar coin. On the front of the golden coin is Sacagawea and her infant son. A Shoshone Indian, Sacagawea helped explorers Lewis and Clark on their expedition to the West.

Write the amount.

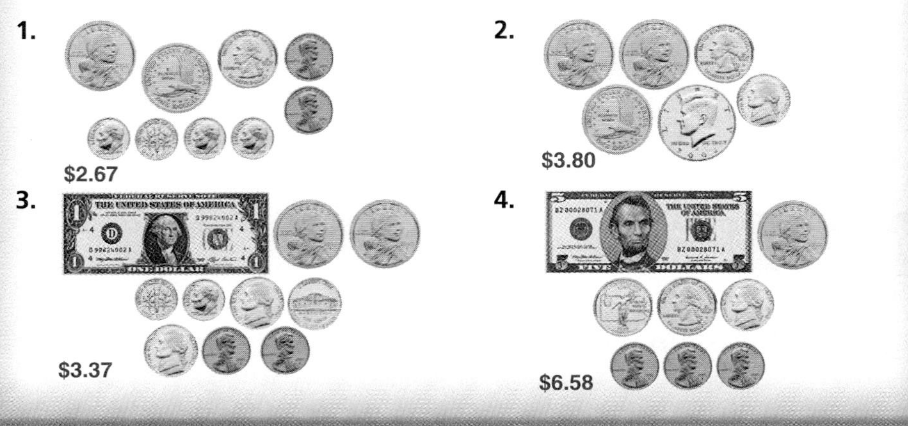

1. $2.67
2. $3.80
3. $3.37
4. $6.58

Reading Strategy

K-W-L CHART Before having students read the Link Up, have them look at the golden coins. Then have students make a three-column chart headed *What I Know, What I Want to Know,* and *What I Learned.* Ask them to fill in the first two columns. Have them fill in the third column as they read through the feature.

K-W-L Chart

What I Know	What I Want to Know	What I Learned

Problem Solving LINKUP . . . to Social Studies

- *Direct students' attention to the exercises.* **What is the difference between the Sacagawea dollar coin and all the other coins?** The color is different.

  REASONING Name some other coins and bills that are equivalent to the golden dollar coin. Possible answers: the $1 bill, 2 half dollars, 4 quarters, 10 dimes, 20 nickels, 100 pennies

4 ASSESS

Summarize the lesson by having students:

DISCUSS What is the easiest way to count a set of bills and coins? Give an example. Begin with the bill or coin that has the greatest value and count on to the bill or coin with the least value. For example, to count three $1 bills, 6 dimes, 1 nickel, and 2 pennies, begin with the dollar bills. Count $3.00, $3.60, $3.65, $3.67.

WRITE Explain how to make $3.46 using the fewest bills and coins. Then explain two different ways to make $3.46. Possible answer: three $1 bills, 1 quarter, 2 dimes, 1 penny; three $1 bills, 4 dimes, 6 pennies; 12 quarters, 3 dimes, 2 nickels, 6 pennies

LESSON QUIZ

Transparency 6.1

Write the amount.

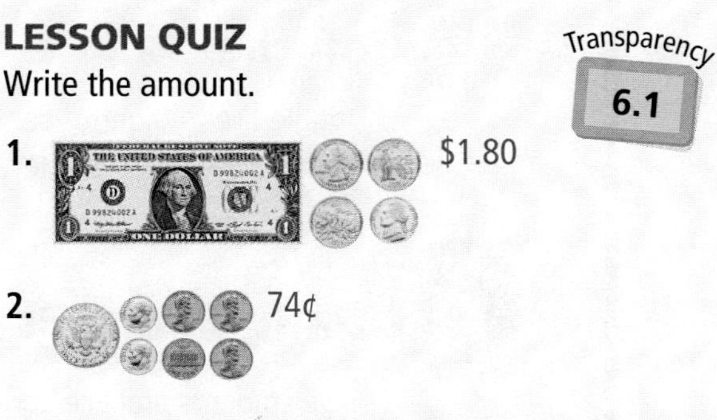

1. $1.80
2. 74¢

Find two equivalent sets for each amount. List the coins and bills for each set.

3. $4.28 **4.** $2.06

3. Possible answer: four $1 bills, 2 dimes, 1 nickel, 3 pennies; 8 half dollars, 2 dimes, 8 pennies

4. Possible answer: two $1 bills, 6 pennies; 8 quarters, 1 nickel, 1 penny

Lesson 6.2

Problem Solving Strategy
Make a Table

Lesson Planning

Objective To use the problem solving strategy *make a table* to solve a problem

Lesson Resources Reading Transparency 6; Intervention • Problem Solving, Strategy/Skill 6

NCTM Standards
1. Number and Operations
5. Data Analysis and Probability
6. Problem Solving
7. Reasoning and Proof
8. Communication
10. Representation

Math Background
These ideas will help students use the strategy *make a table* to solve problems involving equivalent sets of money.

- Different combinations of coins and bills can be used to make equivalent sets of money.
- Students can list and count all the possible combinations in a table to solve a problem.

Warm-Up Resources

Number of the Day

Double the number of cents in a dollar. Then subtract 50. Write the new number. 150

Daily Facts Practice

Have students practice addition and subtraction facts by completing Set D of *Teacher's Resource Book*, p. TR87.

Transparency 6.2

Problem of the Day

In her left hand, Jessica has 2 coins of the same kind. In her right hand, she has 5 coins that are all alike but that are different from the coins in her left hand. She has an equivalent amount of money in each hand. How much money does she have in all? $1.00

Solution Problem of the Day tab, p. PD6

Intervention and Extension Resources

Alternative Teaching Strategy

MATERIALS play money, pp. TR51–52

ESOL/ESL

Have students **identify equivalent sets of money**. Show students the following amounts, one at a time: a $1 bill, a half dollar, a quarter, a dime. Ask them to identify as many equivalent sets as they can for each. Students may model the amounts and then record each set in a table. Check students' work.

KINESTHETIC

BODILY/KINESTHETIC

Reading Strategy

Use Graphic Aids Display the following table to provide practice using graphic aids.

	Quarters	Dimes	Nickels	Pennies
John	3	5	4	5
Keisha	5	0	5	0
Lynn	4	2	5	5

Have students read the table and answer the following questions:

- Who has the most coins? the fewest coins? John; Keisha
- Do John, Keisha, and Lynn have the same amount of money? Explain. Yes; they each have $1.50.

VISUAL

Transparency 6 **Reading Transparency 6**

Multistep and Strategy Problems

The following multistep or strategy problems are provided in Lesson 6.2:

Page	Item
115	1–8

Writing in Mathematics

MATERIALS *For each student* newspapers and/or magazines, scissors, glue, construction paper

Have students **describe tables**. Have each student look through newspapers and/or magazines to find a table. Ask them to cut out the table and glue it to a piece of construction paper. Have students write a 1- or 2-sentence description of their tables. Post students' tables and descriptions. Check students' work.

Health Connection

MATERIALS *For each group* index cards

Have students **make a table**.

- Explain that the U.S. government recommends that we eat two to four servings of fruit each day to stay healthy.
- Ask students to suppose they eat two different kinds of the following fruit each day: apples, oranges, bananas, and pears. Have students write each kind of fruit on an index card and model the possible combinations.
- Have students make a table to find all the possible combinations. Check students' work.

KINESTHETIC

LOGICAL/MATHEMATICAL

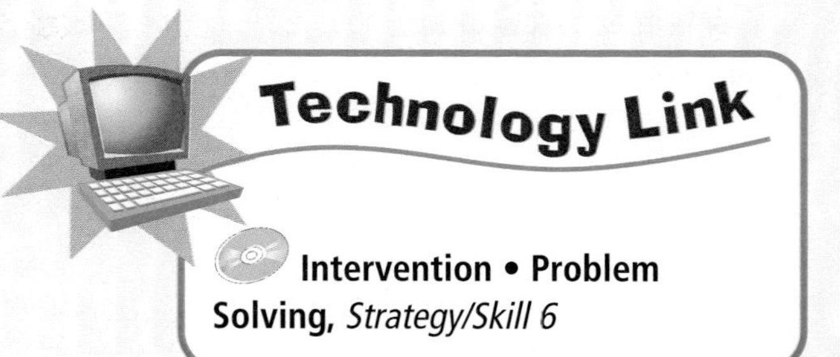

Intervention • Problem Solving, *Strategy/Skill 6*

Lesson 6.2 Organizer

Objective To use the problem solving strategy *make a table* to solve a problem

Lesson Resources Reading Transparency 6; Intervention • Problem Solving, Strategy/Skill 6

1 INTRODUCE

Quick Review provides review of prerequisite skills.

Why Learn This? Making a table can help you keep track of the different coins and bills you can give or receive as change. *Share the lesson objective with students.*

2 TEACH

Guided Instruction

- *Have students read the problem.*
  What makes sets of bills and coins equivalent? The sets are equivalent if they have the same value.
- *Have students look at the Plan question and answer.*
  How can making a table help you find different combinations of bills and coins? Possible answer: A table helps you keep track of the different equivalent sets you can make.
- *Have students look at the table.*
  What happens when you decrease the number of quarters? Possible answer: the number of other coins used increases.
  Which set has the fewest bills and coins? the set with 4 dollars and 3 quarters

Algebraic Thinking Let *b* stand for dollar bill, *c* for quarter, *d* for dime, *n* for nickel, and *p* for penny. Use alphabetical ordering to list possible combinations. For example, list the sets of money in the table as *bbbbccc*, *bbbbccddn*, and so on.

- *Discuss the Check question.*
  How can you tell if each set in the table is equivalent? If the total value of the bills and coins in each row of the table is $4.75, the sets are equivalent.

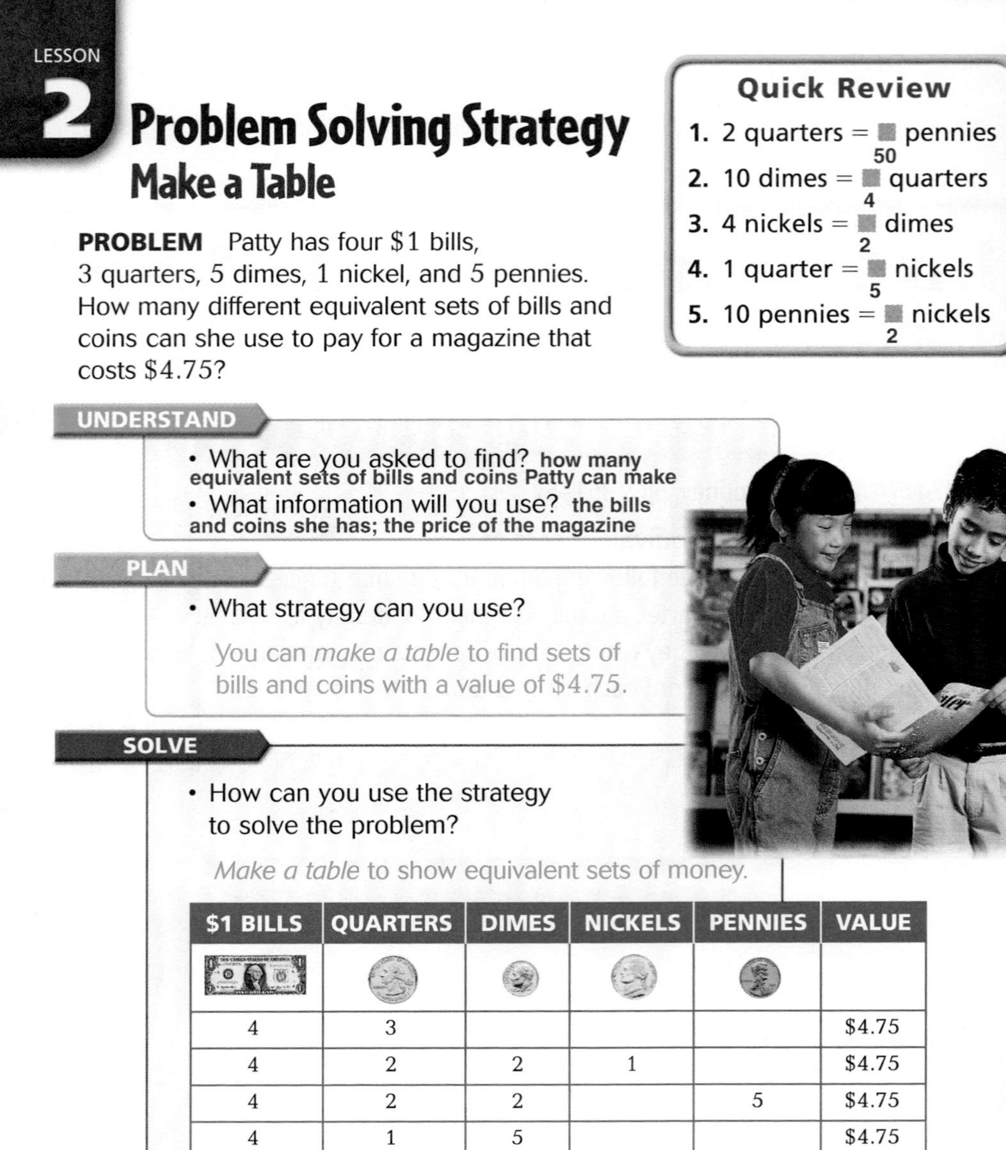

LESSON 2

Problem Solving Strategy
Make a Table

PROBLEM Patty has four $1 bills, 3 quarters, 5 dimes, 1 nickel, and 5 pennies. How many different equivalent sets of bills and coins can she use to pay for a magazine that costs $4.75?

Quick Review

1. 2 quarters = ■ pennies 50
2. 10 dimes = ■ quarters 4
3. 4 nickels = ■ dimes 2
4. 1 quarter = ■ nickels 5
5. 10 pennies = ■ nickels 2

UNDERSTAND

- What are you asked to find? how many equivalent sets of bills and coins Patty can make
- What information will you use? the bills and coins she has; the price of the magazine

PLAN

- What strategy can you use?

You can *make a table* to find sets of bills and coins with a value of $4.75.

SOLVE

- How can you use the strategy to solve the problem?

Make a table to show equivalent sets of money.

$1 BILLS	QUARTERS	DIMES	NICKELS	PENNIES	VALUE
4	3				$4.75
4	2	2	1		$4.75
4	2	2		5	$4.75
4	1	5			$4.75
4	1	4	1	5	$4.75

So, there are 5 equivalent sets.

CHECK

- How can you decide if your answer is correct? Make sure each set is different and each totals $4.75.

114

Reteach 6.2

Problem Solving Strategy

Make a Table

Problem Gerald has three $1 bills, 4 quarters, 1 dime, 6 nickels, and 4 pennies. He buys a yo-yo for $3.28. How many different equivalent sets of bills and coins can he use to pay for the yo-yo?

1. Underline what the problem asks.
2. What information will you use?
   The bills and coins he has; the price of the yo-yo.
3. Complete the table.

$1 bills	Quarters	Dimes	Nickels	Pennies	Value
3	1	0	0	3	$3.28
3	0	1	3	3	$3.28
3	0	0	5	3	$3.28
2	4	1	3	3	$3.28
2	4	0	5	3	$3.28

4. Solve the problem. 5 different sets
5. How many different sets of coins can you use to show 14¢? 4 sets

Dimes	Nickels	Pennies	Value
1	0	4	14¢
0	2	4	14¢
0	1	9	14¢
0	0	14	14¢

RW32 Reteach

Practice 6.2

Problem Solving Stategy

Make a Table

Make a table to solve.

1. Ivy has two $1 bills, 4 quarters, 7 dimes, 1 nickel, and 4 pennies to buy a pack of paper that costs $2.66. How many different equivalent sets of bills and coins can she use? 4 sets

$1 bills	Quarters	Dimes	Nickels	Pennies	Value
2	2	1	1	1	$2.66
2	1	4	0	1	$2.66
2	0	6	1	1	$2.66
1	4	6	1	1	$2.66

2. Show some different combinations of coins you can use to make 23¢.
   Combinations of coins may vary. Examples are shown.

Dimes	Nickels	Pennies	Value
2	0	3	23¢
1	2	3	23¢
1	1	8	23¢
1	0	13	23¢
0	4	3	23¢
0	3	8	23¢
0	2	13	23¢
0	1	18	23¢
0	0	23	23¢

Mixed Review

Add.

3. 152 + 63 + 256 = 471
4. 87 + 84 + 75 = 246
5. 136 + 242 + 192 = 570
6. 101 + 345 + 72 = 518
7. 49¢ + 26¢ = 75¢
8. $1.25 + $0.75 = $2.00
9. 17¢ + 66¢ = 83¢
10. 29¢ + 50¢ = 79¢

PW32 Practice

Problem Solving Practice

Make a table to solve. Check students' tables.

1. **What if** Patty's magazine costs $5.25? What equivalent sets of bills and coins can she use? **four $1 bills, 3 q, 5 d; four $1 bills, 3 q, 4 d, 1 n, 5 p**
2. Tyler has one $1 bill, 5 quarters, 1 dime, and 2 nickels. What equivalent sets of bills and coins can he use to pay for a goldfish that costs $1.35? **one $1 bill, 1 q, 1 d; one $1 bill, 1 q, 2 n; 5 q, 1 d; 5 q, 2 n**

Strategies

- Draw a Diagram or Picture
- Make a Model or Act It Out
- Make an Organized List
- Find a Pattern
- **Make a Table or Graph**
- Predict and Test
- Work Backward
- Solve a Simpler Problem
- Write a Number Sentence
- Use Logical Reasoning

Problem Solving

Kevin has 7 quarters, 4 dimes, and 1 nickel. He wants to buy a bookmark that costs $1.80.

3. Kevin wants to keep 1 quarter. Which set of coins should he use? **B**
   - **A** 6 quarters, 2 dimes, 1 nickel
   - **B** 6 quarters, 3 dimes
   - **C** 7 quarters, 1 dime
   - **D** 6 quarters, 3 dimes, 1 nickel
4. If Kevin uses the fewest coins, which type of coin will he NOT use? **G**
   - **F** quarters
   - **G** dimes
   - **H** nickels
   - **J** none of the above

Mixed Strategy Practice

USE DATA For 5–7, use the table.

Camping Equipment	
Flashlight	$5.99
Canteen	$4.65
Can Opener	$1.05
Bug Spray	$2.49

5. Laura has one $5 bill, four $1 bills, 7 quarters, 2 dimes, 2 nickels, and 4 pennies. Using exact change, how many different ways can she pay for the flashlight? **4 ways**
6. Paco has only quarters and nickels in his pocket. What 9 coins would he use to buy the can opener, using exact change? **3 quarters, 6 nickels**
7. Fran, Geri, Harold, and Ivan each buy a different item. Use the clues to decide what each person buys.
   Fran pays with one $1 bill and 1 nickel. Ivan pays with one $5 bill. Geri pays with three $1 bills. **Fran, can opener; Ivan, canteen; Geri, bug spray; Harold, flashlight**
8. **Write About It** Betty has three $1 bills, 5 quarters, 7 dimes, and 2 nickels. Explain how Betty can trade some of her bills and coins for a $5 bill. **Betty can trade all of her bills and coins except 1 nickel.**

Chapter 6 115

North Carolina Standards 2.01 Solve problems using measurement concepts and procedures olving: b) Equivalent measures within the same measurement system.

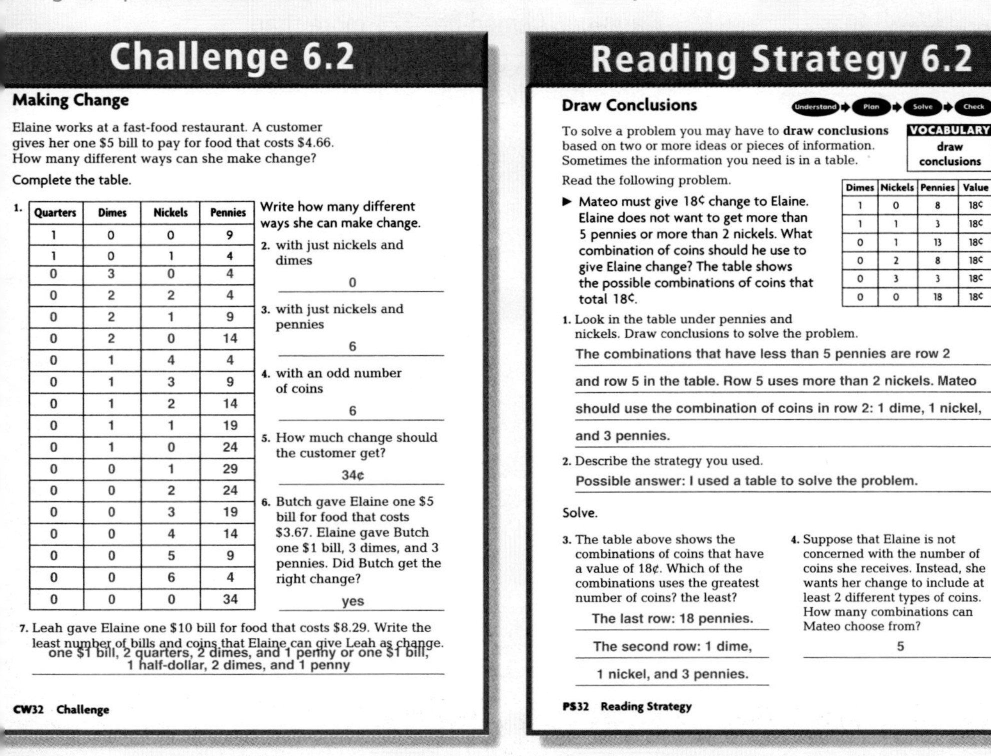

Challenge 6.2

Making Change

Elaine works at a fast-food restaurant. A customer gives her one $5 bill to pay for food that costs $4.66. How many different ways can she make change?

Complete the table.

1.

Quarters	Dimes	Nickels	Pennies
1	0	0	9
1	0	1	4
0	3	0	4
0	2	2	4
0	2	1	9
0	2	0	14
0	1	4	4
0	1	3	9
0	1	2	14
0	1	1	19
0	1	0	24
0	0	1	29
0	0	2	24
0	0	3	19
0	0	4	14
0	0	5	9
0	0	6	4
0	0	0	34

Write how many different ways she can make change.

2. with just nickels and dimes **0**
3. with just nickels and pennies **6**
4. with an odd number of coins **6**
5. How much change should the customer get? **34¢**
6. Butch gave Elaine one $5 bill for food that costs $3.67. Elaine gave Butch one $1 bill, 3 dimes, and 3 pennies. Did Butch get the right change? **yes**
7. Leah gave Elaine one $10 bill for food that costs $8.29. Write the least number of bills and coins that Elaine can give Leah as change. **one $1 bill, 2 quarters, 2 dimes, and 1 penny or one $1 bill, 1 half-dollar, 2 dimes, and 1 penny**

CW32 Challenge

Reading Strategy 6.2

Draw Conclusions

Understand → Plan → Solve → Check

To solve a problem you may have to **draw conclusions** based on two or more ideas or pieces of information. Sometimes the information you need is in a table.

VOCABULARY: draw conclusions

Read the following problem.

▶ Mateo must give 18¢ change to Elaine. Elaine does not want to get more than 5 pennies or more than 2 nickels. What combination of coins should he use to give Elaine change? The table shows the possible combinations of coins that total 18¢.

Dimes	Nickels	Pennies	Value
1	0	8	18¢
1	1	3	18¢
0	1	13	18¢
0	2	8	18¢
0	3	3	18¢
0	0	18	18¢

1. Look in the table under pennies and nickels. Draw conclusions to solve the problem.
   The combinations that have less than 5 pennies are row 2 and row 5 in the table. Row 5 uses more than 2 nickels. Mateo should use the combination of coins in row 2: 1 dime, 1 nickel, and 3 pennies.
2. Describe the strategy you used.
   Possible answer: I used a table to solve the problem.

Solve.

3. The table above shows the combinations of coins that have a value of 18¢. Which of the combinations uses the greatest number of coins? the least?
   The last row: 18 pennies. The second row: 1 dime, 1 nickel, and 3 pennies.
4. Suppose that Elaine is not concerned with the number of coins she receives. Instead, she wants her change to include at least 2 different types of coins. How many combinations can Mateo choose from?
   5

PS32 Reading Strategy

3 PRACTICE

Guided Practice

Do Problem Solving Practice Exercises 1–4 with your students. Identify students who are having difficulty and choose appropriate lesson resources to provide assistance. Note that Exercises 1–4 are **multistep or strategy problems.**

COMMON ERROR ALERT

In listing all the possible combinations of bills and coins in their tables, students may repeat an equivalent set. Have students begin with the coins of greatest value and use them as often as possible. Then have them check their tables to make sure that each equivalent set uses different bills and coins.

Independent Practice

Note that Exercises 5–8 are **multistep or strategy problems.** Assign Exercises 5–8.

SCAFFOLDED INSTRUCTION Use the prompts on Transparency 6 to guide instruction for the multistep or strategy problem in Exercise 7.

4 ASSESS

Summarize the lesson by having students:

DISCUSS How can making a table help you solve Exercises 3 and 4? Possible answer: For Exercise 3, list all the possible equivalent sets for $1.80 with Kevin's coins. Then, count the coins in each set in the table and choose the set with the fewest to answer Exercise 4.

WRITE When can you make a table to help you solve a problem? Possible answer: When there is more than one possible answer and I need to find all of the answers.

LESSON QUIZ Check students' work. Make a table to solve.

Transparency 6.2

1. Sean has one $1 bill, 2 dimes, 5 nickels, and 6 pennies. How many ways can he pay for a card that costs $1.26? 6 ways
2. Allison has three $1 bills, 6 quarters, 1 dime, 3 nickels, and 4 pennies. If she uses the fewest bills and coins to show $3.59, which type of bill or coin will she not use? a dime

Compare Money Amounts

Lesson Planning

Objective To compare money amounts

NCTM Standards

1. Number and Operations
2. Algebra
6. Problem Solving
7. Reasoning and Proof
8. Communication
10. Representation

Math Background

These ideas will help students understand how to compare money amounts.

- The greater amount of money is determined by the value of the money, not by the number of bills and coins.
- When comparing two amounts, compare the dollar amounts first, and then the cents.

Warm-Up Resources

Number of the Day

I am an amount of money. My value is 2 dimes more than a quarter. What amount am I? 45¢

Daily Facts Practice

Have students practice addition facts by completing Set E of *Teacher's Resource Book*, p. TR87.

Problem of the Day

Ahmed has 2 coins of one kind and 2 of another. Katie has different coins, but she also has 2 of one kind and 2 of another. Ahmed has 22¢ more than Katie. What coins does each have if they both have less than $1.00? Ahmed has 2 quarters and 2 pennies, or 52¢. Katie has 2 dimes and 2 nickels, or 30¢.

Solution Problem of the Day tab, p. PD6

Intervention and Extension Resources

Alternative Teaching Strategy

MATERIALS *For each pair* play bills and coins, pp. TR51–53

Help students understand **comparing money amounts**. Remind students that they compare money amounts the same way they compare whole numbers. Give each student a handful of coins and bills. Have students take turns counting the bills and coins and recording the amounts in a table that lists the dollars in one column and the cents in a second column. Then have students work together to compare the amounts. Check students' work.

KINESTHETIC

LOGICAL/MATHEMATICAL, INTERPERSONAL

Special Needs

MATERIALS *For each pair* play coins and bills, pp. TR51–53

Have students **compare money amounts**. Distribute play money to each pair. Ask one student to use the money to show two amounts. Have the partner discuss how to compare the two amounts and tell which is greater. Have students reverse roles and repeat. Check students' work.

KINESTHETIC

BODILY/KINESTHETIC

Multistep and Strategy Problems

The following multistep or strategy problem is provided in Lesson 6.3:

Page	Item
117	6

Math Connection

MATERIALS *For each student* play money, pp. TR51–52

Algebra Have students **compare money amounts**. Have each student take a handful of mixed play coins in each hand. Ask them to determine the amount of money in each hand. Then have them compare the two amounts of money. Remind students to use $<$, $>$, or $=$ between the two amounts. Check students' work.

KINESTHETIC

BODILY/KINESTHETIC

Lesson 6.3 Organizer

Objective To compare money amounts

1 INTRODUCE

QUICK REVIEW provides review of prerequisite skills.

WHY LEARN THIS? Comparing amounts of money can help you find out if you have enough money to buy something. *Share the lesson objective with students.*

Guided Instruction

- *Ask students to read the Learn section.*
  What is the first step to take when you compare two sets of bills and coins? Explain. Count the bills and coins. You need to know the value of the bills and coins that you are going to compare.
  What is the second step? Compare the dollar amounts. 5 = 5. Compare the cents. $75 > 50$, so $\$5.75 > \$5.50$.
- *Have students look at Example A.*
  REASONING What if you added 4 quarters to the first amount and 10 dimes to the second amount? Which amount would be greater? Explain. The amounts would still be equal; Four quarters equal $1.00 and 10 dimes equal $1.00, so $\$3.73 = \$3.73$.
- *Discuss the Reasoning question.*
  Give an example of two sets of coins in which the set with a smaller number of coins has a greater value than the set with a larger number of coins. Possible answer: The value of 2 quarters, or 50¢, is greater than the value of 4 dimes, or 40¢.

MODIFYING INSTRUCTION Suggest students line up the two amounts of money so they can compare place-value positions.

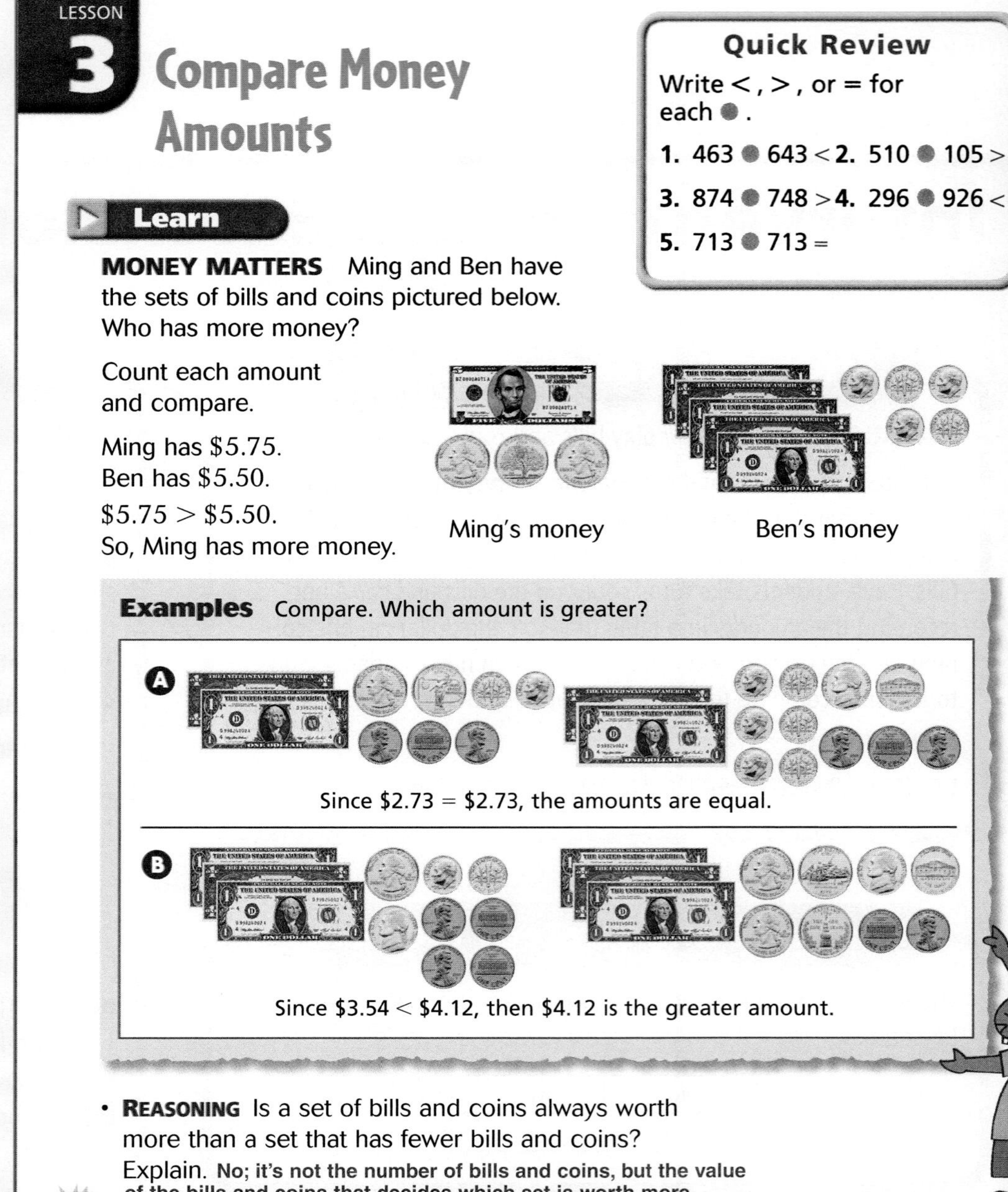

LESSON 3 Compare Money Amounts

Quick Review

Write $<$, $>$, or = for each ●.

1. 463 ● 643 $<$ 2. 510 ● 105 $>$
3. 874 ● 748 $>$ 4. 296 ● 926 $<$
5. 713 ● 713 =

Learn

MONEY MATTERS Ming and Ben have the sets of bills and coins pictured below. Who has more money?

Count each amount and compare.

Ming has $5.75.
Ben has $5.50.
$\$5.75 > \$5.50$.
So, Ming has more money.

Ming's money Ben's money

Examples Compare. Which amount is greater?

A Since $\$2.73 = \$2.73$, the amounts are equal.

B Since $\$3.54 < \$4.12$, then $4.12 is the greater amount.

- **REASONING** Is a set of bills and coins always worth more than a set that has fewer bills and coins? Explain. **No; it's not the number of bills and coins, but the value of the bills and coins that decides which set is worth more.**

MATH IDEA To compare amounts of money, count each set and decide if one is greater than, less than, or equal to the other.

116

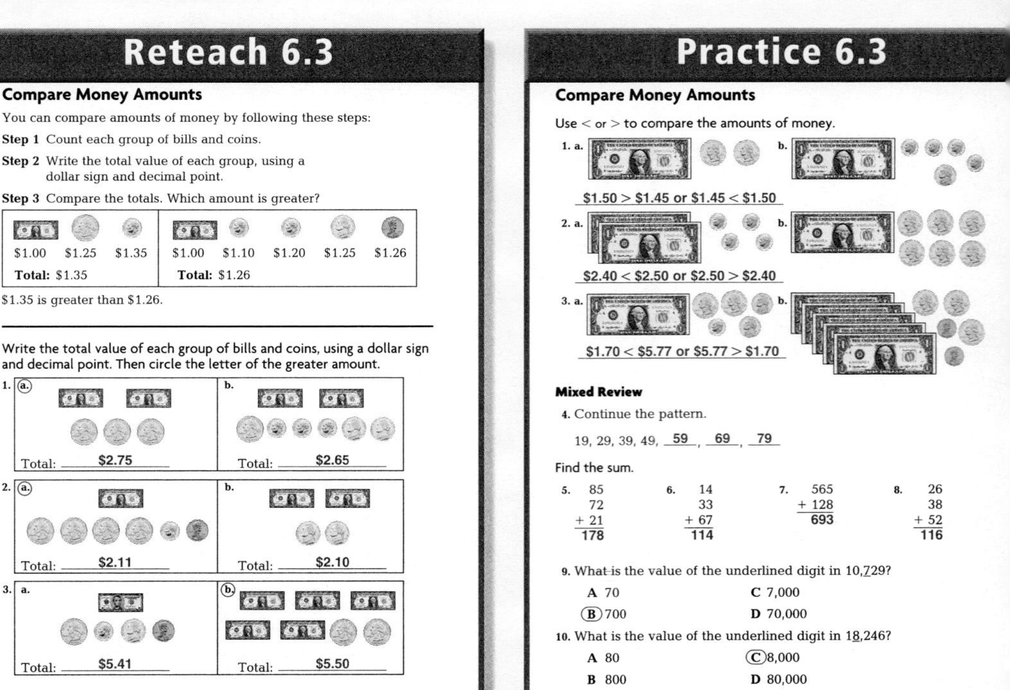

Reteach 6.3

Compare Money Amounts

You can compare amounts of money by following these steps:

Step 1 Count each group of bills and coins.
Step 2 Write the total value of each group, using a dollar sign and decimal point.
Step 3 Compare the totals. Which amount is greater?

$1.00 $1.25 $1.35 — Total: $1.35 | $1.00 $1.10 $1.20 $1.25 $1.26 — Total: $1.26

$1.35 is greater than $1.26.

Write the total value of each group of bills and coins, using a dollar sign and decimal point. Then circle the letter of the greater amount.

1. (a.) Total: $2.75 b. Total: $2.65
2. (a.) Total: $2.11 b. Total: $2.10
3. a. Total: $5.41 (b.) Total: $5.50

Reteach RW33

Practice 6.3

Compare Money Amounts

Use $<$ or $>$ to compare the amounts of money.

1. $\$1.50 > \$1.45$ or $\$1.45 < \$1.50$
2. $\$2.40 < \$2.50$ or $\$2.50 > \$2.40$
3. $\$1.70 < \$5.77$ or $\$5.77 > \$1.70$

Mixed Review

4. Continue the pattern.
19, 29, 39, 49, 59, 69, 79

Find the sum.

5. 85 + 72 + 21 = 178
6. 14 + 33 + 67 = 114
7. 565 + 128 = 693
8. 26 + 38 + 52 = 116

9. What is the value of the underlined digit in 10,729?
A 70 (B) 700 C 7,000 D 70,000

10. What is the value of the underlined digit in 18,246?
A 80 B 800 (C) 8,000 D 80,000

Practice PW33

Check

1. **Explain** how you can use what you know about comparing whole numbers to compare amounts of money. **Possible answer: Think of money amounts in cents and compare as with whole numbers.**

Use < or > to compare the amounts of money.

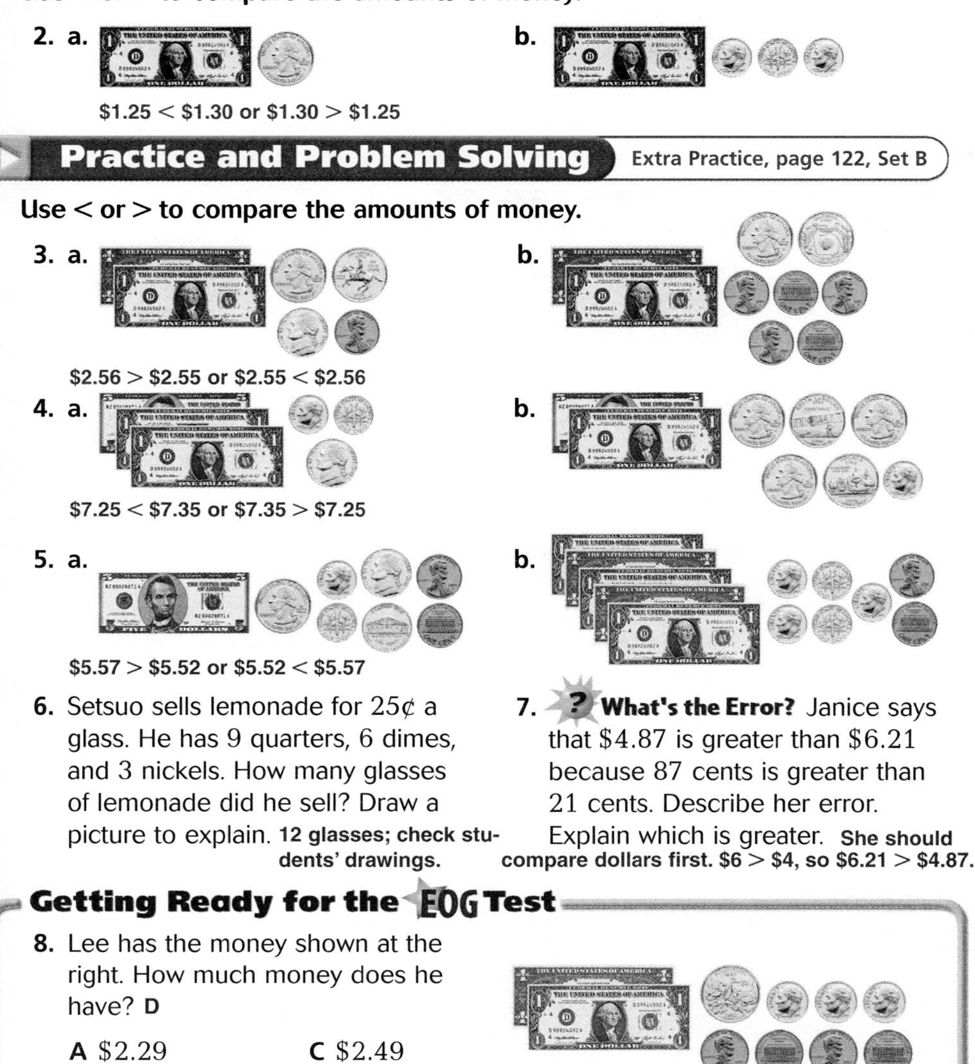

2. a. **$1.25 < $1.30 or $1.30 > $1.25**
   b.

Practice and Problem Solving

Extra Practice, page 122, Set B

Use < or > to compare the amounts of money.

3. a. **$2.56 > $2.55 or $2.55 < $2.56**
   b.
4. a. **$7.25 < $7.35 or $7.35 > $7.25**
   b.
5. a. **$5.57 > $5.52 or $5.52 < $5.57**
   b.
6. Setsuo sells lemonade for 25¢ a glass. He has 9 quarters, 6 dimes, and 3 nickels. How many glasses of lemonade did he sell? Draw a picture to explain. **12 glasses; check students' drawings.**
7. **What's the Error?** Janice says that $4.87 is greater than $6.21 because 87 cents is greater than 21 cents. Describe her error. Explain which is greater. **She should compare dollars first. $6 > $4, so $6.21 > $4.87.**

Getting Ready for the EOG Test

8. Lee has the money shown at the right. How much money does he have? **D**

   A $2.29 **C** $2.49
   B $2.34 **D** $2.59

North Carolina Standards 1.01 Develop number sense for whole numbers through 9,999. c) Compare and order.

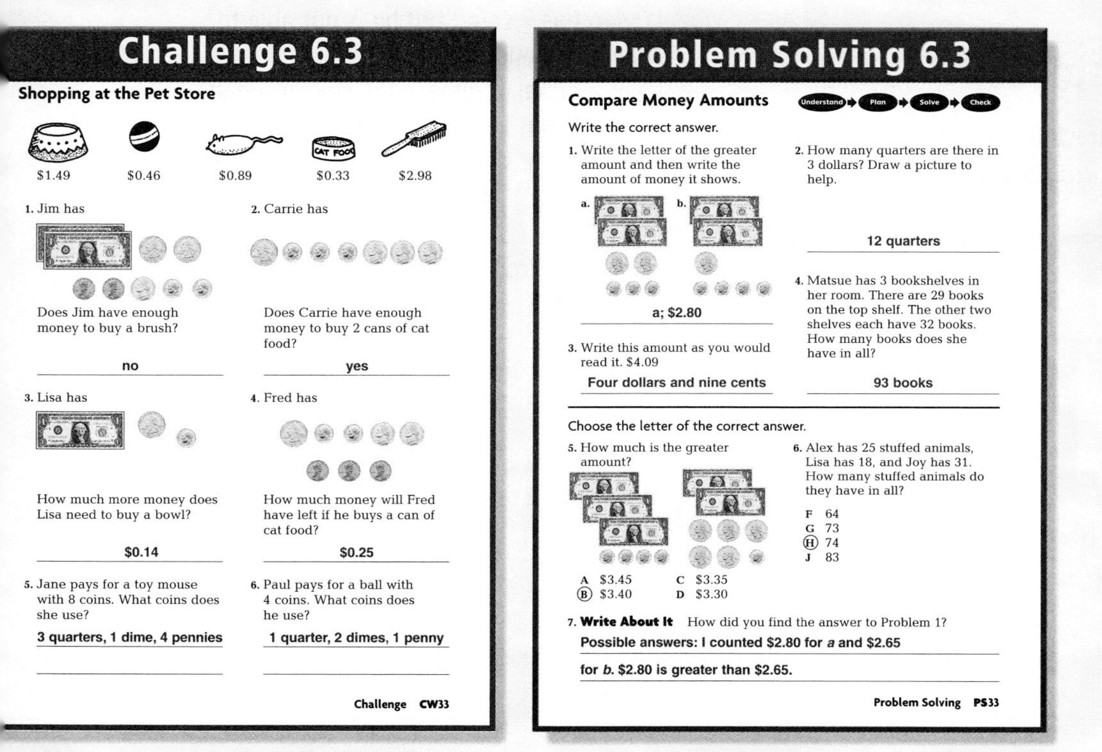

Challenge 6.3

Shopping at the Pet Store

$1.49 $0.46 $0.89 $0.33 $2.98

1. Jim has
   Does Jim have enough money to buy a brush? **no**
2. Carrie has
   Does Carrie have enough money to buy 2 cans of cat food? **yes**
3. Lisa has
   How much more money does Lisa need to buy a bowl? **$0.14**
4. Fred has
   How much money will Fred have left if he buys a can of cat food? **$0.25**
5. Jane pays for a toy mouse with 8 coins. What coins does she use? **3 quarters, 1 dime, 4 pennies**
6. Paul pays for a ball with 4 coins. What coins does he use? **1 quarter, 2 dimes, 1 penny**

Challenge CW33

Problem Solving 6.3

Compare Money Amounts Understand ▸ Plan ▸ Solve ▸ Check

Write the correct answer.

1. Write the letter of the greater amount and then write the amount of money it shows.
   a. b.
   a; $2.80
2. How many quarters are there in 3 dollars? Draw a picture to help.
   12 quarters
3. Write this amount as you would read it. $4.09
   Four dollars and nine cents
4. Matsue has 3 bookshelves in her room. There are 29 books on the top shelf. The other two shelves each have 32 books. How many books does she have in all?
   93 books

Choose the letter of the correct answer.

5. How much is the greater amount?
   A $3.45 C $3.35
   Ⓑ $3.40 D $3.30
6. Alex has 25 stuffed animals, Lisa has 18, and Joy has 31. How many stuffed animals do they have in all?
   F 64
   G 73
   Ⓗ 74
   J 83
7. **Write About It** How did you find the answer to Problem 1?
   Possible answers: I counted $2.80 for *a* and $2.65 for *b*. $2.80 is greater than $2.65.

Problem Solving PS33

3 PRACTICE

Guided Practice

Do Check Exercises 1–2 with your students. Identify students who are having difficulty and choose appropriate lesson resources to provide assistance.

COMMON ERROR ALERT

Students may incorrectly assume that a set of coins has a greater value because it has a greater number of coins.

4 > 2

Correct this by having students compare two sets of coins, such as 4 nickels and 2 dimes, to see that the number of coins does not determine the value.

Independent Practice

Note that Exercise 6 is a **multistep or strategy problem.** Assign Exercises 3–7.

4 ASSESS

Summarize the lesson by having students:

Discuss Which group of coins has the greater value, 3 pennies and 1 quarter or 1 penny and 5 nickels? 3 pennies and 1 quarter

Write Describe the steps you took to compare the amounts of money in Exercise 5. Answers will vary.

LESSON QUIZ Transparency 6.3

Use < or > to compare the amounts of money.

1. a. b.
   $1.90 > $1.36 or $1.36 < $1.90
2. a. b.
   $5.80 < $5.85 or $5.85 > $5.80

Make Change

HANDS ON

Lesson Planning

Objective To use the strategy *counting on* to make change

Materials *For each group* play bills and coins, pp. TR51–53

NCTM Standards

1. Number and Operations
6. Problem Solving
7. Reasoning and Proof
8. Communication
10. Representation

Math Background

These ideas will help students understand how to make change.

- Count on from the price of the object to the amount paid to make change.
- Count the coins and bills with the least value first when making change.
- The price of the object + amount of change = amount paid.

Warm-Up Resources

Number of the Day

Think of your age in years. If you had a quarter for each year you are old, how much money would you have? Answers will vary.

Daily Facts Practice

Have students practice subtraction facts by completing Set F of *Teacher's Resource Book*, p. TR87.

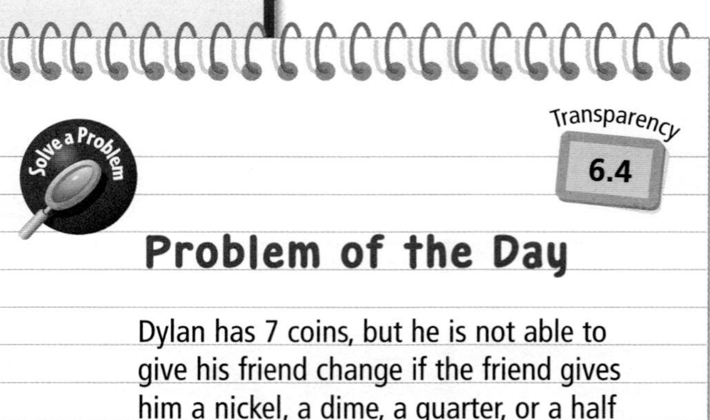

Solve a Problem

Transparency 6.4

Problem of the Day

Dylan has 7 coins, but he is not able to give his friend change if the friend gives him a nickel, a dime, a quarter, or a half dollar. What coins might Dylan have? Possible answers: 1 quarter, 1 dime, 1 nickel, and 4 pennies or 7 half dollars

Solution Problem of the Day tab, p. PD6

Intervention and Extension Resources

Alternative Teaching Strategy

MATERIALS *For each pair* newspapers, scissors, index cards, glue, play bills and coins, pp. TR51–53

Have students **practice making change**.

- Have students cut out from a newspaper pictures of items that cost less than $5.00 and less than $1.00 and glue them on index cards.
- Have one student pay for an item with a $1 bill or a $5 bill, and have the other student make change. The first student then counts to check that he or she received the correct change.
- Have partners reverse roles and continue. Check students' work.

KINESTHETIC

BODILY/KINESTHETIC

Multistep and Strategy Problems

The following multistep or strategy problem is provided in Lesson 6.4:

Page	Item
119	5

Writing in Mathematics

Have students **write a word problem** that involves the following:

- The item purchased is more than $1.50.
- The amount given the clerk is a $5 bill.

Ask students to read their problems aloud for their classmates to solve. Answers will vary.

Social Studies Connection

Have students **explore money from other countries**. Ask students to bring in examples of coins and bills from other countries if possible. Then assign students a country and have them find out the names and denominations of that country's coins and bills. Have students share their findings and make a display. Check students' work.

KINESTHETIC

BODILY/KINESTHETIC

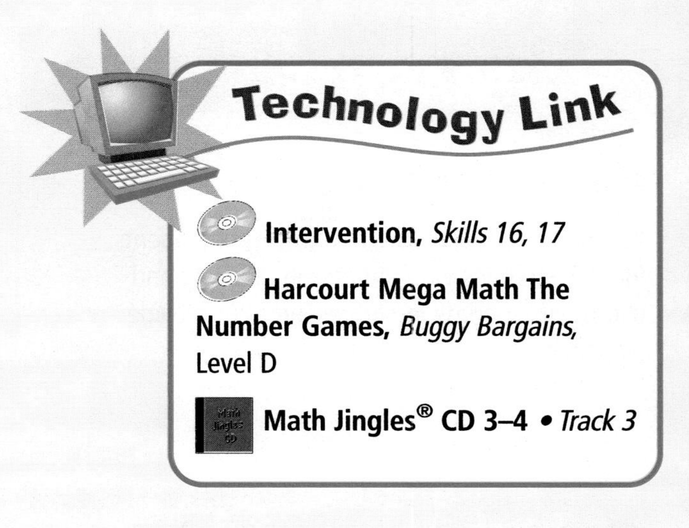

Technology Link

Intervention, *Skills 16, 17*

Harcourt Mega Math The Number Games, *Buggy Bargains,* Level D

Math Jingles® CD 3–4 • *Track 3*

Lesson 6.4 Organizer

Objective To use the strategy *counting on* to make change

Materials *For each group* play bills and coins, pp. TR51–53

1 INTRODUCE

QUICK REVIEW provides review of prerequisite skills.

WHY LEARN THIS? You will know how much change you should get when you buy items. *Share the lesson objective with students.*

2 TEACH

Guided Instruction

- *Discuss the Activity.*
  From what amount did Jessica start counting on? Explain. $2.89; the cost of the kitty toy
  At what amount did she stop counting? Explain. $5.00; the amount she paid
  What are the two steps used to make change? Seller counts on from the cost of the item to the amount buyer paid. Then buyer counts the coins and bills received as change.
- *Direct students' attention to the question beside the photo of the students making change.*
  Do you think the next coin counted should be a dime? no **Explain.** Possible answer: If the next coin is a dime, then you need to add two more coins—another dime and a nickel—before you reach $3.00.
  REASONING How is making change different from counting bills and coins? Possible answer: When you make change, you start with the coin or bill with the least value.

3 PRACTICE

Guided Practice

Complete Try It Exercises a–c with your students. Identify students who are having difficulty and choose appropriate lesson resources to provide assistance.

LESSON 4

HANDS ON Make Change

Quick Review

Add 10¢ to each amount.

1. 55¢ **65¢**
2. 70¢ **80¢**
3. 83¢ **93¢**
4. 29¢ **39¢**
5. 41¢ **51¢**

MATERIALS
play bills and coins

Explore

Jessica buys a kitty toy at Pal's Pet Store. She pays with a $5 bill. How much change will she get?

Activity

Start with $2.89, the cost of the kitty toy. Count on coins and bills to $5.00, the amount Jessica paid.

$2.89

$2.90 → $3.00 → $4.00 → $5.00

Count the coins and bills she received to find the change.

1 penny, 1 dime, and two $1 bills equal $2.11.

PAL'S PET STORE

Dog Leash	$5.99
Dog Shampoo	$3.68
Kitty Toy	$2.89
Fish Food	$1.29
Chew Bone	$3.59
Bird Seed Bell	$2.63

So, Jessica will get $2.11 in change.

- Why do people start with the coin of least value when making change? **Possible answer: It is easier to count on by 1s, 5s, 10s, and 25s by using mental math.**

Try It **Check students' drawings.**

Each person pays with a $5 bill. Use play money to make change. Draw a picture to show the change each person will get. **Check students' drawings.**

a. Tony buys a bird seed bell. **$2.37**

b. Marian buys fish food. Show her change, using the fewest coins.
1 p, 2 d, 2q, three $1 bills; $3.71

c. Emma buys a chew bone. Show at least two different ways to make change. **Possible answers: 1 p, 1 n, 1 d, 1 q, one $1 bill; 1 p, 3 n, 5 q; $1.41**

$2.64, $2.65, $2.75 . . . What should I count next to make change?

a quarter

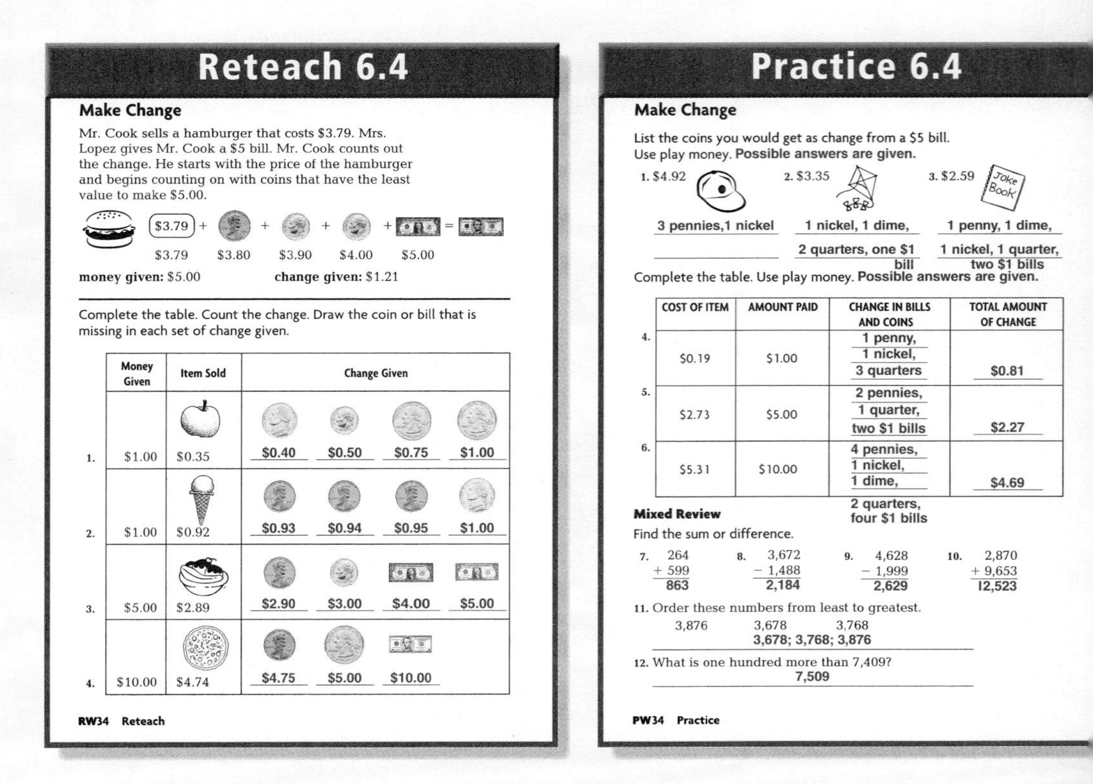

Reteach 6.4

Make Change

Mr. Cook sells a hamburger that costs $3.79. Mrs. Lopez gives Mr. Cook a $5 bill. Mr. Cook counts out the change. He starts with the price of the hamburger and begins counting on with coins that have the least value to make $5.00.

$3.79 + + + + =

$3.79 $3.80 $3.90 $4.00 $5.00

money given: $5.00 **change given:** $1.21

Complete the table. Count the change. Draw the coin or bill that is missing in each set of change given.

	Money Given	Item Sold	Change Given			
1.	$1.00	$0.35	**$0.40**	**$0.50**	**$0.75**	**$1.00**
2.	$1.00	$0.92	**$0.93**	**$0.94**	**$0.95**	**$1.00**
3.	$5.00	$2.89	**$2.90**	**$3.00**	**$4.00**	**$5.00**
4.	$10.00	$4.74	**$4.75**	**$5.00**	**$10.00**	

RW34 Reteach

Practice 6.4

Make Change

List the coins you would get as change from a $5 bill. Use play money. **Possible answers are given.**

1. $4.92 **3 pennies,1 nickel**
2. $3.35 **1 nickel, 1 dime, 2 quarters, one $1 bill**
3. $2.59 **1 penny, 1 dime, 1 nickel, 1 quarter, two $1 bills**

Complete the table. Use play money. **Possible answers are given.**

	COST OF ITEM	AMOUNT PAID	CHANGE IN BILLS AND COINS	TOTAL AMOUNT OF CHANGE
4.	$0.19	$1.00	**1 penny, 1 nickel, 3 quarters**	**$0.81**
5.	$2.73	$5.00	**2 pennies, 1 quarter, two $1 bills**	**$2.27**
6.	$5.31	$10.00	**4 pennies, 1 nickel, 1 dime, 2 quarters, four $1 bills**	**$4.69**

Mixed Review

Find the sum or difference.

7. $264 + 599 =$ **863**
8. $3{,}672 - 1{,}488 =$ **2,184**
9. $4{,}628 - 1{,}999 =$ **2,629**
10. $2{,}870 + 9{,}653 =$ **12,523**

11. Order these numbers from least to greatest.
3,876 3,678 3,768
3,678; 3,768; 3,876

12. What is one hundred more than 7,409?
7,509

PW34 Practice

Connect

1. 1 p, 2 d, 1 q
2. 2 p, 3 q, one $1 bill, one $5 bill
3. 1 p, 1 n, 1 q, two $1 bills

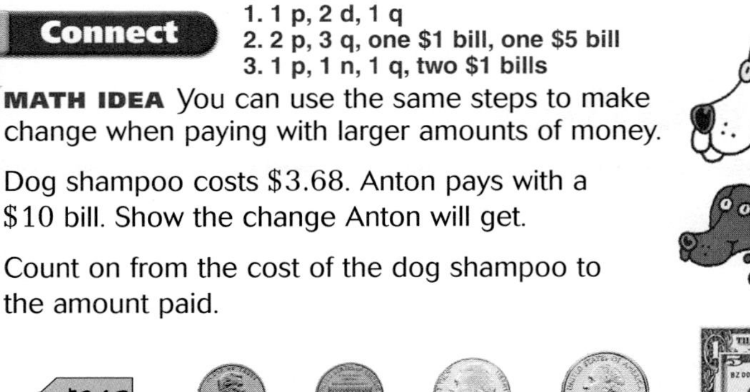

MATH IDEA You can use the same steps to make change when paying with larger amounts of money.

Dog shampoo costs $3.68. Anton pays with a $10 bill. Show the change Anton will get.

Count on from the cost of the dog shampoo to the amount paid.

Count the coins and bills. 2 pennies, 1 nickel, 1 quarter, one $1 bill, and one $5 bill equal $6.32.

So, Anton will get $6.32 in change.

Technology Link
More Practice:
Harcourt Mega Math
The Number Games,
Buggy Bargains,
Level D

Practice and Problem Solving

Copy and complete the table. Use play money. Possible answers are given.

	COST OF ITEM	AMOUNT PAID	CHANGE IN COINS AND BILLS	TOTAL AMOUNT OF CHANGE
1.	$0.54	$1.00	■ See above.	■ $0.46
2.	$3.23	$10.00	■	■ $6.77
3.	$2.69	$5.00	■	■ $2.31

4. **REASONING** Dana buys rocks for her fish tank for $0.65. She pays with a $1 bill. The clerk has run out of quarters. What is the least number of coins Dana can get? List the coins. 4 coins; n, d, d, d

5. **What's the Question?** Evan bought a dog bowl for $2.85 and a chewbone for $3.59. He paid with a $10 bill. The answer is $3.56. How much change should Evan get?

Getting Ready for the EOG Test

6. Erin bought a pen. She paid with $3. Which shows the correct amount of change? B

   A $0.81 C $0.51
   B $0.71 D $0.21

SCHOOL SUPPLIES
Pen.................. $2.29
Notebook...... $4.50
Paper.............. $1.15
Pencils............ $2.79

North Carolina Standards maintains (2) 1.05 Create and solve problems using strategies such as modeling, composing and decomposing quantities, using doubles, and making tens and hundreds.

MODIFYING INSTRUCTION You may wish to have students model the problem shown in the Connect section with play coins and bills.

Independent Practice

Note that Exercise 5 is a **multistep or strategy problem.** Assign Exercises 1–5.

For Exercises 1–3, point out that it makes sense to start counting on with coins of the least value, so you can reach an amount that is easier to count on from, like $0.25 or $0.70.

4 ASSESS

Summarize the lesson by having students:

DISCUSS How can the cashier count out the change when you pay with a $1 bill for a $0.55 item? Possible answer: $0.65, $0.75, $1.00.

WRITE Using as few coins as possible, make change from a $5 bill for groceries that cost $4.77. Explain how you found your answer. 3 pennies, 2 dimes; Possible answer: I counted on with coins of the least value first.

LESSON QUIZ Transparency 6.4

Copy and complete the table.

	Cost of Item	Amount Paid	Coins and Bills	Total Change
1.	$0.36	$1.00	■	■
2.	$4.45	$5.00	■	■

1. Possible answer: 4 pennies, 1 dime, 2 quarters; $0.64
2. Possible answer: 1 nickel, 2 quarters; $0.55

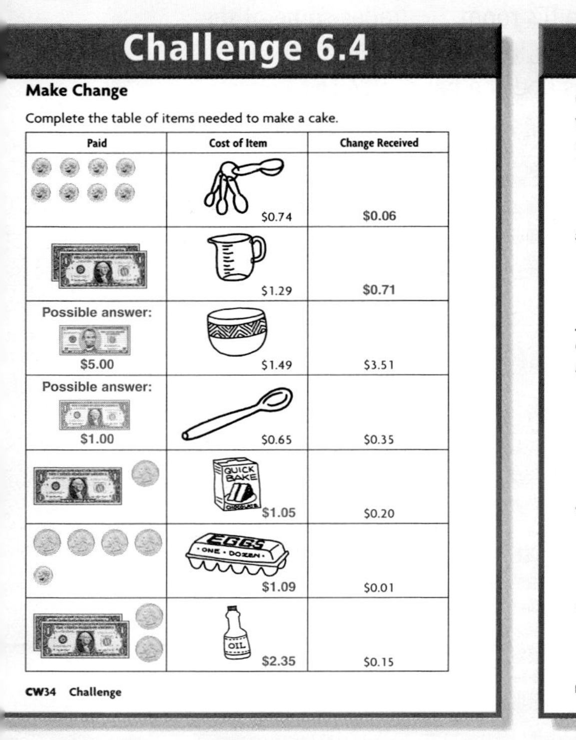

Challenge 6.4

Make Change

Complete the table of items needed to make a cake.

Paid	Cost of Item	Change Received
	$0.74	$0.06
	$1.29	$0.71
Possible answer: $5.00	$1.49	$3.51
Possible answer: $1.00	$0.65	$0.35
	$1.05	$0.20
	$1.09	$0.01
	$2.35	$0.15

CW34 Challenge

Problem Solving 6.4

Make Change Understand → Plan → Solve → Check

Write the correct answer.

1. Matthew's drink cost $0.64. He paid with a $1.00 bill. How much change did he receive? **$0.36**

2. Amy has one $5 bill, three $1 bills, 1 quarter, and 3 dimes. How much money does she have? **$8.55**

3. What is the value of the digit 7 in 74,098? **70,000**

4. Rachel paid for a notebook that cost $1.67 with a $5 bill. What coins and bills did she get for change? **Possible answer: 3 pennies, 1 nickel, 1 quarter, three $1 bills**

Choose the letter of the correct answer.

5. Which numbers are in order from least to greatest?
   A 327, 348, 339
   B 429, 413, 404
   C 198, 179, 199
   (D) 231, 240, 256

6. Marc pays for a model car that cost $4.90 with a $10 bill. What is his change, using the fewest coins and bills?
   F 4 nickels, one $5 bill
   (G) 1 dime, one $5 bill
   H 10 pennies, five $1 bills
   J 1 nickel, 5 pennies, one $5 bill

7. Mrs. Johnson has 345 crayons. If she gives 186 crayons to her students, how many crayons does she have left?
   A 169 C 151
   (B) 159 D 141

8. If Marie pays for a $2.36 pen with a $5 bill, how much change will she receive?
   F $3.66 H $2.66
   G $3.64 (J) $2.64

9. **Write About It** Explain how you found the answer for Problem 8. **Possible answer: I counted on from $2.36 to $5.00 and listed the coins and bills I used. Then I found the value of the coins and bills.**

PS34 Problem Solving

Lesson 6.5

Add and Subtract Money

Lesson Planning

Objective To add and subtract money amounts

NCTM Standards

1. Number and Operations
2. Algebra
6. Problem Solving
8. Communication
10. Representation

Math Background

These ideas will help students understand how to add and subtract money amounts.

- Use rounding to estimate sums or differences of money amounts and to check if your answers are reasonable.
- Add and subtract money amounts like whole numbers.
- Regroup dollars and cents like whole numbers.
- Subtraction is another method to find how much change you should get.

Warm-Up Resources

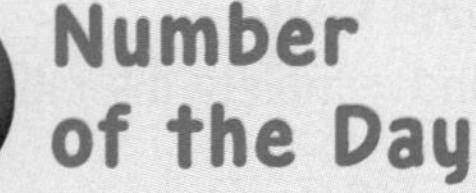

Number of the Day

Think of the number of cents in a quarter. Subtract 9 from the number and add 50 to the difference. What is the new number? 66

Daily Facts Practice

Have students practice addition facts by completing Set G of *Teacher's Resource Book*, p. TR87.

Solve a Problem

Transparency 6.5

Problem of the Day

Phillip has 457 pennies in the piggy bank in his room. He trades some of the pennies in for three $1 bills. How many pennies does he have left? 157 pennies

Solution Problem of the Day tab, p. PD6

Intervention and Extension Resources

Alternative Teaching Strategy

MATERIALS *For each pair* play bills and coins, pp. TR51–53, newspapers or catalogs

ESOL/ESL

Have students **use play money to add and subtract**.

- Have pairs of students look through newspaper advertisements or catalogs and find two items that cost less than $10.00.
- Have students find the total cost of the two items, the difference in price between the two items, and how much change they would receive if they bought one item and paid with a $10 bill.
- Tell students to use play bills and coins to help them. They may combine the bills and coins to find the total cost and count on to find the difference and amount of change. Answers will vary.

KINESTHETIC

LOGICAL/MATHEMATICAL

Multistep and Strategy Problems

The following multistep or strategy problems are provided in Lesson 6.5:

Page	Item
121	19, 20

Writing in Mathematics

Have students **write word problems with money amounts**. Have them write one problem using addition and another using subtraction of money amounts. Have students exchange problems with a partner and solve. Check students' work.

Advanced Learners

Challenge students to **add and subtract money amounts**. Have them solve the following and use the opposite operation to check:

$13.39 + $17.86 = __?__ $31.25

$20.00 − $12.32 = __?__ $7.68

$142.48 + $102.56 = __?__ $245.04

$101.01 − $59.99 = __?__ $41.02

VISUAL

LOGICAL/MATHEMATICAL

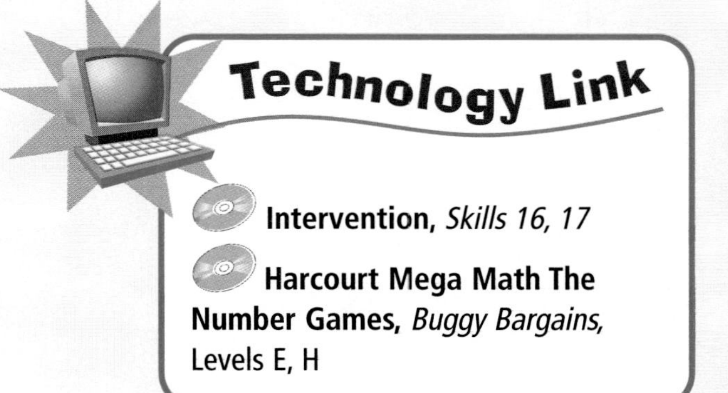

Technology Link

Intervention, *Skills 16, 17*

Harcourt Mega Math The Number Games, *Buggy Bargains,* Levels E, H

Lesson 6.5 Organizer

Objective To add and subtract money amounts

1 INTRODUCE

QUICK REVIEW provides review of prerequisite skills.

WHY LEARN THIS? You can find the total price of more than one item by adding, and you can find how much change you will receive by subtracting. *Share the lesson objective with students.*

2 TEACH

Guided Instruction

- *Have students refer to Steps 1–3 of Example 1.*
  How do you round each amount to the nearest dollar in Step 1? Look at the digit to the right of the decimal point. Since both digits are 5 or more, the dollar amounts increase by 1.
  What do you regroup in Step 2? Regroup 15 tens as 1 hundred, 5 tens.
  How can estimating help you check your answer in Step 3? $8.59 is close to $9.00. $9.00 is the sum that was estimated in Step 1.

MODIFYING INSTRUCTION Have students model the addition problem with play bills and coins.

- *Discuss Steps 1–3 of Example 2.*
  How is regrouping dollars and cents in Step 2 like regrouping whole numbers? Possible answer: You regroup dollars and cents the same way you regroup ones, tens, hundreds, and thousands in whole numbers.

LESSON 5

Add and Subtract Money

Quick Review

1. 863 + 219 = 1,082
2. 673 − 482 = 191
3. 457 + 361 = 818
4. 1,073 − 845 = 228
5. 920 + 549 = 1,469

Learn

CHECK YOUR CHANGE Matthew bought a dog collar for $3.95 and a leash for $4.64. How much money did Matthew spend?

Example 1

Add. $3.95 + $4.64 = ■

STEP 1

Estimate the sum. Round to the nearest dollar.

$3.95 → $4.00
+$4.64 → +$5.00
$9.00

STEP 2

Add money like whole numbers.

$3.95 → 395 (regrouped 1)
+$4.64 → +464
859

STEP 3

Write the sum in dollars and cents.

$3.95
+$4.64
$8.59

So, Matthew spent $8.59. Since $8.59 is close to the estimate of $9.00, the answer is reasonable.

Julia bought a dog bed for $28.98. She paid for it with a $50 bill. How much change should she get?

Example 2

Subtract. $50.00 − $28.98 = ■

STEP 1

Estimate the difference. Round to the nearest ten dollars.

$50.00 → $50.00
−$28.98 → −$30.00
$20.00

STEP 2

Subtract money like whole numbers.

(regrouped: 4 9 9 10)
$50.00 → 5, 0 0 0
−$28.98 → −2, 8 9 8
2, 1 0 2

STEP 3

Write the difference in dollars and cents.

$50.00
−$28.98
$21.02

So, Julia should get $21.02 in change. Since $21.02 is close to the estimate of $20.00, the answer is reasonable.

120

Reteach 6.5

Add and Subtract Money

Adding and subtracting money amounts is similar to adding and subtracting whole numbers.

A. Add. $2.15 + $3.77 = ■

Estimate the sum. Round to the nearest dollar.

$2.15 → $2.00
+$3.77 → +$4.00
$6.00

Step 1
Add money amounts like you add whole numbers.

$2.15 → 215 (regrouped 1)
+$3.77 → +377
592

Step 2
Write the sum in dollars and cents.

$2.15
+$3.77
$5.92

Compare the answer to the estimate. $5.92 is close to $6.00, so the answer is reasonable.

B. Subtract. $70.00 − $35.53 = ■

Estimate the difference. Round to the nearest ten dollars.

$70.00 → $70.00
−$35.53 → −$40.00
$30.00

Step 1
Subtract money amounts like you subtract whole numbers.

(regrouped: 6 9 9 10)
$70.00 → 7,000
−$35.53 → −3,553
3,447

Step 2
Write the difference in dollars and cents.

$70.00
−$35.53
$34.47

$34.47 is close to $30.00, so the answer is reasonable.

Find the sum or difference. Estimate to check.

1. $2.34 + $1.49 = $3.83
2. $25.83 + $43.49 = $69.32
3. $9.62 − $2.17 = $7.45
4. $60.00 − $36.52 = $23.48

Reteach RW35

Practice 6.5

Add and Subtract Money

Find the sum or difference. Estimate to check.

1. $6.43 + $2.15 = $8.58
2. $5.63 − $1.50 = $4.13
3. $2.59 + $1.37 = $3.96
4. $4.93 − $1.78 = $3.15
5. $0.38 + $5.24 = $5.62
6. $3.27 + $2.06 = $5.33
7. $6.55 − $4.90 = $1.65
8. $4.02 − $3.91 = $0.11
9. $3.50 − $1.98 = $1.52
10. $1.90 + $2.64 = $4.54
11. $63.94 + $32.78 = $96.72
12. $28.06 + $52.44 = $80.50
13. $19.78 + $53.98 = $73.76
14. $50.00 − $19.89 = $30.11
15. $75.45 − $36.47 = $38.98
16. $82.02 − $75.93 = $6.09

Mixed Review

Write the missing number.

17. __5__ tens = 50
18. __3__ hundreds = 300
19. __9__ tens = 90
20. __6__ thousands = 6,000
21. __10__ dimes = 4 quarters
22. 15 pennies = __1__ dimes __5__ pennies
23. 12 dimes = __1__ dollars __2__ dimes
24. 8 dimes = __2__ quarters __3__ dimes
25. 26 nickels = __1__ dollars __3__ dimes
26. 15 dimes = __1__ dollars __2__ quarters

Practice PW35

Check

1. **Explain** how you can check the subtraction to be sure Julia got the correct change. **Possible answer: Add to check; $21.02 + $28.98 = $50.00.**

Find the sum or difference. Estimate to check.

2. $1.45 + $2.32 — **$3.77**
3. $5.00 − $1.19 — **$3.81**
4. $14.89 + $22.51 — **$37.40**
5. $31.45 − $19.76 — **$11.69**

Practice and Problem Solving

Extra Practice, page 122, Set C

Find the sum or difference. Estimate to check.

6. $2.63 + $1.74 — **$4.37**
7. $4.55 + $10.48 — **$15.03**
8. $4.64 − $1.80 — **$2.84**
9. $6.73 − $4.85 — **$1.88**
10. $50.00 − $23.46 — **$26.54**
11. $38.26 + $24.87 — **$63.13**
12. $47.69 + $34.54 — **$82.23**
13. $20.00 − $15.25 — **$4.75**
14. $4.28 + $2.59 = ■ **$6.87**
15. $6.72 − $3.94 = ■ **$2.78**
16. $3.26 − $1.09 = ■ **$2.17**

ALGEBRA Write <, >, or = for each ●.

17. $5.00 ● $3.94 + $1.06 **=**
18. $4.57 − $1.14 ● $5.71 **<**

USE DATA For 19–20, use Justin's money at the right.

19. A cat bed costs $8.59. Does Justin have enough money to buy it? **yes**
20. Does Justin have enough money to buy the cat bed and a cat collar that costs $2.99? Explain. **no; Justin has $9.49. $8.59 + $2.99 = $11.58; $11.58 > $9.49**
21. Write a problem using two money amounts greater than $5. Solve. **Check students' problems.**

Getting Ready for the EOG Test

22. Bill bought a turkey sandwich and a lemonade for lunch. How much money did he spend? **D**

A $2.20 C $5.56
B $5.48 D $5.58

BLUE LAKE DINER

Sandwiches		Drinks	
Grilled Cheese	$3.25	Lemonade	$1.69
Tuna	$3.59	Milk	$1.75
Turkey	$3.89		

North Carolina Standards 1.02 Develop fluency with multi-digit addition and subtraction through 9,999 using: a) Strategies for adding and subtracting numbers.

Challenge 6.5

Money Madness

Write the missing numbers.

1. $2.55 + 1.98 = $4.53 (missing: **4**, **3**)
2. $2.95 + 3.69 = $6.64 (missing: **6**)
3. $4.59 + 2.39 = $6.98 (missing: **2**, **9**)
4. $23.91 + 15.39 = $39.30 (missing: **9**, **1**)
5. $3.95 − 1.49 = $2.46 (missing: **2**, **6**)
6. $4.50 − 1.28 = $3.22 (missing: **2**)
7. $6.59 − 1.92 = $4.67 (missing: **1**, **2**)
8. $40.75 − 21.49 = $19.26 (missing: **7**, **1**)

For problems 9–12, use the table.

Sandwiches	
Ham	$3.89
Cheese	$2.35
Chicken	$3.19
Peanut butter and jelly	$1.65

9. Bob buys 2 peanut butter and jelly sandwiches. Should he give the clerk a $1 bill, a $5 bill, or a $10 bill? Explain. **Possible answer: a $5 bill because the cost is between $3.00 and $4.00**
10. Joan buys a sandwich. She gives the clerk a $5 bill. Her change is $2.65. What kind of sandwich does she buy? **cheese**
11. Mr. Riley buys one of each kind of sandwich. How much should he give the clerk? **$11.08**
12. Make up your own problem about sandwiches you will buy for yourself and a friend. Write the problem so that the solver must use estimation, addition, and subtraction. Have a classmate solve it. **Check students' problems. Sample answer: I have $6.00 to buy 2 sandwiches, one for me and one for my friend Ben. Which sandwiches can I buy? How much change will I get?**

Challenge CW35

Problem Solving 6.5

Add and Subtract Money Understand ➔ Plan ➔ Solve ➔ Check

Write the correct answer.

1. Margaret says she needs a little more than $11.00 to buy a book for $6.95 and a calendar for $4.32. Is she right? Explain. **Yes, the exact amount is $11.27.**
2. Rick wants to buy a video for $19.99 and a CD for $13.99. He has $30.00. Is this enough? If not, how much more does he need? **No; Since $19.99 + $13.99 = $33.98, he needs $3.98 more.**
3. Carmen has two $1 bills and 2 quarters. Zach has one $1 bill, 8 dimes, and 10 nickels. Who has more money? How much more? **Carmen; 20¢**
4. Theo paid for a game with a $5 bill, 3 quarters, and 4 pennies. How much did the game cost? **$5.79**

Choose the letter of the correct answer.

5. Jay has 8 more cards than Andy. Andy has 11 fewer cards than Kim. Kim has 26 cards. How many cards does Jay have?
   A 7 C 18
   B 15 **(D) 23**
6. Bridget spent $7.50 to see a movie and $3.95 for popcorn and a drink. About how much did she spend altogether?
   (F) $12.00 H $4.00
   G $4.45 J $3.55
7. Which shows the numbers in order from least to greatest?
   A 352, 299, 399
   B 178, 198, 188
   (C) 516, 606, 610
   D 430, 403, 304
8. Estimate. $10.21 − $6.95
   F $17.00
   G $4.00
   H $3.26
   (J) $3.00
9. **Write About It** How is adding money amounts different from adding whole numbers? **Possible answer: When you add money amounts, you have to put a dollar sign and a decimal point in the answer.**

Problem Solving PS35

3 PRACTICE

Guided Practice

Do Check Exercises 1–5 with your students. Identify students who are having difficulty and choose appropriate lesson resources to provide assistance.

COMMON ERROR ALERT

If students have difficulty subtracting 4-digit numbers across zeros, refer to the model on page 120 and discuss how to regroup for each zero. Provide additional examples, such as $20.00 − $16.37 = __?__, for volunteers to solve. $3.63

Independent Practice

Note that Exercises 19 and 20 are **multistep or strategy problems.** Assign Exercises 6–21.

For Exercises 6–13, students may have difficulty copying exercises. Remind them to place the $ symbol in front of each amount in stacked problems.

4 ASSESS

Summarize the lesson by having students:

DISCUSS Sally bought a magazine for $3.15 and a pen for $0.79. How can you find out how much she spent? by adding $3.15 and $0.79: $3.15 + $0.79 = $3.94

WRITE Explain how you would solve this problem: $4.42 + $3.65 = ■
Possible answer: First, estimate the sum ($4 + $4 = $8). Then find the sum. $4.42 + $3.65 = $8.07 Write the sum in dollars and cents and check it against the estimate.

LESSON QUIZ

Transparency 6.5

Find the sum or difference. Estimate to check.

1. $1.53 + $2.27 — $3.80
2. $43.69 − $21.51 — $22.18
3. $50.00 − $22.76 — $27.24

Extra Practice

Purpose To provide extra practice for the skills presented in this chapter

The blue page references in each set of exercises refer to the lesson pages where each skill is taught.

Internet Resources

Visit THE LEARNING SITE at **www.harcourtschool.com** for a listing of practice activities.

Extra Practice

Set A (pp. 110–113)

Write the amount.

1. 
$0.89

2. 
$7.65

Find two equivalent sets for each. List the coins and bills.
Check students' lists.

3. $0.47 4. $4.38 5. $2.81 6. $6.76

Set B (pp. 116–117)

Use < or > to compare the amounts of money.

1. a. b.

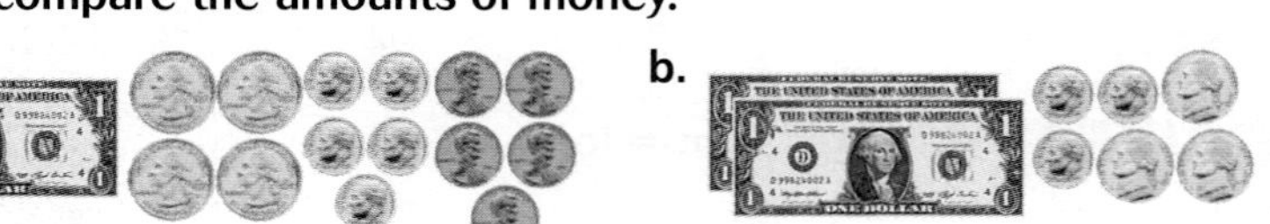

$2.55 > $2.45 or $2.45 < $2.55

2. Maria has 3 quarters, 3 dimes, and 1 nickel. She wants to buy a slice of pie for $1.10. Does she have enough money? Explain.
Yes, she has $1.10.

3. Ronnie has 1 quarter, 4 dimes, and 3 nickels. Lydia has 3 quarters. Who has more money? Explain.
Ronnie; $0.80 > $0.75

Set C (pp. 120–121)

Find the sum or difference. Estimate to check.

1. $3.35 + $2.84 = **$6.19**
2. $8.45 − $4.56 = **$3.89**
3. $10.00 − $5.35 = **$4.65**
4. $25.47 + $32.98 = **$58.45**
5. $63.07 − $54.68 = **$8.39**

USE DATA For 6–7, use the table.

6. How much more does a pint of blueberries cost than an apple?
$1.55 more

7. Ezra buys 2 plums and a pound of grapes and pays with a $5 bill. How much change does Ezra get?
$2.77

FREIDA'S FRUIT STAND

Fruit	Price
Bananas	$0.65 each pound
Plums	$0.45 each
Grapes	$1.33 each pound
Apples	$0.24 each
Blueberries	$1.79 each pint

Review/Test

CHECK VOCABULARY AND CONCEPTS

Choose the best term from the box.

decimal point
equivalent
change

1. Sets of money that have the same value are ? . (p. 111) **equivalent**

Find two equivalent sets for each. List the coins and bills. (pp. 110–113) **Check students' lists.**

2. \$0.78 3. \$3.65 4. \$5.17 5. \$8.42

Copy and complete the table. (pp. 118–119) **Possible answers are given.**

	COST OF ITEM	AMOUNT PAID	CHANGE IN COINS AND BILLS	AMOUNT OF CHANGE
6.	\$4.62	\$10.00	■ See below.	■ \$5.38
7.	\$3.49	\$5.00	■	■ \$1.51

6. 3 p, 1 d, 1 q, one \$5 bill
7. 1 p, 2 q, one \$1 bill

CHECK SKILLS

Use < or > to compare the amounts of money. (pp. 116–117)

8. a.

b. 

\$6.81 > \$6.76 or \$6.76 < \$6.81

Find the sum or difference. Estimate to check. (pp. 120–121)

9. \$2.46 + \$3.37 = **\$5.83**
10. \$6.39 − \$1.81 = **\$4.58**
11. \$9.05 − \$2.88 = **\$6.17**
12. \$60.00 − \$34.72 = **\$25.28**
13. \$62.74 + \$27.46 = **\$90.20**

CHECK PROBLEM SOLVING

Make a table to solve. (pp. 114–115)

14. Michelle has two \$1 bills, 5 quarters, 3 dimes, and 4 nickels. How many different ways can she make \$3.50? **3 ways**

15. Brian has one \$5 bill, one \$1 bill, 5 quarters, 3 dimes, and 3 nickels. How many different ways can he make \$7.35? **4 ways**

Review/Test

Purpose To check understanding of concepts, skills, and problem solving presented in Chapter 6

Using the Page

The Chapter 6 Review/Test can be used as a **review** or a **test**.

- Items 1–7 check understanding of concepts and new vocabulary.
- Items 8–13 check skill proficiency.
- Items 14–15 check students' abilities to choose and apply problem solving strategies to real-life problems.

Suggest that students place the completed Chapter 6 Review/Test in their portfolios.

Using the Assessment Guide

- Multiple-choice format of Chapter 6 Posttest—See *Assessment Guide*, pp. AG37–38.
- Free-response format of Chapter 6 Posttest—See *Assessment Guide*, pp. AG39–40.

Using Student Self-Assessment

The How Did I Do? survey helps students assess what they have learned and how they learned it. This survey is available as a copying master in *Assessment Guide*, p. AGxvii.

Chapter 6 Test, page 1

Choose the correct answer.

1. Which is an equivalent set for \$0.89?
   A 8 dimes, 2 nickels
   B 7 dimes, 5 nickels
   (C) 3 quarters, 1 dime, 4 pennies
   D 3 quarters, 1 nickel, 4 pennies

2. Which is the **greatest** amount of money?
   F 3 quarters, 6 dimes, 4 nickels
   G 3 quarters, 7 dimes, 4 nickels
   (H) 4 quarters, 7 dimes
   J 5 quarters, 2 dimes, 8 pennies

3. A soda costs \$0.86. Darren pays with a \$1 bill. Which set of coins should he get in change?
   A 2 dimes
   B 1 dime, 1 nickel
   C 1 dime, 1 nickel, 4 pennies
   (D) 1 dime, 4 pennies

4. Make a table to find how many ways you can make \$0.30.
   F 4 H 6
   G 5 (J) more than 6

5. \$5.37 + \$4.72 = ■
   (A) \$10.09
   B \$9.45
   C \$9.09
   D \$9.00

6. Which is an equivalent set for \$1.32?
   F one \$1 bill, 1 quarter
   (G) one \$1 bill, 3 dimes, 2 pennies
   H one \$1 bill, 6 nickels
   J one \$1 bill, 2 dimes

7. Andre spent \$2.36. He gave the clerk a \$5 bill. How much change should he get?
   (A) \$2.64 C \$3.36
   B \$2.74 D \$3.74

8. Which is the **greatest** amount of money?
   F two \$1 bills, 10 nickels
   G two \$1 bills, 5 dimes, 4 nickels
   H two \$1 bills, 6 dimes
   (J) two \$1 bills, 3 quarters

9. \$8.34 − \$5.65 = ■
   (A) \$2.69
   B \$2.71
   C \$2.79
   D \$3.31

10. Kamar has 2 quarters, 4 dimes, and 3 nickels. How many ways can he pay for a can of juice that costs \$0.55?
   F 2 (H) 4
   G 3 J 5

Go On

Chapter 6 Test, page 2

11. Which is an **equivalent** set for \$3.55?
   A three \$1 bills, 5 dimes
   B three \$1 bills, 5 nickels
   (C) three \$1 bills, 2 quarters, 1 nickel
   D three \$1 bills, 2 quarters

12. Joan has \$2.68 and Bob has \$4.97. How much money do they have in all?
   F \$2.29 H \$7.55
   G \$6.55 (J) \$7.65

13. Pat has 3 quarters and 5 dimes. Marc has 2 quarters and 7 dimes. Sue has 5 quarters. Tim has 3 quarters and 5 nickels. Which two people have the same amount of money?
   A Pat and Marc
   (B) Pat and Sue
   C Marc and Sue
   D Tim and Marc

14. Make a table to find how many ways you can make \$0.18.
   F 10 H 2
   (G) 6 J 1

15. A box of soap costs \$4.65. Jean pays with a \$5 bill. Which set of coins should she get in change?
   A 1 quarter, 3 nickels
   B 1 quarter, 5 pennies
   (C) 1 quarter, 1 dime
   D 1 quarter, 2 dimes

16. What amount of money is equivalent to four \$1 bills, 1 quarter, and 4 pennies?
   F \$4.39 (H) \$4.29
   G \$4.34 J \$4.24

17. Kim spends \$6.79. Amy spends \$9.33. How much more money does Amy spend than Kim?
   A \$2.46 C \$3.54
   (B) \$2.54 D \$3.56

18. Kay bought a sandwich for \$2.45. She paid for it with three \$1 bills. Which set of coins should she get in change?
   (F) 2 quarters, 1 nickel
   G 4 dimes, 1 nickel
   H 2 quarters, 4 nickels
   J 2 quarters, 1 dime

19. Tao has 5 quarters, 2 dimes, 3 nickels, and 8 pennies. How many different sets of coins could he use to make \$1.22?
   A 10 (C) 4
   B 8 D 1

20. Lynne has one \$1 bill, 2 quarters, and 3 dimes. Leo has 5 quarters and 8 nickels. Meg has 6 quarters and 4 dimes. Jan has 2 quarters and 9 dimes. Who has the **greatest** amount of money?
   F Lynne H Leo
   (G) Meg J Jan

Stop

Getting Ready for the EOG Test
Chapters 1–6

Using the Pages

These pages may be used to help students get ready for the North Carolina EOG Test. The test items are written in the same style and arranged in the same format as those on the EOG Test.

The pages are cumulative. They cover the standards from the North Carolina Mathematics Standard Course of Study that have been taught up to this point in the text or in a previous grade. Each Getting Ready for the EOG Test also reviews the North Carolina mathematics strands shown below.

- Number and Operations
- Measurement
- Geometry
- Data Analysis and Probability
- Algebra

These pages can be assigned at the end of the chapter as classwork or as a homework assignment. You may want to have students use individual recording sheets presented in a multiple-choice (standardized) format. A Test Answer Sheet is available as a blackline master in the *Assessment Guide* (p. AGlii).

You may wish to have students describe how they solved each problem and share their solutions.

Getting Ready for the EOG Test

NUMBER AND OPERATIONS

1. The table shows the heights of volcanoes in the Three Sisters area of Oregon. Which is the height of the North Sister written in word form? C

THREE SISTERS VOLCANOES, OREGON	
Volcano	**Height (in feet)**
North Sister	10,085
Middle Sister	10,047
South Sister	10,358

A ten thousand, eight hundred five
B ten thousand, eight hundred fifty
C ten thousand, eighty-five
D ten thousand, forty-seven

2. Lincoln Elementary has four hundred seventy-six students. How is the number of students written in standard form? C

A 4,076 C 476
B 764 D 467

3. Explain It Eva needs cat food that costs $3.89. She wants to buy a cat toy for $1.69. She has a $5 bill. Explain whether Eva has enough money for both items.
See page 125.

MEASUREMENT AND GEOMETRY

4. Which tool would you use to find the weight of a seashell? A

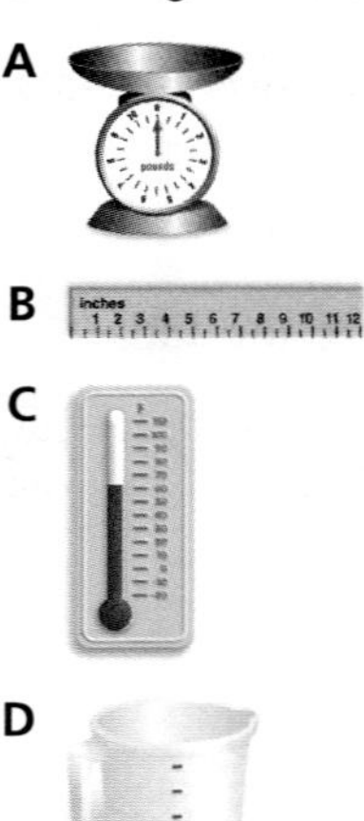

A
B
C
D

5. Which solid figures could describe a basketball and a can of soup? D

A sphere and cube
B cone and cylinder
C sphere and rectangular prism
D sphere and cylinder

6. Explain It Mike looks at this thermometer. He says that the temperature is *about* 50°F. Do you agree with Mike? Explain.
See page 125.

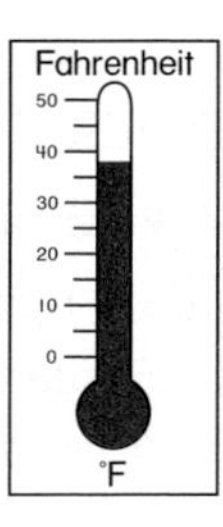

124

ALGEBRA

TIP **Get the information you need.** See item 7. Find the pattern in the figures. Each figure has 1 less side than the figure before it. Think what figure has 1 less than 6 sides.

7. Which is the next figure in this pattern? C

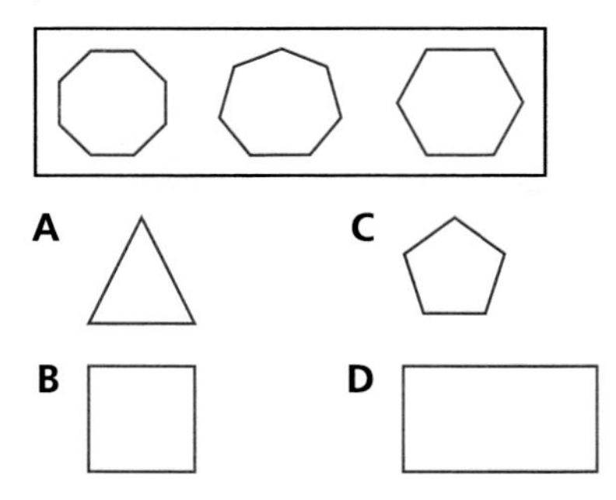

8. Which number sentence is true? C

A $4 + 9 = 12$
B $16 + 4 = 19$
C $18 - 5 = 13$
D $20 - 11 = 8$

9. Explain It Chai wants to know how much it will cost to buy four tickets to the animal farm. Describe how he can find the total cost.

ANIMAL FARM TICKETS	
Number of Tickets	**Cost**
1	\$4.00
2	\$8.00
3	\$12.00
4	■
5	\$20.00

See below.

DATA ANALYSIS AND PROBABILITY

10. Terri asked four of her classmates how many library books they checked out. She made this bar graph of the data.

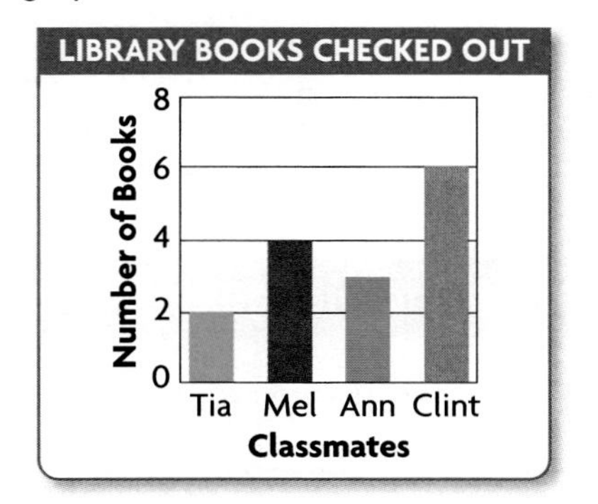

How many books did Clint check out? D

A 2
B 3
C 4
D 6

11. Explain It Pat took a survey of the types of pets her classmates own. The table shows the data she collected. Pat wants to make a pictograph of the data. Explain what key she can use.

MY CLASSMATES' PETS	
Type of Pet	**Number**
Dogs	12
Birds	8
Cats	16
Fish	10

See below.

Chapters 1–6

Item Analysis

You may wish to use the item analysis to determine which North Carolina standards need additional review.

Item	North Carolina Standard	Lesson
1	1.01	2.6
2	1.01	2.2
3	1.06	6.5
4	(2) Goal 2	Grade 2
5	(1) Goal 3	Grade 1
6	(2) 2.01	Grade 2
7	(2) 5.01	Grade 2
8	Goal 5	4.6
9	(2) 5.01	Grade 2
10	(2) 4.01	Grade 2
11	(2) 4.01	Grade 2

SCORING RUBRIC
Explain It

2 Demonstrates a complete understanding of the problem and chooses an appropriate strategy to determine the solution

1 Demonstrates a partial understanding of the problem and chooses a strategy that does not lead to a complete and accurate solution

0 Demonstrates little understanding of the problem and shows little evidence of using any strategy to determine a solution

Explain It • Written Response

3. Possible answer: you could round each amount to the nearest dollar. \$4.00 + \$2.00 = \$6.00. Eva has only \$5.00, so she does not have enough.

6. No; possible answer: the temperature is closer to 40°F than to 50°F.

9. Possible answer: find a pattern in the table. A pattern is add \$4.00 for each ticket. So, four tickets cost \$12.00 + \$4.00, or \$16.00.

11. Possible answer: Pat can use a key of 2, since all the numbers are even.

CHAPTER 7

Understand Time

NCTM Standards 2000

1. Number and Operations
Lessons 7.1, 7.3, 7.4, 7.5, 7.6
2. Algebra
3. Geometry
4. Measurement
Lessons 7.1, 7.2, 7.3, 7.4, 7.5, 7.6
5. Data Analysis and Probability
6. Problem Solving
Lessons 7.1, 7.2, 7.3, 7.4, 7.5, 7.6
7. Reasoning and Proof
Lessons 7.1, 7.2, 7.5, 7.6
8. Communication
Lessons 7.1, 7.2, 7.3, 7.4, 7.5, 7.6
9. Connections
Lessons 7.4, 7.5, 7.6
10. Representation
Lessons 7.2, 7.3, 7.4, 7.5, 7.6

Chapter Planner

Getting Ready for Chapter 7 • Assessing Prior Knowledge and INTERVENTION (See PE and TE page 127.)

LESSON	NORTH CAROLINA STANDARDS	PACING	VOCABULARY*	MATERIALS	RESOURCES AND TECHNOLOGY
7.1 **Tell Time** pp. 128–131 **Objective** To tell time to the nearest minute in various ways	Goal 2 *also* maintains (2) 2.02	1 Day	**half hour** **quarter hour** **clockwise** **counter-clockwise**		Reteach, Practice, Problem Solving, Challenge 7.1 Transparency 7.1 **Intervention,** *Skills 48–50* (CD or Book) **Harcourt Mega Math Country Countdown,** *Clock-a-Doodle-Doo*
7.2 **A.M. and P.M.** pp. 132–133 **Objective** To write and identify times as A.M. or P.M.	Goal 2	1 Day (For Lessons 7.2 and 7.3)	**A.M.** **P.M.** **noon** **midnight**		Reteach, Practice, Problem Solving, Challenge 7.2 Transparency 7.2 **Intervention,** *Skills 48–50* (CD or Book)
7.3 **Hands On: Elapsed Time** pp. 134–135 **Objective** To use a clock to measure elapsed time	2.01a		**elapsed time**	*For each student* clock with movable hands	Reteach, Practice, Problem Solving, Challenge 7.3 Transparency 7.3 **Harcourt Mega Math The Number Games,** *Tiny's Think Tank; Clock-a-Doodle-Doo* **Math Jingles® CD 3–4**
7.4 **Use a Schedule** pp. 136–137 **Objective** To use a schedule to determine elapsed time	2.01a	1 Day	**schedule**		Reteach, Practice, Problem Solving, Challenge 7.4 Transparency 7.4 **Intervention,** *Skills 48–50* (CD or Book)
7.5 **Use a Calendar** pp. 138–141 **Objective** To use a calendar to determine elapsed time	2.01b *also* 2.01a	1 Day	**calendar**		Reteach, Practice, Problem Solving, Challenge 7.5 Transparency 7.5 **Intervention,** *Skill 51* (CD or Book) **Harcourt Mega Math Country Countdown,** *Clock-a-Doodle-Doo*
7.6 **Problem Solving Skill: Sequence Events** pp. 142–143 **Objective** To use a time line to determine a sequence of events	Goal 2 *also* 2.01a	1 Day	**time line**	*For each student* blank number line, p. TR16	Reteach, Practice, Reading Strategy, Challenge Transparency 7.6 Scaffolded Instruction Transparency 7 Reading Transparency 7 **Intervention • Problem Solving,** *Strategy/Skill 7* (CD or Book)

Ending Chapter 7 • **Extra Practice,** p. 144 • **Chapter 7 Review/Test,** p. 145 • **Getting Ready for the EOG Test,** pp. 146–147

Ending Unit 2 • **It's in the Bag,** p. 148; **Challenge,** p. 149; **Study Guide and Review,** pp. 150–151; **Performance Assessment,** p. 152; **Technology Linkup,** p. 153; **Problem Solving In North Carolina,** pp. 154–155

*****Boldfaced** terms are the key mathematical terms for the chapter.

Vocabulary Power

Review Vocabulary

To be ready for Chapter 7, students should know the following vocabulary term:

- **hour** (p. 128)—a unit used to measure time; 1 hour = 60 minutes

Develop Key Chapter Vocabulary

The **boldfaced** words are some key vocabulary terms in the chapter.

- **quarter hour** (p. 129)—15 minutes
- **clockwise** (p. 131)—direction that the hands of a clock move in
- **counterclockwise** (p. 131)—opposite of the direction that the hands of a clock move in
- **A.M.** (p. 132)—describes times of the day from midnight to noon
- **P.M.** (p. 132)—describes times of the day from noon to midnight
- **noon** (p. 132)—12:00 in the day
- **midnight** (p. 132)—12:00 at night
- **elapsed time** (p. 134)—the amount of time that passes from the start to the end of an activity
- **schedule** (p. 136)—a table of activities and the times they happen
- **time line** (p. 142)—a drawing that shows when and in what order events took place

Vocabulary Cards

Have students use the Vocabulary Cards on *Teacher's Resource Book* pages TR147–150 for the key terms in the chapter. The cards can be added to a file of mathematics terms.

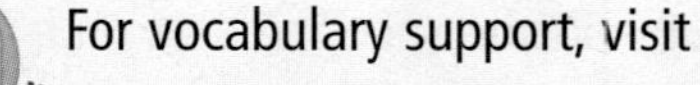

Multimedia Math Glossary

GO ON-LINE For vocabulary support, visit **www.harcourtschool.com/mathglossary**

Math Journal

Have students define the key vocabulary terms: minute, half hour, quarter hour, clockwise, counterclockwise, A.M., P.M., elapsed time, schedule, calendar, and time line. Have students use their own words and give an example of each.

MATH Word Work

Objective To reinforce vocabulary concepts
Use after Lesson 7.4.

Materials *For each pair* clock with movable hands

Display the Zoo Movie Schedule. Ask each pair to display the time in response to each question below. Have students describe each time as *A.M.* or *P.M.*

1. The elapsed time of *A Giraffe's View* is 1 hour 20 minutes. At what time does this movie end? **4:20 P.M.**
2. *Insect Adventures* ends a half hour before *Ocean Tides* begins. At what time does *Insect Adventures* end? **12:15 P.M.**
3. Seating for each movie begins a quarter hour before the start time of the movie. When does seating begin for *A Giraffe's View?* **2:45 P.M.**
4. George's family arrived at the movie theatre 25 minutes before *Insect Adventures* began. At what time did they arrive? **10:50 A.M.**

ZOO MOVIE SCHEDULE

Movie	Start Time
Insect Adventures	11:15 A.M.
Ocean Tides	12:45 P.M.
A Giraffe's View	3:00 P.M.

Understand Time

Mathematics Across the Grades

LOOKING BACK • Prerequisite Skills

To be ready for Chapter 7, students should have the following understandings and skills:

- **Tell Time**—read and write times on an analog clock
- **Calendar**—locate specific dates on a calendar

Check What You Know

Use page 127 to determine students' knowledge of prerequisite concepts and skills.

Intervention

Help students prepare for the chapter by using the intervention resources described on TE page 127.

LOOKING AT CHAPTER 7 • Essential Skills

Students will

- tell time to the nearest minute.
- write and identify times as A.M. or P.M.
- **use a clock to measure elapsed time.**
- use a schedule and a calendar to determine elapsed time.
- use a time line to determine a sequence of events.

Example

John went jogging from 3:30 P.M. to 4:25 P.M. How long did he jog?

Count by fives from 3:30 to 4:25. Elapsed time: 55 minutes. So, John jogged for 55 minutes.

LOOKING AHEAD • Applications

Students will apply what they learn in Chapter 7 to the following new concepts:

- Find Time to the Nearest Second (Grade 4)
- Find Elapsed Time Using Addition or Subtraction (Grade 4)
- Solve Problems by Using the Skill *Sequence Information* (Grade 4)

Differentiated Instruction

Meeting the Needs of All Learners

Extra Support	Activities for All	Enrichment
Alternative Teaching Strategy TE Lessons 7.1, 7.2, 7.3, 7.4, 7.5, 7.6 **Special Needs** TE Lesson 7.5 **ESOL/ESL** TE Lessons 7.1, 7.2, 7.3, 7.4, 7.5, 7.6	**Cross-Curricular Connections** **Career:** TE Lesson 7.1 **Reading:** TE Lesson 7.6 **Social Studies:** TE/PE Chapter Opener, TE Lessons 7.1 and 7.5 **Vocabulary:** TE p. 126B, PE p. 127, TE Lesson 7.2 **Writing:** TE Lesson 7.4	**Advanced Learners** TE Lessons 7.3, 7.4 **Early Finishers** TE Lessons 7.2, 7.6

Combination and Multi-age Classrooms

Grade 2	Grade 3	Grade 4
Skills Trace Across the Grades		
Tell time to the hour, half hour, and 15 minutes; sequence months; read a calendar.	**Tell time to the minute; identify times as A.M. or P.M.; find elapsed time using a clock; find elapsed time using a calendar; read a time line.**	Tell time to the nearest second; sequence information; find elapsed time using addition or subtraction.
Instructional Strategies		
Students on this level may require more time to build conceptual understanding. **Assignments** **Grade 3 Pupil Edition** • Have students work in pairs on Lessons 7.1, 7.2, 7.3, and 7.4. • Have them skip Lessons 7.5 and 7.6. **Grade 2 Pupil Edition**—pages 241–256 and 259–272	Students on this level should be able to complete all the lessons in the Pupil Edition and all the activities in the Teacher's Edition with minimal adjustments. **Assignment** **Grade 3 Pupil Edition**—pages 126–145	Students on this level will probably require less time to build conceptual understanding. **Assignments** **Grade 3 Pupil Edition** • Compact Lessons 7.3, 7.4, 7.5, and 7.6. **Grade 4 Pupil Edition**—pages 94–109

CHAPTER 7

Understand Time

Introducing the Chapter

Tell students that clocks can be used to tell the time to the minute by looking at the positions of the hour hand and the minute hand. Have students locate the clock on the Wrigley Building. Ask: What time is shown on the clock? Possible answer: 12:46 P.M.

Using Data

To begin the study of this chapter, have students

- Determine how much longer the 7:45 P.M. boat tour lasts than the 3:00 P.M. boat tour. 30 minutes longer
- Determine the end times for the boat tours if the length of each tour was 1 hour. 12:30 P.M.; 2:15 P.M.; 4:00 P.M.; 8:45 P.M.
- Find the elapsed time from the start of the earliest boat tour to the start of the latest boat tour. 8 hours 15 minutes

Problem Solving Project

Purpose To calculate elapsed time

Grouping small groups

Background William Wrigley, Jr. wished to build an impressive building as the headquarters for his chewing gum company. He wanted the building to look like a birthday cake.

UNDERSTAND • PLAN • SOLVE • CHECK

Have students

- Tell what time they go to bed and what time they get up.
- Make a 4-column table with students' names in the first column and the times in the second and third columns.
- Find the elapsed time for each student and write it in the fourth column.

Suggest that students place the tables in their portfolios.

Graphing Investigations
Begin Week 7.

CHAPTER 7 Understand Time

FAST FACT • SOCIAL STUDIES The Wrigley Building is in Chicago, Illinois. This clock on the Wrigley Building has an hour hand that is 6 feet 4 inches long, and a minute hand that is 9 feet 2 inches long.

PROBLEM SOLVING Boat tours on the Chicago River pass by the Wrigley Building. Find the end time for each tour.

BOAT TOURS

Start Time	Length of Tour
11:30 A.M.	1 hour 30 minutes
1:15 P.M.	1 hour 30 minutes
3:00 P.M.	1 hour 30 minutes
7:45 P.M.	2 hours

1:00 P.M.; 2:45 P.M.; 4:30 P.M.; 9:45 P.M.

The Wrigley Building

126

WHY LEARN MATH? A baker needs to make sure that foods are in the oven for the right amount of time so that they will be baked properly. Ask: If a pie is supposed to bake for 50 minutes and it is put in the oven at 4:15 P.M., at what time should the pie be taken out of the oven? 5:05 P.M.

Family Involvement Activities

These activities provide:

- Letter to the Family
- Math Vocabulary
- Family Game
- Practice (Homework)

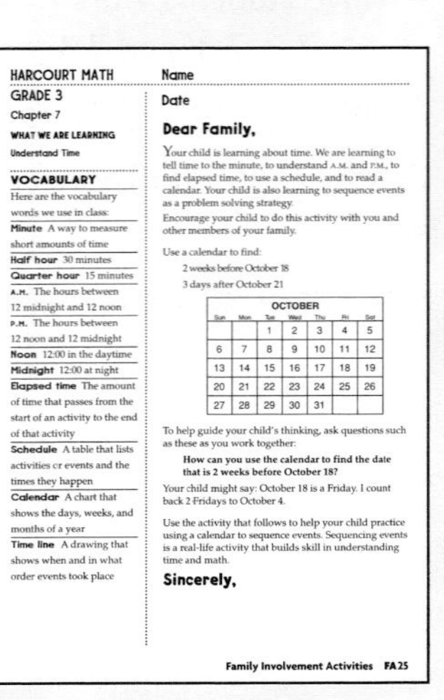

HARCOURT MATH
GRADE 3
Chapter 7
WHAT WE ARE LEARNING
Understand Time

VOCABULARY
Here are the vocabulary words we use in class:
Minute A way to measure short amounts of time
Half hour 30 minutes
Quarter hour 15 minutes
A.M. The hours between 12 midnight and 12 noon
P.M. The hours between 12 noon and 12 midnight
Noon 12:00 in the daytime
Midnight 12:00 at night
Elapsed time The amount of time that passes from the start of an activity to the end of that activity
Schedule A table that lists activities or events and the times they happen
Calendar A chart that shows the days, weeks, and months of a year
Time line A drawing that shows when and in what order events took place

Name
Date

Dear Family,

Your child is learning about time. We are learning to tell time to the minute, to understand A.M. and P.M., to find elapsed time, to use a schedule, and to read a calendar. Your child is also learning to sequence events as a problem solving strategy.

Encourage your child to do this activity with you and other members of your family.

Use a calendar to find:
2 weeks before October 18
3 days after October 21

OCTOBER

Sun	Mon	Tue	Wed	Thu	Fri	Sat
		1	2	3	4	5
6	7	8	9	10	11	12
13	14	15	16	17	18	19
20	21	22	23	24	25	26
27	28	29	30	31		

To help guide your child's thinking, ask questions such as these as you work together:

How can you use the calendar to find the date that is 2 weeks before October 18?

Your child might say: October 18 is a Friday. I count back 2 Fridays to October 4.

Use the activity that follows to help your child practice using a calendar to sequence events. Sequencing events is a real-life activity that builds skill in understanding time and math.

Sincerely,

Family Involvement Activities FA25

Family Involvement Activities, p. FA25

Use this page to help you review and remember important skills needed for Chapter 7.

TELL TIME

Read and write the time.

1.
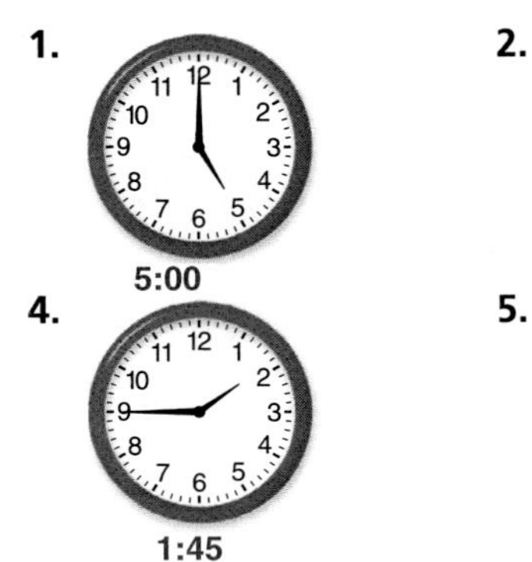
5:00

2.

12:35

3.

6:15

4. 1:45

5. 4:30

6. 8:05

CALENDAR

For 7–9, use the calendar.

7. There are _?_ Fridays in November. four

8. The second Monday in November is _?_. November 8

9. The third Wednesday in November is _?_. November 17

November						
Sun	Mon	Tue	Wed	Thu	Fri	Sat
	1	2	3	4	5	6
7	8	9	10	11	12	13
14	15	16	17	18	19	20
21	22	23	24	25	26	27
28	29	30				

VOCABULARY POWER

REVIEW

minute [min′it] *noun*

Minute has meanings other than "small amount of time." When pronounced as [mī•n(y)o͞ot′], it is an adjective that means "very small." Can you think of other words that mean "very small"?
Check students' answers.

PREVIEW

half hour
quarter hour
A.M.
P.M.
noon
midnight
elapsed time
schedule
calendar
time line

GO ON-LINE www.harcourtschool.com/mathglossary

Assessing Prior Knowledge

Use the **Check What You Know** page to determine whether your students have mastered the prerequisite skills critical for this chapter.

Intervention

- **Diagnose and Prescribe**
Evaluate your students' performance on this page to determine whether intervention is necessary or if enrichment is appropriate. Options that provide instruction, practice, and a check are listed in the chart below.

CHECK WHAT YOU KNOW RESOURCES

Intervention Copying Masters or CD-ROMs
Enrichment Copying Masters

VOCABULARY POWER

For activities and information about the vocabulary in this chapter, see page 126B.

ADDITIONAL PREVIEW VOCABULARY
clockwise, counterclockwise

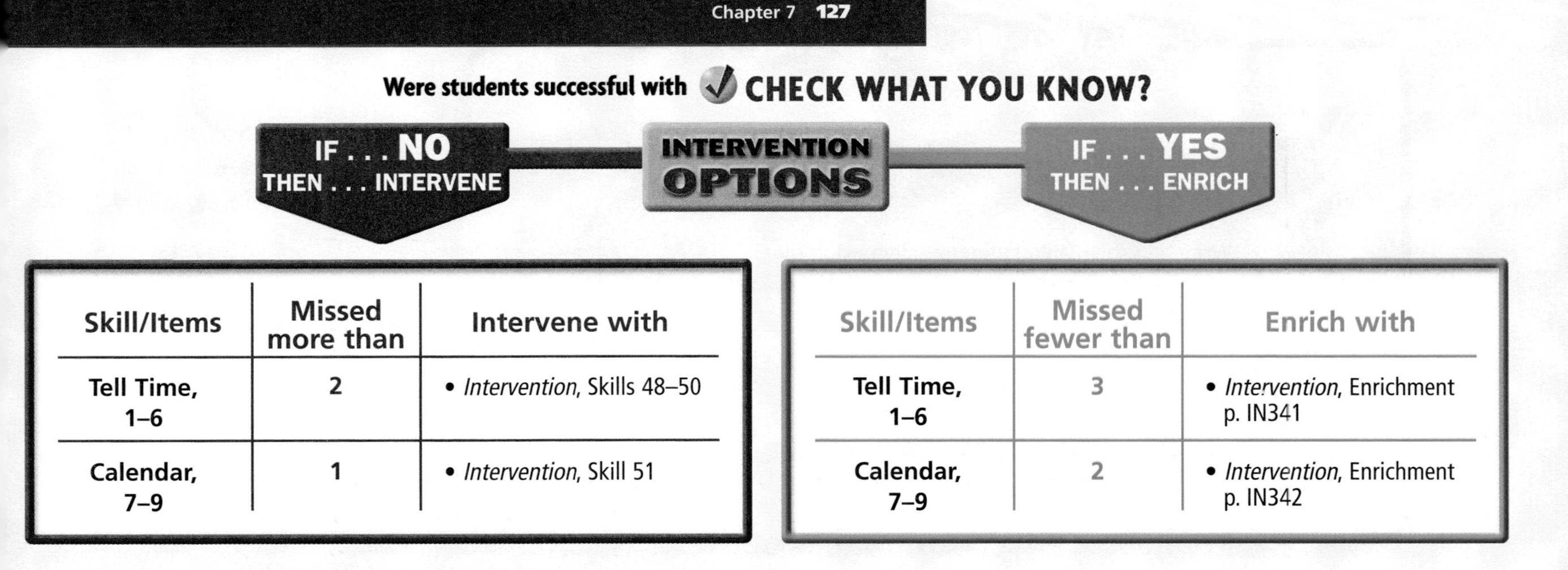

Were students successful with CHECK WHAT YOU KNOW?

IF . . . NO THEN . . . INTERVENE — INTERVENTION OPTIONS — IF . . . YES THEN . . . ENRICH

Skill/Items	Missed more than	Intervene with
Tell Time, 1–6	2	• *Intervention*, Skills 48–50
Calendar, 7–9	1	• *Intervention*, Skill 51

Skill/Items	Missed fewer than	Enrich with
Tell Time, 1–6	3	• *Intervention*, Enrichment p. IN341
Calendar, 7–9	2	• *Intervention*, Enrichment p. IN342

Lesson 7.1

Tell Time

Lesson Planning

Objective To tell time to the nearest minute in various ways

NCTM Standards

1. Number and Operations
4. Measurement
6. Problem Solving
7. Reasoning and Proof
8. Communication

Math Background

These ideas will help students understand how to tell time to the nearest minute:

- To find the number of minutes *after* the hour, count by fives and ones from the 12 to where the minute hand is pointing.
- When a clock shows 31 or more minutes *after* the hour, you can read the time as a number of minutes *before* the next hour by counting back by fives and ones from the 12 to where the minute hand is pointing.

Vocabulary

minute the amount of time it takes for the minute hand to move from one mark to the next

half hour 30 minutes, or one half of one hour

quarter hour 15 minutes, or one fourth of one hour

clockwise in the same direction in which the hands of a clock move

counterclockwise in the opposite direction in which the hands of a clock move

Warm-Up Resources

Number of the Day

Write and solve an addition problem using the number of minutes in one hour. Answers will vary.

Daily Facts Practice

Have students practice addition facts by completing Set A of *Teacher's Resource Book*, p. TR88.

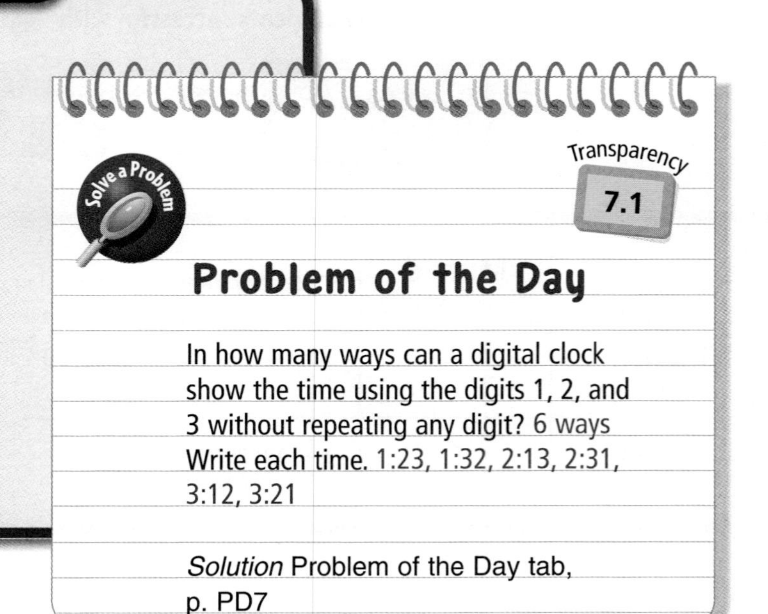

Problem of the Day

In how many ways can a digital clock show the time using the digits 1, 2, and 3 without repeating any digit? 6 ways
Write each time. 1:23, 1:32, 2:13, 2:31, 3:12, 3:21

Solution Problem of the Day tab, p. PD7

Intervention and Extension Resources

Alternative Teaching Strategy

Help students **practice telling time**. Have students draw two clockfaces. Tell students to have one clock show 3:00. First, have them count by fives from 3:00 to 4:00, and write each time. Have students show 10:00 on the second clock. Then, ask them to count by tens from 10:00 to 11:00, and write each time. Ask volunteers to read the times aloud. Check students' work.

See also page 130.

VISUAL

MUSICAL/RHYTHMIC

Multistep and Strategy Problems

The following multistep or strategy problem is provided in Lesson 7.1:

Page	Item
130	24

Career Connection

Help students **understand the necessity of learning to tell time**. Ask students to give some examples of jobs for which time is very important. List students' responses and have them discuss why time is important to each job. Possible answers: airline pilot, passengers depend on planes to depart and arrive on time; teacher, schools expect classes to begin on time

AUDITORY

INTERPERSONAL/SOCIAL

Social Studies Connection

Challenge students to **expand the concept of telling time**. Explain to students that the clocks we use today are not the only ways to tell time. Time-telling instruments have changed over the years and different cultures may have different ways of telling time.

Ask students to research other ways they can tell time without looking at a clock. Possible answers: position of the sun, sundial, hourglass with sand, water clock, bells from a tower

AUDITORY

VERBAL/LINGUISTIC

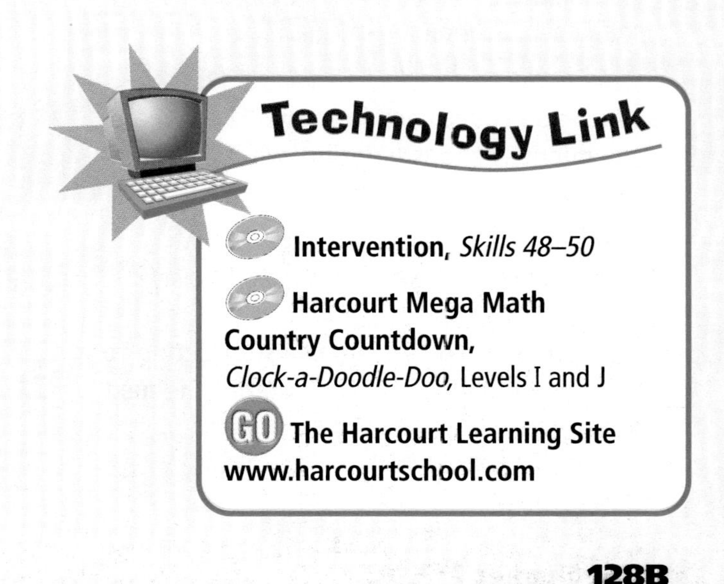

Technology Link
Intervention, *Skills 48–50*
Harcourt Mega Math Country Countdown, *Clock-a-Doodle-Doo,* Levels I and J
GO The Harcourt Learning Site www.harcourtschool.com

Lesson 7.1 Organizer

Objective To tell time to the nearest minute in various ways

Vocabulary half hour, quarter hour, clockwise, counterclockwise

1 INTRODUCE

Quick Review provides review of prerequisite skills.

Why Learn This? You can arrive on time for school or sporting events. *Share the lesson objective with students.*

2 TEACH

Guided Instruction

- *Have students read the Learn section and review students' understanding of the concepts of 5 minutes, 1 minute, and 1 hour.*

  How many minutes have passed when the minute hand moves from the 6 to the 7 on a clock? 5 minutes

  How many minutes are there from one mark to the next on a clock? 1 minute

  Reasoning How many hours have passed when the hour hand moves from the 4 to the 7? 3 hours

- *Refer to the analog clock showing 9:26.*

  Why do you start counting the minutes from the 12? When the minute hand is on the 12, the time is 9:00. Start counting the minutes from the 12 to find the number of minutes after 9:00.

  Why do you think the hour hand is positioned between 9 and 10 on the clock? Since the minute hand is almost halfway around the clockface, the hour hand will be almost halfway to the next hour on the clockface.

- *Refer to the analog clock showing 1:42.*

  When you count back from the 12 to where the minute hand is pointing, what do you find out? how many minutes there are before the next hour

- *Direct students' attention to the digital clock showing 7:52.*

  Reasoning How can you use subtraction to find the number of minutes before the next hour? Possible answer: You can subtract 52 from 60, the number of minutes in one hour.

Tell Time

Quick Review

Add 5 to each number.

1. 25 30
2. 10 15
3. 15 20
4. 5 10
5. 30 35

VOCABULARY
half hour
quarter hour
clockwise
counterclockwise

Learn

WHAT TIME IS IT? The hands, numbers, and marks on a clock help you tell what time it is. In one minute, the minute hand moves from one mark to the next.

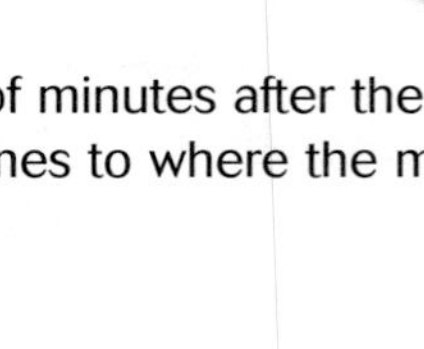

To find the number of minutes after the hour, count by fives and ones to where the minute hand is pointing.

Read: nine twenty-six, or 26 minutes after nine

Write: 9:26

Remember

In five minutes, the minute hand moves from one number to the next.

When a clock shows 31 or more minutes *after* the hour, you can read the time as a number of minutes *before* the next hour.

Count back by fives and ones to where the minute hand is pointing.

5 minutes, 10 minutes, 15 minutes, 16 minutes, 17 minutes, 18 minutes

Read: 18 minutes before two

Write: 1:42

A digital clock uses numbers to show the hour and the number of minutes after the hour.

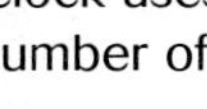

Read: seven fifty-two, or 8 minutes before eight

Write: 7:52

Read: one twenty, or 20 minutes after one

Write: 1:20

Reteach 7.1

Tell Time

What time does the clock show?

To count the number of minutes after the hour, follow these steps:

Start at the 12 on the clock. Count by fives as far as you can.

5 minutes, 10 minutes, 15 minutes, 20 minutes, 25 minutes, 30 minutes, 35 minutes, **40 minutes**

Then count by ones to where the minute hand is pointing. Add.

1 minute, **2 minutes**

40 + 2 = 42

So, it is 42 minutes after ten, or 10:42.

Record the numbers you count as fives and ones. Find the total number of minutes after the hour. Then write the time. The first one is done for you.

1. 15 + 3 = 18
   The time is 10:18.
2. 30 + 4 = 34
   The time is 10:34.
3. 55 + 2 = 57
   The time is 10:57.
4. 20 + 1 = 21
   The time is 10:21.

RW36 Reteach

Practice 7.1

Tell Time Possible answers are given.

Write each time. Then write two ways you can read each time.

1. 6:30
   half past six
   30 minutes after six
2. 7:48
   seven forty-eight
   12 minutes before eight

Write two ways you can read each time. Possible answers are given.

3. 9:17
   nine seventeen
   17 minutes after nine
4. 3:31
   three thirty-one
   29 minutes before four

Estimate each time to the nearest half hour.

5. 4:00
6. 1:00
7. 1:30

Mixed Review

8. 632 + 421 + 267 = 1,320
9. 2,345 + 1,827 + 4,558 = 8,730
10. 4,414 − 3,399 = 1,015
11. 7,212 − 3,946 = 3,266

PW36 Practice

Half Hour and Quarter Hour

You can also tell time by parts of an hour. On the clocks below, you can see how one hour can be divided into 2 equal parts, or half hours, or into 4 equal parts, or quarter hours. A **half hour** has 30 minutes, and a **quarter hour** has 15 minutes.

Read: half past seven

Write: 7:30

Read: quarter past ten

Write: 10:15

Read: quarter to three

Write: 2:45

ESTIMATION Sometimes an estimate of the time is asked for. Look at where the minute hand is pointing to estimate the time to the nearest half hour.

Is the time closer to 8:00 or 8:30?

The minute hand is closer to the hour mark, so the estimated time is about 8:00.

Is the time closer to 3:30 or 4:00?

The minute hand is closer to the half hour mark, so the estimated time is about 3:30.

Check

2. 3:23; three twenty-three; 23 minutes after three

4. 11:45; quarter to twelve; eleven forty-five

1. Explain why 30 minutes is called a half hour. **Possible answer: The minute hand moves halfway around the clock in 30 minutes.**

Write each time. Then write two ways you can read each time.
Possible answers are given.

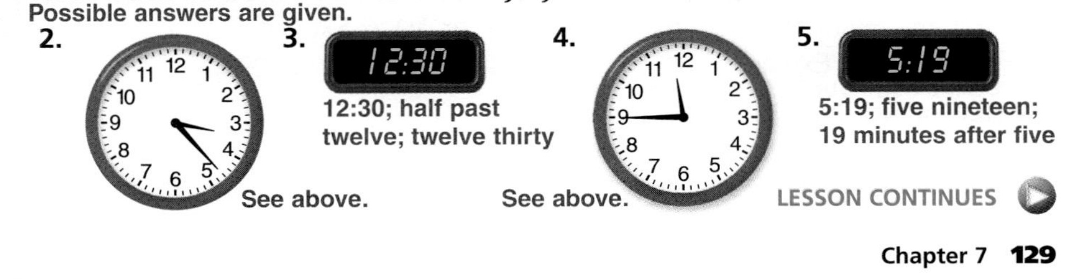

2. See above.

3. 12:30; half past twelve; twelve thirty

4. See above.

5. 5:19; five nineteen; 19 minutes after five

LESSON CONTINUES

North Carolina Standards Goal 2 The learner will recognize and use standard units of metric and customary measurement. *also* maintains (2) 2.02

COMMON ERROR ALERT

Students may confuse the minute and hour hands.

9:20

Correct by pointing out that the word *hour* is shorter than the word *minute*. Likewise, the hour hand is shorter than the minute hand. Have students use clocks with movable hands to show specified times between one hour and the next.

- *Have students read the Half Hour and Quarter Hour section.*

  REASONING Look at the clock showing 7:30. Explain why the time can be read as "half" past seven. The minute hand moved halfway from 7:00 to 8:00.

  REASONING When would you want to estimate the time? Possible answer: when it's almost time to go somewhere; when it's almost dinnertime

3 PRACTICE

Guided Practice

Do Check Exercises 1–5 with your students. Identify students who are having difficulty and choose appropriate lesson resources to provide assistance.

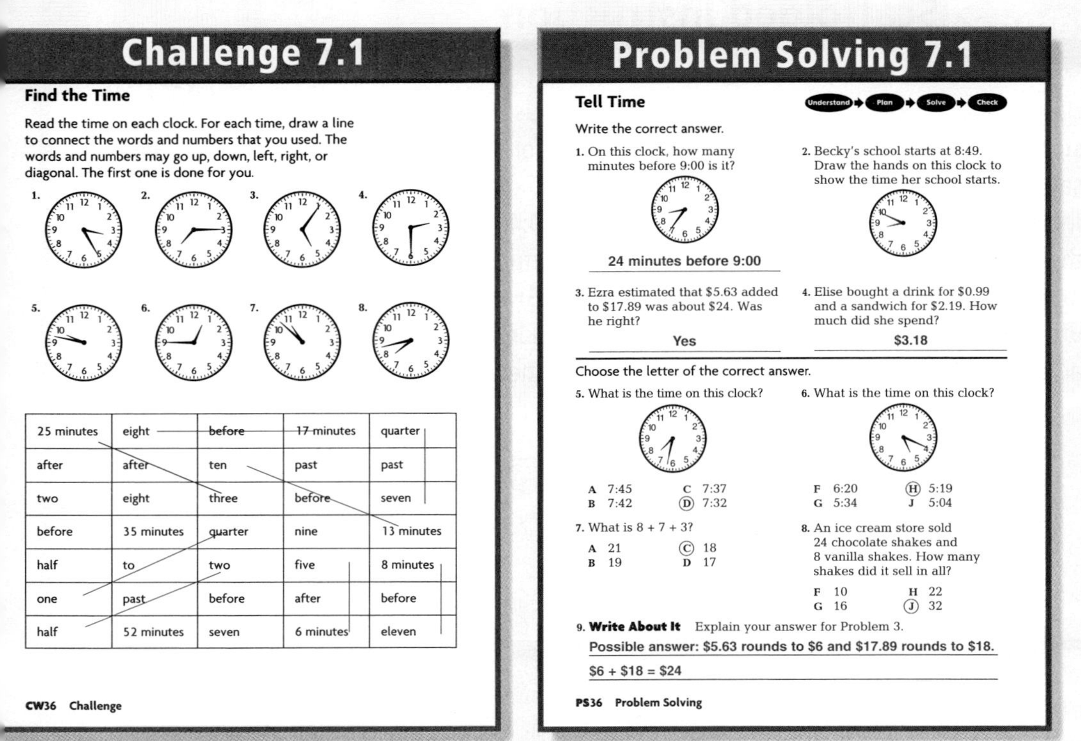

Challenge 7.1

Find the Time

Read the time on each clock. For each time, draw a line to connect the words and numbers that you used. The words and numbers may go up, down, left, right, or diagonal. The first one is done for you.

25 minutes	eight	before	17 minutes	quarter
after	after	ten	past	past
two	eight	three	before	seven
before	35 minutes	quarter	nine	13 minutes
half	to	two	five	8 minutes
one	past	before	after	before
half	52 minutes	seven	6 minutes	eleven

CW36 Challenge

Problem Solving 7.1

Tell Time

Understand → Plan → Solve → Check

Write the correct answer.

1. On this clock, how many minutes before 9:00 is it?
   24 minutes before 9:00

2. Becky's school starts at 8:49. Draw the hands on this clock to show the time her school starts.

3. Ezra estimated that \$5.63 added to \$17.89 was about \$24. Was he right?
   Yes

4. Elise bought a drink for \$0.99 and a sandwich for \$2.19. How much did she spend?
   \$3.18

Choose the letter of the correct answer.

5. What is the time on this clock?
   A 7:45 C 7:37
   B 7:42 (D) 7:32

6. What is the time on this clock?
   F 6:20 (H) 5:19
   G 5:34 J 5:04

7. What is 8 + 7 + 3?
   A 21 (C) 18
   B 19 D 17

8. An ice cream store sold 24 chocolate shakes and 8 vanilla shakes. How many shakes did it sell in all?
   F 10 H 22
   G 16 (J) 32

9. **Write About It** Explain your answer for Problem 3.
   Possible answer: \$5.63 rounds to \$6 and \$17.89 rounds to \$18. \$6 + \$18 = \$24

PS36 Problem Solving

Independent Practice

Note that Exercise 24 is a **multistep or strategy problem.** Assign Exercises 6–28.

For Exercises 6–9, remind students that counting by fives and ones can help them find the time before and after the hour.

For Exercises 10–13, students may wish to show the times on clocks with movable hands, and then count by fives and ones to find the number of minutes before or after the hour.

For Exercises 14–19, tell students that some of the clocks will be used more than once.

MULTISTEP OR STRATEGY PROBLEM To solve Exercise 24, students will need to determine that a half hour is the same as 30 minutes. Next, students will compare 28 minutes and 30 minutes. Since $30 > 28$, Rob has the longer walk.

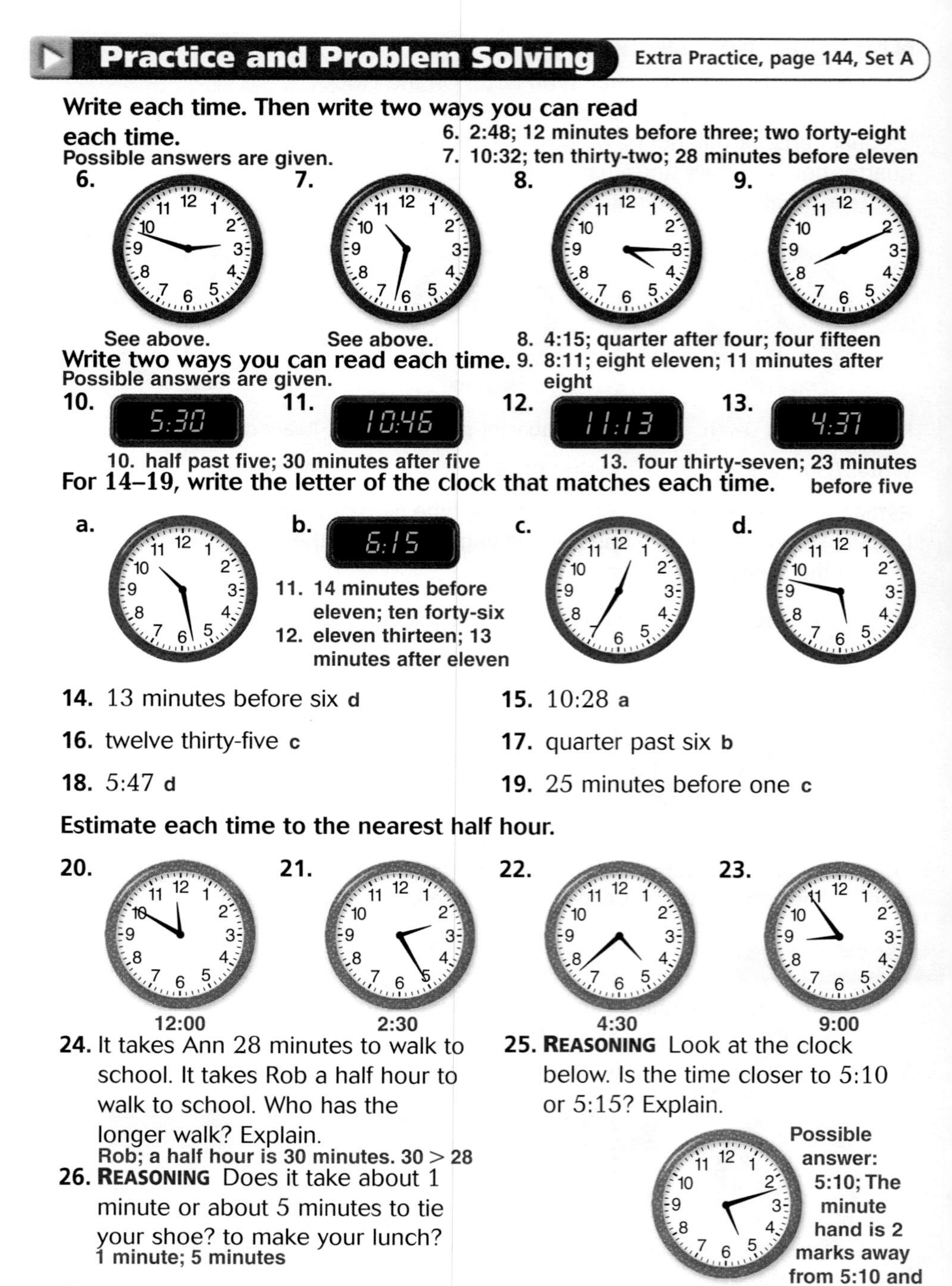

Practice and Problem Solving Extra Practice, page 144, Set A

Write each time. Then write two ways you can read each time.
Possible answers are given.

6. 7. 8. 9.

See above. See above.

6. 2:48; 12 minutes before three; two forty-eight
7. 10:32; ten thirty-two; 28 minutes before eleven
8. 4:15; quarter after four; four fifteen
9. 8:11; eight eleven; 11 minutes after eight

Write two ways you can read each time.
Possible answers are given.

10. 5:30 11. 10:46 12. 11:13 13. 4:37

10. half past five; 30 minutes after five
11. 14 minutes before eleven; ten forty-six
12. eleven thirteen; 13 minutes after eleven
13. four thirty-seven; 23 minutes before five

For 14–19, write the letter of the clock that matches each time.

a. b. 6:15 c. d.

14. 13 minutes before six **d**
15. 10:28 **a**
16. twelve thirty-five **c**
17. quarter past six **b**
18. 5:47 **d**
19. 25 minutes before one **c**

Estimate each time to the nearest half hour.

20. 12:00
21. 2:30
22. 4:30
23. 9:00

24. It takes Ann 28 minutes to walk to school. It takes Rob a half hour to walk to school. Who has the longer walk? Explain.
Rob; a half hour is 30 minutes. $30 > 28$

25. **REASONING** Look at the clock below. Is the time closer to 5:10 or 5:15? Explain.

Possible answer: 5:10; The minute hand is 2 marks away from 5:10 and 3 marks away from 5:15.

26. **REASONING** Does it take about 1 minute or about 5 minutes to tie your shoe? to make your lunch?
1 minute; 5 minutes

130

Alternative Teaching Strategy

Scaffolded Instruction

PROFESSIONAL DEVELOPMENT

PURPOSE Students will model different times on a clock.

MATERIALS *For each student* clock with movable hands

- Have students identify the hour hand and minute hand on their clocks. Explain that in one minute the minute hand moves from one tick mark to the next. Explain that the hour hand moves much slower than the minute hand. In one hour, the minute hand moves all the way around the clockface; however, in one hour, the hour hand moves from one number to the next.
- Have students point to the 12. Then have students move their finger to the 1 and say "5." Have students skip-count by fives as they move from one number to the next. Ask: How many minutes are marked around the clockface? 60 minutes What is another name for this amount of time? 1 hour

- List the following times for students to show on their clocks: 12:05, 2:33, 9:45, and 11:37. You may wish to have students work in pairs.
- Give students the opportunity to choose some times on their own and show these times on their clocks.

27. Joni needs to leave at about 5:30. If the minute hand is on the 2, is it closer to 5:00 or 5:30? **5:00**

28. Mr. Olsen bought 8 copies of the newspaper for his class. He spent $16. How much did each newspaper cost? **$2 each**

Getting Ready for the EOG Test

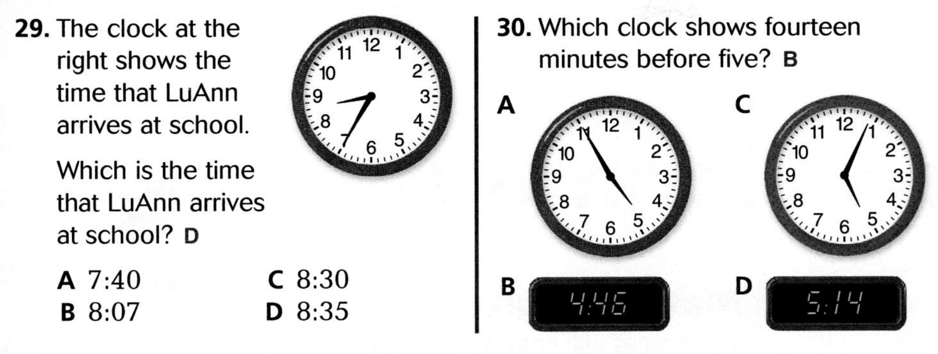

29. The clock at the right shows the time that LuAnn arrives at school.

Which is the time that LuAnn arrives at school? **D**

A 7:40 **C** 8:30
B 8:07 **D** 8:35

30. Which clock shows fourteen minutes before five? **B**

A C

B 4:46 D 5:14

Problem Solving Thinker's Corner

VISUAL THINKING You can describe the direction of turns by knowing how the hands of a clock move.

Think:
Turn to
the right.

Think: Turn
to the
left.

The turns that the hands of a clock make are called **clockwise** turns.

Turns in the opposite direction are called **counterclockwise** turns.

Describe each turn. Write *clockwise* or *counterclockwise*.

1. 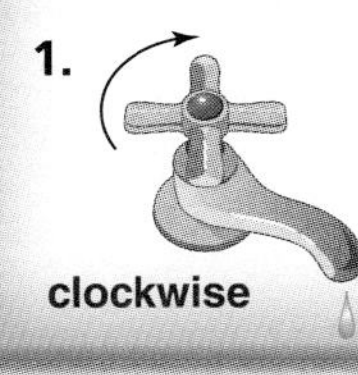
clockwise

2. **counterclockwise**

3. 
clockwise

Problem Solving Thinker's Corner

- *Have students read the Thinker's Corner. Explain that when* counter *is the first part of a word, it can mean* "opposite" *or* "against."
Which exercises have a picture of a clockwise turn? Exercises 1 and 3
How do you know that these are clockwise turns? The turns are to the right, like the turns made by the hands on a clock.
Which exercise shows a counterclockwise turn? Explain. Exercise 2; the turn is the opposite direction of the turns made by the hands on a clock.

4 ASSESS

Summarize the lesson by having students:

Discuss How would you draw the hour hand and minute hand on a clockface to show the time 6:43? Possible answer: the hour hand would be between the 6 and the 7. The minute hand would be pointing at the third tick mark past the 8.

Write Draw a clockface showing 3:18. Write the time in words in two ways. eighteen minutes after three, three eighteen

LESSON QUIZ

Read and write each time.

Transparency 7.1

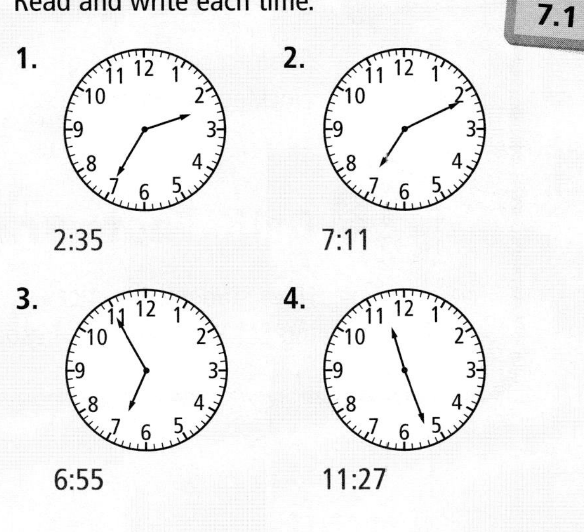

1. 2:35
2. 7:11
3. 6:55
4. 11:27

Lesson 7.2

A.M. and P.M.

Lesson Planning

Objective To write and identify times as A.M. or P.M.

NCTM Standards

4. Measurement
6. Problem Solving
7. Reasoning and Proof
8. Communication
10. Representation

Math Background

These ideas will help students understand how to write and identify times as A.M. or P.M.:

- There are 24 hours in one day.
- The 12 hours between midnight and noon are A.M.
- The 12 hours between noon and midnight are P.M.

Vocabulary

A.M. the times from midnight to noon

P.M. the times from noon to midnight

noon 12:00 in the day

midnight 12:00 at night

Warm-Up Resources

Number of the Day

Subtract 5 from the greatest number that is on a clockface. Write the new number. 7

Daily Facts Practice

Have students practice addition facts by completing Set B of *Teacher's Resource Book*, p. TR88.

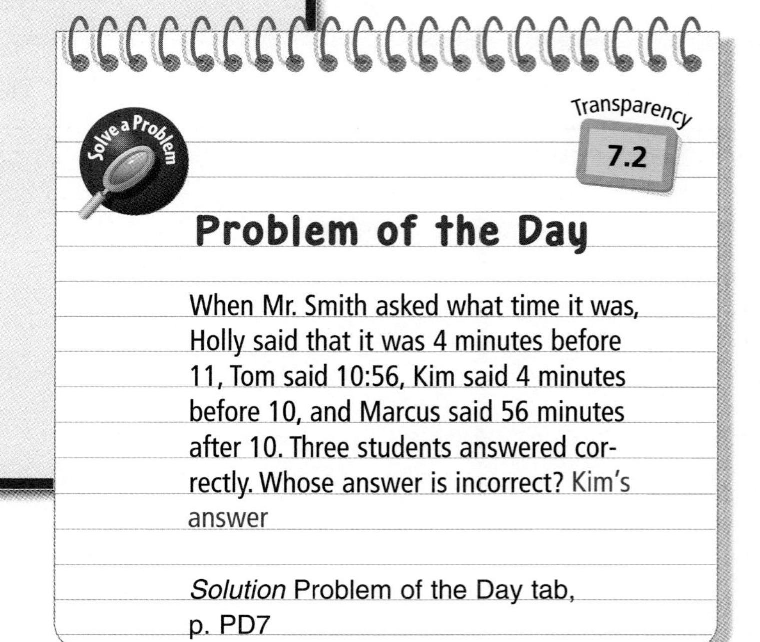

Problem of the Day

When Mr. Smith asked what time it was, Holly said that it was 4 minutes before 11, Tom said 10:56, Kim said 4 minutes before 10, and Marcus said 56 minutes after 10. Three students answered correctly. Whose answer is incorrect? Kim's answer

Solution Problem of the Day tab, p. PD7

Intervention and Extension Resources

Alternative Teaching Strategy

MATERIALS *For each pair* clocks with movable hands, paper

Help students **identify time as A.M. or P.M.** On a slip of paper, have one student write a time of day and an activity that takes place at that time and show it to his or her partner. Make sure that students write A.M. or P.M.

Ask the partner to read the time aloud in two ways and then to show it on the clockface. Have students reverse roles and continue for several rounds.

AUDITORY, KINESTHETIC

BODILY/KINESTHETIC

Multistep and Strategy Problems

The following multistep or strategy problem is provided in Lesson 7.2:

Page	Item
133	16

Vocabulary Strategy

Help students **reinforce the concept of A.M. and P.M.** Have students write a short story using the terms *A.M., P.M., noon*, and *midnight*. Ask students to take turns reading their stories aloud to the class.

VISUAL

INTRAPERSONAL/INTROSPECTIVE

Early Finishers

Challenge students to **make a list of school activities that happen in the A.M. and P.M.** Have students first make a schedule of school activities. From the schedule, have them choose activities that happen during A.M. hours and during P.M. hours, and ask them to write the time each activity occurs. Check students' work.

VISUAL

LOGICAL/MATHEMATICAL

Lesson 7.2 Organizer

Objective To write and identify times as A.M. or P.M.

Vocabulary A.M., P.M., **noon**, **midnight**

1 INTRODUCE

QUICK REVIEW provides review of prerequisite skills.

WHY LEARN THIS? You can tell if an appointment or game is in the morning or afternoon. *Share the lesson objective with students.*

2 TEACH

Guided Instruction

- *Ask students to read the Learn section.*
  What kinds of activities happen in the A.M.? Possible answers: the sun comes up, I eat breakfast, I take the bus to school
  What things happen in the P.M.? Possible answers: the sun goes down, I eat dinner, I go to sleep
- *Ask students to read the Math Idea.*
  What are some different ways you could read 12:30 A.M.? Possible answers: half past midnight, thirty minutes after midnight, twelve thirty A.M.

3 PRACTICE

Guided Practice

Do Check Exercises 1–6 with your students. Identify students who are having difficulty and choose appropriate lesson resources to provide assistance.

LESSON 2

A.M. and P.M.

Quick Review
Possible answers given.
Write one way to read each time.
1. 3:22 22 minutes after three
2. 12:34 26 minutes before one
3. 9:45 quarter to ten
4. 5:10 10 minutes after five
5. 11:55 5 minutes before twelve

VOCABULARY
A.M. noon
P.M. midnight

Learn

IT'S ABOUT TIME Using A.M. and P.M. helps you know what time of the day or night it is. **A.M.** is used for the hours from 12 midnight to 12 noon. **P.M.** is used for the hours from 12 noon to 12 midnight.

12:00 in the day is **noon**.
12:00 at night is **midnight**.

Here are some ways to read and write times.

quarter to midnight
eleven forty-five P.M.
11:45 P.M.

quarter past seven
seven fifteen A.M.
7:15 A.M.

half past three
three thirty P.M.
3:30 P.M.

MATH IDEA The hours between midnight and noon are A.M. hours. The hours between noon and midnight are P.M. hours.

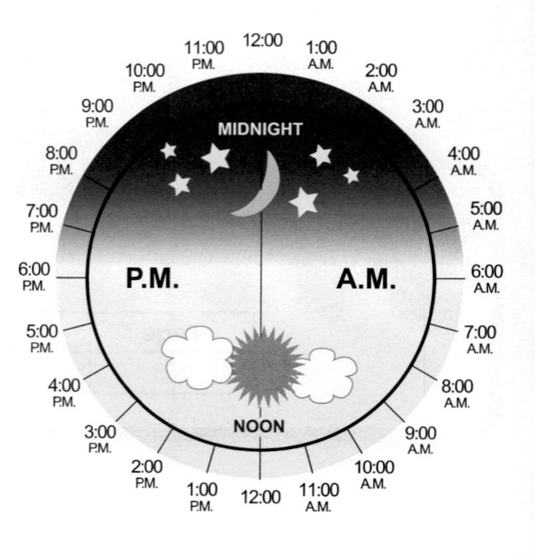

Check

1. **List** three things that you do in the A.M. hours. **Possible answers: sleep, read, go to school**
2. **Name** something you do at 9:00 A.M. and something you do at 9:00 P.M. Explain how these times are different. **Possible answer: Go to school; go to sleep; 9:00 A.M. comes between midnight and noon; 9:00 P.M. comes between noon and midnight.**

132

Reteach 7.2

A.M. and P.M.

A day has 24 hours.

A new day starts just after midnight. The hours from midnight to noon are **A.M.**

The hours from noon to midnight are **P.M.** A day ends at midnight.

Marcie gets on the school bus at 8:05 A.M. The bus comes at five minutes after eight.

Kyle eats dinner with his family at 6:15 P.M. Dinner is ready at quarter past six.

Here is a diagram of one day.

Midnight	Sunrise	Noon	Sunset	Midnight
12:00	6:00 A.M.	12:00	6:00 P.M.	12:00

Write the time, using A.M. or P.M.

1. recess at school **2:15 P.M.**
2. eat breakfast **7:30 A.M.**
3. bedtime **8:45 P.M.**
4. sound asleep **12:06 A.M.**

Write two ways you can read each time. Then write the time, using A.M. or P.M. **Possible answers are given.**

5. Saturday morning basketball game **quarter after eleven; eleven fifteen A.M.; 11:15 A.M.**
6. a trip to the shoe store **one-thirty P.M.; half past one; 1:30 P.M.**

Reteach **RW37**

Practice 7.2

A.M. and P.M.

Write the time, using A.M. or P.M.

1. still sleeping **5:12 A.M.**
2. dentist appointment **10:30 A.M.**
3. paint a picture **3:17 P.M.**
4. lunch time **12:06 P.M.**
5. the sunrise **6:05 A.M.**
6. this is a new day **12:01 A.M.**
7. this day is almost over **11:44 P.M.**
8. do the dishes **5:36 P.M.**
9. eat breakfast **8:12 A.M.**

Mixed Review

Write + or − to make the number sentence true.

10. 36 (−) 27 = 9
11. 16 = 14 (+) 2
12. 35 (+) 18 = 53
13. 15 = 22 (−) 7

Subtract.

14. $1.68 − $0.09 = **$1.59**
15. $5.62 − $3.17 = **$2.45**
16. $8.13 − $3.59 = **$4.54**
17. $12.72 − $ 7.49 = **$5.23**

Practice **PW37**

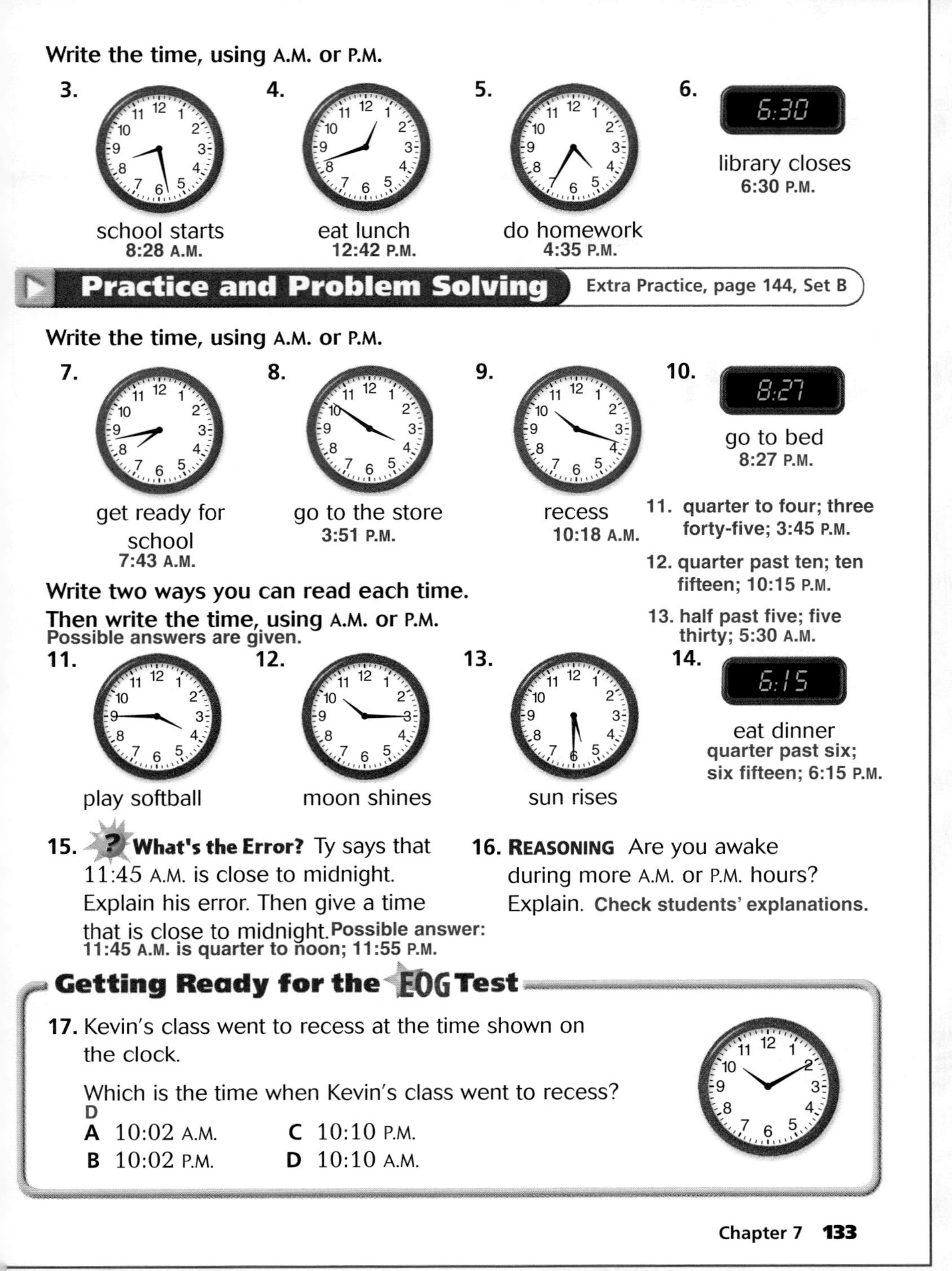

Write the time, using A.M. or P.M.

3. school starts 8:28 A.M.
4. eat lunch 12:42 P.M.
5. do homework 4:35 P.M.
6. 6:30 library closes 6:30 P.M.

Practice and Problem Solving

Extra Practice, page 144, Set B

Write the time, using A.M. or P.M.

7. get ready for school 7:43 A.M.
8. go to the store 3:51 P.M.
9. recess 10:18 A.M.
10. 8:27 go to bed 8:27 P.M.

Write two ways you can read each time. Then write the time, using A.M. or P.M. Possible answers are given.

11. play softball
12. moon shines
13. sun rises
14. 6:15 eat dinner quarter past six; six fifteen; 6:15 P.M.

11. quarter to four; three forty-five; 3:45 P.M.
12. quarter past ten; ten fifteen; 10:15 P.M.
13. half past five; five thirty; 5:30 A.M.

15. **What's the Error?** Ty says that 11:45 A.M. is close to midnight. Explain his error. Then give a time that is close to midnight. Possible answer: 11:45 A.M. is quarter to noon; 11:55 P.M.

16. **REASONING** Are you awake during more A.M. or P.M. hours? Explain. Check students' explanations.

Getting Ready for the EOG Test

17. Kevin's class went to recess at the time shown on the clock.

Which is the time when Kevin's class went to recess? D

A 10:02 A.M.
B 10:02 P.M.
C 10:10 P.M.
D 10:10 A.M.

Chapter 7 133

COMMON ERROR ALERT

Students may confuse the terms *quarter to* and *quarter past.* You may correct this by having students shade in and label quarters of an hour on the Analog Clockfaces in *Teacher's Resource Book*, p. TR49.

Independent Practice

Note that Exercise 16 is a **multistep or strategy problem.** Assign Exercises 7–16.

4 ASSESS

Summarize the lesson by having students:

DISCUSS John has a music lesson at 4:10. How do you know if that time is A.M. or P.M.? Possible answer: The time is P.M. because 4:10 P.M. is in the day. John is probably asleep at 4:10 A.M.

WRITE List two ways to read the time 10:45 A.M. Then describe an activity that could happen at that time. Possible answers: ten forty-five A.M., quarter to eleven; math class begins

LESSON QUIZ

Transparency 7.2

Write the time using A.M. or P.M.

1. 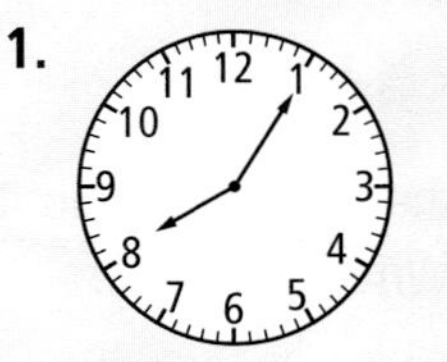
school begins
8:05 A.M.

2. 
dinner time
5:30 P.M.

3. 
I am asleep.
3:00 A.M.

4. 
halfway through a school day
11:15 A.M.

North Carolina Standards Goal 2 The learner will recognize and use standard units of metric and customary measurement.

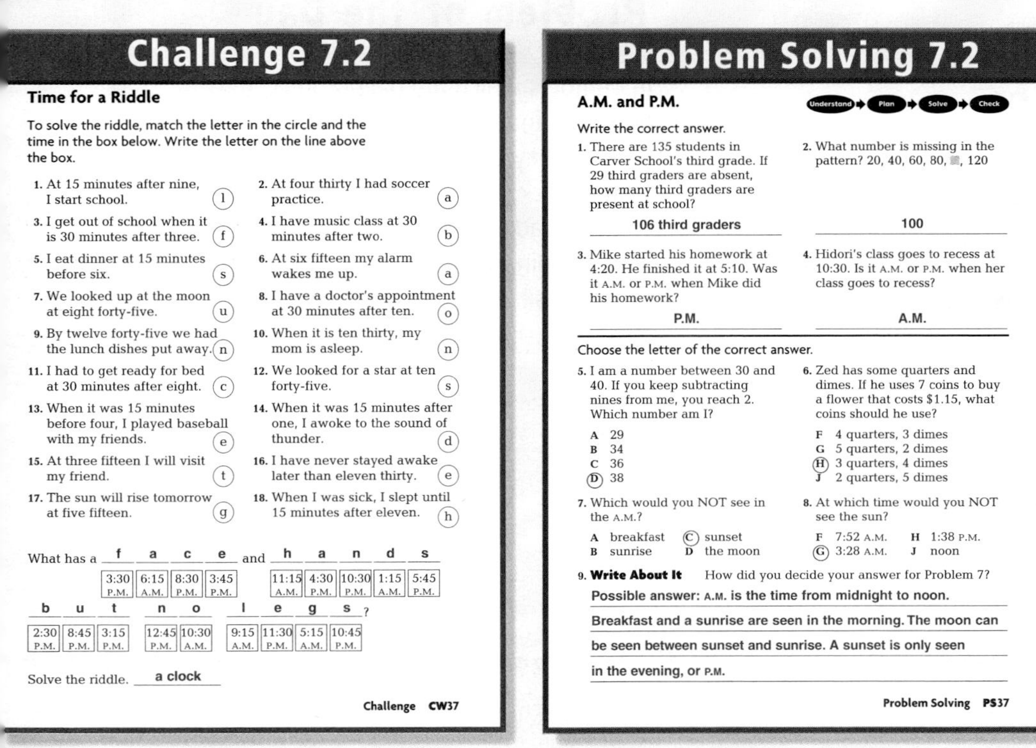

Challenge 7.2

Time for a Riddle

To solve the riddle, match the letter in the circle and the time in the box below. Write the letter on the line above the box.

1. At 15 minutes after nine, I start school. (l)
2. At four thirty I had soccer practice. (a)
3. I get out of school when it is 30 minutes after three. (f)
4. I have music class at 30 minutes after two. (b)
5. I eat dinner at 15 minutes before six. (s)
6. At six fifteen my alarm wakes me up. (a)
7. We looked up at the moon at eight forty-five. (u)
8. I have a doctor's appointment at 30 minutes after ten. (o)
9. By twelve forty-five we had the lunch dishes put away. (n)
10. When it is ten thirty, my mom is asleep. (n)
11. I had to get ready for bed at 30 minutes after eight. (c)
12. We looked for a star at ten forty-five. (s)
13. When it was 15 minutes before four, I played baseball with my friends. (e)
14. When it was 15 minutes after one, I awoke to the sound of thunder. (d)
15. At three fifteen I will visit my friend. (t)
16. I have never stayed awake later than eleven thirty. (e)
17. The sun will rise tomorrow at five fifteen. (g)
18. When I was sick, I slept until 15 minutes after eleven. (h)

What has a f a c e and h a n d s

f	a	c	e		h	a	n	d	s
3:30 P.M.	6:15 A.M.	8:30 P.M.	3:45 P.M.	and	11:15 A.M.	4:30 P.M.	10:30 P.M.	1:15 A.M.	5:45 P.M.

b u t n o l e g s?

b	u	t		n	o		l	e	g	s
2:30 P.M.	8:45 P.M.	3:15 P.M.		12:45 P.M.	10:30 A.M.		9:15 A.M.	11:30 P.M.	5:15 A.M.	10:45 P.M.

Solve the riddle. a clock

Challenge CW37

Problem Solving 7.2

A.M. and P.M.

Understand → Plan → Solve → Check

Write the correct answer.

1. There are 135 students in Carver School's third grade. If 29 third graders are absent, how many third graders are present at school?
106 third graders

2. What number is missing in the pattern? 20, 40, 60, 80, ■, 120
100

3. Mike started his homework at 4:20. He finished it at 5:10. Was it A.M. or P.M. when Mike did his homework?
P.M.

4. Hidori's class goes to recess at 10:30. Is it A.M. or P.M. when her class goes to recess?
A.M.

Choose the letter of the correct answer.

5. I am a number between 30 and 40. If you keep subtracting nines from me, you reach 2. Which number am I?
A 29
B 34
C 36
(D) 38

6. Zed has some quarters and dimes. If he uses 7 coins to buy a flower that costs $1.15, what coins should he use?
F 4 quarters, 3 dimes
G 5 quarters, 2 dimes
(H) 3 quarters, 4 dimes
J 2 quarters, 5 dimes

7. Which would you NOT see in the A.M.?
A breakfast
B sunrise
(C) sunset
D the moon

8. At which time would you NOT see the sun?
F 7:52 A.M.
(G) 3:28 A.M.
H 1:38 P.M.
J noon

9. **Write About It** How did you decide your answer for Problem 7?
Possible answer: A.M. is the time from midnight to noon. Breakfast and a sunrise are seen in the morning. The moon can be seen between sunset and sunrise. A sunset is only seen in the evening, or P.M.

Problem Solving PS37

Lesson 7.3

Elapsed Time

Lesson Planning

Objective To use a clock to measure elapsed time

Materials *For each student* clock with movable hands

NCTM Standards
1. Number and Operations
4. Measurement
6. Problem Solving
8. Communication
10. Representation

Math Background

These ideas will help students understand how to measure elapsed time:

- Elapsed time is the amount of time that passes from the start of an activity to the end of that activity.
- Counting by fives on a clock can help you find elapsed time.
- If you know the time an activity begins and the elapsed time, you can find the end time in hours and minutes by counting on.

Vocabulary

elapsed time the amount of time that passes from the start of an activity to the end of that activity

Warm-Up Resources

Build Number Sense

Number of the Day

Transparency 7.3

I am the number of minutes in three quarters of an hour. What number am I? 45

Daily Facts Practice

Have students practice addition and subtraction facts by completing Set C of *Teacher's Resource Book*, p. TR88.

Solve a Problem

Transparency 7.3

Problem of the Day

In numbers which are palindromes, the digits are in the same order from left to right as they are from right to left. On a digital clock, 1:01 is a palindrome number. We read: 1 minute after 1. Write at least 5 palindrome numbers for a digital clock. Possible answers: 2:32, 3:13, 4:24, 5:45, 6:56, 11:11, 12:21

Solution Problem of the Day tab, p. PD7

Intervention and Extension Resources

Alternative Teaching Strategy

MATERIALS *For each group* clocks with movable hands

Help students **practice finding elapsed time**. Organize students into groups to play a game. Distribute clocks to each group.

Read a start time and an end time aloud to students. You may want to vary how you read the times aloud.

Have students work together to find the elapsed time. Have each group choose a student to give the answer. The first team to get the correct answer receives 1 point. The group that reaches 5 points first wins.

KINESTHETIC

BODILY/KINESTHETIC

ESOL/ESL

Help students **build understanding of finding elapsed time**. Have several students work together to write sentences with missing times. Provide this example: Math begins at ______. Recess is ______ later. What time is recess? ______

- Have students fill in each blank.
- Encourage students to write other incomplete sentences involving time.
- Have students trade with a partner, complete, and share their completed sentences. Check students' work.

VISUAL

VERBAL/LINGUISTIC

Multistep and Strategy Problems

The following multistep or strategy problem is provided in Lesson 7.3:

Page	Item
135	8

Advanced Learners

Challenge students to **solve elapsed time problems**. Problems should involve longer periods of time in a day and times that do not use multiples of five.

Ask the following questions:

- School starts at 7:55 A.M. and ends at 2:32 P.M. How long is the school day? 6 hours 37 minutes
- Jane goes to sleep at 9:48 P.M. and wakes up at 6:30 A.M. For how long does she sleep? 8 hours 42 minutes
- Mr. Taylor's meeting lasted 7 hours and 43 minutes. The meeting started at 10:25 A.M. When did the meeting end? 6:08 P.M.

AUDITORY

LOGICAL/MATHEMATICAL

Technology Link

Intervention, *Skills 48–50*

Math Jingles® CD 3–4 • *Track 4*

Harcourt Mega Math Country Countdown, *Clock-a-Doodle-Doo,* Level K

Harcourt Mega Math The Number Games, *Tiny's Think Tank,* Level D

Lesson 7.3 Organizer

Objective To use a clock to measure elapsed time

Vocabulary elapsed time

Materials *For each student* clock with movable hands

1 INTRODUCE

QUICK REVIEW provides review of prerequisite skills.

WHY LEARN THIS? You can find out how long it takes to complete an activity. *Share the lesson objective with students.*

2 TEACH

Guided Instruction

- *Have students read the Explore section.*

  Why do you count by fives between 8:15 and 8:45? Possible answer: It is faster to count by fives than to count by ones.

  When an activity ends more than an hour after it begins, should you only count by fives to find the elapsed time? Explain. No, it is better to count by hours first and then by fives to count the additional minutes.

  REASONING An activity starts at 11:00 A.M. and lasts 2 hours. Will you use A.M. or P.M. when you write the end time? P.M.

MODIFYING INSTRUCTION Have students use the Analog Clockfaces in *Teacher's Resource Book*, p. TR49.

3 PRACTICE

Guided Practice

Do Try It Exercises a–f with your students. Identify students who are having difficulty and choose appropriate lesson resources to provide assistance.

LESSON 3

HANDS ON

Elapsed Time

Explore

Abby and her father played basketball from 8:15 P.M. to 8:45 P.M. How long did they play basketball?

Activity

Move the minute hand on your clock to find the elapsed time.

Start: 8:15

Count the minutes: 30 minutes

So, they played basketball for 30 minutes.

Elapsed time is the amount of time that passes from the start of an activity to the end of that activity.

- Find the elapsed time from 1:15 P.M. to 1:45 P.M. 30 minutes, or a half hour

Try It

Use a clock to find the elapsed time.

d. 1 hour 30 minutes, or one and a half hours

a. start: 9:15 A.M.
end: 10:00 A.M.
45 minutes

b. start: 3:45 P.M.
end: 5:45 P.M.
2 hours

c. start: 10:00 A.M.
end: 11:15 A.M.
1 hour 15 minutes

d. start: 11:45 A.M.
end: 1:15 P.M.
See above.

e. start: 5:10 P.M.
end: 9:20 P.M.
4 hours 10 minutes

f. start: 11:30 P.M.
end: 12:30 A.M.
1 hour

The start time was 9:15. The end time is 10:00. How much time has elapsed? 45 minutes

134

Quick Review

Skip-count by fives.

1. 5, 10, 15, ■ 20
2. 15, 20, 25, ■ 30
3. 30, 35, 40, ■ 45
4. 10, 15, 20, ■ 25
5. 40, 45, 50, ■ 55

VOCABULARY

elapsed time

MATERIALS

clocks with movable hands

Technology Link

More Practice: Harcourt Mega Math Country Countdown, *Clock-a-Doodle-Doo*, Level K

Reteach 7.3

Elapsed Time

Elapsed time is the time that passes from the start of an activity to the end of that activity. To find the elapsed time, count the number of minutes between the start time and the end time.

Start: 6:15 End: 6:45 Elapsed time: 30 minutes

Remember:
- When the minute hand moves from one number to the next number on the clock, five minutes have passed.

Find the elapsed time.

	Start	End	Elapsed Time
1.	6:00	6:15	15 minutes
2.	6:45	7:30	45 minutes
3.	10:00	11:15	1 hour 15 minutes
4.	5:30	6:00	30 minutes

RW38 Reteach

Practice 7.3

Elapsed Time

Use a clock to find the elapsed time.

1. start: 4:15 P.M. end: 4:30 P.M. 15 min
2. start: 5:30 P.M. end: 7:50 P.M. 2 hrs 20 min
3. start: 3:30 A.M. end: 4:15 A.M. 45 min

Use a clock to find the end time.

4. starting time: 4:15 P.M. elapsed time: 30 minutes 4:45 P.M.
5. starting time: 2:00 A.M. elapsed time: 3 hours and 30 minutes 5:30 A.M.
6. starting time: 7:30 A.M. elapsed time: 45 minutes 8:15 A.M.
7. starting time: 3:45 P.M. elapsed time: 5 hours 8:45 P.M.

Mixed Review

Write <, >, or = in each ◯.

8. 1,980 (=) 1,980
9. 13,886 (>) 13,688
10. 6,807 (<) 6,870
11. 499 − 107 (>) 307

Write in standard form.

12. six thousand, three hundred forty-two 6,342
13. 10,000 + 5,000 + 900 + 30 + 2 15,932
14. 20,000 + 7,000 + 400 + 80 + 7 27,487
15. eighty-four thousand, thirty-three 84,033

PW38 Practice

Connect

Soccer practice starts at 11:00 A.M. It lasts 2 hours 15 minutes. Use your clock to find the time that practice ends.

Start: 11:00

Count the hours.

Count the minutes.

So, practice ends at 1:15 P.M.

MATH IDEA If you know when an activity starts and how long it takes, you can find the time it ends.

Practice and Problem Solving

Use a clock to find the elapsed time.

1. start: 7:00 A.M.
   end: 10:00 A.M.
   3 hours
2. start: 5:15 P.M.
   end: 7:20 P.M.
   2 hours 5 minutes
3. start: 1:30 P.M.
   end: 2:15 P.M.
   45 minutes

Use a clock to find the end time.

4. start: 4:15 P.M.
   elapsed time: 1 hour 15 minutes **5:30 P.M.**
5. start: 11:45 A.M.
   elapsed time: 65 minutes
   12:50 P.M.
6. **What's the Question?** The basketball game started at 11:30 A.M. It ended at 1:15 P.M. The answer is 1 hour 45 minutes.
   Possible question: How long did the game last?
7. **Write About It** Explain how you can use a clock to find the elapsed time from 10:30 A.M. to 1:15 P.M. **Check students' answers. The elapsed time is 2 hours 45 minutes.**

Getting Ready for the EOG Test

8. Tia went to Splash Time for 30 minutes. She rested for 15 minutes, then went home. At what time did she go home? **B**

   A 11:15 A.M.
   B 5:00 P.M.
   C 4:45 P.M.
   D 11:30 A.M.

SWIMMING POOL SESSIONS	
Session	**Start Time**
Minnow Team	11:00 A.M.
Dolphin Team	2:30 P.M.
Splash Time	4:15 P.M.

Independent Practice

Note that Exercise 8 is a **multistep or strategy problem.** Assign Exercises 1–8.

To help students with Exercises 4–7, have them review the steps in the Connect activity.

Summarize the lesson by having students:

DISCUSS If math class started at 10:15 A.M. and ended at 11:00 A.M., how would you find how long it lasted? Possible answer: Count by fives from 10:15 to 11:00.

WRITE You know that an activity starts at 6:45 P.M. and ends 2 hours and 20 minutes later. At what time does the activity end? Describe the steps you took to find the answer. 9:05 P.M.; Start at 6:45, count 2 hours to 8:45, count by fives to 20 minutes, end at 9:05.

LESSON QUIZ

Transparency 7.3

Use a clock to find the elapsed time.

1. start: 9:30 A.M.
   end: 9:50 A.M.
   20 minutes
2. start: 2:00 P.M.
   end: 3:15 P.M.
   1 hour 15 minutes
3. start: 6:15 P.M.
   end: 7:25 P.M.
   1 hour 10 minutes
4. start: 11:45 A.M.
   end: 12:30 P.M.
   45 minutes

North Carolina Standards 2.01 Solve problems using measurement concepts and procedures volving: a) Elapsed time.

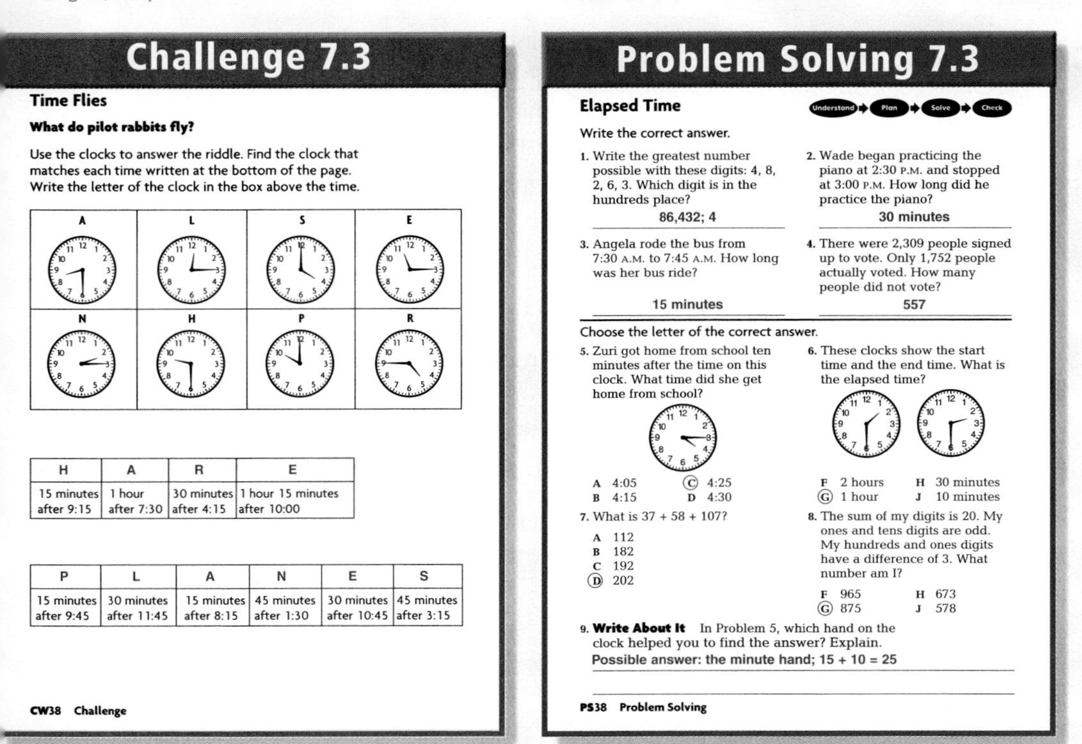

Challenge 7.3

Time Flies

What do pilot rabbits fly?

Use the clocks to answer the riddle. Find the clock that matches each time written at the bottom of the page. Write the letter of the clock in the box above the time.

A	L	S	E
N	H	P	R

H	A	R	E
15 minutes after 9:15	1 hour after 7:30	30 minutes after 4:15	1 hour 15 minutes after 10:00

P	L	A	N	E	S
15 minutes after 9:45	30 minutes after 11:45	15 minutes after 8:15	45 minutes after 1:30	30 minutes after 10:45	45 minutes after 3:15

CW38 Challenge

Problem Solving 7.3

Elapsed Time

Understand ➔ Plan ➔ Solve ➔ Check

Write the correct answer.

1. Write the greatest number possible with these digits: 4, 8, 2, 6, 3. Which digit is in the hundreds place?
   86,432; 4
2. Wade began practicing the piano at 2:30 P.M. and stopped at 3:00 P.M. How long did he practice the piano?
   30 minutes
3. Angela rode the bus from 7:30 A.M. to 7:45 A.M. How long was her bus ride?
   15 minutes
4. There were 2,309 people signed up to vote. Only 1,752 people actually voted. How many people did not vote?
   557

Choose the letter of the correct answer.

5. Zuri got home from school ten minutes after the time on this clock. What time did she get home from school?
   A 4:05
   B 4:15
   (C) 4:25
   D 4:30
6. These clocks show the start time and the end time. What is the elapsed time?
   F 2 hours
   (G) 1 hour
   H 30 minutes
   J 10 minutes
7. What is 37 + 58 + 107?
   A 112
   B 182
   C 192
   (D) 202
8. The sum of my digits is 20. My ones and tens digits are odd. My hundreds and ones digits have a difference of 3. What number am I?
   F 965
   (G) 875
   H 673
   J 578
9. **Write About It** In Problem 5, which hand on the clock helped you to find the answer? Explain.
   Possible answer: the minute hand; 15 + 10 = 25

PS38 Problem Solving

Lesson 7.4

Use a Schedule

Lesson Planning

Objective To use a schedule to determine elapsed time

NCTM Standards

1. Number and Operations
4. Measurement
6. Problem Solving
8. Communication
9. Connections
10. Representation

Math Background

These ideas will help students understand how to use a schedule:

- Count the hours and minutes between two times to find the elapsed time.
- From the start time, count on, using the elapsed time to find the end time.

Vocabulary

schedule a table that lists activities or events and the times they happen

Warm-Up Resources

Number of the Day

Think of the number of hours between noon and midnight, and double it. Write the new number. 24

Daily Facts Practice

Have students practice subtraction facts by completing Set D of *Teacher's Resource Book*, p. TR88.

Solve a Problem

Transparency 7.4

Problem of the Day

Lucas is painting a poster with the words HELP KEEP AMERICA GREEN on it. It takes him 5 minutes to paint each giant letter. If he starts at 10:15 A.M., will he be finished before lunch at noon? How do you know? Yes, he will be finished before noon; he will finish at 11:55 A.M.

Solution Problem of the Day tab, p. PD7

Intervention and Extension Resources

Alternative Teaching Strategy

MATERIALS *For each student* local TV listings from a newspaper or magazine

Help students **practice using a schedule**. Using the local television listings, have students record the following:

- The day, start time, and length of their favorite TV show
- The number of movies on TV Monday night between the hours of 6 and 11
- The start and end times of their favorite TV shows on Saturday

VISUAL

LOGICAL/MATHEMATICAL

Multistep and Strategy Problems

The following multistep or strategy problem is provided in Lesson 7.4:

Page	Item
137	14

Writing in Mathematics

MATERIALS *For each group* a variety of schedules, including train, bus, plane, TV, and movie schedules

Help students **reinforce the concept of using a schedule**. Distribute a few schedules to each group of students. Have students write 5 problems whose solutions require the use of a schedule. Collect each group's schedules and problems, and distribute them to another group to solve. Ask volunteers to share problems and solutions. Check students' work.

VISUAL

INTERPERSONAL/SOCIAL

Advanced Learners

Challenge students to **make schedules** for activities that they would like to learn or improve upon if they had extra time. Choices may include spelling, guitar playing, or playing soccer.

Then have students follow these steps:

- Select an activity.
- Make a schedule for one weekday and include two 10-minute periods for the new activity.
- Make a different schedule for a weekend day.

Have students share their activities and schedules. Check students' work.

VISUAL

LOGICAL/MATHEMATICAL

Lesson 7.4 Organizer

Objective To use a schedule to determine elapsed time

Vocabulary schedule

1 INTRODUCE

QUICK REVIEW provides review of prerequisite skills.

WHY LEARN THIS? You can plan how to spend your day. *Share the lesson objective with students.*

2 TEACH

Guided Instruction

- *Have students read the Learn section.*
  What do you need to know to finish Stacy's schedule? how long it takes Stacy to do her homework and what time she finishes walking the dog
- *Ask students to read the question about homework.*
  How would you count to find the elapsed time? Start at 4:05 P.M. and count 1 hour and then 5 minutes to get to 5:10 P.M.
- *Read the second question with students.*
  What information will help you find the end time for walking the dog? the start time and the elapsed time
- *Ask students to read the Math Idea.*
  REASONING What if Stacy plays outside for 30 minutes after walking her dog? What will the end time be? Explain. 6:05 P.M.; you know the start time is 5:35 P.M. Count by fives to 6:05 P.M.

3 PRACTICE

Guided Practice

Do Check Exercises 1–3 with your students. Identify students who are having difficulty and choose appropriate lesson resources to provide assistance.

LESSON 4 Use a Schedule

Quick Review

1. 15 + 5 = ■ **20**
2. 15 + ■ = 25 **10**
3. ■ + 15 = 30 **15**
4. 15 + 30 = ■ **45**
5. 30 + ■ = 45 **15**

VOCABULARY
schedule

Learn

RIGHT ON TIME A **schedule** is a table that lists activities or events and the times they happen.

You can use what you know about elapsed time to finish Stacy's schedule.

STACY'S SCHEDULE		
Activity	**Time**	**Elapsed Time**
Eat snack	3:45 P.M.–4:05 P.M.	20 minutes
Do homework	4:05 P.M.–5:10 P.M.	■
Walk dog	5:10 P.M.–■	25 minutes

How long will Stacy do homework?

Think: Find the elapsed time.
4:05 P.M. to 5:05 P.M. 1 hour
5:05 P.M. to 5:10 P.M. 5 minutes

So, Stacy will do homework for 1 hour 5 minutes.

When will Stacy walk her dog?

Think: Find the end time.
Start: 5:10 P.M.
Count on 25 minutes to 5:35 P.M.

So, Stacy will walk her dog from 5:10 P.M. to 5:35 P.M.

MATH IDEA You can use a schedule to find elapsed times of events. If you know the elapsed times, you can find start or end times on a schedule.

Check

1. **Explain** why Stacy won't start walking her dog at 5:00 P.M. **She will still be doing her homework.**

USE DATA For 2–3, use Stacy's schedule above.

2. What time does Stacy finish her homework? **5:10 P.M.**
3. How long does it take Stacy to do her homework and walk the dog? **1 hour 30 minutes**

136

Reteach 7.4

Use a Schedule

A **schedule** is a table that lists activities or events and the times they happen.

You can use a schedule to find elapsed times of events. If you know the elapsed times, you can find start and end times on a schedule.

THE ARTS CHANNEL SCHEDULE		
Show	**Time**	**Elapsed Time**
Painting	9:00 A.M. — 10:30 A.M.	1 hour 30 minutes
Drawing	10:30 A.M. — 11:30 A.M.	■
Pottery	11:30 A.M. — ■	1 hour
Jewelry	■ — 1:00 P.M.	30 minutes

For 1–4, use a clock with movable hands and the schedule above.

1. At what time does the painting show end? **10:30 A.M.**
2. How long is the drawing show? **1 hour**
3. At what time does the pottery show end? **12:30 P.M.**
4. At what time does the jewelry show begin? **12:30 P.M.**

Reteach RW39

Practice 7.4

Use a Schedule

Complete the schedule.

	CAMP WINDY SCHEDULE		
	Activity	**Time**	**Elapsed Time**
1.	Tennis	9:00 A.M. – 10:00 A.M.	1 hour
2.	Snack	10:00 A.M. – 10:25 A.M.	**25 minutes**
3.	Crafts	**10:25 A.M.** – 11:30 A.M.	1 hour 5 minutes
4.	Lunch	11:30 A.M. – **12:15 P.M.**	45 minutes
5.	Reading and Games	**12:15 P.M.** – 1:00 P.M.	45 minutes
6.	Swimming	1:00 P.M. – 2:15 P.M.	**1 hour 15 minutes**

For 7–10, use the schedule you completed.

7. Which activity ends at 10:25 A.M.? 11:30 A.M.? **snack; crafts**
8. Reading and games begins _?_ minutes after lunch begins. **45**
9. Crafts ends _?_ hours _?_ minutes after 9:00 A.M. **2; 30**
10. Which activity is the longest? **swimming**

Mixed Review

Write the greatest number possible with these digits.

11. 3, 7, 1, 5 **7,531**
12. 4, 1, 1, 5, 4 **54,411**
13. 6, 7, 3, 8, 5 **87,653**

Tell whether the number is *odd* or *even*.

14. 16 **even**
15. 3,451 **odd**
16. 5,467 **odd**
17. 834 **even**

Find 1,000 more.

18. 398 **1,398**
19. 1,309 **2,309**
20. 5,833 **6,833**
21. 10 **1,010**

Compare the numbers. Write <, >, or = in each ○.

22. 56 **>** 29
23. 247 **<** 417
24. 702 **=** 702
25. 212 **>** 199

Practice PW39

Practice and Problem Solving

Extra Practice, page 144, Set C

USE DATA For 4–6, use the class schedule.

MORNING CLASS SCHEDULE	
Activity	**Time**
Reading	8:30 A.M. – 9:15 A.M.
Math	9:15 A.M. – 10:15 A.M.
Recess	10:15 A.M. – 10:35 A.M.
Music	10:35 A.M. – 11:20 A.M.
Art	11:20 A.M. – 12:05 P.M.

4. Which activities last 45 minutes each? **reading, music, and art**
5. Which activity is the longest? **math**
6. **ESTIMATION** About how long are the reading and math activities altogether? **about 2 hours**

Copy and complete the schedule.

THE SCIENCE CHANNEL SCHEDULE			
	Program	**Time**	**Elapsed Time**
7.	Animals Around Us	■ – 7:00 P.M. **6:00 P.M.**	1 hour
8.	Wonderful Space	7:00 P.M. – ■ **7:25 P.M.**	25 minutes
9.	Weather in Your Town	7:25 P.M. – 7:30 P.M.	**5 min** ■
10.	Earthly Treasures	7:30 P.M. – ■ **8:00 P.M.**	30 minutes

For 11–12, use the schedule you completed.

11. Find the time when *Wonderful Space* ends. Then estimate this time to the nearest half hour. Explain. **Possible answer: 7:25 P.M.; 7:30 P.M.; 7:25 is closer to 7:30 than to 7:00.**
12. *Earthly Treasures* begins ■ hour and ■ minutes after *Animals Around Us* begins. **1; 30**
13. **REASONING** Sean needs at least 30 minutes to get ready for school. If he leaves for school at 8:05 A.M., what is the latest he can start getting ready? **7:35 A.M.**
14. **Write About It** Think about activities you do on a school day and how much time each takes. Make a schedule. Be sure to include start and end times. **Check students' schedules.**

Getting Ready for the EOG Test

15. At Sam's birthday party, the children made pizzas. For how long did the children make pizzas? **A**

    A 1 hour
    B 45 minutes
    C 30 minutes
    D 15 minutes

SAM'S PARTY SCHEDULE	
Activity	**Time**
Play games	10:30 A.M. – 11:30 A.M.
Make pizzas	11:30 A.M. – 12:30 P.M.
Open presents	12:30 P.M. – 1:00 P.M.
Swim	1:00 P.M. – 2:00 P.M.

Independent Practice

Note that Exercise 14 is a **multistep or strategy problem.** Assign Exercises 4–14.

Point out the Reasoning exercise to students. Suggest that they count back to help solve the problem.

Summarize the lesson by having students:

DISCUSS When you read a schedule, what two things must you look at to find the elapsed time for an activity? the start time and the end time of the activity

WRITE What column labels would you use to set up a schedule for students to go to the library? Possible answer: Grade, Starting Time, Ending Time, Elapsed Time

LESSON QUIZ

For 1–3, use the Morning Class Schedule on page 137.

1. Which activity ends at 10:15 A.M. and begins at 9:15 A.M.? Math
2. Which activity lasts 1 hour? Math
3. Which activity is the shortest? Recess

North Carolina Standards 2.01 Solve problems using measurement concepts and procedures involving: a) Elapsed time.

Challenge 7.4

Make a Schedule

Mr. Frank's class is going to a nature center. Mr. Frank drew these clocks to show when each activity begins. Each activity ends just as the next activity begins.

Arrive at nature center · Hike in woods · Visit nature center library · Explore pond · Eat picnic lunch · Explore meadow · Play outdoor games · Get on bus

1. Complete this schedule.

Activity	Time	Elapsed Time
Arrive	9:00 A.M.–9:15 A.M.	15 minutes
Hike	**9:15 A.M.–10:40 A.M.**	**1 hour 25 minutes**
Visit library	**10:40 A.M.–11:25 A.M.**	**45 minutes**
Explore pond	**11:25 A.M.–12:15 P.M.**	**50 minutes**
Eat lunch	**12:15 P.M.–12:50 P.M.**	**35 minutes**
Explore meadow	**12:50 P.M.–1:35 P.M.**	**45 minutes**
Play games	**1:35 P.M.–2:05 P.M.**	**30 minutes**

2. Which activity lasts the longest? **hike**
3. How much time in all will the class spend at the nature center? **5 hours 5 minutes**

Challenge CW39

Problem Solving 7.4

Use a Schedule

Understand → Plan → Solve → Check

Write the correct answer.

Ellen's Schedule	
Class	**Time**
Social Studies	9:00 A.M. – 9:45 A.M.
Language Arts	9:45 A.M. – 10:30 A.M.
Health	10:30 A.M. – 11:15 A.M.
Art	11:15 A.M. – 11:50 A.M.

1. How long is Health class? **45 minutes**
2. How long is Art class? **35 minutes**
3. Write the value of the digit 7 in the number 678. **70**
4. How many quarters are equal to $2.25? **9**

Choose the letter of the correct answer.

5. Math class starts at 12:20 P.M. and lasts 50 minutes. What time is Math class over?
   A 12:50 P.M.
   B 1:00 P.M.
   (C) 1:10 P.M.
   D 1:20 P.M.
6. Kelly needs at least 35 minutes to get ready for school. If she gets on the bus at 8:45 A.M., what is the latest she can start getting ready?
   (F) 8:10 A.M.
   G 8:05 A.M.
   H 8:00 A.M.
   J 7:55 A.M.
7. Which number is greater than 182 + 399 and less than 187 + 396?
   A 580
   B 581
   (C) 582
   D 583
8. What is the missing number? 1,132 − □ = 1,102
   F 3
   (G) 30
   H 132
   J 300
9. **Write About It** Explain why you chose the answer you did for Problem 5. **Possible answer: 12:20 – 12:30 is 10 minutes. 12:30 – 1:00 is 30 minutes. 1:00 – 1:10 is 10 minutes. This is a total of 50 minutes.**

Problem Solving PS39

Lesson 7.5 Use a Calendar

Lesson Planning

Objective To use a calendar to determine elapsed time

NCTM Standards

1. Number and Operations
4. Measurement
6. Problem Solving
7. Reasoning and Proof
8. Communication
9. Connections
10. Representation

Math Background

These ideas will help students understand how to use a calendar to determine elapsed time:

- There are 7 days in 1 week and 12 months in 1 year.
- Count by months, weeks, and days on a calendar to find elapsed time.

Vocabulary

calendar a chart that shows the days, weeks, and months of a year

Warm-Up Resources

Number of the Day

An addition problem adds the number of days in the month of April and the number of days in the month of October. What is the sum? 61

Daily Facts Practice

Have students practice addition facts by completing Set E of *Teacher's Resource Book*, p. TR88.

Transparency 7.5

Problem of the Day

To find the secret number, add the number of months in a year as many times as there are days in a week. From that sum, subtract the number of minutes in an hour. Is the secret number the number of minutes in an hour, the number of hours in a day, or the number of days in a year? The secret number is 24, the number of hours in a day.

Solution Problem of the Day tab, p. PD7

Intervention and Extension Resources

Alternative Teaching Strategy

Help students **practice finding elapsed time**. Have them make calendars of their birth months for the current year and circle the dates of their birthdays. Within the same month, have them circle another date that is special to them or is a holiday. Ask students to find the elapsed time from the earlier date to the later date. Display students' calendars. Check students' work.

See also page 140.

KINESTHETIC

BODILY/KINESTHETIC

Special Needs

MATERIALS *For each pair* calendar

Help students **understand the concept of elapsed time by playing a game**. One student names a date that he or she is leaving on vacation and says how many days he or she will be gone. The second student uses a calendar to find the date the first student will return. Students should then trade roles. Answers will vary.

KINESTHETIC

VISUAL/SPATIAL

Multistep and Strategy Problems

The following multistep and strategy problems are provided in Lesson 7.5:

Page	Item
140	10, 17

Social Studies Connection

MATERIALS *For each group* encyclopedia or other reference materials

Provide students the opportunity to **explore different kinds of calendars**. Explain that different cultures in the past and present have used different kinds of calendars. For example, in the Chinese calendar, the New Year does not begin on January 1. Also, years in the Chinese calendar are named for different animals.

Have students research the calendar of another modern or ancient culture and make a presentation to the class. Check students' work.

AUDITORY

VERBAL/LINGUISTIC

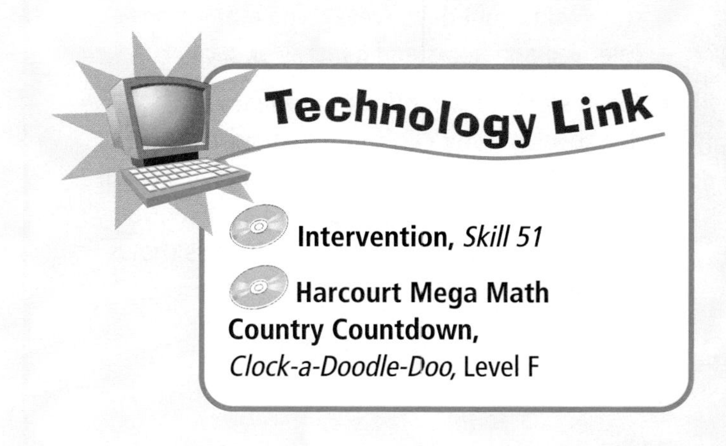

Technology Link
Intervention, *Skill 51*
Harcourt Mega Math Country Countdown, *Clock-a-Doodle-Doo,* Level F

Lesson 7.5 Organizer

Objective To use a calendar to determine elapsed time

Vocabulary calendar

1 INTRODUCE

QUICK REVIEW provides review of prerequisite skills.

WHY LEARN THIS? You can find the elapsed time of events that last days, weeks, or months, such as summer vacations. *Share the lesson objective with students.*

2 TEACH

Guided Instruction

- *Have students review two 12-month calendars, one of which is for a leap year.*

MODIFYING INSTRUCTION Explain that leap years occur every four years, and during a leap year the month of February has 29 days. Tell students that scientists discovered that a year lasts for $365 + \frac{1}{4}$ days, and that is why we have a leap year once every 4 years.

- *Display a calendar of the current month and year.* **What is a different way to write today's date? Explain.** Possible answer: 10/23/04; October is the tenth calendar month, 23 is the day of the month, and 04 represents the last two digits of the year 2004.
  REASONING Moving down two weeks on the calendar is like counting on twice by what number of days? 7 days
- *Lead a discussion on finding elapsed time.* **How is finding elapsed time on a calendar similar to finding elapsed time on a clock? How is it different?** Possible answer: you count on to find elapsed time on a calendar and on a clock; you count days, weeks, and months on a calendar, and hours and minutes on a clock.
- *Direct students' attention to Example A.* **REASONING Why can't you just subtract 11 from 15?** That would give you 4. You must count October 11 as the first day of the fair. When you count October 11, 12, 13, 14, and 15, this shows that the correct answer is 5 days.

LESSON 5

Use a Calendar

Quick Review

What day of the week is

1. after Monday? **Tuesday**
2. before Saturday? **Friday**
3. after Wednesday? **Thursday**
4. before Tuesday? **Monday**
5. after Thursday? **Friday**

VOCABULARY
calendar

Learn

DAYS AND DATES A calendar is a chart that shows the days, weeks, and months of a year. There are 12 months in one year.

MATH IDEA You can use a calendar to find elapsed time in days, weeks, and months.

Examples

A The Book Fair begins on October 11. The last day will be October 15. How long will the Book Fair last?

Think: The dates of the fair are October 11, 12, 13, 14, and 15.
Count each day.

So, the Book Fair will last 5 days.

B Miss Hanson is painting a picture in the school lunchroom. She will paint from November 29 to December 15. For how long will she paint?

Think: Start: Monday, November 29.
Move down 2 weeks to December 13.
Then count on 2 days to December 15.

So, Miss Hanson will paint for 2 weeks and 2 days, or 16 days.

October

Sun	Mon	Tue	Wed	Thu	Fri	Sat
					1	2
3	4	5	6	7	8	9
10	11	12	13	14	15	16
17	18	19	20	21	22	23
24/31	25	26	27	28	29	30

November

Sun	Mon	Tue	Wed	Thu	Fri	Sat
	1	2	3	4	5	6
7	8	9	10	11	12	13
14	15	16	17	18	19	20
21	22	23	24	25	26	27
28	29	30				

December

Sun	Mon	Tue	Wed	Thu	Fri	Sat
			1	2	3	4
5	6	7	8	9	10	11
12	13	14	15	16	17	18
19	20	21	22	23	24	25
26	27	28	29	30	31	

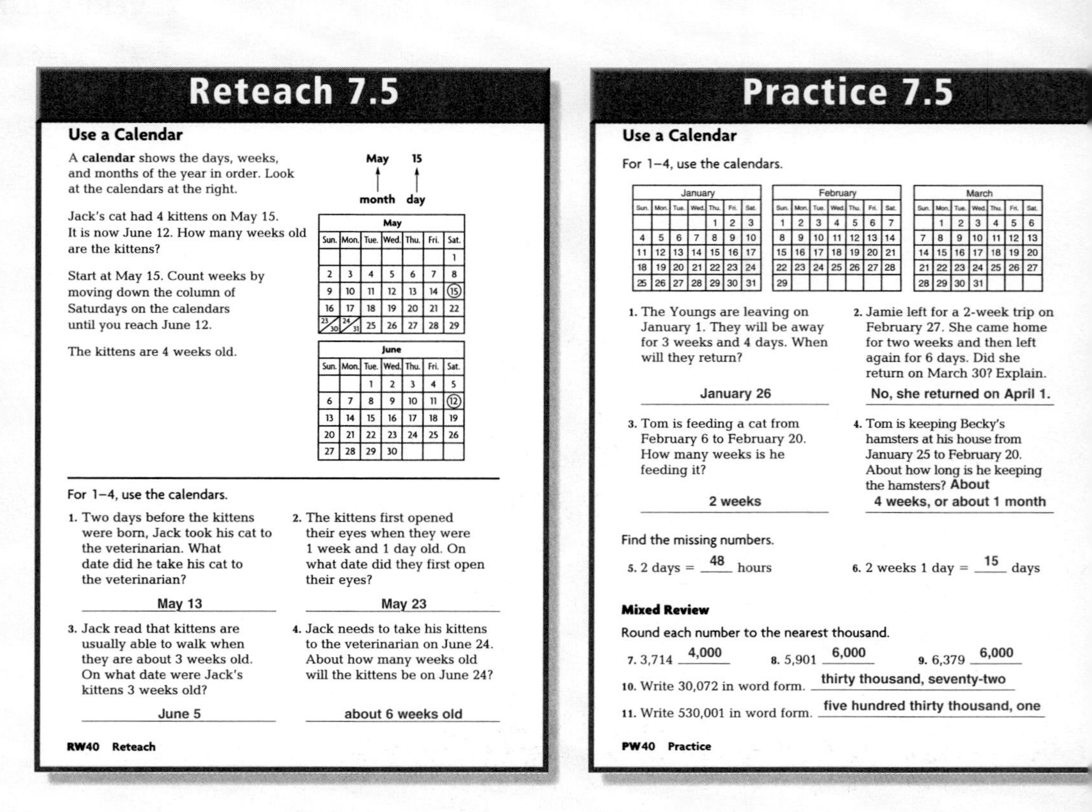

Reteach 7.5

Use a Calendar

A **calendar** shows the days, weeks, and months of the year in order. Look at the calendars at the right.

May 15 (May = month, 15 = day)

Jack's cat had 4 kittens on May 15. It is now June 12. How many weeks old are the kittens?

Start at May 15. Count weeks by moving down the column of Saturdays on the calendars until you reach June 12.

The kittens are 4 weeks old.

May

Sun.	Mon.	Tue.	Wed.	Thu.	Fri.	Sat.
						1
2	3	4	5	6	7	8
9	10	11	12	13	14	(15)
16	17	18	19	20	21	22
23/30	24/31	25	26	27	28	29

June

Sun.	Mon.	Tue.	Wed.	Thu.	Fri.	Sat.
		1	2	3	4	5
6	7	8	9	10	11	(12)
13	14	15	16	17	18	19
20	21	22	23	24	25	26
27	28	29	30			

For 1–4, use the calendars.

1. Two days before the kittens were born, Jack took his cat to the veterinarian. What date did he take his cat to the veterinarian? **May 13**
2. The kittens first opened their eyes when they were 1 week and 1 day old. On what date did they first open their eyes? **May 23**
3. Jack read that kittens are usually able to walk when they are about 3 weeks old. On what date were Jack's kittens 3 weeks old? **June 5**
4. Jack needs to take his kittens to the veterinarian on June 24. About how many weeks old will the kittens be on June 24? **about 6 weeks old**

RW40 Reteach

Practice 7.5

Use a Calendar

For 1–4, use the calendars.

January

Sun.	Mon.	Tue.	Wed.	Thu.	Fri.	Sat.
				1	2	3
4	5	6	7	8	9	10
11	12	13	14	15	16	17
18	19	20	21	22	23	24
25	26	27	28	29	30	31

February

Sun.	Mon.	Tue.	Wed.	Thu.	Fri.	Sat.
1	2	3	4	5	6	7
8	9	10	11	12	13	14
15	16	17	18	19	20	21
22	23	24	25	26	27	28
29						

March

Sun.	Mon.	Tue.	Wed.	Thu.	Fri.	Sat.
	1	2	3	4	5	6
7	8	9	10	11	12	13
14	15	16	17	18	19	20
21	22	23	24	25	26	27
28	29	30	31			

1. The Youngs are leaving on January 1. They will be away for 3 weeks and 4 days. When will they return? **January 26**
2. Jamie left for a 2-week trip on February 27. She came home for two weeks and then left again for 6 days. Did she return on March 30? Explain. **No, she returned on April 1.**
3. Tom is feeding a cat from February 6 to February 20. How many weeks is he feeding it? **2 weeks**
4. Tom is keeping Becky's hamsters at his house from January 25 to February 20. About how long is he keeping the hamsters? **About 4 weeks, or about 1 month**

Find the missing numbers.

5. 2 days = **48** hours
6. 2 weeks 1 day = **15** days

Mixed Review

Round each number to the nearest thousand.

7. 3,714 **4,000**
8. 5,901 **6,000**
9. 6,379 **6,000**
10. Write 30,072 in word form. **thirty thousand, seventy-two**
11. Write 530,001 in word form. **five hundred thirty thousand, one**

PW40 Practice

Units of Time

Short amounts of time are measured with a clock. Greater amounts of time are measured with a calendar. The table of measures shows how the different units of time are related.

TABLE OF MEASURES	
60 minutes = 1 hour	12 months = 1 year
24 hours = 1 day	365 days = 1 year
7 days = 1 week	

You can use these units of time to describe elapsed time in more than one way.

Examples

A The reading program at the library lasts for 3 weeks. For how many days does the program last?

Think: 7 days = 1 week
$7 + 7 + 7 = 21$

So, the program lasts for 21 days.

B Zack read a book for 1 hour 20 minutes. For how many minutes did he read?

Think: 60 minutes = 1 hour
$60 + 20 = 80$

So, Zack read for 80 minutes.

Check

Technology Link
More Practice: Harcourt Mega Math Country Countdown, *Clock-a-Doodle-Doo*, Level F

1. **Explain** how you know 3 weeks and 4 days is the same amount of time as 25 days. **Find the number of days in 3 weeks. 7 + 7 + 7 = 21 days. 21 + 4 = 25 days.**

For 2–3, use the calendars.

June						
Sun	Mon	Tue	Wed	Thu	Fri	Sat
		1	2	3	4	5
6	7	8	9	10	11	12
13	14	15	16	17	18	19
20	21	22	23	24	25	26
27	28	29	30			

July						
Sun	Mon	Tue	Wed	Thu	Fri	Sat
				1	2	3
4	5	6	7	8	9	10
11	12	13	14	15	16	17
18	19	20	21	22	23	24
25	26	27	28	29	30	31

August						
Sun	Mon	Tue	Wed	Thu	Fri	Sat
1	2	3	4	5	6	7
8	9	10	11	12	13	14
15	16	17	18	19	20	21
22	23	24	25	26	27	28
29	30	31				

2. The photo contest is on July 23. Today is June 21. How much time does Emily have to get her photos ready for the contest? **Possible answer: 4 weeks and 4 days**

3. Brian's grandparents are visiting from July 17 to August 14. How many weeks is this? How many days? **Possible answer: 4 weeks; 28 days**

LESSON CONTINUES

- *Discuss the different units of time in the Table of Measures.*
  REASONING How could you use addition to find the number of months in 2 years? 12 + 12 = 24 months
- *Direct students' attention to Example A.*
  Why are three 7s added to find the total number of days? There are 7 days in one week, so you need to add three 7s together to find the total number of days in 3 weeks.

3 PRACTICE

Guided Practice

Do Check Exercises 1–3 with your students. Identify students who are having difficulty and choose appropriate lesson resources to provide assistance.

North Carolina Standards 2.01 Solve problems using measurement concepts and procedures involving: b) Equivalent measures within the same measurement system. *also* **2.01a**

Challenge 7.5

Calendar Challenge

Sam cut out a column of numbers from his calendar.

He noticed that each number is 7 more than the number above it.

4
11 — 4 + 7 = 11
18 — 11 + 7 = 18
25 — 18 + 7 = 25

MARCH						
S	M	T	W	T	F	S
	1	2	3	4	5	6
7	8	9	10	11	12	13
14	15	16	17	18	19	20
21	22	23	24	25	26	27
28	29	30	31			

Find other patterns on the calendar. Add along the diagonals of two-by-two squares of numbers.

1. 1, 2 / 8, 9 — 10, 10
2. 3, 4 / 10, 11 — 14, 14
3. 5, 6 / 12, 13 — 18, 18

4. Can you find a two-by-two square of numbers on the calendar where this relationship does not happen? Explain.
No; the sums of the diagonals of each of the possible two-by-two squares of numbers are always the same.

Add along the diagonals of three-by-three squares of numbers.

5. 1, 2, 3 / 8, 9, 10 / 15, 16, 17 — 27, 27
6. 4, 5, 6 / 11, 12, 13 / 18, 19, 20 — 36, 36
7. 7, 8, 9 / 14, 15, 16 / 21, 22, 23 — 45, 45

8. Can you find a three-by-three square of numbers on the calendar where this relationship does not happen? Explain.
No; the sums of the diagonals of each of the possible three-by-three squares of numbers are always the same.

9. Add the diagonals of a four-by-four square of numbers on the calendar. What do you notice?
The sums are the same.

CW40 Challenge

Problem Solving 7.5

Use a Calendar

JULY						
Sun	Mon	Tues	Wed	Thurs	Fri	Sat
				1	2	3
4	5	6	7	8	9	10
11	12	13	14	15	16	17
18	19	20	21	22	23	24
25	26	27	28	29	30	31

AUGUST						
Sun	Mon	Tues	Wed	Thurs	Fri	Sat
1	2	3	4	5	6	7
8	9	10	11	12	13	14
15	16	17	18	19	20	21
22	23	24	25	26	27	28
29	30	31				

Write the correct answer.

1. The Robinsons are going on a vacation for 2 weeks. Their vacation begins July 10. When will they be back?
July 24

2. I am a number on the calendar. The difference of my digits is 2. The sum of my digits is 6. What number am I?
24

3. Steve's birthday is August 2. His brother's birthday is 3 weeks later. When is his brother's birthday?
August 23

4. Jane has 9 quarters, 6 dimes, and 4 nickels. How much money does she have?
$3.05

Choose the letter of the correct answer.

5. Mrs. Daly's piano students practiced for a recital from July 1 to August 5. How many weeks did they practice?
A 7 B 6 (C) 5 D 4

6. Tiffany read a 129-page book last week. This week she plans to read a 285-page book. How many pages is this altogether?
(F) 414 G 404 H 385 J 314

7. Swimming lessons are from August 2 to August 16. How many weeks is this?
A 1 week (B) 2 weeks C 3 weeks D 4 weeks

8. Tell which digit is in the hundreds place in the number 34,578.
F 4 (G) 5 H 7 J 8

9. **Write About It** In Problem 1, how many days long is the Robinsons' vacation? Explain.
14 days; 7 + 7 = 14 days

PS40 Problem Solving

Independent Practice

Note that Exercises 10 and 17 are **multistep or strategy problems.** Assign Exercises 4–20.

For Exercises 11–16, remind students that they can use the Table of Measures on page 139.

MULTISTEP OR STRATEGY PROBLEM To solve Exercise 17, students can subtract 3 from 32, then add 5 to the difference to find the number of pencils that Carol had.

Practice and Problem Solving

Extra Practice, page 144, Set D

For 4–7, use the calendars.

August						
Sun	Mon	Tue	Wed	Thu	Fri	Sat
1	2	3	4	5	6	7
8	9	10	11	12	13	14
15	16	17	18	19	20	21
22	23	24	25	26	27	28
29	30	31				

September						
Sun	Mon	Tue	Wed	Thu	Fri	Sat
			1	2	3	4
5	6	7	8	9	10	11
12	13	14	15	16	17	18
19	20	21	22	23	24	25
26	27	28	29	30		

October						
Sun	Mon	Tue	Wed	Thu	Fri	Sat
					1	2
3	4	5	6	7	8	9
10	11	12	13	14	15	16
17	18	19	20	21	22	23
24/31	25	26	27	28	29	30

Possible answers are given.

4. Doug went on vacation from August 24 to September 14. How many weeks was his vacation? **3 weeks**
5. Mr. Todd left for a 4-week trip on August 9. Did he return by August 31? Explain. **No; he returned on September 6.**
6. **ESTIMATION** Ms. Green's team practiced from September 13 to October 9. About how long did the team practice? **about 4 weeks, or about 1 month**
7. Chantel started her art project on October 1. She worked for 3 weeks and 4 days. When did she finish? **October 25**

USE DATA For 8–10, use the calendars above and the pictograph.

8. "Raisins in the Sun" first hit number 1 on August 11. When did it lose its first-place spot? **August 25**
9. Which song was number 1 for the longest time? **"Dance and Sing"**
10. **REASONING** How many more days was "Dance and Sing" number 1 than "Music Time"? **7 days**

TOP-OF-THE-CHART SONGS

Song	Weeks
Dance and Sing	♪ ♪ ♪ ♪
Raisins in the Sun	♪ ♪
Music Time	♪ ♪ ♪

Key: Each ♪ = 1 week.

Find the missing numbers.

11. 2 weeks = ■ days **14**
12. ■ hours = 1 day **24**
13. 2 years = ■ months **24**
14. 1 year = ■ months **12**
15. 4 weeks = ■ days **28**
16. ■ minutes = 2 hours **120**
17. Carol had 32 pencils. She gave 3 pencils to a friend. Then she bought 5 more. How many pencils did she have then? **34 pencils**
18. **Write a problem** about elapsed time, using minutes and hours. Explain how these units of time are related. **Check students' work.**

140

Alternative Teaching Strategy — Scaffolded Instruction

PURPOSE Students review the months of the year and how to use a calendar.

MATERIALS *For each group* one 12-month calendar; *For each student* blank calendar, p. TR46

STEP 1
Review with students the months of the year. Ask: Which month is just before March? February Ask: Which month follows September? October
For students that are having difficulty remembering the order of the months, you may wish to give them each 12 index cards and a 12-month calendar and have them make a card for each month that includes the ordinal number for that month.

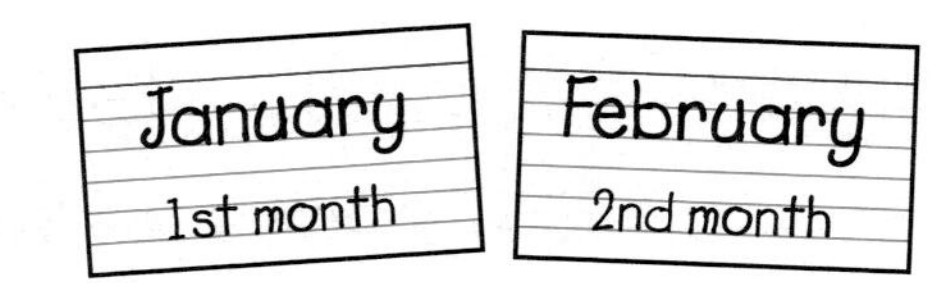

STEP 2
Give each student a blank calendar to make a calendar for the present month. Ask: Which month is it right now? Students should name the present month. Point out the blank line where they should write the name of the month. Tell students where the first day of the month should be written, and how many days there are in the month. Have each student fill in the dates for the month.

STEP 3
Ask: How many Fridays are there in this month? Check responses for accuracy. Ask students for the date of the second Tuesday in the month. Check responses for accuracy. Ask: What is the date of the Tuesday that is one week after this date? Check responses for accuracy.

19. **Vocabulary Power** The word *quarter* can mean one of four equal parts. How does this meaning relate to *quarter hour*? What is another math meaning for *quarter*?

20. **FAST FACT** • SCIENCE Brown bears will hibernate for up to 7 months in a year. About how many months are they not hibernating in a year? **about 5 months**

19. Possible responses: In fifteen minutes, the minute hand moves one quarter of the way around the clock. The word *quarter* is also the name of coin worth 25¢.

Getting Ready for the EOG Test

21. Tiffany's aunt is coming to visit on January 5. She will stay for six nights. On what day will Tiffany's aunt leave? **C**

January						
Sun	Mon	Tue	Wed	Thu	Fri	Sat
				1	2	3
4	5	6	7	8	9	10
11	12	13	14	15	16	17
18	19	20	21	22	23	24
25	26	27	28	29	30	31

A Friday
B Saturday
C Sunday
D Monday

22. Pat begins training for his job on January 12. The training lasts for 21 days. How many weeks will Pat's training last? **B**

A 2 weeks
B 3 weeks
C 4 weeks
D 5 weeks

Problem Solving Thinker's Corner

VISUAL THINKING Use the knuckles on your fists to help you remember the number of days in each month.

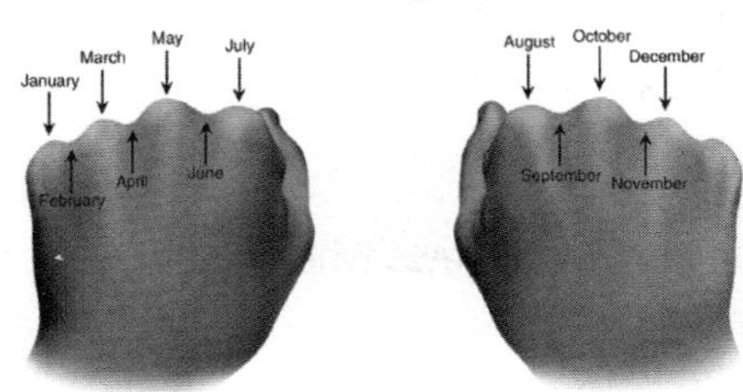

The months on the knuckles have 31 days. The months on the spaces have 30 days, except for February.

Write the number of days in each month.

1. September **30**
2. May **31**
3. June **30**

Vocabulary Power The word *quarter* is used in many everyday situations. Discuss with students how some sporting contests that are timed events are divided into 4 equal parts. Ask students if they are familiar with the *first quarter, second quarter, third quarter,* and *fourth quarter* of a basketball game.

4 ASSESS

Summarize the lesson by having students:

Discuss What differences do you notice between the calendars for September and October on page 140? Possible answer: There are different numbers of days in the months. There are 30 days in September and 31 days in October.

Write Tevin and Matt worked together on a social studies project. They worked on their research from March 12 through April 27 and then took 2 more weeks to finish the project. Explain how you would figure out how long it took them to complete the entire project. Begin at March 12 and move down 6 weeks to April 23. Then count on 4 days to April 27. Add 2 more weeks. 6 + 2 = 8 weeks + 4 days

LESSON QUIZ

Transparency 7.5

For 1–2, use the calendars on page 139.

1. Alexis went on vacation from June 27 to July 18. How long was her vacation? 3 weeks
2. Bill built a doghouse in 2 weeks and 5 days. He started on August 1. When did he finish? August 20

Problem Solving Skill

Sequence Events

Lesson Planning

Objective To use a time line to determine a sequence of events

Materials *For each student* blank number line, p. TR16

Lesson Resources Reading Transparency 7; Intervention • Problem Solving, Strategy/Skill 7

NCTM Standards

1. Number and Operations
4. Measurement
6. Problem Solving
7. Reasoning and Proof
8. Communication
9. Connections
10. Representation

Math Background

These ideas will help students understand how to use a time line to determine a sequence of events:

- A time line is read from left to right, showing the order in which events happened.
- Familiarity with number lines that have intervals will help students understand time lines that have intervals.
- A single unit of time is used on a time line. The unit of time will depend on the events: hours could be used for events in a single day, while centuries could be used for events in the history of a country.

Vocabulary

time line a drawing that shows when and in what order events took place

Warm-Up Resources

Number of the Day

Identify the number of months with 31 days and subtract the number of months with 30 or fewer days. What is the difference? 2

Daily Facts Practice

Have students practice addition facts by completing Set F of *Teacher's Resource Book*, p. TR88.

Solve a Problem

Transparency 7.6

Problem of the Day

Hilary's birthday is exactly 6 weeks before Henry's. Rosa is 40 days older than Hilary. Hilary's birthday is the last day of April. When are Rosa and Henry's birthdays? Rosa's birthday is on March 21 and Henry's birthday is on June 11.

Solution Problem of the Day tab, p. PD7

Intervention and Extension Resources

Alternative Teaching Strategy

MATERIALS *For each pair* blank time line, p. TR16; 1 index card cut into 4 small cards: one small card with the current year and 3 small cards with other years

Help students **practice using a time line to show the sequence of events.**

- Distribute the prepared cards.
- Have students place the cards on the time line. Then have students explain their placement. Check students' work.

KINESTHETIC

VISUAL/SPATIAL

Reading Strategy

Put Things in Sequence Tell students that sequence is an arrangement of one thing after another. Sometimes, sequence clues, such as the words *first, next, then, after,* and *last,* are used to show the order of events in a problem. Have students underline the sequence clues and solve the following problem.

Juan planned to hang posters on one wall of the classroom. After he measured the wall and found the length to be 30 feet, he hung the first poster 6 feet from the left end. Then he hung 1 poster every 6 feet. The last poster he hung was 6 feet from the right end of the wall. How many posters did Juan hang? 4 posters

Transparency 7 **Reading Transparency 7**

Multistep and Strategy Problems

The following multistep or strategy problem is provided in Lesson 7.6:

Page	Item
143	7

ESOL/ESL

MATERIALS *For each pair* 13 index cards: 9 labeled 1950, 1955, 1960, 1965, 1970, 1975, 1980, 1985, 1990 and 4 labeled 1962, 1976, 1954, 1987

ESOL/ESL

Help students **understand the concept of sequence of events.** Have pairs shuffle the cards. Then have them place the cards in order. They should begin with the dates ending with 5 or 0. Then they should place the remaining 4 cards.

Encourage students to discuss how to order the dates. When the cards are placed, have students explain what they did.

KINESTHETIC, AUDITORY

BODILY/KINESTHETIC

Early Finishers

Challenge students to **determine the sequence of events**. Have students plan their own birthday parties. Ask them to write at least three things they must do before the party and determine the dates when these things must be completed. Things to do might include reserving an ice skating rink, sending invitations, and ordering the cake. Have them sketch a time line and place the dates on it. Students then explain what interval they chose for the time line. Check students' work.

VISUAL

INTRAPERSONAL/INTROSPECTIVE

Technology Link

Intervention • Problem Solving, *Strategy/Skill 7*

Lesson 7.6 Organizer

Objective To use a time line to determine a sequence of events

Vocabulary time line

Materials *For each student* blank number line, p. TR16

Lesson Resources Reading Transparency 7; Intervention • Problem Solving, Strategy/Skill 7

1 INTRODUCE

QUICK REVIEW provides review of prerequisite skills.

WHY LEARN THIS? You can use a time line to find out the order in which events happened. *Share the lesson objective with students.*

2 TEACH

Guided Instruction

- *Ask students to read the Old and New section. Have them look at the time line.*
  How is the time line like a number line as you look from left to right? The numbers become greater as you look from left to right.
  Why do you think that the time line is labeled with only every tenth year? Possible answers: there isn't room for all of the years to be labeled; just like on a number line, you know what numbers go between the labels
- *Discuss Talk About It.*
  How many toys on the time line were introduced after Tonka trucks? 4 **Explain how you know.** Possible answer: The point for Tonka trucks would be to the right of Slinky, so Play-Doh, Hot Wheels, Rollerblades, and Beanie Babies would be to the right of Tonka trucks.

LESSON 6

Problem Solving Skill
Sequence Events

UNDERSTAND PLAN SOLVE CHECK

Quick Review

Tell which number is greater.

1. 76 or 68 **76**
2. 52 or 60 **60**
3. 34 or 31 **34**
4. 245 or 243 **245**
5. 591 or 597 **597**

VOCABULARY
time line

OLD AND NEW Gina and Nick wanted to show the years that some toys were introduced. They made a time line.

A **time line** is a drawing that shows when and in what order events took place. It is read from left to right. The dates at the left happened first. The dates at the right happened later.

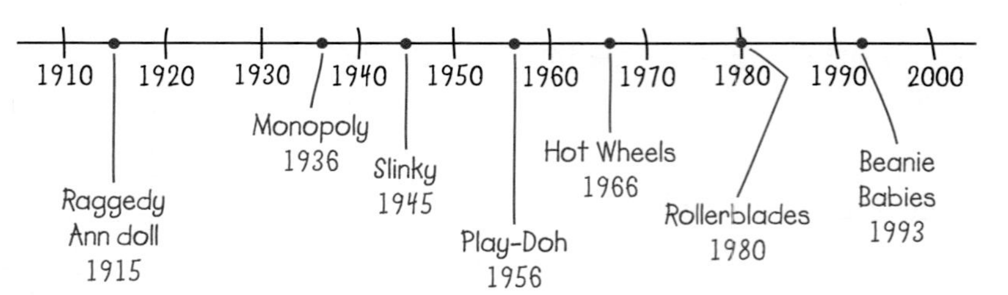

Use the time line to decide if Play-Doh was introduced before or after Hot Wheels.

Since Play-Doh is to the left of Hot Wheels, it was introduced before Hot Wheels.

Talk About It

- **REASONING** Suppose you knew the years that Play-Doh and Hot Wheels were introduced, but they were not on the time line. How would you know which toy was introduced first? **Possible answer: The lesser number would be the earlier of the two years.**
- Tonka trucks were introduced in 1947. Describe where the point for Tonka trucks should be placed on the time line. **Possible answer: The point should be a little to the right of the point for Slinky, since 1947 is 2 years after 1945.**

142

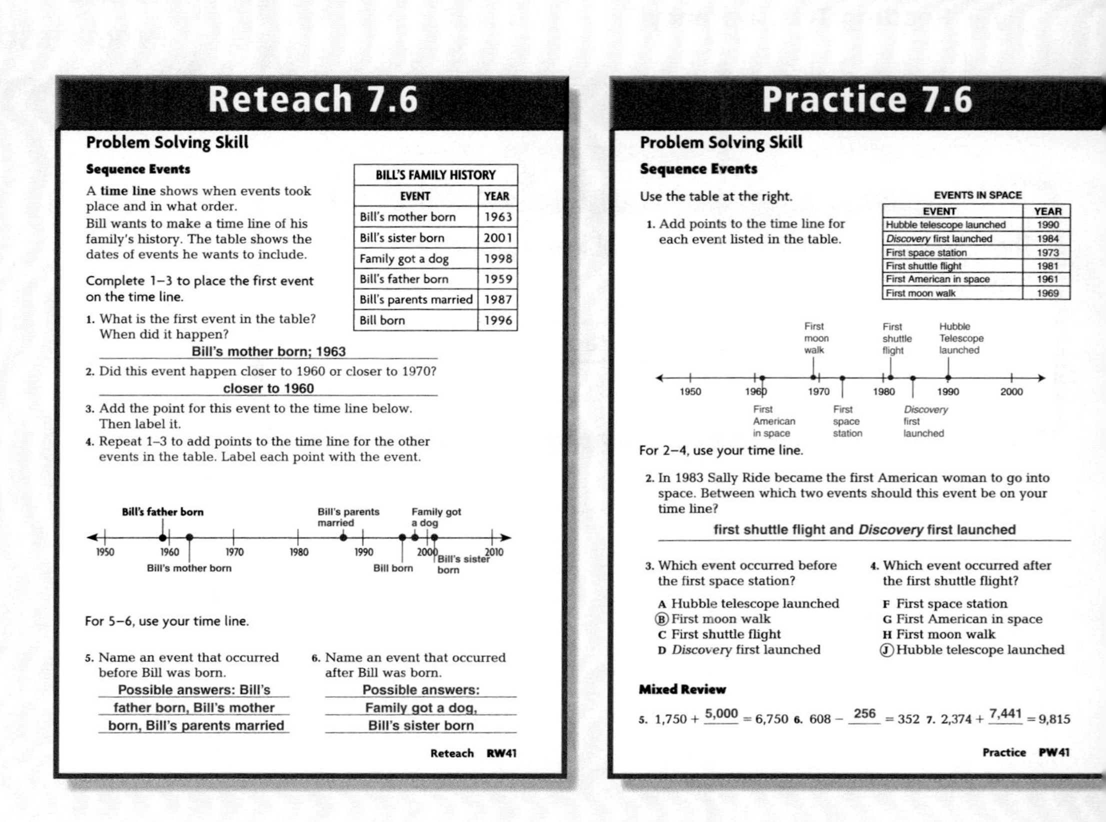

Reteach 7.6

Problem Solving Skill

Sequence Events

A **time line** shows when events took place and in what order.
Bill wants to make a time line of his family's history. The table shows the dates of events he wants to include.

BILL'S FAMILY HISTORY	
EVENT	YEAR
Bill's mother born	1963
Bill's sister born	2001
Family got a dog	1998
Bill's father born	1959
Bill's parents married	1987
Bill born	1996

Complete 1–3 to place the first event on the time line.

1. What is the first event in the table? When did it happen?
   Bill's mother born; 1963
2. Did this event happen closer to 1960 or closer to 1970?
   closer to 1960
3. Add the point for this event to the time line below. Then label it.
4. Repeat 1–3 to add points to the time line for the other events in the table. Label each point with the event.

For 5–6, use your time line.

5. Name an event that occurred before Bill was born.
   Possible answers: Bill's father born, Bill's mother born, Bill's parents married
6. Name an event that occurred after Bill was born.
   Possible answers: Family got a dog, Bill's sister born

Reteach **RW41**

Practice 7.6

Problem Solving Skill

Sequence Events

Use the table at the right.

1. Add points to the time line for each event listed in the table.

EVENTS IN SPACE

EVENT	YEAR
Hubble telescope launched	1990
Discovery first launched	1984
First space station	1973
First shuttle flight	1981
First American in space	1961
First moon walk	1969

For 2–4, use your time line.

2. In 1983 Sally Ride became the first American woman to go into space. Between which two events should this event be on your time line?
   first shuttle flight and *Discovery* first launched
3. Which event occurred before the first space station?
   A Hubble telescope launched
   Ⓑ First moon walk
   C First shuttle flight
   D *Discovery* first launched
4. Which event occurred after the first shuttle flight?
   F First space station
   G First American in space
   H First moon walk
   Ⓙ Hubble telescope launched

Mixed Review

5. 1,750 + **5,000** = 6,750 6. 608 − **256** = 352 7. 2,374 + **7,441** = 9,815

Practice **PW41**

Problem Solving Practice

USE DATA For 1–2, use the table at the right.

INTRODUCTION OF TOYS	
Toy	**Year**
Nerf ball	1969
Lincoln Logs	1916
Crayola crayons	1903
Mr. Potato Head	1952
Erector set	1913
Lego blocks	1949

1. Copy the time line below. Add a point to the time line for each toy listed. Label each point with the name of the toy.

1900 1910 1920 1930 1940 1950 1960 1970

Crayola crayons, Erector set, Lincoln Logs, Lego blocks, Mr. Potato Head, Nerf ball

2. Etch-A-Sketch was introduced in 1960. Between which two toys should it be on your time line? **between Mr. Potato Head and Nerf ball**

For 3–4, use your time line.

3. Which toy was introduced after Lego blocks? **B**
   - **A** Crayola crayons
   - **B** Mr. Potato Head
   - **C** Erector set
   - **D** Lincoln Logs

4. Which toy was introduced before Lincoln Logs? **J**
   - **F** Nerf ball
   - **G** Mr. Potato Head
   - **H** Lego blocks
   - **J** Erector set

Mixed Applications

5. Mr. Brooks will need chairs for 8 adults and 14 children for a party. Should Mr. Brooks estimate to decide how many chairs to rent? Explain. **No; everyone needs a chair, so he should find the exact number needed.**
6. Ms. Tate leaves on May 15. She must reserve a room 10 days before she leaves and a flight 2 weeks before she leaves. Which should she do first? **Reserve a flight.**
7. The sum of two numbers is 72. Their difference is 24. What are the numbers? **48 and 24**
8. **Write a problem** you can solve by using a time line. Trade problems with a partner and solve. **Check students' problems.**

Problem Solving

3 PRACTICE

Guided Practice

Do Problem Solving Practice Exercises 1–4 with your students. Identify students who are having difficulty and choose appropriate lesson resources to provide assistance.

You may wish to give students blank number lines to use when they are making their time lines.

Independent Practice

Note that Exercise 7 is a **multistep or strategy problem.** Assign Exercises 5–8.

SCAFFOLDED INSTRUCTION Use the prompts on Transparency 7 to guide instruction for the multistep or strategy problem in Exercise 7.

Transparency 7

4 ASSESS

Summarize the lesson by having students:

DISCUSS How would you order the following dates: 1925, 1917, 1921, and 1933? Explain. 1917, 1921, 1925, 1933; They go in order from left to right.

WRITE Compare the time line that you made for Exercise 1 with the table on page 143. Which do you think is easier to read? Why? Possible answer: The time line is easier to read because the dates are in order. The table would be easy to read if the dates were in order from top to bottom.

LESSON QUIZ

Transparency 7.6

For 1–3, use the time line on page 142.

1. Which toys were introduced before Slinky? Raggedy Ann doll, Monopoly
2. Which toys were introduced after Hot Wheels? Rollerblades, Beanie Babies
3. Which toys were introduced between 1940 and 1970? Slinky, Play-Doh, and Hot Wheels

North Carolina Standards Goal 2 The learner will recognize and use standard units of metric and customary measurement. *also* 2.01a

Challenge 7.6

State Facts

The table shows when some places in the United States became states. Add points to the time line for each state in the table. The finished time line will show the order in which the places became states.

STATEHOOD			
State	**Year**	**State**	**Year**
Colorado	1876	Minnesota	1858
Florida	1845	Missouri	1821
Illinois	1818	Nevada	1864
Michigan	1837	North Dakota	1889

1810 1820 1830 1840 1850 1860 1870 1880 1890 1900

Illinois, Missouri, Michigan, Florida, Minnesota, Nevada, Colorado, North Dakota

Write the states in time order in the boxes below. Write the first state to become a state in box one, the second state in box two, and so on. The first one is done for you.

1. **Illinois** has the tallest building in the United States.
2. **Missouri** is the state where the first ice-cream cone is believed to have been sold.
3. **Michigan** borders on the largest lake in the United States.
4. **Florida** has orange juice as its official state beverage.
5. **Minnesota** has more than 15,000 lakes.
6. **Nevada** usually gets less rain than any other state.
7. **Colorado** has more mountains higher than 14,000 feet than any other state.
8. **North Dakota** is an important wheat-growing state.

Challenge CW41

Reading Strategy 7.6

Sequence Information

Understand → Plan → Solve → Check

A **time line** is a drawing that shows when and in what order events took place. Events at the left happened first. Events at the right happened later.

The table at the right shows when some United States Presidents were born.

PRESIDENTS' BIRTH DATES

PRESIDENT	YEAR
George W. Bush	1946
Jimmy Carter	1924
Gerald Ford	1913
Lyndon Johnson	1908
John Kennedy	1917
Ronald Reagan	1911

1. Add a point to the time line for each President listed in the table. Label each point with the name of the President.

1900 1910 1920 1930 1940 1950

Lyndon Johnson, Ronald Reagan, Gerald Ford, John Kennedy, Jimmy Carter, George W. Bush

2. Describe the strategy you used to make the time line.
   Possible answer: For each President, I found the two dates on the time line between which his birth date fell. Then I found which date it was closer to, added the point to the time line, and labeled it.
3. Name a President born before John Kennedy. Explain your thinking.
   Possible answers: Johnson, Reagan, or Ford; his birth date is to the left of Kennedy's on the time line.
4. Name a President born after Gerald Ford. Explain your thinking.
   Possible answers: Kennedy, Carter, or Bush; his birth date is to the right of Ford's on the time line.

Reading Strategy PS41

Extra Practice

Purpose To provide extra practice for the skills presented in this chapter

The blue page references in each set of exercises refer to the lesson pages where each skill is taught.

Internet Resources

Visit THE LEARNING SITE at **www.harcourtschool.com** for a listing of practice activities.

Extra Practice

Set A (pp. 128–131) **1. 14 minutes after seven; seven fourteen**

Write two ways you can read each time. **Possible answers are given.**

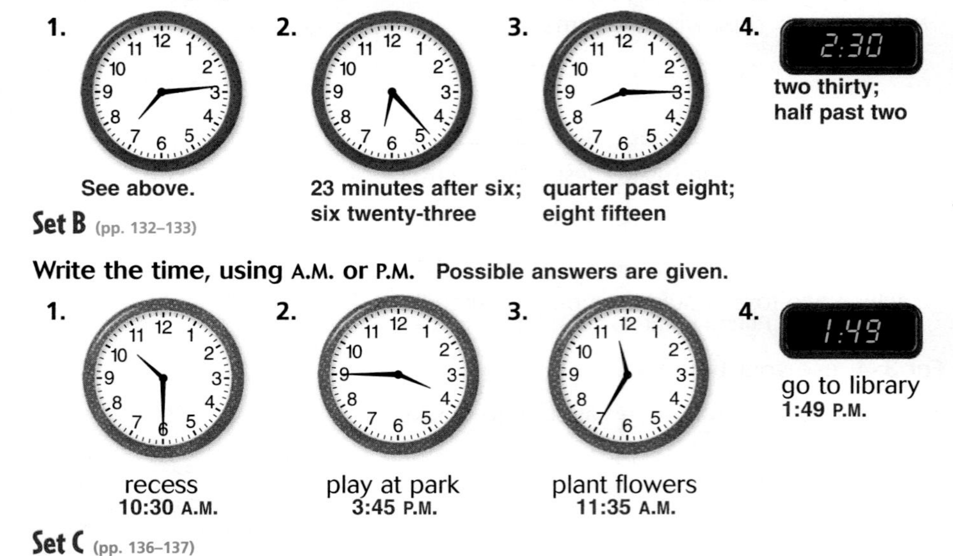

1. See above.
2. 23 minutes after six; six twenty-three
3. quarter past eight; eight fifteen
4. 2:30 — two thirty; half past two

Set B (pp. 132–133)

Write the time, using A.M. or P.M. **Possible answers are given.**

1. recess **10:30 A.M.**
2. play at park **3:45 P.M.**
3. plant flowers **11:35 A.M.**
4. 1:49 — go to library **1:49 P.M.**

Set C (pp. 136–137)

Copy and complete the schedule.

	MONDAY NIGHT ON CHANNEL 8			
	Program	**Time**	**Elapsed Time**	
1.	Game Show	4:30 P.M. – 5:00 P.M.	■	**30 minutes**
2.	Evening News	5:00 P.M. – 5:45 P.M.	■	**45 minutes**
3.	Basketball Game	5:45 P.M. – ■ **8:00 P.M.**	2 hours 15 minutes	
4.	Mystery Theater	■ – 10:00 P.M. **8:00 P.M.**	2 hours	

Set D (pp. 138–141)

Solve. Use the calendar.

1. What date is 3 weeks after July 9? **July 30**
2. Enya went on a trip for 2 weeks and 3 days. She left on July 11. When did Enya return? **Possible answer: July 28**

July						
Sun	Mon	Tue	Wed	Thu	Fri	Sat
				1	2	3
4	5	6	7	8	9	10
11	12	13	14	15	16	17
18	19	20	21	22	23	24
25	26	27	28	29	30	31

144

Review/Test

CHECK VOCABULARY

Choose the best term from the box.

midnight
noon
schedule
elapsed time

1. 12:00 at night is _?_. (p. 132) **midnight**
2. The amount of time that passes from the start of an activity to the end of that activity is _?_. (p. 134) **elapsed time**
3. A _?_ is a table that lists activities or events and the times they happen. (p. 136) **schedule**

CHECK SKILLS

Write two ways you can read each time. Then write the time, using A.M. or P.M. (pp. 128–131, 132–133) **Possible answers are given.**

4. 
dance class
three twenty-seven; 27 min after three; 3:27 P.M.

5. 
bedtime
eight forty-two; 18 min before nine; 8:42 P.M.

6. eat lunch
twelve two; 2 min after twelve; 12:02 P.M.

7. 7:38
eat breakfast
seven thirty-eight, 22 min before eight, 7:38 A.M.

8. Estimate the time shown in Exercise 5 to the nearest half hour. (p. 129) **8:30 P.M.**

USE DATA For 9–10, use the schedule. (pp. 136–137)

BOB'S SATURDAY SCHEDULE	
Activity	**Time**
Breakfast	7:30 A.M. – 8:00 A.M.
Read book	8:00 A.M. – 8:45 A.M.
Play baseball	8:45 A.M.–10:15 A.M.

9. At what time does Bob start to read? **8:00 A.M.**
10. Which activity is the shortest? **breakfast**

CHECK PROBLEM SOLVING

For 11–12, use the time line. (pp. 142–143)

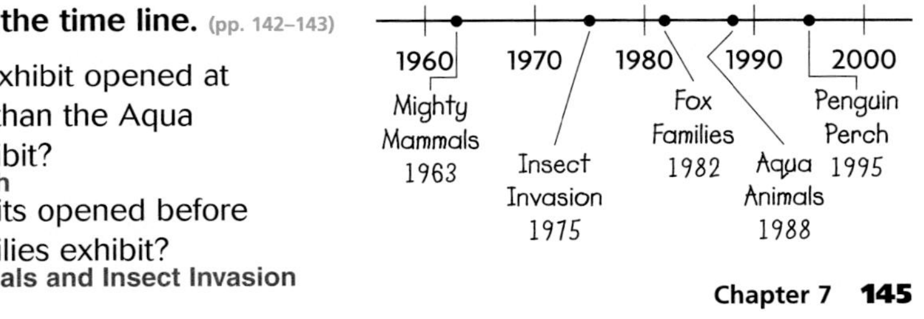

11. Which zoo exhibit opened at a later date than the Aqua Animals exhibit? **Penguin Perch**
12. Which exhibits opened before the Fox Families exhibit? **Mighty Mammals and Insect Invasion**

Review/Test

Purpose To check understanding of concepts, skills, and problem solving presented in Chapter 7

Using the Page

The Chapter 7 Review/Test can be used as a **review** or a **test**.

- Items 1–3 check understanding of concepts and new vocabulary.
- Items 4–10 check skill proficiency.
- Items 11–12 check students' abilities to choose and apply problem solving strategies to real-life time problems.

Suggest that students place the completed Chapter 7 Review/Test in their portfolios.

Using the Assessment Guide

- Multiple-choice format of Chapter 7 Posttest— See *Assessment Guide*, pp. AG41–42.
- Free-response format of Chapter 7 Posttest— See *Assessment Guide*, pp. AG43–44.

Using Student Self-Assessment

The How Did I Do? survey helps students assess what they have learned and how they learned it. This survey is available as a copying master in *Assessment Guide*, p. AGxvii.

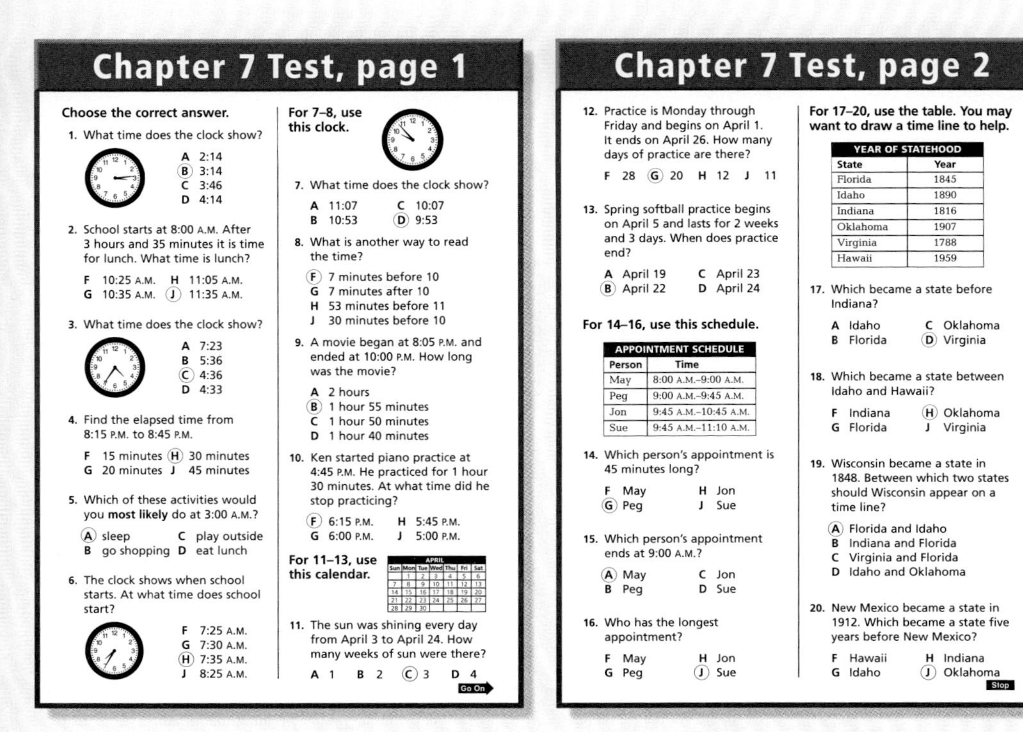

Chapter 7 Test, page 1

Choose the correct answer.

1. What time does the clock show?
A 2:14 (B) 3:14 C 3:46 D 4:14
2. School starts at 8:00 A.M. After 3 hours and 35 minutes it is time for lunch. What time is lunch?
F 10:25 A.M. H 11:05 A.M. G 10:35 A.M. (J) 11:35 A.M.
3. What time does the clock show?
A 7:23 B 5:36 (C) 4:36 D 4:33
4. Find the elapsed time from 8:15 P.M. to 8:45 P.M.
F 15 minutes (H) 30 minutes G 20 minutes J 45 minutes
5. Which of these activities would you **most likely** do at 3:00 A.M.?
(A) sleep C play outside B go shopping D eat lunch
6. The clock shows when school starts. At what time does school start?
F 7:25 A.M. G 7:30 A.M. (H) 7:35 A.M. J 8:25 A.M.

For 7–8, use this clock.

7. What time does the clock show?
A 11:07 C 10:07 B 10:53 (D) 9:53
8. What is another way to read the time?
(F) 7 minutes before 10 G 7 minutes after 10 H 53 minutes before 11 J 30 minutes before 10
9. A movie began at 8:05 P.M. and ended at 10:00 P.M. How long was the movie?
A 2 hours (B) 1 hour 55 minutes C 1 hour 50 minutes D 1 hour 40 minutes
10. Ken started piano practice at 4:45 P.M. He practiced for 1 hour 30 minutes. At what time did he stop practicing?
(F) 6:15 P.M. H 5:45 P.M. G 6:00 P.M. J 5:00 P.M.

For 11–13, use this calendar.

11. The sun was shining every day from April 3 to April 24. How many weeks of sun were there?
A 1 B 2 (C) 3 D 4

Go On

Chapter 7 Test, page 2

12. Practice is Monday through Friday and begins on April 1. It ends on April 26. How many days of practice are there?
F 28 (G) 20 H 12 J 11
13. Spring softball practice begins on April 5 and lasts for 2 weeks and 3 days. When does practice end?
A April 19 C April 23 (B) April 22 D April 24

For 14–16, use this schedule.

APPOINTMENT SCHEDULE	
Person	Time
May	8:00 A.M.–9:00 A.M.
Peg	9:00 A.M.–9:45 A.M.
Jon	9:45 A.M.–10:45 A.M.
Sue	9:45 A.M.–11:10 A.M.

14. Which person's appointment is 45 minutes long?
F May H Jon (G) Peg J Sue
15. Which person's appointment ends at 9:00 A.M.?
(A) May C Jon B Peg D Sue
16. Who has the longest appointment?
F May H Jon G Peg (J) Sue

For 17–20, use the table. You may want to draw a time line to help.

YEAR OF STATEHOOD	
State	Year
Florida	1845
Idaho	1890
Indiana	1816
Oklahoma	1907
Virginia	1788
Hawaii	1959

17. Which became a state before Indiana?
A Idaho C Oklahoma B Florida (D) Virginia
18. Which became a state between Idaho and Hawaii?
F Indiana (H) Oklahoma G Florida J Virginia
19. Wisconsin became a state in 1848. Between which two states should Wisconsin appear on a time line?
(A) Florida and Idaho B Indiana and Florida C Virginia and Florida D Idaho and Oklahoma
20. New Mexico became a state in 1912. Which became a state five years before New Mexico?
F Hawaii H Indiana G Idaho (J) Oklahoma

Stop

Getting Ready for the EOG Test

Chapters 1–7

Using the Pages

These pages may be used to help students get ready for the North Carolina EOG Test. The test items are written in the same style and arranged in the same format as those on the EOG Test.

The pages are cumulative. They cover the standards from the North Carolina Mathematics Standard Course of Study that have been taught up to this point in the text or in a previous grade. Each Getting Ready for the EOG Test also reviews the North Carolina mathematics strands shown below.

- Number and Operations
- Measurement
- Geometry
- Data Analysis and Probability
- Algebra

These pages can be assigned at the end of the chapter as classwork or as a homework assignment. You may want to have students use individual recording sheets presented in a multiple-choice (standardized) format. A Test Answer Sheet is available as a blackline master in the *Assessment Guide* (p. AGlii).

You may wish to have students describe how they solved each problem and share their solutions.

Getting Ready for the EOG Test

NUMBER AND OPERATIONS

1. Shannon spent $19 for a pair of pants and $8 for a T-shirt. She has $16 left. How much money did Shannon have before she bought the pants and shirt? **A**

A $43
B $39
C $34
D $31

2. Sam has 208 trading cards. Josh has 15 fewer cards than Sam. How many cards does Josh have? **B**

A 223
B 193
C 188
D 183

3. Which group of numbers is in order from *least* to *greatest*? **D**

A 371, 317, 731
B 568, 685, 658
C 924, 429, 294
D 578, 758, 875

4. Explain It Gina has 2 quarters, 3 dimes, and 2 nickels. Explain how to find the total value of these coins. See page 147.

MEASUREMENT AND GEOMETRY

5. Which unit would be *best* for measuring the amount of water used to fill a bathtub? **C**

A quart
B pint
C gallon
D cup

TIP **Understand the problem.** See item 6. The problem is asking for the unit that would be used to measure the length of a crayon. Read each choice to find the unit that would be used to measure the length of a small object.

6. Will wants to measure the length of a crayon. Which unit should he use? **D**

A yard
B foot
C pint
D inch

7. Explain It What is the length of this piece of yarn measured to the nearest inch? Explain your answer. See page 147.

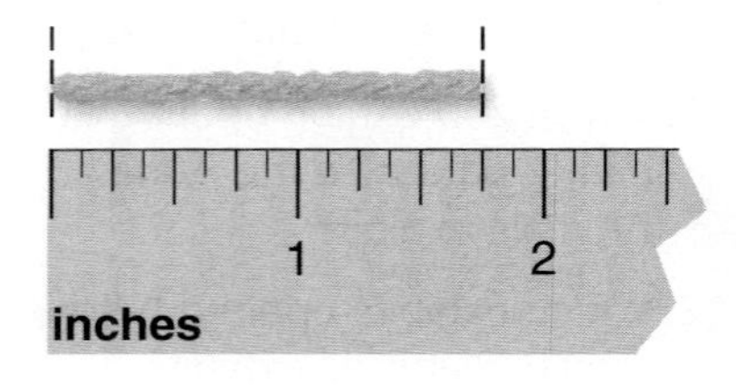

146

ALGEBRA

8. Which number will be next in this pattern? D

5, 10, 15, 20, 25

A 20
B 26
C 28
D 30

9. Rebecca went to art class on June 1, June 5, June 9, and June 13.

If this pattern continues, what is the next date when Rebecca will go to art class? C

A June 14
B June 15
C June 17
D June 19

10. Which number is the missing addend? B

9 + ■ = 17

A 9
B 8
C 7
D 6

11. **Explain It** Dan had 46 marbles. Russ gave Dan some more marbles. Then Dan had a total of 60 marbles. Write a number sentence to find how many marbles Russ gave to Dan. Explain how you chose the operation for your number sentence. **See below.**

DATA ANALYSIS AND PROBABILITY

12. Paul surveyed the students in his class to find the favorite color. How many votes were there for red? C

FAVORITE COLOR	
Color	Number of Votes
Red	卌 ||
Blue	卌 卌 |
Green	||||
Yellow	卌
Purple	|||

A 5
B 6
C 7
D 10

13. Look at the table above. How many more votes were there for blue than for yellow? D

A 3
B 4
C 5
D 6

14. **Explain It** How many members are there in the drama club? Explain how you found your answer. **See below.**

SCHOOL CLUBS	
Art Club	□□□
Drama Club	□□□□
Singing Club	□□□
Key: Each □ = 4 members.	

Chapters 1–7

Item Analysis

You may wish to use the item analysis to determine which North Carolina standards need additional review.

Item	North Carolina Standard	Lesson
1	1.02	1.4
2	1.02	5.4
3	1.01	3.3
4	1.06	6.1
5	(2) 2.01	Grade 2
6	(2) 2.01	Grade 2
7	(2) 2.01	Grade 2
8	5.01	2.5
9	5.01	2.5
10	5.04	1.2
11	5.04	1.6
12	(2) Goal 4	Grade 2
13	(2) Goal 4	Grade 2
14	(2) 4.01	Grade 2

SCORING RUBRIC
Explain It

2 Demonstrates a complete understanding of the problem and chooses an appropriate strategy to determine the solution

1 Demonstrates a partial understanding of the problem and chooses a strategy that does not lead to a complete and accurate solution

0 Demonstrates little understanding of the problem and shows little evidence of using any strategy to determine a solution

Explain It • Written Response

4. Possible answer: count on starting with the quarters and then the dimes and nickels: 25, 50, 60, 70, 80, 85, 90; 90¢ is the total value of the coins.

7. Possible answer: 2 inches; the length of the piece of yarn is closer to 2 inches than to 1 inch.

11. Possible answer: 46 + ■ = 60; a number was added to 46 to get a total of 60, so I used addition in the number sentence.

14. Possible answer: 16 members; each square stands for 4 members. Since there are 4 squares next to Drama Club, I skip-counted by 4s to find the total number of members.

UNIT 2

It's in the Bag

My Coin Keeper

Purpose To make a coin keeper and practice making change
Materials 35-mm film canister, eye screw, 2 feet of cord, 3 or 4 beads, play coins and bills, product cards, p. TR185, label for canister, tape

Using the Page

Preparing the Materials

- Assemble the materials needed for each student. You may wish to prepare the canisters as directed in Step 1 and cut the cord in 2-foot lengths. Play coins and bills are available in *Teacher's Resource Book*, pp. TR51–53.

Making the Project

- After students lace the cord through the eye screw, help them push both ends of the cording through the beads and tie a knot. After students have practiced with the problems on the product cards, help them write new problems on blank cards.

Extending the Project

- Help students set up a store with empty food boxes, cans, and cartons. Have students apply pressure-sensitive labels to the containers and write prices on the labels. Have students take turns as shopper and store clerk so each gets practice counting coins and bills and making change. Challenge students to make change using the fewest bills and coins. Or have students pay for items using equivalent sets of coins and bills.

IT'S IN THE BAG

My Coin Keeper

PROJECT Make your own coin keeper, and practice making change.

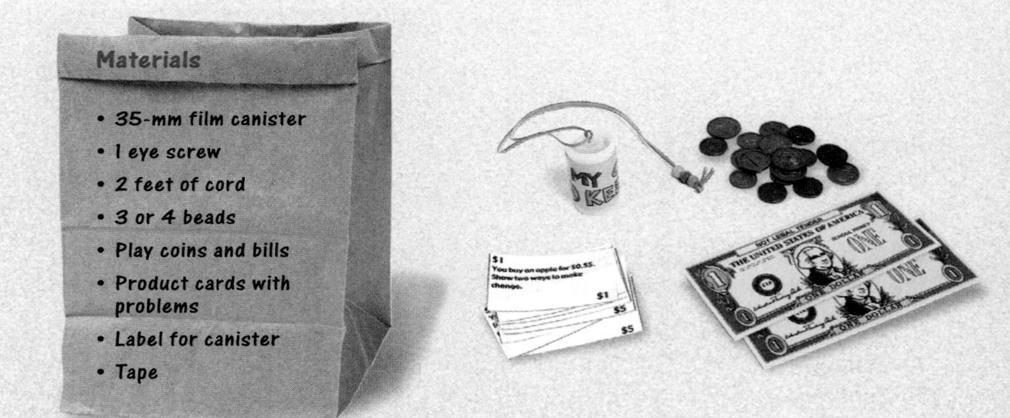

Directions

1. Push the eye screw into the lid of the canister (if this is difficult, poke a hole in the lid with a pen tip first). *(Picture A)*

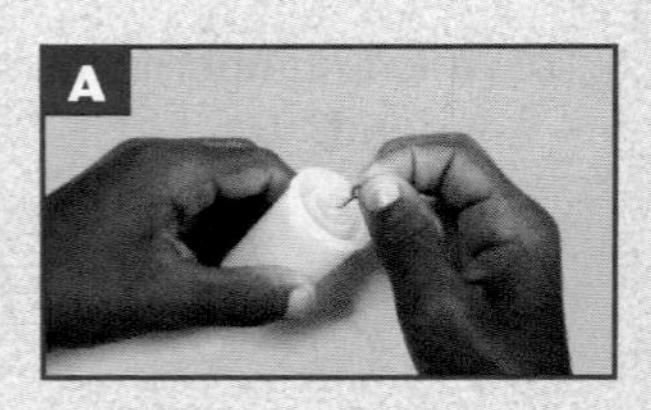

2. Lace one end of the cord through the eye screw, and then add 3 or 4 beads by pushing both ends of the cord through the beads. Tie a knot at the ends of the cord to make a loop. *(Picture B)*

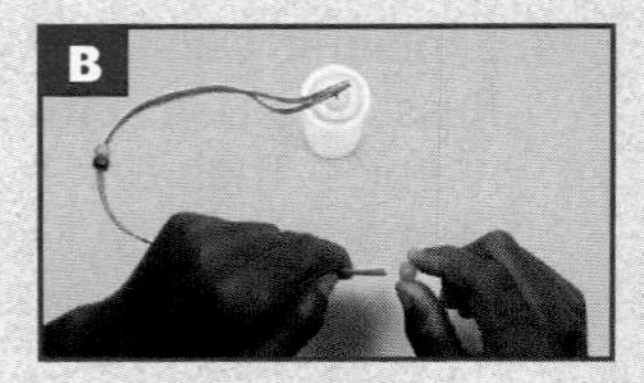

3. Write *My Coin Keeper* on the label, and tape it to the canister. Fill the canister with play coins and bills. *(Picture C)*
4. Work with a partner. Cut out and use the product cards to practice making change. Use the blank cards to write your own problems for the class to solve.

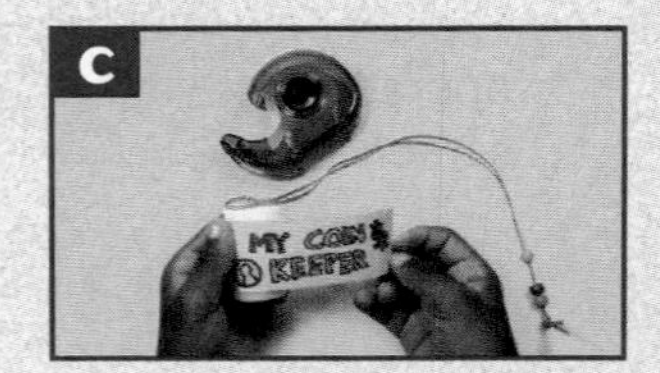

Challenge

Money Amounts to $100

Kari and her brother want to compare the amounts of money they saved. Kari saved $71.50, and her brother saved the amount shown below.

$50.00 → $70.00 → $75.00 → $75.10 → $75.15 → $75.16 → $75.17

So, Kari saved $71.50, and her brother saved $75.17. Who saved more?

$71.50 < $75.17, so Kari's brother saved more.

Talk About It

- How is comparing money amounts similar to comparing whole numbers? How is it different? **Possible answer: Similar: You compare the digits from left to right, just as you do with whole numbers. Different: You include a decimal point and a dollar sign with money amounts.**

Try It

For 1–2, use the sets of money below.

a. **b.**

1. What is the value of each set of money? **a: $81.61; b: $90.40**
2. Which set of money has the lesser value? **Set a**
3. Rodrigo has two $20 bills, one $10 bill, one $5 bill, one $1 bill, two quarters, one dime, and one nickel. Does he have enough money to buy a pair of gym shoes for $57.75? Explain. **No; Rodrigo has $56.65. $56.65 < $57.75**

Challenge

Money Amounts to $100

Objective **To extend the concepts and skills of Chapters 4–7**

Using the Page

- *Direct students' attention to the set of money for Kari's brother.*

  Reasoning **Why are the bills and coins arranged in this way?** It is simpler to count on from the bill with the greatest value to the coin with the least value.

  What skip-counting patterns can be used to count money? Possible answer: you can skip-count by fives, tens, twenties, and twenty-fives.

MODIFYING INSTRUCTION Use play bills and coins to model the amount of money Kari saved and the amount her brother saved. Ask volunteers to count aloud to find the total value.

Try It Provide play bills and coins for students to use when completing Exercises 1–3. Remind students that images include the heads and tails of coins.

Have students draw two different amounts of money that equal $100. Have students place the drawings in their portfolios.

Intervention and Extension Resources

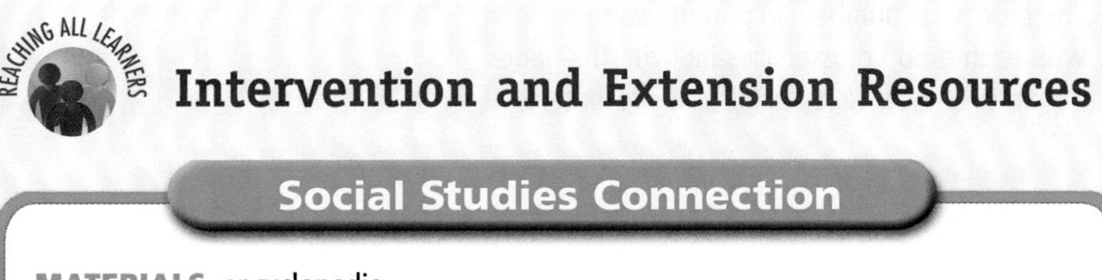

Social Studies Connection

MATERIALS encyclopedia

To **recognize the different denominations of bills,** have students research the Presidents shown on the $50, $20, $10, $5, and $1 bills. Have students write a paragraph about each President and make a poster of their findings. Have students present their posters to the class.

VISUAL

UNIT 2

Study Guide and Review

Purpose To help students review concepts and skills presented in Chapters 4–7

Using the Pages

✓ Assessment Checkpoint

The Study Guide and Review includes content from Chapters 4–7.

Chapter 4

4.1 Estimate Sums
4.2 Hands On: Addition with Regrouping
4.3 Add 3- and 4-Digit Numbers
4.4 Problem Solving Strategy: *Predict and Test*
4.5 Choose a Method
4.6 Algebra: Expressions and Number Sentences

Chapter 5

5.1 Estimate Differences
5.2 Hands On: Subtraction with Regrouping
5.3 Subtract Across Zeros
5.4 Subtract 3- and 4-Digit Numbers
5.5 Choose a Method
5.6 Problem Solving Skill: *Estimate or Exact Answer*

Chapter 6

6.1 Count Bills and Coins
6.2 Problem Solving Strategy: *Make a Table*
6.3 Compare Money Amounts
6.4 Hands On: Make Change
6.5 Add and Subtract Money

Chapter 7

7.1 Tell Time
7.2 A.M. and P.M.
7.3 Hands On: Elapsed Time
7.4 Use a Schedule
7.5 Use a Calendar
7.6 Problem Solving Skill: *Sequence Events*

UNIT 2

Study Guide and Review

VOCABULARY

Choose the best term from the box.

calendar
schedule
A.M.
P.M.

1. A table that lists activities or events and the times they happen is called a __?__. (p. 136) **schedule**
2. The hours from 12 midnight to 12 noon are __?__ hours. (p. 132) **A.M.**

STUDY AND SOLVE

Chapter 4

Add 3- and 4-digit numbers.

$$\begin{array}{r} \overset{1}{4}37 \\ +155 \\ \hline 592 \end{array} \qquad \begin{array}{r} 3,\overset{1}{9}\overset{1}{8}7 \\ +2,532 \\ \hline 6,519 \end{array}$$

Find the sum. Estimate to check. (pp. 72–73, 76–79)

3. 192 + 432 = **624**
4. 643 + 289 = **932**
5. 534 + 846 = **1,380**
6. 4,276 + 1,071 = **5,347**
7. 2,008 + 6,439 = **8,447**
8. 5,976 + 8,668 = **14,644**

Chapter 5

Subtract 3- and 4-digit numbers.

$$\begin{array}{r} \overset{8\,13}{8\,9\,3} \\ -5\,0\,8 \\ \hline 3\,8\,5 \end{array} \qquad \begin{array}{r} \overset{2\;\;9\;\;10\;10}{3,0\,0\,0} \\ -1,6\,5\,0 \\ \hline 1,3\,5\,0 \end{array}$$

Subtract. (pp. 90–99)

9. 562 − 313 = **249**
10. 430 − 287 = **143**
11. 406 − 89 = **317**
12. 6,314 − 2,509 = **3,805**
13. 2,000 − 1,734 = **266**
14. 3,508 − 2,779 = **729**

Chapter 6

Add or subtract money amounts.

Add or subtract money amounts like whole numbers. Then write the sum or difference in dollars and cents.

$$\begin{array}{r} \$\overset{1}{2}.59 \\ +\$3.17 \\ \hline \$5.76 \end{array} \qquad \begin{array}{r} \$7.\overset{3}{4}\overset{12}{2} \\ -\$2.23 \\ \hline \$5.19 \end{array}$$

Find the sum or difference. Estimate to check. (pp. 120–121)

15. \$3.58 + \$2.21 = **\$5.79**
16. \$2.46 + \$6.54 = **\$9.00**
17. \$5.75 − \$2.30 = **\$3.45**
18. \$50.00 − \$ 6.49 = **\$43.51**

The blue page numbers in parentheses provided with each group of exercises indicate the pages on which the concept or skill was presented.

Count on to make change.

A comb costs $0.69. Nikki pays with a $1 bill. How much change should she get?

$0.69

$0.69 → $0.70 → $0.75 → $1.00

1 penny, 1 nickel, and 1 quarter equal $0.31. So, Nikki will get $0.31.

Copy and complete the table. (pp. 118–119)

	COST OF ITEM	AMOUNT PAID	AMOUNT OF CHANGE
19.	$1.25	$2.00	■ **$0.75**
20.	$3.72	$5.00	■ **$1.28**
21.	$6.34	$10.00	■ **$3.66**
22.	$0.17	$1.00	■ **$0.83**

Chapter 7

Find elapsed time.

Jerry played basketball from 11:30 A.M. to 1:45 P.M. How long did Jerry play?

Think:
From 11:30 A.M. to 1:30 P.M. is 2 hours.
From 1:30 P.M. to 1:45 P.M. is 15 minutes.

So, Jerry played for 2 hours 15 minutes.

Copy and complete the schedule. (pp. 134–135)

	Activity	Time	Elapsed Time
23.	Reading	11:45 A.M.–12:30 P.M.	■ **45 minutes**
24.	Lunch	12:30 P.M.–1:00 P.M.	■ **30 minutes**
25.	Soccer	1:00 P.M.–■ **2:30 P.M.**	1 hour 30 minutes

PROBLEM SOLVING PRACTICE

Solve. (pp. 74–75, 102–103, 114–115)

26. Joyce bought 14 yellow apples and 17 red apples to bake holiday pies. How many apples did she buy in all? **31 apples**

27. Susan has 10 more goldfish than Gary. Together, they own 50 goldfish. How many goldfish does each have? **Susan has 30 goldfish; Gary has 20 goldfish.**

28. Ann has one $1 bill, 8 dimes, and 7 nickels. What equivalent sets of bills and coins can she use to buy a notebook that costs $1.35? **one $1 bill, 3d, 1n; one $1 bill, 2d, 3n; one $1 bill, 1d, 5n; one $1 bill, 7n**

29. Jim has one $5 bill, two $1 bills, 5 quarters, 2 dimes, and 4 nickels. What equivalent sets of bills and coins can he use to make $7.65? **See above.**

29. one $5 bill, two $1 bills, 2q, 1d, 1n; one $5 bill, two $1 bills, 1q, 2d, 4n; one $5 bill, one $1 bill, 5q, 2d, 4n

✓ Assessment Checkpoint

Portfolio

Portfolio Suggestions The portfolio represents the growth, talents, achievements, and reflections of the mathematics learner. Students might spend a short time selecting work samples for their portfolios and completing A Guide to My Math Portfolio from *Assessment Guide*, page AGxix.

You may want to have students respond to the following questions:

- **What new understanding of math have I developed in the past several weeks?**
- **What growth in understanding or skills can I see in my work?**
- **What can I do to improve my understanding of math ideas?**
- **What would I like to learn more about?**

For information on how to organize, share, and evaluate portfolios, see *Assessment Guide*, page AGxviii.

Use the item analysis in the **Intervention** chart to diagnose students' errors. You may wish to reinforce content or remediate misunderstandings by using the text pages or lesson resources.

Unit Test

- Multiple-choice format of Unit 2 Posttest–See *Assessment Guide*, pp. AG45–48.
- Free-Response format of Unit 2 Posttest–See *Assessment Guide*, pp. AG49–52.

Study Guide and Review Intervention • How to Help Options

Items	Text Pages	Reteach and Practice Resources
3–8	72–73, 76–79	Worksheets for Lessons 4.3, 4.5
9–14	90–99	Worksheets for Lessons 5.2, 5.3, 5.4, 5.5
15–18	120–121	Worksheets for Lesson 6.5
19–22	118–119	Worksheets for Lesson 6.4
23–25	134–135	Worksheets for Lesson 7.3
26–29	74–75, 102–103, 114–115	Worksheets for Lessons 4.4, 5.6, 6.2

UNIT 2

Performance Assessment

Purpose To provide performance assessment tasks for Chapters 4–7

Using the Page

- *Have students work individually or in pairs as an alternative to formal assessment.*
- *Use the performance indicators and work samples below to evaluate Tasks A–B.*

See *Performance Assessment* for

- a complete scoring rubric, p. PAx for this unit.
- additional student work samples for this unit.
- copying masters for this unit.

Portfolio You may suggest that students place completed *Performance Assessment* tasks in their portfolios.

PERFORMANCE ASSESSMENT

TASK A • MEETING A GOAL

The third-grade classes at Cliffside Elementary School are collecting toys to donate to the children's hospital. The chart shows how many toys have already been collected.

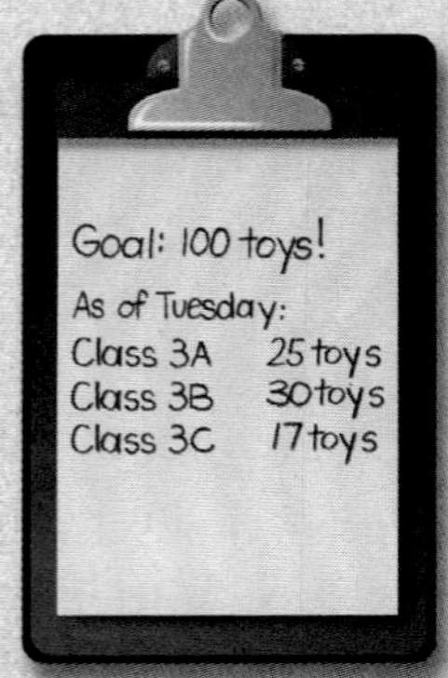

a. Explain how you can find out how the three classes have done so far with the toy collection. Show all your work. **See below.**

b. What do the third graders need to do to reach their goal? Show all of your work. **They need to collect 28 more toys to meet the goal of 100 toys. 100 – 72 = 28**

a. Possible answer: Add the number of toys the classes have collected so far; 25 + 30 + 17, or 72 toys have been collected so far.

b. Possible answer: any amount from $3.01 through $5.62

c. Possible answer: They could have saved between $8.64 and $11.25; not enough; all amounts between $8.64 and $11.25 are less than $12.

TASK B • SAVING MONEY

Materials: bills and coins

Becka and Martin are saving money to buy a soccer ball.

a. Becka has saved $5.63. Use bills and coins to show $5.63 in different ways. Copy and complete the table. **Check students' tables.**

b. Martin has saved more than $3.00 but less than Becka. Write an amount Martin could have saved. **See above.**

c. How much could Becka and Martin have saved in all? Is this enough to buy a soccer ball that costs $12.00? Explain. **See above.**

Possible answers:

$1 bills	Quarters	Dimes	Nickels	Pennies
4	6	1	0	3
4	5	3	1	3
3	8	5	2	3
3	7	8	1	3

Performance Indicators

Task A

A student with a Level 3 paper

✓ Interprets a chart.

✓ Finds the sum of three whole numbers.

✓ Finds the difference of two whole numbers.

Task B

A student with a Level 3 paper

✓ Completes the table with equivalent amounts of money.

✓ Determines an amount of money between two given amounts.

✓ Finds the sum of two amounts of money.

✓ Determines whether the children have enough money for their purchase and explains the answer.

Work Samples for Task A and Task B

Name ______ UNIT 2 • TASK A

Meeting a Goal

The third grade classes at Cliffside Elementary School are collecting toys to donate to the children's hospital. The chart shows how many toys have already been collected.

a. Explain how you can find out how the three classes have done so far with the toy collection. Show all your work.

b. What do the third graders need to do to make their goal? Show all your work.

Goal: 100 toys! As of Tuesday: Class 3A 25 toys, Class 3B 30 toys, Class 3C 17 toys

Show your work.

25 + 30 + 17 = 72; 100 – 72 = 28. They have 72 toys & they need 28 more. I took 72 away from 100 & got 28. I added 25+30+17 & I got 72.

Level 3 This student shows a good understanding of reading a chart. Computation is complete and accurate. Explanations are included.

Name ______ UNIT 2 • TASK B

Saving Money

Materials: bills and coins

Becka and Martin are saving money to buy a soccer ball.

a. Becka has saved $5.63. Use bills and coins to show $5.63 in different ways. Complete the table to show the ways you find.

$1 bills	Quarters	Dimes	Nickels	Pennies
4	4	6	0	3
4	2	10	2	3
3	8	4	4	3
3	7	4	8	3

b. Martin has saved more than $3.00, but less than Becka. Write an amount Martin could have saved. $4.00

c. How much could Becka and Martin have saved in all? Is this enough to buy a soccer ball that costs $12.00? Explain. NO

Show your work.

Because they did not have enough money

$5.63 + $4.00 = $9.63

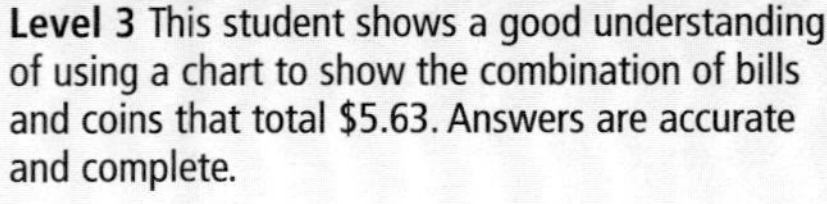

Level 3 This student shows a good understanding of using a chart to show the combination of bills and coins that total $5.63. Answers are accurate and complete.

Add and Subtract Money

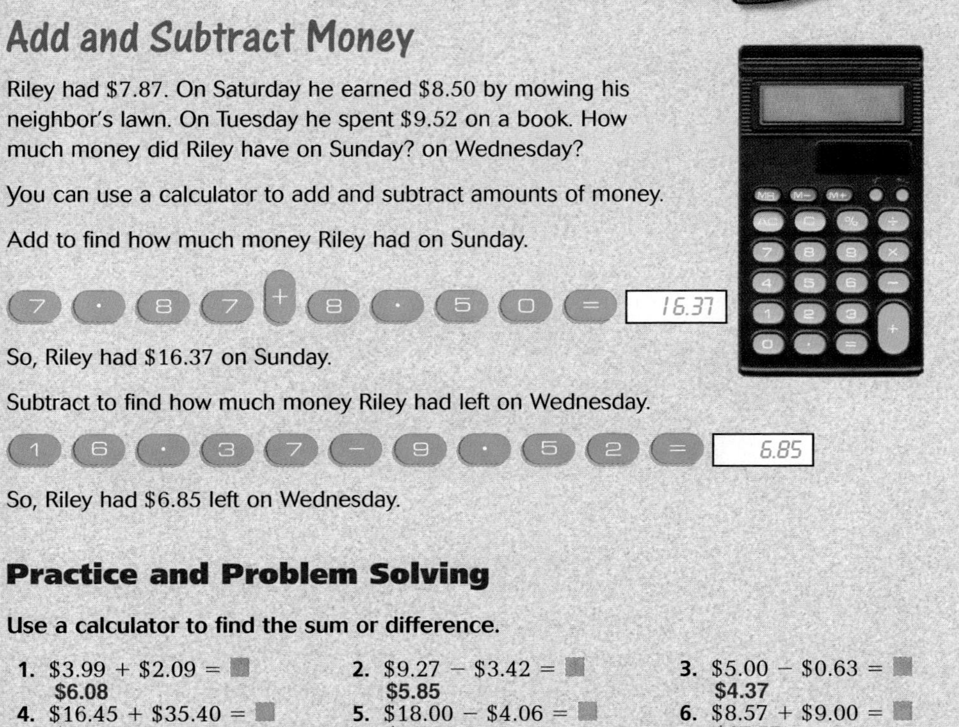

Riley had $7.87. On Saturday he earned $8.50 by mowing his neighbor's lawn. On Tuesday he spent $9.52 on a book. How much money did Riley have on Sunday? on Wednesday?

You can use a calculator to add and subtract amounts of money.

Add to find how much money Riley had on Sunday.

7 . 8 7 + 8 . 5 0 = 16.37

So, Riley had $16.37 on Sunday.

Subtract to find how much money Riley had left on Wednesday.

1 6 . 3 7 − 9 . 5 2 = 6.85

So, Riley had $6.85 left on Wednesday.

Practice and Problem Solving

Use a calculator to find the sum or difference.

1. $3.99 + $2.09 = ■ **$6.08**
2. $9.27 − $3.42 = ■ **$5.85**
3. $5.00 − $0.63 = ■ **$4.37**
4. $16.45 + $35.40 = ■ **$51.85**
5. $18.00 − $4.06 = ■ **$13.94**
6. $8.57 + $9.00 = ■ **$17.57**
7. Josh wants to buy a CD that costs $11.50. He has $8.63. How much more money does Josh need to buy the CD? **$2.87 more**
8. **REASONING** Tanya has 3 quarters, 2 dimes, and 4 pennies. She spends $0.53. How much money does Tanya have left? **$0.46**
9. Amber has $3.45. Then she gets a birthday gift of $12.00. How much money does Amber have in all? **$15.45**
10. **Write a problem** about adding or subtracting money. Use a calculator to solve. **Check students' problems.**

GO ON-LINE **Multimedia Math Glossary** www.harcourtschool.com/mathglossary

Vocabulary Power Look up *decimal point* in the Multimedia Math Glossary. Write a money amount that uses a dollar sign and decimal point. **Check students' work.**

Technology Linkup

Objective To add and subtract money on a calculator.

Using the Page

Point out to students that this problem is a multi-step problem. Have students identify the operations needed and in which order they will be used.

- *Direct students' attention to the second step of the problem.*

  Reasoning After you find how much money Riley had on Sunday, is it necessary to clear your calculator before you subtract the amount he spent on Tuesday? Explain. No; after you find the total Riley earned, $16.37, you can simply enter the minus sign, the amount Riley spent, $9.52, and the equal sign. The calculator will automatically subtract $9.52 from the sum.

Using the Calculator

Explain to students that when performing more than one related operation on a calculator, they should not clear the screen each time they perform a new operation. On some calculator models, to clear all previous operations, students can press Clear and On/Off together. The display will read MEM CLEARED to show that all operations have been deleted.

Practice and Problem Solving

Remind students that they do not need to look for a dollar sign key on the calculator. All they need to enter are the numbers and the decimal point to find the answer. They will need to write the dollar sign when recording the sums and differences.

Multimedia Math Glossary

Decimal point, estimate, rounding, and all other vocabulary words in this unit can be found in the Harcourt Multimedia Math Glossary. **www.harcourtschool.com/mathglossary**

Problem Solving

in North Carolina

Purpose To provide additional practice for concepts and skills in Chapters 4–7

Using the Page

MOREHEAD PLANETARIUM AND SCIENCE CENTER

- *Direct students' attention to the sign.*
  Jeff and his father left the planetarium 25 minutes before it closed on Saturday evening. At what time did they leave the planetarium? 9:05 P.M.
  In addition to buying 1 adult ticket and 1 child's ticket, Jeff's father bought a poster that cost $2.49. How much did Jeff's father spend in all? $10.49
- *After students complete Exercise 1, ask:*
  Suppose Mr. Williams purchased 3 adult tickets with a $20 bill. How much change would he receive? $6.50
  List the fewest coins and bills that could be used to make the change. one $5 bill, one $1 bill, 2 quarters

Extension Challenge students to plan a new schedule for the planetarium. Their schedules should keep the planetarium open the same number of hours each week. The planetarium should be closed on Monday. Check students' work. The planetarium should be open for 43 hours each week.

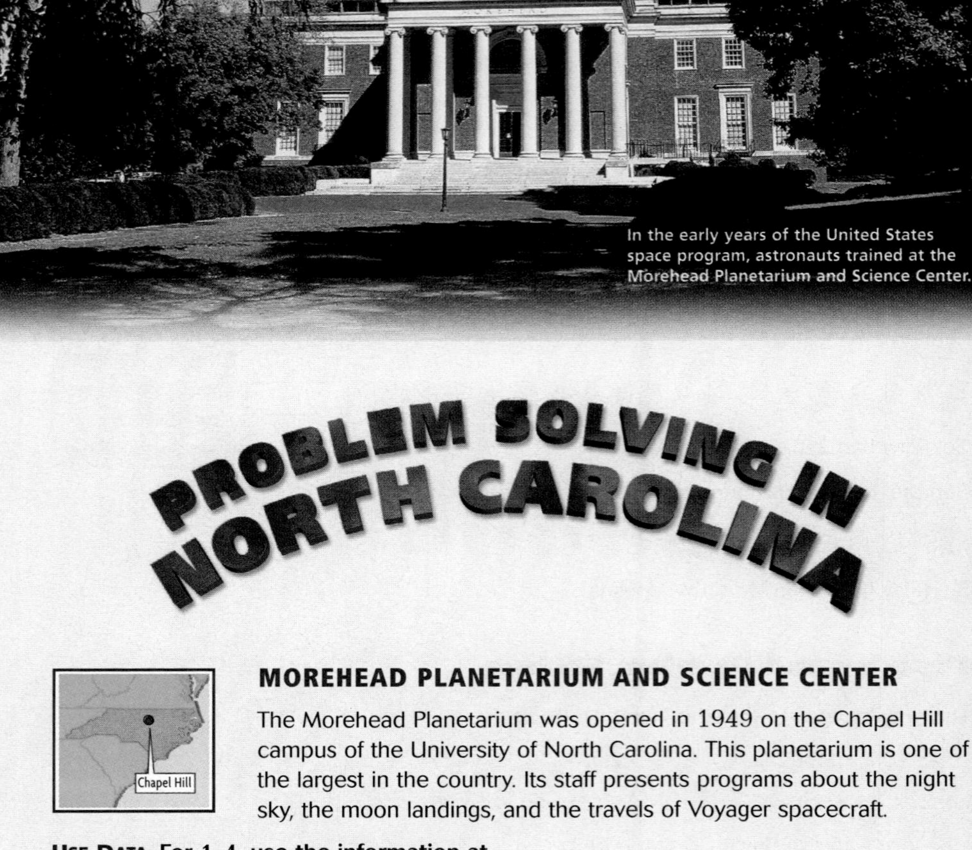
In the early years of the United States space program, astronauts trained at the Morehead Planetarium and Science Center.

PROBLEM SOLVING IN NORTH CAROLINA

MOREHEAD PLANETARIUM AND SCIENCE CENTER

Chapel Hill

The Morehead Planetarium was opened in 1949 on the Chapel Hill campus of the University of North Carolina. This planetarium is one of the largest in the country. Its staff presents programs about the night sky, the moon landings, and the travels of Voyager spacecraft.

USE DATA For 1–4, use the information at the right.

1. What is the total cost of admission for two adults and two children? **$16.00**
2. Mrs. Barnes pays for her admission with a $10 bill. How much change should she receive? **$5.50**
3. Jason arrived at the planetarium at 11:30 A.M. and stayed until 5:00 P.M. How many hours was he there? **$5\frac{1}{2}$ hours**
4. **STRETCH YOUR THINKING** How many hours a week is the planetarium open? **43 hours**

Admission
Adults $4.50
Children $3.50
Hours
Sunday–Friday 12:30 P.M. – 5:00 P.M.
Saturday 10:00 A.M. – 5:00 P.M.
Thursday–Saturday 6:30 P.M. – 9:30 P.M.

THE STAR THEATER

At shows in the planetarium's Star Theater, you can sit under a stainless-steel dome and watch the movements of the sun, moon, planets, and stars.

USE DATA For 1–2, use the table.

1. Tickets go on sale 30 minutes before each show begins. Adam wants to see *Carolina Skies* on Friday. At what time should he arrive at the theater to make sure he gets a ticket? **6:30 P.M.**
2. On Saturday, Jessie went to see *Larry, Cat in Space* and *Solar System Adventure. Solar System Adventure* ended at 12:30 P.M. How long was she in the Star Theater? **2 hours**
3. The Star Theater has 300 seats. There were 182 people at one show. How many seats were empty? **118 seats**
4. The Star Theater has been used as a giant classroom since 1949. For how many years has it been used as a classroom? **Answers will vary; in 2004, 55 years**
5. Each year more than 80,000 students attend Star Theater shows and classes. About how many students visit the Star Theater in 3 years? **about 240,000 children**

SHOW SCHEDULE

Day	Program	Time
Friday	Carolina Skies	7:00 P.M.
	Sky Safari	8:00 P.M.
Saturday	Larry, Cat in Space	10:30 A.M.
	Solar System Adventure	11:30 A.M., 3:30 P.M.
	Extreme Weather	12:30 P.M.
	Sky Safari	1:30 P.M., 8:00 P.M.
	Sol & Company	2:30 P.M.
	Carolina Skies	7:00 P.M.

▼ This star projector displays about 8,900 stars on the dome ceiling of the Star Theater. The projector weighs 5,000 pounds.

Using the Page

THE STAR THEATER

- *After students complete Exercise 3, ask:* **On Thursday, a section of the theater was reserved for a visiting class that included 32 students, 1 teacher, and 2 parents. Write an expression that could be used to find the number of seats in the theater that were not reserved.** 300 − 35
- *Direct students' attention to the Show Schedule and the planetarium hours on page 154.* **Reasoning The Star Theater closes on Saturday after the last showing of *Solar System Adventure* and reopens before the start of *Carolina Skies.* If *Solar System Adventure* lasts 1 hour, how long is the Star Theater closed before reopening on Saturday evenings?** 2 hr 30 min

Extension Encourage students to write problems based on the data given in the show schedule. Have them exchange problems with a classmate and solve. Check students' work.

Teaching Notes

Additional Ideas:

Good Questions to Ask:

Additional Resources:

Notes for Next Time:

Unit at a Glance

CHAPTER 8

CHAPTER 9

CHAPTER 10

CHAPTER 11

PROFESSIONAL DEVELOPMENT

EXCERPTS FROM THE RESEARCH

"Instructional materials and classroom teaching should help students learn increasingly abbreviated procedures for producing number combinations rapidly and accurately without always having to refer to tables or other aids." (Kilpatrick, Swafford, and Bradford, 2001)

Assessment Options

Assessing Prior Knowledge

Determine whether students have the required prerequisite concepts and skills.

Check What You Know, PE pp. 157, 175, 193, 211

Test Preparation

Provide review and practice for chapter and standardized tests.

Getting Ready for the EOG Test, PE pp. 159, 161, 163, 167, 172–173, 177, 179, 185, 187, 190–191, 195, 197, 201, 205, 208–209, 215, 217, 219, 226–227

Study Guide and Review, PE pp. 230–231

Formal Assessment

Assess students' mastery of chapter concepts and skills.

Chapter Review/Test, PE pp. 171, 189, 207, 225

Pretest and Posttest Options

Chapter Test, Form A

pp. AG53–54, 57–58, 61–62, 65–66

Chapter Test, Form B

pp. AG55–56, 59–60, 63–64, 67–68

Unit 3 Test • Chapters 8–11

Form A, pp. AG69–72

Form B, pp. AG73–76

Daily Assessment

Obtain daily feedback on students' understanding of concepts.

Quick Review, See the first page of each PE lesson.

Getting Ready for the EOG Test

See the last page of each PE skill lesson.

Number of the Day

See the first page of each TE lesson.

Problem of the Day

See the first page of each TE lesson.

Lesson Quiz

See the *Assess* section of each TE lesson.

Performance Assessment

Assess students' understanding of concepts applied to real-world situations.

Performance Assessment (Tasks A–B); PE p. 232; pp. PA21–22

Student Self-Assessment

Have students evaluate their own work.

How Did I Do?, p. AGxvii

A Guide to My Math Portfolio, p. AGxix

Math Journal

See *Write* in the *Assess* section of each TE lesson and TE pages 168B, 182B, 186B, 198B, 202B, 222B.

Harcourt Assessment System

Make and grade chapter tests electronically.

This software includes:

- **multiple-choice items**
- **free-response items**
- **customizable tests**
- **the means to build your own tests from available items**
- **customizable student and class reports**

Portfolio

Portfolio opportunities appear throughout the Pupil and Teacher's Editions.

Suggested work samples:

Problem Solving Project, TE pp. 156, 174, 192, 210

Write About It, PE pp. 163, 177, 187, 195, 221

Chapter Review/Test, PE pp. 171, 189, 207, 225

AG Assessment Guide **TE** Teacher's Edition **PA** Performance Assessment **PE** Pupil Edition

Correlation to STANDARDIZED TESTS

LEARNING GOAL		TAUGHT IN LESSONS	CAT/ TERRA NOVA	CTBS/ TERRA NOVA	ITBS FORM A	MAT 8	STANFORD 10	NORTH CAROLINA STANDARDS
8A	To connect multiplication sentences with addition sentences and to draw arrays to represent multiplication sentences	8.1, 8.3	•	•	•	•	•	1.03
8B	To write multiplication facts with factors 2 and 5 using a variety of formats and strategies	8.2	•	•	•	•	•	1.03
8C	To write multiplication facts with the factor 3 and to write products by using the Order Property of Multiplication	8.4	•	•	•	•	•	1.03 1.04
8D	To solve problems by using an appropriate skill such as *evaluate too much/too little information*	8.5	•	•	•	•	•	1.03 1.06
9A	To write multiplication facts with factors 0, 1, and 4 using a variety of formats and strategies	9.1, 9.2, 9.4	•	•	•	•	•	1.03 1.04
9B	To identify and write missing factors	9.5		•	•	•		1.03 5.04
9C	To solve problems by using an appropriate strategy such as *find a number pattern*	9.3	•	•		•	•	5.01
10A	To write multiplication facts with factors 6, 7, and 8 using a variety of formats and strategies	10.1, 10.2, 10.4, 10.5	•	•	•	•	•	1.03
10B	To solve problems by using an appropriate strategy such as *use a pictograph*	10.3	•	•	•	•	•	1.03 4.01
11A	To write multiplication facts with factors 9 and 10 using a variety of formats and strategies	11.1	•	•	•	•	•	1.03 5.01
11B	To identify and write the rule for a linear pattern, and to extend the pattern and solve problems by using the rule	11.2	•	•	•	•	•	5.01
11C	To write products of 2 or 3 factors by using multiplication Properties such as the Identity, Zero, Commutative, Associative, and Distributive Properties to solve problems	11.3, 11.4	•	•		•	•	1.03 1.04
11D	To solve problems by using an appropriate skill such as *solve multistep problems*	11.5	•	•	•	•	•	1.06

Technology Links

The Harcourt Learning Site

www.harcourtschool.com

Visit **THE LEARNING SITE** at **www.harcourtschool.com** for a variety of activities and resources that can be used to explore, reinforce, practice, and extend the learning of the chapter.

- Multimedia Math Glossary
- Activities and instructional resources
- E-Lab activities
- Show Me math models

Intervention CD-ROMs

These CD-ROMs help you

- assess prerequisite concepts and skills for each chapter and assess problem-solving at point of use.
- diagnose to determine whether intervention is necessary or if enrichment is appropriate for a concept or skill.
- diagnose to determine whether intervention is necessary for a specific problem-solving strategy or skill.
- prescribe intervention for concepts, skills, and problem-solving strategies and skills.
- provide enrichment for students who mastered the prerequisite concepts and skills.

Harcourt Mega Math CD-ROM Series

The learning activities in this exciting, new, comprehensive math software series complement, enrich, and enhance the Pupil Edition lessons.

Harcourt Mega Math Correlation

Lesson	Activity/Level	Skill
8.1	Country Countdown, Counting Critters/Level V	Connect Addition and Multiplication
8.2	Country Countdown, Counting Critters/Level Z	Multiply with 2 and 5
8.3	Country Countdown, Counting Critters/Level W	Arrays
9.2 & 9.4	The Number Games, Up, Up, and Array/Level A	Multiplication Facts to 5
10.3	The Number Games, Arachna Graph/Level A	Use a Pictograph
10.4	The Number Games, Up, Up, and Array/Level B	Multiplication Facts Through 8
11.1	The Number Games, Up, Up, and Array/Level C Ice Station Exploration Arctic Algebra, Level C	Multiplication Facts Through 10
11.2	Ice Station Exploration, Arctic Algebra, Level D	Find a Rule

For the Student

The following technology can be used with students that need more instruction with skills or problem solving, and with students that will benefit from reinforcement, practice, and extension of skills from this chapter.

Intervention CD-ROMs

- Support and enrichment for prerequisite skills
- Support for problem solving

Harcourt Mega Math CD-ROMs

- Reinforcement, practice and extension

Counting Critters
Skill Level W

The Harcourt Learning Site
www.harcourtschool.com

- Multimedia Math Glossary
- E-Lab activities
- Show me math models
- Games and activities

For the Teacher

Intervention CD-ROMs

- Diagnose and prescribe intervention for prerequisite skills.
- Provide enrichment for prerequisite skills.
- Diagnose and prescribe intervention for problem-solving strategies and skills.

Harcourt Mega Math CD-ROMs

- Customize additional practice for each student in your class.
- The leveled activities increase in difficulty as students progress.

The Harcourt Learning Site
www.harcourtschool.com

- Find activities and other resources.

Harcourt Assessment System

This software includes:

- Online test taking and automatic scoring
- A bank of items from which to build tests
- Immediate feedback on students' performance
- Correlation of items to textbook and state standards
- Comprehensive program management and class reporting
- Prescriptive reports

ePlanner

This on-line resource allows you to:

- Customize planning and pacing.
- Select resources for daily instruction.
- Reorder content to meet your state, district, or local needs.

For the Parent

The Harcourt Learning Site
www.harcourtschool.com

Encourage parents to visit the Math section of the Harcourt Learning Site to help them reinforce mathematics vocabulary, concepts, and skills with their children.

- Multimedia Math Glossary
- E-Lab interactive learning experiences
- Show Me math models
- Family Involvement tips and activities

Cross-Curricular Connections

Use these topics to help integrate mathematics into your daily planning.

See the pages indicated to find out more about each topic.

Science

- **Spiders,** TE p. 196B
- **Space missions,** TE p. 198B

Writing

- **Word problems,** TE p. 168B
- **Short paragraph,** TE p. 182B
- **Explanation,** TE p. 186B
- **Questions,** TE p. 198B
- **Mystery number clues,** TE p. 202B
- **Multistep word problem,** TE p. 222B

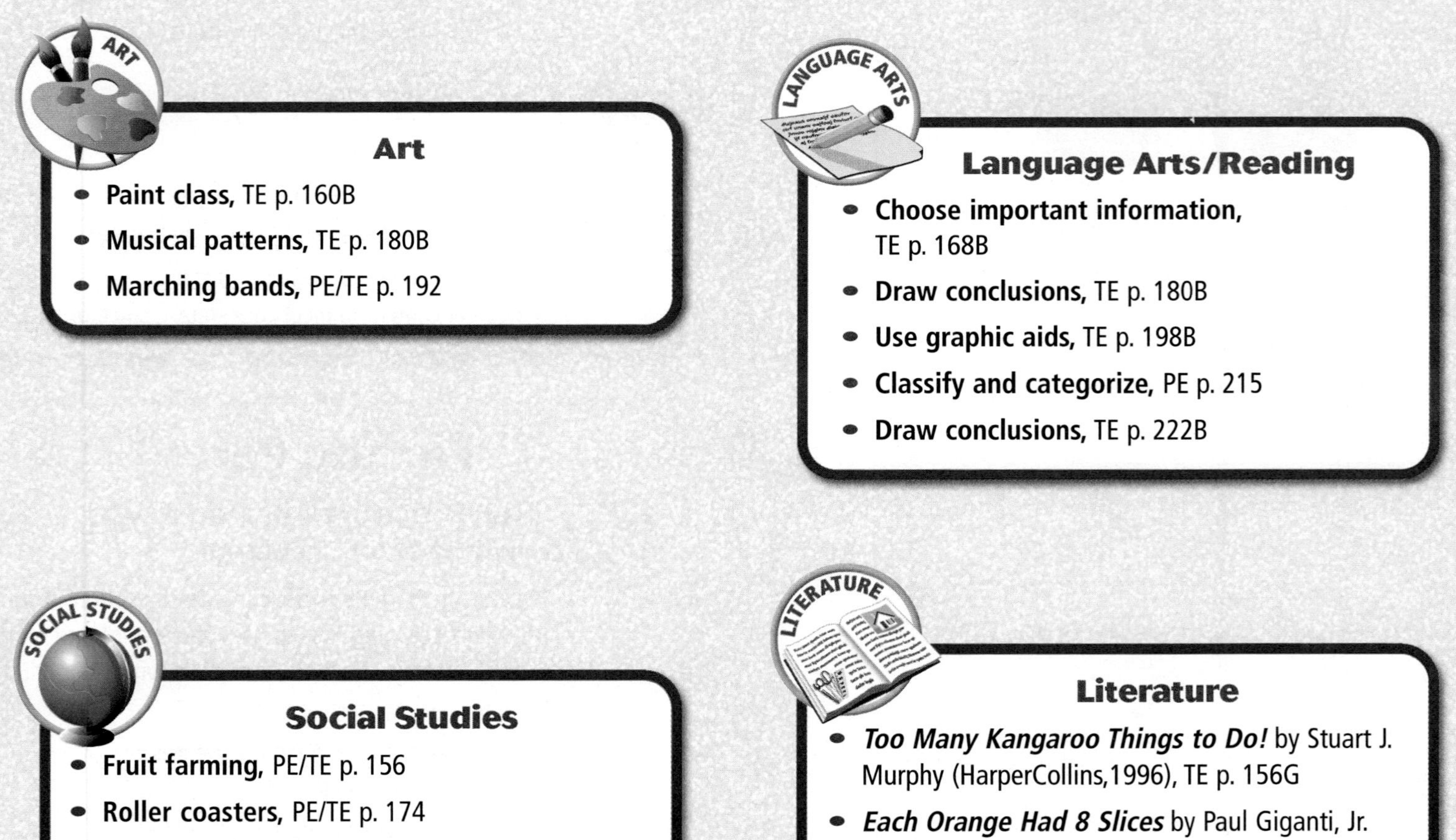

Art

- **Paint class,** TE p. 160B
- **Musical patterns,** TE p. 180B
- **Marching bands,** PE/TE p. 192

Language Arts/Reading

- **Choose important information,** TE p. 168B
- **Draw conclusions,** TE p. 180B
- **Use graphic aids,** TE p. 198B
- **Classify and categorize,** PE p. 215
- **Draw conclusions,** TE p. 222B

Social Studies

- **Fruit farming,** PE/TE p. 156
- **Roller coasters,** PE/TE p. 174
- **Dog sled teams,** PE/TE p. 210

Literature

- ***Too Many Kangaroo Things to Do!*** by Stuart J. Murphy (HarperCollins,1996), TE p. 156G
- ***Each Orange Had 8 Slices*** by Paul Giganti, Jr. (Greenwillow Books,1992), TE p. 156G

Reaching All Learners

Differentiated Instruction

PURPOSE To practice multiplication facts through 10

USING THE ACTIVITY WHEEL Have each student choose one activity to complete independently. *Use after Lesson 11.1.*

*The Activity Wheel provides each student with a choice, according to learning style, for practicing an important skill.

Check students' work.

ACTIVITY WHEEL*

Write two different ways to represent 5 groups of 4. Explain how both number sentences have the same product.

Choose a percussion instrument and invent a rhythm to use when reciting any group of multiplication facts.

Describe 3 different arrays of objects you have seen in a store. Include the number in each row and the number of rows. Find the total numer of objects in each array.

Literature Connections

These books provide ways to explore multiplication.

Too Many Kangaroo Things to Do! by Stuart J. Murphy (HarperCollins, 1996) Kangaroo's friends use multiplication to figure out how many things they have to do to plan a surprise party for him.

- Have students draw animals and find how many legs there are if they have 2, 3, or 4 animals. *Use with Lessons 8.2, 8.4, and 9.2.*

Each Orange Had 8 Slices by Paul Giganti, Jr. (Greenwillow Books, 1992) is an engaging book that provides opportunities to count equal groups.

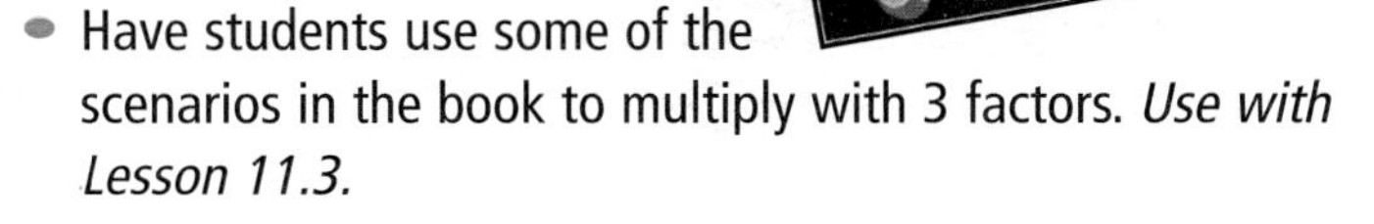

- Have students use some of the scenarios in the book to multiply with 3 factors. *Use with Lesson 11.3.*

PRACTICE GAME

Around the Moon

PURPOSE To practice multiplication facts with factors 0–9

MATERIALS *For each pair* game board and game cards, p. TR73; timer

ABOUT THE GAME

- Player A mixes all the cards and places 1 card face up on the moon, and the rest of the cards face up on the rockets.
- Starting on any rocket, Player A tells the product of the number on the moon and each of the numbers on the rockets. Player B keeps time.
- Player B then mixes the rocket cards, places them back on the rocket, and takes a turn.
- The player who names the products in the shortest time gets a point. After 5 rounds, the player with the greater number of points wins the game. *Use with Lessons 10.5 and 11.1.*

VISUAL

VISUAL/SPATIAL

Understand Multiplication

NCTM Standards 2000

1. Number and Operations
Lessons 8.1, 8.2, 8.3, 8.4, 8.5
2. Algebra
Lessons 8.1, 8.2, 8.3, 8.4, 8.5
3. Geometry
4. Measurement
5. Data Analysis and Probability
6. Problem Solving
Lessons 8.1, 8.2, 8.3, 8.4, 8.5
7. Reasoning and Proof
Lessons 8.1, 8.2, 8.3, 8.4, 8.5
8. Communication
Lessons 8.1, 8.2, 8.3, 8.4, 8.5
9. Connections
Lessons 8.1, 8.4, 8.5
10. Representation
Lesson 8.4

Chapter Planner

Getting Ready for Chapter 8 • Assessing Prior Knowledge and INTERVENTION (See PE and TE page 157.)

LESSON	NORTH CAROLINA STANDARDS	PACING	VOCABULARY*	MATERIALS	RESOURCES AND TECHNOLOGY
8.1 Algebra: Connect Addition and Multiplication pp. 158–159 **Objective** To connect multiplication to repeated addition	1.03c	1 Day	**multiply**		Reteach, Practice, Problem Solving, Challenge 8.1 Worksheets Transparency 8.1 **Intervention,** *Skills 19, 61* (CD or Book) **Harcourt Mega Math Country Countdown,** *Counting Critters*
8.2 Multiply with 2 and 5 pp. 160–161 **Objective** To multiply with 2 and 5	1.03a	1 Day (For Lessons 8.2 and 8.3)	**factors** **product**		Reteach, Practice, Problem Solving, Challenge 8.2 Worksheets Transparency 8.2 **Math Jingles® CD 3–4** **Intervention,** *Skills 19, 61* (CD or Book) **Harcourt Mega Math Country Countdown,** *Counting Critters*
8.3 Hands On: Arrays pp. 162–163 **Objective** To use arrays and the Commutative Property to explore the concept of multiplication	1.03a		**array** **Commutative Property of Multiplication**	*For each group* square tiles	Reteach, Practice, Problem Solving, Challenge 8.3 Worksheets Transparency 8.3 **Intervention,** *Skills 19, 61* (CD or Book) Scaffolded Instruction Transparency 8 **Harcourt Mega Math Country Countdown,** *Counting Critters*
8.4 Multiply with 3 pp. 164–167 **Objective** To multiply with 3 and use the Commutative Property	1.03a *also* 1.04	1 Day			Reteach, Practice, Problem Solving, Challenge 8.4 Worksheets Transparency 8.4 **Math Jingles® CD 3–4** **Intervention,** *Skill 61* (CD or Book)
8.5 Problem Solving Skill: Too Much/Too Little Information pp. 168–169 **Objective** To identify which information is needed and if there is enough information to solve a problem	1.03a *also* 1.06	1 Day			Reteach, Practice, Reading Strategy, Challenge 8.5 Worksheets Transparency 8.5 Reading Transparency 8 **Intervention • Problem Solving,** *Strategy/Skill 8* (CD or Book)

Ending Chapter 8 • Extra Practice, p. 170 • Chapter 8 Review/Test, p. 171 • Getting Ready for the EOG Test, pp. 172–173

* **Boldfaced** terms are the key mathematical terms for the chapter.

Vocabulary Power

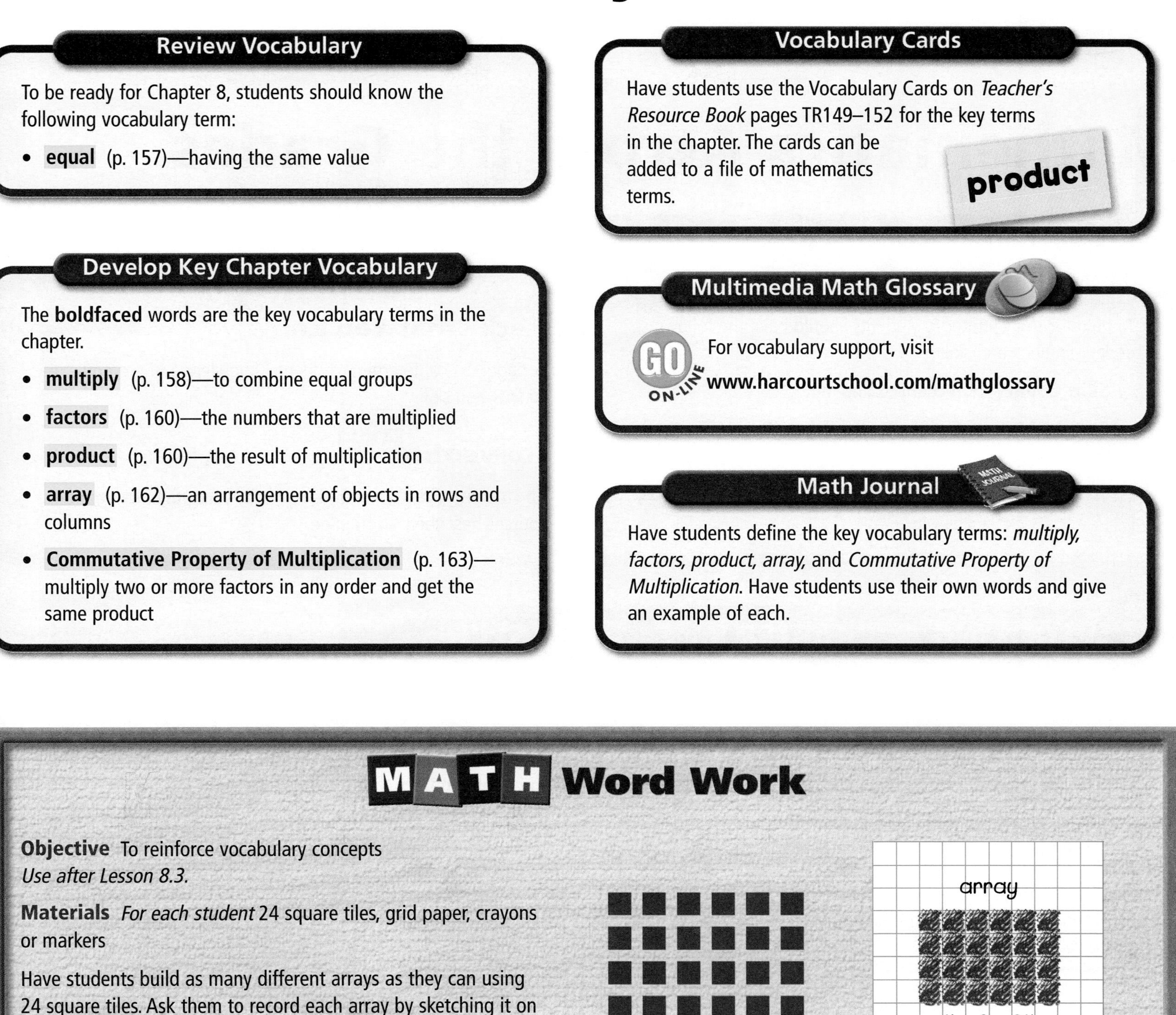

Review Vocabulary

To be ready for Chapter 8, students should know the following vocabulary term:

- **equal** (p. 157)—having the same value

Vocabulary Cards

Have students use the Vocabulary Cards on *Teacher's Resource Book* pages TR149–152 for the key terms in the chapter. The cards can be added to a file of mathematics terms.

Develop Key Chapter Vocabulary

The **boldfaced** words are the key vocabulary terms in the chapter.

- **multiply** (p. 158)—to combine equal groups
- **factors** (p. 160)—the numbers that are multiplied
- **product** (p. 160)—the result of multiplication
- **array** (p. 162)—an arrangement of objects in rows and columns
- **Commutative Property of Multiplication** (p. 163)—multiply two or more factors in any order and get the same product

Multimedia Math Glossary

GO ON-LINE For vocabulary support, visit **www.harcourtschool.com/mathglossary**

Math Journal

Have students define the key vocabulary terms: *multiply, factors, product, array,* and *Commutative Property of Multiplication.* Have students use their own words and give an example of each.

MATH Word Work

Objective To reinforce vocabulary concepts
Use after Lesson 8.3.

Materials *For each student* 24 square tiles, grid paper, crayons or markers

Have students build as many different arrays as they can using 24 square tiles. Ask them to record each array by sketching it on grid paper and writing a multiplication sentence to describe it. Have students label the arrays, factors, and products on their sketches using the appropriate vocabulary terms.

Understand Multiplication

Mathematics Across the Grades

LOOKING BACK • Prerequisite Skills

To be ready for Chapter 8, students should have the following understandings and skills:

- **Skip-Count**—skip-count to find multiples
- **Equal Groups**—find the total number of items in equal groups

Check What You Know

Use page 157 to determine students' knowledge of prerequisite concepts and skills.

Intervention

Help students prepare for the chapter by using the intervention resources described on TE page 157.

LOOKING AT CHAPTER 8 • Essential Skills

Students will

- connect multiplication to repeated addition.
- use arrays and the Commutative Property to explore the concept of multiplication.
- **multiply with 2, 3, and 5.**
- identify which information is needed and whether there is enough information to solve a problem.

Example

Ricky caught 3 fish each day for 5 days. Ronnie caught 5 fish each day for 3 days. Who caught more fish, Ricky or Ronnie?

Model	Algorithm
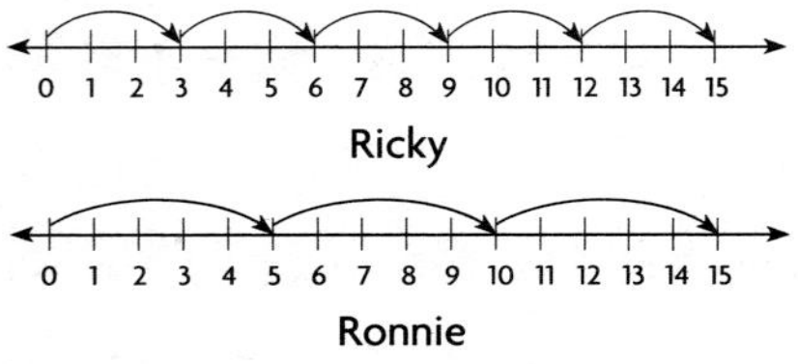	$\begin{array}{r} 5 \\ \times 3 \\ \hline 15 \end{array}$ $\begin{array}{r} 3 \\ \times 5 \\ \hline 15 \end{array}$ Ricky and Ronnie caught the same number of fish.

LOOKING AHEAD • Applications

Students will apply what they learn in Chapter 8 to the following new concepts:

- Multiply with 0, 1, and 4 (Chapter 9)
- Multiply with 6, 7, and 8 (Chapter 10)
- Find Missing Factors (Chapter 9)
- Multiply with 9 and 10 (Chapter 11)

Differentiated Instruction

Meeting the Needs of All Learners

Extra Support	Activities for All	Enrichment
Alternative Teaching Strategy TE Lessons 8.1, 8.2, 8.3, 8.4, 8.5 **ESOL/ESL** TE Lessons 8.1, 8.2, 8.3, 8.4, 8.5 **Special Needs** TE Lesson 8.3	**Cross-Curricular Connection** **Fine Arts:** TE Lesson 8.2 **Reading:** TE Lesson 8.5 **Social Studies:** Chapter Opener **Vocabulary:** TE p. 156I, PE/TE p. 157, TE Lesson 8.4 **Writing:** TE Lesson 8.5	**Advanced Learners** TE Lessons 8.2, 8.3, 8.5 **Early Finishers** TE Lessons 8.1, 8.4

Combination and Multi-age Classrooms

Grade 2	Grade 3	Grade 4
Skills Trace Across the Grades		
Relate addition and multiplication; use arrays to model multiplication; multiply in any order and across and down.	**Relate addition and multiplication; multiply with 2, 3, and 5; draw arrays to represent multiplication sentences; use the Commutative Property of Multiplication.**	Relate multiplication and division; multiply and divide facts through 12; use the properties of multiplication.
Instructional Strategies		
Students on this level may require more time to build conceptual understanding. **Assignments** **Grade 3 Pupil Edition** • Have students use counters with Lessons 8.1, 8.2, and 8.4. • Have students work in pairs on Lessons 8.1, 8.2, 8.3, and 8.4. Skip Lesson 8.5. **Grade 2 Pupil Edition**—pages 521–528	Students on this level should be able to complete all the lessons in the Pupil Edition and all the activities in the Teacher's Edition with minimal adjustments. **Assignment** **Grade 3 Pupil Edition**—pages 156–171	Students on this level will probably require less time to build conceptual understanding. **Assignments** **Grade 3 Pupil Edition** • Compact Lessons 8.2 and 8.4. • Work quickly through Lesson 8.3. **Grade 4 Pupil Edition**—pages 162–179

CHAPTER 8

Understand Multiplication

Introducing the Chapter

Tell students that multiplication helps them find the total number of items when there are equal groups. Have students focus on the pictograph to determine about how many plums equal the weight of 1 apple. 3 plums

Using Data

To begin the study of this chapter, have students

- Use the pictograph to find how much 2 peaches weigh. 6 ounces
- Write a subtraction sentence to compare the weight of 5 kiwi fruit with 5 pears. $30 - 15 = 15$ ounces
- Determine how many apples equal the weight of 3 bananas. 2 apples

Problem Solving Project

Purpose To connect repeated addition and multiplication

Background The majority of the apple crop in the United States is produced in Washington, New York, Michigan, California, Pennsylvania, Virginia, and the New England states. Washington produces more than 2 million tons of apples a year.

UNDERSTAND • PLAN • SOLVE • CHECK
Have students

- Draw 4 bowls of apples with 5 apples in each bowl.
- Write an addition sentence to find the number of apples in all. $5 + 5 + 5 + 5 = 20$
- Write a multiplication sentence to find the total number of apples and compare the answer to their sum. $4 \times 5 = 20$; They are both 20.

Graphing Investigations
Begin Week 8.

CHAPTER 8

Understand Multiplication

FAST FACT • SOCIAL STUDIES Apples are grown in all 50 states. Millions of pounds of fruit are grown each year. Knowing how much different fruits weigh can help you decide how much fruit to buy.

PROBLEM SOLVING **Use the pictograph. About how many plums should you buy to equal the weight of 1 apple?**

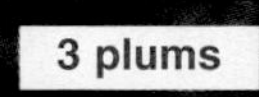

WEIGHT OF FRUITS

Fruit	Weight
Apple	🧺🧺🧺🧺🧺🧺
Orange	🧺🧺🧺🧺🧺
Peach	🧺🧺🧺
Banana	🧺🧺🧺🧺
Kiwi	🧺🧺🧺
Plum	🧺🧺
Pear	🧺🧺🧺🧺🧺🧺

Key: Each 🧺 = 1 ounce.

Apple orchard—Hope, Maine

156

WHY LEARN MATH? People who purchase food for hospitals, schools, and other large facilities need to know how to multiply, since they buy food in large quantities. Ask: If 1 can of corn feeds 5 people, how can you find how many people 4 cans will feed? Possible answer: Multiply: $4 \times 5 = 20$ people

Family Involvement Activities

These activities provide:

- Letter to the Family
- Math Vocabulary
- Family Game
- Practice (Homework)

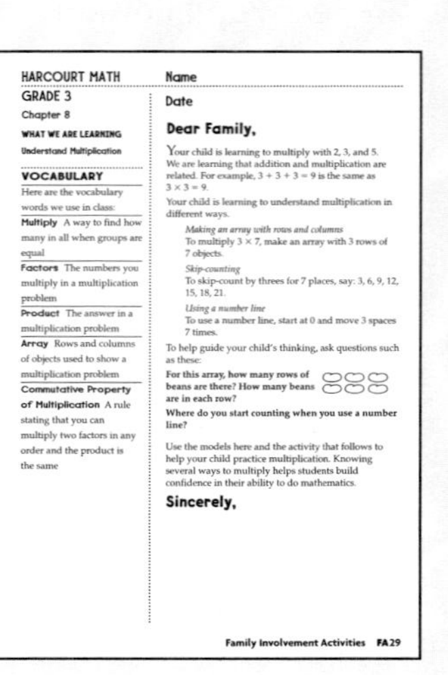
HARCOURT MATH
GRADE 3
Chapter 8
WHAT WE ARE LEARNING
Understand Multiplication

VOCABULARY
Here are the vocabulary words we use in class:
Multiply A way to find how many in all when groups are equal
Factors The numbers you multiply in a multiplication problem
Product The answer in a multiplication problem
Array Rows and columns of objects used to show a multiplication problem
Commutative Property of Multiplication A rule stating that you can multiply two factors in any order and the product is the same

Name
Date

Dear Family,

Your child is learning to multiply with 2, 3, and 5. We are learning that addition and multiplication are related. For example, $3 + 3 + 3 = 9$ is the same as $3 \times 3 = 9$.

Your child is learning to understand multiplication in different ways.

Making an array with rows and columns
To multiply 3×7, make an array with 3 rows of 7 objects.

Skip-counting
To skip-count by threes for 7 places, say: 3, 6, 9, 12, 15, 18, 21.

Using a number line
To use a number line, start at 0 and move 3 spaces 7 times.

To help guide your child's thinking, ask questions such as these:

For this array, how many rows of beans are there? How many beans are in each row?

Where do you start counting when you use a number line?

Use the models here and the activity that follows to help your child practice multiplication. Knowing several ways to multiply helps students build confidence in their ability to do mathematics.

Sincerely,

Family Involvement Activities FA29

Family Involvement Activities, p. FA29

Use this page to help you review and remember important skills needed for Chapter 8.

SKIP-COUNT

Skip-count to find the missing numbers.

1. 2, 4, 6, ■, ■, ■, 14, 16, ■, ■ 8, 10, 12, 18, 20
2. 3, 6, ■, 12, ■, ■, 21 9, 15, 18
3. 5, 10, ■, ■, 25, ■, ■, ■, ■, 50 15, 20, 30, 35, 40, 45
4. 10, 20, ■, ■, 50, ■, ■, ■, 90 30, 40, 60, 70, 80

EQUAL GROUPS

Write how many there are in all.

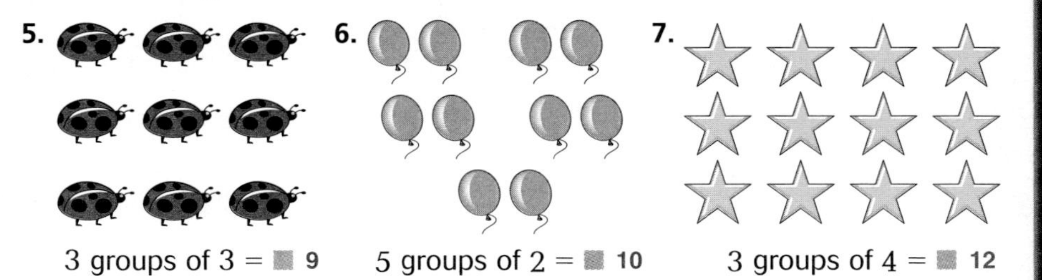

5. 3 groups of 3 = ■ 9
6. 5 groups of 2 = ■ 10
7. 3 groups of 4 = ■ 12

Find how many in all. You may wish to draw a picture. Check students' drawings.

8. 2 groups of 6 12
9. 3 groups of 5 15
10. 4 groups of 2 8

VOCABULARY POWER

REVIEW

equal [ē′kwəl] *adjective*

When two things are *equal,* they have the same measure or amount. Name two amounts that are equal. Use an equal sign (=) to show that two amounts are equal.
Check students' answers.

PREVIEW

multiply
product
Commutative Property of Multiplication
factors
array

GO ON-LINE www.harcourtschool.com/mathglossary

Assessing Prior Knowledge

Use the **Check What You Know** page to determine whether your students have mastered the prerequisite skills critical for this chapter.

Intervention

- **Diagnose and Prescribe**
  Evaluate your students' performance on this page to determine whether intervention is necessary or if enrichment is appropriate. Options that provide instruction, practice, and a check are listed in the chart below.

CHECK WHAT YOU KNOW RESOURCES

Intervention Copying Masters or CD-ROMs

Enrichment Copying Masters

VOCABULARY POWER

For activities and information about the vocabulary in this chapter, see page 156I.

Were students successful with CHECK WHAT YOU KNOW?

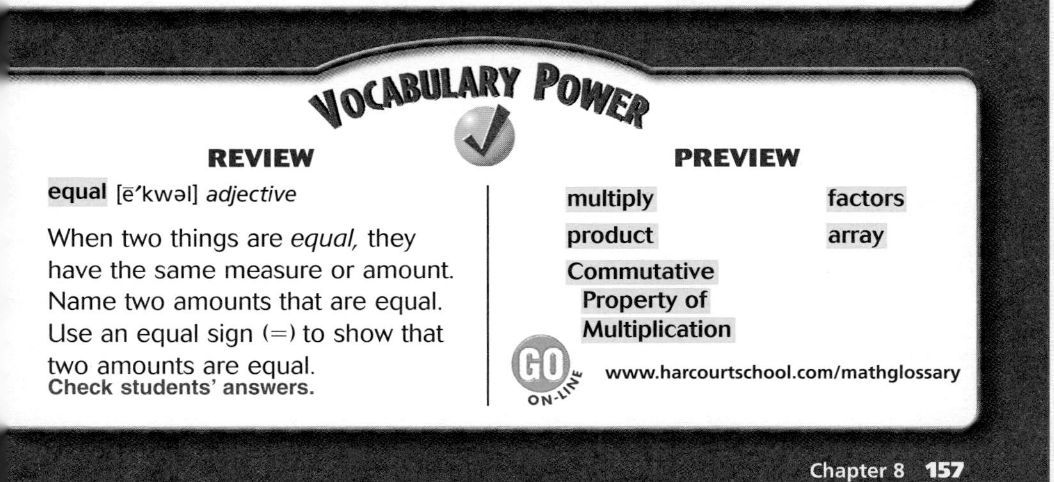

IF . . . NO THEN . . . INTERVENE | **INTERVENTION OPTIONS** | **IF . . . YES THEN . . . ENRICH**

Skill/Items	Missed more than	Intervene with
Skip Count, 1–4	1	• *Intervention*, Skill 61
Equal Groups, 5–10	2	• *Intervention*, Skill 19

Skill/Items	Missed fewer than	Enrich with
Skip Count, 1–4	2	• *Intervention*, Enrichment p. IN343
Equal Groups, 5–10	3	• *Intervention*, Enrichment p. IN344

Algebra: Connect Addition and Multiplication

Lesson Planning

Objective To connect multiplication to repeated addition

NCTM Standards
1. Number and Operations
2. Algebra
6. Problem Solving
7. Reasoning and Proof
8. Communication
9. Connections

Math Background

Keep the following ideas in mind when helping students connect multiplication to repeated addition.

- Start with zero when skip-counting or repeatedly adding a number.
- Multiplication connects directly to addition only when equal groups are used.

Vocabulary

multiply a way to find how many in all, when groups have the same number of items

Warm-Up Resources

Number of the Day

Take the number of pennies in a dollar and add it to the number of pennies in a quarter to find the number of the day. 125

Daily Facts Practice

Have students practice addition facts by completing Set G of *Teacher's Resource Book*, p. TR88.

Solve a Problem

Transparency 8.1

Problem of the Day

Darrell is buying a notepad for 75¢. He wants to pay for it with coins that are all the same kind. What type of coins and how many of each could Darrell use to pay for the notepad? He can use 3 quarters, 15 nickels, or 75 pennies.

Solution Problem of the Day tab, p. PD8

Intervention and Extension Resources

Alternative Teaching Strategy

MATERIALS *For each student* number line, p. TR5

Have students **model equal groups using a number line**. Have students use a number line to help them model addition and multiplication sentences for exercises in the lesson. Check students' work.

VISUAL

VISUAL/SPATIAL

Multistep and Strategy Problems

The following multistep or strategy problem is provided in Lesson 8.1:

Page	Item
159	10

ESOL/ESL

Have students complete these steps to **connect repeated addition and multiplication**.

- Fold a sheet of paper into thirds.
- Draw sets with equal groups of objects in the first section.
- Write an addition sentence that describes the drawing in the second section and a multiplication sentence for the drawing in the third section.
- Have students share their work. Check students' work.

KINESTHETIC

BODILY/KINESTHETIC

Early Finishers

Have students solve the following exercises to help them **connect repeated addition and multiplication**.

1. $6 + 6 + 6 = \blacksquare$ 18 $\quad 9 + 9 = \blacksquare$ 18
$3 + 3 + 3 + 3 + 3 + 3 = \blacksquare$ 18

2. $3 \times 6 = \blacksquare$ 18 $\quad 2 \times 9 = \blacksquare$ 18
$6 \times 3 = \blacksquare$ 18

Ask: What similarity can you find between the number sentences in Exercises 1 and 2? All equal 18.

Then have students write number sentences with equal groups whose sum or product is 12. Possible answers: $6 + 6 = 12$; $2 \times 6 = 12$; $3 + 3 + 3 + 3 = 12$; $4 \times 3 = 12$; $2 + 2 + 2 + 2 + 2 + 2 = 12$; $6 \times 2 = 12$; $4 + 4 + 4 = 12$; $3 \times 4 = 12$

VISUAL

LOGICAL/MATHEMATICAL

Technology Link

Intervention, *Skills 19, 61*

Harcourt Mega Math Country Countdown, *Counting Critters,* Level V

The Harcourt Learning Site www.harcourtschool.com

Lesson 8.1 Organizer

Objective To connect multiplication to repeated addition

Vocabulary multiply

1 INTRODUCE

QUICK REVIEW provides review of prerequisite skills.

WHY LEARN THIS? Many things in the world come in equal groups. *Share the lesson objective with students.*

2 TEACH

Guided Instruction

- *Ask students to look at the Learn section.*
  What does each circle represent? a package
  Why do you multiply 5 packages times 3? Each of the 5 packages has 3 juice boxes.
- *Have students read the Math Idea.*
  How would you explain the Math Idea to a friend? Possible answer: When each group has the same number of objects, you can multiply to find how many in all.
- *Refer students to the Reasoning question on page 158.*
  REASONING When would you write an addition number sentence instead of a multiplication sentence to find an answer? when the groups are not equal

3 PRACTICE

Guided Practice

Do Check Exercises 1–3 with your students. Identify students who are having difficulty and choose appropriate lesson resources to provide assistance.

LESSON 1

Algebra: Connect Addition and Multiplication

Quick Review

1. $3 + 3 + 3$ 9
2. $5 + 5 + 5$ 15
3. $2 + 2 + 2$ 6
4. $2 + 2 + 2 + 2$ 8
5. $4 + 4 + 4$ 12

VOCABULARY
multiply

Learn

SLURP! There are 3 juice boxes in a package. If Cara buys 5 packages, how many juice boxes will she have?

You can add to find how many in all.

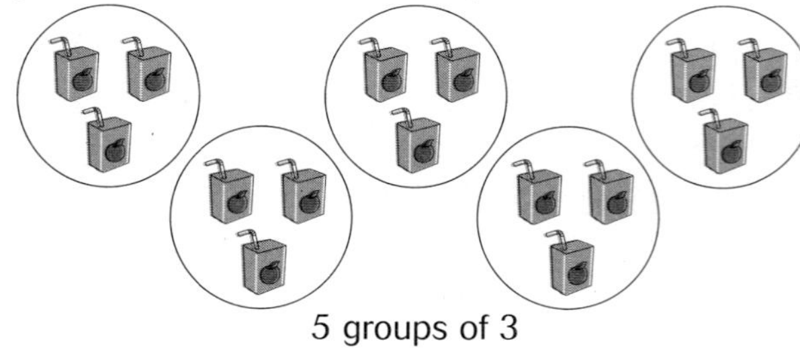

5 groups of 3

Write: $3 + 3 + 3 + 3 + 3 = 15$

Say: 5 threes equal 15.

You can multiply to find how many in all.

Write: $5 \times 3 = 15$

Say: 5 times 3 equals 15.

So, Cara will have 15 juice boxes.

Remember
You can use a number sentence to show addition.
$2 + 2 + 2 = 6$

MATH IDEA When you combine equal groups, you can multiply to find how many in all.

REASONING Can you use multiplication to find $2 + 3 + 2$? Why or why not?
Possible answer: no; the groups are not equal.

Technology Link
More Practice: Harcourt Mega Math Country Countdown, *Counting Critters*, Level V

Check

1. **Explain** two ways to find the total if the juice boxes come in packages of 4, and Cara buys 3 packages.
Possible answer: One way is to add: 4 + 4 + 4 = 12 and another way is to multiply: 3 × 4 = 12.

158

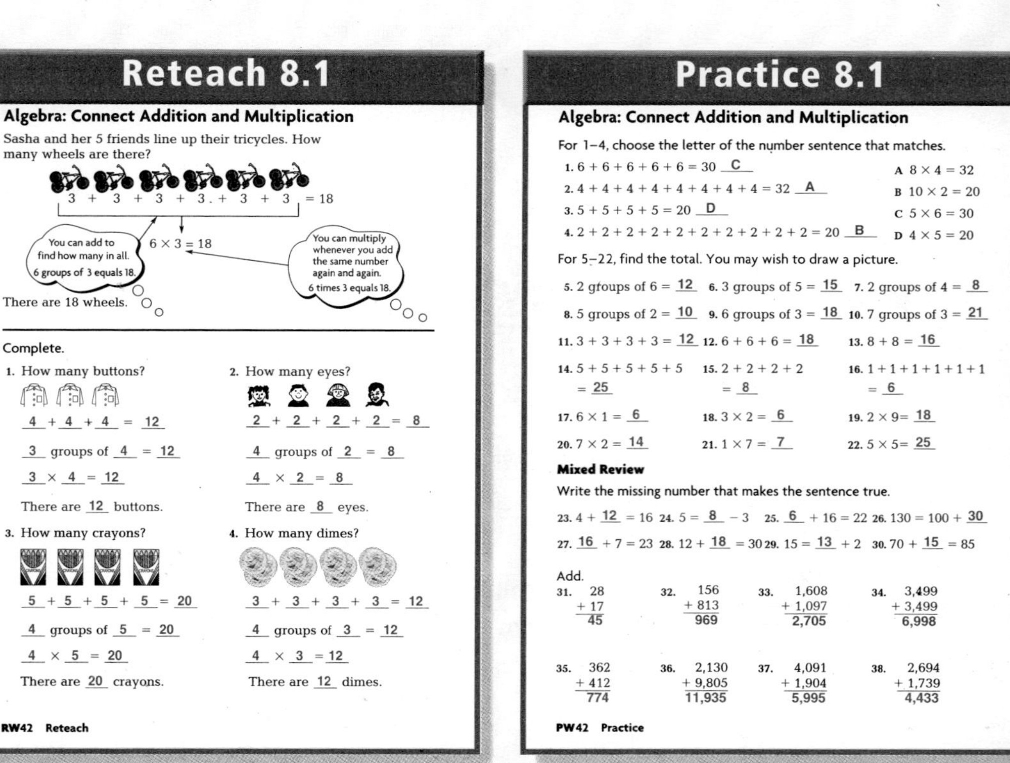

Reteach 8.1

Algebra: Connect Addition and Multiplication

Sasha and her 5 friends line up their tricycles. How many wheels are there?

$3 + 3 + 3 + 3 + 3 + 3 = 18$

$6 \times 3 = 18$

You can add to find how many in all. 6 groups of 3 equals 18.

You can multiply whenever you add the same number again and again. 6 times 3 equals 18.

There are 18 wheels.

Complete.

1. How many buttons?
4 + 4 + 4 = 12
3 groups of 4 = 12
3 × 4 = 12
There are 12 buttons.

2. How many eyes?
2 + 2 + 2 + 2 = 8
4 groups of 2 = 8
4 × 2 = 8
There are 8 eyes.

3. How many crayons?
5 + 5 + 5 + 5 = 20
4 groups of 5 = 20
4 × 5 = 20
There are 20 crayons.

4. How many dimes?
3 + 3 + 3 + 3 = 12
4 groups of 3 = 12
4 × 3 = 12
There are 12 dimes.

RW42 Reteach

Practice 8.1

Algebra: Connect Addition and Multiplication

For 1–4, choose the letter of the number sentence that matches.

1. $6 + 6 + 6 + 6 + 6 = 30$ C
2. $4 + 4 + 4 + 4 + 4 + 4 + 4 + 4 = 32$ A
3. $5 + 5 + 5 + 5 = 20$ D
4. $2 + 2 + 2 + 2 + 2 + 2 + 2 + 2 + 2 + 2 = 20$ B

A $8 \times 4 = 32$
B $10 \times 2 = 20$
C $5 \times 6 = 30$
D $4 \times 5 = 20$

For 5–22, find the total. You may wish to draw a picture.

5. 2 groups of 6 = 12
6. 3 groups of 5 = 15
7. 2 groups of 4 = 8
8. 5 groups of 2 = 10
9. 6 groups of 3 = 18
10. 7 groups of 3 = 21
11. $3 + 3 + 3 + 3 = 12$
12. $6 + 6 + 6 = 18$
13. $8 + 8 = 16$
14. $5 + 5 + 5 + 5 + 5 = 25$
15. $2 + 2 + 2 + 2 = 8$
16. $1 + 1 + 1 + 1 + 1 + 1 = 6$
17. $6 \times 1 = 6$
18. $3 \times 2 = 6$
19. $2 \times 9 = 18$
20. $7 \times 2 = 14$
21. $1 \times 7 = 7$
22. $5 \times 5 = 25$

Mixed Review

Write the missing number that makes the sentence true.

23. $4 + 12 = 16$
24. $5 = 8 - 3$
25. $6 + 16 = 22$
26. $130 = 100 + 30$
27. $16 + 7 = 23$
28. $12 + 18 = 30$
29. $15 = 13 + 2$
30. $70 + 15 = 85$

Add.

31. $28 + 17 = 45$
32. $156 + 813 = 969$
33. $1,608 + 1,097 = 2,705$
34. $3,499 + 3,499 = 6,998$
35. $362 + 412 = 774$
36. $2,130 + 9,805 = 11,935$
37. $4,091 + 1,904 = 5,995$
38. $2,694 + 1,739 = 4,433$

PW42 Practice

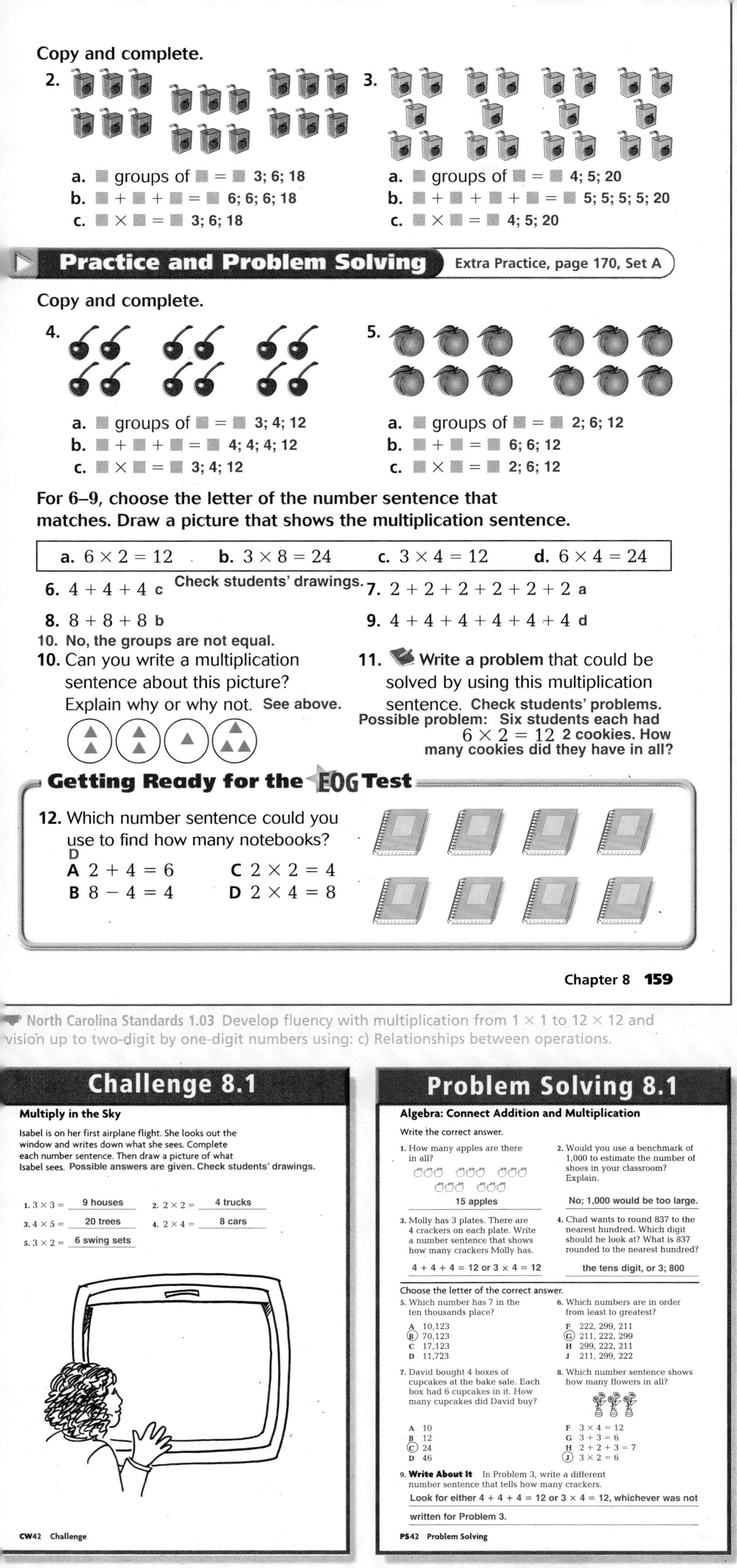

Copy and complete.

2.

a. ■ groups of ■ = ■ 3; 6; 18
b. ■ + ■ + ■ = ■ 6; 6; 6; 18
c. ■ × ■ = ■ 3; 6; 18

3.

a. ■ groups of ■ = ■ 4; 5; 20
b. ■ + ■ + ■ + ■ = ■ 5; 5; 5; 5; 20
c. ■ × ■ = ■ 4; 5; 20

Practice and Problem Solving

Extra Practice, page 170, Set A

Copy and complete.

4.

a. ■ groups of ■ = ■ 3; 4; 12
b. ■ + ■ + ■ = ■ 4; 4; 4; 12
c. ■ × ■ = ■ 3; 4; 12

5.

a. ■ groups of ■ = ■ 2; 6; 12
b. ■ + ■ = ■ 6; 6; 12
c. ■ × ■ = ■ 2; 6; 12

For 6–9, choose the letter of the number sentence that matches. Draw a picture that shows the multiplication sentence.

a. $6 \times 2 = 12$	b. $3 \times 8 = 24$	c. $3 \times 4 = 12$	d. $6 \times 4 = 24$

Check students' drawings.

6. $4 + 4 + 4$ c
7. $2 + 2 + 2 + 2 + 2 + 2$ a
8. $8 + 8 + 8$ b
9. $4 + 4 + 4 + 4 + 4 + 4$ d

10. No, the groups are not equal.

10. Can you write a multiplication sentence about this picture? Explain why or why not. See above.

11. **Write a problem** that could be solved by using this multiplication sentence. Check students' problems. Possible problem: Six students each had 2 cookies. How many cookies did they have in all?
$6 \times 2 = 12$

Getting Ready for the EOG Test

12. Which number sentence could you use to find how many notebooks? D

A $2 + 4 = 6$
B $8 - 4 = 4$
C $2 \times 2 = 4$
D $2 \times 4 = 8$

North Carolina Standards 1.03 Develop fluency with multiplication from 1×1 to 12×12 and vision up to two-digit by one-digit numbers using: c) Relationships between operations.

Challenge 8.1

Multiply in the Sky

Isabel is on her first airplane flight. She looks out the window and writes down what she sees. Complete each number sentence. Then draw a picture of what Isabel sees. Possible answers are given. Check students' drawings.

1. $3 \times 3 =$ 9 houses
2. $2 \times 2 =$ 4 trucks
3. $4 \times 5 =$ 20 trees
4. $2 \times 4 =$ 8 cars
5. $3 \times 2 =$ 6 swing sets

CW42 Challenge

Problem Solving 8.1

Algebra: Connect Addition and Multiplication

Write the correct answer.

1. How many apples are there in all?
15 apples

2. Would you use a benchmark of 1,000 to estimate the number of shoes in your classroom? Explain.
No; 1,000 would be too large.

3. Molly has 3 plates. There are 4 crackers on each plate. Write a number sentence that shows how many crackers Molly has.
$4 + 4 + 4 = 12$ or $3 \times 4 = 12$

4. Chad wants to round 837 to the nearest hundred. Which digit should he look at? What is 837 rounded to the nearest hundred?
the tens digit, or 3; 800

Choose the letter of the correct answer.

5. Which number has 7 in the ten thousands place?
A 10,123
(B) 70,123
C 17,123
D 11,723

6. Which numbers are in order from least to greatest?
F 222, 299, 211
(G) 211, 222, 299
H 299, 222, 211
J 211, 299, 222

7. David bought 4 boxes of cupcakes at the bake sale. Each box had 6 cupcakes in it. How many cupcakes did David buy?
A 10
B 12
(C) 24
D 46

8. Which number sentence shows how many flowers in all?
F $3 \times 4 = 12$
G $3 + 3 = 6$
H $2 + 2 + 3 = 7$
(J) $3 \times 2 = 6$

9. **Write About It** In Problem 3, write a different number sentence that tells how many crackers.
Look for either $4 + 4 + 4 = 12$ or $3 \times 4 = 12$, whichever was not written for Problem 3.

PS42 Problem Solving

COMMON ERROR ALERT

If students confuse the plus (+) and the multiplication (×) signs, have them read aloud each sentence, using the word *times* for the multiplication sign. Talk about the difference in the meaning and appearance of the signs. Using language gives meaning to the multiplication symbol:

3 groups of 5	3 rows of 5
3 × 5	3 × 5

Independent Practice

Note that Exercise 10 is a **multistep or strategy problem.** Assign Exercises 4–11.

4 ASSESS

Summarize the lesson by having students:

Discuss Juan and three friends want to buy enough chocolate chip cookies so that each can have 5 cookies. Show two ways to solve this problem. $5 + 5 + 5 + 5 = 20$; $4 \times 5 = 20$

Write In your own words, explain when you can use multiplication to solve a problem. Give an example. Possible answer: when you have equal groups of something, such as items in packages, you can multiply to find how many in all.

LESSON QUIZ

Transparency 8.1

Choose the letter of the number sentence that matches.

1. $2 + 2 + 2$ c
2. $3 + 3 + 3 + 3$ a
3. $8 + 8 + 8 + 8$ d
4. $5 + 5$ b

a. $4 \times 3 = 12$
b. $2 \times 5 = 10$
c. $3 \times 2 = 6$
d. $4 \times 8 = 32$

Lesson 8.2

Multiply with 2 and 5

Lesson Planning

Objective **To multiply with 2 and 5**

NCTM Standards

1. **Number and Operations**
2. **Algebra**
6. **Problem Solving**
7. **Reasoning and Proof**
8. **Communication**

Math Background

Consider the following when helping students multiply with 2 and 5.

- When you multiply with 2, the product is always even. (There is a 0, 2, 4, 6, or 8 in the ones place.)
- When you multiply with 5, the product always has a 0 or 5 in the ones place.

Vocabulary

factors numbers that are multiplied to find a product
product the answer in a multiplication problem

Warm-Up Resources

Number of the Day

Transparency 8.2

Take the number of people in your home. Compare it to the number of pets in your home. Which is greater? Answers will vary.

Daily Facts Practice

Have students practice subtraction facts by completing Set A of *Teacher's Resource Book*, p. TR89.

Solve a Problem

Transparency 8.2

Problem of the Day

Complete each pattern. Describe the patterns in your own words.
2, ■, ■, 17, 22, ■, 32 7, 12, 27; add 5
2, ■, 8, ■, 32, 64 4, 16; double the number, or multiply by 2

Solution Problem of the Day tab, p. PD8

Intervention and Extension Resources

Alternative Teaching Strategy

Have students **model multiplication sentences**. Some students may have trouble visualizing a multiplication sentence. Display a multiplication problem and then form equal groups of students to model the numbers in the sentence. Ask a volunteer to count the students and write the answer. Repeat the procedure if necessary. Check students' work.

VISUAL, KINESTHETIC

BODILY/KINESTHETIC

Multistep and Strategy Problems

The following multistep or strategy problem is provided in Lesson 8.2:

Page	Item
161	26

Fine Arts Connection

Have students **multiply with 5.** Have them suppose that they are helping the teacher get paint ready for art class. Share the following: There are 6 groups of students. Each group needs 5 different colors of paint. How many dishes of paint do they need?
$6 \times 5 = 30$ dishes

VISUAL

LOGICAL/MATHEMATICAL

Advanced Learners

MATERIALS *For each group* base-ten blocks

Challenge students to **use patterns to find products.** Display the following exercises:

$3 \times 5 = 15$; $3 \times 50 = 150$; $3 \times 500 = 1,500$

Have students find the first product and use that answer to help them predict what the products for the other two are. Students may use base-ten blocks if needed. Discuss the pattern.

VISUAL

LOGICAL/MATHEMATICAL

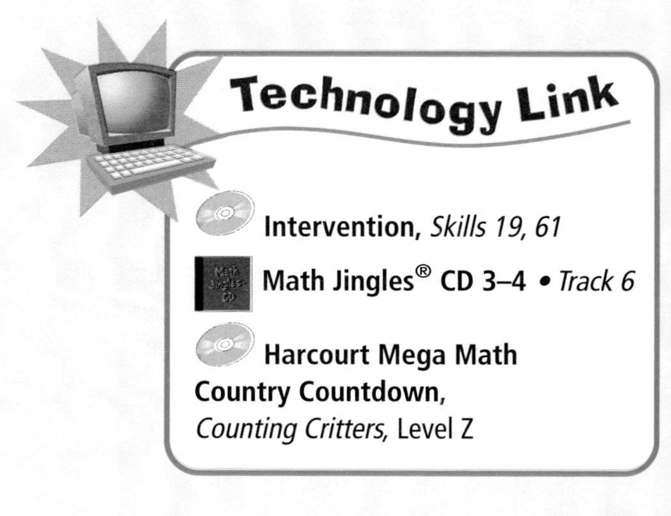

Technology Link

Intervention, *Skills 19, 61*

Math Jingles® CD 3–4 • *Track 6*

Harcourt Mega Math Country Countdown, *Counting Critters,* Level Z

Lesson 8.2 Organizer

Objective To multiply with 2 and 5

Vocabulary factors, product

1 INTRODUCE

Quick Review provides review of prerequisite skills.

Why Learn This? You can use multiplication as a quick way to find the total number when items are in equal groups. *Share the lesson objective with students.*

2 TEACH

Guided Instruction

- *Ask students to read the Learn section.*
  Why can you multiply to solve this problem? The groups are equal.
  How can you skip-count to solve the problem? Count by 2's five times.
  Reasoning How is multiplication like addition? In both, you find how many in all.
  How is multiplication different from addition? In multiplication, you have equal groups. In addition, groups may not be equal.
- *Ask students to read the Math Idea.*
  What two multiplication sentences can you write in which the digits 4 and 5 are the factors and 20 is the product? $4 \times 5 = 20$; $5 \times 4 = 20$

Modifying Instruction Have students use counters, as needed, to represent items in problems presented in this lesson.

3 PRACTICE

Guided Practice

Do Check Exercises 1–4 with your students. Identify students who are having difficulty and choose appropriate lesson resources to provide assistance.

Help students conclude that when you multiply with 5, the product always has a 5 or 0 in the ones place. When you multiply with 2, the product is always an even number.

LESSON 2

Multiply with 2 and 5

Quick Review

How many are in all?

1. 1 group of 8 **8**
2. 3 groups of 2 **6**
3. 2 groups of 5 **10**
4. 4 groups of 2 **8**
5. 3 groups of 3 **9**

VOCABULARY
factors
product

Learn

SMART ROCKS The chips that run computers are made from a mineral found in rocks. Mrs. Frank asked 5 students to bring in 2 rocks each for a science project. How many rocks does she need?

Use counters.

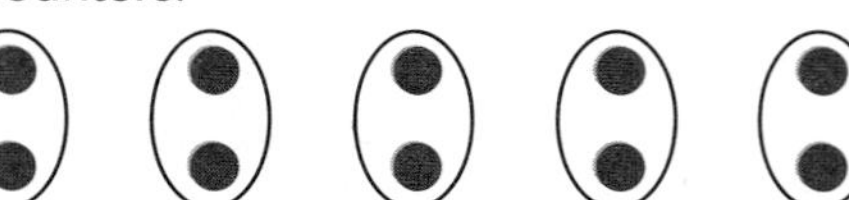
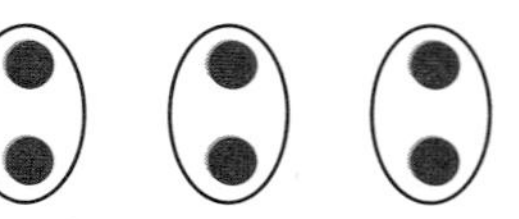
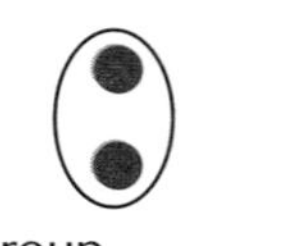

There are 5 groups, with 2 in each group.

Since each group has the same number, you can multiply to find how many in all.

$5 \times 2 = 10$ (factor, factor, product)

$$\begin{array}{rl} 2 & \leftarrow \text{factor} \\ \times 5 & \leftarrow \text{factor} \\ \hline 10 & \leftarrow \text{product} \end{array}$$

So, Mrs. Frank needs 10 rocks in all.

Computer chip

Crystal

MATH IDEA The numbers that you multiply are **factors**. The answer is the **product**.

- Name the factors and product in $3 \times 2 = 6$. **factors: 3, 2; product: 6**

Check

1. **Find** the products 1×2 through 9×2. What do you notice about the products? Are they always even numbers or always odd numbers? Explain. **2, 4, 6, 8, 10, 12, 14, 16, 18; even numbers; when you count by 2's from 2, the numbers are all even.**

Find the product.

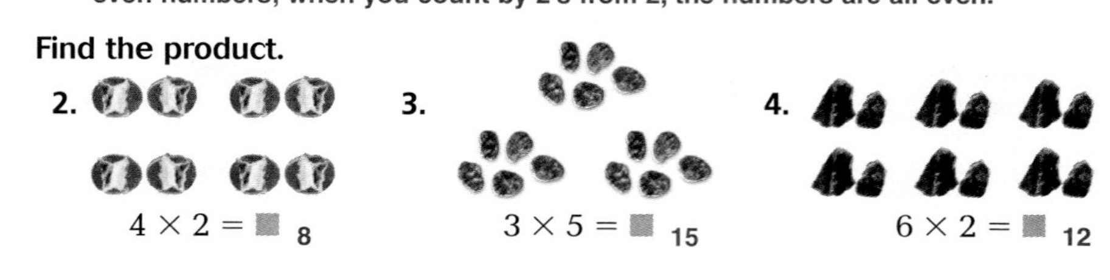

2. $4 \times 2 = ■$ **8**
3. $3 \times 5 = ■$ **15**
4. $6 \times 2 = ■$ **12**

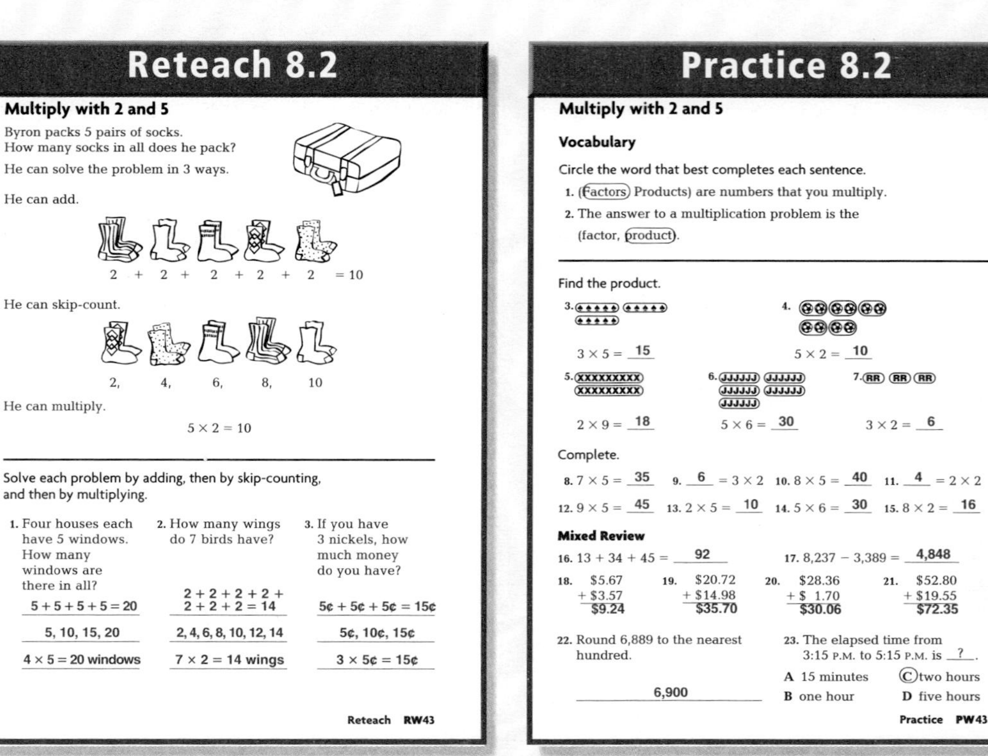

Reteach 8.2

Multiply with 2 and 5

Byron packs 5 pairs of socks.
How many socks in all does he pack?

He can solve the problem in 3 ways.

He can add.

2 + 2 + 2 + 2 + 2 = 10

He can skip-count.

2, 4, 6, 8, 10

He can multiply.

5 × 2 = 10

Solve each problem by adding, then by skip-counting, and then by multiplying.

1. Four houses each have 5 windows. How many windows are there in all?
   5 + 5 + 5 + 5 = 20
   5, 10, 15, 20
   4 × 5 = 20 windows
2. How many wings do 7 birds have?
   2 + 2 + 2 + 2 + 2 + 2 + 2 = 14
   2, 4, 6, 8, 10, 12, 14
   7 × 2 = 14 wings
3. If you have 3 nickels, how much money do you have?
   5¢ + 5¢ + 5¢ = 15¢
   5¢, 10¢, 15¢
   3 × 5¢ = 15¢

Reteach RW43

Practice 8.2

Multiply with 2 and 5

Vocabulary

Circle the word that best completes each sentence.

1. (Factors, Products) are numbers that you multiply. [Factors circled]
2. The answer to a multiplication problem is the (factor, product). [product circled]

Find the product.

3. 3 × 5 = 15
4. 5 × 2 = 10
5. 2 × 9 = 18
6. 5 × 6 = 30
7. 3 × 2 = 6

Complete.

8. 7 × 5 = 35
9. 6 = 3 × 2
10. 8 × 5 = 40
11. 4 = 2 × 2
12. 9 × 5 = 45
13. 2 × 5 = 10
14. 5 × 6 = 30
15. 8 × 2 = 16

Mixed Review

16. 13 + 34 + 45 = 92
17. 8,237 − 3,389 = 4,848
18. $5.67 + $3.57 = $9.24
19. $20.72 + $14.98 = $35.70
20. $28.36 + $ 1.70 = $30.06
21. $52.80 + $19.55 = $72.35
22. Round 6,889 to the nearest hundred. 6,900
23. The elapsed time from 3:15 P.M. to 5:15 P.M. is ? .
    A 15 minutes
    B one hour
    C two hours [circled]
    D five hours

Practice PW43

Practice and Problem Solving

Extra Practice, page 170, Set B

Find the product.

5. $2 \times 2 = ■$ 4

6. $5 \times 5 = ■$ 25

7. $4 \times 5 = ■$ 20

Copy and complete.

25. Check students' problems. Possible problem: Sally bought 3 bags of rocks with 2 rocks in each bag. How many rocks does she have in all? 6 rocks

	×	1	2	3	4	5	6	7	8	9
8.	2	■ 2	■ 4	■ 6	■ 8	■ 10	■ 12	■ 14	■ 16	■ 18
9.	5	■ 5	■ 10	■ 15	■ 20	■ 25	■ 30	■ 35	■ 40	■ 45

Complete.

10. $8 \times 2 = ■$ 16
11. $■ = 4 \times 5$ 20
12. $6 \times 2 = ■$ 12
13. $■ = 7 \times 5$ 35
14. $■ = 9 \times 5$ 45
15. $8 \times 5 = ■$ 40
16. $■ = 7 \times 2$ 14
17. $6 \times 5 = ■$ 30
18. 2×8 16
19. 5×8 40
20. 2×9 18
21. 5×9 45
22. $3 + 3 = 2 \times ■$ 3
23. $4 \times ■ = 4 + 4 + 4$ 3
24. $2 \times 5 = ■ + 5$ 5

25. Write a multiplication problem about the rocks below. Then solve. See above.

26. **REASONING** Drew has 5 pairs of white socks and 2 pairs of black socks. How many more white socks than black socks does Drew have? 6 more white socks

27. **FAST FACT** • SCIENCE Six Apollo space missions brought back 842 pounds of rocks, pebbles, sand, and dust from the surface of the moon. Write 842 in expanded form. 800 + 40 + 2

Getting Ready for the EOG Test

28. The pictograph shows the numbers of players on two teams. Which number sentence could be used to find the number of players on the Red Team? B

NUMBER OF PLAYERS PER TEAM	
Red Team	● ● ● ● ●
Green Team	● ● ● ● ● ●
Each ● = 2 players.	

A $5 \times 1 = 5$ B $5 \times 2 = 10$ C $6 \times 2 = 12$ D $5 \times 6 = 30$

COMMON ERROR ALERT

Watch for students who get products that do not end in 0 or 5 when they multiply by 5.

$$\begin{array}{r} 6 \\ \times 5 \\ \hline 24 \end{array} \qquad \begin{array}{r} 7 \\ \times 5 \\ \hline 28 \end{array}$$

Reinforce that all multiples of 5 have the digit 5 or the digit 0 in the ones place. Demonstrate that the pattern for products, when multiplying with 5, is odd, even, odd, even, and so on by having students color the numbers as they skip-count by 5 on a hundred chart.

Independent Practice

Note that Exercise 26 is a **multistep or strategy problem.** Assign Exercises 5–27.

Point out that the multiplication table in Exercises 8–9 must be completed. Encourage volunteers to explain how they would complete the table.

North Carolina Standards 1.03 Develop fluency with multiplication from 1 × 1 to 12 × 12 and division up to two-digit by one-digit numbers using: a) Strategies for multiplying and dividing numbers.

Challenge 8.2

Pattern Plot

Find the next numbers.
Write a rule used to make the pattern. Possible rules are given.

1. 22, 24, 26, 28, 30, 32, 34, 36
   Rule: add 2
2. 80, 85, 90, 95, 100, 105, 110, 115
   Rule: add 5
3. 117, 122, 127, 132, 137, 142, 147, 152
   Rule: add 5
4. 211, 213, 215, 217, 219, 221, 223, 225
   Rule: add 2
5. 317, 319, 324, 326, 331, 333, 338, 340, 345, 347, 352, 354, 359, 361
   Rule: add 2, then add 5

Make up your own pattern using differences of 2 or 5. Write your rule under your pattern. Patterns will vary. Check students' work.

6. ____, ____, ____, ____, ____, ____, ____
   Rule: ____
7. ____, ____, ____, ____, ____, ____, ____
   Rule: ____

Challenge CW43

Problem Solving 8.2

Multiply with 2 and 5

Understand → Plan → Solve → Check

Write the correct answer.

1. $2 + 2 + 2 + 2 + 2 = ■$ 10
2. $5 \times 2 = ■$ 10
3. Sebastian has 3 pairs of shoes. How many individual shoes does he have? 6 shoes
4. Jenny buys 3 packs of pencils. There are 5 pencils in each pack. How many pencils does she have in all? 15 pencils

Choose the letter of the correct answer.

5. Which addition sentence can be used to tell how many there are in all?
   A $4 + 4 = ■$
   B $2 + 4 = ■$
   C $4 + 4 + 4 + 4 = ■$
   (D) $2 + 2 + 2 + 2 = ■$
6. Which multiplication sentence can be used to tell how many there are in all?
   F $20 \times 5 = ■$
   G $5 \times 5 = ■$
   (H) $5 \times 4 = ■$
   J $5 \times 20 = ■$
7. **Write About It** How are the number sentences in Problems 1 and 2 related? Possible answer: Both number sentences find out how many there are in 5 groups of 2.

Problem Solving PS43

4 ASSESS

Summarize the lesson by having students:

DISCUSS Describe how you would find 10 × 5. Write the product. Possible answer: skip-count; 50

WRITE Compose a word problem for the multiplication sentence 8 × 5 = 40. Answers will vary.

LESSON QUIZ

Transparency 8.2

Complete.

1. $7 \times 2 = ■$ 14
2. $5 \times 7 = ■$ 35
3. $2 \times 9 = ■$ 18
4. $5 \times 5 = ■$ 25

Lesson 8.3

Arrays

Lesson Planning

Objective To use arrays and the Commutative Property to explore the concept of multiplication

Materials *For each group* square tiles

NCTM Standards

1. Number and Operations
2. Algebra
6. Problem Solving
7. Reasoning and Proof
8. Communication

Math Background

These ideas will help students use arrays and the Commutative Property to multiply.

- Multiplication sentences can be represented by rectangular arrays with equal numbers in each row and in each column.
- Numbers that can be represented in square arrays have the same number of rows and columns. These arrays are later identified as perfect squares.
- The Commutative Property of Multiplication states that $a \times b = c$ and $b \times a = c$.

Vocabulary

array an arrangement that shows objects in rows and columns

Commutative Property of Multiplication a rule stating that two factors can be multiplied in any order and the product is the same.

Warm-Up Resources

Number of the Day

How many days are in three weeks? 21 days

Daily Facts Practice

Have students practice addition and subtraction facts by completing Set B of *Teacher's Resource Book*, p. TR89.

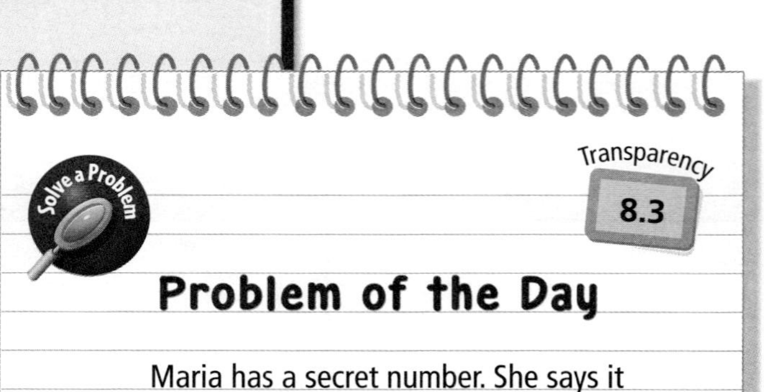

Problem of the Day

Maria has a secret number. She says it when she counts by twos and threes. She does not say it when she counts by fours. What could the number be? Possible answers: 6,18

Solution Problem of the Day tab, p. PD8

Intervention and Extension Resources

Alternative Teaching Strategy

MATERIALS *For each group* grid paper

Have students **write multiplication sentences for arrays.** Have them use grid paper to color arrays. Let a volunteer write a multiplication sentence for each array. Check students' work.

VISUAL

VISUAL/SPATIAL

Special Needs

MATERIALS *For each group* square tiles

Have students **use tiles to make arrays.** Have them see how many ways they can arrange 8 tiles, 10 tiles, and 12 tiles in equal groups. 4 groups of 2, 2 groups of 4; 5 groups of 2, 2 groups of 5; 6 groups of 2, 2 groups of 6; 3 groups of 4, 4 groups of 3

KINESTHETIC

BODILY/KINESTHETIC

Multistep and Strategy Problems

The following multistep or strategy problems are provided in Lesson 8.3:

Page	Item
163	8, 9

Advanced Learners

MATERIALS scissors, cardboard or paper

Challenge students to **make arrays**. Have them make paper or cardboard squares with sides of 1 foot. Let them estimate how many squares they will need to arrange in each row and column in order to cover their desk or a section of the classroom floor. Students can check their estimates by using their squares to measure the width and length of the room or designated area. Check students' work.

VISUAL, KINESTHETIC

BODILY/KINESTHETIC

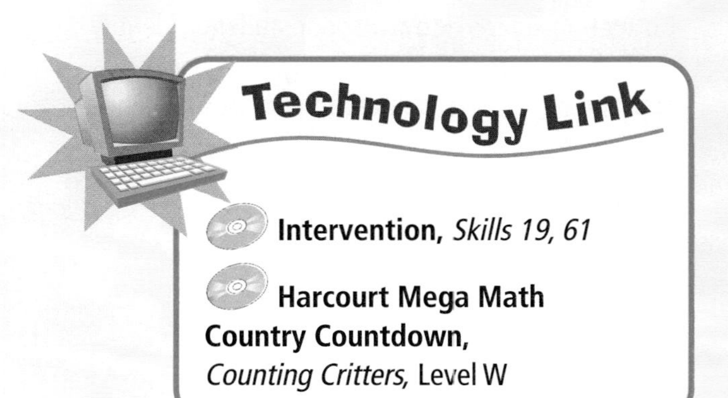

Technology Link

Intervention, *Skills 19, 61*

Harcourt Mega Math Country Countdown, *Counting Critters,* Level W

Lesson 8.3 Organizer

Objective To use arrays and the Commutative Property to explore the concept of multiplication

Vocabulary array, Commutative Property of Multiplication

Materials *For each group* square tiles

1 INTRODUCE

QUICK REVIEW provides review of prerequisite skills.

WHY LEARN THIS? You can make arrays to solve multiplication sentences. *Share the lesson objective with students.*

2 TEACH

Guided Instruction

- *Ask students to read the definition of array.*
  What is a row? A row goes across the page.
  What is a column? A column goes down the page.
- *Have students complete Steps 1 and 2.*
  Why is 15 the total number represented by the tiles? There are 3 rows with 5 tiles in each or 15 tiles in all.
- *Direct students to the questions in Explore.*
  How would you form an array in the shape of a rectangle? Make an array with different numbers of rows and columns.
  How would you form an array in the shape of a square? Make an array with equal numbers of rows and columns.

3 PRACTICE

Guided Practice

Do Try It Exercises a–b with your students. Identify students who are having difficulty and choose appropriate lesson resources to provide assistance.

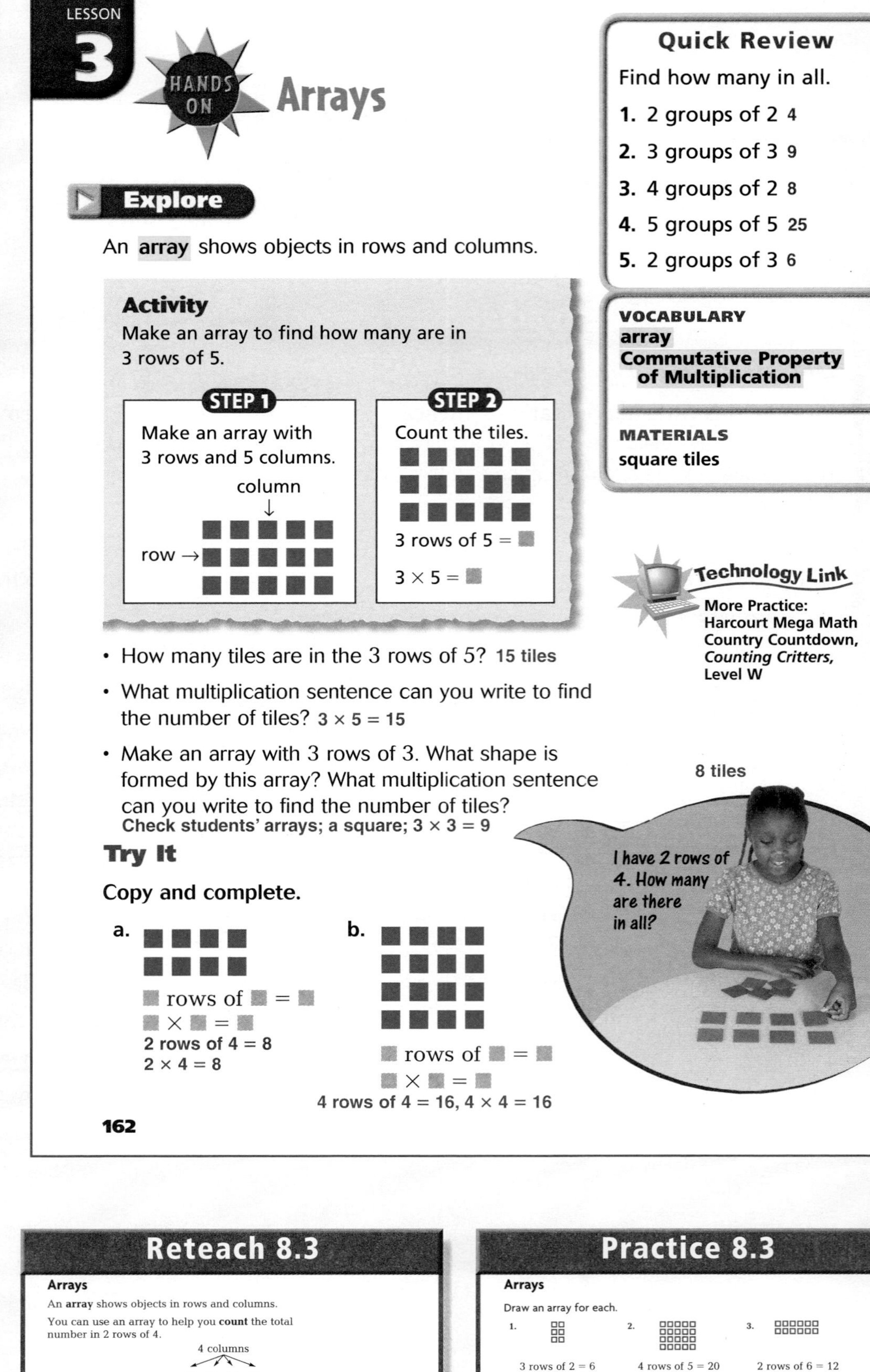

LESSON 3

HANDS ON

Arrays

Quick Review

Find how many in all.

1. 2 groups of 2 **4**
2. 3 groups of 3 **9**
3. 4 groups of 2 **8**
4. 5 groups of 5 **25**
5. 2 groups of 3 **6**

VOCABULARY
array
Commutative Property of Multiplication

MATERIALS
square tiles

Explore

An **array** shows objects in rows and columns.

Activity

Make an array to find how many are in 3 rows of 5.

STEP 1 Make an array with 3 rows and 5 columns.

column ↓

row →

STEP 2 Count the tiles.

3 rows of 5 = ■

$3 \times 5 =$ ■

- How many tiles are in the 3 rows of 5? **15 tiles**
- What multiplication sentence can you write to find the number of tiles? **$3 \times 5 = 15$**
- Make an array with 3 rows of 3. What shape is formed by this array? What multiplication sentence can you write to find the number of tiles? **Check students' arrays; a square; $3 \times 3 = 9$**

Technology Link
More Practice: Harcourt Mega Math Country Countdown, *Counting Critters,* Level W

8 tiles

I have 2 rows of 4. How many are there in all?

Try It

Copy and complete.

a. ■ rows of ■ = ■
■ × ■ = ■
2 rows of 4 = 8
$2 \times 4 = 8$

b. ■ rows of ■ = ■
■ × ■ = ■
4 rows of 4 = 16, $4 \times 4 = 16$

162

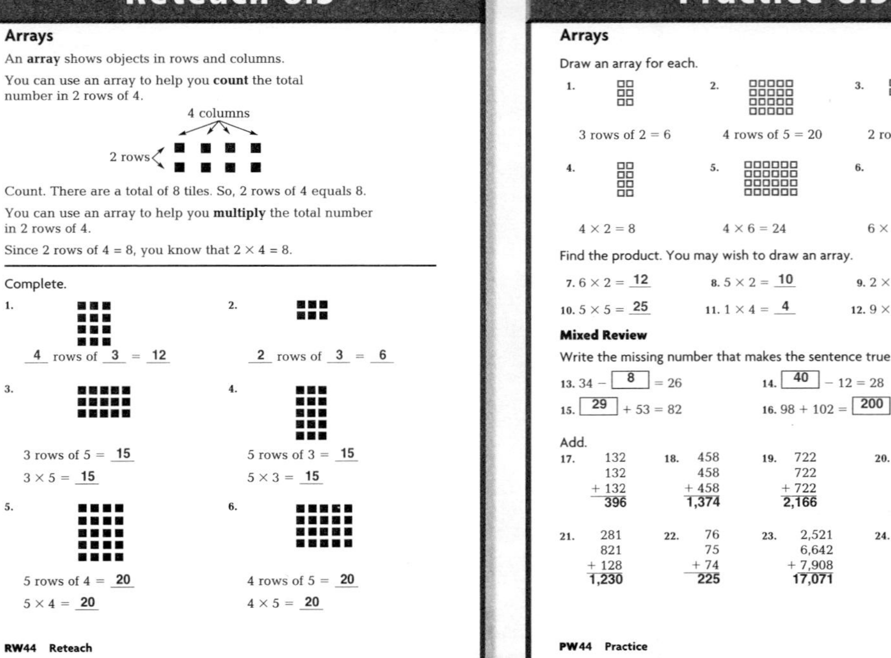

Reteach 8.3

Arrays

An **array** shows objects in rows and columns.

You can use an array to help you **count** the total number in 2 rows of 4.

4 columns

2 rows

Count. There are a total of 8 tiles. So, 2 rows of 4 equals 8.

You can use an array to help you **multiply** the total number in 2 rows of 4.

Since 2 rows of 4 = 8, you know that $2 \times 4 = 8$.

Complete.

1. 4 rows of 3 = 12
2. 2 rows of 3 = 6
3. 3 rows of 5 = 15; $3 \times 5 =$ 15
4. 5 rows of 3 = 15; $5 \times 3 =$ 15
5. 5 rows of 4 = 20; $5 \times 4 =$ 20
6. 4 rows of 5 = 20; $4 \times 5 =$ 20

RW44 Reteach

Practice 8.3

Arrays

Draw an array for each.

1. 3 rows of 2 = 6
2. 4 rows of 5 = 20
3. 2 rows of 6 = 12
4. $4 \times 2 = 8$
5. $4 \times 6 = 24$
6. $6 \times 3 = 18$

Find the product. You may wish to draw an array.

7. $6 \times 2 =$ 12
8. $5 \times 2 =$ 10
9. $2 \times 7 =$ 14
10. $5 \times 5 =$ 25
11. $1 \times 4 =$ 4
12. $9 \times 3 =$ 27

Mixed Review

Write the missing number that makes the sentence true.

13. 34 − [8] = 26
14. [40] − 12 = 28
15. [29] + 53 = 82
16. 98 + 102 = [200]

Add.

17. 132 + 132 + 132 = 396
18. 458 + 458 + 458 = 1,374
19. 722 + 722 + 722 = 2,166
20. 537 + 537 + 537 = 1,611
21. 281 + 821 + 128 = 1,230
22. 76 + 75 + 74 = 225
23. 2,521 + 6,642 + 7,908 = 17,071
24. 3,715 + 6,142 + 4,143 = 14,000

PW44 Practice

Connect

The **Commutative Property of Multiplication**, or Order Property, states that two factors can be multiplied in any order. The product is the same.

Use arrays to show the Commutative Property of Multiplication.

Examples

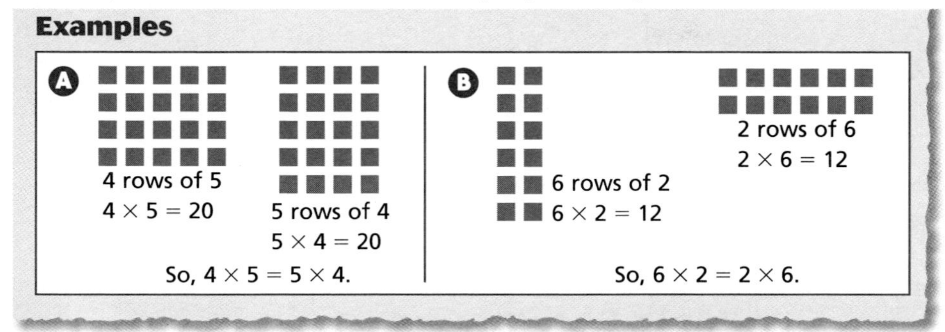

Practice and Problem Solving

Copy and complete.

1. 3 rows of 6 = 18; $3 \times 6 = 18$
   ■ rows of ■ = ■
   ■ × ■ = ■
2. 2 rows of 3 = 6; $2 \times 3 = 6$
   ■ rows of ■ = ■
   ■ × ■ = ■
3. 3 rows of 2 = 6; $3 \times 2 = 6$
   ■ rows of ■ = ■
   ■ × ■ = ■

Find the product. You may wish to draw an array.

4. $2 \times 5 =$ ■ 10
5. $6 \times 4 =$ ■ 24
6. $8 \times 3 =$ ■ 24
7. $3 \times 5 =$ ■ 15
8. **Write About It** Miguel needs a book cover that costs \$1.99 and a package of markers that costs \$2.79. He has \$5.00. Does he have enough money to buy both items?
   Yes; the two items cost \$4.78 altogether.
9. **REASONING** The sum of Jarrod's age and Kayla's age is 21. Kayla is 5 years older than Jarrod. How old are Kayla and Jarrod?
   Kayla: 13; Jarrod: 8

Getting Ready for the EOG Test

10. Jan is laying tiles. How many tiles are in 5 rows of 6? **D**

   A 11 C 25
   B 15 D 30

North Carolina Standards 1.03 Develop fluency with multiplication from 1×1 to 12×12 and division to two-digit by one-digit numbers using: a) Strategies for multiplying and dividing numbers.

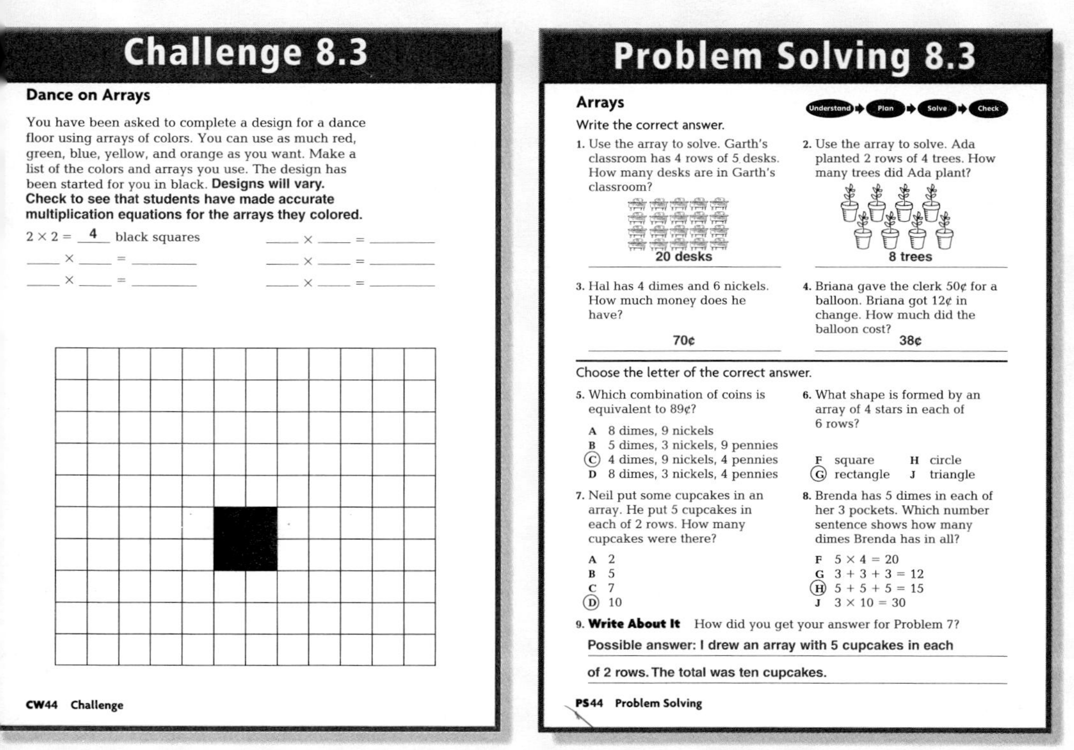

Challenge 8.3

Dance on Arrays

You have been asked to complete a design for a dance floor using arrays of colors. You can use as much red, green, blue, yellow, and orange as you want. Make a list of the colors and arrays you use. The design has been started for you in black. **Designs will vary. Check to see that students have made accurate multiplication equations for the arrays they colored.**

$2 \times 2 =$ 4 black squares

___ × ___ = ______

CW44 Challenge

Problem Solving 8.3

Arrays

Understand → Plan → Solve → Check

Write the correct answer.

1. Use the array to solve. Garth's classroom has 4 rows of 5 desks. How many desks are in Garth's classroom?
   20 desks
2. Use the array to solve. Ada planted 2 rows of 4 trees. How many trees did Ada plant?
   8 trees
3. Hal has 4 dimes and 6 nickels. How much money does he have?
   70¢
4. Briana gave the clerk 50¢ for a balloon. Briana got 12¢ in change. How much did the balloon cost?
   38¢

Choose the letter of the correct answer.

5. Which combination of coins is equivalent to 89¢?
   A 8 dimes, 9 nickels
   B 5 dimes, 3 nickels, 9 pennies
   (C) 4 dimes, 9 nickels, 4 pennies
   D 8 dimes, 3 nickels, 4 pennies
6. What shape is formed by an array of 4 stars in each of 6 rows?
   F square H circle
   (G) rectangle J triangle
7. Neil put some cupcakes in an array. He put 5 cupcakes in each of 2 rows. How many cupcakes were there?
   A 2
   B 5
   C 7
   (D) 10
8. Brenda has 5 dimes in each of her 3 pockets. Which number sentence shows how many dimes Brenda has in all?
   F $5 \times 4 = 20$
   G $3 + 3 + 3 = 12$
   (H) $5 + 5 + 5 = 15$
   J $3 \times 10 = 30$
9. **Write About It** How did you get your answer for Problem 7?
   Possible answer: I drew an array with 5 cupcakes in each of 2 rows. The total was ten cupcakes.

PS44 Problem Solving

Independent Practice

Note that Exercises 8–9 are **multistep or strategy problems.** Assign Exercises 1–9.

SCAFFOLDED INSTRUCTION Use the prompts on Transparency 8 to guide instruction for the multistep or strategy problem in Exercise 8.

Summarize the lesson by having students:

DISCUSS What would the product be for Exercise 7 if you added 3 more rows of 5 each to the array? Write the new multiplication sentence. 30; $6 \times 5 = 30$

WRITE Give an example of a multiplication problem, and draw an array to picture the problem. Exchange problems with another student and solve. Answers will vary.

LESSON QUIZ

Find the product. You may wish to draw an array.

1. $2 \times 6 =$ ■ 12
2. $5 \times 3 =$ ■ 15
3. $6 \times 3 =$ ■ 18
4. $3 \times 4 =$ ■ 12

Lesson 8.4

Multiply with 3

Lesson Planning

Objective To multiply with 3 and use the Commutative Property

NCTM Standards

1. Number and Operations
2. Algebra
6. Problem Solving
7. Reasoning and Proof
8. Communication
9. Connections
10. Representation

Math Background

These ideas will help students multiply with 3 and use the Commutative Property of Multiplication to solve problems.

- When you multiply 3 by an even number, the product is even. When you multiply 3 by an odd number, the product is odd.
- The Commutative Property of Multiplication says you can multiply two factors in any order. The product is always the same.
- Students can use the Commutative Property of Multiplication to help them solve problems by reversing the order of factors of products they already know.

You can illustrate the Commutative Property of Multiplication by using a number line to show that while the jumps may be different, the product is always the same.

Warm-Up Resources

Number of the Day

Write and solve two multiplication sentences using the number of school days in one week as one factor and a number of weeks as the other factor. Possible answer: $3 \times 5 = 15$, $5 \times 7 = 35$

Daily Facts Practice

Have students practice addition facts by completing Set C of *Teacher's Resource Book*, p. TR89.

Solve a Problem

Transparency 8.4

Problem of the Day

I am a number between 30 and 40. You say my name when you count by threes. You also say my name when you count by twos. What number am I? 36

Solution Problem of the Day tab, p. PD8

Intervention and Extension Resources

Alternative Teaching Strategy

MATERIALS *For each student* number line, p. TR5

Help students **multiply with 3.** Use a number line from 0 to 30 to help students see the pattern of odd and even products when skip-counting by threes. Have students write the corresponding multiplication sentence for each jump on the number line as they move to the right. Discuss the odd/even pattern in the products. Check students' work.

See also page 166.

VISUAL

VISUAL/SPATIAL

Multistep and Strategy Problems

The following multistep or strategy problems are provided in Lesson 8.4:

Page	Item
166	34, 35
167	41

Vocabulary Strategy

Help students **use the Commutative Property of Multiplication.**

- Have students write three multiplication sentences and draw arrays to model each sentence.
- Below each number sentence, have them reverse the order of the factors. Have them draw arrays to model the new sentences to show that the product remains the same. Check students' work.

VISUAL

VISUAL/SPATIAL

Early Finishers

Have students **use a number line to multiply**. Display a large number line from 0 to 25. Have students who finish early show how to make jumps of 2, 3, and 5 on the number line. Then have students show where they will land if they make:

3 jumps of 8 24   8 jumps of 3 24
4 jumps of 5 20   2 jumps of 9 18
6 jumps of 2 12   5 jumps of 5 25

VISUAL, KINESTHETIC

BODILY/KINESTHETIC

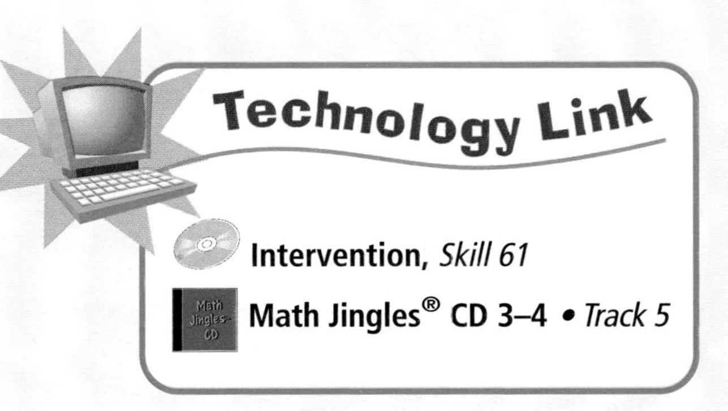

Intervention, *Skill 61*

Math Jingles® CD 3–4 • *Track 5*

Lesson 8.4 Organizer

Objective To multiply with 3 and use the Commutative Property

1 INTRODUCE

QUICK REVIEW provides review of prerequisite skills.

WHY LEARN THIS? Using the Commutative Property of Multiplication will help you memorize multiplication facts. *Share the lesson objective with students.*

2 TEACH

Guided Instruction

- *Ask students to read the Learn section.*
  How are the jumps on the two number lines different? The first number line has 3 jumps of 2; the second number line has 2 jumps of 3.
  How are the jumps on the number lines alike? The jumps begin at 0 and end at 6.
  ALGEBRAIC THINKING How is the Commutative Property of Multiplication similar to the Order Property of Addition? The order in which two numbers are multiplied does not affect the product, just as the order in which two numbers are added does not affect the sum.
- *Ask students to read the Reasoning item.*
  Can you subtract numbers in any order and get the same difference? Give an example. No; Possible answer: you subtract the lesser number from the greater number; $5 - 3 = 2$, not $3 - 5$.

MODIFYING INSTRUCTION Discuss the reason you can multiply a number by 3 by adding the number to its double. Provide examples for students.

LESSON 4

Multiply with 3

Quick Review

1. $2 + 2 = 2 \times$ ■ 2
2. $3 \times$ ■ $= 5 + 5 + 5$ 5
3. $2 \times 6 = 6 +$ ■ 6
4. ■ $\times 5 = 10$ 2
5. $2 \times 4 =$ ■ 8

Learn

PRACTICE, PRACTICE, PRACTICE

Pat practiced soccer 2 hours each day for 3 days. How many hours did he practice in all?

For 2 hours, move 2 spaces. For 3 days, make 3 jumps of 2 spaces.

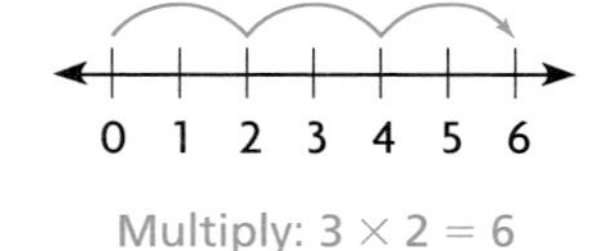

Multiply: $3 \times 2 = 6$

Val practiced soccer 3 hours each day for 2 days. How many hours did she practice in all?

For 3 hours, move 3 spaces. For 2 days, make 2 jumps of 3 spaces.

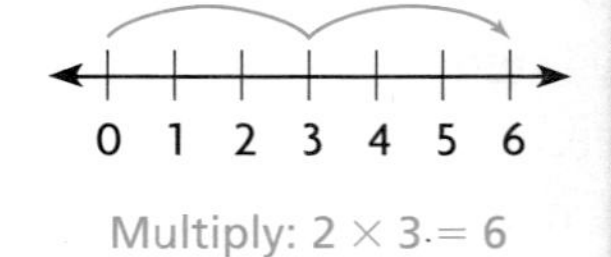

Multiply: $2 \times 3 = 6$

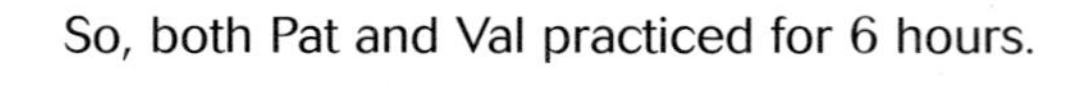

So, both Pat and Val practiced for 6 hours.

A number line can help you understand the Commutative Property of Multiplication.

One Way Use a number line.

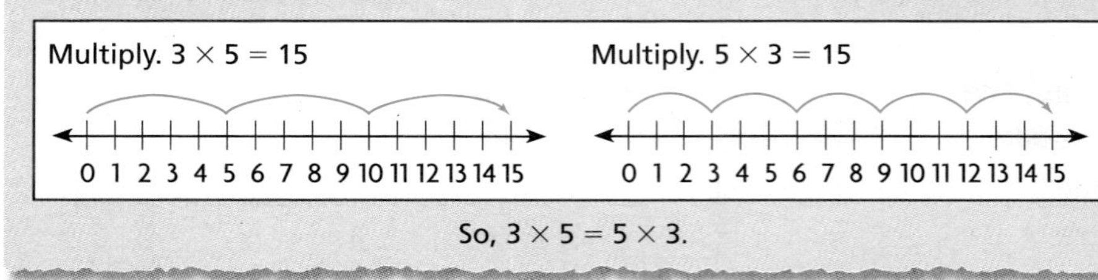

So, $3 \times 5 = 5 \times 3$.

- **REASONING** Use the factors 3 and 6 to explain the Commutative Property of Multiplication. **Possible answer: $3 \times 6 = 18$ and $6 \times 3 = 18$. The product is the same but the order of the factors changed.**

164

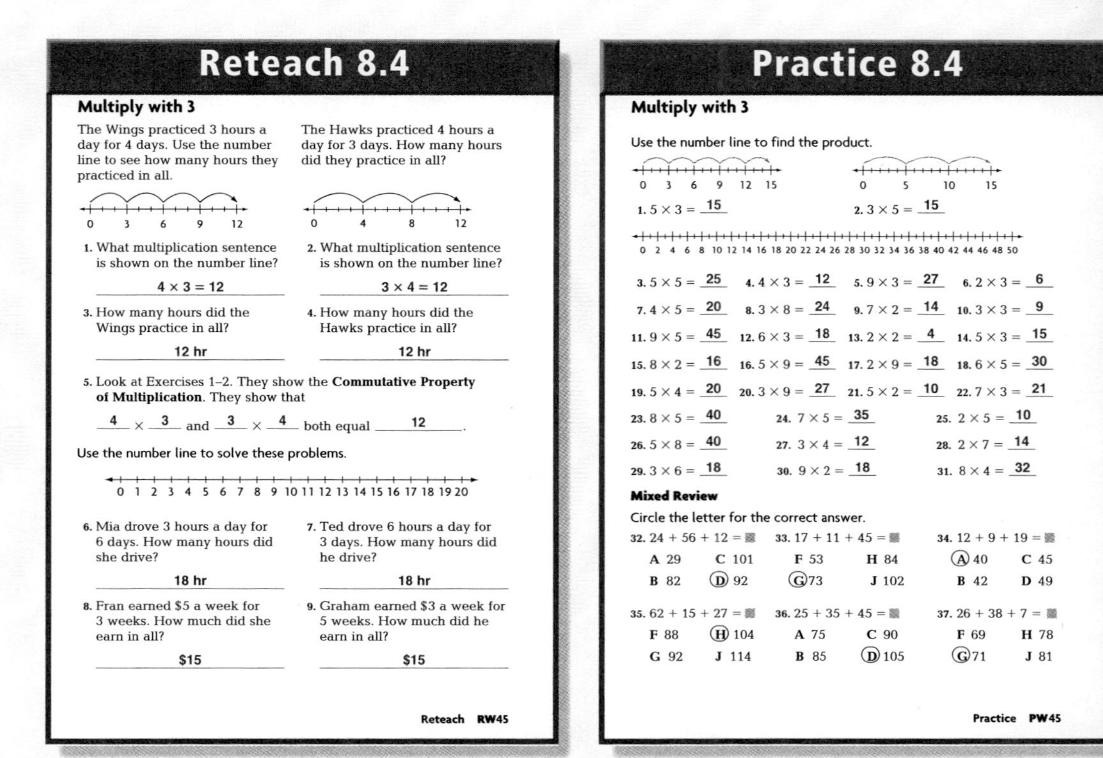

Reteach 8.4

Multiply with 3

The Wings practiced 3 hours a day for 4 days. Use the number line to see how many hours they practiced in all.

0 3 6 9 12

The Hawks practiced 4 hours a day for 3 days. How many hours did they practice in all?

0 4 8 12

1. What multiplication sentence is shown on the number line? **$4 \times 3 = 12$**
2. What multiplication sentence is shown on the number line? **$3 \times 4 = 12$**
3. How many hours did the Wings practice in all? **12 hr**
4. How many hours did the Hawks practice in all? **12 hr**
5. Look at Exercises 1–2. They show the **Commutative Property of Multiplication**. They show that **4** × **3** and **3** × **4** both equal **12**.

Use the number line to solve these problems.

0 1 2 3 4 5 6 7 8 9 10 11 12 13 14 15 16 17 18 19 20

6. Mia drove 3 hours a day for 6 days. How many hours did she drive? **18 hr**
7. Ted drove 6 hours a day for 3 days. How many hours did he drive? **18 hr**
8. Fran earned $5 a week for 3 weeks. How much did she earn in all? **$15**
9. Graham earned $3 a week for 5 weeks. How much did he earn in all? **$15**

Reteach RW45

Practice 8.4

Multiply with 3

Use the number line to find the product.

0 3 6 9 12 15

0 5 10 15

1. $5 \times 3 =$ **15**
2. $3 \times 5 =$ **15**

0 2 4 6 8 10 12 14 16 18 20 22 24 26 28 30 32 34 36 38 40 42 44 46 48 50

3. $5 \times 5 =$ **25**
4. $4 \times 3 =$ **12**
5. $9 \times 3 =$ **27**
6. $2 \times 3 =$ **6**
7. $4 \times 5 =$ **20**
8. $3 \times 8 =$ **24**
9. $7 \times 2 =$ **14**
10. $3 \times 3 =$ **9**
11. $9 \times 5 =$ **45**
12. $6 \times 3 =$ **18**
13. $2 \times 2 =$ **4**
14. $5 \times 3 =$ **15**
15. $8 \times 2 =$ **16**
16. $5 \times 9 =$ **45**
17. $2 \times 9 =$ **18**
18. $6 \times 5 =$ **30**
19. $5 \times 4 =$ **20**
20. $3 \times 9 =$ **27**
21. $5 \times 2 =$ **10**
22. $7 \times 3 =$ **21**
23. $8 \times 5 =$ **40**
24. $7 \times 5 =$ **35**
25. $2 \times 5 =$ **10**
26. $5 \times 8 =$ **40**
27. $3 \times 4 =$ **12**
28. $2 \times 7 =$ **14**
29. $3 \times 6 =$ **18**
30. $9 \times 2 =$ **18**
31. $8 \times 4 =$ **32**

Mixed Review

Circle the letter for the correct answer.

32. $24 + 56 + 12 =$ ■
    A 29 C 101 B 82 (D) 92
33. $17 + 11 + 45 =$ ■
    F 53 H 84 (G) 73 J 102
34. $12 + 9 + 19 =$ ■
    (A) 40 C 45 B 42 D 49
35. $62 + 15 + 27 =$ ■
    F 88 (H) 104 G 92 J 114
36. $25 + 35 + 45 =$ ■
    A 75 C 90 B 85 (D) 105
37. $26 + 38 + 7 =$ ■
    F 69 H 78 (G) 71 J 81

Practice PW45

Multiplication Practice

What if Pat scored 4 goals in each of 3 games and Val scored 3 goals in each of 4 games? Which example shows Pat's goals? Val's goals? How many goals did each player score?

Another Way Draw a picture.

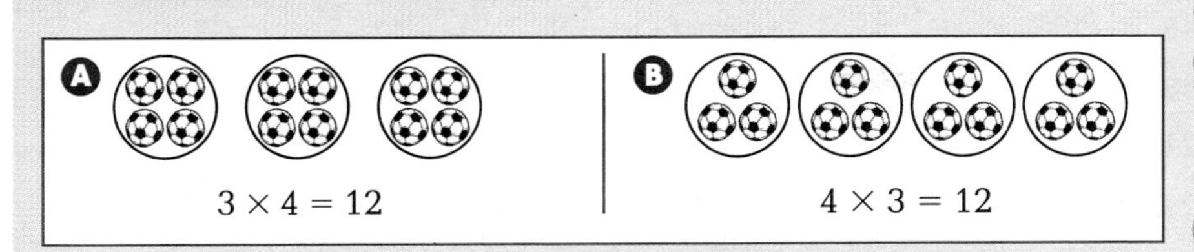

Example A shows Pat's goals. Example B shows Val's goals.

Each player scored 12 goals.

- **What if** Val scored 8 goals in each of 3 games and Pat scored 3 goals in each of 8 games? How many goals did each player score? **Each scored 24 goals.**

Check

1. **Explain** how knowing the product 7×3 can help you find the product 3×7. **Possible answer: The factors are the same, so the product will be the same; $7 \times 3 = 21$ so $3 \times 7 = 21$.**
2. Is the product even or odd when you multiply 3 by an even number? by an odd number? Explain. **The product is even when you multiply 3 by an even number and odd when you multiply 3 by an odd number.**

Use the number line or draw a picture to find the product.

0 1 2 3 4 5 6 7 8 9 10 11 12 13 14 15 16 17 18 19 20 21 22 23 24 25 26 27 28 29 30

3. $4 \times 3 = ■$ **12**
4. $■ = 3 \times 4$ **12**
5. $7 \times 3 = ■$ **21**
6. $■ = 3 \times 7$ **21**
7. $■ = 6 \times 3$ **18**
8. $■ = 3 \times 6$ **18**
9. $3 \times 8 = ■$ **24**
10. $■ = 8 \times 3$ **24**
11. 5×3 **15**
12. 3×5 **15**
13. 3×9 **27**
14. 9×3 **27**

LESSON CONTINUES

North Carolina Standards 1.03 Develop fluency with multiplication from 1×1 to 12×12 and division to two-digit by one-digit numbers using: a) Strategies for multiplying and dividing numbers. *also* 1.04

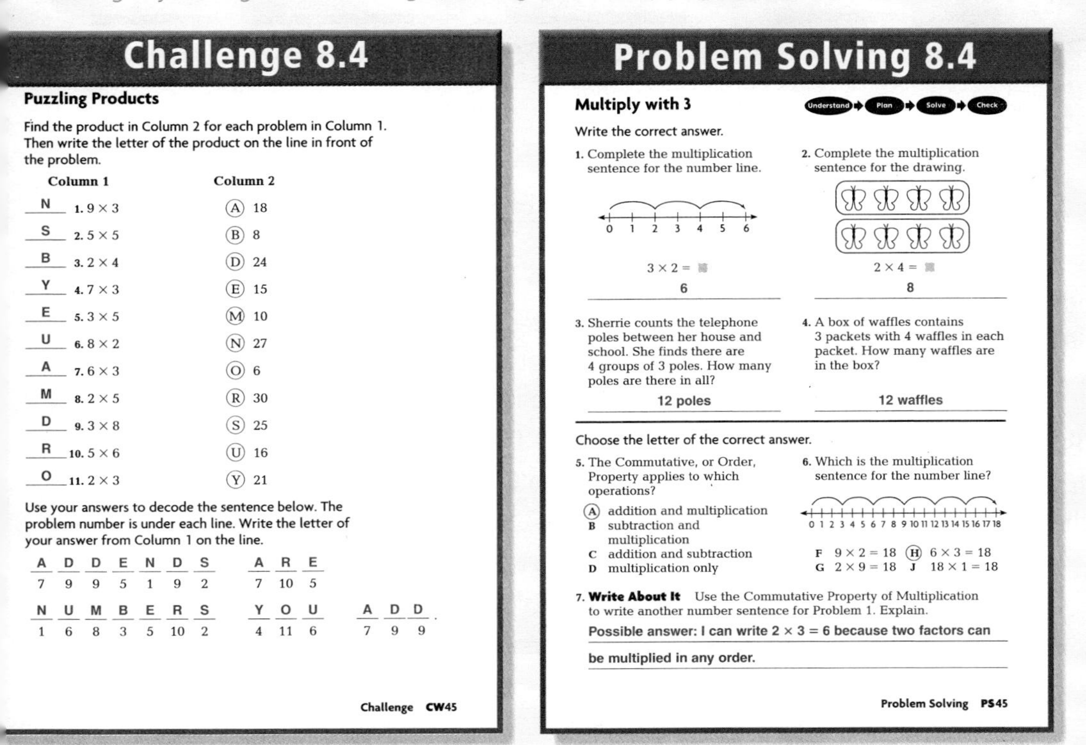

Challenge 8.4

Puzzling Products

Find the product in Column 2 for each problem in Column 1. Then write the letter of the product on the line in front of the problem.

Column 1	Column 2
N 1. 9 × 3	(A) 18
S 2. 5 × 5	(B) 8
B 3. 2 × 4	(D) 24
Y 4. 7 × 3	(E) 15
E 5. 3 × 5	(M) 10
U 6. 8 × 2	(N) 27
A 7. 6 × 3	(O) 6
M 8. 2 × 5	(R) 30
D 9. 3 × 8	(S) 25
R 10. 5 × 6	(U) 16
O 11. 2 × 3	(Y) 21

Use your answers to decode the sentence below. The problem number is under each line. Write the letter of your answer from Column 1 on the line.

A D D E N D S (7 9 9 5 1 9 2) A R E (7 10 5)

N U M B E R S (1 6 8 3 5 10 2) Y O U (4 11 6) A D D. (7 9 9)

Challenge CW45

Problem Solving 8.4

Multiply with 3

Understand → Plan → Solve → Check

Write the correct answer.

1. Complete the multiplication sentence for the number line.
$3 \times 2 = ■$ 6
2. Complete the multiplication sentence for the drawing.
$2 \times 4 = ■$ 8
3. Sherrie counts the telephone poles between her house and school. She finds there are 4 groups of 3 poles. How many poles are there in all? 12 poles
4. A box of waffles contains 3 packets with 4 waffles in each packet. How many waffles are in the box? 12 waffles

Choose the letter of the correct answer.

5. The Commutative, or Order, Property applies to which operations?
(A) addition and multiplication
B subtraction and multiplication
C addition and subtraction
D multiplication only
6. Which is the multiplication sentence for the number line?
F $9 \times 2 = 18$
(H) $6 \times 3 = 18$
G $2 \times 9 = 18$
J $18 \times 1 = 18$
7. **Write About It** Use the Commutative Property of Multiplication to write another number sentence for Problem 1. Explain.
Possible answer: I can write $2 \times 3 = 6$ because two factors can be multiplied in any order.

Problem Solving PS45

- *Discuss the first What If problem.*
What if Pat scored 2 goals in each game for 6 games and Val scored 6 goals in each game for 2 games? Would either player have scored more goals than the other? Explain. No; $6 \times 2 = 12$ and $2 \times 6 = 12$, so both would have scored the same number of goals.
- *Have students work through the second What If problem.*
What if Val scored 3 goals in 7 games and Pat scored 7 goals in 2 games? Would either player have scored more? Explain. Yes; Val would have scored more because $7 \times 3 = 21$, which is more than $2 \times 7 = 14$.

3 PRACTICE

Guided Practice

Do Check Exercises 1–14 with your students. Identify students who are having difficulty and choose appropriate lesson resources to provide assistance.

REASONING Have students explain how they can tell, without multiplying, if the product $3 \times 1{,}387$ is an odd or even number. Possible answer: Since 1,387 is an odd number, the product will be an odd number.

After they have completed Exercises 3–14, ask students what would change if the order of the factors in each problem were switched. Students should conclude that nothing would change—the products would be the same.

COMMON ERROR ALERT

Watch for students who get odd numbers when they multiply an even number by 3 or even numbers when they multiply an odd number by 3. Remind them that an even number multiplied by 3 is *always* even and an odd number multiplied by 3 is *always* odd.

Independent Practice

Note that Exercises 34–35 and 41 are **multistep or strategy problems.** Assign Exercises 15–41.

Have students skim Exercises 15–26 without solving them. Ask them to identify the exercises with odd products and those with even products. Students should conclude that Exercises 16, 17, 18, 20, 25, and 26 have odd products; they should also conclude that Exercises 15, 19, 21, 22, 23, and 24 have even products.

Practice and Problem Solving

Extra Practice, page 170, Set C

Use the number line or draw a picture to find the product.

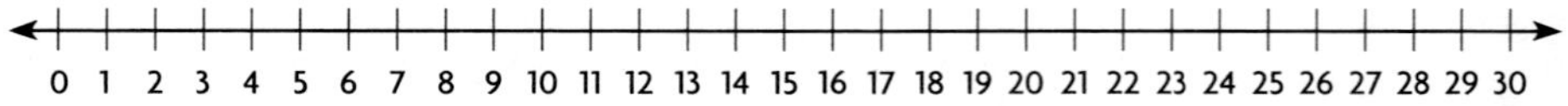

15. $3 \times 6 = ■$ **18**
16. $■ = 5 \times 5$ **25**
17. $3 \times 9 = ■$ **27**
18. $■ = 9 \times 3$ **27**
19. $■ = 9 \times 2$ **18**
20. $7 \times 3 = ■$ **21**
21. $■ = 4 \times 5$ **20**
22. $2 \times 8 = ■$ **16**
23. $7 \times 2 = ■$ **14**
24. 3×8 **24**
25. 1×5 **5**
26. 3×9 **27**

Copy and complete.

27.

×	1	2	3	4	5	6	7	8	9
3	■ 3	■ 6	■ 9	■ 12	■ 15	■ 18	■ 21	■ 24	■ 27

Write the missing factor.

28. $2 \times 3 = ■ \times 2$ **3**
29. $3 \times ■ = 7 \times 3$ **7**
30. $5 \times 3 = ■ \times 5$ **3**
31. $6 \times 3 = ■ \times 2$ **9**
32. $4 \times 3 = 6 \times ■$ **2**
33. $8 \times 3 = ■ \times 8$ **3**

34. **What's the Error?** Sam played soccer for 2 hours a day, 3 days a week, for 4 weeks. Sam said he played soccer for a total of 6 hours during the month. What is Sam's error? **Possible answer: He didn't multiply the number of hours a week by the number of weeks.**

35. REASONING If you add 3 to an odd number, is the sum even or odd? If you multiply an odd number by 3, is the product even or odd? Explain. **even; odd; Check students' explanations.**

USE DATA For 36–39, use the bar graph.

36. How many more goals did Matt's soccer team score in Game 4 than in Game 1? **3 goals**

37. How many goals did Matt's team score in the four games? **18 goals**

38. If Matt's team scores twice as many goals in Game 5 as in Game 3, how many goals will it score? **8 goals**

39. **Write a problem** using the bar graph. **Possible problem: How many more goals did the team score in Game 4 than in Game 3? 2 goals**

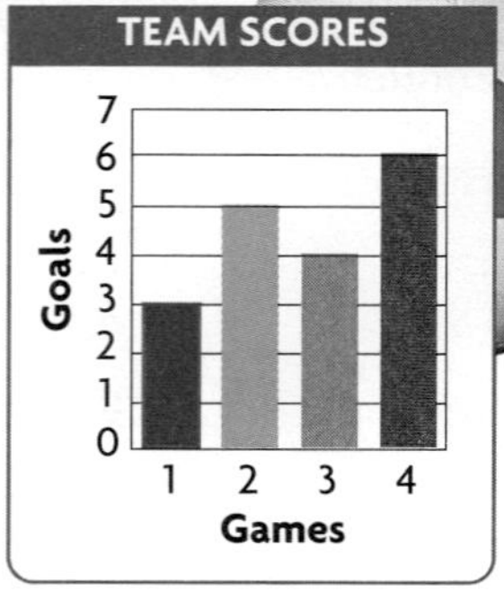

166

Alternative Teaching Strategy

Scaffolded Instruction

PURPOSE Students use numbers on spinners to reinforce understanding of the Commutative Property of Multiplication.

MATERIALS *For each pair* 2 spinners, one with numerals 2, 3, 5, one with numerals 2–6, pp. TR67–68; number line, p. TR5

Step 1

Students spin both spinners to get 2 numbers.

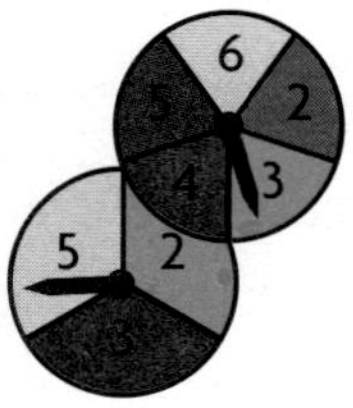

Step 2

One student makes up a multiplication sentence using the two numbers, such as $6 \times 2 = 12$.

Step 3

Another student makes up a related number sentence using the same two numbers.

$2 \times 6 = 12$

Step 4

Both students show their number sentences on the number line.

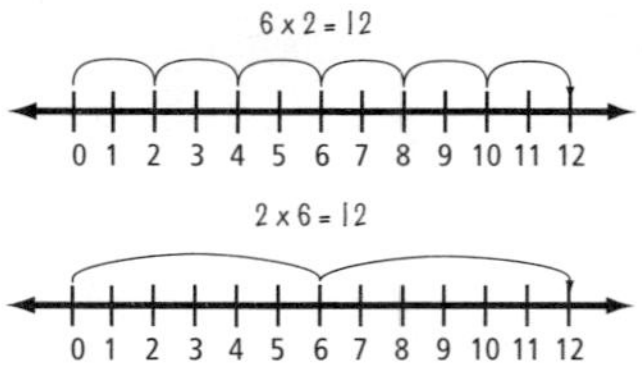

PROFESSIONAL DEVELOPMENT

Step 5

Students discuss and draw conclusions about the order of two numbers in a multiplication sentence. The order of the factors does not change the product.

Step 6

Students spin again and repeat the procedure with two different numbers. Check students' work.

40. Vocabulary Power One number *times* another means that you multiply. Write a multiplication sentence. Circle the "times" sign, ×. Then draw a picture to show your sentence. **See below.**

41. Matt needs 25 tennis balls. There are 5 balls in 1 package. If he buys 4 packages, will he have enough tennis balls? Draw a picture to show your answer. **Check students' drawings. No; 4 × 5 = 20; he needs 5 packages.**

Getting Ready for the EOG Test

42. Tim practiced 2 days for 3 hours each day. Jon practiced 3 days for 2 hours each day. For how many hours did each boy practice in all? **C**

A 2
B 4
C 6
D 8

43. Abby has 3 boxes of shells. There are 6 shells in each box. How many shells does Abby have altogether? **C**

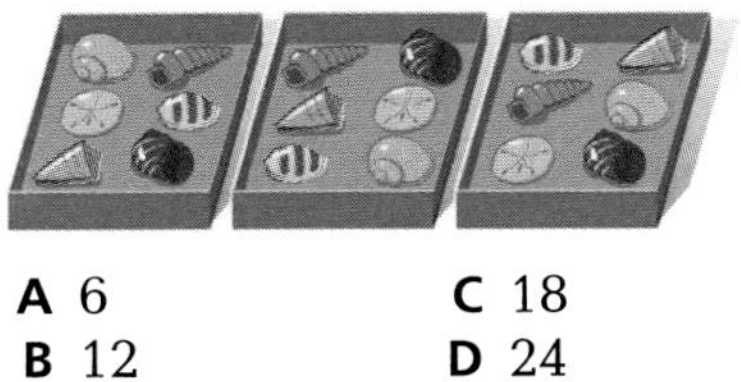

A 6
B 12
C 18
D 24

Problem Solving Thinker's Corner

40. Check students' work. Possible answer: 2 × 4 = 8. Drawings can be any array, number line, or grouped items that illustrate the students' multiplication sentence.

SOLVE THE RIDDLE! Find the product. To answer the riddle, match the letters to the products below.

6 I ×3 **18**	6 A ×5 **30**	5 H ×3 **15**	3 J ×4 **12**
9 Q ×5 **45**	2 S ×7 **14**	8 N ×3 **24**	3 L ×2 **6**

■ = 2 × 8 D **16**	2 × 2 = ■ K **4**	■ = 4 × 2 M **8**
7 × 3 = ■ E **21**	■ = 9 × 3 U **27**	■ = 8 × 5 G **40**

What is a mouse's favorite game? **Hide and Squeak**

?/15 ?/18 ?/16 ?/21 ?/30 ?/24 ?/16 ?/14 ?/45 ?/27 ?/21 ?/30 ?/4

MULTISTEP AND STRATEGY PROBLEM To solve Exercise 41, students can multiply: 5 balls × 4 packages = 20 tennis balls. Then they can subtract: 25 − 20 = 5 tennis balls. So, Tim needs 5 more tennis balls, or 1 more package.

Vocabulary Power Discuss with students the meaning of *times*. Have students write a multiplication sentence and draw a picture to show its meaning. Check students' drawings.

Problem Solving Thinker's Corner

- *Have students look at the Solve the Riddle! puzzle.* **What strategy can you use to find the products?** Possible answer: Use a number line.

4 ASSESS

Summarize the lesson by having students:

DISCUSS How does knowing the Commutative Property of Multiplication help you learn multiplication facts more easily? Possible answer: If you know that 2 × 9 = 18, then by using the Commutative Property of Multiplication you know that 9 × 2 = 18.

WRITE How are the jumps on a number line for 3 × 7 and for 7 × 3 different? How are they alike? For 3 × 7, there are 3 jumps of 7 spaces each. For 7 × 3, there are 7 jumps of 3 spaces each. For both, the jumps begin at 0 and end at 21.

LESSON QUIZ

Transparency 8.4

Find the product. You may use a number line.

1. 2 × 6 = ■ 12
2. 3 × 9 = ■ 27
3. 6 ×2 = 12
4. 4 ×3 = 12
5. 5 ×6 = 30
6. 3 ×7 = 21

Lesson 8.5

Problem Solving Skill

Too Much/Too Little Information

Lesson Planning

Objective To identify which information is needed and if there is enough information to solve a problem

Lesson Resources Reading Transparency 8; Intervention • Problem Solving, Strategy/Skill 8

NCTM Standards

1. Number and Operations
2. Algebra
6. Problem Solving
7. Reasoning and Proof
8. Communication
9. Connections

Math Background

These ideas will help students develop the problem solving skill of recognizing too much or too little information.

- Check for too much or too little information before trying to solve a problem.
- In the case of too much information, the extra information may not be related to the question asked.
- Too little information prevents you from finding a solution.

Warm-Up Resources

Number of the Day

Multiply the number of pennies in a nickel by 2 to find the number of the day. 10

Daily Facts Practice

Have students practice addition facts by completing Set D of *Teacher's Resource Book*, p. TR89.

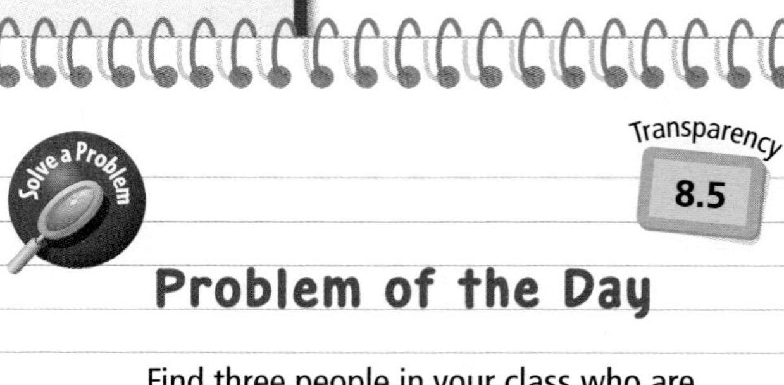

Problem of the Day

Find three people in your class who are the same age in years. Use a calendar to help you put them in order from oldest to youngest. Answers will vary.

Solution Problem of the Day tab, p. PD8

Intervention and Extension Resources

Alternative Teaching Strategy

MATERIALS *For each group* counters, egg carton

ESOL/ESL

Use this activity to **help students see multiplication as the most efficient way to find the total of repeated addends.**

Students count out 12 counters and distribute them equally among 4 sections of the carton. Ask:

- How many groups are formed? 4
- How many counters are in the first section? second? third? fourth? 3, 3, 3, 3
- How many counters are there in all? 12 Have students write a multiplication sentence. $4 \times 3 = 12$

Redistribute counters and ask similar questions about different numbers of equal groups.

VISUAL, KINESTHETIC

VISUAL/SPATIAL

Reading Strategy

Choose Important Information Tell students that sometimes not all the details or information given is needed to solve a problem. Choose a problem with too much information and ask students to:

1. Read each fact.
2. Make a list of the given facts.
3. Beside each fact, write *yes* if it is needed to solve the problem or *no* if it is not needed.
4. Solve the problem.
5. Describe the strategy they used to solve the problem. Check students' work.

Transparency 8 **Reading Transparency 8**

Multistep and Strategy Problems

The following multistep or strategy problems are provided in Lesson 8.5:

Page	Item
169	6, 7

Writing in Mathematics

Have each student **write or tell three word problems: one giving too much information, one giving too little information, and one giving just enough information.** Have students exchange problems and solve. Check students' work.

Advanced Learners

Challenge students to **use multiplication** to solve the following problem.

Jones is 5 times as old as Ricky. Jean is 3 times as old as Ricky. The sum of Jean's age and Ricky's age is 12. If each person is younger than 20, how old is each person? Jones is 15; Ricky is 3; Jean is 9.

Let each student make up 3 similar problems. Pairs of students can exchange papers and solve.

VISUAL

LOGICAL/MATHEMATICAL

Technology Link

Intervention • Problem Solving, *Strategy/Skill 8*

Lesson 8.5 Organizer

Objective To identify which information is needed and if there is enough information to solve a problem

Lesson Resources Reading Transparency 8; Intervention • Problem Solving, Strategy/Skill 8

1 INTRODUCE

QUICK REVIEW provides review of prerequisite skills.

WHY LEARN THIS? In the future, you will need to solve problems in which you are given too much or too little information. *Share the lesson objective with students.*

2 TEACH

Guided Instruction

- *Read the problem and discuss Steps 1 and 2.*
  How do you know what facts are needed to solve the problem? You have to understand the question and choose the facts that help you answer the question.

MODIFYING INSTRUCTION Some students may have difficulty deciding what a question asks. Have students rephrase questions in their own words so they can better identify problems and how to solve them.

- *Have students look at Steps 3 and 4.*
  What do you do with the extra information? Ignore it.
  Why was multiplication used to solve the problem? There are an equal number of pieces of poster board for each student.
  What other operation could you use? addition
- *Discuss Talk About It.*
  What happens when there is too little information? You cannot solve the problem.

LESSON 5

Problem Solving Skill
Too Much/Too Little Information

Quick Review

1. 3×5 15
2. 4×3 12
3. 3×3 9
4. 9×3 27
5. 3×6 18

UNDERSTAND › PLAN › SOLVE › CHECK

FIND THE FACTS Three students walked 6 blocks to the craft store. Each one bought 5 pieces of poster board to make posters for the school book fair. They stayed at the store for 45 minutes. How many pieces of poster board did the students buy in all?

Example

STEP 1

Find what the problem asks.
- How many pieces of poster board did the students buy in all?

STEP 2

Find what facts are needed to solve the problem.
- the number of students
- the number of pieces of poster board each one buys

STEP 3

Look for extra information.
- how far they walked
- how long they were at the store

Do you need this information to solve the problem?

STEP 4

Solve the problem.
- multiply
  3 students × 5 pieces = 15 pieces

So, the students bought 15 pieces of poster board in all.

Talk About It

- Is there too much or too little information in the problem above? **too much**
- Three students went to a restaurant. They each bought a sandwich. How much did they spend in all? Does this problem have too much, too little, or the right amount of information? What information is missing from the problem? **too little information; The cost of each sandwich is missing.**

168

Reteach 8.5

Problem Solving Skill

Too Much/Too Little Information

Alexa and Carl are on the diving team. Alexa has been on the team 1 year longer than Carl. They practice diving with the team 2 hours 3 times a week.

How many hours a week do they practice diving with the team?	How many years has Alexa been on the team?
Ask Yourself What do I know? They practice <u>2</u> hours <u>3</u> times a week. Solve the problem. • Multiply. <u>2</u> × <u>3</u> = <u>6</u> hours	**Ask Yourself** What do I know? Alexa has been on the team <u>1</u> year longer than Carl. I need to know how many years Carl has been on the team. Can I find the information I need? No; the number of years Carl has been on the team is not given.

For 1–4, use the table. Write *a*, *b*, or *c* to tell whether the problem has:
a. too much information.
b. too little information.
c. the right amount of information.
Solve those with too much or the right amount of information.

Art Supplies	
box of colored pencils	$4
box of crayons	$2
pad of drawing paper	$5

1. Tyrone bought 2 boxes of crayons. He used a $10 bill to pay for them. How much change did Tyrone get? *c*; $6
2. Laura bought 3 items at the Art Supply store. She gave the clerk $20. How much change did she get? *b*
3. Preston had $17. He bought 3 pads of drawing paper and 4 stencils. How much did he spend? *b*
4. Rene bought 2 pads of drawing paper. Treva bought 3 boxes of colored pencils. How much did Treva spend? *a*; $12

RW46 Reteach

Practice 8.5

Problem Solving Skill

Too Much/Too Little Information

Garden Supplies	
hoe	$9
rake	$8
package of seeds	$2

For 1–6, use the table.
For 1–4, write *a*, *b*, or *c* to tell whether the problem has *a.* too much information, *b.* too little information, or *c.* the right amount of information. Solve those with too much or the right amount of information.

1. Mario bought 2 rakes. He was in the garden store 15 minutes. How much did Mario spend? a; $16
2. Cecil left at 5:00 P.M. to go to the garden store. He spent more on seeds than he did on other garden supplies. How much did he spend on seeds? b
3. Jerome had $20. He bought 7 packages of seeds. How much did he spend? a; $14
4. Elaine had $20. She bought one hoe and two shovels. How much did she spend? b
5. You have $25 to spend on garden supplies. Which items can you buy?
   A 2 hoes, 2 rakes
   B 3 rakes, a package of seeds
   C 2 hoes, 4 packages of seeds
   (D) 1 hoe, 2 rakes
6. You have $30. How much more money do you need if you choose to buy 4 packages of seeds, 2 rakes and 2 hoes?
   F $42
   G $13
   (H) $12
   J $10

Mixed Review

Write the time.

7. 2:45
8. 6:15
9. 5:00
10. 8:25

11. Are the hours between midnight and noon A.M. or P.M.? A.M.

PW46 Practice

Problem Solving Practice

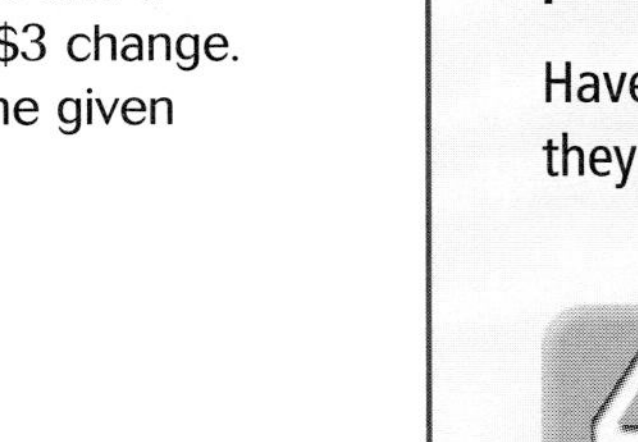

USE DATA For 1–4, use the table. Write *a*, *b*, or *c* to tell whether the problem has

a. too much information. **b.** too little information. **c.** the right amount of information.

Solve those with too much or the right amount of information. Tell what is missing for those with too little information.

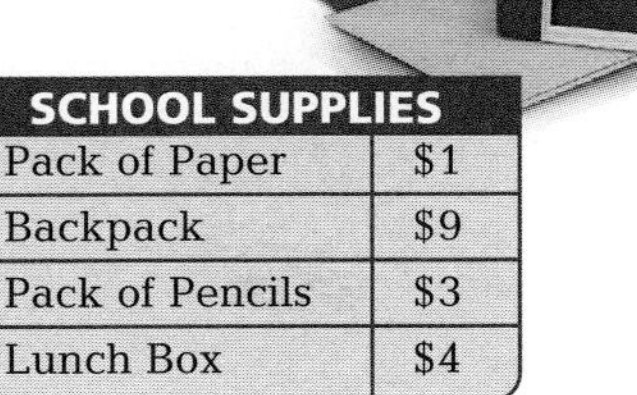

SCHOOL SUPPLIES	
Pack of Paper	$1
Backpack	$9
Pack of Pencils	$3
Lunch Box	$4

1. Felix wants to buy a backpack and a box of crayons. How much will he spend? **b; the cost of the crayons**
2. Marisa bought 2 packs of pencils. She was second in line to pay for her supplies. How much did Marisa spend? **a; $6**
3. Sam bought 2 backpacks and a lunch box. He received $3 change. How much money had he given the clerk? **c; $25**
4. Sally had $15. She bought 5 packs of paper and a lunch box. How much did she spend? **a; $9**

Mixed Applications

USE DATA For 5–6, use the table above.

You have $15 to spend on school supplies.

5. Which items can you buy? **C**
   - **A** a backpack, 3 packs of pencils
   - **B** a backpack, a pack of pencils, a lunch box
   - **C** a lunch box, 2 packs of paper, a backpack
   - **D** 4 packs of pencils, a backpack
6. How much more money do you need if you choose to buy 2 packs of pencils, a lunch box, and a backpack? **J**
   - **F** $1
   - **G** $2
   - **H** $3
   - **J** $4
7. Joe bought two tapes at the music store. They cost $7.28 and $7.71. How much change did he receive from $20.00? **$5.01**
8. **What's the Question?** There are 4 people in the Tamura family. Movie tickets cost $6 each. The answer is $24. **Possible question: How much did the family spend for movie tickets?**

North Carolina Standards 1.03 Develop fluency with multiplication from 1×1 to 12×12 and ivision up to two-digit by one-digit numbers using: a) Strategies for multiplying and dividing umbers. *also* 1.06

Challenge 8.5

What's the Question?

For 1–6, complete the problem with a question so that the answer given is correct. **Possible questions are given.**

1. Four friends walked 4 blocks to school. Each one is carrying 3 books.
   How many books are there?
   Too much information; 12 books
2. Doug bought 6 pencils. They were on sale today for 5¢ less than they were yesterday.
   How much did he spend on pencils?
   Not enough information
3. Xavier bought 4 ice-cream cones. The clerk gave him $0.50 in change.
   How much did he spend on ice-cream cones?
   Not enough information
4. Misty's piggy bank has 3 times as many nickels as dimes. She has 3 more dimes than quarters. Misty has 8 dimes.
   How many nickels does she have?
   Too much information; 24 nickels
5. When all of Pam's cousins come to visit, the number of children in her house will double. Pam has 2 cousins.
   How many children will be in her house?
   Right amount of information 4 children
6. A three-digit number has a ones digit that is 4 times its tens digit. The tens digit is 2. The hundreds digit is 1 less than the tens digit.
   What is the ones digit?
   Too much information; 8

CW46 Challenge

Reading Strategy 8.5

Choose Important Information Understand → Plan → Solve → Check

Read the entire problem. Then look for important information. Underline details that help you understand the problem.

▶ Casey needs 18 baseballs for each team practice. He has 5 bats. He has 3 boxes of 5 baseballs. How many more baseballs does he need?

The problem asks about baseballs. Underline important information about baseballs. Then write what each detail tells you. **Possible answer is given.**

Information	What this tells me
Casey needs 18 baseballs for each team practice. He has 5 bats.	how many baseballs Casey needs
He has 3 boxes of 5 baseballs. How many more baseballs does he need?	**how many baseballs Casey has**

1. Solve the problem. Describe what you did.
   Casey has 15 baseballs, $3 \times 5 = 15$; Casey needs 3 more to have 18, $15 + 3 = 18$ or $18 - 15 = 3$. Therefore, Casey needs 3 more baseballs.

Underline information that you will use.
Solve.

2. Mr. Kular needs 25 sets of colored pencils for his art class. He has 4 boxes of 6 sets. His class will make posters for the book fair. How many more sets of pencils does he need?
   1 more set
3. Mrs. Brooks has 8 boxes of 5 calculators. Her 28 math students will use them today in class. How many calculators will be left over?
   12 calculators

PS46 Reading Strategy

3 PRACTICE

Guided Practice

Do Problem Solving Practice Exercises 1–4 with your students. Identify students who are having difficulty and choose appropriate lesson resources to provide assistance.

Independent Practice

Note that Exercises 6–7 are **multistep or strategy problems.** Assign Exercises 5–8.

Have students refer to Steps 1–4 on page 168 as they solve the problems.

4 ASSESS

Summarize the lesson by having students:

DISCUSS You made 45 party favors. Trish made 30 party favors, and Nick made 15. How many party favors did you and Trish make altogether? Is there too much or too little information to solve this problem? Explain. 75 party favors. There is too much information. You don't need to know that Nick made 15.

WRITE Explain why there is too little information to solve the following problem: Lynda buys 5 markers. She gives the clerk $5. How much change does she receive? You need to know the cost of the markers.

LESSON QUIZ

Transparency 8.5

1. Mr. Lorca gave 7 quarters and 5 dimes to each of his 3 children. How many quarters did he give in all? 21 quarters
2. Amy bought 3 magnets for $1 each. The cashier gave her $2 in change. What bill did she give the cashier? a five-dollar bill

CHAPTER 8

Extra Practice

Purpose To provide extra practice for the skills presented in this chapter

The blue page references in each set of exercises refer to the lesson pages where each skill is taught.

Internet Resources

GO ON-LINE Visit THE LEARNING SITE at **www.harcourtschool.com** for a listing of practice activities.

Extra Practice

Set A (pp. 158–159)

Copy and complete.

1.

a. ■ groups of ■ = ■ **5, 2, 10**

b. ■ + ■ + ■ + ■ + ■ = ■ **2, 2, 2, 2, 2, 10**

c. ■ × ■ = ■ **5, 2, 10**

2.

a. ■ groups of ■ = ■ **4, 6, 24**

b. ■ + ■ + ■ + ■ = ■ **6, 6, 6, 6, 24**

c. ■ × ■ = ■ **4, 6, 24**

For 3–8, find how many in all.

3. 5 groups of 3 **15**
4. $4 + 4 + 4 + 4$ **16**
5. $7 + 7 + 7$ **21**
6. 5×4 **20**
7. 4 groups of 5 **20**
8. 5×5 **25**
9. Ana bought 6 packages of 5 cards each. How many cards did she buy? **30 cards**

Set B (pp. 160–161)

Find the product.

1. $7 \times 2 =$ ■ **14**
2. $5 \times 2 =$ ■ **10**
3. $7 \times 5 =$ ■ **35**
4. $8 \times 2 =$ ■ **16**
5. $4 \times 5 =$ ■ **20**
6. $9 \times 5 =$ ■ **45**
7. ■ $= 6 \times 5$ **30**
8. ■ $= 2 \times 2$ **4**
9. ■ $= 5 \times 5$ **25**
10. Keith bought 5 packages of 3 toy cars each. David has 16 toy cars. Who has more cars? How do you know? **David; 5 × 3 = 15, and 15 < 16.**

Set C (pp. 164–167)

Find the product.

1. $7 \times 3 =$ ■ **21**
2. $5 \times 3 =$ ■ **15**
3. ■ $= 3 \times 9$ **27**
4. 6×3 **18**
5. 5×6 **30**
6. 3×8 **24**
7. 3×9 **27**
8. 5×9 **45**

Find the missing factor.

9. $4 \times 3 =$ ■ $\times 4$ **3**
10. $5 \times$ ■ $= 9 \times 5$ **9**
11. ■ $\times 8 = 8 \times 3$ **3**

170

Review/Test

✓ CHECK VOCABULARY AND CONCEPTS

Choose the best term from the box.

array
factors
multiply
product

1. When groups have the same number, you can __?__ to find how many in all. (p. 158) **multiply**
2. The numbers you multiply are __?__. (p. 160) **factors**
3. The answer to a multiplication problem is the __?__. (p. 160) **product**

Find the product. You may wish to draw an array. (pp. 162–166)

4. $4 \times 5 = $ ■ **20**
5. $3 \times 2 = $ ■ **6**
6. $3 \times 6 = $ ■ **18**
7. $7 \times 3 = $ ■ **21**

✓ CHECK SKILLS

For 8–9, choose the letter of the number sentence that matches. (pp. 158–159)

8. $3 + 3 + 3 + 3$ **c**
9. $4 + 4 + 4 + 4 + 4$ **a**

a. $5 \times 4 = 20$
b. $6 \times 2 = 12$
c. $4 \times 3 = 12$

Find the product. (pp. 160–167)

10. $3 \times 8 = $ ■ **24**
11. $3 \times 7 = $ ■ **21**
12. ■ $= 5 \times 6$ **30**
13. $4 \times 2 = $ ■ **8**
14. 3×9 **27**
15. 6×3 **18**
16. 8×5 **40**
17. 7×5 **35**
18. 5×9 **45**

✓ CHECK PROBLEM SOLVING

Write *a*, *b*, or *c* to tell whether the problem has

a. too much information.
b. too little information.
c. the right amount of information.

Solve those with too much or the right amount of information. Tell what is missing for those with too little information. (pp. 168–169)

19. Pete practices 3 hours a day, Monday through Friday. How many hours does he practice each week? **c; 15 hours**

20. Ramiro worked on his science project 3 hours longer than Sue. How much time did each of them spend on the project? **b; length of time Sue spent on project**

Review/Test

Purpose To check understanding of concepts, skills, and problem solving presented in Chapter 8

Using the Page

The Chapter 8 Review/Test can be used as a **review** or a **test**.

- Items 1–7 check understanding of concepts and new vocabulary.
- Items 8–18 check skill proficiency.
- Items 19–20 check students' abilities to choose and apply problem solving strategies to real-life multiplication problems.

Portfolio: Suggest that students place the completed Chapter 8 Review/Test in their portfolios.

Using the Assessment Guide

- Multiple-choice format of Chapter 8 Posttest—See *Assessment Guide*, pp. AG53–54.
- Free-response format of Chapter 8 Posttest—See *Assessment Guide*, pp. AG55–56.

Using Student Self-Assessment

The How Did I Do? survey helps students assess what they have learned and how they learned it. This survey is available as a copying master in *Assessment Guide*, p. AGxvii.

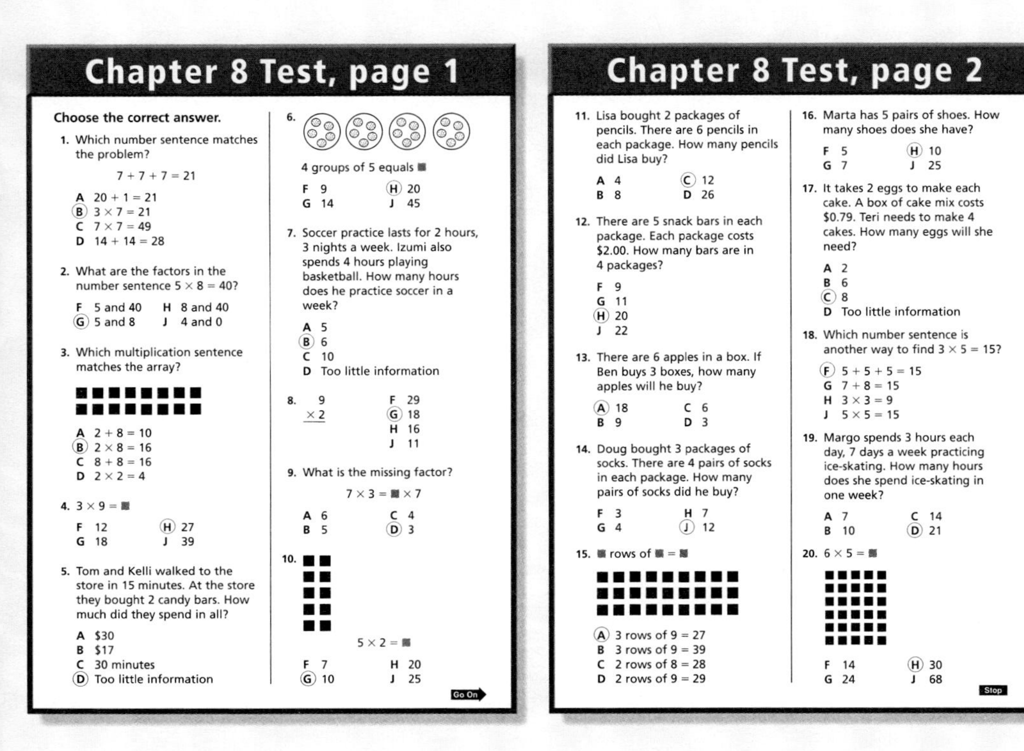

Chapter 8 Test, page 1

Choose the correct answer.

1. Which number sentence matches the problem? $7 + 7 + 7 = 21$
   A $20 + 1 = 21$ (B) $3 \times 7 = 21$ C $7 \times 7 = 49$ D $14 + 14 = 28$
2. What are the factors in the number sentence $5 \times 8 = 40$?
   F 5 and 40 H 8 and 40 (G) 5 and 8 J 4 and 0
3. Which multiplication sentence matches the array?
   A $2 + 8 = 10$ (B) $2 \times 8 = 16$ C $8 + 8 = 16$ D $2 \times 2 = 4$
4. $3 \times 9 = $ ■
   F 12 (H) 27 G 18 J 39
5. Tom and Kelli walked to the store in 15 minutes. At the store they bought 2 candy bars. How much did they spend in all?
   A \$30 B \$17 C 30 minutes (D) Too little information
6. 4 groups of 5 equals ■
   F 9 (H) 20 G 14 J 45
7. Soccer practice lasts for 2 hours, 3 nights a week. Izumi also spends 4 hours playing basketball. How many hours does he practice soccer in a week?
   A 5 (B) 6 C 10 D Too little information
8. 9×2
   F 29 (G) 18 H 16 J 11
9. What is the missing factor? $7 \times 3 = $ ■ $\times 7$
   A 6 C 4 B 5 (D) 3
10. $5 \times 2 = $ ■
    F 7 H 20 (G) 10 J 25

Go On

Chapter 8 Test, page 2

11. Lisa bought 2 packages of pencils. There are 6 pencils in each package. How many pencils did Lisa buy?
    A 4 (C) 12 B 8 D 26
12. There are 5 snack bars in each package. Each package costs \$2.00. How many bars are in 4 packages?
    F 9 G 11 (H) 20 J 22
13. There are 6 apples in a box. If Ben buys 3 boxes, how many apples will he buy?
    (A) 18 C 6 B 9 D 3
14. Doug bought 3 packages of socks. There are 4 pairs of socks in each package. How many pairs of socks did he buy?
    F 3 H 7 G 4 (J) 12
15. ■ rows of ■ = ■
    (A) 3 rows of 9 = 27 B 3 rows of 9 = 39 C 2 rows of 8 = 28 D 2 rows of 9 = 29
16. Marta has 5 pairs of shoes. How many shoes does she have?
    F 5 (H) 10 G 7 J 25
17. It takes 2 eggs to make each cake. A box of cake mix costs \$0.79. Teri needs to make 4 cakes. How many eggs will she need?
    A 2 B 6 (C) 8 D Too little information
18. Which number sentence is another way to find $3 \times 5 = 15$?
    (F) $5 + 5 + 5 = 15$ G $7 + 8 = 15$ H $3 \times 3 = 9$ J $5 \times 5 = 15$
19. Margo spends 3 hours each day, 7 days a week practicing ice-skating. How many hours does she spend ice-skating in one week?
    A 7 C 14 B 10 (D) 21
20. $6 \times 5 = $ ■
    F 14 (H) 30 G 24 J 68

Stop

Getting Ready for the EOG Test

Chapters 1–8

Using the Pages

These pages may be used to help students get ready for the North Carolina EOG Test. The test items are written in the same style and arranged in the same format as those on the EOG Test.

The pages are cumulative. They cover the standards from the North Carolina Mathematics Standard Course of Study that have been taught up to this point in the text or in a previous grade. Each Getting Ready for the EOG Test also reviews the North Carolina mathematics strands shown below.

- Number and Operations
- Measurement
- Geometry
- Data Analysis and Probability
- Algebra

These pages can be assigned at the end of the chapter as classwork or as a homework assignment. You may want to have students use individual recording sheets presented in a multiple-choice (standardized) format. A Test Answer Sheet is available as a blackline master in the *Assessment Guide* (p. AGlii).

You may wish to have students describe how they solved each problem and share their solutions.

Getting Ready for the EOG Test

NUMBER AND OPERATIONS

1. Carl wrote this number sentence about the picture. Which number does ■ stand for? **B**

$3 \times ■ = 15$

A 3 **C** 7
B 5 **D** 12

2. Karen has 17 postcards. Shelly has 14 more postcards than Karen. How many postcards does Shelly have? **D**

A 13
B 21
C 23
D 31

3. Mrs. Ruiz buys 5 packs of plant seeds. Each pack holds 8 seeds. How many seeds does she buy? **C**

A 13 **C** 40
B 25 **D** 85

4. Explain It Can you write a multiplication sentence about this picture? Explain why or why not. **See page 173.**

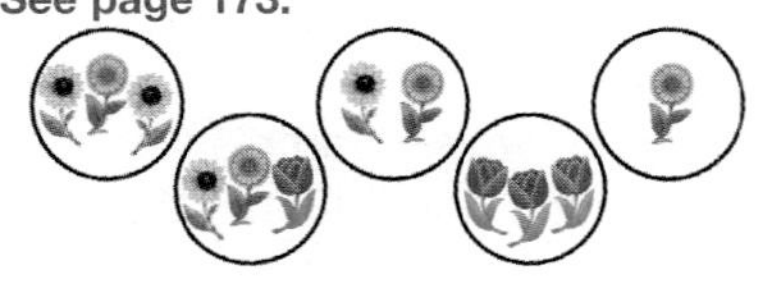

MEASUREMENT AND GEOMETRY

> **TIP** **Check your work.** See item 5.
> Check your work by adding one hour to your answer. The sum should be the time shown on the clock.

5. Rhonda has been at the library for one hour. This clock shows the time it is now. At what time did Rhonda arrive at the library? **A**

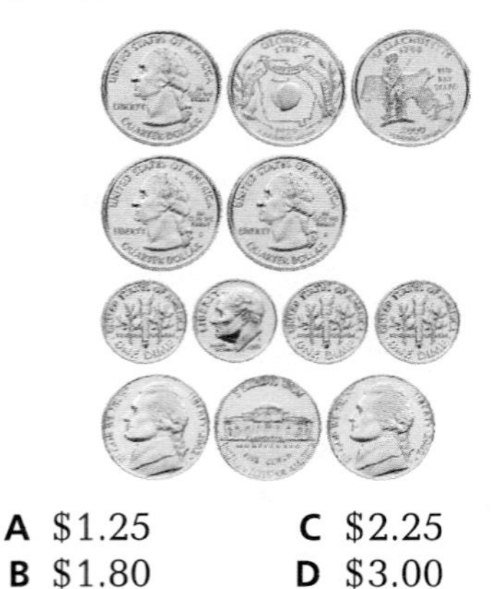

A 12:15 **C** 1:45
B 1:00 **D** 2:15

6. Ben put these coins in a bank. How much money did Ben put in the bank? **B**

A $1.25 **C** $2.25
B $1.80 **D** $3.00

7. Explain It Megan said the length of a dollar bill is about 6 feet. Explain her error. **See page 173.**

ALGEBRA

8. The table shows how many people attended the town fair from Monday to Thursday.

FAIR ATTENDANCE	
Day	Number of People
Monday	104
Tuesday	106
Wednesday	108
Thursday	110
Friday	■

If the pattern continues, how many people will be at the town fair on Friday? **D**

A 118
B 116
C 114
D 112

9. What is the next number in this pattern? **D**

200, 190, 180, 170, ■

A 130
B 140
C 150
D 160

10. Explain It Mr. Dalby asks Bob to skip-count by twos from 2 to 20. Then he asks Marie to skip-count by fives from 5 to 20. Are there any numbers that both Bob and Marie will name? Explain why or why not. **See below.**

DATA ANALYSIS AND PROBABILITY

11. Which statement is true about this spinner? **D**

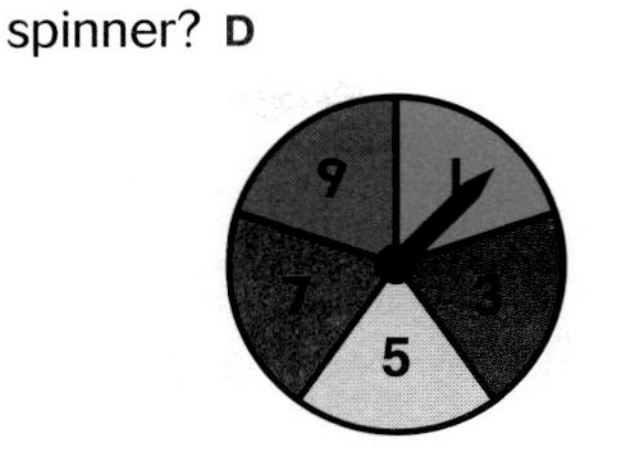

A It is certain that the pointer will land on an even number.
B It is certain that the pointer will land on a number greater than 3.
C It is certain that the pointer will land on a number less than 2.
D It is certain that the pointer will land on an odd number.

12. Mike asks six classmates how many hats they own. The table shows their answers. How many hats do they own in all? **B**

HATS OWNED	
Roger	5
Heather	7
Bill	4
Nancy	3
Lisa	4
David	6

A 39 **C** 28
B 29 **D** 26

13. Explain It Mike said that the boys have more hats than the girls. Is he correct? Use Mike's survey above to explain your answer. **See below.**

Chapters 1–8

Item Analysis

You may wish to use the item analysis to determine which North Carolina standards need additional review.

Item	North Carolina Standard	Lesson
1	1.03	8.2
2	1.02	1.4
3	1.03	8.2
4	1.03	8.1
5	2.01	7.3
6	Goal 2	6.1
7	(2) 2.01	Grade 2
8	(2) Goal 5	Grade 2
9	(2) 5.01	Grade 2
10	5.01	2.5
11	(2) 4.02	Grade 2
12	(2) Goal 4	Grade 2
13	(2) Goal 4	Grade 2

SCORING RUBRIC
Explain It

2 Demonstrates a complete understanding of the problem and chooses an appropriate strategy to determine the solution

1 Demonstrates a partial understanding of the problem and chooses a strategy that does not lead to a complete and accurate solution

0 Demonstrates little understanding of the problem and shows little evidence of using any strategy to determine a solution

Explain It • Written Response

4. No, the groups are not the same.

7. Possible answer: she should have said *inches* instead of *feet.*

10. Possible answer: yes, they will both name 10 and 20. Skip-counting by twos names all even numbers. Skip-counting by fives names multiples of tens which are even numbers.

13. Possible answer: yes, the boys have 15 hats and the girls have 14 hats.

Multiplication Facts Through 5

NCTM Standards 2000

1. Number and Operations
Lessons 9.1, 9.2, 9.3, 9.4, 9.5
2. Algebra
Lessons 9.1, 9.2, 9.3, 9.4, 9.5
3. Geometry
4. Measurement
5. Data Analysis and Probability
Lesson 9.3
6. Problem Solving
Lessons 9.1, 9.2, 9.3, 9.4, 9.5
7. Reasoning and Proof
Lessons 9.1, 9.2, 9.3, 9.4
8. Communication
Lessons 9.1, 9.3
9. Connections
Lesson 9.4
10. Representation
Lessons 9.2, 9.3, 9.4

Chapter Planner

Getting Ready for Chapter 9 • Assessing Prior Knowledge and INTERVENTION (See PE and TE page 175.)

LESSON	NORTH CAROLINA STANDARDS	PACING	VOCABULARY*	MATERIALS	RESOURCES AND TECHNOLOGY
9.1 Multiply with 1 and 0 pp. 176–177 **Objective** To use the Identity Property and the Zero Property for Multiplication	1.03a *also* 1.04	1 Day			Reteach, Practice, Problem Solving, Challenge 9.1 Worksheets Transparency 9.1 **Intervention,** *Skills 20, 22* (CD or Book)
9.2 Multiply with 4 on a Multiplication Table pp. 178–179 **Objective** To multiply with 4 using a multiplication table	1.03a	1 Day	**multiple**		Reteach, Practice, Problem Solving, Challenge 9.2 Worksheets Transparency 9.2 **Intervention,** *Skills 20, 22* (CD or Book) **Harcourt Mega Math The Number Games,** *Up, Up, and Array*
9.3 Problem Solving Strategy: Find a Pattern pp. 180–181 **Objective** To use the problem solving strategy *find a pattern* to solve problems	1.06 *also* 5.01	1 Day			Reteach, Practice, Reading Strategy, Challenge 9.3 Worksheets Transparency 9.3 Reading Transparency 9 **Intervention • Problem Solving,** *Strategy/Skill 9* (CD or Book) **Math Jingles® CD 3–4**
9.4 Practice Multiplication pp. 182–185 **Objective** To practice multiplication facts 0–5	1.03a *also* 1.04	1 Day			Reteach, Practice, Problem Solving, Challenge 9.4 Worksheets Transparency 9.4 **Intervention,** *Skills 20, 22* (CD or Book) **Harcourt Mega Math The Number Games,** *Up, Up, and Array* **Math Jingles® CD 3–4**
9.5 Algebra: Missing Factors pp. 186–187 **Objective** To use an array and a multiplication table to find missing factors	1.03a *also* 5.03	1 Day			Reteach, Practice, Problem Solving, Challenge 9.5 Worksheets Transparency 9.5 Scaffolded Instruction Transparency 9 **Intervention,** *Skills 20, 22* (CD or Book)

Ending Chapter 9 • **Extra Practice,** p. 188 • **Chapter 9 Review/Test,** p. 189 • **Getting Ready for the EOG Test,** pp. 190–191

* **Boldfaced** terms are the key mathematical terms for the chapter.

Use this page to help you review and remember important skills needed for Chapter 9.

MODEL MULTIPLICATION

Copy and complete.

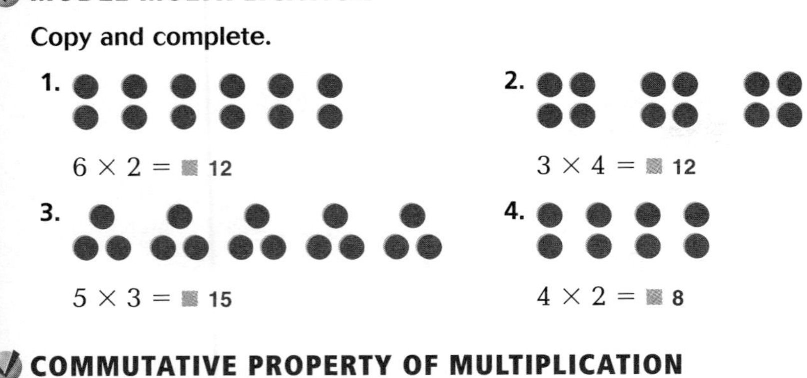

1. $6 \times 2 = \blacksquare$ 12
2. $3 \times 4 = \blacksquare$ 12
3. $5 \times 3 = \blacksquare$ 15
4. $4 \times 2 = \blacksquare$ 8

COMMUTATIVE PROPERTY OF MULTIPLICATION

Complete.

5. $4 \times 5 = \blacksquare \times 4$ 5
6. $3 \times 6 = \blacksquare \times 3$ 6
7. $2 \times 7 = \blacksquare \times 2$ 7
8. $5 \times 8 = \blacksquare \times 5$ 8
9. $4 \times 7 = \blacksquare \times 4$ 7
10. $3 \times 9 = \blacksquare \times 3$ 9

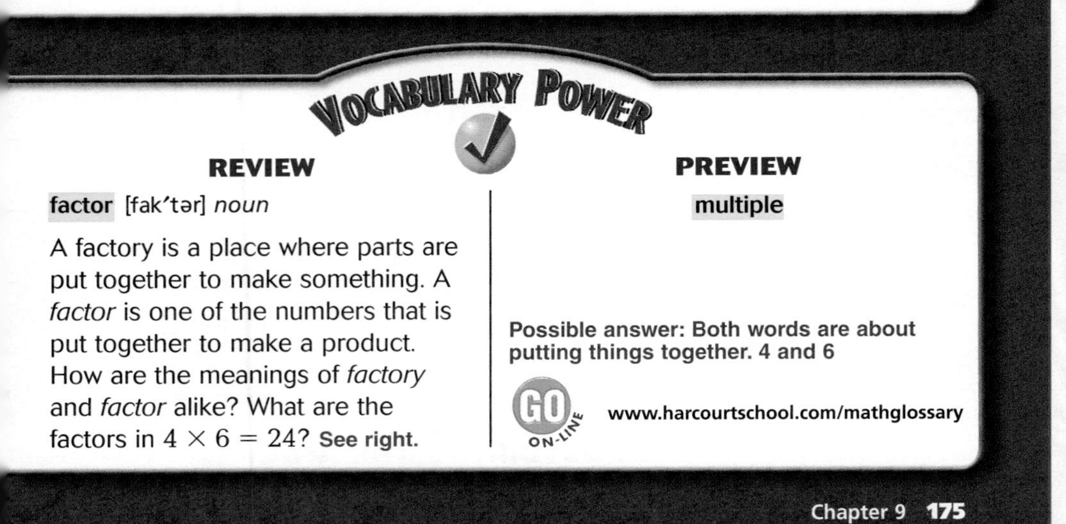

VOCABULARY POWER

REVIEW

factor [fak′tər] *noun*

A factory is a place where parts are put together to make something. A *factor* is one of the numbers that is put together to make a product. How are the meanings of *factory* and *factor* alike? What are the factors in $4 \times 6 = 24$? See right.

PREVIEW

multiple

Possible answer: Both words are about putting things together. 4 and 6

GO ON-LINE www.harcourtschool.com/mathglossary

Assessing Prior Knowledge

Use the **Check What You Know** page to determine whether your students have mastered the prerequisite skills critical for this chapter.

Intervention

- **Diagnose and Prescribe**
  Evaluate your students' performance on this page to determine whether intervention is necessary or if enrichment is appropriate. Options that provide instruction, practice, and a check are listed in the chart below.

CHECK WHAT YOU KNOW RESOURCES

Intervention Copying Masters, or CD-ROMs
Enrichment Copying Masters

VOCABULARY POWER

For activities and information about the vocabulary in this chapter, see page 174B.

Were students successful with CHECK WHAT YOU KNOW?

IF . . . NO THEN . . . INTERVENE — INTERVENTION OPTIONS — IF . . . YES THEN . . . ENRICH

Skill/Items	Missed more than	Intervene with
Model Multiplication, 1–4	1	• *Intervention*, Skill 20
Commutative Property of Multiplication, 5–10	2	• *Intervention*, Skill 22

Skill/Items	Missed fewer than	Enrich with
Model Multiplication, 1–4	2	• *Intervention*, Enrichment p. IN345
Commutative Property of Multiplication, 5–10	3	• *Intervention*, Enrichment p. IN346

Lesson 9.1

Multiply with 1 and 0

Lesson Planning

Objective To use the Identity Property and the Zero Property for Multiplication

NCTM Standards

1. Number and Operations
2. Algebra
6. Problem Solving
7. Reasoning and Proof
8. Communication

Math Background

These ideas will help students understand how to multiply with 1 and 0.

- The number of groups multiplied by the number in each group equals the number in all.
- The product of 1 and any number equals that number.
- The product of 0 and any number equals 0.

Warm-Up Resources

Build Number Sense

Number of the Day

Think of your age in years. Write and solve three addition sentences in which you add that number more than twice. Answers will vary.

Daily Facts Practice

Have students practice addition facts by completing Set E of *Teacher's Resource Book*, p. TR89.

Solve a Problem

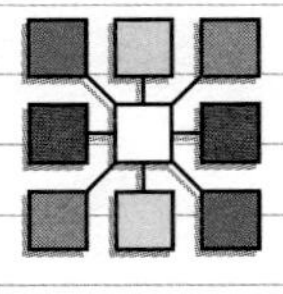

Problem of the Day

Write the numbers 0–8 so that the sum of each connected line of three numbers is 15. First row: 4; 0; 1; Second row: 5; 8; 2; Third row: 6; 7; 3

Solution Problem of the Day tab, p. PD9

Intervention and Extension Resources

Alternative Teaching Strategy

MATERIALS *For each pair* 5 counters, 5 small boxes or bags

Help students **model multiplication with 1 and 0.** Ask them to place a counter in each bag and write the multiplication sentence that shows how many counters are in the bags. $5 \times 1 = 5$ Then have students remove the counters from the bags and write the multiplication sentence that shows how many counters are now in the bags. $5 \times 0 = 0$

KINESTHETIC

BODILY/KINESTHETIC, VERBAL/LINGUISTIC

Multistep and Strategy Problems

The following multistep or strategy problem is provided in Lesson 9.1:

Page	Item
177	29

ESOL/ESL

MATERIALS *For each pair* 4 strips of paper or cardboard

ESOL/ESL

Help students **develop the concept of multiplication with 1 and 0** by writing the following multiplication sentences on strips of paper or cardboard:

$1 \times 9 = 9$ $9 \times 1 = 9$

$0 \times 9 = 0$ $9 \times 0 = 0$

Cut the sentences into parts, so that each number and symbol is separate.

Distribute the cut-up sentences to students. Have students use the pieces to make four different multiplication sentences. Then have students take turns reading each multiplication sentence aloud. Check students' work.

KINESTHETIC, AUDITORY

BODILY/KINESTHETIC, VERBAL/LINGUISTIC

Early Finishers

Challenge students to **write a word problem that can be solved by multiplying with either 1 or 0.** Have students exchange problems with a partner and solve. Check students' work.

VISUAL

VISUAL/SPATIAL, VERBAL/LINGUISTIC

Intervention, *Skills 20, 22*

The Harcourt Learning Site
www.harcourtschool.com

Lesson 9.1 Organizer

Objective To use the Identity Property and the Zero Property for Multiplication

1 INTRODUCE

QUICK REVIEW provides review of prerequisite skills.

WHY LEARN THIS? You can find the product of greater numbers and 1 or 0. *Share the lesson objective with students.*

2 TEACH

Guided Instruction

- *Ask students to read the first problem in the Learn section.*
  REASONING What addition sentence can you write for this problem? $1 + 1 + 1 + 1 + 1 = 5$
  If there were a different number of cars, what could you say about the product when multiplying by 1? When you multiply any number by 1, the product is that number.
- *Have students read the second problem in the Learn section.*
  REASONING What if Tina saw 255 cars with 0 clowns in each car? Would the solution to the problem change? Explain. No; the product would still be 0. There would still be 0 clowns in all.
- *Discuss the Reasoning question.*
  How can rules help you answer the Reasoning question? Possible answer: you can use a rule for multiplying greater numbers with 1 or 0.

LESSON 1

Multiply with 1 and 0

Quick Review

1. $2 \times 5 = ■$ 10
2. $3 \times 4 = 4 + 4 + ■$ 4
3. $6 \times 2 = ■$ 12
4. $5 + 5 + 5 = ■ \times 5$ 3
5. $3 \times 2 = ■$ 6

Learn

ALL OR NOTHING Tina saw 5 cars. One clown sat in each car. How many clowns were there in all?

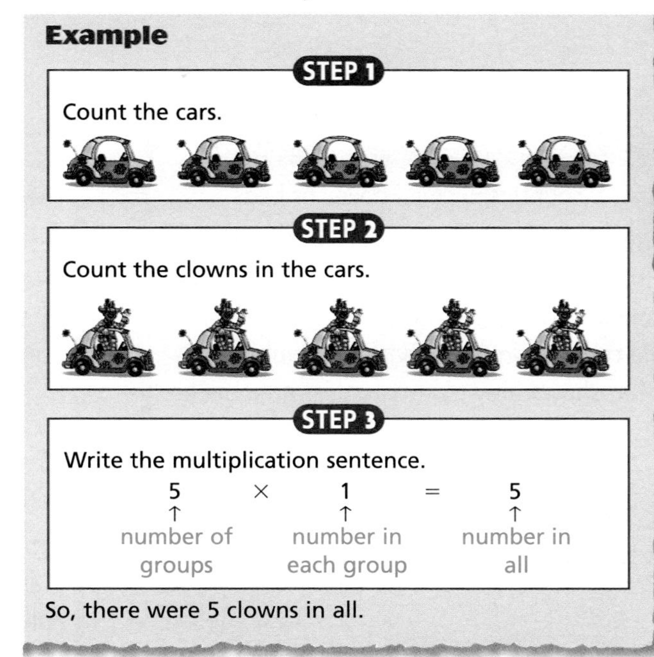

Example
STEP 1
Count the cars.
STEP 2
Count the clowns in the cars.
STEP 3
Write the multiplication sentence.
5 × 1 = 5
number of groups
number in each group
number in all
So, there were 5 clowns in all.

Suppose Tina saw 3 cars with 0 clowns in each car. How many clowns were there in all?

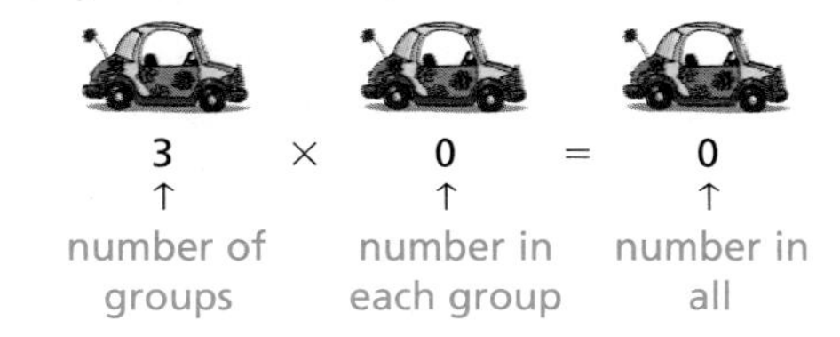

$3 \times 0 = 0$

number of groups ↑ number in each group ↑ number in all

So, there were 0 clowns in all.

MATH IDEA The product of 1 and any number equals that number. The product of 0 and any number equals 0.

REASONING What is 498×1? 498×0? How do you know?
498; 0. Possible answer: The product of a number and 1 is that number; the product of a number and 0 is 0.

Reteach 9.1

Multiply with 1 and 0

- Pam put 1 muffin in each of 6 bags. How many muffins did she put in the bags?

You can draw a picture to find the answer.

Draw 6 bags, with 1 muffin in each bag.

1. What multiplication sentence can you write for 6 bags with 1 muffin in each bag? **6 × 1 = 6**
2. What happens when you multiply any number by 1? **The product is the number being multiplied.**

- Pam gave each bag holding a muffin to a friend. Each friend ate the muffin. Now how many muffins are there?

You can draw another picture to find the answer.

Draw 6 empty bags, 0 muffins in each.

3. What multiplication sentence can you write for 6 bags with 0 muffins in each bag? **6 × 0 = 0**
4. What happens when you multiply any number by 0? **The product is 0.**

Find the product.

5. $1 \times 9 =$ **9**	6. $0 \times 6 =$ **0**	7. $8 \times 0 =$ **0**	8. $5 \times 1 =$ **5**
9. $7 \times 1 =$ **7**	10. $0 \times 0 =$ **0**	11. $3 \times 1 =$ **3**	12. $9 \times 0 =$ **0**
13. $1 \times 4 =$ **4**	14. $0 \times 2 =$ **0**	15. $6 \times 1 =$ **6**	16. $5 \times 0 =$ **0**

Reteach RW47

Practice 9.1

Multiply with 1 and 0

Complete the multiplication sentence to show the number of sneakers.

1. $3 \times 1 =$ **3** 2. $6 \times 0 =$ **0** 3. $1 \times 2 =$ **2**

Find the product.

4. $8 \times 0 =$ **0**	5. $1 \times 6 =$ **6**	6. $0 \times 5 =$ **0**	7. $9 \times 1 =$ **9**
8. $1 \times 4 =$ **4**	9. $0 \times 3 =$ **0**	10. $1 \times 8 =$ **8**	11. $0 \times 1 =$ **0**
12. $0 \times 0 =$ **0**	13. $5 \times 1 =$ **5**	14. $7 \times 0 =$ **0**	15. $2 \times 5 =$ **10**
16. $5 \times 4 =$ **20**	17. $6 \times 3 =$ **18**	18. $3 \times 7 =$ **21**	19. $8 \times 2 =$ **16**

Mixed Review

20. Find the value of the bold digit.

43,975	**70**	78,214	**8,000**
90,255	**90,000**	33,436	**3,000**
29,467	**400**	89,612	**600**

21. Find the sum of 198 and 864. **1,062**
22. Put the numbers in order from least to greatest.
    74 44 62 47
    44, 47, 62, 74
23. Put the numbers in order from greatest to least.
    29 59 13 68
    68, 59, 29, 13
24. $3 + 3 + 3 + 3 =$ **12** 25. $2 + 2 + 2 =$ **6**

Practice PW47

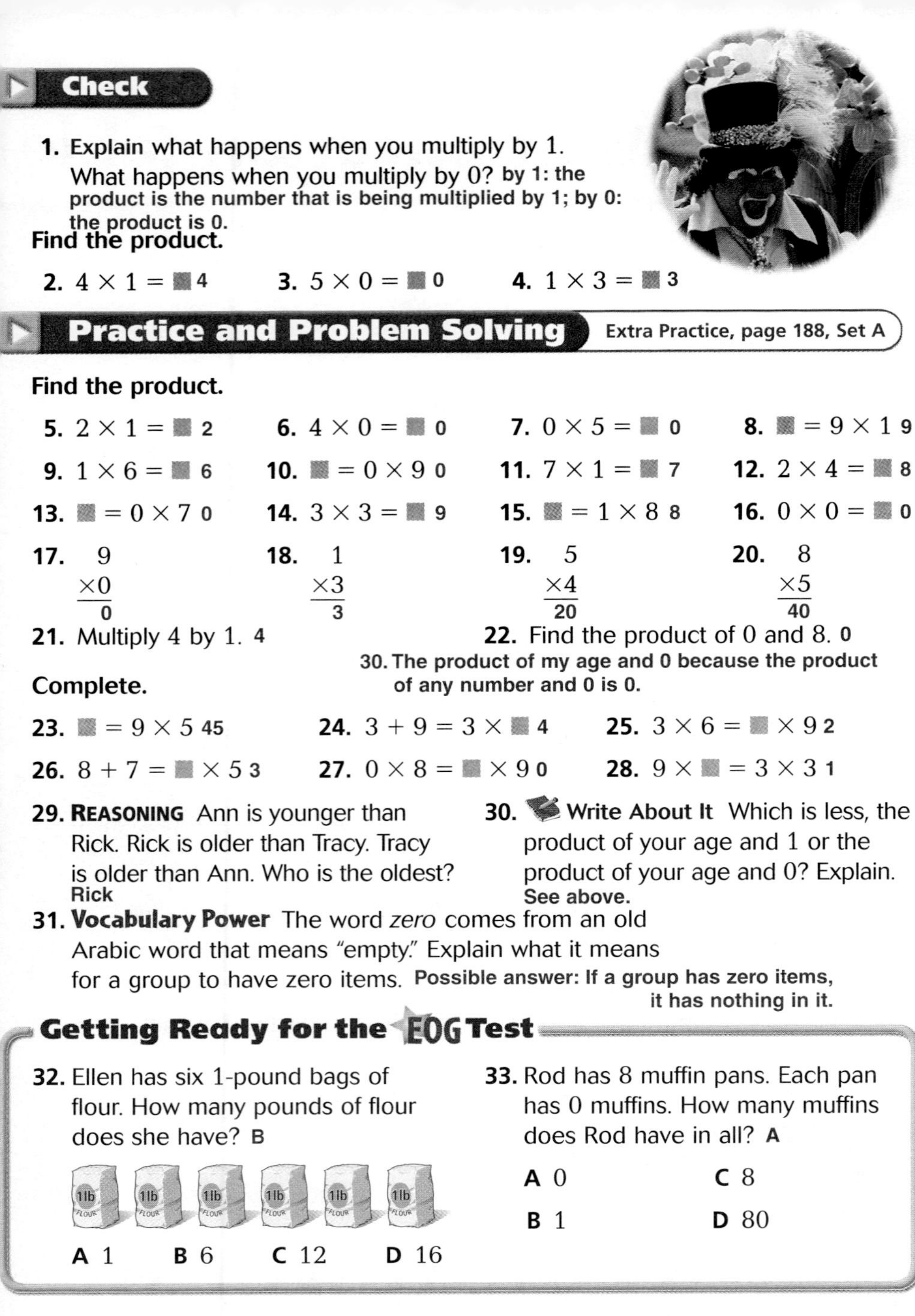

Check

1. Explain what happens when you multiply by 1. What happens when you multiply by 0? **by 1: the product is the number that is being multiplied by 1; by 0: the product is 0.**

Find the product.

2. $4 \times 1 = \blacksquare$ **4**
3. $5 \times 0 = \blacksquare$ **0**
4. $1 \times 3 = \blacksquare$ **3**

Practice and Problem Solving

Extra Practice, page 188, Set A

Find the product.

5. $2 \times 1 = \blacksquare$ **2**
6. $4 \times 0 = \blacksquare$ **0**
7. $0 \times 5 = \blacksquare$ **0**
8. $\blacksquare = 9 \times 1$ **9**
9. $1 \times 6 = \blacksquare$ **6**
10. $\blacksquare = 0 \times 9$ **0**
11. $7 \times 1 = \blacksquare$ **7**
12. $2 \times 4 = \blacksquare$ **8**
13. $\blacksquare = 0 \times 7$ **0**
14. $3 \times 3 = \blacksquare$ **9**
15. $\blacksquare = 1 \times 8$ **8**
16. $0 \times 0 = \blacksquare$ **0**
17. 9×0 **0**
18. 1×3 **3**
19. 5×4 **20**
20. 8×5 **40**
21. Multiply 4 by 1. **4**
22. Find the product of 0 and 8. **0**

Complete.

23. $\blacksquare = 9 \times 5$ **45**
24. $3 + 9 = 3 \times \blacksquare$ **4**
25. $3 \times 6 = \blacksquare \times 9$ **2**
26. $8 + 7 = \blacksquare \times 5$ **3**
27. $0 \times 8 = \blacksquare \times 9$ **0**
28. $9 \times \blacksquare = 3 \times 3$ **1**
29. **REASONING** Ann is younger than Rick. Rick is older than Tracy. Tracy is older than Ann. Who is the oldest? **Rick**
30. **Write About It** Which is less, the product of your age and 1 or the product of your age and 0? Explain. **See above.**
    30. The product of my age and 0 because the product of any number and 0 is 0.
31. **Vocabulary Power** The word *zero* comes from an old Arabic word that means "empty." Explain what it means for a group to have zero items. **Possible answer: If a group has zero items, it has nothing in it.**

Getting Ready for the EOG Test

32. Ellen has six 1-pound bags of flour. How many pounds of flour does she have? **B**
    A 1 B 6 C 12 D 16
33. Rod has 8 muffin pans. Each pan has 0 muffins. How many muffins does Rod have in all? **A**
    A 0 B 1 C 8 D 80

North Carolina Standards 1.03 Develop fluency with multiplication from 1 × 1 to 12 × 12 and division to two-digit by one-digit numbers using: a) Strategies for multiplying and dividing numbers. o 1.04

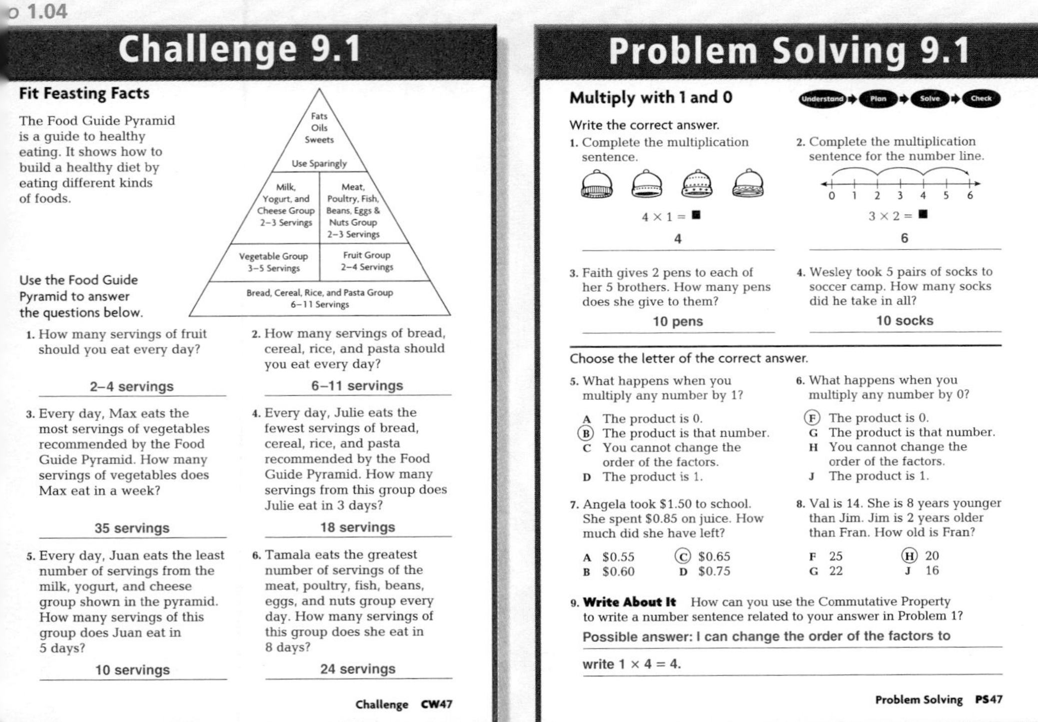

Challenge 9.1

Fit Feasting Facts

The Food Guide Pyramid is a guide to healthy eating. It shows how to build a healthy diet by eating different kinds of foods.

Use the Food Guide Pyramid to answer the questions below.

1. How many servings of fruit should you eat every day? **2–4 servings**
2. How many servings of bread, cereal, rice, and pasta should you eat every day? **6–11 servings**
3. Every day, Max eats the most servings of vegetables recommended by the Food Guide Pyramid. How many servings of vegetables does Max eat in a week? **35 servings**
4. Every day, Julie eats the fewest servings of bread, cereal, rice, and pasta recommended by the Food Guide Pyramid. How many servings from this group does Julie eat in 3 days? **18 servings**
5. Every day, Juan eats the least number of servings from the milk, yogurt, and cheese group shown in the pyramid. How many servings of this group does Juan eat in 5 days? **10 servings**
6. Tamala eats the greatest number of servings of the meat, poultry, fish, beans, eggs, and nuts group every day. How many servings of this group does she eat in 8 days? **24 servings**

Challenge CW47

Problem Solving 9.1

Multiply with 1 and 0

Write the correct answer.

1. Complete the multiplication sentence. $4 \times 1 = \blacksquare$ **4**
2. Complete the multiplication sentence for the number line. $3 \times 2 = \blacksquare$ **6**
3. Faith gives 2 pens to each of her 5 brothers. How many pens does she give to them? **10 pens**
4. Wesley took 5 pairs of socks to soccer camp. How many socks did he take in all? **10 socks**

Choose the letter of the correct answer.

5. What happens when you multiply any number by 1?
   A The product is 0.
   B The product is that number.
   C You cannot change the order of the factors.
   D The product is 1.
6. What happens when you multiply any number by 0?
   F The product is 0.
   G The product is that number.
   H You cannot change the order of the factors.
   J The product is 1.
7. Angela took \$1.50 to school. She spent \$0.85 on juice. How much did she have left?
   A \$0.55 B \$0.60 **C \$0.65** D \$0.75
8. Val is 14. She is 8 years younger than Jim. Jim is 2 years older than Fran. How old is Fran?
   F 25 G 22 **H 20** J 16
9. **Write About It** How can you use the Commutative Property to write a number sentence related to your answer in Problem 1?
   Possible answer: I can change the order of the factors to write 1 × 4 = 4.

Problem Solving PS47

3 PRACTICE

Guided Practice

Do Check Exercises 1–4 with your students. Identify students who are having difficulty and choose appropriate lesson resources to provide assistance.

COMMON ERROR ALERT

Students may confuse the Identity Property of Addition with the Zero Property of Multiplication.

$$5 \times 0 = 5$$

To correct this, draw 5 circles and have students model 5 × 0. Help students to understand that they do not need counters to model 5 groups of zero.

Independent Practice

Note that Exercise 29 is a **multistep or strategy problem.** Assign Exercises 5–33.

Vocabulary Power Have students act out the meaning of *zero*. Discuss why a symbol is needed to represent *zero* in math.

4 ASSESS

Summarize the lesson by having students:

DISCUSS How does knowing rules for multiplying with 1 and 0 help you find products more easily? Possible answer: You do not have to memorize multiplication facts for 1 and 0. You only need to remember two rules.

WRITE What is the missing factor for $\blacksquare \times 9 = 0$? How do you know? 0; The product is 0.

LESSON QUIZ

Transparency 9.1

Find the product.

1. $0 \times 5 = \blacksquare$ 0
2. $1 \times 7 = \blacksquare$ 7
3. $1 \times 1 = \blacksquare$ 1
4. $23 \times 0 = \blacksquare$ 0

Lesson 9.2 Multiply with 4 on a Multiplication Table

Lesson Planning

Objective To multiply with 4 using a multiplication table

NCTM Standards

1. Number and Operations
2. Algebra
6. Problem Solving
7. Reasoning and Proof
10. Representation

Math Background

These ideas will help students understand how to multiply with 4.

- When you multiply two factors, the result is called the product.
- On a multiplication table, the product is found where the factor row and the factor column meet.
- All multiplication facts that have 4 as a factor have an even product.
- A multiple of 4 is any product that has 4 as a factor.

Vocabulary

multiple the product of a given whole number and another whole number

Warm-Up Resources

Number of the Day

The minute hand on a clock moved from the 1 to the 2. Multiply the number of minutes elapsed by 2. Write the product. 10

Daily Facts Practice

Have students practice subtraction facts by completing Set F of *Teacher's Resource Book*, p. TR89.

Transparency 9.2

Problem of the Day

0	■	■	6	8
10	■	14	■	■
■	22	■	26	■
■	■	■	■	■

Complete this chart. 2, 4; 12, 16, 18; 20, 24, 28; 30, 32, 34, 36, 38. By what number did you count? 2 What pattern do you see in the ones digits? Possible answer: the numbers 0, 2, 4, 6, and 8 repeat.

Solution Problem of the Day tab, p. PD9

Intervention and Extension Resources

Alternative Teaching Strategy

MATERIALS *For each student* color tiles

Help students **model multiplying with 4**. Tell students that they can double the product of 2 × 3 to find the product of 4 × 3.

- Have students make a 2 × 3 array with tiles.
- Ask students to make another 2 × 3 array with tiles and then add the products of the two arrays.
- Now have students make a 4 × 3 array. Ask: How are the two 2 × 3 arrays and the 4 × 3 array alike? The two arrays of 2 × 3 show the same number of tiles as the array for 4 × 3.

Have students repeat the steps above to find the following products: 4 × 4, 4 × 7, 4 × 9. Check students' work.

KINESTHETIC, VISUAL

BODILY/KINESTHETIC, VISUAL/SPATIAL

Multistep and Strategy Problems

The following multistep or strategy problem is provided in Lesson 9.2:

Page	Item
179	37

Special Needs

MATERIALS *For each pair* one spinner labeled 0–4, one spinner labeled 1–5, p. TR68

Help students **practice multiplication facts to 5**. Have students spin both spinners and use the numbers the pointers land on as factors. One student makes up a multiplication problem, using the factors in any order. The second student names the product. Students then reverse roles. Check students' work.

KINESTHETIC

BODILY/KINESTHETIC, INTERPERSONAL/SOCIAL

Early Finishers

Have students form groups of four to **practice multiplying with 4**. Invite them to list items they each have in common. For example, they may each have one backpack, two sneakers, or four textbooks. Then have them show the total number of items owned by the group by writing a multiplication sentence for each item on the list. Have each group explain their multiplication sentences to the class. Check students' work.

AUDITORY

VERBAL/LINGUISTIC, INTERPERSONAL/SOCIAL

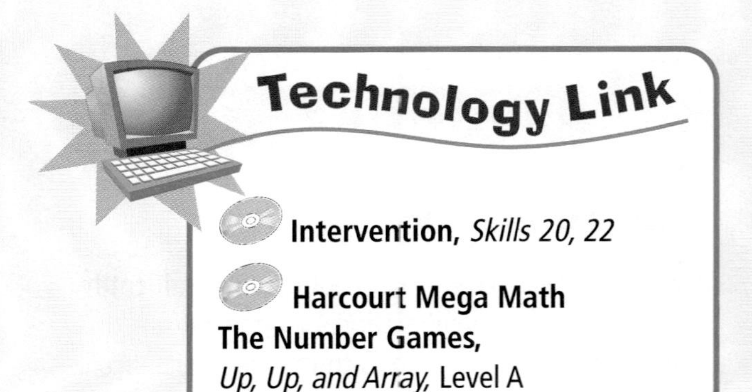

Lesson 9.2 Organizer

Objective To multiply with 4 using a multiplication table

Vocabulary multiple

1 INTRODUCE

QUICK REVIEW provides review of prerequisite skills.

WHY LEARN THIS? You can use a multiplication table to help you find products. *Share the lesson objective with students.*

2 TEACH

Guided Instruction

- *Have students look at the multiplication table.*
  What pattern do you see as you read across each row? down each column? Possible answers: The rows show skip-counting by the number that heads the row; the columns show skip-counting by the number that heads the column.
  How do you find the product of two factors in a multiplication table? Look across the row for the first factor and down the column for the second factor. The product is where the row and the column meet.
  How can you use a hundred chart to find multiples? a calendar? Possible answers: look for patterns on a hundred chart; find multiples of 7 on a calendar.
- *Discuss the Reasoning question.*
  How can you find 4 × 7? Possible answer: 2×7 plus 2×7

MODIFYING INSTRUCTION Distribute copies of p. TR17. Have students fill in the facts they already know. Suggest strategies they can use to find the remaining 4's facts.

3 PRACTICE

Guided Practice

Do Check Exercises 1–5 with your students. Identify students who are having difficulty and choose appropriate lesson resources to provide assistance.

LESSON 2

Multiply with 4 on a Multiplication Table

Quick Review

1. 0×3 0
2. 4×2 8
3. 1×9 9
4. 8×1 8
5. 2×5 10

VOCABULARY
multiple

Learn

TWISTS AND TURNS There are 6 cars in the Twister ride at the amusement park. Each car holds 4 people. How many people does the Twister ride hold?

$$6 \times 4 = ■$$

- How could you use an array to find 6×4? **Make 6 rows of 4 or 4 rows of 6; 24**

You can use a multiplication table to find the product. The product is found where row 6 and column 4 meet.

$6 \times 4 = 24$ (6 ↑ factor, 4 ↑ factor, 24 ↑ product)

4 ← factor
×6 ← factor
24 ← product

So, the Twister ride holds 24 people.

Multiplication Table (column ↓ 4; row → 6)

×	0	1	2	3	4	5	6	7	8	9
0	0	0	0	0	0	0	0	0	0	0
1	0	1	2	3	4	5	6	7	8	9
2	0	2	4	6	8	10	12	14	16	18
3	0	3	6	9	12	15	18	21	24	27
4	0	4	8	12	16	20	24	28	32	36
5	0	5	10	15	20	25	30	35	40	45
6	0	6	12	18	24	30	36	42	48	54
7	0	7	14	21	28	35	42	49	56	63
8	0	8	16	24	32	40	48	56	64	72
9	0	9	18	27	36	45	54	63	72	81

MATH IDEA A multiple of 4 is any product that has 4 as a factor. 4, 8, 12, 16, and so on are all multiples of 4. **Possible answer: Look across the row for 4 or down the column for 4, and all the numbers are multiples of 4; 4, 8, 12, 16, 20, 24, 28, 32 and 36.**

REASONING How can you use the multiplication table to find other multiples of 4? **See above.**

- Name the multiples of 3 in the multiplication table. **3, 6, 9, 12, 15, 18, 21, 24, and 27**
- Are the multiples of 5 all even numbers? Explain. **Possible answer: No; the multiples ending with 0 are even numbers, but the multiples ending with 5 are odd.**

Check

1. **Explain** how you can use the multiplication table to find 4×8. **Find where the row for 4 and the column for 8 meet; 4 × 8 = 32.**

Find the product.

2. $2 \times 4 = ■$ **8**
3. $9 \times 4 = ■$ **36**
4. $■ = 4 \times 5$ **20**
5. $4 \times 3 = ■$ **12**

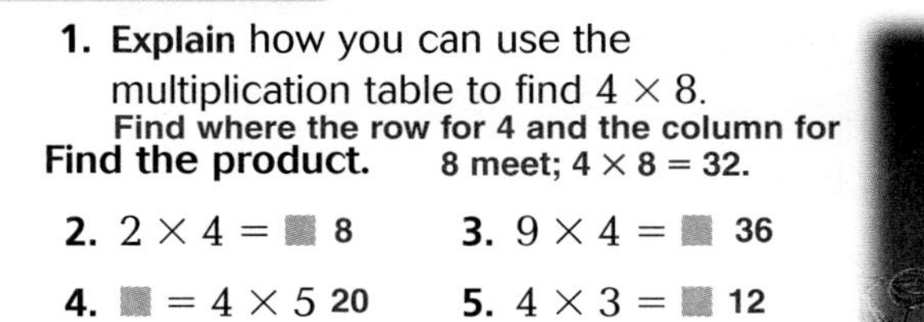

Reteach 9.2

Multiply with 4 on a Multiplication Table

Nate counted his baseball cards. He made 9 stacks with 4 cards in each stack. How many cards did he have?

You can use a multiplication table to find the number of cards.

Step 1 Nate has 9 stacks of cards. So, 9 is a factor. Find the row marked 9.

Step 2 There are 4 cards in each stack. So, 4 is a factor. Find the column marked 4.

Step 3 Find the box where row 9 and column 4 meet. This box shows the product of 9 and 4.

×	0	1	2	3	4	5	6	7	8	9
0	0	0	0	0	0	0	0	0	0	0
1	0	1	2	3	4	5	6	7	8	9
2	0	2	4	6	8	10	12	14	16	18
3	0	3	6	9	12	15	18	21	24	27
4	0	4	8	12	16	20	24	28	32	36
5	0	5	10	15	20	25	30	35	40	45
6	0	6	12	18	24	30	36	42	48	54
7	0	7	14	21	28	35	42	49	56	63
8	0	8	16	24	32	40	48	56	64	72
9	0	9	18	27	36	45	54	63	72	81

Using the multiplication table, you find that Nate had 36 cards.

Name the factors in each of the problems below. Then, use the multiplication table to solve.

1. Mia uses 7 ribbons on every card she makes. Mia wants to make 4 cards. How many ribbons does she need?
   Factors: **7, 4;**
   28 ribbons
2. Akio gets an allowance of \$4 each week. He spends \$3 and saves the rest. How much does he save every 8 weeks?
   Factors: **1, 8;**
   \$8
3. Norman practices basketball 1 hour on school days and 2 hours each day of the weekend. How many hours does he practice in 4 weeks?
   Factors: **9, 4;**
   36 hours
4. Tamisha counted the dimes in her bank. She made 6 stacks with 4 dimes in each stack. How many dimes did she count?
   Factors: **6, 4;**
   24 dimes

RW48 Reteach

Practice 9.2

Multiply with 4 on a Multiplication Table

Find the product.

1. $4 \times 4 = $ **16**
2. $1 \times 4 = $ **4**
3. $4 \times 7 = $ **28**
4. $9 \times 4 = $ **36**
5. $4 \times 3 = $ **12**
6. $2 \times 4 = $ **8**
7. $4 \times 8 = $ **32**
8. $0 \times 4 = $ **0**
9. $5 \times 4 = $ **20**
10. $3 \times 2 = $ **6**
11. $4 \times 2 = $ **8**
12. $4 \times 1 = $ **4**
13. $7 \times 3 = $ **21**
14. $9 \times 2 = $ **18**
15. $8 \times 2 = $ **16**
16. $3 \times 5 = $ **15**
17. $5 \times 1 = $ **5**
18. $6 \times 5 = $ **30**
19. $0 \times 3 = $ **0**
20. $1 \times 2 = $ **2**
21. $7 \times 0 = $ **0**
22. $4 \times 6 = $ **24**
23. $1 \times 0 = $ **0**
24. $5 \times 3 = $ **15**
25. $0 \times 9 = $ **0**
26. $4 \times 0 = $ **0**
27. $5 \times 4 = $ **20**
28. $1 \times 0 = $ **0**
29. $8 \times 3 = $ **24**

Mixed Review

30. \$6.27 + \$2.66 = **\$8.93**
31. \$7.99 − \$4.44 = **\$3.55**
32. \$8.31 − \$5.98 = **\$2.33**
33. \$2.28 + \$7.95 = **\$10.23**
34. 305 + 882 + 406 = **1,593**
35. 761 + 75 = **836**
36. Which shows the numbers in order from least to greatest?
   A 786 867 678
   B 867 678 786
   (C) 678 786 867

What is the value of the 4 in each of these numbers?

37. 9,412 **400**
38. 24 **4**
39. 46,118 **40,000**

PW48 Practice

Practice and Problem Solving

Extra Practice, page 188, Set B

Find the product.

6. $4 \times 2 = ■$ 8
7. $9 \times 0 = ■$ 0
8. $4 \times 5 = ■$ 20
9. $■ = 5 \times 8$ 40
10. $4 \times 4 = ■$ 16
11. $1 \times 9 = ■$ 9
12. $■ = 4 \times 7$ 28
13. $3 \times 0 = ■$ 0
14. $■ = 8 \times 4$ 32
15. 2×3 = 6
16. 5×1 = 5
17. 4×6 = 24
18. 0×4 = 0
19. 7×4 = 28
20. 5×5 = 25
21. 3×6 = 18
22. 4×9 = 36
23. 8×2 = 16
24. 7×5 = 35
25. 4×8 = 32
26. 9×4 = 36

Copy and complete. 31. 2, 4, 6, 8, 10, 12, 14, 16, 18. A multiple of 2 is any product that has 2 as a factor.

27.

×	0	1	2	3	4	5	6	7	8	9
4	■ 0	■ 4	■ 8	■ 12	■ 16	■ 20	■ 24	■ 28	■ 32	■ 36

28. $9 \times 0 = ■ \times 4$ 0
29. $2 \times 9 = ■ \times 3$ 6
30. $4 \times 4 = ■ \times 2$ 8
31. Name some multiples of 2. Explain. See above.
32. Find the product of 4 and 9. 36
33. Find the product of 7 and 0. 0
34. Is 12 a multiple of 6? Explain. Yes, because 12 is the product of 2 × 6.
35. Each ride costs 4 tickets. If Tonya went on 7 different rides, how many tickets did she use? Draw a picture to show your answer. Check students' drawings; 28 tickets.
36. **FAST FACT** • SOCIAL STUDIES There are 520 steel roller coasters and 124 wooden roller coasters in North America. How many more steel than wooden ones are there? 396 more
37. Ahmed has 3 packs of 8 baseball cards and 11 extra cards. How many cards does he have in all? 35 cards
38. Since $9 \times 4 = 36$ and $10 \times 4 = 40$, what is 11×4? How do you know? Possible answer: Since 10 × 4 is 4 more than 9 × 4, 11 × 4 is 4 more than 10 × 4, or 44.

Getting Ready for the EOG Test

39. Lenny set 7 tables for his party. He put 4 plates at each table. How many plates did he set? D

A 18
B 20
C 24
D 28

40. Caleb has a butterfly book. There are 4 butterflies on each of 6 pages. How many butterflies are there in all? D

A 10
B 12
C 18
D 24

North Carolina Standards 1.03 Develop fluency with multiplication from 1 × 1 to 12 × 12 and division to two-digit by one-digit numbers using: a) Strategies for multiplying and dividing numbers. *also* 1.04

COMMON ERROR ALERT

Students may confuse the terms *row* and *column*. To correct this, display a multiplication table and label one row and one column. Ask volunteers to identify other rows and columns on the table.

Independent Practice

Note that Exercise 37 is a **multistep or strategy problem.** Assign Exercises 6–38.

4 ASSESS

Summarize the lesson by having students:

Discuss How can you use a multiplication table to find the product of two factors? You find the row for one factor and the column for the other factor. The product is found where the row and the column meet.

Write List two multiplication facts with a factor of 4. Draw a picture to show the product for each fact you listed. Check students' work.

LESSON QUIZ

Transparency 9.2

Find the product.

1. $7 \times 4 = ■$ 28
2. $3 \times 4 = ■$ 12
3. 5×4 = 20
4. 4×0 = 0

Challenge 9.2

Pondering Products

Find the product for each Column 1 problem in Column 2. Then write the product's circled letter on the line in front of the problem.

Column 1	Column 2
I 1. 4 × 9	(E) 8
T 2. 3 × 2	(F) 0
O 3. 2 × 8	(I) 36
F 4. 0 × 4	(X) 45
R 5. 8 × 4	(M) 40
U 6. 5 × 7	(N) 20
E 7. 4 × 2	(O) 16
S 8. 2 × 7	(R) 32
X 9. 5 × 9	(S) 14
M 10. 8 × 5	(T) 6
N 11. 5 × 4	(U) 35

Use your answers to decode the sentence below. The problem number under each blank tells you where to look in Column 1. Write the letter of your answer from Column 1 on the blank.

F O U R (4. 3. 6. 5.) T I M E S (2. 1. 10. 7. 8.) F O U R (4. 3. 6. 5.)

I S (1. 8.) S I X T E E N (8. 1. 9. 2. 7. 7. 11.)

CW48 Challenge

Problem Solving 9.2

Multiply with 4 on a Multiplication Table

Write the correct answer.

1. A group of 6 children each drink 4 glasses of milk a day. How many glasses do they drink in all each day? 24 glasses
2. Every day this week, James drew 3 pictures. How many pictures did he draw in 7 days? 21 pictures
3. Solve. 9×4 = 36
4. Solve. 0×8 = 0

Choose the letter of the correct answer.

5. Which statement is *not* true about the number sentence $0 \times 9 = 0$?
   A 0 is a factor.
   B 9 is a factor.
   C 0 is the product.
   (D) 9 is the only factor.
6. Which multiplication sentence can be used for this addition sentence: 2 + 2 + 2 + 2 = 8?
   (F) 4 × 2 = 8
   G 8 × 2 = 16
   H 2 × 8 = 16
   J 2 × 6 = 12
7. There are 7 tables in Mr. Jones' classroom. There are 4 students at each table. How many students are there in all?
   (A) 28
   B 26
   C 24
   D 11
8. Which number is the same as four thousand, five hundred sixty-eight?
   (F) 4,568
   G 40,568
   H 45,068
   J 45,608
9. **Write About It** If you change the order of the factors in Problem 4, does the product change? Explain. Possible answer: No; both orders give a product of 0.

PS48 Problem Solving

Problem Solving Strategy
Find a Pattern

Lesson Planning

Objective To use the problem solving strategy *find a pattern* to solve problems

Lesson Resources Reading Transparency 9; Intervention • Problem Solving, Strategy/Skill 9

NCTM Standards
1. Number and Operations
2. Algebra
5. Data Analysis and Probability
6. Problem Solving
7. Reasoning and Proof
8. Communication
10. Representation

Math Background

Consider the following when introducing the strategy *find a pattern* to solve problems.

- Use a number line to find patterns.
- Some patterns use more than one operation.
- Write a rule to describe a pattern.
- Growing patterns increase or decrease in a predictable way. Repeating patterns show a pattern unit repeated.

Warm-Up Resources

Number of the Day

Transparency 9.3

Here is a plan "four" finding me. Start with 4 and then skip-count by 4 four times. What number am I? 20

Daily Facts Practice

Have students practice addition and subtraction facts by completing Set G of *Teacher's Resource Book*, p. TR89.

Problem of the Day

Amy started at 0 and skip-counted by 3 until she reached 30. Lila started at 0 and skip-counted by 4 until she reached 32. What numbers did Amy and Lila both count? 12 and 24

Solution Problem of the Day tab, p. PD9

Intervention and Extension Resources

Alternative Teaching Strategy

MATERIALS *For each student* index cards

Help students **find a pattern** to solve a problem. Display the following pattern:

2, 4, 6, 8, __?__, 12, __?__, 16

Ask: What are the missing numbers in the pattern? 10, 14 What is the rule? Add 2.

Have students make up a number pattern with missing numbers. Ask them to write the pattern on the front of an index card and write the missing numbers and the rule on the back. Then have students exchange cards with a partner to find the missing numbers and rule. Check students' work.

KINESTHETIC

VERBAL/LINGUISTIC, LOGICAL/MATHEMATICAL

Special Needs

Help students **develop the concept of finding a pattern** to solve a problem. Ask four volunteers to come to the front of the class and stand in a line. Have the first student wave once and hop once. Have the second student wave once and hop twice. Have the third student wave once and hop three times, and have the fourth student wave once and hop four times. Ask students:

- What pattern do you see? always wave once, increase hops by 1 each time
- What would the next person in line do to continue the pattern? wave once, hop five times

KINESTHETIC

BODILY/KINESTHETIC, INTERPERSONAL/SOCIAL

Reading Strategy

Draw Conclusions Explain that when you draw conclusions to solve a problem, you must use what information you already know to find the answer.

Read the following problem to students: John set his alarm clock to ring every 5 minutes starting at 1:07 P.M. Karen set her alarm clock to ring every 4 minutes starting at 1:14 P.M. Whose alarm clock will ring more times before 2:00 P.M., John's or Karen's? Karen's

Ask:

- How can you use patterns to solve the problem? For John's clock, start at 1:07 and add 5 minutes until you get to 2:00. For Karen's clock, start at 1:14 and add 4 minutes until you get to 2:00.

Transparency 9 **Reading Transparency 9**

Fine Arts Connection

Have students make up musical patterns with rhythmic sounds to **practice finding patterns**. Have them use hand clapping, finger snapping, or tapping the desk. They can also sing or say words or sounds. Have students demonstrate their patterns and challenge the class to describe and repeat them.

AUDITORY

MUSICAL/RHYTHMIC, VERBAL/LINGUISTIC

Multistep and Strategy Problems

The following multistep or strategy problems are provided in Lesson 9.3:

Page	Items
181	1–10

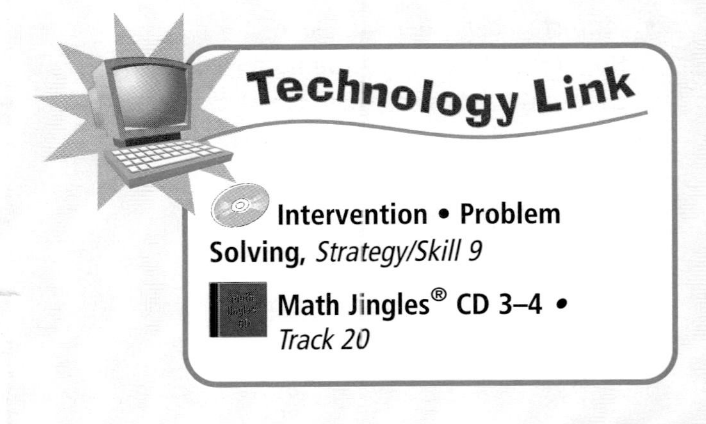

Technology Link

Intervention • Problem Solving, *Strategy/Skill 9*

Math Jingles® CD 3–4 • *Track 20*

Lesson 9.3 Organizer

Objective To use the problem solving strategy *find a pattern* to solve problems

Lesson Resources Reading Transparency 9; Intervention • Problem Solving, Strategy/Skill 9

INTRODUCE

QUICK REVIEW provides review of prerequisite skills.

WHY LEARN THIS? You can find patterns when you use everyday things like clocks and calendars. *Share the lesson objective with students.*

2 TEACH

Guided Instruction

- *Have students look at the number line.*
  Why do you start with 3 on the number line? It is the first number in the pattern.
  Why do you show all of the numbers in the pattern on the number line? so that you have enough information to find the rule for the pattern
  How do you use the number line to find a rule for the pattern? Count the number of spaces between each number in the pattern.
  How do you find the next four numbers in the pattern? Start with 23, add 2, then 3, then 2, then 3. $23 + 2 = 25$, $25 + 3 = 28$, $28 + 2 = 30$, $30 + 3 = 33$
  REASONING If the rule is add 2 and then add 3, give the first 9 numbers in the pattern starting with 0. 0, 2, 5, 7, 10, 12, 15, 17, 20
  How does this pattern compare to the previous one? The rule is the same, but the pattern starts with a different number. Some, but not all, of the numbers are the same.

MODIFYING INSTRUCTION Have students use a hundred chart, p. TR15, to shade numbers to find the pattern.

- *Instruct students to read Check.*
  How else can you use the number line to check your answer? From 33 you can reverse the rule and subtract 3, then 2, then 3, and then 2. $33 - 3 = 30$, $30 - 2 = 28$, $28 - 3 = 25$, $25 - 2 = 23$

Problem Solving Strategy
Find a Pattern

Quick Review

1. $3 \times ■ = 6$ 2
2. $3 + ■ = 9$ 6
3. $■ \times 2 = 12$ 6
4. $12 + ■ = 15$ 3
5. $14 + ■ = 18$ 4

PROBLEM Emily is playing a number pattern game. She says the numbers 3, 5, 8, 10, 13, 15, 18, 20, and 23. What is a rule for her pattern? What are the next four numbers she will say?

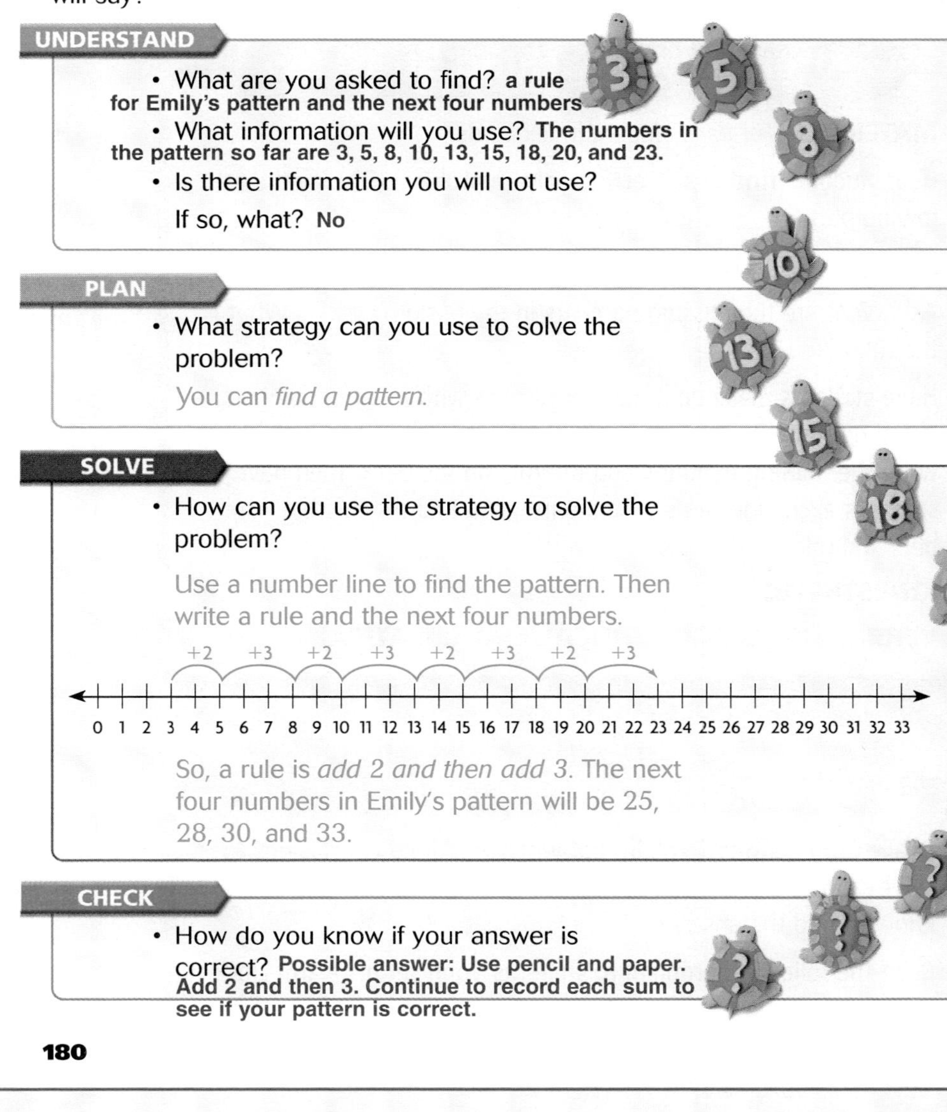

UNDERSTAND

- What are you asked to find? **a rule for Emily's pattern and the next four numbers**
- What information will you use? **The numbers in the pattern so far are 3, 5, 8, 10, 13, 15, 18, 20, and 23.**
- Is there information you will not use? If so, what? **No**

PLAN

- What strategy can you use to solve the problem?
  You can *find a pattern.*

SOLVE

- How can you use the strategy to solve the problem?
  Use a number line to find the pattern. Then write a rule and the next four numbers.

+2 +3 +2 +3 +2 +3 +2 +3

0 1 2 3 4 5 6 7 8 9 10 11 12 13 14 15 16 17 18 19 20 21 22 23 24 25 26 27 28 29 30 31 32 33

So, a rule is *add 2 and then add 3*. The next four numbers in Emily's pattern will be 25, 28, 30, and 33.

CHECK

- How do you know if your answer is correct? **Possible answer: Use pencil and paper. Add 2 and then 3. Continue to record each sum to see if your pattern is correct.**

180

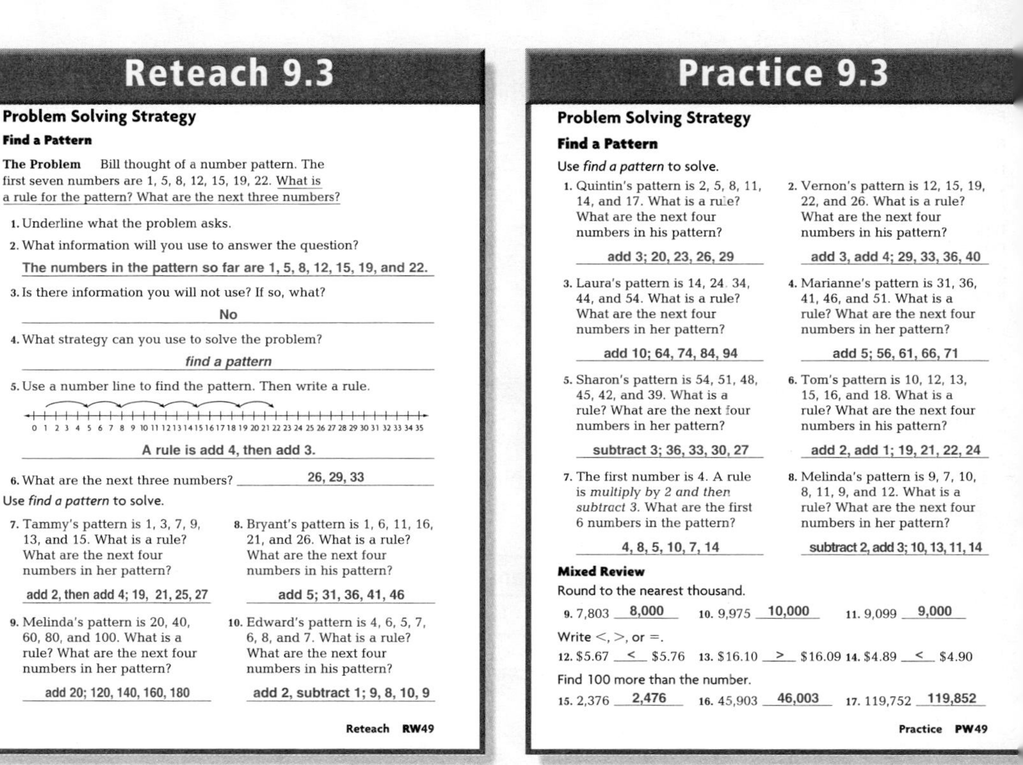

Reteach 9.3

Problem Solving Strategy

Find a Pattern

The Problem Bill thought of a number pattern. The first seven numbers are 1, 5, 8, 12, 15, 19, 22. What is a rule for the pattern? What are the next three numbers?

1. Underline what the problem asks.
2. What information will you use to answer the question? **The numbers in the pattern so far are 1, 5, 8, 12, 15, 19, and 22.**
3. Is there information you will not use? If so, what? **No**
4. What strategy can you use to solve the problem? ***find a pattern***
5. Use a number line to find the pattern. Then write a rule.
   0 1 2 3 4 5 6 7 8 9 10 11 12 13 14 15 16 17 18 19 20 21 22 23 24 25 26 27 28 29 30 31 32 33 34 35
   A rule is add 4, then add 3.
6. What are the next three numbers? **26, 29, 33**

Use *find a pattern* to solve.

7. Tammy's pattern is 1, 3, 7, 9, 13, and 15. What is a rule? What are the next four numbers in her pattern? **add 2, then add 4; 19, 21, 25, 27**
8. Bryant's pattern is 1, 6, 11, 16, 21, and 26. What is a rule? What are the next four numbers in his pattern? **add 5; 31, 36, 41, 46**
9. Melinda's pattern is 20, 40, 60, 80, and 100. What is a rule? What are the next four numbers in her pattern? **add 20; 120, 140, 160, 180**
10. Edward's pattern is 4, 6, 5, 7, 6, 8, and 7. What is a rule? What are the next four numbers in his pattern? **add 2, subtract 1; 9, 8, 10, 9**

Reteach RW49

Practice 9.3

Problem Solving Strategy

Find a Pattern

Use *find a pattern* to solve.

1. Quintin's pattern is 2, 5, 8, 11, 14, and 17. What is a rule? What are the next four numbers in his pattern? **add 3; 20, 23, 26, 29**
2. Vernon's pattern is 12, 15, 19, 22, and 26. What is a rule? What are the next four numbers in his pattern? **add 3, add 4; 29, 33, 36, 40**
3. Laura's pattern is 14, 24, 34, 44, and 54. What is a rule? What are the next four numbers in her pattern? **add 10; 64, 74, 84, 94**
4. Marianne's pattern is 31, 36, 41, 46, and 51. What is a rule? What are the next four numbers in her pattern? **add 5; 56, 61, 66, 71**
5. Sharon's pattern is 54, 51, 48, 45, 42, and 39. What is a rule? What are the next four numbers in her pattern? **subtract 3; 36, 33, 30, 27**
6. Tom's pattern is 10, 12, 13, 15, 16, and 18. What is a rule? What are the next four numbers in his pattern? **add 2, add 1; 19, 21, 22, 24**
7. The first number is 4. A rule is *multiply by 2 and then subtract 3*. What are the first 6 numbers in the pattern? **4, 8, 5, 10, 7, 14**
8. Melinda's pattern is 9, 7, 10, 8, 11, 9, and 12. What is a rule? What are the next four numbers in her pattern? **subtract 2, add 3; 10, 13, 11, 14**

Mixed Review

Round to the nearest thousand.

9. 7,803 **8,000** 10. 9,975 **10,000** 11. 9,099 **9,000**

Write $<$, $>$, or $=$.

12. \$5.67 **$<$** \$5.76 13. \$16.10 **$>$** \$16.09 14. \$4.89 **$<$** \$4.90

Find 100 more than the number.

15. 2,376 **2,476** 16. 45,903 **46,003** 17. 119,752 **119,852**

Practice PW49

Problem Solving Practice

- Draw a Diagram or Picture
- Make a Model or Act It Out
- Make an Organized List
- **Find a Pattern**
- Make a Table or Graph
- Predict and Test
- Work Backward
- Solve a Simpler Problem
- Write a Number Sentence
- Use Logical Reasoning

Problem Solving

Use *find a pattern* to solve.

1. **What if** the first number in Emily's pattern is 3 and the rule is *multiply by 2 and then subtract 2*? What are the first five numbers in her pattern? **3, 6, 4, 8, 6**
2. Albert's pattern is 3, 6, 9, and 12. What is a rule for his pattern? What are the next four numbers? **rule: add 3; 15, 18, 21, 24**

Karen is thinking of a number pattern. The first four numbers are 4, 8, 12, and 16.

3. What are the next three numbers in Karen's pattern? **D**

   A 16, 20, 24 **C** 18, 20, 22
   B 17, 19, 21 **D** 20, 24, 28

4. Which number doesn't fit in Karen's pattern? **J**

   F 20 **H** 32
   G 28 **J** 35

6. 60; Pattern is count by 10's starting with 11, so 60 should be 61.

Mixed Strategy Practice

5. Bo bicycled 4 miles a day last week. He did not bicycle on Saturday or Sunday. How far did he bicycle last week? **20 mi**
6. **What's the Error?** Look at this pattern. Which number doesn't fit this pattern? Explain.
   11, 21, 31, 41, 51, 60, 71
   See above.
7. **Reasoning** Use the digits 0–9 to write the greatest possible 4-digit number using 4 different digits. Write the least possible 4-digit number using 4 different digits. **9,876; 1,023**
8. If this is the time now, what time will it be in 2 hours 35 minutes? **1:35**

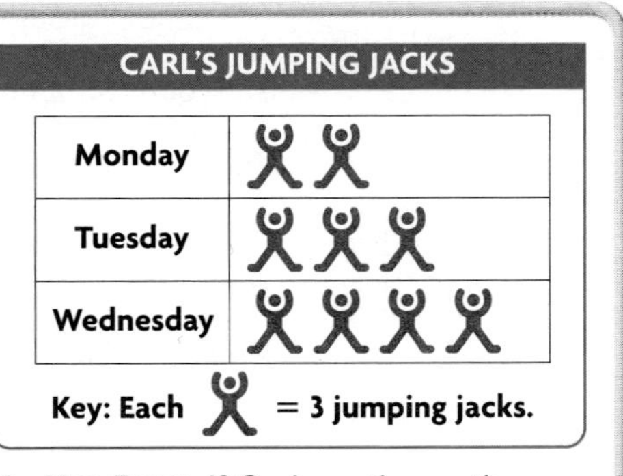

CARL'S JUMPING JACKS
Monday
Tuesday
Wednesday
Key: Each = 3 jumping jacks.

9. **Use Data** If Carl continues the pattern above, how many jumping jacks will he do on Saturday? **21 jumping jacks**
10. **Write a problem** about a number pattern. Tell how you would explain to a second grader how to find the next number in your pattern. **Check students' patterns and explanations.**

North Carolina Standards 1.06 Develop flexibility in solving problems by selecting strategies and using ntal computation, estimation, calculators or computers, and paper and pencils. *also* 5.01

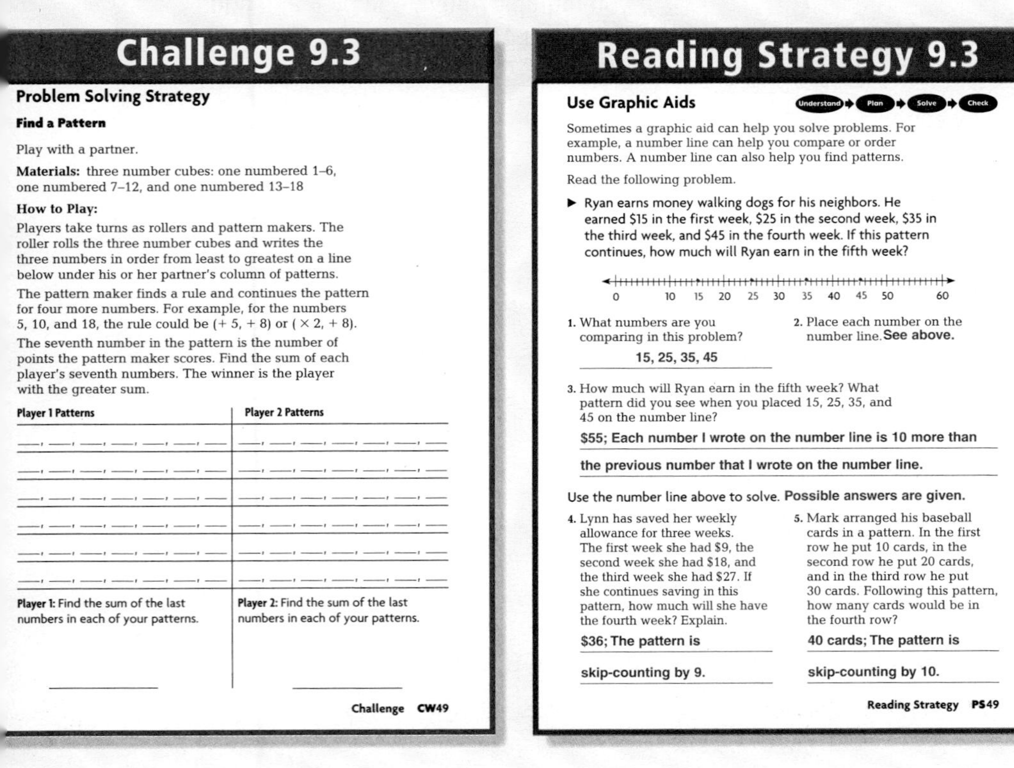

Challenge 9.3

Problem Solving Strategy

Find a Pattern

Play with a partner.

Materials: three number cubes: one numbered 1–6, one numbered 7–12, and one numbered 13–18

How to Play:

Players take turns as rollers and pattern makers. The roller rolls the three number cubes and writes the three numbers in order from least to greatest on a line below under his or her partner's column of patterns.

The pattern maker finds a rule and continues the pattern for four more numbers. For example, for the numbers 5, 10, and 18, the rule could be (+ 5, + 8) or (× 2, + 8).

The seventh number in the pattern is the number of points the pattern maker scores. Find the sum of each player's seventh numbers. The winner is the player with the greater sum.

Player 1 Patterns	Player 2 Patterns
___, ___, ___, ___, ___, ___, ___	___, ___, ___, ___, ___, ___, ___
___, ___, ___, ___, ___, ___, ___	___, ___, ___, ___, ___, ___, ___
___, ___, ___, ___, ___, ___, ___	___, ___, ___, ___, ___, ___, ___
___, ___, ___, ___, ___, ___, ___	___, ___, ___, ___, ___, ___, ___
___, ___, ___, ___, ___, ___, ___	___, ___, ___, ___, ___, ___, ___
___, ___, ___, ___, ___, ___, ___	___, ___, ___, ___, ___, ___, ___
Player 1: Find the sum of the last numbers in each of your patterns. ______	**Player 2:** Find the sum of the last numbers in each of your patterns. ______

Challenge CW49

Reading Strategy 9.3

Use Graphic Aids Understand → Plan → Solve → Check

Sometimes a graphic aid can help you solve problems. For example, a number line can help you compare or order numbers. A number line can also help you find patterns.

Read the following problem.

▶ Ryan earns money walking dogs for his neighbors. He earned $15 in the first week, $25 in the second week, $35 in the third week, and $45 in the fourth week. If this pattern continues, how much will Ryan earn in the fifth week?

0 10 15 20 25 30 35 40 45 50 60

1. What numbers are you comparing in this problem? **15, 25, 35, 45**
2. Place each number on the number line. **See above.**
3. How much will Ryan earn in the fifth week? What pattern did you see when you placed 15, 25, 35, and 45 on the number line? **$55; Each number I wrote on the number line is 10 more than the previous number that I wrote on the number line.**

Use the number line above to solve. **Possible answers are given.**

4. Lynn has saved her weekly allowance for three weeks. The first week she had $9, the second week she had $18, and the third week she had $27. If she continues saving in this pattern, how much will she have the fourth week? Explain. **$36; The pattern is skip-counting by 9.**
5. Mark arranged his baseball cards in a pattern. In the first row he put 10 cards, in the second row he put 20 cards, and in the third row he put 30 cards. Following this pattern, how many cards would be in the fourth row? **40 cards; The pattern is skip-counting by 10.**

Reading Strategy PS49

3 PRACTICE

Guided Practice

Do Problem Solving Practice Exercises 1–4 with your students. Identify students who are having difficulty and choose appropriate lesson resources to provide assistance. Note that Exercises 1–4 are **multistep or strategy problems.**

Discuss the use of multiplication in the pattern in Exercise 1.

Independent Practice

Note that Exercises 5–10 are **multistep or strategy problems.** Assign Exercises 5–10.

Summarize the lesson by having students:

Discuss How can you find a rule for Karen's pattern in Exercises 3 and 4? Describe the rule. Possible answer: Find the first four numbers for the pattern on a number line. Count 4 spaces between each number; add 4.

Write The rule for a pattern is to subtract 1 and add 3. The pattern starts at 3 and ends at 11. Write the numbers in the pattern. 3, 2, 5, 4, 7, 6, 9, 8, 11

LESSON QUIZ

Transparency 9.3

Use *find a pattern* to solve.

1. David's pattern is 6, 10, 8, 12, 10, 14, 12, and 16. What are the rule and the next four numbers? rule: add 4, subtract 2; 14, 18, 16, 20
2. Shelly's pattern is 52, 49, 46, and 43. What are the rule and the next four numbers? rule: subtract 3; 40, 37, 34, 31

Lesson 9.4

Practice Multiplication

Lesson Planning

Objective To practice multiplication facts 0–5

NCTM Standards

1. Number and Operations
2. Algebra
6. Problem Solving
7. Reasoning and Proof
9. Connections
10. Representation

Math Background

These strategies will help students practice multiplication facts 0–5.

- Make equal groups or arrays to find a product.
- Skip-count on a number line to find a product.
- Double a fact you already know.
- Use the Commutative Property of Multiplication and a fact that you already know.
- Use a multiplication table to find a product.

Warm-Up Resources

Number of the Day

I am a two-digit number. The sum of my digits is 6 and the product of my digits is 8. What number could I be? 24 or 42

Daily Facts Practice

Have students practice addition facts by completing Set A of *Teacher's Resource Book*, p. TR90.

Solve a Problem

Transparency 9.4

Problem of the Day

If you multiply Andy's age by 3 and add 1, you'll get 16. How old is Andy?
5 years old

Solution Problem of the Day tab, p. PD9

Intervention and Extension Resources

Alternative Teaching Strategy

MATERIALS *For each pair* two number cubes labeled 0–5

Help students **practice multiplication facts**. Have one student toss the number cubes and the second student write or say a multiplication sentence using the two numbers. Tell students to use a variety of methods to find the product. Have students reverse roles and keep playing until each has completed ten multiplication sentences. Check students' work.

See also page 184.

KINESTHETIC, AUDITORY

VERBAL/LINGUISTIC, INTERPERSONAL/SOCIAL

Multistep and Strategy Problems

The following multistep or strategy problems are provided in Lesson 9.4:

Page	Items
184	45–46
185	50

Writing in Mathematics

Help **reinforce multiplication concepts** by having students write a short paragraph about their preferred way of finding a product. Tell students to give reasons why they prefer this method to each of the other methods they have learned about. Check students' work.

VISUAL

VERBAL/LINGUISTIC, INTRAPERSONAL/INTROSPECTIVE

Advanced Learners

MATERIALS *For each group* poster board, construction paper, markers, scissors

Challenge students to make a board game in which players advance by **solving multiplication problems with facts 0–5**.

Students will need to:

- make the board and game pieces.
- determine the number of squares to advance for a correct answer.
- decide if there will be penalties for incorrect answers.

Have students explain their games to the class and then exchange games and play. Check students' work.

VISUAL

VISUAL/SPATIAL, LOGICAL/MATHEMATICAL

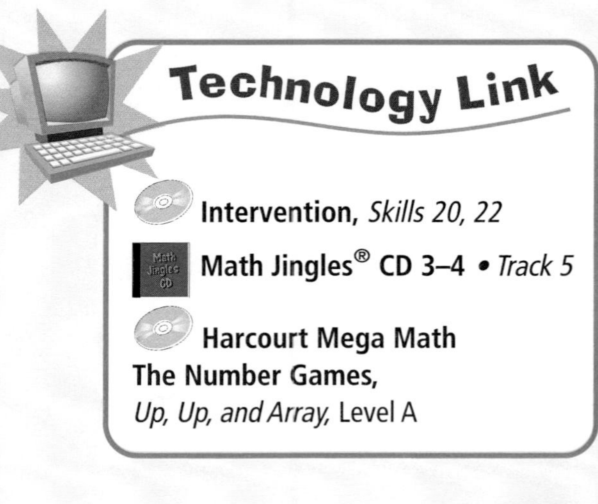

Technology Link

Intervention, *Skills 20, 22*

Math Jingles® CD 3–4 • *Track 5*

Harcourt Mega Math The Number Games, *Up, Up, and Array,* Level A

Lesson 9.4 Organizer

Objective To practice multiplication facts 0–5

1 INTRODUCE

QUICK REVIEW provides review of prerequisite skills.

WHY LEARN THIS? If you can't find a product one way, you can use a different method to find the product. *Share the lesson objective with students.*

2 TEACH

Guided Instruction

- *Have students read the Learn section.*
  Why is it helpful to learn different ways to find a product? Possible answer: I can use a different method depending on the factors being multiplied.
  How is making equal groups similar to making an array? Possible answer: In both methods, you show 6 groups of 3.
  In which of the methods do you use multiplication facts that you already know? double a fact you know and the Commutative Property of Multiplication
  How do you use the facts you know to find a product? In doubling you double a fact that you know to find a fact that you don't know; with the Commutative Property of Multiplication, you reverse the factors of a fact that you know to find a product.

LESSON 4

Practice Multiplication

Quick Review

1. $3 \times$ ■ $= 12$ 4
2. $2 \times 6 =$ ■ 12
3. $0 \times 8 =$ ■ 0
4. $4 \times 5 =$ ■ 20
5. $9 \times$ ■ $= 9$ 1

Learn

FACTS IN FLIGHT At the airport, Nicole saw 6 jets waiting to take off. Each jet had 3 engines. How many engines were there in all?

$6 \times 3 =$ ■

There are many ways to find a product.

A. You can make equal groups or arrays.

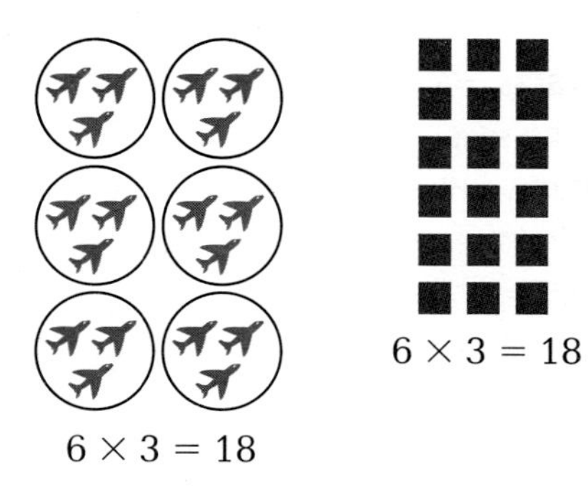

$6 \times 3 = 18$ $6 \times 3 = 18$

B. You can skip-count on a number line.

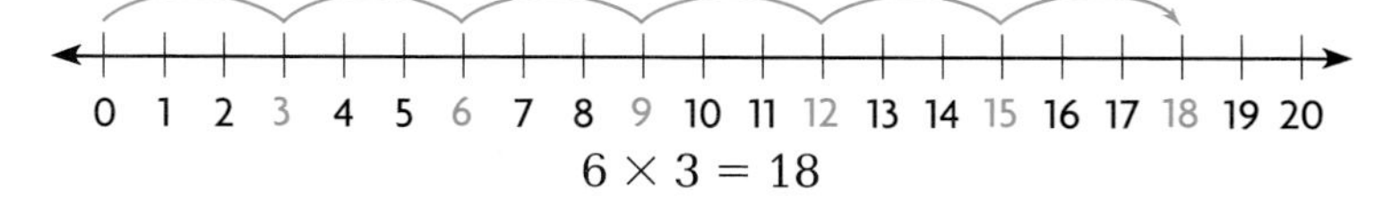

$6 \times 3 = 18$

C. You can double a fact that you already know.

Think: $3 \times 3 = 9$ and $9 + 9 = 18$, so $6 \times 3 = 18$.

D. You can use the Commutative Property of Multiplication.

Think: $3 \times 6 = 6 \times 3 = 18$.

Technology Link

More Practice: Harcourt Mega Math The Number Games, *Up, Up, and Array,* Level A

182

Reteach 9.4

Practice Multiplication

There are many ways to find a product. Here are a few of them.

Find 2×5.

Example A
You can make equal groups.
So, $2 \times 5 = 10$.

Example B
You can make an array.
So, $2 \times 5 = 10$.

Example C
You can skip-count on a number line.
0 1 2 3 4 5 6 7 8 9 10
So, $2 \times 5 = 10$.

Example D
You can double a fact you already know.
Think: $1 \times 5 = 5$ and $5 + 5 = 10$
So, $2 \times 5 = 10$.

Example E
You can use a multiplication table.
Think: The product is found where row 2 and column 5 meet.
So, $2 \times 5 = 10$.

×	0	1	2	3	4	5	6	7	8	9
0	0	0	0	0	0	0	0	0	0	0
1	0	1	2	3	4	5	6	7	8	9
2	0	2	4	6	8	10	12	14	16	18
3	0	3	6	9	12	15	18	21	24	27
4	0	4	8	12	16	20	24	28	32	36
5	0	5	10	15	20	25	30	35	40	45

Find the product.

1. $7 \times 3 =$ 21
2. $5 \times 4 =$ 20
3. $2 \times 8 =$ 16
4. $6 \times 2 =$ 12
5. $8 \times 5 =$ 40
6. $3 \times 9 =$ 27
7. $0 \times 5 =$ 0
8. $4 \times 9 =$ 36
9. $3 \times 8 =$ 24
10. $2 \times 7 =$ 14
11. $8 \times 4 =$ 32
12. $7 \times 4 =$ 28

RW50 Reteach

Practice 9.4

Practice Multiplication

Complete the tables.

1.

×	3	6	7	2	5
4	12	24	28	8	20

2.

×	5	4	6	7	8
5	25	20	30	35	40

3.

×	6	7	8	3	5
3	18	21	24	9	15

4.

×	8	2	4	3	6
2	16	4	8	6	12

Find the product.

5. $1 \times 6 =$ 6
6. $2 \times 8 =$ 16
7. $2 \times 7 =$ 14
8. $4 \times 8 =$ 32
9. $3 \times 7 =$ 21
10. $4 \times 2 =$ 8
11. $8 \times 3 =$ 24
12. $4 \times 6 =$ 24
13. $2 \times 9 =$ 18
14. $4 \times 1 =$ 4
15. $5 \times 5 =$ 25
16. $1 \times 3 =$ 3

Mixed Review

17. What is the elapsed time from 11:30 P.M. to 11:45 P.M.? 15 minutes

18. $\$5.98 + \$2.07 = \$8.05$
19. $702 - 67 = 635$
20. $\$0.71 + \$10.49 = \$11.20$
21. $6{,}498 - 3{,}512 = 2{,}986$

22. 8 $+ 21 = 29$
23. $72 - 33 =$ 39
24. $923 + 765 =$ 1,688
25. $4{,}099 - 170 =$ 3,929

26. Which shows the numbers in order from greatest to least?
A 789 897 987
(B) 987 897 789
C 897 987 789

PW50 Practice

Another Way to Find a Product

E. You can use a multiplication table.

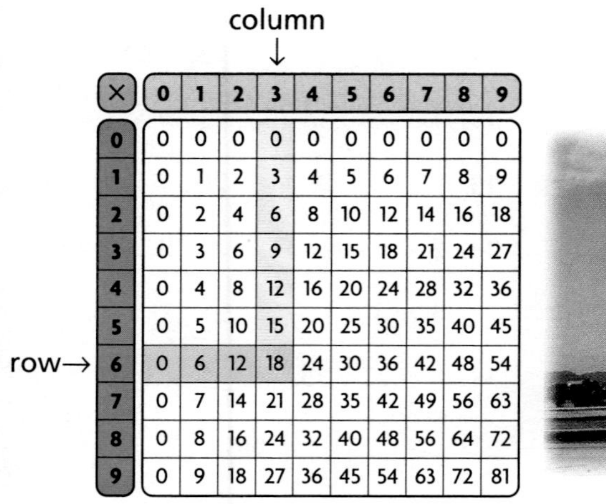

column ↓

row → 6

×	0	1	2	3	4	5	6	7	8	9
0	0	0	0	0	0	0	0	0	0	0
1	0	1	2	3	4	5	6	7	8	9
2	0	2	4	6	8	10	12	14	16	18
3	0	3	6	9	12	15	18	21	24	27
4	0	4	8	12	16	20	24	28	32	36
5	0	5	10	15	20	25	30	35	40	45
6	0	6	12	18	24	30	36	42	48	54
7	0	7	14	21	28	35	42	49	56	63
8	0	8	16	24	32	40	48	56	64	72
9	0	9	18	27	36	45	54	63	72	81

Think: The product is found where row 6 and column 3 meet.

$$6 \times 3 = 18$$

So, there are 18 engines in all.

MATH IDEA You can use equal groups, arrays, skip-counting, doubles, the Commutative Property of Multiplication, or a multiplication table to help you find products or multiples.

- Are the multiples of 6 always even numbers? Explain why or why not. **Possible answer: yes; all multiples of 6 end with 0, 2, 4, 6, or 8.**

Check

1. **Explain** two ways to find 4×8. **Possible answers: Since $2 \times 8 = 16$, then $4 \times 8 = 16 + 16$, or 32; since $8 \times 4 = 32$, then $4 \times 8 = 32$.**

Write a multiplication sentence for each.

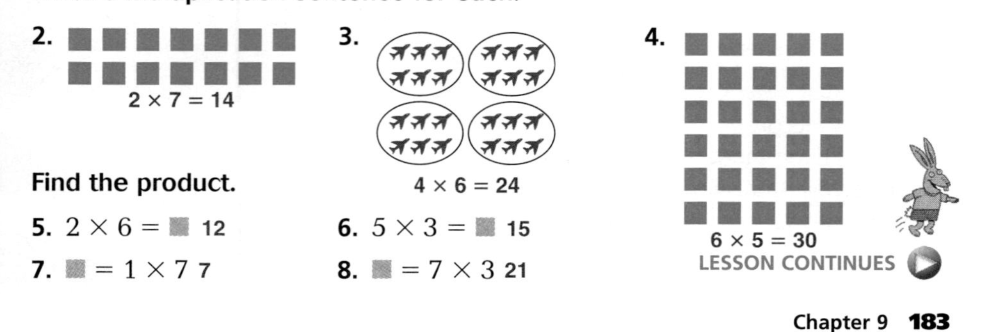

2. $2 \times 7 = 14$

3. $4 \times 6 = 24$

4. $6 \times 5 = 30$

Find the product.

5. $2 \times 6 = ■$ **12**
6. $5 \times 3 = ■$ **15**
7. $■ = 1 \times 7$ **7**
8. $■ = 7 \times 3$ **21**

LESSON CONTINUES

North Carolina Standards 1.03 Develop fluency with multiplication from 1 × 1 to 12 × 12 and division to two-digit by one-digit numbers using: a) Strategies for multiplying and dividing numbers. *also* **1.04**

- *Direct students' attention to the multiplication table on page 183.*

REASONING If you know that the first factor in a multiplication sentence is 4 and the product is 20, how can you use the multiplication table to find the second factor? Look across the row for 4 to 20. Move up the column to find 5.

How are multiples shown on the multiplication table? Give an example. Multiples for each number are listed in rows and columns on the multiplication table. Possible answer: some multiples of 4 are 4, 8, 12, 16, 20, 24, 28, 32, and 36.

- *Have students read the Math Idea.*

Are there any other methods you can use to find a product? Possible answers: draw a picture, use repeated addition

3 PRACTICE

Guided Practice

Do Check Exercises 1–8 with your students. Identify students who are having difficulty and choose appropriate lesson resources to provide assistance.

Challenge 9.4

The Factor Game

Play with a partner.

Materials: 2 game tokens
30 number cards including ten 7s, ten 8s, and ten 9s

How to Play:
Place the game tokens on Start. Shuffle the number cards. Turn the number cards upside down or place them in a bag.

Take turns drawing a number card. Move to the closest space with a missing factor that matches the number on the card. Write the factor in the space. The first player to reach Finish wins!

Start
- $3 \times ■ = 24$ (8)
- $■ \times 3 = 21$ (7)
- $■ \times 4 = 36$ (9)
- $■ \times 3 = 27$ (9)
- $■ \times 5 = 35$ (7)
- Take another turn! $6 \times ■ = 48$ (8)
- $8 \times ■ = 64$ (8)
- $■ \times 1 = 9$ (9)
- $■ \times 10 = 90$ (9)
- $2 \times ■ = 14$ (7)
- $■ \times 9 = 72$ (8)
- Take another turn! $■ \times 7 = 49$ (7)
- $■ \times 4 = 32$ (8)
- $■ \times 4 = 28$ (7)
- $■ \times 5 = 40$ (8)
- $■ \times 5 = 45$ (9)
- Lose one turn. $■ \times 6 = 42$ (7)
- $■ \times 6 = 54$ (9)
- $7 \times ■ = 56$ (8)
- $■ \times 10 = 80$ (8)
- $■ \times 1 = 7$ (7)
- $■ \times 1 = 8$ (8)
- $■ \times 2 = 16$ (8) Lose one turn.
- $■ \times 2 = 18$ (9)
- $■ \times 10 = 70$ (7)
- Finish $■ \times 9 = 81$ (9)

CW50 Challenge

Problem Solving 9.4

Practice Multiplication

Understand → Plan → Solve → Check

Write the correct answer.

1. What products are missing from the table?

×	8	4	3	6	2
4	32	■	12	■	■

16; 24; 8

2. Which product is greater, 5×3 or 4×4?

4 × 4

3. Leslie is going to the theater to buy tickets. The tickets are $7 each. How much will five tickets cost?

$35

4. Each person gets 2 dinner rolls. There are 8 people at the table. How many rolls will be needed?

16 rolls

Choose the letter of the correct answer.

5. Which number is less than 3,231 and greater than 3,132?
   A 3,321
   (B) 3,213
   C 3,123
   D 3,032

6. Bill eats 3 servings of vegetables each day. How many servings does he eat each week?
   F 28
   G 24
   (H) 21
   J 14

7. Peter's birthday is April 17. Dana's birthday is 5 days before Peter's but 6 days after Jeff's. When is Jeff's birthday?
   A April 28
   B April 12
   C April 7
   (D) April 6

8. What is the missing number in the pattern?
   210, 200, 190, 180, ■
   F 190
   G 180
   (H) 170
   J 160

9. **Write About It** How can multiplication help you find $7 + 7 + 7 + 7 + 7 + 7$?
I can use the multiplication fact $6 \times 7 = 42$.

PS50 Problem Solving

Independent Practice

Note that Exercises 45–46 and 50 are **multistep or strategy problems.** Assign Exercises 9–50.

Encourage students to use different methods to find the products in Exercises 9–34.

For Exercises 39–44, remind students to find each product first and then compare the products.

Reasoning In Exercise 45, suggest that students make a table to find the number of cookies baked and pecans used.

Cookies	1	2	3	4	5	6
Pecans	2	4	6	8	10	12
Chips	4	8	12	16	20	24

Tell students that practicing multiplication facts helps them memorize them. The strategies in this lesson will help students remember the facts that are difficult for them. Help students work toward a goal of giving a product in less than 3 seconds.

Practice and Problem Solving

Extra Practice, page 188, Set C

Find the product.

9. $7 \times 4 = ■$ 28
10. $2 \times 8 = ■$ 16
11. $7 \times 5 = ■$ 35
12. $4 \times 2 = ■$ 8
13. $■ = 5 \times 4$ 20
14. $9 \times 4 = ■$ 36
15. $■ = 2 \times 5$ 10
16. $9 \times 1 = ■$ 9
17. $■ = 1 \times 9$ 9
18. $6 \times 2 = ■$ 12
19. $5 \times 6 = ■$ 30
20. $■ = 8 \times 4$ 32
21. $5 \times 1 = ■$ 5
22. $3 \times 0 = ■$ 0
23. $2 \times 9 = ■$ 18
24. $6 \times 5 = ■$ 30
25. $2 \times 4 = ■$ 8
26. $■ = 3 \times 7$ 21
27. $8 \times 5 = ■$ 40
28. $■ = 9 \times 3$ 27
29. 9×3 27
30. 0×6 0
31. 5×7 35
32. 8×3 24
33. 4×9 36
34. 4×4 16

Copy and complete.

35.

×	2	4	7	8	9
2	■	■	■	■	■
	4	8	14	16	18

36.

×	3	5	7	8	9
3	■	■	■	■	■
	9	15	21	24	27

37.

×	2	7	5	3	8
4	■	■	■	■	■
	8	28	20	12	32

38.

×	1	6	9	7	8
5	■	■	■	■	■
	5	30	45	35	40

Compare. Write $<$, $>$, or $=$ for each ●.

39. 3×2 ● 4×1 $>$
40. 7×4 ● 4×8 $<$
41. 5×8 ● $35 + 6$ $<$
42. 4×6 ● 8×3 $=$
43. 3×6 ● 5×4 $<$
44. 7×5 ● 8×3 $>$

45. **Reasoning** Jenny baked some cookies. She put 4 chocolate chips and 2 pecans on each cookie. If she used 24 chocolate chips in all, how many pecans did she use? **12 pecans**

46. Pedro and Jon have 20 toy cars altogether. If Jon buys another toy car, he will have twice as many toy cars as Pedro. How many toy cars does Pedro have? **7 toy cars**

47. **What's the Error?** To find the product 5×6, Ellen made this array. What did Ellen do wrong? **Possible answer: she made an array of $5 \times 5 = 25$ instead of $5 \times 6 = 30$.**

48. **Reasoning** Look at this number pattern. What is a rule? What are the missing numbers?

8, 11, 14, ■, ■, ■, 26 **rule: add 3; 17, 20, 23**

184

Alternative Teaching Strategy

Scaffolded Instruction

PURPOSE Students will draw a picture to find a product.

Present the following problem: Jennifer wants to plant 3 equal rows of 6 flowers each in her garden. How many flowers will she plant?

Have students draw a picture to solve the problem. Ask: How did you begin your picture? Possible answer: by drawing 3 rows

Ask: What is the next step? Possible answer: place 6 flowers in each row.

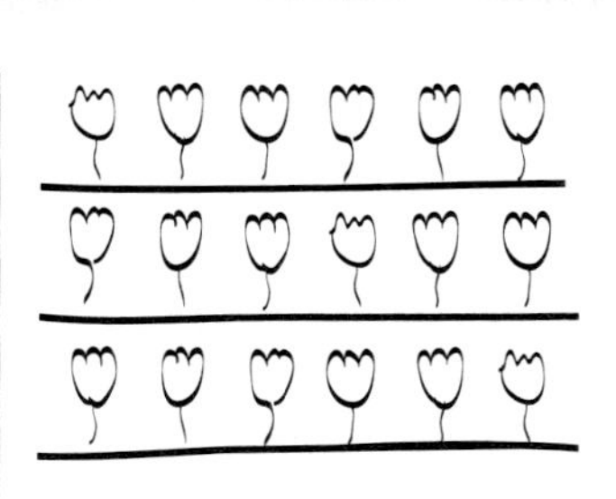

Professional Development

Ask:

- How do you find the answer to the question? Count the flowers; 18
- What if Jennifer plants 4 equal rows of 8 flowers each? How many flowers does she plant? 32 flowers

49. Three vans are going to the airport. There are 9 people in each van. How many people are going to the airport?
27 people

50. Marie has 4 loose stamps and 5 sheets of 8 stamps each. How many stamps does she have in all? **44 stamps**

Getting Ready for the EOG Test

51. Shanna mailed 9 postcards. Each postcard had 2 stamps. How many stamps did she use? **C**

A 92   C 18
B 27   D 11

52. Ben went on vacation for 5 days. He mailed 4 postcards each day. How many postcards did he mail in all? **A**

A 20   C 10
B 15   D 9

53. Which array models 3×4? **B**

A   C

B   D

Problem Solving Thinker's Corner

FINDING MULTIPLES

You can use a hundred chart to show multiples.

MATERIALS: hundred chart, crayons

a. Start at 2. Shade all of the multiples of 2 with a yellow crayon.
all multiples of 2 should be shaded yellow

b. Start at 3. Shade all of the multiples of 3 with a blue crayon.
all multiples of 3 should be shaded blue

c. What numbers are now shaded both yellow and blue (green)?
6, 12, 18, 24, 30, 36, 42, 48, 54, 60, 66, 72, 78, 84, 90, and 96

d. Look at the green numbers. These numbers are multiples of which number?
multiples of 6

1	2	3	4	5	6	7	8	9	10
11	12	13	14	15	16	17	18	19	20
21	22	23	24	25	26	27	28	29	30
31	32	33	34	35	36	37	38	39	40
41	42	43	44	45	46	47	48	49	50
51	52	53	54	55	56	57	58	59	60
61	62	63	64	65	66	67	68	69	70
71	72	73	74	75	76	77	78	79	80
81	82	83	84	85	86	87	88	89	90
91	92	93	94	95	96	97	98	99	100

MULTISTEP OR STRATEGY PROBLEM To solve Exercise 50, students can multiply 5 times the number of stamps on one sheet, 8, and then add the 4 loose stamps. Guide students to conclude that the multiplication must be completed before the addition.

Problem Solving Thinker's Corner

- *Have students complete Steps a and b.*
  What patterns do you notice? Possible answers: the multiples of 2 are in the 2, 4, 6, 8, and 10 columns; the multiples of 3 make diagonals across the chart.
- *Have students answer c and d.*
  REASONING If you shade multiples of 2 and 5 on a hundred chart, the multiples of which number are shown with both colors? 10

Summarize the lesson by having students:

DISCUSS How would you explain to a second grader how to make an array to find 2 × 4? Possible answer: Use tiles. Make 2 rows with 4 tiles in each row. Count the number of tiles. There are 8 tiles, so $2 \times 4 = 8$.

WRITE Choose two different ways to find 3 × 5. Describe how to use each method to find the product. Possible answers: skip-count on a number line by 5 three times; make an array with 3 rows of 5.

LESSON QUIZ

Transparency 9.4

Find the product.

1. $4 \times 5 = ■$ 20
2. $■ = 7 \times 3$ 21
3. $■ = 8 \times 2$ 16
4. $1 \times 9 = ■$ 9

Lesson 9.5

Algebra: Missing Factors

Lesson Planning

Objective To use an array and a multiplication table to find missing factors

NCTM Standards

1. Number and Operations
2. Algebra
6. Problem Solving

Math Background

These steps will help students find missing factors.

- You can build an array to find the missing factor. Use the product as the total number of tiles. Use the known factor as the number in each row. Count out the tiles. The number of rows is the missing factor.
- When you know the product and one factor, a multiplication table can help you find the missing factor.
- To use a multiplication table, locate the given factor in either the factor row or factor column and then locate the product. The product will be in the missing factor's row or column.

Warm-Up Resources

Number of the Day

Each basket that Pete scored in a basketball game was worth 2 points. Write and solve a multiplication sentence using the number of points earned for each basket. Possible answer: $9 \times 2 = 18$

Daily Facts Practice

Have students practice addition facts by completing Set B of *Teacher's Resource Book,* p. TR90.

Solve a Problem

Transparency 9.5

Problem of the Day

The answer to a multiplication problem is 12. What could the factors be?
1 and 12, 2 and 6, 3 and 4

Solution Problem of the Day tab, p. PD9

CHAPTER 9

Multiplication Facts Through 5

Introducing the Chapter

Remind students that multiplication is the joining of equal-sized groups. Tell students to focus on the picture. Ask them how many equivalent groups are in the roller coaster and how many are in each group. 8 groups of 4

Using Data

To begin the study of this chapter, have students

- Compare to find which roller coaster can hold the most riders. Mamba
- Multiply the number of riders in each car by 6 cars to determine which roller coaster on the chart holds this many riders. 24 riders, Hercules
- Find how many riders each car on a roller coaster can hold if there are 4 rows of seats in a car and 2 seats in each row. 8 riders

Problem Solving Project

Purpose To make and record equivalent groups

Grouping pairs

Materials *For each pair* 20 counters

Background Roller coasters are built to look dangerous, but they can be quite safe—as long as riders follow the rules! The fastest roller coaster in the world is in Japan. Its top speed is more than 100 miles per hour.

UNDERSTAND • PLAN • SOLVE • CHECK

Have students

- Design a roller coaster train that has 20 seats.
- Use counters to show different ways of arranging the seats so that each row has the same number.
- Record the different groupings.
- Repeat the activity using 30 counters.

Graphing Investigations
Begin Week 9.

CHAPTER 9

Multiplication Facts Through 5

Mantis is a stand-up roller coaster in Sandusky, Ohio. Each train has eight rows of four riders.

FAST FACT • SOCIAL STUDIES There are more than 600 roller coasters in North America today. Some can reach speeds greater than 70 miles per hour!

PROBLEM SOLVING Compare the number of riders on the roller coasters in the pictograph with the coaster in the photo. Which roller coasters have the same number of riders per train as the Mantis?

Wicked Twister and Alpengeist

ROLLER COASTER RIDERS PER TRAIN

Hercules (Pennsylvania)	
Wicked Twister (Ohio)	
Alpengeist (Virginia)	
Mamba (Missouri)	

Key: Each [train car] = 4 riders.

174

WHY LEARN MATH? Amusement park ride operators use multiplication to figure out how many people can ride on a roller coaster at one time. If the roller coaster has 8 cars and each car holds 4 people, how many people can ride on the roller coaster at once? 32 people

Family Involvement Activities

These activities provide:

- Letter to the Family
- Math Vocabulary
- Family Game
- Practice (Homework)

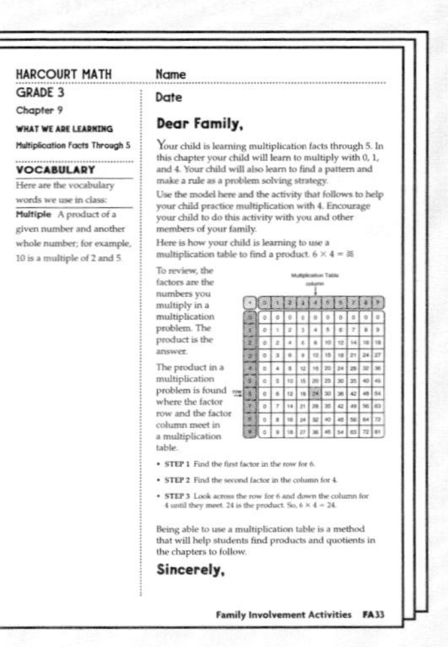

HARCOURT MATH
GRADE 3
Chapter 9
WHAT WE ARE LEARNING
Multiplication Facts Through 5

VOCABULARY
Here are the vocabulary words we use in class:
Multiple A product of a given number and another whole number; for example, 10 is a multiple of 2 and 5.

Name
Date

Dear Family,

Your child is learning multiplication facts through 5. In this chapter your child will learn to multiply with 0, 1, and 4. Your child will also learn to find a pattern and make a rule as a problem solving strategy.

Use the model here and the activity that follows to help your child practice multiplication with 4. Encourage your child to do this activity with you and other members of your family.

Here is how your child is learning to use a multiplication table to find a product. 6 × 4 = ■

To review, the factors are the numbers you multiply in a multiplication problem. The product is the answer.

The product in a multiplication problem is found where the factor row and the factor column meet in a multiplication table.

- STEP 1 Find the first factor in the row for 6.
- STEP 2 Find the second factor in the column for 4.
- STEP 3 Look across the row for 6 and down the column for 4 until they meet. 24 is the product. So, 6 × 4 = 24.

Being able to use a multiplication table is a method that will help students find products and quotients in the chapters to follow.

Sincerely,

Family Involvement Activities FA33

Family Involvement Activities, p. FA33

Differentiated Instruction

Meeting the Needs of All Learners

Extra Support	Activities for All	Enrichment
Alternative Teaching Strategy TE Lessons 9.1, 9.2, 9.3, 9.4, 9.5 **ESOL/ESL** TE Lessons 9.1, 9.2, 9.3, 9.4, 9.5 **Special Needs** TE Lessons 9.2, 9.3	**Cross-Curricular Connections** **Fine Arts:** TE Lesson 9.3 **Reading:** TE Lesson 9.3 **Social Studies:** Chapter Opener **Vocabulary:** TE p. 174B, PE/TE p. 175 **Writing:** TE Lessons 9.4, 9.5	**Advanced Learners** TE Lessons 9.4, 9.5 **Early Finishers** TE Lessons 9.1, 9.2

Combination and Multi-age Classrooms

Grade 2	Grade 3	Grade 4
Skills Trace Across the Grades		
Relate addition and multiplication; use arrays to model multiplication; multiply in any order and across and down.	**Multiply with 0, 1, and 4; identify and write missing factors.**	Relate multiplication and division; multiply and divide facts through 12; write and evaluate multiplication and division expressions and equations that contain variables.
Instructional Strategies		
Students on this level may require more time to build conceptual understanding. **Assignments** **Grade 3 Pupil Edition** • Have students work in pairs on Lessons 9.3, 9.4, and 9.5. Skip Lessons 9.1 and 9.2. **Grade 2 Pupil Edition**—pages 521–528	Students on this level should be able to complete all the lessons in the Pupil Edition and all the activities in the Teacher's Edition with minimal adjustments. **Assignment** **Grade 3 Pupil Edition**—pages 174–189	Students on this level will probably require less time to build conceptual understanding. **Assignments** **Grade 3 Pupil Edition** • Compact Lessons 9.1 and 9.2. **Grade 4 Pupil Edition**—pages 162–201

Multiplication Facts Through 5

Mathematics Across the Grades

LOOKING BACK • Prerequisite Skills

To be ready for Chapter 9, students should have the following understandings and skills:

- **Model Multiplication**—review of equal groups
- **Commutative Property of Multiplication**—review of the Commutative Property of Multiplication

Check What You Know

Use page 175 to determine students' knowledge of prerequisite concepts and skills.

Intervention

Help students prepare for the chapter by using the intervention resources described on TE page 175.

LOOKING AT CHAPTER 9 • Essential Skills

Students will

- use the Identity Property and the Zero Property for Multiplication.
- use a multiplication table to multiply with 4.
- **use a multiplication table to find missing factors.**
- use the problem solving strategy *find a pattern* to solve problems.
- practice multiplication facts 0–5.

Example

■ $\times$ 4 = 36

×	0	1	2	3	4	5	6	7	8	9
0	0	0	0	0	0	0	0	0	0	0
1	0	1	2	3	4	5	6	7	8	9
2	0	2	4	6	8	10	12	14	16	18
3	0	3	6	9	12	15	18	21	24	27
4	0	4	8	12	16	20	24	28	32	36
5	0	5	10	15	20	25	30	35	40	45
6	0	6	12	18	24	30	36	42	48	54
7	0	7	14	21	28	35	42	49	56	63
8	0	8	16	24	32	40	48	56	64	72
9	0	9	18	27	36	45	54	63	72	81

Start at the column for 4. Look down to the product 36. Look left across the row from 36.

So, the missing factor is 9.

Check:

9 $\times$ 4 = 36

LOOKING AHEAD • Applications

Students will apply what they learn in Chapter 9 to the following new concepts:

- Multiplication with 6, 7, and 8 (Chapter 10)
- Find a Rule (Chapter 11)
- Relate Multiplication and Division (Chapter 12)
- Multiplication with 9 and 10 (Chapter 11)
- Multiplication with 3 Factors (Chapter 11)
- Write Fact Families (Chapter 12)

Vocabulary Power

Review Vocabulary

To be ready for Chapter 9, students should know the following vocabulary term:

- **factor** (p. 175)—one of the numbers in a multiplication problem

Develop Key Chapter Vocabulary

The **boldfaced** word is the key vocabulary term in the chapter.

- **multiple** (p. 178)—the product of a given number and another whole number

Vocabulary Cards

Have students use the Vocabulary Card on *Teacher's Resource Book* pages TR151–152 for the key term in the chapter. The card can be added to a file of mathematics terms.

multiple

Multimedia Math Glossary

GO ON-LINE For vocabulary support, visit **www.harcourtschool.com/mathglossary**

Math Journal

Have students define the key vocabulary term: *multiple*. Have students use their own words and give an example.

MATH Word Work

Objective To reinforce vocabulary concepts
Use after Lesson 9.2.

Materials *For each student* blank Multiplication Table, *Teacher's Resource Book* p. TR17, crayons or colored pencils

Have students write the multiples of 3, 4, and 5 on a blank multiplication table. Direct students to use yellow to shade multiples of 3, blue to shade multiples of 4, and red to shade multiples of 5. Ask students to write about the patterns they notice in their tables. Have them describe the multiples that are shaded green, orange, and purple.

×	0	1	2	3	4	5	6	7	8	9	10
0				0	0	0					
1				3	4	5					
2				6	8	10					
3	0	3	6	9	12	15	18	21	24	27	30
4	0	4	8	12	16	20	24	28	32	36	40
5	0	5	10	15	20	25	30	35	40	45	50
6				18	24	30					
7				21	28	35					
8				24	32	40					
9				27	36	45					
10				30	40	50					

Intervention and Extension Resources

Alternative Teaching Strategy

MATERIALS *For each pair* 35 counters

Help students model with the counters to **find the missing factor** in this multiplication sentence:
3 × __?__ = 21.

- Have students count out 21 counters for the product.
- Have students divide the counters into 3 equal rows.
- Ask students how many rows of 3 there are. 7

Have students make arrays with counters to find missing factors in the following exercises.

2 × ■ = 12 6 ■ × 5 = 20 4

■ × 9 = 27 3 4 × ■ = 32 8

KINESTHETIC

BODILY/KINESTHETIC, VISUAL/SPATIAL

Multistep and Strategy Problems

The following multistep or strategy problem is provided in Lesson 9.5:

Page	Item
187	27

Writing in Mathematics

Ask students to write a paragraph explaining how to **find a missing factor on a multiplication table**. Encourage them to tell what needs to be done and the exact order in which it should be done. Remind students to use linking words such as *first, second, next*, and *then* to help make their writing clear. Check students' work.

VISUAL

VERBAL/LINGUISTIC, LOGICAL/MATHEMATICAL

Advanced Learners

MATERIALS *For each student* multiplication table, p. TR17

Challenge students to **determine how many multiplication sentences can be written with two factors of one digit each**. Ask: How many different multiplication sentences can be made by using a multiplication table with factors from 0 to 9? Explain. There are 10 choices for the first factor and 10 choices for the second factor. 10 rows of 10 = 100 different multiplication sentences

VISUAL

VISUAL/SPATIAL, LOGICAL/MATHEMATICAL

Lesson 9.5 Organizer

Objective To use an array and a multiplication table to find missing factors

Quick Review provides review of prerequisite skills.

Why Learn This? You can complete multiplication sentences for which you know the product and one of the factors. *Share the lesson objective with students.*

2 TEACH

Guided Instruction

- *Discuss the problem in the Learn section and the first model.*
  What does the missing factor in the multiplication sentence represent? Since each plate had 5 muffins, the missing factor must be the number of plates that Mike used.
  What does the product represent? the total number of muffins
  Reasoning How do you know to use 5 tiles in each row? Because 5 is the one factor you know. Model 35 with rows of 5. The number of rows, 7, is the missing factor.
- *Direct students' attention to the second model.*
  Reasoning What if, instead of starting at column 5, you started at row 5? How would you find the missing factor? Follow the row across until you reach the product. Then look up the column to find the missing factor.

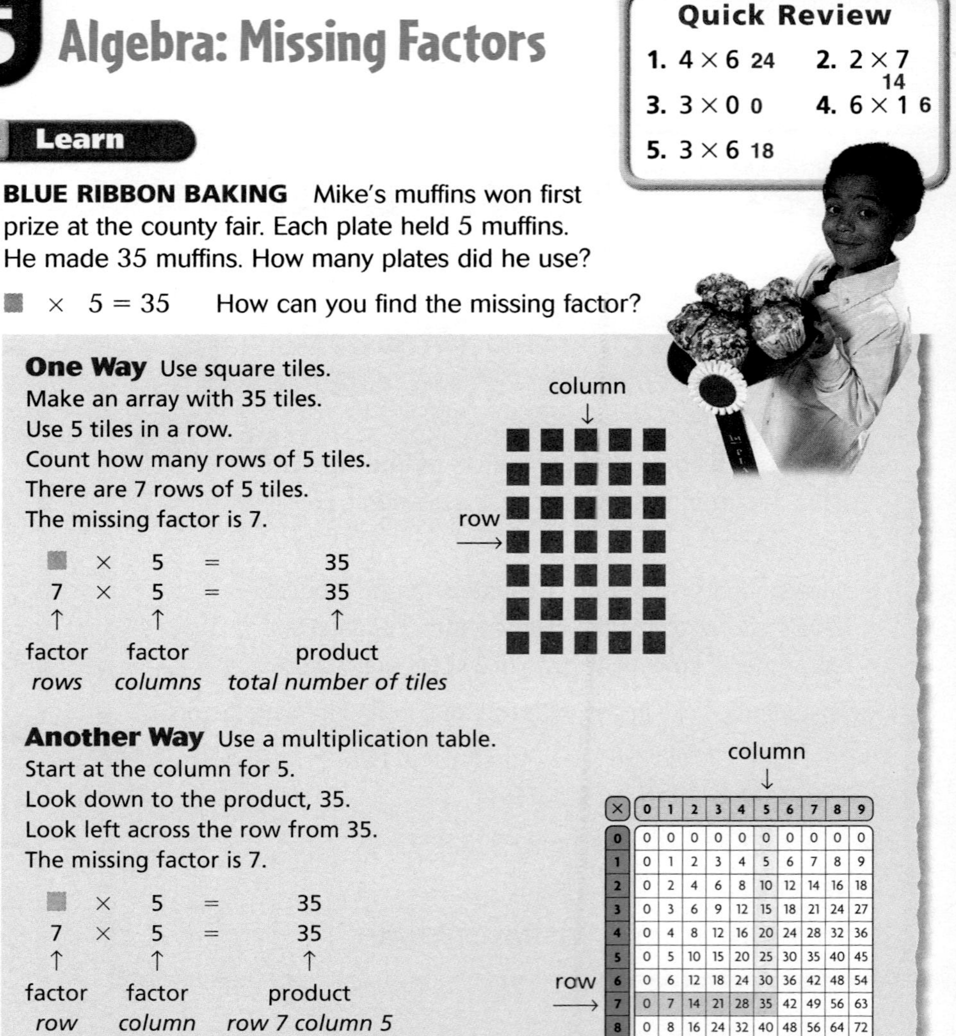

LESSON 5

Algebra: Missing Factors

Quick Review

1. 4 × 6 24
2. 2 × 7 14
3. 3 × 0 0
4. 6 × 1 6
5. 3 × 6 18

Learn

BLUE RIBBON BAKING Mike's muffins won first prize at the county fair. Each plate held 5 muffins. He made 35 muffins. How many plates did he use?

■ × 5 = 35 How can you find the missing factor?

One Way Use square tiles.
Make an array with 35 tiles.
Use 5 tiles in a row.
Count how many rows of 5 tiles.
There are 7 rows of 5 tiles.
The missing factor is 7.

■	×	5	=	35
7	×	5	=	35
↑		↑		↑
factor		factor		product
rows		*columns*		*total number of tiles*

Another Way Use a multiplication table.
Start at the column for 5.
Look down to the product, 35.
Look left across the row from 35.
The missing factor is 7.

■	×	5	=	35
7	×	5	=	35
↑		↑		↑
factor		factor		product
row		*column*		*row 7 column 5*

So, Mike used 7 plates.

×	0	1	2	3	4	5	6	7	8	9
0	0	0	0	0	0	0	0	0	0	0
1	0	1	2	3	4	5	6	7	8	9
2	0	2	4	6	8	10	12	14	16	18
3	0	3	6	9	12	15	18	21	24	27
4	0	4	8	12	16	20	24	28	32	36
5	0	5	10	15	20	25	30	35	40	45
6	0	6	12	18	24	30	36	42	48	54
7	0	7	14	21	28	35	42	49	56	63
8	0	8	16	24	32	40	48	56	64	72
9	0	9	18	27	36	45	54	63	72	81

MATH IDEA When you know the product and one factor, square tiles or a multiplication table can help you find the missing factor.

Reasoning How can you use square tiles or a multiplication table to find factors for 24? **Possible answers: Tiles: make as many different arrays for 24 as possible. Count the tiles in each row and column to find the factors. Multiplication table: find 24 on a multiplication table. Then look up the column to find one factor and across the row to find the other; factors: 3, 4, 6, 8.**

Reteach 9.5

Algebra: Missing Factors

When you know the product and one factor, you can use skip-counting to find the missing factor.

Find each missing factor.

Example A	Example B
_?_ × 4 = 28	6 × _?_ = 30
missing factor, factor, product	factor, missing factor, product
Skip-count by 4s until you reach 28.	Skip-count by 6s until you reach 30.
4, 8, 12, 16, 20, 24, 28	6, 12, 18, 24, 30
You counted 7 numbers. So, **7** × 4 = 28.	You counted 5 numbers. So, **5** × 6 = 30.

Find the missing factor. You may wish to skip-count or use a multiplication table.

1. _4_ × 3 = 12
2. 8 × _5_ = 40
3. _7_ × 2 = 14
4. 9 × _3_ = 27
5. _2_ × 4 = 8
6. 2 × _8_ = 16
7. _1_ × 7 = 7
8. _9_ × 5 = 45
9. 9 × _2_ = 18
10. 5 × _6_ = 30
11. _4_ × 9 = 36
12. _7_ × 4 = 28
13. _8_ × 5 = 40
14. 5 × _5_ = 25
15. 6 × _3_ = 18
16. 3 × _2_ = 6
17. 4 × _9_ = 36
18. _5_ × 4 = 20
19. 4 × _6_ = 24
20. _1_ × 9 = 9
21. 3 × _8_ = 24

Reteach RW51

Practice 9.5

Algebra: Missing Factors

Find the missing factor.

1. _5_ × 4 = 20
2. 7 × _5_ = 35
3. _3_ × 6 = 18
4. 8 × _4_ = 32
5. _9_ × 3 = 27
6. 5 × _6_ = 30
7. _3_ × 5 = 15
8. _7_ × 3 = 21
9. 8 × _3_ = 24
10. 5 × _5_ = 25
11. _6_ × 4 = 24
12. _9_ × 4 = 36
13. _8_ × 4 = 32
14. 4 × _5_ = 20
15. 2 × _6_ = 12
16. 5 × _9_ = 45
17. 8 × _3_ = 24
18. _5_ × 2 = 10
19. 3 × _9_ = 27
20. _1_ × 3 = 3
21. 4 × _4_ = 16
22. 7 × _2_ = 2 × _7_
23. 5 × _8_ = 45 − 5

Mixed Review

Add 8 to each.

24. 42 _50_
25. 216 _224_
26. 181 _189_
27. 437 _445_

Write the total value of each.

28. 2 dimes, 3 nickels, 4 pennies _$0.39_
29. 3 quarters, 5 nickels, 8 pennies _$1.08_
30. 3 $1-bills, 4 quarters, 10 dimes _$5.00_
31. 2 $1-bills, 2 quarters, 2 dimes _$2.70_
32. $17.25 + $6.00 = _$23.25_
33. $0.79 + $0.40 + $0.88 = _$2.07_

Complete the tables.

34.

×	9	5	1	4	6
2	18	10	2	8	12

35.

×	4	0	3	8	7
0	0	0	0	0	0

Practice PW51

Check

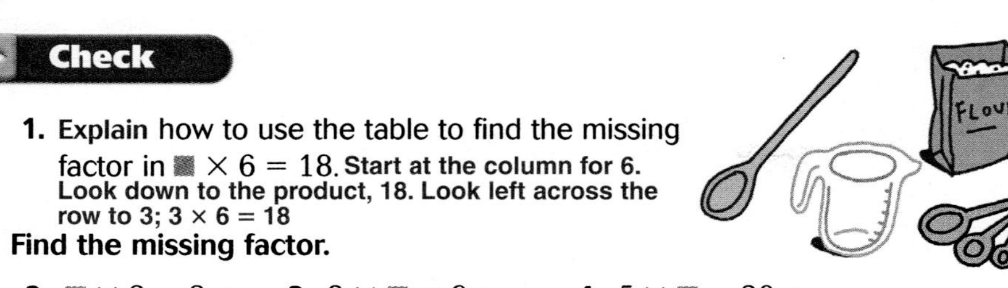

1. Explain how to use the table to find the missing factor in $\blacksquare \times 6 = 18$. **Start at the column for 6. Look down to the product, 18. Look left across the row to 3; 3 x 6 = 18**

Find the missing factor.

2. $\blacksquare \times 2 = 8$ **4**
3. $3 \times \blacksquare = 9$ **3**
4. $5 \times \blacksquare = 20$ **4**

Practice and Problem Solving

Extra Practice, page 188, Set D

Find the missing factor.

5. $\blacksquare \times 4 = 12$ **3**
6. $\blacksquare \times 3 = 21$ **7**
7. $5 \times \blacksquare = 0$ **0**
8. $2 \times \blacksquare = 12$ **6**
9. $1 \times \blacksquare = 9$ **9**
10. $8 \times \blacksquare = 24$ **3**
11. $\blacksquare \times 6 = 30$ **5**
12. $\blacksquare \times 4 = 32$ **8**
13. $\blacksquare \times 2 = 18$ **9**
14. $4 \times \blacksquare = 16$ **4**
15. $5 \times \blacksquare = 15$ **3**
16. $\blacksquare \times 6 = 24$ **4**
17. $\blacksquare \times 4 = 36$ **9**
18. $\blacksquare \times 3 = 27$ **9**
19. $6 \times \blacksquare = 18$ **3**
20. $8 \times \blacksquare = 40$ **5**
21. $4 \times 6 = \blacksquare \times 3$ **8**
22. $9 \times \blacksquare = 50 - 5$ **5**
23. $7 \times \blacksquare = 32 - 4$ **4**
24. The product of 4 and another factor is 28. What is the other factor? **7**
25. If you multiply 9 by a number, the product is 27. What is the number? **3**
26. There are 2 chairs at each table. If there are 14 chairs, how many tables are there? Write a multiplication sentence to solve. **$2 \times \blacksquare = 14$ or $\blacksquare \times 2 = 14$; 7 tables**
27. There are 4 oatmeal cookies and 3 sugar cookies on each plate. How many cookies are on 5 plates? **35 cookies**
28. **Write About It** How can you use a multiplication table to find the multiples of 6? **Possible answer: Look at a row or column for 6. All the numbers are multiples of 6: 6, 12, 18, 24, 30, 36, 42, 48, and 54.**
29. **What's the Question?** Pies are on sale for $3 each. Carly spent $12 on pies. The answer is 4 pies. **How many pies did Carly buy?**

Getting Ready for the EOG Test

30. Nancy put 9 books in each box. She packed 18 books. How many boxes were filled? **A**

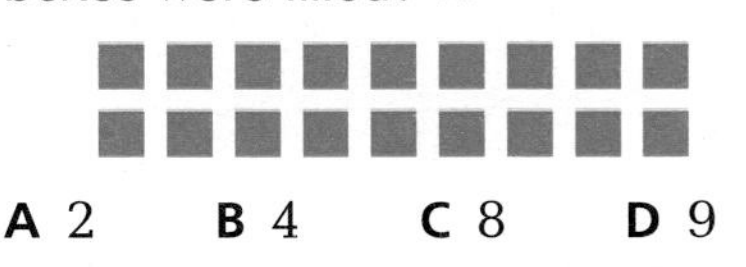

A 2   B 4   C 8   D 9

31. Jon put 72 rocks into 9 bags. Each bag has the same number of rocks. How many rocks are in each bag? **C**

A 6   B 7   C 8   D 9

North Carolina Standards 1.03 Develop fluency with multiplication from 1×1 to 12×12 and division to two-digit by one-digit numbers using: a) Strategies for multiplying and dividing numbers. *also* **5.03**

3 PRACTICE

Guided Practice

Do Check Exercises 1–4 with your students. Identify students who are having difficulty and choose appropriate lesson resources to provide assistance.

Independent Practice

Note that Exercise 27 is a **multistep or strategy problem.** Assign Exercises 5–29.

SCAFFOLDED INSTRUCTION Use the prompts on Transparency 9 to guide instruction for the multistep or strategy problem in Exercise 27.

Transparency 9

4 ASSESS

Summarize the lesson by having students:

DISCUSS Suppose that the first factor in a multiplication sentence is 5 and the product is 20. What steps can you take to find the missing second factor using a multiplication table? Start at the row for 5. Look across to the product, 20. Look up the column from 20. The column is for 4, so 4 is the missing factor.

WRITE Jackie wrote the following two multiplication sentences: $\blacksquare \times 3 = 21$ and $3 \times \blacksquare = 21$. How can finding the missing factor in the first sentence help you find the missing factor in the second sentence? Explain. Possible answer: I can build an array or use the multiplication table to find the first factor in the first sentence, 7. If I know that $7 \times 3 = 21$, I also know that $3 \times 7 = 21$.

LESSON QUIZ

Transparency 9.5

Find the missing factor.

1. $3 \times \blacksquare = 18$ 6
2. $\blacksquare \times 9 = 36$ 4
3. $\blacksquare \times 5 = 25$ 5
4. $2 \times \blacksquare = 14$ 7

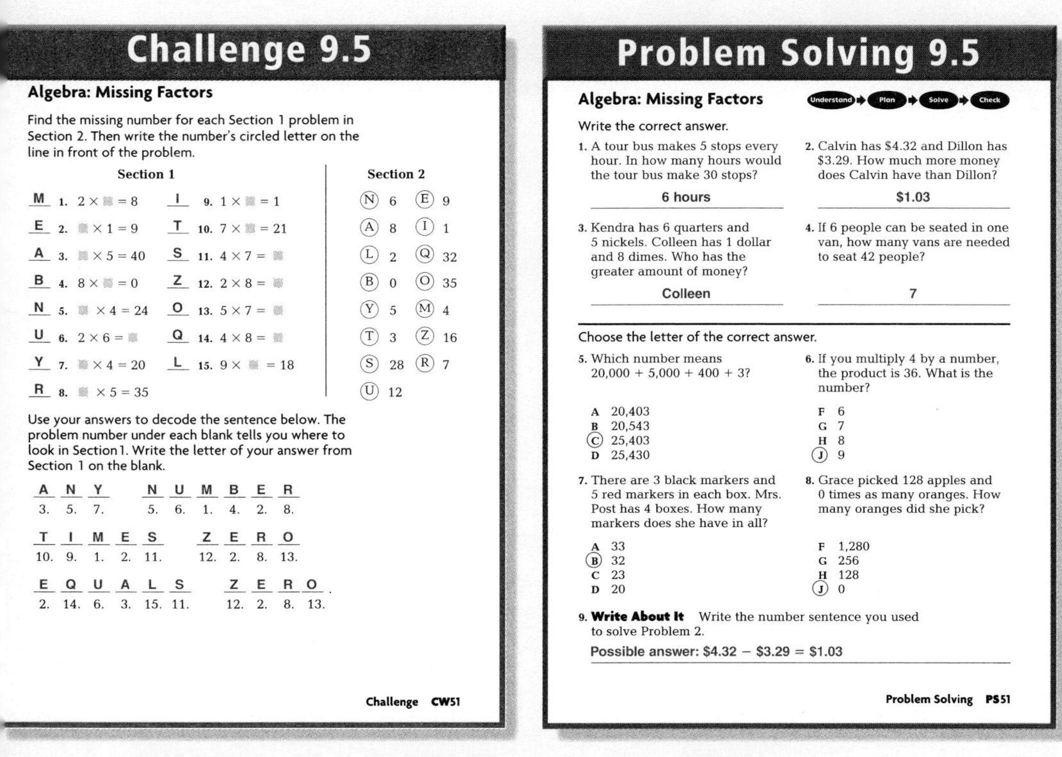

Challenge 9.5

Algebra: Missing Factors

Find the missing number for each Section 1 problem in Section 2. Then write the number's circled letter on the line in front of the problem.

Section 1

M	1. $2 \times \blacksquare = 8$	I	9. $1 \times \blacksquare = 1$
E	2. $\blacksquare \times 1 = 9$	T	10. $7 \times \blacksquare = 21$
A	3. $\blacksquare \times 5 = 40$	S	11. $4 \times 7 = \blacksquare$
B	4. $8 \times \blacksquare = 0$	Z	12. $2 \times 8 = \blacksquare$
N	5. $\blacksquare \times 4 = 24$	O	13. $5 \times 7 = \blacksquare$
U	6. $2 \times 6 = \blacksquare$	Q	14. $4 \times 8 = \blacksquare$
Y	7. $\blacksquare \times 4 = 20$	L	15. $9 \times \blacksquare = 18$
R	8. $\blacksquare \times 5 = 35$		

Section 2

(N)	6	(E)	9
(A)	8	(I)	1
(L)	2	(Q)	32
(B)	0	(O)	35
(Y)	5	(M)	4
(T)	3	(Z)	16
(S)	28	(R)	7
(U)	12		

Use your answers to decode the sentence below. The problem number under each blank tells you where to look in Section 1. Write the letter of your answer from Section 1 on the blank.

A N Y   N U M B E R
3. 5. 7.   5. 6. 1. 4. 2. 8.

T I M E S   Z E R O
10. 9. 1. 2. 11.   12. 2. 8. 13.

E Q U A L S   Z E R O.
2. 14. 6. 3. 15. 11.   12. 2. 8. 13.

Challenge CW51

Problem Solving 9.5

Algebra: Missing Factors

Understand → Plan → Solve → Check

Write the correct answer.

1. A tour bus makes 5 stops every hour. In how many hours would the tour bus make 30 stops?
   6 hours
2. Calvin has $4.32 and Dillon has $3.29. How much more money does Calvin have than Dillon?
   $1.03
3. Kendra has 6 quarters and 5 nickels. Colleen has 1 dollar and 8 dimes. Who has the greater amount of money?
   Colleen
4. If 6 people can be seated in one van, how many vans are needed to seat 42 people?
   7

Choose the letter of the correct answer.

5. Which number means 20,000 + 5,000 + 400 + 3?
   A 20,403
   B 20,543
   (C) 25,403
   D 25,430
6. If you multiply 4 by a number, the product is 36. What is the number?
   F 6
   G 7
   H 8
   (J) 9
7. There are 3 black markers and 5 red markers in each box. Mrs. Post has 4 boxes. How many markers does she have in all?
   A 33
   (B) 32
   C 23
   D 20
8. Grace picked 128 apples and 0 times as many oranges. How many oranges did she pick?
   F 1,280
   G 256
   H 128
   (J) 0
9. **Write About It** Write the number sentence you used to solve Problem 2.
   Possible answer: $4.32 − $3.29 = $1.03

Problem Solving PS51

CHAPTER 9 Extra Practice

Purpose To provide extra practice for the skills presented in this chapter

The blue page references in each set of exercises refer to the lesson pages where each skill is taught.

Internet Resources

Visit THE LEARNING SITE at **www.harcourtschool.com** for a listing of practice activities.

Extra Practice

Set A (pp. 176–177)

Find the product.

1. $0 \times 5 = $ ■ **0**
2. $3 \times 7 = $ ■ **21**
3. $1 \times 7 = $ ■ **7**
4. $4 \times 3 = $ ■ **12**
5. ■ $= 6 \times 3$ **18**
6. ■ $= 8 \times 5$ **40**
7. ■ $= 0 \times 9$ **0**
8. ■ $= 1 \times 1$ **1**
9. Is the product of 3 and 0 *greater than, less than,* or *equal to* the product of 0 and 6? Explain. **equal to; $3 \times 0 = 0$ and $0 \times 6 = 0$**

Set B (pp. 178–179)

Find the product.

1. $\begin{array}{r} 8 \\ \times 4 \\ \hline 32 \end{array}$
2. $\begin{array}{r} 4 \\ \times 0 \\ \hline 0 \end{array}$
3. $\begin{array}{r} 4 \\ \times 6 \\ \hline 24 \end{array}$
4. $\begin{array}{r} 4 \\ \times 4 \\ \hline 16 \end{array}$
5. $\begin{array}{r} 4 \\ \times 9 \\ \hline 36 \end{array}$
6. $3 \times 4 = $ ■ **12**
7. ■ $= 2 \times 4$ **8**
8. ■ $= 4 \times 7$ **28**
9. $5 \times 4 = $ ■ **20**
10. Mario has 4 packs of 8 stickers. He also has 19 loose stickers. How many stickers does he have in all? **51 stickers**

Set C (pp. 182–185)

Find the product.

1. $4 \times 6 = $ ■ **24**
2. $5 \times 3 = $ ■ **15**
3. $8 \times 0 = $ ■ **0**
4. $9 \times 5 = $ ■ **45**
5. $5 \times 8 = $ ■ **40**
6. $3 \times 6 = $ ■ **18**
7. $7 \times 4 = $ ■ **28**
8. $3 \times 9 = $ ■ **27**
9. $8 \times 2 = $ ■ **16**
10. $3 \times 7 = $ ■ **21**
11. $6 \times 5 = $ ■ **30**
12. $4 \times 8 = $ ■ **32**
13. A movie is shown 5 times each day. How many times is that movie shown in one week? **35 times**

Set D (pp. 186–187)

Find the missing factor.

1. ■ $\times 9 = 18$ **2**
2. $5 \times$ ■ $= 20$ **4**
3. ■ $\times 1 = 8$ **8**
4. ■ $\times 9 = 9$ **1**
5. $2 \times$ ■ $= 14$ **7**
6. $4 \times$ ■ $= 16$ **4**
7. $3 \times$ ■ $= 21$ **7**
8. ■ $\times 8 = 32$ **4**
9. Jill has 9 baskets with an equal number of eggs in each. If she has 36 eggs in all, how many are in each basket? **4 eggs**

Review/Test

CHECK VOCABULARY

Choose the best term from the box.

array
zero
multiple
one
factor

1. The product of _?_ and any number equals that number. (p. 176) **one**
2. The product of _?_ and any number equals zero. (p. 176) **zero**
3. A _?_ of 5 is any product that has 5 as a factor, such as 5, 10, 15, and so on. (p. 178) **multiple**

CHECK SKILLS

Find the product. (pp. 176–177)

4. $5 \times 1 = ■$ **5**
5. $0 \times 6 = ■$ **0**
6. $■ = 1 \times 8$ **8**
7. $■ = 9 \times 0$ **0**

Find the product. (pp. 178–179)

8. $■ = 4 \times 3$ **12**
9. $2 \times 4 = ■$ **8**
10. $5 \times 4 = ■$ **20**
11. $■ = 8 \times 4$ **32**
12. $4 \times 9 = ■$ **36**
13. $4 \times 4 = ■$ **16**
14. $■ = 6 \times 4$ **24**
15. $4 \times 0 = ■$ **0**

Find the missing factor. (pp. 186–187)

16. $2 \times ■ = 8$ **4**
17. $■ \times 5 = 30$ **6**
18. $1 \times ■ = 9$ **9**
19. $■ \times 6 = 18$ **3**
20. $■ \times 1 = 9$ **9**
21. $4 \times ■ = 32$ **8**
22. $■ \times 3 = 18$ **6**
23. $7 \times ■ = 0$ **0**

CHECK PROBLEM SOLVING

Solve. (pp. 180–181)

24. The first four numbers in the pattern are 4, 8, 12, 16. What is a rule? What are the next three numbers? **rule: add 4; 20, 24, 28**
25. Lin saw this number pattern: 10, 13, 16, 19, 22, 25, and 28. What is a rule? What are the next three numbers? **rule: add 3; 31, 34, 37**

Review/Test

Purpose To check understanding of concepts, skills, and problem solving presented in Chapter 9

Using the Page

The Chapter 9 Review/Test can be used as a **review** or a **test**.

- Items 1–3 check understanding of concepts and new vocabulary.
- Items 4–23 check skill proficiency.
- Items 24–25 check students' abilities to choose and apply problem solving strategies to real-life multiplication problems.

Suggest that students place the completed Chapter 9 Review/Test in their portfolios.

Using the Assessment Guide

- Multiple-choice format of Chapter 9 Posttest—See *Assessment Guide*, pp. AG57–58.
- Free-response format of Chapter 9 Posttest—See *Assessment Guide*, pp. AG59–60.

Using Student Self-Assessment

The How Did I Do? survey helps students assess what they have learned and how they learned it. This survey is available as a copying master in *Assessment Guide*, p. AGxvii.

Chapter 9 Test, page 1

Choose the correct answer.

1. 1×4
   A 1 B 3 (C) 4 D 5
2. $8 \times 1 = ■$
   F 0 G 1 (H) 8 J 9
3. What is the missing factor? $5 \times ■ = 25$
   A 2 B 3 C 4 (D) 5
4. $6 \times 1 = ■$
   F 7 (G) 6 H 5 J 0
5. What are the next 3 numbers in the pattern?
   5, 7, 9, 11, ___, ___, ___
   A 12, 14, 16
   (B) 13, 15, 17
   C 14, 17, 20
   D 15, 19, 23
6. What is the product of 4 and 7?
   F 3 G 11 (H) 28 J 47
7. Amy made 4 cups of hot chocolate. She put 4 small marshmallows in each cup. How many marshmallows did she use?
   A 20 (B) 16 C 12 D 8
8. Jill is thinking of a number pattern. The first four numbers in her pattern are 5, 10, 15, and 20. What is a rule for her pattern?
   F multiply by 2
   (G) add 5
   H subtract 4
   J add 10
9. A classroom has 6 rows with 4 desks in each row. How many desks are in the room?
   (A) 24 B 20 C 12 D 10
10. What is the product of 0 and 8?
    (F) 0 G 4 H 8 J 12

Go On

Chapter 9 Test, page 2

11. When 8 is multiplied by a number, the answer is 24. What is the number?
    A 2 (B) 3 C 4 D 5
12. Each package of pens contains 3 blue and 5 black pens. How many pens are in 4 packages?
    F 12 G 17 H 23 (J) 32
13. Abby is thinking of a number pattern. Her pattern starts with 8, 14, 20, 26, and 32. Which number doesn't fit the pattern if it continues?
    A 56 (B) 52 C 50 D 44
14. $9 \times ■ = 0$
    (F) 0 G 1 H 9 J 90
15. Eric has 4 nickels. Each nickel is worth 5 cents. How much money does Eric have?
    A 4¢ B 5¢ C 9¢ (D) 20¢
16. The product of 2 and another factor is 18. Which number sentence could be used to find the missing factor?
    F $2 + ■ = 18$
    (G) $2 \times ■ = 18$
    H $18 - ■ = 2$
    J $■ - 2 = 18$
17. There are 4 apartments in each building. How many apartments are there in 9 buildings?
    A 5 B 13 C 18 (D) 36
18. Phil's mom buys 5 boxes of cereal. Each box should have 1 prize in it. Phil found 0 prizes in each box. How many prizes did he get?
    F 6 G 5 H 4 (J) 0
19. Josh's number pattern starts with 38, 36, 37, 35, 36, 34, and 35. What are the next 3 numbers in the number pattern?
    A 36, 35, 37
    (B) 33, 34, 32
    C 34, 36, 35
    D 31, 32, 29
20. A number multiplied by 4 equals 12. What is the number?
    F 2 (G) 3 H 8 J 16

Stop

Getting Ready for the EOG Test

Chapters 1–9

Using the Pages

These pages may be used to help students get ready for the North Carolina EOG Test. The test items are written in the same style and arranged in the same format as those on the EOG Test.

The pages are cumulative. They cover the standards from the North Carolina Mathematics Standard Course of Study that have been taught up to this point in the text or in a previous grade. Each Getting Ready for the EOG Test also reviews the North Carolina mathematics strands shown below.

- Number and Operations
- Measurement
- Geometry
- Data Analysis and Probability
- Algebra

These pages can be assigned at the end of the chapter as classwork or as a homework assignment. You may want to have students use individual recording sheets presented in a multiple-choice (standardized) format. A Test Answer Sheet is available as a blackline master in the *Assessment Guide* (p. AGlii).

You may wish to have students describe how they solved each problem and share their solutions.

Getting Ready for the EOG Test

NUMBER AND OPERATIONS

TIP **Understand the problem.** See item 1. The shaded box stands for the *same* number in all of the fact family sentences. Replace the shaded box with each answer choice to find which number makes all of the sentences true.

1. What number completes this fact family? B

$\blacksquare + 5 = 8$ $\quad 5 + \blacksquare = 8$

$8 - 5 = \blacksquare$ $\quad 8 - \blacksquare = 5$

A 0 **C** 5
B 3 **D** 8

2. What multiplication sentence does the array show? C

A $5 \times 5 = 25$ **C** $4 \times 5 = 20$
B $2 \times 5 = 10$ **D** $4 \times 4 = 16$

3. Explain It There are 157 third-grade students. Tana wants to give each student an ice pop at the third-grade picnic. She estimates she will need 5 boxes of pops. Each box holds 30 pops. Explain whether you agree with Tana's estimate. See page 191.

MEASUREMENT AND GEOMETRY

4. The clock shows when Mark finished a science project. He had been working on it for two hours. At what time did Mark start his science project? D

A 3:15 **C** 1:15
B 2:30 **D** 11:15

5. If October 21 falls on a Monday, what day does October 29 fall on? B

A Monday **C** Sunday
B Tuesday **D** Thursday

6. Jill measured the height of her school desk. She wrote 1 as her answer. What unit of measure should Jill use to label her answer? C

A cup **C** yard
B pound **D** gallon

7. Explain It It takes 25 minutes to bake 1 batch of brownies in Jack's oven. Jack estimates that he could bake 4 batches of brownies in 1 hour. Do you agree with his estimate? Explain why or why not. See page 191.

ALGEBRA

8. What is the missing number in this pattern? **C**

4, 8, 12, 16, ■, 24

A 4 **C** 20
B 18 **D** 22

9. Which rule could be used to find the numbers in column B? **D**

A	B
6	18
7	21
8	24
9	27

A Add 6 to the number in column A.
B Multiply the number in column A by 4.
C Subtract 2 from the number in column A.
D Multiply the number in column A by 3.

10. Explain It Jan is making a bracelet. She strings the beads according to this pattern.

Describe the next three beads that Jan will use. Explain how you found your answer. **See below.**

DATA ANALYSIS AND PROBABILITY

11. The graph shows the number of cans collected at Bryce Elementary School. How many more cans did Grade 3 students collect than Grade 5 students? **D**

CANS COLLECTED

Grade 5	🥫🥫🥫🥫🥫
Grade 4	🥫🥫🥫🥫🥫🥫🥫
Grade 3	🥫🥫🥫🥫🥫🥫🥫🥫
Grade 2	🥫🥫🥫🥫🥫🥫

Key: Each 🥫 = 4 cans.

A 52 **C** 18
B 22 **D** 12

12. Which shows the grades shown in the graph above in order from the *least* number of cans collected to the *greatest* number? **B**

A grade 2, grade 3, grade 5, grade 4
B grade 5, grade 2, grade 4, grade 3
C grade 3, grade 4, grade 2, grade 5
D grade 5, grade 4, grade 3, grade 2

13. Explain It Gail also made a pictograph of the data above. Explain why Gail's pictograph has twice as many symbols as the graph above. **See below.**

Chapters 1–9

Item Analysis

You may wish to use the item analysis to determine which North Carolina standards need additional review.

Item	North Carolina Standard	Lesson
1	1.02	1.1
2	1.03	8.2
3	1.06	8.5
4	2.01	7.3
5	(2.01	7.5
6	(2) Goal 2	Grade 2
7	2.01	7.1
8	5.01	2.5
9	5.01	9.3
10	(2) 5.01	Grade 2
11	(2) 4.01	Grade 2
12	(2) 4.01	Grade 2
13	(2) Goal 4	Grade 2

SCORING RUBRIC
Explain It

2 Demonstrates a complete understanding of the problem and chooses an appropriate strategy to determine the solution

1 Demonstrates a partial understanding of the problem and chooses a strategy that does not lead to a complete and accurate solution

0 Demonstrates little understanding of the problem and shows little evidence of using any strategy to determine a solution

Explain It • Written Response

3. Possible answer: no; Tana's estimate is too low: 30 + 30 + 30 + 30 + 30 = 150. She will need 6 boxes of ice pops.

7. Possible answer: no; Jack's estimate is wrong. He should round 25 minutes to 30 minutes. He can bake 2 batches of brownies in 1 hour.

10. Possible answer: a rule for the pattern is 2 red beads, 1 white bead, 2 blue beads. Add to right side: blue, red, and red. Add to left side: blue, blue, white.

13. Gail used a different key. One symbol on her pictograph represents 2 cans instead of 4 cans.

Multiplication Facts and Strategies

NCTM Standards 2000

1. Number and Operations
Lessons 10.1, 10.2, 10.3, 10.4, 10.5
2. Algebra
Lessons 10.1, 10.2, 10.3, 10.4, 10.5
3. Geometry
4. Measurement
5. Data Analysis and Probab lity
Lesson 10.3
6. Problem Solving
Lessons 10.1, 10.2, 10.3, 10.4, 10.5
7. Reasoning and Proof
Lessons 10.1, 10.2, 10.4, 10.5
8. Communication
Lessons 10.1, 10.2, 10.4, 10.5
9. Connections
Lessons 10.1, 10.2, 10.4, 10.5
10. Representation
Lessons 10.1, 10.2, 10.4, 10.5

Chapter Planner

Getting Ready for Chapter 10 • Assessing Prior Knowledge and INTERVENTION (See PE and TE page 193.)

LESSON	NORTH CAROLINA STANDARDS	PACING	VOCABULARY*	MATERIALS	RESOURCES AND TECHNOLOGY
10.1 Multiply with 6 pp. 194–195 Objective To multiply with 6	1.03a	1 Day			Reteach, Practice, Problem Solving, Challenge 10.1 Worksheets Transparency 10.1 **Intervention,** *Skills 21–25* (CD or Book)
10.2 Multiply with 8 pp. 196–197 Objective To multiply with 8	1.03a	1 Day			Reteach, Practice, Problem Solving, Challenge 10.2 Worksheets Scaffolded Instruction Transparency 10 Transparency 10.2 **Intervention,** *Skills 21–25* (CD or Book)
10.3 Problem Solving Skill: ***Use a Pictograph*** pp. 198–199 Objective To use the problem solving skill *use a pictograph* to solve problems	1.03a *also* 4.01	1 Day			Reteach, Practice, Reading Strategy, Challenge 10.3 Worksheets Transparency 10.3 Reading Transparency 10 **Intervention • Problem Solving,** *Strategy/Skill 10* (CD or Book) **Harcourt Mega Math The Number Games,** *ArachnaGraph*
10.4 Multiply with 7 pp. 200–201 Objective To multiply with 7	1.03a	1 Day			Reteach, Practice, Problem Solving, Challenge 10.4 Worksheets Transparency 10.4 **Intervention,** *Skills 21–25* (CD or Book) **Harcourt Mega Math The Number Games,** *Up, Up, and Array*
10.5 Algebra: Practice the Facts pp. 202–205 Objective To review multiplication strategies and apply them to 0–8 basic facts	1.03a	2 Days			Reteach, Practice, Problem Solving, Challenge 10.5 Worksheets Transparency 10.5 **Intervention,** *Skills 21–25* (CD or Book) **Math Jingles® CD 3–4**

Ending Chapter 10 • **Extra Practice,** p. 206 • **Chapter 10 Review/Test,** p. 207 • **Getting Ready for the EOG Test,** pp. 208–209

Vocabulary Power

Review Vocabulary

To be ready for Chapter 10, students should know the following vocabulary term:

- **array** (p. 193)—an arrangement of objects in rows and columns

Multimedia Math Glossary

GO ON-LINE For vocabulary support, visit **www.harcourtschool.com/mathglossary**

Vocabulary Cards

There are no key words in this chapter, but mathematics vocabulary is reinforced visually and verbally. Encourage students to review the mathematics vocabulary in their journals.

Math Journal

Have students write the review vocabulary term. Then have them use the vocabulary term in a sentence.

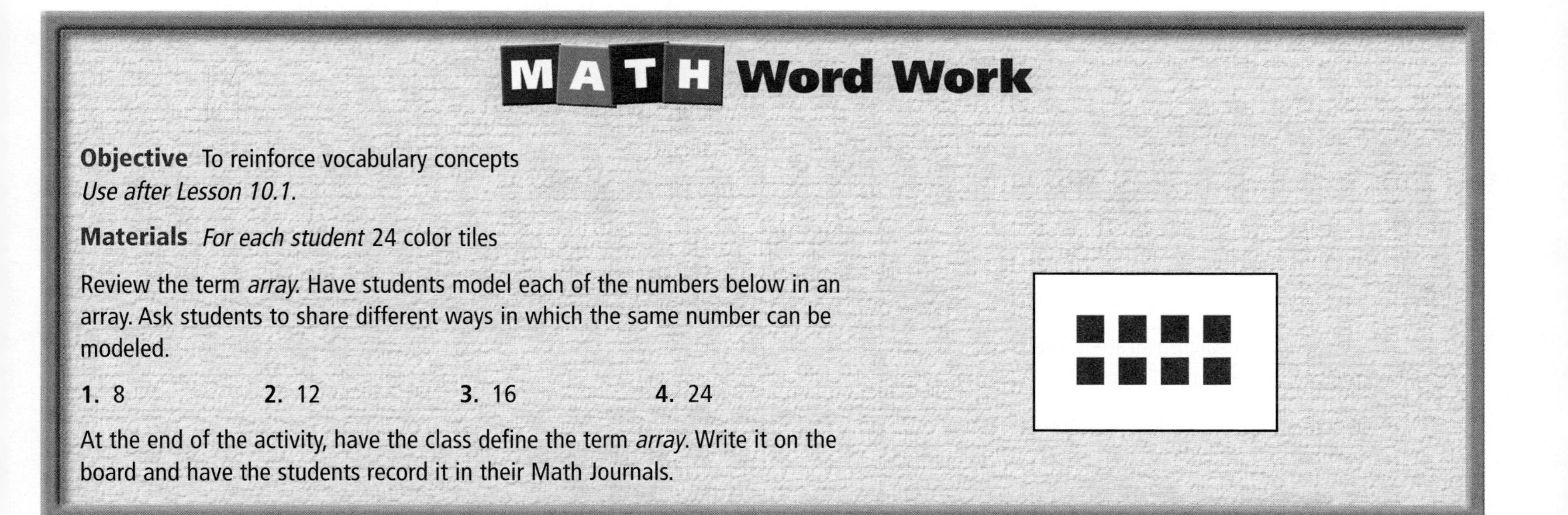

MATH Word Work

Objective To reinforce vocabulary concepts
Use after Lesson 10.1.

Materials *For each student* 24 color tiles

Review the term *array.* Have students model each of the numbers below in an array. Ask students to share different ways in which the same number can be modeled.

1. 8 **2.** 12 **3.** 16 **4.** 24

At the end of the activity, have the class define the term *array.* Write it on the board and have the students record it in their Math Journals.

Multiplication Facts and Strategies

Mathematics Across the Grades

LOOKING BACK • Prerequisite Skills

To be ready for Chapter 10, students should have the following understandings and skills:

- **Arrays**—review modeling multiplication with arrays
- **Multiplication Facts Through 5**—find products for factors of 0–5

Check What You Know

Use page 193 to determine students' knowledge of prerequisite concepts and skills.

Intervention

Help students prepare for the chapter by using the intervention resources described on TE page 193.

LOOKING AT CHAPTER 10 • Essential Skills

Students will

- **multiply with 6, 7, and 8 using arrays.**
- use the problem solving strategy *use a pictograph* to solve problems.
- review multiplication strategies and apply them to 0–8 basic facts.

Example

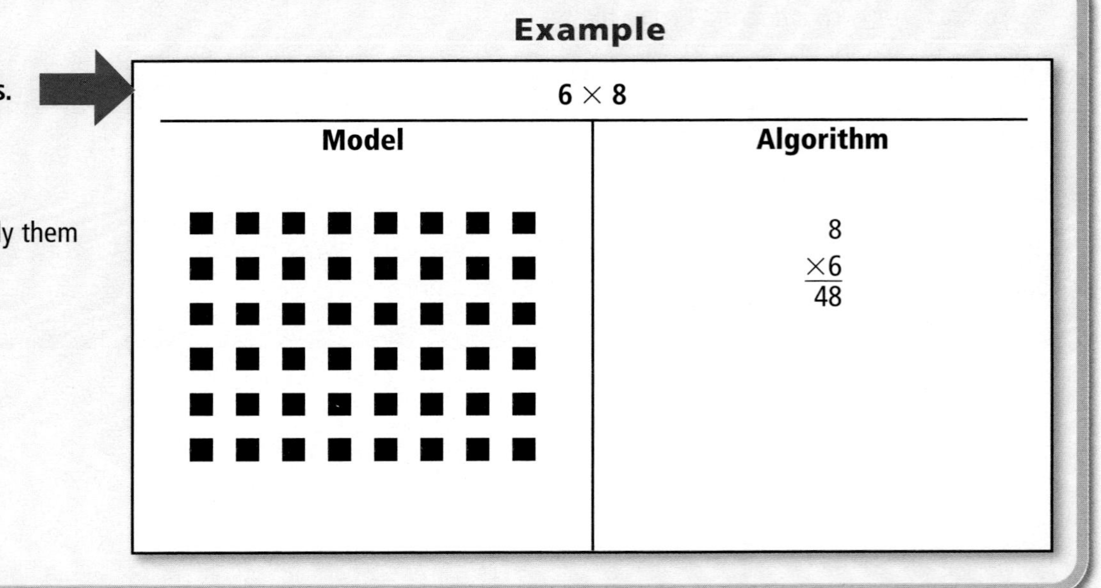

LOOKING AHEAD • Applications

Students will apply what they learn in Chapter 10 to the following new concepts:

- Multiply with 9 and 10 (Chapter 11)
- Divide by 6, 7, and 8 (Chapter 14)
- Multiply with 3 Factors (Chapter 11)
- Multiply 2-Digit Numbers (Chapter 29)

Differentiated Instruction

Meeting the Needs of All Learners

Extra Support	Activities for All	Enrichment
Alternative Teaching Strategy TE Lessons 10.1, 10.2, 10.3, 10.4, 10.5 **ESOL/ESL** TE Lessons 10.1, 10.2, 10.3, 10.4, 10.5 **Special Needs** TE Lessons 10.1, 10.2	**Cross-Curricular Connections** **Reading:** TE Lesson 10.3 **Science:** TE Lessons 10.2, 10.3 **Vocabulary:** TE p. 192B, PE/TE p. 193 **Writing:** TE Lessons 10.3, 10.5 **Music:** Chapter Opener	**Advanced Learners** TE Lesson 10.5 **Early Finishers** TE Lessons 10.1, 10.4

Combination and Multi-age Classrooms

Grade 2	Grade 3	Grade 4
Skills Trace Across the Grades		
Explore multiplication concepts; relate addition and multiplication.	**Multiply with 6, 7, and 8; practice basic multiplication facts.**	Practice multiplication and division facts; write expressions with multiplication and division.
Instructional Strategies		
Students on this level may require more time to build conceptual understanding. **Assignments** **Grade 3 Pupil Edition** • Have students use counters for Lessons 10.1, 10.2, and 10.4. Skip Lessons 10.3 and 10.5. **Grade 2 Pupil Edition**—pages 521–528	Students on this level should be able to complete all the lessons in the Pupil Edition and all the activities in the Teacher's Edition with minimal adjustments. **Assignment** **Grade 3 Pupil Edition**—pages 192–207	Students on this level will probably require less time to build conceptual understanding. **Assignments** **Grade 3 Pupil Edition** • Compact Lessons 10.1, 10.2, and 10.4. **Grade 4 Pupil Edition**—pages 162–201

CHAPTER 10

Multiplication Facts and Strategies

Introducing the Chapter

Tell students that they will learn strategies for multiplying with 6, 7, and 8. Have students look at the photograph. Ask them how they could find the total number of drumsticks if there are 8 drummers in the band. Possible answer: Add 8 groups of 2: $2 + 2 + 2 + 2 + 2 + 2 + 2 + 2 = 16$ drumsticks

Using Data

To begin the study of this chapter, have students

- Find the number of brass players in the Loch Raven band. 12 brass players
- Determine which band has a greater number of brass players—Loch Raven or Patapsco. Patapsco
- Find the total number of brass players shown in the graph and explain how they got their answers. 72 brass players; $3 \times 4 = 12$; $8 \times 4 = 32$; $7 \times 4 = 28$; $12 + 32 + 28 = 72$

Problem Solving Project

Purpose To draw arrays to solve a problem

Grouping partners

Background Marching bands generally have brass, wind, and percussion sections. They also usually have color guards that march in formations with flags.

UNDERSTAND • PLAN • SOLVE • CHECK

Have students

- Draw an array that shows a marching band of 5 rows of 8 people. Check students' work.
- Draw an array that shows a marching band of 10 rows of 4 people. Check students' work.
- Decide which marching band has more people. Both bands have 40 people.

Graphing Investigations
Begin Week 10.

CHAPTER 10

Multiplication Facts and Strategies

FAST FACT • MUSIC
A marching band plays music and moves in formation. Marching bands are popular at parades and football games. Many bands compete in state and national marching band contests.

PROBLEM SOLVING **Look at the pictograph. Draw an array that each band could use as a formation for its brass players.**

Check students' drawings.

MARYLAND MARCHING BANDS

High School	Brass Players
Loch Raven	🎺🎺🎺
Patapsco	🎺🎺🎺🎺🎺🎺🎺🎺
Severna Park	🎺🎺🎺🎺🎺🎺🎺

Key: Each 🎺 = 4 Brass Players.

192

WHY LEARN MATH? A marching band is a group of people that moves in formation. The director of a marching band may organize the band members into equal groups to march in a parade. If there are 8 band members marching in 7 equal rows, how many members are in the marching band? 56 members Ask: How do people in other careers use multiplication? Possible answer: Salespeople use multiplication to find the total cost when several items with the same price are sold.

Family Involvement Activities

These activities provide:

- Letter to the Family
- Math Vocabulary
- Family Game
- Practice (Homework)

Family Involvement Activities, p. FA37

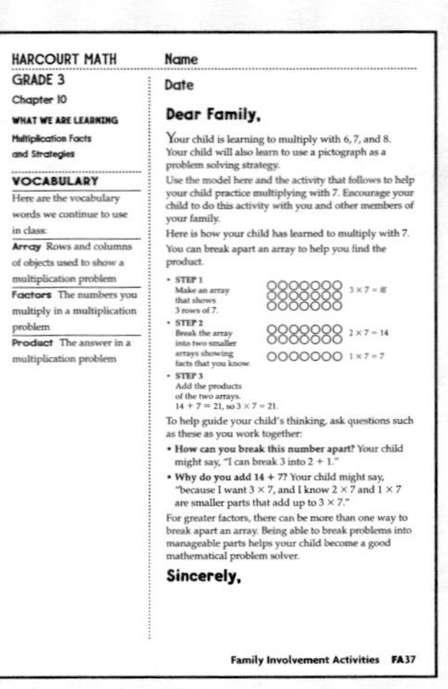

HARCOURT MATH
GRADE 3
Chapter 10
WHAT WE ARE LEARNING
Multiplication Facts and Strategies

VOCABULARY
Here are the vocabulary words we continue to use in class:
Array Rows and columns of objects used to show a multiplication problem
Factors The numbers you multiply in a multiplication problem
Product The answer in a multiplication problem

Name
Date

Dear Family,

Your child is learning to multiply with 6, 7, and 8. Your child will also learn to use a pictograph as a problem solving strategy.

Use the model here and the activity that follows to help your child practice multiplying with 7. Encourage your child to do this activity with you and other members of your family.

Here is how your child has learned to multiply with 7. You can break apart an array to help you find the product.

- **STEP 1** Make an array that shows 3 rows of 7. $3 \times 7 =$ [illegible]
- **STEP 2** Break the array into two smaller arrays showing facts that you know. $2 \times 7 = 14$ $1 \times 7 = 7$
- **STEP 3** Add the products of the two arrays. $14 + 7 = 21$, so $3 \times 7 = 21$.

To help guide your child's thinking, ask questions such as these as you work together:

- **How can you break this number apart?** Your child might say, "I can break 3 into 2 + 1."
- **Why do you add 14 + 7?** Your child might say, "because I want 3×7, and I know 2×7 and 1×7 are smaller parts that add up to 3×7."

For greater factors, there can be more than one way to break apart an array. Being able to break problems into manageable parts helps your child become a good mathematical problem solver.

Sincerely,

Family Involvement Activities FA37

CHECK WHAT YOU KNOW

Use this page to help you review and remember important skills needed for Chapter 10.

ARRAYS

Find the product.

1. $2 \times 4 = ■$ 8
2. $3 \times 6 = ■$ 18
3. $4 \times 5 = ■$ 20
4. $5 \times 6 = ■$ 30
5. $4 \times 4 = ■$ 16
6. $3 \times 7 = ■$ 21

MULTIPLICATION FACTS THROUGH 5

Find the product.

7. $7 \times 3 = ■$ 21
8. $5 \times 5 = ■$ 25
9. $■ = 7 \times 4$ 28
10. $1 \times 2 = ■$ 2
11. $4 \times 1 = ■$ 4
12. $6 \times 3 = ■$ 18
13. $9 \times 5 = ■$ 45
14. $■ = 6 \times 1$ 6
15. 6×4 24
16. 4×2 8
17. 2×3 6
18. 8×4 32
19. 3×1 3

REVIEW

array [ə•rā′] *noun*

An array is an orderly arrangement of objects, pictures, or numbers in rows and columns. Why can you use an array to show 4×6 but not $4 + 6$?

Possible answer: All rows and all columns in an array are equal. 4 + 6 cannot be shown with two equal rows.

GO ON-LINE www.harcourtschool.com/mathglossary

Assessing Prior Knowledge

Use the **Check What You Know** page to determine whether your students have mastered the prerequisite skills critical for this chapter.

Intervention

- **Diagnose and Prescribe**
  Evaluate your students' performance on this page to determine whether intervention is necessary or if enrichment is appropriate. Options that provide instruction, practice, and a check are listed in the chart below.

CHECK WHAT YOU KNOW RESOURCES

Intervention Copying Masters or CD-ROMs

Enrichment Copying Masters

VOCABULARY POWER

For activities and information about the vocabulary in this chapter, see page 192B.

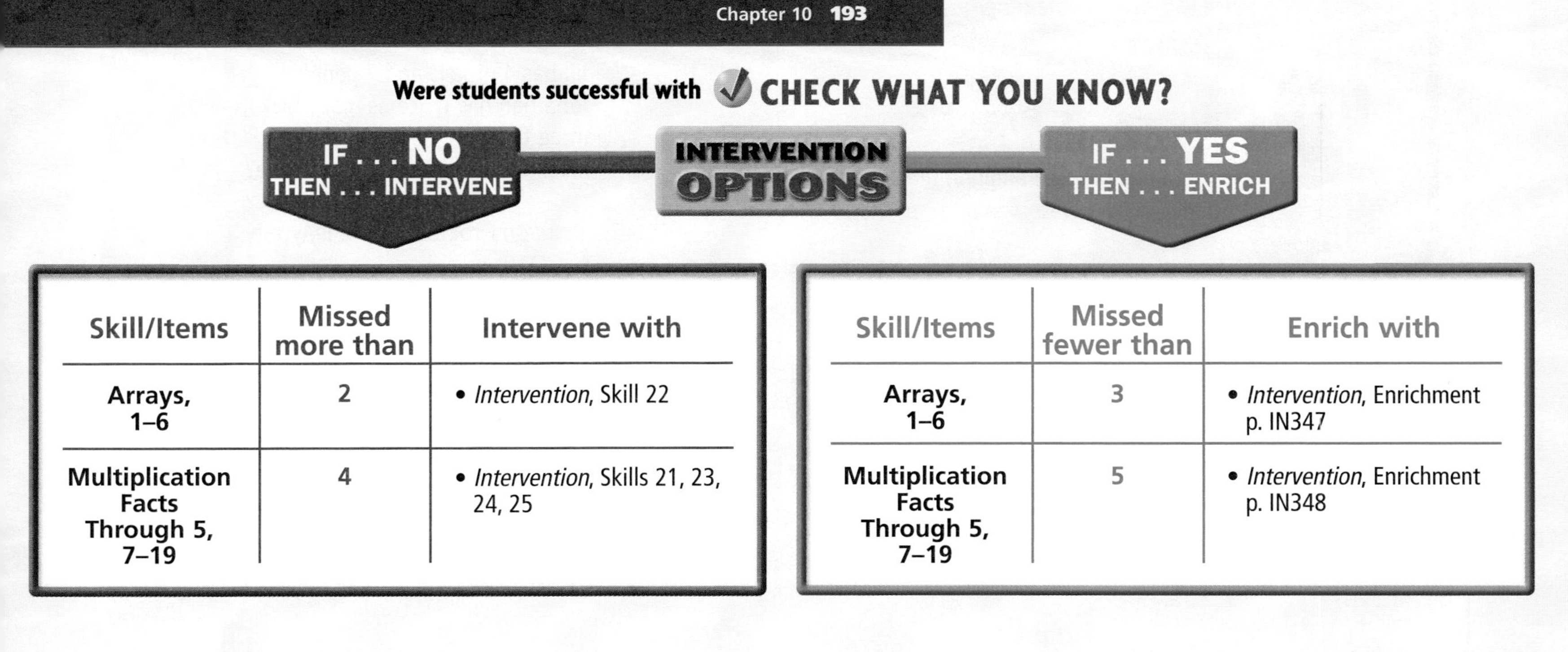

Skill/Items	Missed more than	Intervene with
Arrays, 1–6	2	• *Intervention*, Skill 22
Multiplication Facts Through 5, 7–19	4	• *Intervention*, Skills 21, 23, 24, 25

Skill/Items	Missed fewer than	Enrich with
Arrays, 1–6	3	• *Intervention*, Enrichment p. IN347
Multiplication Facts Through 5, 7–19	5	• *Intervention*, Enrichment p. IN348

Lesson 10.1

Multiply with 6

Lesson Planning

Objective To multiply with 6

NCTM Standards

1. Number and Operations
2. Algebra
6. Problem Solving
7. Reasoning and Proof
8. Communication
9. Connections
10. Representation

Math Background

These ideas will help students understand how to multiply with 6.

- Break apart an array with 6 rows into two smaller arrays, and then add the two products.
- The product of a 6's fact is double the product of the corresponding 3's fact.
- Use multiplication facts you already know to help multiply with 6.

Warm-Up Resources

Build Number Sense

Number of the Day

Use the number of days in April as the product in a multiplication sentence. If one factor in the sentence is 5, what is the other factor? 6

Daily Facts Practice

Have students practice addition facts by completing Set C of *Teacher's Resource Book*, p. TR90.

Solve a Problem

Transparency 10.1

Problem of the Day

Jill has 4 nickels and 7 pennies. Jonathan has twice as many nickels and three times as many pennies as Jill. How much money does Jonathan have? 61¢

Solution Problem of the Day tab, p. PD10

Intervention and Extension Resources

Alternative Teaching Strategy

MATERIALS *For each pair* square tiles

Help students **model doubling the product of a 3's fact to find a 6's fact**. Have students make a 4×3 array. Then have them make another 4×3 array beside the first array. Ask: What multiplication sentence can you write if you combine the two arrays? $4 \times 6 = 24$

Have students repeat with 5×3, 6×3, 7×3, 8×3, and 9×3. Ask: What pattern do you notice in the products? Possible answer: Each product increases by 3.

KINESTHETIC

BODILY/KINESTHETIC

Special Needs

MATERIALS *For each group* counters, 12 items that come in packages of 6 such as juice or bagels

Help students **multiply with 6**. Have each group show a package of 6 items. Ask: What multiplication sentence can you write? $1 \times 6 = 6$ Then have students show the second package. Ask them to write a multiplication sentence for the two packages. $2 \times 6 = 12$

Have groups continue arranging packages of 6 to show all of the 6's facts through 9×6. Check students' work.

KINESTHETIC

VISUAL/SPATIAL

Multistep and Strategy Problems

The following multistep or strategy problems are provided in Lesson 10.1:

Page	Item
195	38–39

Early Finishers

MATERIALS *For each pair* number cube labeled 4–9, p. TR65

Help **reinforce students' knowledge of multiplication patterns** by completing the following steps:

- Have one student toss a number cube.
- Ask the partner to multiply the number on the cube by 3 and then by 6 and to say each product aloud.
- Have partners reverse roles and repeat for 10 tosses.

Check students' work.

AUDITORY

VERBAL/LINGUISTIC

Intervention, *Skills 21–25*

The Harcourt Learning Site
www.harcourtschool.com

Lesson 10.1 Organizer

Objective To multiply with 6

1 INTRODUCE

QUICK REVIEW provides review of prerequisite skills.

WHY LEARN THIS? You can figure out the total number of items that come in several packages of 6, such as bagels or cans of juice. *Share the lesson objective with students.*

Guided Instruction

- *Have students read the Learn section.*
  What are the factors in the problem? 6 and 6
  Why is it important to add the two products of the smaller arrays? Possible answer: You have to combine the products of the smaller arrays to find the product of 6 × 6.

MODIFYING INSTRUCTION Have students use square tiles to model and break apart the array.

- *Discuss Another Way to multiply with 6.*
  REASONING Are the products of 3's facts half the products of 6's facts? Explain. Possible answer: Yes, since 3 is half of 6, the product of any number multiplied by 3 is half the product of that number multiplied by 6.
  What fact could you double to find 3 × 8? 3 × 4

LESSON 1

Multiply with 6

Quick Review

1. 5 × 3 = ■ 15
2. 5 × ■ = 25 5
3. 5 × 9 = ■ 45
4. ■ × 5 = 30 6
5. 40 = 5 × ■ 8

Learn

MARCHING MULTIPLES The school band has 6 rows, with 6 students in each row. How many students are in the band?

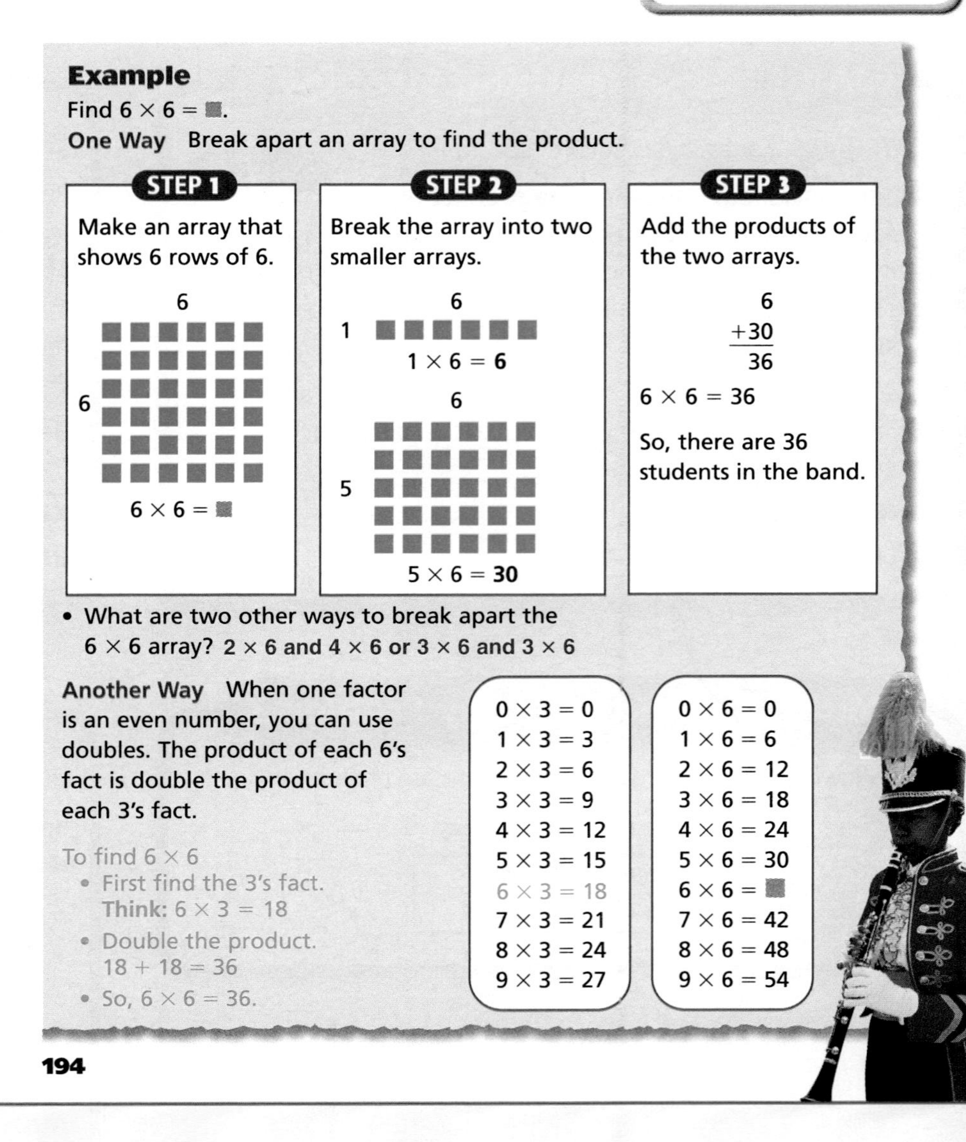

Example

Find 6 × 6 = ■.

One Way Break apart an array to find the product.

STEP 1 Make an array that shows 6 rows of 6.

6 × 6 = ■

STEP 2 Break the array into two smaller arrays.

1 × 6 = 6

5 × 6 = 30

STEP 3 Add the products of the two arrays.

$$\begin{array}{r} 6 \\ +30 \\ \hline 36 \end{array}$$

6 × 6 = 36

So, there are 36 students in the band.

- What are two other ways to break apart the 6 × 6 array? 2 × 6 and 4 × 6 or 3 × 6 and 3 × 6

Another Way When one factor is an even number, you can use doubles. The product of each 6's fact is double the product of each 3's fact.

To find 6 × 6

- First find the 3's fact. **Think:** 6 × 3 = 18
- Double the product. 18 + 18 = 36
- So, 6 × 6 = 36.

3's facts	6's facts
0 × 3 = 0	0 × 6 = 0
1 × 3 = 3	1 × 6 = 6
2 × 3 = 6	2 × 6 = 12
3 × 3 = 9	3 × 6 = 18
4 × 3 = 12	4 × 6 = 24
5 × 3 = 15	5 × 6 = 30
6 × 3 = 18	6 × 6 = ■
7 × 3 = 21	7 × 6 = 42
8 × 3 = 24	8 × 6 = 48
9 × 3 = 27	9 × 6 = 54

194

Reteach 10.1

Multiply with 6

An **array** shows objects in rows and columns.
An array can be used to show a multiplication sentence.

Show 3 × 6.

The array has 3 rows.
Each row has 6 circles.
3 × 6 = 18

You can break apart an array to help you find a product.

Add the products of the two smaller arrays.

3 × 3 = 9 3 × 3 = 9

9 + 9 = 18

Complete the number sentence to show how many in all.

1. 2 × 6 = 12
2. 4 × 6 = 24
3. 5 × 6 = 30

Draw the array for each exercise below.
Write the product. Check students' drawings.

4. 6 rows of 2 — 6 × 2 = 12
5. 1 row of 6 — 1 × 6 = 6
6. 6 rows of 4 — 6 × 4 = 24

RW52 Reteach

Practice 10.1

Multiply with 6

Find each product.

1. 4 × 6 = 24
2. 3 × 8 = 24
3. 6 × 2 = 12
4. 5 × 4 = 20
5. 8 × 6 = 48
6. 6 × 5 = 30
7. 7 × 6 = 42
8. 3 × 9 = 27
9. 6 × 6 = 36
10. 6 × 0 = 0
11. 1 × 6 = 6
12. 4 × 9 = 36
13. 9 × 6 = 54
14. 7 × 4 = 28
15. 6 × 3 = 18
16. 3 × 4 = 12

Complete each table.

	Multiply by 2.	
17.	5	10
18.	8	16
19.	9	18

	Multiply by 6.	
20.	3	18
21.	5	30
22.	8	48

	Multiply by 4.	
23.	4	16
24.	6	24
25.	8	32

Mixed Review

Solve.

26. 4,009 − 2,389 = 1,620
27. 387 + 906 = 1,293
28. \$62.85 − \$34.99 = \$27.86
29. 1,709 + 5,913 = 7,622
30. \$5.49 + \$3.89 = \$9.38
31. 7,360 − 2,507 = 4,853
32. 6,906 − 6,079 = 827
33. \$47.88 + \$ 6.13 = \$54.01

PW52 Practice

Check

1. Explain how you can use 8×3 to find 8×6.
$8 \times 3 = 24$; $24 + 24 = 48$; so, $8 \times 6 = 48$.

Find each product.

2. $7 \times 6 =$ ■ **42**
3. $4 \times 6 =$ ■ **24**
4. $5 \times 6 =$ ■ **30**

Practice and Problem Solving

Extra Practice, page 206, Set A

Find each product.

5. $3 \times 6 =$ ■ **18**
6. $6 \times 5 =$ ■ **30**
7. $5 \times 9 =$ ■ **45**
8. ■ $= 8 \times 6$ **48**
9. $4 \times 7 =$ ■ **28**
10. ■ $= 3 \times 4$ **12**
11. $4 \times 9 =$ ■ **36**
12. $6 \times 0 =$ ■ **0**
13. ■ $= 2 \times 9$ **18**
14. ■ $= 8 \times 4$ **32**
15. $3 \times 5 =$ ■ **15**
16. $9 \times 6 =$ ■ **54**
17. $5 \times 7 =$ **35**
18. $6 \times 7 =$ **42**
19. $8 \times 3 =$ **24**
20. $6 \times 1 =$ **6**
21. $5 \times 8 =$ **40**
22. $6 \times 6 =$ **36**

Copy and complete each table.

	Multiply by 3.		
23.	4	■	**12**
24.	6	■	**18**
25.	9	■	**27**

	Multiply by 5.		
26.	6	■	**30**
27.	3	■	**15**
28.	8	■	**40**

	Multiply by 6.		
29.	4	■	**24**
30.	7	■	**42**
31.	9	■	**54**

Complete.

32. ■ $\times 4 = 12$ **3**
33. ■ $\times 6 = 42$ **7**
34. $48 = 8 \times$ ■ **6**
35. ■ $\times 4 = 4 \times 3$ **3**
36. $3 \times 6 =$ ■ $\times 2$ **9**
37. ■ $\times 6 = 40 + 8$ **8**

38. ***FAST FACT*** • MUSIC A guitar has 6 strings. A banjo has 5 strings. How many strings are on 4 guitars and 2 banjos? **34 strings**

39. **Write About It** Draw arrays to show that 6×4 is the same as 1×4 plus 5×4. **Drawings should show a 6×4 array broken into a 1×4 array and a 5×4 array.**

Getting Ready for the EOG Test

40. Pet Palace has 7 fish tanks. Each tank has 6 fish. How many fish are in all of the tanks? **B**

A 30
B 42
C 45
D 47

North Carolina Standards 1.03 Develop fluency with multiplication from 1×1 to 12×12 and division to two-digit by one-digit numbers using: a) Strategies for multiplying and dividing numbers.

3 PRACTICE

Guided Practice

Do Check Exercises 1–4 with your students. Identify students who are having difficulty and choose appropriate lesson resources to provide assistance.

Independent Practice

Note that Exercises 38–39 are **multistep or strategy problems.** Assign Exercises 5–39.

4 ASSESS

Summarize the lesson by having students:

DISCUSS How would you make an array for 4×6? Make 4 rows of 6. **How would you make one for 6×4?** Make 6 rows of 4.

WRITE Describe how to find the product of 9×6 by either breaking apart an array or doubling a 3's fact. Possible answer: $9 \times 3 = 27$; $27 + 27 = 54$; $9 \times 6 = 54$

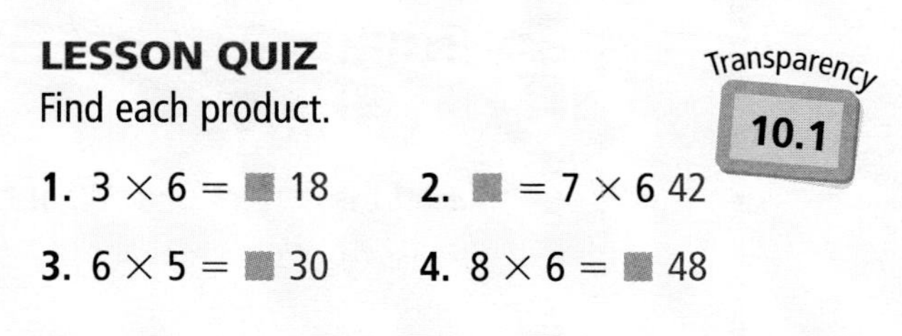

LESSON QUIZ
Find each product.

1. $3 \times 6 =$ ■ 18
2. ■ $= 7 \times 6$ 42
3. $6 \times 5 =$ ■ 30
4. $8 \times 6 =$ ■ 48

Challenge 10.1

The Array Game

Play alone or with a partner.

Materials: 10×10 grid for each player, two number cubes labeled 1–6, crayons or colored pencils

How to Play:

- Roll the number cubes. If you are playing with a partner, take turns rolling.
- Shade an array on your grid with a length and width that correspond to the numbers you rolled.
  Example: Suppose you roll ⚁ and ⚅.
  Shade an array that is 2 squares wide and 6 squares long or 6 squares wide and 2 squares long. You may place the array anywhere on your grid. Arrays cannot overlap.
- The object of the game is to shade as much of the grid as possible during the time that you have to play the game.

Score: Your score is the total number of squares that you have shaded when time runs out.

Game 1 Score is ______

Game 2 Score is ______

CW52 Challenge

Problem Solving 10.1

Multiply with 6

Understand → Plan → Solve → Check

Write the correct answer.

1. Every time the Kinner family plays tennis they need 3 cans of tennis balls. If there are 3 balls in each can, how many tennis balls do they need?
9 tennis balls

2. Name two smaller arrays you can use to find the product.
$6 \times 9 =$ ■
Possible answer: 3×9, 3×9; 54

3. Find the product.
$6 \times 7 =$ ■
42

4. Justin has 28 days of vacation every July. How many weeks is this?
4 weeks

Choose the letter of the correct answer.

5. Bill and Ted have 15 quarters. Bill has 3 more than Ted. How many does Ted have?
(A) 6
B 7
C 9
D 12

6. Which product is less than the product 5×7?
F 6×6
G 7×6
(H) 4×8
J 8×5

7. Ivy has a set of blocks that fit into a box only when they are in 6 rows of 8. How many blocks does she have?
A 14
B 24
C 36
(D) 48

8. Roderic had $6.13. He spent $1.89. How much does he have left?
F $8.02
G $5.76
H $4.34
(J) $4.24

9. **Write About It** Explain how you solved Problem 2.
Possible answer: I multiplied 3×9 and 3×9. Then I added the products: $27 + 27 = 54$.

PS52 Problem Solving

Lesson 10.2

Multiply with 8

Lesson Planning

Objective To multiply with 8

NCTM Standards
1. Number and Operations
2. Algebra
6. Problem Solving
7. Reasoning and Proof
8. Communication
9. Connections
10. Representation

Math Background

These ideas will help students understand how to multiply with 8.

- Break apart an array into two smaller arrays, and then add the two products.
- The product of each 8's fact is double the product of the corresponding 4's fact.

Warm-Up Resources

Number of the Day

Find the current time. What time was it $2\frac{1}{2}$ hours ago? Answers will vary.

Daily Facts Practice

Have students practice addition and subtraction facts by completing Set D of *Teacher's Resource Book*, p. TR90.

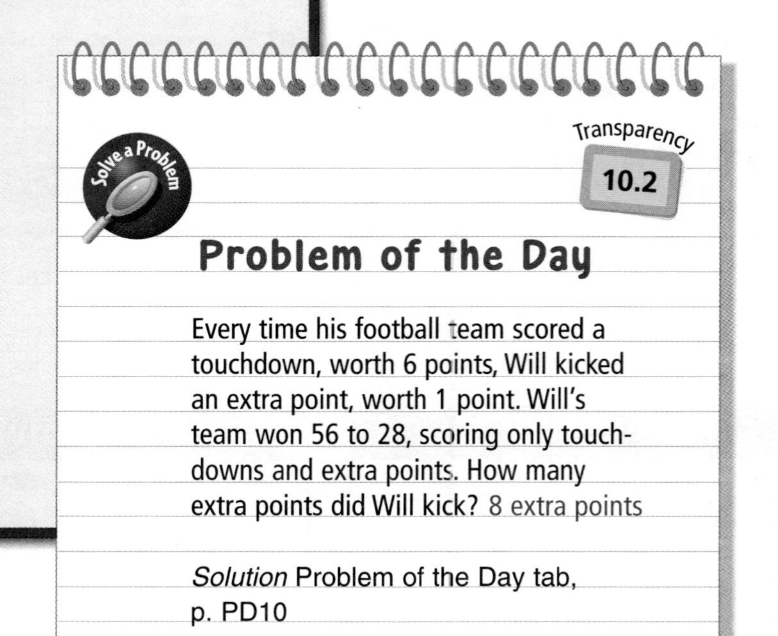

Transparency 10.2

Problem of the Day

Every time his football team scored a touchdown, worth 6 points, Will kicked an extra point, worth 1 point. Will's team won 56 to 28, scoring only touchdowns and extra points. How many extra points did Will kick? 8 extra points

Solution Problem of the Day tab, p. PD10

Intervention and Extension Resources

Alternative Teaching Strategy

MATERIALS *For each pair* a spinner with ten sections labeled 0–9, p. TR70

Help students **practice multiplying with 8** by using a spinner. Tell students that the numbers on the spinner represent groups of 8. For example, the number 2 stands for 2 groups of 8. Have one student spin the pointer and have the partner write the multiplication sentence for the number of groups shown. Have students reverse roles after 10 spins. Check students' work.

KINESTHETIC

BODILY/KINESTHETIC

Multistep and Strategy Problems

The following multistep or strategy problems are provided in Lesson 10.2:

Page	Item
197	36–37

Special Needs

MATERIALS *For each pair* a hundred chart, p. TR15

Help students **practice skip-counting by 8's**. Have students count by 8's on the hundred chart until they reach 72. Tell them to draw an X on each number that they land on. Then ask students the following questions:

- How many times did you skip-count by 8's to reach 72? 9 times What 8's fact is that? $9 \times 8 = 72$
- When you skip-count 6 times, what number do you land on? 48 What 8's fact is that? $6 \times 8 = 48$
- What do all the numbers with Xs have in common? Possible answers: They are all products of facts with 8; they are even numbers.

VISUAL

VISUAL/SPATIAL

Science Connection

Help students **reinforce the concept of multiplication with 8** by sharing information about spiders. Remind students that all spiders—from daddy longlegs spiders to tarantulas—have 8 legs.

Have students work in pairs to make a table. Have them title the first column *Number of Spiders* and list the numbers 1–8. Have students take turns completing the second column, which they have titled *Total Number of Legs.* Check students' work.

AUDITORY

VERBAL/LINGUISTIC

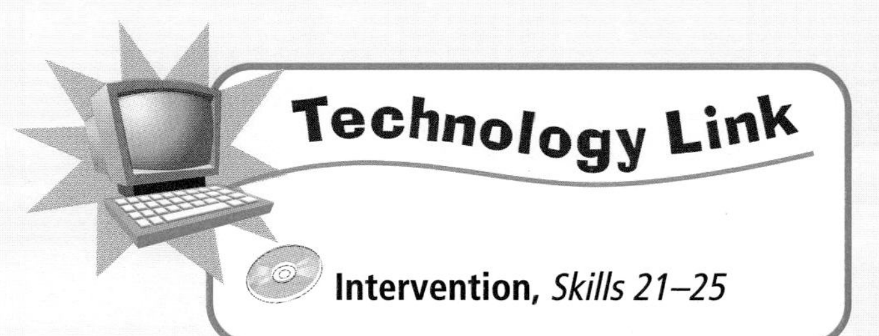

Lesson 10.2 Organizer

Objective To multiply with 8

QUICK REVIEW provides review of prerequisite skills.

WHY LEARN THIS? You can figure out the total number of items when there are 8 items in a group. *Share the lesson objective with students.*

2 TEACH

Guided Instruction

- *Ask students to read the Learn section.*
  What do the two factors, 6 and 8, represent in the problem? 6 represents the number of pies and 8 represents the number of peaches in each pie.
  How many other ways could you break the array? Possible answers: into 6 rows of 1 and 6 rows of 7; 6 rows of 2 and 6 rows of 6; 6 rows of 3 and 6 rows of 5
  Is there another way you could solve the problem? Explain. Possible answers: Yes; Draw 6 groups of 8 peaches; add $8 + 8 + 8 + 8 + 8 + 8$ to find the total number of peaches.

MODIFYING INSTRUCTION Have students use counters to model and break apart the array.

- *Discuss Another Way with students.*
  REASONING What fact could you double to find 10×8? Possible answers: 10×4; 5×8

LESSON 2

Multiply with 8

Quick Review

1. $30 = ■ \times 6$ 5
2. $2 \times 6 = ■$ 12
3. $6 \times 3 = ■$ 18
4. $6 \times ■ = 42$ 7
5. $7 \times 6 = ■$ 42

Learn

BAKE-OFF Mr. Lee baked 6 peach pies for the state fair. He used 8 peaches in each pie. How many peaches did he use in all?

Example

Find $6 \times 8 = ■$.

One Way Break apart an array to find the product.

STEP 1

Make an array that shows 6 rows of 8.

8

6

$6 \times 8 = ■$

STEP 2

Break the array into two smaller arrays.

4 4

6 6

$6 \times 4 = 24$ $6 \times 4 = 24$

STEP 3

Add the products of the two arrays.

$$\begin{array}{r} 24 \\ +24 \\ \hline 48 \end{array}$$

$6 \times 8 = 48$

So, Mr. Lee used 48 peaches in all.

- What are two other ways to break apart the 6×8 array? **Possible answers: 6×2 and 6×6; 6×3 and 6×5; 6×1 and 6×7**

Another Way When one factor is an even number, you can use doubles. The product of each 8's fact is double the product of each 4's fact.

4's facts	8's facts
$0 \times 4 = 0$	$0 \times 8 = 0$
$1 \times 4 = 4$	$1 \times 8 = 8$
$2 \times 4 = 8$	$2 \times 8 = 16$
$3 \times 4 = 12$	$3 \times 8 = 24$
$4 \times 4 = 16$	$4 \times 8 = 32$
$5 \times 4 = 20$	$5 \times 8 = 40$
$6 \times 4 = 24$	$6 \times 8 = ■$
$7 \times 4 = 28$	$7 \times 8 = 56$
$8 \times 4 = 32$	$8 \times 8 = 64$
$9 \times 4 = 36$	$9 \times 8 = 72$

To find 6×8
- First find the 4's fact.
  Think: $6 \times 4 = 24$
- Double the product.
  $24 + 24 = 48$
- So, $6 \times 8 = 48$.

196

Reteach 10.2

Multiply with 8

You can use the multiplication facts you know to learn new facts. The examples show two different ways to learn 6×8.

5×8 40
$+ 1 \times 8$ $+ 8$
6×8 = 48

3×8 24
$+ 3 \times 8$ $+ 24$
6×8 = 48

Complete the number sentences.

1. $3 \times 8 =$ 24
   $1 \times 8 =$ 8
   $4 \times 8 =$ 32
2. $2 \times 8 =$ 16
   $2 \times 8 =$ 16
   $4 \times 8 =$ 32

Find the product. You may use the facts that are given to help you.

3. $5 \times 8 = 40$, $1 \times 8 = 8$, $6 \times 8 =$ 48
4. $4 \times 8 = 32$, $1 \times 8 = 8$, $5 \times 8 =$ 40
5. $3 \times 8 = 24$, $3 \times 8 = 24$, $6 \times 8 =$ 48
6. $7 \times 8 = 56$, $2 \times 8 = 16$, $9 \times 8 =$ 72

Find the product for each pair of factors.

7. $8 \times 7 = 56$; $7 \times 8 = 56$
8. $8 \times 5 = 40$; $5 \times 8 = 40$
9. $8 \times 9 = 72$; $9 \times 8 = 72$
10. $8 \times 3 = 24$; $3 \times 8 = 24$
11. $4 \times 8 = 32$; $8 \times 4 = 32$
12. $0 \times 8 = 0$; $8 \times 0 = 0$
13. $6 \times 8 = 48$; $8 \times 6 = 48$
14. $2 \times 8 = 16$; $8 \times 2 = 16$

Reteach RW53

Practice 10.2

Multiply with 8

Find each product.

1. $4 \times 8 =$ 32
2. $7 \times 8 =$ 56
3. $4 \times 6 =$ 24
4. $3 \times 8 =$ 24
5. $8 \times 9 =$ 72
6. $7 \times 6 =$ 42
7. $8 \times 0 =$ 0
8. $2 \times 8 =$ 16
9. $5 \times 8 =$ 40
10. $7 \times 2 = 14$
11. $1 \times 8 = 8$
12. $8 \times 6 = 48$
13. $8 \times 8 = 64$

Complete each table.

	Multiply by 5.	
14.	7	35
15.	8	40
16.	9	45

	Multiply by 6.	
17.	4	24
18.	6	36
19.	7	42

	Multiply by 8.	
20.	5	40
21.	4	32
22.	7	56

Compare. Write <, >, or = in each ◯.

23. 8×4 (>) 2×6
24. 8×3 (<) 6×8
25. 7×0 (=) 8×0
26. 4×5 (<) 7×6
27. 8×9 (>) 3×4
28. 5×5 (<) 8×8

Mixed Review

Solve.

29. $32 + 44 + 81 =$ 157
30. $56 + 14 + 39 =$ 109
31. $82 + 8 + 18 =$ 108
32. $28 + 27 + 42 =$ 97
33. $4{,}290 - 3{,}735 =$ 555
34. $8{,}802 - 6{,}529 =$ 2,273

Practice PW53

Check

1. **Explain** how you can use $4 \times 5 = 20$ to find 8×5.
Possible answer: Double 4×5 to find 8×5; $4 \times 5 = 20$, so $8 \times 5 = 40$.

Find each product.

2. $4 \times 8 = ■$ **32**
3. $7 \times 8 = ■$ **56**
4. $6 \times 8 = ■$ **48**
5. $8 \times 8 = ■$ **64**

Practice and Problem Solving

Extra Practice, page 206, Set B

Find each product.

6. $5 \times 4 = ■$ **20**
7. $8 \times 3 = ■$ **24**
8. $9 \times 8 = ■$ **72**
9. $7 \times 4 = ■$ **28**
10. $8 \times 6 = ■$ **48**
11. $3 \times 4 = ■$ **12**
12. $7 \times 5 = ■$ **35**
13. $8 \times 8 = ■$ **64**
14. $2 \times 9 = ■$ **18**
15. $7 \times 8 = ■$ **56**
16. $5 \times 9 = ■$ **45**
17. $6 \times 6 = ■$ **36**
18. 4×8 = **32**
19. 6×7 = **42**
20. 9×6 = **54**
21. 4×9 = **36**
22. 3×7 = **21**
23. 6×8 = **48**

Copy and complete each table.

	Multiply by 4.		
24.	5	■	**20**
25.	6	■	**24**
26.	8	■	**32**

	Multiply by 6.		
27.	7	■	**42**
28.	9	■	**54**
29.	8	■	**48**

	Multiply by 8.		
30.	9	■	**72**
31.	6	■	**48**
32.	8	■	**64**

Compare. Write <, >, or = for each ●.

33. 2×3 ● 2×4 **<**
34. 5×8 ● 8×5 **=**
35. 5×5 ● 4×6 **>**

36. **ALGEBRA** Hal has 7 bags of 8 green apples and 1 bag of red apples. He has 60 apples in all. How many red apples does he have?
4 red apples

37. **What's the Error?** Robin says, "I can find 8×6 by thinking of $3 \times 6 = 18$ and doubling it."
She should think of $4 \times 6 = 24$ or $3 \times 8 = 24$ and double it.

Getting Ready for the EOG Test

38. Mr. Rossini orders 3 pizzas. Each pizza has 8 slices. How many slices are there in all? **A**

A 24 B 21 C 18 D 11

39. The Perfect Pizza Restaurant has 5 tables. Each table has 8 seats. How many seats are there in all? **A**

A 40 B 42 C 45 D 48

North Carolina Standards 1.03 Develop fluency with multiplication from 1×1 to 12×12 and division to two-digit by one-digit numbers using: a) Strategies for multiplying and dividing numbers.

Challenge 10.2

Number Patterns

A **multiple** is a number that is the product of a given number and another whole number. Some of the multiples of 3 are: 3, 6, 9, and 12.

1. On the number chart below, put a triangle around the numbers that are multiples of 4.
Check students' charts.
2. Circle all the numbers that are multiples of 6.
Check students' charts.
3. Shade all the numbers that are multiples of 8.
Check students' charts.
4. List the numbers that have triangles around them and are also circled and shaded. **24, 48, 72**
5. Are there any shaded numbers that do not have triangles around them? **no**

1	2	3	4	5	6	7	8	9	10
11	12	13	14	15	16	17	18	19	20
21	22	23	24	25	26	27	28	29	30
31	32	33	34	35	36	37	38	39	40
41	42	43	44	45	46	47	48	49	50
51	52	53	54	55	56	57	58	59	60
61	62	63	64	65	66	67	68	69	70
71	72	73	74	75	76	77	78	79	80

Complete the number sentences.

6. **3** $\times 8 = 24$
7. **6** $\times 8 = 48$
8. **4** $\times 8 = 32$
9. **4** $\times 6 = 24$
10. **8** $\times 6 = 48$
11. **5** $\times 6 = 30$

Challenge CW53

Problem Solving 10.2

Multiply with 8

Understand → Plan → Solve → Check

Write the correct answer.

1. Name two smaller arrays you can use to find the product.
$8 \times 6 = ■$
Possible answer: 4×6, 4×6; 48

2. Find the product.
$7 \times 5 = ■$
35

3. Every time the Sims family eats together they need 8 plates. If they eat together 3 times in a day, how many plates will they use?
24 plates

4. Ed made 4 baskets each game for the first 4 games of the season. How many baskets is that in all?
16 baskets

Choose the letter of the correct answer.

5. Which number sentence would *not* help you find the product 5×8?
A $5 \times 4 = 20$
(B) $4 \times 9 = 36$
C $5 \times 5 = 25$
D $3 \times 8 = 24$

6. Which number sentence can you use to show 6 boxes with 1 sweater in each box?
F $6 \times 0 = 0$
G $6 + 1 = 7$
H $2 \times 6 = 12$
(J) $6 \times 1 = 6$

7. Lee and Carol bought 13 gifts altogether. Lee bought one more than Carol did. How many gifts did Carol buy?
A 8
B 7
(C) 6
D 5

8. Victor had \$5.75. He earned \$2.15 more. How much does he have now?
F \$5.90
(G) \$7.90
H \$7.95
J \$10.05

9. **Write About It** Explain how you solved Problem 4.
Possible answer: I multiplied 4×4, so my answer is 16 baskets.

Problem Solving PS53

3 PRACTICE

Guided Practice

Do Check Exercises 1–5 with your students. Identify students who are having difficulty and choose appropriate lesson resources to provide assistance.

Independent Practice

Note that Exercises 36–37 are **multistep or strategy problems.** Assign Exercises 6–37.

SCAFFOLDED INSTRUCTION Use the prompts on Transparency 10 to guide instruction for the multistep or strategy problem in Exercise 36.

ALGEBRAIC THINKING Discuss the operations and number sentences students may use to solve Exercise 36.

4 ASSESS

Summarize the lesson by having students:

DISCUSS How does an array show a multiplication fact? Possible answer: The number of rows represents one factor, and the number of columns represents the other factor. The total number is the product.

WRITE Explain how you would multiply 7×8. Possible answer: I would double the product of a 4's fact that I already know. $7 \times 4 = 28$, $28 + 28 = 56$, so $7 \times 8 = 56$.

LESSON QUIZ

Transparency 10.2

Find each product.

1. $5 \times 8 = ■$ 40
2. $9 \times 8 = ■$ 72
3. 8×8 = 64
4. 8×6 = 48

Problem Solving Skill
Use a Pictograph

Lesson Planning

Objective To use the problem solving skill *use a pictograph* to solve problems

Lesson Resources Reading Transparency 10; Intervention • Problem Solving, Strategy/Skill 10

NCTM Standards
1. Number and Operations
2. Algebra
5. Data Analysis and Probability
6. Problem Solving
10. Representation

Math Background

These ideas will help students understand how to use a pictograph.

- Pictographs organize and display data by using a title, labels, a key, and picture symbols.
- Pictographs use pictures as symbols to represent information. The pictures may represent one unit or multiple units.
- You can use multiplication to find out how many each row of symbols represents.

Warm-Up Resources

Number of the Day

The number of the day is the number of hours in one day. Double this number. Then write a multiplication sentence using that number as the product. 24 hours; 48; Possible answers: $6 \times 8 = 48$ or $8 \times 6 = 48$

Daily Facts Practice

Have students practice subtraction facts by completing Set E of *Teacher's Resource Book,* p. TR90.

Solve a Problem

Transparency 10.3

Problem of the Day

Jason watered the plants in his vegetable garden every fourth day. If he began on March 3, how many times did he water the plants during the month of March? 8 times

Solution Problem of the Day tab, p. PD10

Intervention and Extension Resources

Alternative Teaching Strategy

To help students **use a pictograph**, draw a pictograph with the following information: School Store Supplies; pencils, 50; notebooks, 15; construction paper, 35; erasers, 25; markers, 20. Choose a symbol to equal 5 objects. Include a key. Have students practice skip-counting by 5's. Then ask students to generate questions about the pictograph. Guide them to find how many in all there are of a certain object, and how many of each item in the graph there are.

VISUAL

VERBAL/LINGUISTIC, LOGICAL/MATHEMATICAL

Reading Strategy

Use Graphic Aids Explain that sometimes information is presented in a graph, table, or chart. Draw a pictograph with the following information: School Store Supplies; pens, 24; pencil holders, 16; folders, 20; pencil symbol = 2. Have students practice reading the graph. For students having trouble, suggest they use a straightedge such as a ruler to guide their reading across the line of information.

Ask:

What kind of information can you find on this graph? kinds and numbers of school supplies

How do you know? The title tells what the graph is about.

How many folders are available? 20 folders

How did you find out? I read straight across the line, counted the number of symbols, and multiplied that number by 2.

Transparency 10 **Reading Transparency 10**

Multistep and Strategy Problems

The following multistep or strategy problems are provided in Lesson 10.3:

Page	Item
199	6–9

Writing in Mathematics

MATERIALS *For each student* paper and pencil

Have students look at any of the graphs in the lesson and write 3 additional questions about the information. Guide students to ask questions that compare quantities, find the totals, or ask how to use and interpret the symbols. Have students exchange questions and find the answers.

VISUAL

VERBAL/LINGUISTIC

Science Connection

Put this pictograph on the board.

NASA SPACE MISSIONS	
Mercury Program	✷ ✷ ✷
Gemini Program	✷ ✷ ✷ ✷ ✷ ✷
Apollo Program	✷ ✷ ✷ ✷ ✷ ✷ ✷ ✷ (half ✷)

Key: Each ✷ = 2 missions.

Ask:

How many Apollo missions were there? 17 missions

If there were 1 more Gemini mission, how would you show it on the graph? use $\frac{1}{2}$ symbol

Have students look up information about one of the space missions and make a pictograph using the information.

VISUAL

LOGICAL/MATHEMATICAL

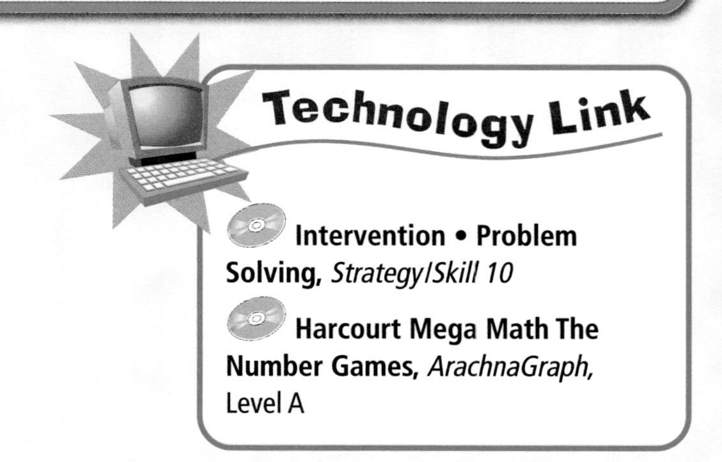

Intervention • Problem Solving, *Strategy/Skill 10*

Harcourt Mega Math The Number Games, *ArachnaGraph,* Level A

Lesson 10.3 Organizer

Objective To use the problem solving skill *use a pictograph* to solve problems

Lesson Resources Reading Transparency 10; Intervention • Problem Solving, Strategy/Skill 10

1 INTRODUCE

Quick Review provides review of prerequisite skills.

Why Learn This? You can use this skill to read and understand graphs you see in magazines and newspapers. *Share the lesson objective with students.*

2 TEACH

Guided Instruction

- *Introduce the skill by having students study the graph.*
  Reasoning What information is found on this pictograph? The graph shows the number of named moons the outer planets have.
  What does the phrase "Named Moons" in the title mean? It means the moons that have been given names so far.
  How many named moons does Uranus have? 20 named moons
  Reasoning If the key were 1 symbol equals 5 moons, how many symbols would Uranus have? 4 symbols
- *Look at the multiplication sentence.*
  How can you use multiplication instead of skip-counting to find the number of moons Neptune has? Multiply: $4 \times 2 = 8$; Neptune has 8 named moons.

LESSON 3

Problem Solving Skill
Use a Pictograph

Quick Review

1. $6 \times 4 = ■$ 24
2. $■ = 9 \times 2$ 18
3. $7 \times 2 = ■$ 14
4. $8 \times 4 = ■$ 32
5. $7 \times ■ = 28$ 4

OUTER PLANETS Madison read in her science book that the five planets farthest from the sun are called the outer planets. How many named moons does Saturn have?

OUTER PLANETS: NUMBER OF NAMED MOONS	
Jupiter	● ● ● ● ● ● ● ●
Saturn	● ● ● ● ● ● ● ● ●
Uranus	● ● ● ● ● ● ● ● ● ●
Neptune	● ● ● ●
Pluto	◐
Key: Each ● = 2 moons.	

Look at the pictograph. Saturn has 9 symbols.

You can use multiplication to find the number of named moons Saturn has.

9	×	2	=	18
factor		factor		product
number of symbols		each symbol stands for 2 moons		number of Saturn's named moons

Talk About It

- The number of moons Pluto has is shown with $\frac{1}{2}$ of a symbol. How many named moons does Pluto have? **one moon**
- How would you find the number of named moons Jupiter has? Multiply: $8 \times 2 = 16$.
- If Neptune had 11 named moons, how many symbols would be needed in all? **$5\frac{1}{2}$ symbols**

REASONING Why do you think a key of 2 was used on this pictograph? **Possible answer: Three of the numbers needed are 8, 16, and 18. All are multiples of 2. The number of moons for each planet was less than 20, so 2 was a good choice.**

Reteach 10.3

Problem Solving Skill

Use a Pictograph

A **pictograph** uses pictures or symbols to show information.

Joey surveyed students to find out what their favorite kind of pizza is. The results are shown in the pictograph. How many people named sausage pizza?

FAVORITE KINDS OF PIZZA	
Cheese	웃 웃
Pepperoni	웃 웃 웃 웃 웃 웃
Sausage	웃 웃 웃 ½
Pineapple	웃 ½
Key: Each 웃 = 4 people	

Step 1 Locate Sausage in the pictograph. Count the symbols next to it. There are $3\frac{1}{2}$ symbols.

Step 2 Look at the key. It shows that each symbol in the graph stands for 4 people.

Step 3 Multiply the whole number of symbols for Sausage (3) times the number of people each symbol stands for (4).
$3 \times 4 = 12$ people

Step 4 Figure out how many people half of a symbol stands for.
$\frac{1}{2}$ of $4 = 2$ people

Step 5 Add to find how many people altogether are represented by $3\frac{1}{2}$ symbols.
$12 + 2 = 14$ people

14 people named sausage pizza.

For 1–4, use the pictograph above.

1. How many people named cheese pizza? 8 people
2. What kind of pizza was named most often? pepperoni
   How do you know?
   Possible answer: Pepperoni has more symbols than any other kind of pizza.
3. How many people named sausage or pineapple? 20 people
4. How many more people named pepperoni than named sausage?
   10 people

RW54 Reteach

Practice 10.3

Problem Solving Skill

Use a Pictograph

For 1–3, use the pictograph.

Third-Graders at Myra's School	
Mr. Adam's Class	웃 웃 웃 웃 웃 웃
Miss Green's Class	웃 웃 웃 웃 웃
Mrs. Ortez's Class	웃 웃 웃 웃 웃 ½
Mr. Hill's Class	웃 웃 웃 웃 ½
Key: Each 웃 = 4 students.	

1. Explain how to use this pictograph to find which class has the fewest students. How many students are in this class?
   Possible answer: Find the class with the fewest symbols. Mr. Hill's class has $4\frac{1}{2}$. Multiply. $4 \times 4 = 16$. Then add 2. 18 students
2. How many students are in Mrs. Ortez's class?
   22 students
3. How many more students are in Mr. Adam's class than are in Mr. Hill's class?
   6 more students

For 4–5, use the pictograph.

Animals in Pet Parade	
Birds	½
Cats	▭ ▭
Dogs	▭ ▭ ▭ ▭ ▭
Horses	▭ ▭ ▭ ½
Key: Each ▭ = 6 animals.	

4. How many animals are in the parade?
   A 11
   B 64
   (C) 66
   D 72
5. Which numbers represented on the pictograph are multiples of 6?
   F 21 and 30
   (G) 12 and 30
   H 12, 21, and 30
   J 3, 12, and 30

Mixed Review

Write how many there are in all.

6. 3 groups of 8 — 24
7. 7 groups of 4 — 28
8. 3 groups of 5 — 15

PW54 Practice

1. Possible answer: Find the planet with the most symbols: Neptune has $9\frac{1}{2}$. Multiply $9 \times 2 = 18$. Then add 1. 19 Earth hours

Problem Solving Practice

USE DATA For 1–3, use the pictograph.

PLANETS: LENGTH OF DAY	
Jupiter	☼☼☼☼☼
Saturn	☼☼☼☼☼
Uranus	☼☼☼☼☼☼☼☼◖
Neptune	☼☼☼☼☼☼☼☼☼◖

Key: Each ☼ = 2 Earth hours.

1. Explain how to use this pictograph to find which of these planets has the longest day. How many Earth hours long is it? See above.
2. How many Earth hours are in a day on Uranus? 17 Earth hours
3. How much longer is a day on Neptune than a day on Jupiter? 9 Earth hours

USE DATA For 4–5, use the pictograph.

NEW SCIENCE BOOKS IN THE LIBRARY	
Solar System	📖📖📖📖📖📖
Plants	📖📖📖📖▮
Mammals	📖📖📖📖📖📖📖
Reptiles	📖📖📖

Key: Each 📖 = 4 books.

4. How many new science books are in the library? C
   A 81 C 82
   B 41 D 72
5. Which three numbers represented on the pictograph are multiples of 4? G
   F 12, 18, 24 H 18, 24, 28
   G 12, 24, 28 J 12, 18, 28

Mixed Applications

USE DATA For 6–9, use the table.

SCIENCE CENTER	
Activity	**Tickets**
Admission	5
Space exhibits	3
Dinosaur exhibits	4
Animal exhibits	2

6. How many tickets do Brandon and his 3 friends need in all for admission to the Science Center? 20 tickets
7. Brandon and his 3 friends used 28 tickets. They used 4 more tickets for dinosaur exhibits than for space exhibits. How many tickets did they use for each? 16 for Dinosaur exhibits; 12 for space exhibits
8. Abigail's father gave her 14 tickets. She used tickets for admission and the space exhibits. How many tickets did she have left? $14 - 8 = 6$; 6 tickets left
9. **Write a problem** about tickets used at the Science Center in which the product is greater than 15 and is a multiple of 3. Possible problem: Hillary and 5 friends saw the dinosaur exhibits. How many tickets did they use? 24 tickets

North Carolina Standards 1.03 Develop fluency with multiplication from 1×1 to 12×12 and division up to two-digit by one-digit numbers using: a) Strategies for multiplying and dividing numbers. *also* 4.01

Challenge 10.3

Square Time

A **square array** is an array that is the same number of squares long as it is wide.

Complete the table, listing the sizes and products of some square arrays.

Square Arrays		
Length	Width	Total Squares
1	1	1
2	2	4
3	3	9
4	4	16
5	5	25
6	6	36
7	7	49
8	8	64

Use the table to solve. See students' work.

1. Jay and Barb each made a square array. Barb used more squares than Jay. Together they used 100 squares. How big was each array? Jay's was 6×6; Barb's was 8×8.
2. Tim, Mark, Dave, and Paul each made a square array. Together they used 100 squares. How big was each array? Possible answer: Each made a 5×5 square.
3. Sharon, Gayle, Joy, and Bev each made a square array. Joy and Bev used 22 more squares than Sharon and Gayle. Altogether the 4 girls used 122 squares. How big was each array? Joy and Bev each made a 6×6 array; Sharon and Gayle each made a 5×5 array.

CW54 Challenge

Reading Strategy 10.3

Paraphrase Understand → Plan → Solve → Check

Sometimes it is helpful to **paraphrase**, or tell again in your own words, what a problem is asking you to do. This helps you to understand the problem better.

VOCABULARY paraphrase

Read the following problem.

► Mr. Wilson will let Jamie display her antique doll house furniture along with his model planes at the model show. Her space is 4 floor tiles long and has a total of 12 floor tiles. How wide is it?

1. Use your own words to paraphrase the problem. Answers will vary.
2. Solve the problem. Possible answer: An array of 12 floor tiles with 4 columns would have 3 rows; it is 3 tiles wide.
3. Describe the problem solving strategy you used. Possible answer: I drew a picture using squares to make an array of 12.

Paraphrase the problem. Then solve.

4. Mrs. Gomez asked Jeff to paint an array of 40 daisies on her flower box. Jeff thinks that 5 rows of daisies will fit on the flower box. How many daisies would he have to put in each row? Answers will vary; 8 daisies
5. Dave and Lisa have their own garden. This year they bought 56 strawberry plants. They planted 8 equal rows of strawberry plants. How many plants are in each row? Answers will vary; 7 strawberry plants

PS54 Reading Strategy

3 PRACTICE

Guided Practice

Do Problem Solving Practice Exercises 1–5 with your students. Identify students who are having difficulty and choose appropriate lesson resources to provide assistance.

Independent Practice

Note that Exercises 6–9 are multistep or strategy problems. Assign Exercises 6–9.

Summarize the lesson by having students:

DISCUSS How can you use the pictograph on the top of page 199 to find how long a day on Saturn is? Multiply the 5 symbols times 2; $5 \times 2 = 10$ hours.

What information is found on the second pictograph on page 199? the kinds of new science books in the library

WRITE If the library bought 10 books on insects, how could you add that information to the pictograph? Possible answer: in a new row, write a label for insects and draw $2\frac{1}{2}$ book symbols to stand for 10 books.

LESSON QUIZ

Transparency 10.3

For 1–3, use the pictograph.

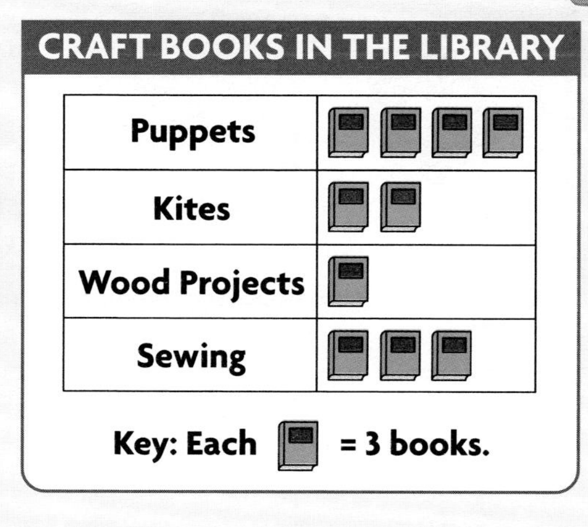

1. How many books about making puppets are there? 12 books
2. How many more books about sewing are there than books about wood projects? 6 more sewing books
3. How many books about kites and wood projects are there altogether? 9 books

Multiply with 7

Lesson Planning

Objective To multiply with 7

NCTM Standards

1. Number and Operations
2. Algebra
6. Problem Solving
7. Reasoning and Proof
8. Communication
9. Connections
10. Representation

Math Background

These ideas will help students understand how to multiply with 7.

- Break apart an array into two smaller arrays, and then add the two products.
- Skip-count by 5's and skip-count by 2's, and then add the two products.

Warm-Up Resources

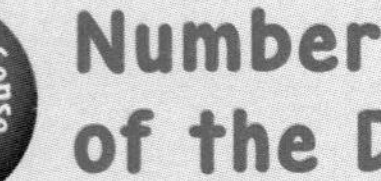

Number of the Day

Take the number of nickels you can exchange for 1 quarter and multiply it by 6. Write the value of the nickels after the multiplication. $1.50

Daily Facts Practice

Have students practice subtraction facts by completing Set F of *Teacher's Resource Book*, p. TR90.

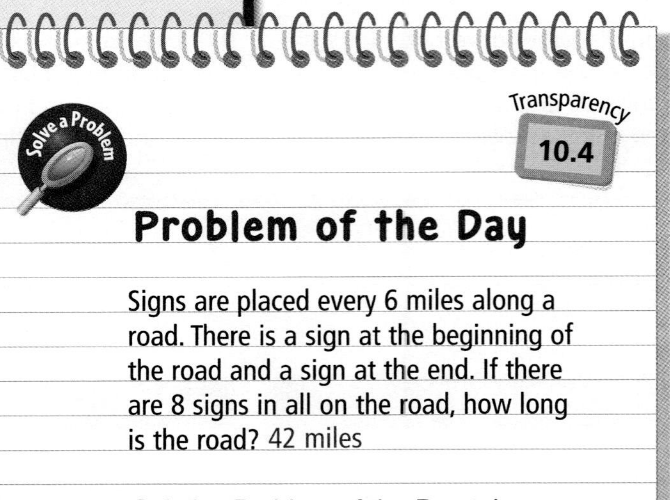

Problem of the Day

Signs are placed every 6 miles along a road. There is a sign at the beginning of the road and a sign at the end. If there are 8 signs in all on the road, how long is the road? 42 miles

Solution Problem of the Day tab, p. PD10

Intervention and Extension Resources

Alternative Teaching Strategy

MATERIALS *For each pair* counters, 10 index cards with 7's facts (0–9) on the front and answers on the back

Help students **model multiplication with 7's facts.**

- Have one student select a card and show it to his or her partner.
- The partner will then find the product by arranging the counters in an array to show the multiplication fact on the card.
- The first student checks the answer.
- Have students reverse roles and continue until they have used all of the cards. Check students' work.

KINESTHETIC

VISUAL/SPATIAL

ESOL/ESL

MATERIALS *For each pair* a calendar for 2 months

Help students **reinforce multiplication with 7**.

- Review with students the number of days in a week. 7 days
- Ask students to name the number of days in 2 weeks, 4 weeks, and 8 weeks and to show examples of each set of weeks on the calendar. 14, 28, 56
- Have students write a multiplication sentence for each set of weeks. $2 \times 7 = 14$; $4 \times 7 = 28$; $8 \times 7 = 56$

VISUAL

VERBAL/LINGUISTIC

Multistep and Strategy Problems

The following multistep or strategy problems are provided in Lesson 10.4:

Page	Item
201	36, 38

Early Finishers

MATERIALS *For each student* square tiles

Challenge students to **practice multiplication with 7** by using square tiles to make arrays for 7×7, 8×7, and 9×7. Ask students to

- break each array into three smaller arrays.
- write three multiplication sentences.
- add the products to solve.

Check students' work.

KINESTHETIC

BODILY/KINESTHETIC

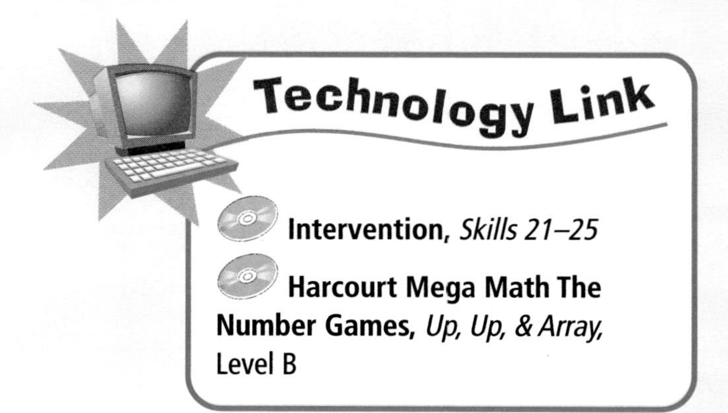

Intervention, *Skills 21–25*

Harcourt Mega Math The Number Games, *Up, Up, & Array,* Level B

Lesson 10.4 Organizer

Objective To multiply with 7

1 INTRODUCE

QUICK REVIEW provides review of prerequisite skills.

WHY LEARN THIS? You can find the number of days when you know the number of weeks. *Share the lesson objective with students.*

2 TEACH

Guided Instruction

- *Ask students to read the Learn section.*
  In Step 1, what do the factors represent? 8: the number of weeks; 7: there are 7 days in a week.
  In Step 2, what do you notice about the two smaller arrays? Possible answer: They use multiplication facts we already know.
  Can you make an array to show 0×7? Explain. No; 0×7 represents 0 rows of 7.
- *Discuss the first Check question.*
  REASONING How can you find 10×7? Possible answer: You know $5 \times 7 = 35$; $35 + 35 = 70$; so, $10 \times 7 = 70$

MODIFYING INSTRUCTION Have students use square tiles to model and break apart the array.

3 PRACTICE

Guided Practice

Do Check Exercises 1–5 with your students. Identify students who are having difficulty and choose appropriate lesson resources to provide assistance.

LESSON 4

Multiply with 7

Quick Review

1. $8 \times 5 = ■$ 40
2. $6 \times 4 = ■$ 24
3. $3 \times 8 = ■$ 24
4. $2 \times 6 = ■$ 12
5. $5 \times 6 = ■$ 30

Learn

PARADE! PARADE! Students built a float for a parade. They worked on the float for 8 weeks. How many days did they work on the float?

Example

Find $8 \times 7 = ■$.
Break apart an array to find the product.

STEP 1

Make an array that shows 8 rows of 7.

7

8

$8 \times 7 = ■$

STEP 2

Break the array into two smaller arrays.

3 4

8 8

$8 \times 3 = \mathbf{24}$ $8 \times 4 = \mathbf{32}$

STEP 3

Add the products of the two arrays.

$$\begin{array}{r} 24 \\ +32 \\ \hline 56 \end{array}$$

$8 \times 7 = 56$

So, the students worked on the float for 56 days.

- What are two other ways to break apart the 8×7 array?

Possible answers: 8×1 and 8×6; 8×2 and 8×5

Check

1. **Explain** how you could break apart 7×5 into two arrays to help you find the product. **Possible answer: I can make arrays to show $4 \times 5 = 20$ and $3 \times 5 = 15$ and then find $20 + 15 = 35$**

Technology Link
More Practice: Harcourt Mega Math The Number Games, *Up, Up, and Array,* Level B

Find each product.

2. $4 \times 7 = ■$ **28**
3. $0 \times 7 = ■$ **0**
4. $8 \times 7 = ■$ **56**
5. $6 \times 7 = ■$ **42**

200

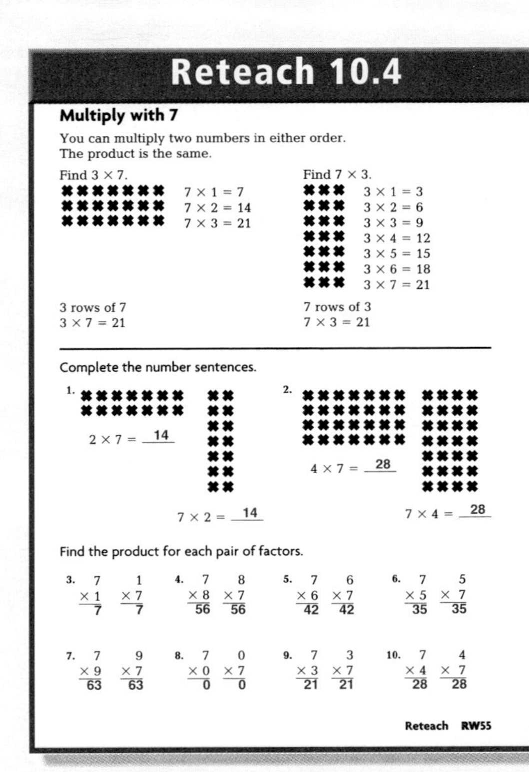

Reteach 10.4

Multiply with 7

You can multiply two numbers in either order.
The product is the same.

Find 3×7.

$7 \times 1 = 7$
$7 \times 2 = 14$
$7 \times 3 = 21$

3 rows of 7
$3 \times 7 = 21$

Find 7×3.

$3 \times 1 = 3$
$3 \times 2 = 6$
$3 \times 3 = 9$
$3 \times 4 = 12$
$3 \times 5 = 15$
$3 \times 6 = 18$
$3 \times 7 = 21$

7 rows of 3
$7 \times 3 = 21$

Complete the number sentences.

1. $2 \times 7 =$ **14** $7 \times 2 =$ **14**
2. $4 \times 7 =$ **28** $7 \times 4 =$ **28**

Find the product for each pair of factors.

3. $7 \times 1 = \mathbf{7}$; $1 \times 7 = \mathbf{7}$
4. $7 \times 8 = \mathbf{56}$; $8 \times 7 = \mathbf{56}$
5. $7 \times 6 = \mathbf{42}$; $6 \times 7 = \mathbf{42}$
6. $7 \times 5 = \mathbf{35}$; $5 \times 7 = \mathbf{35}$
7. $7 \times 9 = \mathbf{63}$; $9 \times 7 = \mathbf{63}$
8. $7 \times 0 = \mathbf{0}$; $0 \times 7 = \mathbf{0}$
9. $7 \times 3 = \mathbf{21}$; $3 \times 7 = \mathbf{21}$
10. $7 \times 4 = \mathbf{28}$; $4 \times 7 = \mathbf{28}$

Reteach RW55

Practice 10.4

Multiply with 7

Find each procuct.

1. $7 \times 6 =$ **42**
2. $5 \times 8 =$ **40**
3. $3 \times 7 =$ **21**
4. $7 \times 4 =$ **28**
5. $6 \times 7 =$ **42**
6. $4 \times 8 =$ **32**
7. $9 \times 7 =$ **63**
8. $5 \times 1 =$ **5**
9. $7 \times 0 =$ **0**
10. $1 \times 7 =$ **7**
11. $7 \times 5 =$ **35**
12. $7 \times 8 =$ **56**

Complete each table.

	Multiply by 6.	
13.	3	18
14.	7	42
15.	8	48

	Multiply by 7.	
16.	7	49
17.	9	63
18.	4	28

	Multiply by 8.	
19.	5	40
20.	9	72
21.	8	64

Complete.

22. $9 \times 7 =$ **30** $+ 33$
23. $7 \times$ **3** $= 34 - 13$
24. **2** $\times 7 = 7 + 7$

Mixed Review

Write the value of the underlined digit.

25. 53,009 **3,000**
26. 6,842 **40**
27. 92,106 **90,000**
28. 4,222 **200**
29. 11,001 **1,000**
30. 6,681 **80**

Round to the nearest hundred.

31. 5,349 **5,300**
32. 478 **500**
33. 14,780 **14,800**
34. 26,318 **26 300**
35. 1,159 **1,200**
36. 879 **900**

Subtract 475 from each number.

37. 690 **215**
38. 4,330 **3,855**
39. 2,065 **1,590**

Practice PW55

Practice and Problem Solving

Extra Practice, page 206, Set C

Find each product.

6. $2 \times 7 = \blacksquare$ 14
7. $2 \times 9 = \blacksquare$ 18
8. $3 \times 7 = \blacksquare$ 21
9. $6 \times 6 = \blacksquare$ 36
10. $7 \times 6 = \blacksquare$ 42
11. $\blacksquare = 6 \times 9$ 54
12. $\blacksquare = 5 \times 9$ 45
13. $7 \times 7 = \blacksquare$ 49
14. $4 \times 7 = \blacksquare$ 28
15. $3 \times 6 = \blacksquare$ 18
16. $\blacksquare = 4 \times 9$ 36
17. $\blacksquare = 5 \times 5$ 25
18. 1×7 = 7
19. 7×9 = 63
20. 6×8 = 48
21. 8×8 = 64
22. 4×5 = 20
23. 8×7 = 56

Copy and complete each table.

	Multiply by 6.		
24.	4	■	24
25.	6	■	36
26.	9	■	54

	Multiply by 7.		
27.	6	■	42
28.	5	■	35
29.	8	■	56

	Multiply by 8.		
30.	6	■	48
31.	7	■	56
32.	9	■	72

Complete.

33. $7 \times 6 = \blacksquare + 21$ 21
34. $\blacksquare \times 4 = 30 - 2$ 7
35. $8 + 6 = 7 \times \blacksquare$ 2

36. **REASONING** How can you tell without multiplying that 7×9 is less than 9×8? **7 × 9 is one less group of 9 than 8 × 9.**

37. **What's the Question?** Joanna has 9 boxes of pears. She has 72 pears in all. The answer is 8 pears. **How many pears are in each box?**

38. Shayla was on vacation for 7 weeks. She spent 3 weeks at band camp and the rest of the time at home. How many days did she spend at home? **28 days**

39. Break apart the array. Then write the multiplication fact. (array: 4 rows of 7) **Possible answer: 2 × 4 and 5 × 4 arrays; 8 + 20 = 28; 7 × 4 = 28**

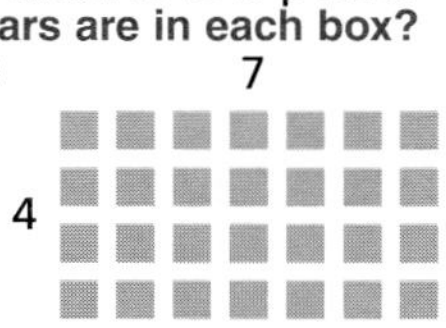

40. **ALGEBRA** Find a one-digit number to make this number sentence true. $\blacksquare \times 7 + 10 > 67 - 9$ **Possible answers: 7, 8, 9**

Getting Ready for the EOG Test

41. Tasha bought 8 hardcover books. How much did she spend in all? **C**

A $64 B $58 C $56 D $40

Used Books: $3 Paperback, $7 Hardcover

North Carolina Standards 1.03 Develop fluency with multiplication from 1 × 1 to 12 × 12 and division up to two-digit by one-digit numbers using: a) Strategies for multiplying and dividing numbers.

COMMON ERROR ALERT

Some students may have trouble finding products of new 7's facts. Remind students that when they know one multiplication fact of 7, they can add 7 to the product to find the next one. Display $5 \times 7 = 35$. Then write $6 \times 7 = 35 + 7 = 42$. Have students continue the pattern for the remaining 7's facts through 9×7.

Independent Practice

Note that Exercises 36 and 38 are **multistep or strategy problems.** Assign Exercises 6–40.

4 ASSESS

Summarize the lesson by having students:

DISCUSS How would you make an array that shows the factors of 49? Make 7 rows of 7.

WRITE Make up a multiplication word problem about a family that took 2 summer vacations, one that lasted 2 weeks and one that lasted 3 weeks. Show an array that can be used to solve the problem. Check students' work.

LESSON QUIZ

Transparency 10.4

Find each product.

1. $4 \times 7 = \blacksquare$ 28
2. $\blacksquare = 9 \times 7$ 63
3. $7 \times 6 = \blacksquare$ 42
4. $5 \times 7 = \blacksquare$ 35

Challenge 10.4

Finding Factor Pairs

What kind of fruit is always grumpy?

To find out, draw a line to match each clue to the correct factor pair. Write the factor pair's code letter above the clue number at the bottom of page.

1. Their product is equal to 15 + 15.
2. Their product is odd. Their difference is 2.
3. Their product is equal to 3 × 8.
4. Their product is between 40 and 50. Their sum is even.
5. Their product is equal to 14 + 14.
6. Their product is about 40. Their difference is 1.
7. Their product is between 35 and 40.
8. Their product is greater than 50. Their difference is 1.
9. Their product is equal to 28 − 7.
10. Their product is even. Their difference is 4.

Factor Pairs	Code Letter
4,6	A
6,7	P
4,8	S
5,6	C
4,7	A
7,9	R
7,8	L
3,7	E
6,6	P
6,8	B

C R A B A P P L E S

1. 2. 3. 4. 5. 6. 7. 8. 9. 10.

Challenge CW55

Problem Solving 10.4

Multiply with 7

Understand → Plan → Solve → Check

Write the correct answer.

1. Name two smaller arrays you can use to find the product.
   $7 \times 6 = \blacksquare$
   Possible answer: 7 × 3, 7 × 3; 42
2. Find the product.
   $4 \times 7 = \blacksquare$
   28
3. Hiroshi takes a 3-week vacation every August. How many days is his vacation?
   21 days
4. Sarah had 6 bags. She put 5 tennis balls in each bag. How many tennis balls did she have?
   30 tennis balls

Choose the letter of the correct answer.

5. Emilio feeds his puppies 4 times a day. How many times does he feed them each week?
   A 11 times C 24 times
   B 21 times (D) 28 times
6. Which of the following has the same answer as 7 × 6?
   F 7 + 6 (H) 6 × 7
   G 7 − 6 J 6 + 7
7. Nicole's garden has 6 rows with 5 plants in each row. Which of the following could you use to find the number of plants in the garden?
   A 5 + 6 C 6 + 5
   B 6 − 5 (D) 6 × 5
8. Brian is 7 years old. Sandra is twice as old as he is. Kate is 3 years younger than Sandra. How old is Kate?
   F 17 (H) 11
   G 12 J 4
9. **Write About It** How did you solve Problem 1?
   Possible answer: I multiplied 7 × 3 and 7 × 3. Then I added the products: 21 + 21 = 42

Problem Solving PS55

Lesson 10.5

Algebra: Practice the Facts

Lesson Planning

Objective To review multiplication strategies and apply them to 0–8 basic facts

NCTM Standards

1. Number and Operations
2. Algebra
6. Problem Solving
7. Reasoning and Proof
8. Communication
9. Connections
10. Representation

Math Background

These ideas will help students review multiplication strategies and practice facts for 0–8:

- To multiply 1-digit numbers with factors greater than 5, break an array into known facts and add the products.
- Use the Commutative Property of Multiplication to find a multiplication fact that you don't know.
- Double a 3's fact to find a 6's fact and double a 4's fact to find an 8's fact.
- Find the place where the factor row and the factor column meet on a multiplication table to find a product.

Warm-Up Resources

Build Number Sense

Number of the Day

Write the current time. What time will it be in 11 hours? Answers will vary.

Daily Facts Practice

Have students practice subtraction facts by completing Set G of *Teacher's Resource Book*, p. TR90.

Solve a Problem

Transparency 10.5

Problem of the Day

On grid paper, Gina wrote the numbers 1–99, putting 8 numbers in each row. What is the last number she wrote on the third line? 24 What multiplication fact does this show? $3 \times 8 = 24$ Where did she write the number 56? at the end of the seventh row What is the greatest two-digit number she wrote in the ninth row? 72

Solution Problem of the Day tab, p. PD10

REACHING ALL LEARNERS

Intervention and Extension Resources

Alternative Teaching Strategy

MATERIALS *For each pair* 10 index cards

Help students **practice multiplication strategies and review 0–8's facts**.

- Have students name the ten multiplication facts they have learned that are the most difficult for them to remember.
- Ask them to write the two factors for each fact on the front of a card and the product and a strategy on the back.
- Have students alternate showing the factors on the front of the card and finding the products using the strategies. Check students' work.

See also page 204.

AUDITORY, VISUAL

VISUAL/SPATIAL

Multistep and Strategy Problems

The following multistep or strategy problems are provided in Lesson 10.5:

Page	Item
204	67–68
205	70–71

Writing in Mathematics

Help students **practice using a multiplication table to find products**. Suggest they use the table on page 202 to help them find the mystery number described by these clues:

- If you count by 8's, you'll say my name.
- If you count by 5's, you won't.
- One of my factors is 7.

Ask: What number am I? 56

Have students pick another mystery number and write clues about it. Have students exchange clues and solve. Check students' work.

Advanced Learners

Challenge students to **extend their understanding of multiplication facts**. Have students copy the following sentences and write *All*, *Some*, or *No* to make each sentence true:

- __?__ products of 6's facts are odd. No
- __?__ products of 6's facts are even. All
- __?__ products of 6's facts are 2-digit numbers. Some
- __?__ products of 6's facts are greater than 30. Some

Challenge students to write similar statements for 7's facts and 8's facts.

VISUAL

VISUAL/SPATIAL

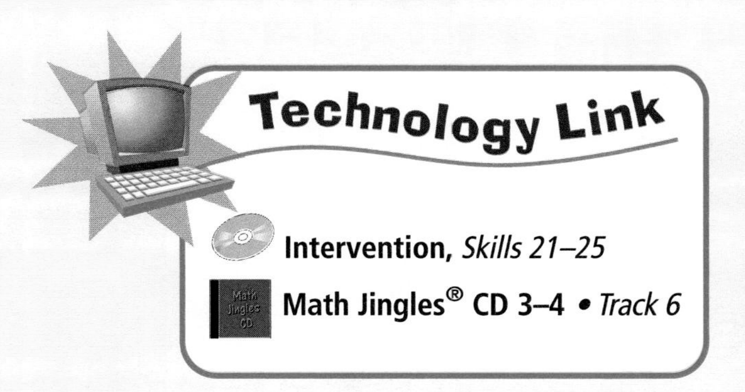

Technology Link

Intervention, *Skills 21–25*

Math Jingles® CD 3–4 • *Track 6*

Lesson 10.5 Organizer

Objective To review multiplication strategies and apply them to 0–8 basic facts

Quick Review provides review of prerequisite skills.

Why Learn This? You can use different methods to find products. *Share the lesson objective with students.*

2 TEACH

Guided Instruction

- *Have students read the Learn section and review the four different ways to find a product.*

  Which of the four methods do you like to use? Explain. Possible answer: the Commutative Property of Multiplication because I don't have to do a lot of different calculations

  How could you break the array in Example A so that the two smaller arrays have the same number of rows? Possible answer: Break the array between the second and third columns into 7 rows of 2 and 7 rows of 4.

  Reasoning Can you use doubles to find 3 × 7? Explain. No; there is no number that when doubled equals 7; you can only use doubles when one of the factors is an even number.

  What other strategies can you use to multiply 7 × 6? Possible answers: skip-count on a number line, draw equal groups, use repeated addition

LESSON 5

Algebra: Practice the Facts

Quick Review

1. $6 \times 3 = \blacksquare$ 18
2. $5 \times 4 = \blacksquare$ 20
3. $2 \times 8 = \blacksquare$ 16
4. $4 \times 9 = \blacksquare$ 36
5. $7 \times 8 = \blacksquare$ 56

Learn

SPLASH! Each instructor teaches a group of 6 children. If there are 7 instructors, how many children are taking swimming lessons?

$$7 \times 6 = \blacksquare$$

You have learned many ways to find 7×6.

A. Break an array into known facts.

6

2 ■■■■■■ / ■■■■■■

$2 \times 6 = \mathbf{12}$

6

5 ■■■■■■ (5 rows)

$5 \times 6 = \mathbf{30}$

$12 + 30 = 42$, so $7 \times 6 = 42$.

B. Use a multiplication table.

×	0	1	2	3	4	5	6	7	8	9
0	0	0	0	0	0	0	0	0	0	0
1	0	1	2	3	4	5	6	7	8	9
2	0	2	4	6	8	10	12	14	16	18
3	0	3	6	9	12	15	18	21	24	27
4	0	4	8	12	16	20	24	28	32	36
5	0	5	10	15	20	25	30	35	40	45
6	0	6	12	18	24	30	36	42	48	54
7	0	7	14	21	28	35	42	49	56	63
8	0	8	16	24	32	40	48	56	64	72
9	0	9	18	27	36	45	54	63	72	81

$7 \times 6 = 42$

C. Use the Commutative Property of Multiplication.

Try changing the order of the factors:

Think: If $6 \times 7 = 42$, then $7 \times 6 = 42$.

D. When one of the factors is an even number, you can use doubles.

To find a 6's fact, you can double a 3's fact.

- First find the 3's fact.
  Think: $7 \times 3 = 21$
- Double the product. $21 + 21 = 42$
  $7 \times 6 = 42$

So, 42 children are taking lessons.

202

Reteach 10.5

Algebra: Practice the Facts

Here are some ways you have learned to find 5×8.

A. Break an array into known facts.

8 8

2 ▪▪▪▪▪▪▪▪ 3 ▪▪▪▪▪▪▪▪

$2 \times 8 = 16$ $3 \times 8 = 24$

$16 + 24 = 40$

$5 \times 8 = 40$

B. Use a multiplication table.

×	0	1	2	3	4	5	6	7	8
0	0	0	0	0	0	0	0	0	0
1	0	1	2	3	4	5	6	7	8
2	0	2	4	6	8	10	12	14	16
3	0	3	6	9	12	15	18	21	24
4	0	4	8	12	16	20	24	28	32
5	0	5	10	15	20	25	30	35	40
6	0	6	12	18	24	30	36	42	48
7	0	7	14	21	28	35	42	49	56
8	0	8	16	24	32	40	48	56	64

$5 \times 8 = 40$

C. Use doubles.

To find an 8's fact, you can double a 4's fact.

Think: $5 \times 4 = 20$

Double the product. $20 + 20 = 40$

$5 \times 8 = 40$

D. Use the Commutative Property of Multiplication.

Try switching the order of the factors:

Think: $8 \times 5 = 40$, so $5 \times 8 = 40$.

$5 \times 8 = 40$

Find each product.

1. $7 \times 8 =$ 56
2. $5 \times 9 =$ 45
3. $8 \times 8 =$ 64
4. $6 \times 9 =$ 54
5. $8 \times 9 =$ 72
6. $4 \times 9 =$ 36
7. $0 \times 7 =$ 0
8. $7 \times 6 =$ 42
9. $9 \times 6 =$ 54
10. $2 \times 9 =$ 18
11. $8 \times 4 =$ 32
12. $6 \times 4 =$ 24
13. $1 \times 9 =$ 9
14. $7 \times 7 =$ 49
15. $6 \times 6 =$ 36
16. $4 \times 8 =$ 32
17. $3 \times 9 =$ 27
18. $7 \times 9 =$ 63
19. $8 \times 0 =$ 0
20. $2 \times 7 =$ 14
21. $6 \times 8 =$ 48

RW56 Reteach

Practice 10.5

Algebra: Practice the Facts

Find each product.

1. $5 \times 4 =$ 20
2. $6 \times 6 =$ 36
3. $8 \times 6 =$ 48
4. $7 \times 7 =$ 49
5. $3 \times 5 =$ 15
6. $6 \times 9 =$ 54
7. $8 \times 9 =$ 72
8. $6 \times 7 =$ 42
9. $5 \times 6 =$ 30
10. $8 \times 5 =$ 40
11. $8 \times 7 =$ 56
12. $8 \times 8 =$ 64
13. $5 \times 7 =$ 35
14. $9 \times 7 =$ 63
15. $5 \times 9 =$ 45
16. $5 \times 2 =$ 10
17. $8 \times 4 =$ 32
18. $7 \times 8 =$ 56
19. $7 \times 6 =$ 42
20. $9 \times 8 =$ 72
21. $4 \times 4 =$ 16
22. $9 \times 3 =$ 27
23. $4 \times 7 =$ 28

Find each missing factor.

24. $5 \times$ 9 $= 45$
25. $9 \times$ 4 $= 36$
26. $8 \times$ 2 $= 16$
27. $3 \times$ 9 $= 27$
28. $7 \times$ 9 $= 63$
29. 3 $\times 8 = 24$
30. 9 $\times 6 = 54$
31. 7 $\times 4 = 28$
32. $6 \times$ 4 $= 24$

Mixed Review

Add.

33. $45 + 16 + 27 =$ 88
34. $43 + 57 + 87 =$ 187
35. $44 + 55 + 66 =$ 165
36. $73 + 64 + 46 + 11 =$ 194

PW56 Practice

Ways to Find a Product

What if there are 8 instructors with 5 swimmers each? How many children are taking lessons?

$8 \times 5 = ■$

David and Niam use different ways to find 8×5.

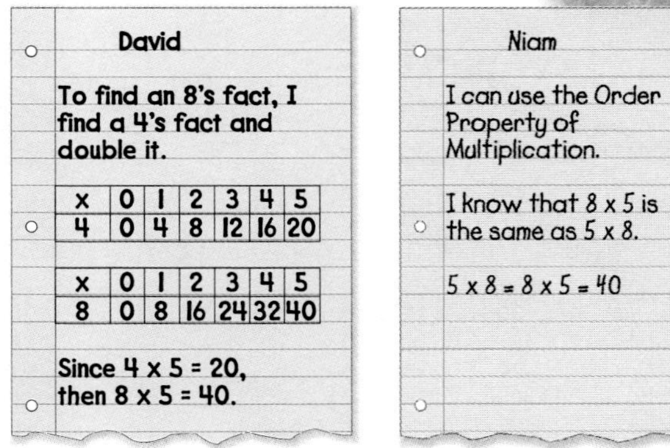

David

To find an 8's fact, I find a 4's fact and double it.

x	0	1	2	3	4	5
4	0	4	8	12	16	20

x	0	1	2	3	4	5
8	0	8	16	24	32	40

Since 4 x 5 = 20, then 8 x 5 = 40.

Niam

I can use the Order Property of Multiplication.

I know that 8 x 5 is the same as 5 x 8.

5 x 8 = 8 x 5 = 40

- What is another way that David or Niam could find 8×5? **Possible answer: Make an array of 8 rows of 5.**

REASONING As you multiply two factors, when is the product *less than* the greater factor? *equal to* the greater factor? *greater than* either of the factors? Explain. **Possible answer: When one factor is a zero, the product is less than the greater factor; when one factor is a 1, the product is equal to the greater factor; and when one factor is 2 or greater, the product is greater than either of the two factors.**

Check

1. **Explain** how you could use $9 \times 5 = 45$ to find 8×5. **Subtract one group of 5 from 45 to get 40.**
2. **Describe** how you could use doubles to find 6×9. **3 x 9 = 27; 27 + 27 = 54**

Find each product.

3. $4 \times 5 = ■$ **20**
4. $3 \times 7 = ■$ **21**
5. $6 \times 4 = ■$ **24**
6. $7 \times 6 = ■$ **42**
7. $2 \times 5 = ■$ **10**
8. $6 \times 6 = ■$ **36**
9. $■ = 4 \times 3$ **12**
10. $2 \times 2 = ■$ **4**
11. $1 \times 8 = ■$ **8**
12. $■ = 5 \times 3$ **15**
13. $9 \times 2 = ■$ **18**
14. $5 \times 5 = ■$ **25**
15. 5×9 = **45**
16. 6×3 = **18**
17. 7×7 = **49**
18. 4×8 = **32**
19. 0×4 = **0**
20. 3×3 = **9**

LESSON CONTINUES ▶ Chapter 10

- *Have students read the What If question.* **Which strategy would you use, doubles or the Commutative Property of Multiplication? Explain.** Possible answer: the Commutative Property of Multiplication; I don't have to add. **Describe a third way you could solve the problem.** Possible answer: Break an 8×5 array into a 2×5 and 6×5 array; add the products $10 + 30 = 40$.

MODIFYING INSTRUCTION Discuss the Reasoning question with the class. On the board, show examples of one factor multiplied by each number 0–9.

3 PRACTICE

Guided Practice

Do Check Exercises 1–20 with your students. Identify students who are having difficulty and choose appropriate lesson resources to provide assistance.

COMMON ERROR ALERT

Students may not remember that the order of factors does not matter when finding products.

$7 \times 4 = 28$ What is 4×7?

To help them, have students make a 4×7 array and then a 7×4 array. Point out that the products of the two arrays are equal.

North Carolina Standards 1.03 Develop fluency with multiplication from 1×1 to 12×12 and division to two-digit by one-digit numbers using: a) Strategies for multiplying and dividing numbers.

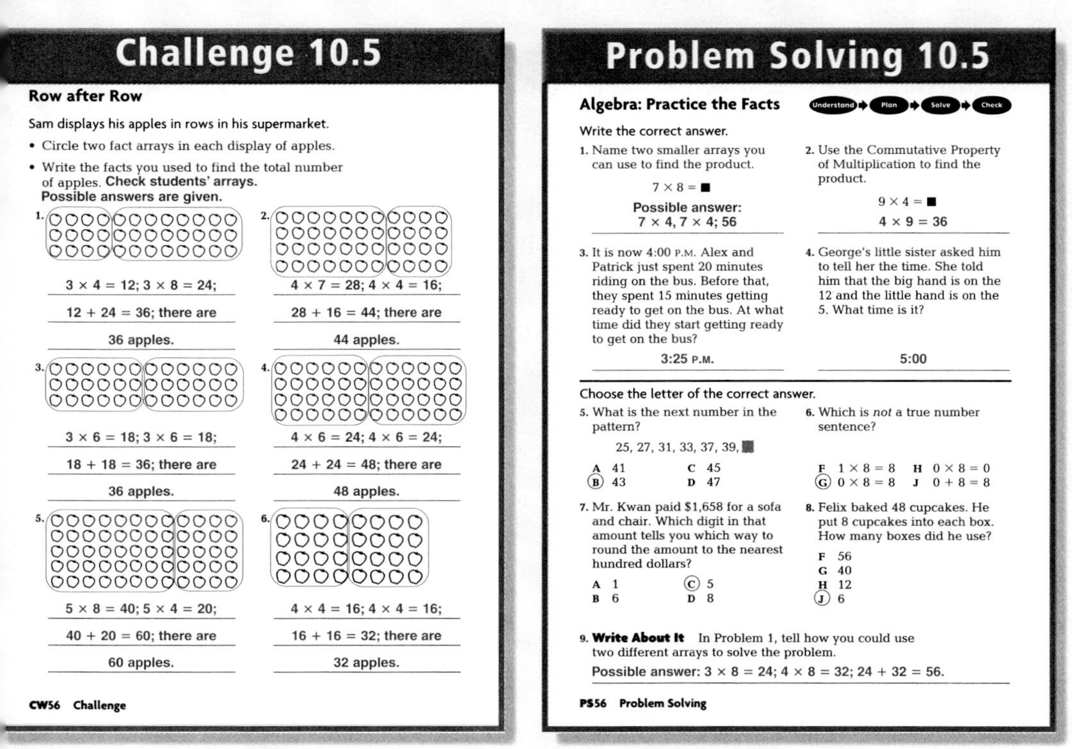

Challenge 10.5

Row after Row

Sam displays his apples in rows in his supermarket.
- Circle two fact arrays in each display of apples.
- Write the facts you used to find the total number of apples. **Check students' arrays. Possible answers are given.**

1. 3 × 4 = 12; 3 × 8 = 24; 12 + 24 = 36; there are 36 apples.
2. 4 × 7 = 28; 4 × 4 = 16; 28 + 16 = 44; there are 44 apples.
3. 3 × 6 = 18; 3 × 6 = 18; 18 + 18 = 36; there are 36 apples.
4. 4 × 6 = 24; 4 × 6 = 24; 24 + 24 = 48; there are 48 apples.
5. 5 × 8 = 40; 5 × 4 = 20; 40 + 20 = 60; there are 60 apples.
6. 4 × 4 = 16; 4 × 4 = 16; 16 + 16 = 32; there are 32 apples.

CW56 Challenge

Problem Solving 10.5

Algebra: Practice the Facts Understand ▶ Plan ▶ Solve ▶ Check

Write the correct answer.

1. Name two smaller arrays you can use to find the product. 7 × 8 = ■ **Possible answer: 7 × 4, 7 × 4; 56**
2. Use the Commutative Property of Multiplication to find the product. 9 × 4 = ■ **4 × 9 = 36**
3. It is now 4:00 P.M. Alex and Patrick just spent 20 minutes riding on the bus. Before that, they spent 15 minutes getting ready to get on the bus. At what time did they start getting ready to get on the bus? **3:25 P.M.**
4. George's little sister asked him to tell her the time. She told him that the big hand is on the 12 and the little hand is on the 5. What time is it? **5:00**

Choose the letter of the correct answer.

5. What is the next number in the pattern? 25, 27, 31, 33, 37, 39, ■
   A 41 (B) 43 C 45 D 47
6. Which is *not* a true number sentence?
   F 1 × 8 = 8 (G) 0 × 8 = 8 H 0 × 8 = 0 J 0 + 8 = 8
7. Mr. Kwan paid $1,658 for a sofa and chair. Which digit in that amount tells you which way to round the amount to the nearest hundred dollars?
   A 1 B 6 (C) 5 D 8
8. Felix baked 48 cupcakes. He put 8 cupcakes into each box. How many boxes did he use?
   F 56 G 40 H 12 (J) 6
9. **Write About It** In Problem 1, tell how you could use two different arrays to solve the problem. **Possible answer: 3 × 8 = 24; 4 × 8 = 32; 24 + 32 = 56.**

PS56 Problem Solving

Independent Practice

Note that Exercises 67–68 and 70–71 are **multistep or strategy problems.** Assign Exercises 21–71.

These rules will help students find products:

- *even number × even number = even number*
- *odd number × odd number = odd number*
- *even number × odd number = even number*

Vocabulary Power Discuss with students other ways in which the word *double* is used, such as a double-decker sandwich or a double play in baseball.

ALGEBRAIC THINKING Before students complete Exercise 66, remind them of these rules for multiplying with 0 and with 1:

- *The product of 0 and any number is 0.*
- *The product of 1 and any number is that number.*

MULTISTEP OR STRATEGY PROBLEM To solve Exercise 68, students can multiply \$3 × 2 to find the cost of 2 cakes. \$3 × 2 = \$6. They can then add the cost of 1 cupcake to find the total cost. \$6.00 + \$0.50 = \$6.50. Finally students can subtract the total cost from \$10.00 to find the amount of change. \$10.00 − \$6.50 = \$3.50. Guide students to conclude they must find the total cost before they can find the change.

Practice and Problem Solving

Extra Practice, page 206, Set D

Find each product.

21. $8 \times 5 = \blacksquare$ 40
22. $0 \times 6 = \blacksquare$ 0
23. $9 \times 3 = \blacksquare$ 27
24. $5 \times 6 = \blacksquare$ 30
25. $9 \times 8 = \blacksquare$ 72
26. $8 \times 3 = \blacksquare$ 24
27. $\blacksquare = 1 \times 8$ 8
28. $8 \times 8 = \blacksquare$ 64
29. $6 \times 8 = \blacksquare$ 48
30. $\blacksquare = 4 \times 9$ 36
31. $\blacksquare = 2 \times 8$ 16
32. $8 \times 7 = \blacksquare$ 56
33. 2×6 12
34. 6×7 42
35. 8×9 72
36. 5×7 35
37. 5×1 5
38. 4×4 16
39. 2×9 18
40. 0×3 0
41. 2×4 8
42. 4×7 28
43. 9×6 54
44. 7×9 63

Find each missing factor.

45. $\blacksquare \times 4 = 20$ 5
46. $8 \times \blacksquare = 56$ 7
47. $\blacksquare \times 6 = 0$ 0
48. $6 \times \blacksquare = 42$ 7
49. $8 \times \blacksquare = 24$ 3
50. $\blacksquare \times 5 = 40$ 8
51. $4 \times \blacksquare = 16$ 4
52. $3 \times \blacksquare = 12$ 4

Write <, >, or = for each ●.

53. 3×2 ● 6 =
54. 4×2 ● $5 + 2$ >
55. 6×3 ● 7×2 >
56. 4×9 ● 6×6 =
57. 3×4 ● 18 <
58. 5×9 ● 6×8 <
59. 7×4 ● $30 - 4$ >
60. 3×8 ● 6×4 =
61. 5×7 ● 6×6 <
62. $8 + 9$ ● 8×9 <
63. 7×7 ● 50 <
64. 9×3 ● $9 + 9$ >

65. **Vocabulary Power** The word *double* means "twice as many." A double scoop is two scoops of ice cream. What number is the double of 8? 16

66. **ALGEBRA** Write *true* or *false* for each. a. false, b. true, c. true, d. false
 a. $1 \times 8 = 9$
 b. $0 \times 7 = 0$
 c. $0 \times 0 = 0$
 d. $1 \times 9 = 1$

USE DATA For 67–68, use the table.

BAKE SALE
Cake - \$3
Brownie - \$1
Cupcake - \$0.50
Loaf of Bread - \$2

67. Sara buys 4 cakes and 1 loaf of bread at the bake sale. How much does she pay? \$14

68. Greg buys 2 cakes and one cupcake. How much change does he get from a \$10 bill? \$3.50

69. **REASONING** List as many factors as you can for each of the following numbers: 12, 18, and 24. Possible answers: 12: 2 and 6, 3 and 4, 12 and 1; 18: 2 and 9, 3 and 6, 18 and 1; 24: 3 and 8, 4 and 6, 2 and 12, 24 and 1

204

Alternative Teaching Strategy — Scaffolded Instruction

PURPOSE Students use different strategies to practice multiplication facts for 0–8.

MATERIALS *For each group* counters, square tiles

Step 1

Display 5 × 8 and have students find the product using counters or square tiles.

Step 2

Have students use the same materials to find 8 × 5. Ask:

- Is the product the same? yes
- What is different? Possible answer: For the first step I made 5 rows of 8 counters. This time I made 8 rows of 5 counters.

Step 3

Ask students to use square tiles to break apart an array to find 5 × 8. Then have students write the two multiplication facts. Possible answers: 1 × 8 and 4 × 8; 2 × 8 and 3 × 8; 1 × 5 and 7 × 5; 2 × 5 and 6 × 5; 3 × 5 and 5 × 5

Step 4

PROFESSIONAL DEVELOPMENT

Then have students demonstrate finding the product again using the multiplication table, doubles, and the Commutative Property of Multiplication.

Discuss opinions about which strategy is most useful. Help students understand that no one strategy is the *only right* one.

You may want to have students continue using the strategy of their choice to practice finding products for problems such as 9 × 3, 7 × 4, and 6 × 8.

70. Mr. Wu taught 3 lessons each day for 6 days. Then he taught 2 lessons each day for 3 days. How many lessons did he teach? **24 lessons**

71. Ed arranged 5 rows of 6 pennies each. He had one more coin in his pocket. If he had a total of $0.35, what coin was in his pocket? **a nickel**

Getting Ready for the EOG Test

72. Which figure shows 3×7? **D**

A (3 rows of 5 dots) C (2 rows of 7 dots)

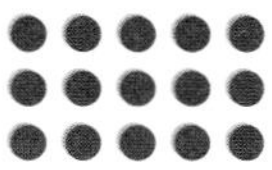

B (2 rows of 3 dots) D (3 rows of 7 dots)

73. Alison makes model cars. She put 4 wheels on each of 6 cars. How many wheels did she use? **C**

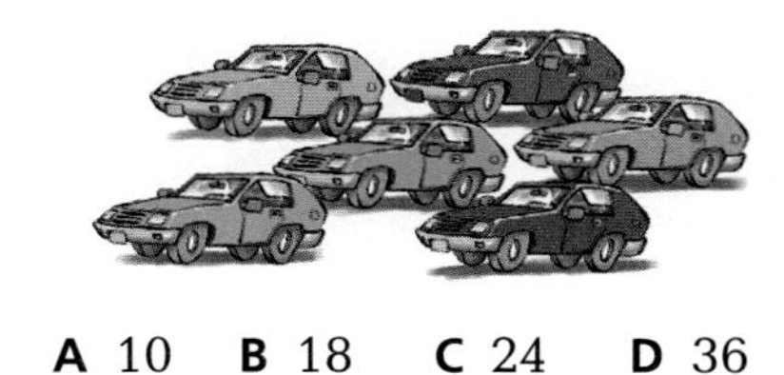

A 10 **B** 18 **C** 24 **D** 36

Problem Solving Thinker's Corner

MULTIPLICATION CONCENTRATION
MATERIALS: 40 index cards
PLAYERS: 2

Using index cards, record all of the multiplication facts for 7's and 8's. Write a fact on one card and the product on another card.

Shuffle cards and place cards in 5 rows with numbers face down.

a. Player One turns over two cards and tries to match a multiplication sentence and a product.

b. If there is a match, Player One keeps the two cards. If there is no match, the cards are turned face down again.

c. Players take turns turning over cards. When all of the pairs have been matched, the player with the greater number of cards wins.

Chapter 10 205

Problem Solving Thinker's Corner

- *Have students work in pairs to play Multiplication Concentration.* **Which facts have the same products?** 0×7 and 0×8 are both equal to 0; 7×8 and 8×7 are both equal to 56.

MODIFYING INSTRUCTION For more practice, have students make game cards for other multiplication facts and include these when playing the game.

Summarize the lesson by having students:

DISCUSS What facts could you double to find 6 × 8? $3 \times 8 = 24$ and $6 \times 4 = 24$

WRITE Choose two different strategies to find the product of 9 × 6. Describe the steps you used for each method. Possible answer: skip-count by 9's; use the Commutative Property of Multiplication because I know $6 \times 9 = 54$, so $9 \times 6 = 54$

LESSON QUIZ
Find each product.

Transparency 10.5

1. $5 \times 6 = ■$ 30 **2.** $■ = 8 \times 7$ 56

3. 9×8 = 72 **4.** 7×6 = 42

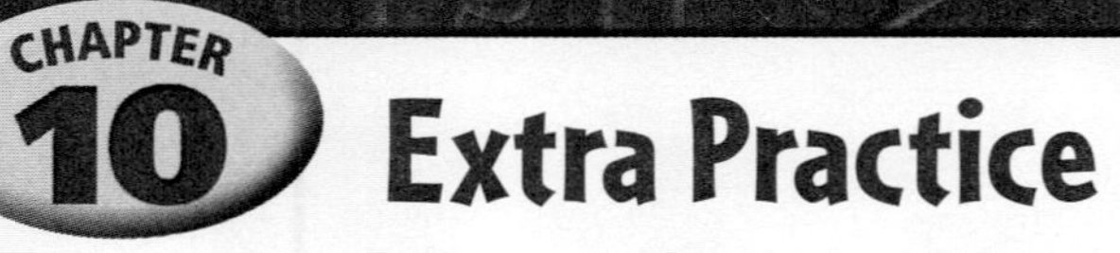

Extra Practice

Purpose To provide extra practice for the skills presented in this chapter

The blue page references in each set of exercises refer to the lesson pages where each skill is taught.

Internet Resources

Visit THE LEARNING SITE at **www.harcourtschool.com** for a listing of practice activities.

Extra Practice

Set A (pp. 194–195)

Find each product.

1. $5 \times 6 =$ ■ **30** 2. $6 \times 2 =$ ■ **12** 3. $0 \times 6 =$ ■ **0** 4. $6 \times 7 =$ ■ **42**
5. $6 \times 4 =$ ■ **24** 6. $6 \times 3 =$ ■ **18** 7. ■ $= 8 \times 6$ **48** 8. $4 \times 7 =$ ■ **28**
9. $8 \times 2 =$ ■ **16** 10. ■ $= 6 \times 6$ **36** 11. $6 \times 1 =$ ■ **6** 12. $6 \times 9 =$ ■ **54**

Complete.

13. ■ $\times 4 = 16$ **4** 14. ■ $\times 5 = 35$ **7** 15. $2 \times$ ■ $= 8$ **4** 16. $8 \times$ ■ $= 24$ **3**

Set B (pp. 196–197)

Find each product.

1. $7 \times 8 =$ ■ **56** 2. $8 \times 0 =$ ■ **0** 3. $8 \times 3 =$ ■ **24** 4. $6 \times 8 =$ ■ **48**
5. ■ $= 8 \times 4$ **32** 6. ■ $= 2 \times 5$ **10** 7. $8 \times 1 =$ ■ **8** 8. $8 \times 8 =$ ■ **64**
9. $8 \times 2 =$ ■ **16** 10. $5 \times 8 =$ ■ **40** 11. $2 \times 2 =$ ■ **4** 12. $8 \times 9 =$ ■ **72**

13. Dolores has 8 bags of 4 apples. Ruth has 3 bags of 8 apples. How many more apples does Dolores have? **8 more apples**

Set C (pp. 200–201)

Find each product.

1. $1 \times 7 =$ ■ **7** 2. ■ $= 7 \times 5$ **35** 3. $6 \times 7 =$ ■ **42** 4. $3 \times 7 =$ ■ **21**
5. $2 \times 7 =$ ■ **14** 6. $3 \times 3 =$ ■ **9** 7. $7 \times 7 =$ ■ **49** 8. $4 \times 7 =$ ■ **28**
9. $8 \times 1 =$ ■ **8** 10. $0 \times 7 =$ ■ **0** 11. ■ $= 7 \times 8$ **56** 12. $9 \times 7 =$ ■ **63**

13. Alex has 8 bags of rocks. Each bag has 7 rocks. Vera takes 3 bags. How many rocks does Alex have left? **35 rocks**

Set D (pp. 202–205)

Find each product.

1. $8 \times 7 =$ ■ **56** 2. $6 \times 7 =$ ■ **42** 3. ■ $= 6 \times 4$ **24** 4. $7 \times 3 =$ ■ **21**
5. $9 \times 8 =$ ■ **72** 6. $8 \times 6 =$ ■ **48** 7. $7 \times 7 =$ ■ **49** 8. $3 \times 5 =$ ■ **15**
9. $9 \times 7 =$ ■ **63** 10. ■ $= 6 \times 5$ **30** 11. $8 \times 8 =$ ■ **64** 12. $9 \times 6 =$ ■ **54**

13. List the factors for 16. **Possible answers: 1 and 16; 2 and 8; 4 and 4**

Review/Test

✓ CHECK CONCEPTS

Name a way to break apart each array. Then write the product. (pp. 194–195, 200–201)

Possible responses are given.

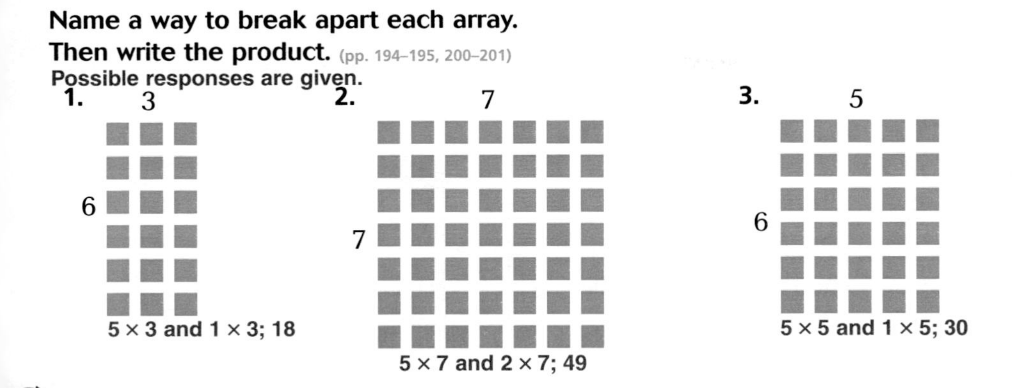

✓ CHECK SKILLS

Find each product. (pp. 194–195, 196–197, 200–201)

4. $6 \times 7 = ■$ 42
5. $■ = 8 \times 7$ 56
6. $4 \times 6 = ■$ 24
7. $9 \times 7 = ■$ 63
8. $■ = 5 \times 8$ 40
9. $6 \times 0 = ■$ 0
10. $3 \times 8 = ■$ 24
11. $5 \times 7 = ■$ 35
12. $6 \times 6 = ■$ 36
13. $8 \times 9 = ■$ 72
14. $8 \times 6 = ■$ 48
15. $6 \times 9 = ■$ 54
16. 8×8 64
17. 8×4 32
18. 2×7 14
19. 7×3 21
20. 6×2 12
21. 7×4 28

✓ CHECK PROBLEM SOLVING

Solve. (pp. 198–199)

For 22–25, use the pictograph.

22. How many more students voted for summer than for winter? 4 students
23. Which season received the most votes? summer
24. How many more students voted for summer and winter than voted for spring and fall? 16 students
25. How many students voted in all? 40 students

FAVORITE SEASONS	
Spring	
Summer	
Fall	
Winter	

Key: Each [leaf] = 2 student votes.

Review/Test

Purpose To check understanding of concepts, skills, and problem solving presented in Chapter 10

Using the Page

The Chapter 10 Review/Test can be used as a **review** or a **test**.

- Items 1–3 check understanding of concepts.
- Items 4–21 check skill proficiency.
- Items 22–25 check students' abilities to choose and apply problem solving strategies to real-life multiplication problems.

Portfolio

Suggest that students place the completed Chapter 10 Review/Test in their portfolios.

Using the Assessment Guide

- Multiple-choice format of Chapter 10 Posttest—See *Assessment Guide*, pp. AG61–62.
- Free-response format of Chapter 10 Posttest—See *Assessment Guide*, pp. AG63–64.

Using Student Self-Assessment

The How Did I Do? survey helps students assess what they have learned and how they learned it. This survey is available as a copying master in *Assessment Guide*, p. AGxvii.

Chapter 10 Test, page 1

Choose the correct answer.

1. $2 \times 7 = ■$
   A 5 (C) 14
   B 9 D 27

2. Which of the following is true?
   F $7 \times 3 > 4 \times 6$
   G $7 \times 5 < 6 \times 5$
   H $8 \times 4 = 7 \times 6$
   (J) $3 \times 8 = 4 \times 6$

3. What is the missing factor?
   $5 \times ■ = 30$
   (A) 6 C 4
   B 5 D 3

4. Which symbol makes the following true?
   $7 \times 7 ● 6 \times 8$
   F < (G) > H =

5. Keith's father works 6 days each week. How many days does his father work in 7 weeks?
   A 13 (C) 42
   B 21 D 67

6. 9×6
   F 48
   (G) 54
   H 56
   J 63

7. Steve bought 7 boxes of cupcakes. There were 4 cupcakes in each box. Twelve cupcakes had white icing and the rest had chocolate icing. How many had chocolate icing?
   A 13 C 20
   (B) 16 D 28

8. What is the product of 8 and 9?
   F 1 (H) 72
   G 17 J 89

9. What number completes the number sentence?
   $3 \times ■ = 20 + 1$
   A 10 C 8
   B 9 (D) 7

10. The product of two factors is 54. One of the factors is 6. What is the other factor?
    F 6 H 8
    G 7 (J) 9

Go On

Chapter 10 Test, page 2

11. Emily has 2 jobs. At one job she works 6 hours each day, 3 days a week. At her other job she works 8 hours each day, 2 days a week. How many hours does she work in one week?
    A 36 C 30
    (B) 34 D 28

12. Each bicycle has 2 wheels. What expression shows how many wheels there are on 6 bicycles?
    F $2 + 6$
    G $6 - 2$
    (H) 6×2
    J 6×6

13. There are 4 small pizzas in each box. Mrs. Owens buys 8 boxes. How many pizzas will she have?
    A 4 C 24
    B 12 (D) 32

14. Danny has 48 plants to arrange in his garden. He wants 6 rows with the same number of plants in each row. How many plants should be in each row?
    F 9 H 7
    (G) 8 J 6

15. Each roll of ribbon has 9 yards on it. Megan needs 63 yards. How many rolls should she buy in order to have enough?
    (A) 7 C 5
    B 6 D 4

16. Each week, Nate goes to school 5 days and spends 2 days at home. How many days does he spend at school in 7 weeks?
    F 14 (H) 35
    G 17 J 49

17. Cheryl was playing a math game. The answer was 40. Which of these could have been the problem?
    A $8 \times 6 = ■$ C $7 \times 6 = ■$
    (B) $8 \times 5 = ■$ D $7 \times 5 = ■$

For 18–20, use the pictograph.

FAVORITE PLACES TO VISIT	
City Park	
Lake	
Mountains	
Amusement Park	
Zoo	
Nature Trail	

Key: Each [car] = 4 votes.

18. How many more votes did the lake receive than the nature trail?
    F 1 (H) 4
    G 2 J 10

19. How many people altogether voted for the amusement park and the zoo?
    A 32 C 36
    (B) 34 D 40

20. Which three numbers represented on the pictograph are multiples of 4?
    F 4, 8, 10 H 8, 14, 16
    G 8, 10, 16 (J) 8, 12, 20

Stop

Getting Ready for the EOG Test

Chapters 1–10

Using the Pages

These pages may be used to help students get ready for the North Carolina EOG Test. The test items are written in the same style and arranged in the same format as those on the EOG Test.

The pages are cumulative. They cover the standards from the North Carolina Mathematics Standard Course of Study that have been taught up to this point in the text or in a previous grade. Each Getting Ready for the EOG Test also reviews the North Carolina mathematics strands shown below.

- Number and Operations
- Measurement
- Geometry
- Data Analysis and Probability
- Algebra

These pages can be assigned at the end of the chapter as classwork or as a homework assignment. You may want to have students use individual recording sheets presented in a multiple-choice (standardized) format. A Test Answer Sheet is available as a blackline master in the *Assessment Guide* (p. AGlii).

You may wish to have students describe how they solved each problem and share their solutions.

Getting Ready for the EOG Test

NUMBER AND OPERATIONS

1. Desi bought 7 boxes of crayons. There are 8 crayons in each box. How many crayons did Desi buy? **D**

A 15 **C** 32
B 28 **D** 56

2. Which of the following should Mindy choose to complete the number sentence? **B**

$6 \times 4 = \blacksquare$

A 10
B 24
C 30
D 36

3. What multiplication fact does the array show? **A**

■■■■■■■■■
■■■■■■■■■
■■■■■■■■■
■■■■■■■■■
■■■■■■■■■
■■■■■■■■■

A $6 \times 9 = 54$
B $6 \times 6 = 36$
C $5 \times 9 = 45$
D $6 \times 8 = 48$

4. Explain It Akiko has read 28 pages of a book that has 96 pages. Estimate the number of pages Akiko needs to read to finish the book. **See page 209.**

MEASUREMENT AND GEOMETRY

5. The schedule below shows Steve's day at school. Where is Steve at 10:30? **C**

STEVE'S SCHEDULE	
Time	**Class**
8:15–8:30	Homeroom
8:35–9:25	Math
9:30–10:20	Social studies
10:25–11:15	Science
11:20–12:10	Reading
12:15–12:45	Lunch

A reading **C** science
B lunch **D** math

TIP **Understand the problem.** See item 6. Find the difference between the time that the lunch period starts and the time it ends.

6. Look at Steve's schedule above. How long is Steve's lunch period? **C**

A 50 minutes
B 45 minutes
C 30 minutes
D 15 minutes

7. Explain It Lucy cooked a turkey from 2:15 P.M. to 6:20 P.M. *About* how many hours did the turkey cook? Explain how you found your answer. **See page 209.**

ALGEBRA

8. This week, Marian jogged on Tuesday, Thursday, and Saturday. If she continues this pattern, on what day will Marian jog next? B

A Sunday
B Monday
C Wednesday
D Friday

9. Jon made this number pattern. What is the missing number in his pattern? B

115, 125, 135, ■, 155, 165

A 130
B 145
C 185
D 205

10. The table shows Carly's pattern.

CARLY'S PATTERN TABLE	
1	7
3	21
5	35
7	■
9	63

Which number should replace the ■ in the table? D

A 42
B 45
C 47
D 49

11. **Explain It** What rule was used to make the table above? Explain how you found your answer. See below.

DATA ANALYSIS AND PROBABILITY

12. Leo made the graph below to show how much money he saved. How much more money did Leo save in Week 3 than he saved in Week 1? C

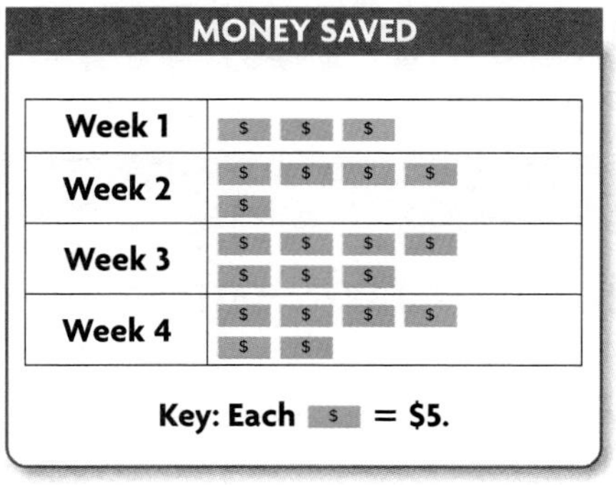

MONEY SAVED	
Week 1	$ $ $
Week 2	$ $ $ $ $
Week 3	$ $ $ $ $ $ $
Week 4	$ $ $ $ $ $

Key: Each $ = $5.

A $5 C $20
B $10 D $35

13. Look at the graph above. Which shows the weeks in order from the *least* amount to ***greatest*** amount of money saved? C

A 4, 2, 3, 1 C 1, 2, 4, 3
B 3, 2, 4, 1 D 2, 4, 1, 3

14. **Explain It** Todd put marbles in this bag. Which two colors is Todd equally likely to pull? Explain how you know. See below.

Chapters 1–10

Item Analysis

You may wish to use the item analysis to determine which North Carolina standards need additional review.

Item	North Carolina Standard	Lesson
1	1.03	10.2
2	1.03	9.2
3	1.03	10.1
4	1.06	5.1
5	2.01	7.4
6	2.01	7.4
7	2.01	7.3
8	5.02	2.5
9	5.01	2.5
10	5.01	10.4
11	5.01	10.4
12	(2) 4.01	Grade 2
13	(2) 4.01	Grade 2
14	(2) 4.02	Grade 2

SCORING RUBRIC
Explain It

2 Demonstrates a complete understanding of the problem and chooses an appropriate strategy to determine the solution

1 Demonstrates a partial understanding of the problem and chooses a strategy that does not lead to a complete and accurate solution

0 Demonstrates little understanding of the problem and shows little evidence of using any strategy to determine a solution

Explain It • Written Response

4. Possible answer: about 70 pages; I rounded 28 to 30 and 96 to 100. Then I subtracted: $100 - 30 = 70$.

7. Possible answer: about 4 hours; from 2:15 P.M. until 6:15 P.M. is 4 hours and 6:20 P.M. is 5 minutes longer, so the turkey cooked about 4 hours.

11. Possible answer: multiply the numbers in the first column by 7; the numbers in the second column are all products of the numbers in the first column times 7.

14. Possible answer: a red or yellow marble because there are 2 of each in the bag

Multiplication Facts and Patterns

NCTM Standards 2000

1. Number and Operations
Lessons 11.1, 11.2, 11.3, 11.4, 11.5
2. Algebra
Lessons 11.2, 11.3, 11.4
3. Geometry
4. Measurement
5. Data Analysis and Probability
6. Problem Solving
Lessons 11.1, 11.2, 11.3, 11.4, 11.5
7. Reasoning and Proof
Lessons 11.2, 11.3, 11.4
8. Communication
Lessons 11.1, 11.2, 11.3, 11.4, 11.5
9. Connections
10. Representation
Lessons 11.1, 11.2, 11.3, 11.4, 11.5

Chapter Planner

Getting Ready for Chapter 11 • Assessing Prior Knowledge and INTERVENTION (See PE and TE page 211.)

LESSON	NORTH CAROLINA STANDARDS	PACING	VOCABULARY*	MATERIALS	RESOURCES AND TECHNOLOGY
11.1 **Multiply with 9 and 10** pp. 212–215 **Objective** To multiply with 9 and 10	1.03a 5.01	1 Day		*For Linkup to Reading* hundred charts, p. TR14; colored pencils	Reteach, Practice, Problem Solving, Challenge 11.1 Scaffolded Instruction Transparency 11 Transparency 11.1 **Math Jingles® CD 3–4** **Intervention,** *Skill 61* (CD or Book) **Harcourt Mega Math The Number Games,** *Up, Up, and Array* and **Ice Station Exploration,** *Arctic Algebra*
11.2 **Algebra: Find a Rule** pp. 216–217 **Objective** To recognize a rule in a linear pattern and extend the pattern	1.03a *also* 5.01	1 Day			Reteach, Practice, Problem Solving, Challenge 11.2 Transparency 11.2 **Intervention,** *Skills 61–62* (CD or Book) **Harcourt Mega Math Ice Station Exploration,** *Arctic Algebra*
11.3 **Algebra: Multiply with 3 Factors** pp. 218–219 **Objective** To multiply with 3 factors and use the Associative (Grouping) Property of Multiplication	1.03a *also* 1.04	1 Day	**Associative Property of Multiplication**		Reteach, Practice, Problem Solving, Challenge 11.3 Transparency 11.3 **Math Jingles® CD 3–4** **Intervention,** *Skills 61–62* (CD or Book)
11.4 **Algebra: Multiplication Properties** pp. 220–221 **Objective** To use multiplication properties to find products	1.04 *also* 1.03a	1 Day	**Identity Property** **Zero Property** **Distributive Property**		Reteach, Practice, Problem Solving, Challenge 11.4 **Intervention,** *Skills 61–62* (CD or Book) Transparency 11.4
11.5 **Problem Solving Skill: Multistep Problems** pp. 222–223 **Objective** To solve multistep problems using basic multiplication facts, addition, and subtraction	1.06	1 Day	**multistep problem**		Reteach, Practice, Reading Strategy, Challenge 11.5 Transparency 11.5 Reading Transparency 11 **Intervention • Problem Solving,** *Strategy/Skill 11* (CD or Book)

Ending Chapter 11 • **Extra Practice,** p. 224 • **Chapter 11 Review/Test,** p. 225 • **Getting Ready for the EOG Test,** pp. 226–227

Ending Unit 3 • **It's in the Bag,** p. 228; **Challenge,** p. 229; **Study Guide and Review,** pp. 230–231; **Performance Assessment,** p. 232; **Technology Linkup,** p. 233; **Problem Solving in North Carolina,** pp. 234–235

***Boldfaced** terms are the key mathematical terms for the chapter.

Vocabulary Power

Review Vocabulary

To be ready for Chapter 11, students should know the following vocabulary term:

- **product** (p. 211)—the results in a multiplication problem

Develop Key Chapter Vocabulary

The **boldfaced** words are the key vocabulary terms in the chapter.

- **Associative (Grouping) Property** (p. 218)—grouping factors in different ways does not change the product
- **Identity Property of Multiplication** (p. 220)—the product of 1 and any number is that number
- **Zero Property** (p. 220)—the product of 0 and any number is equal to 0
- **Distributive Property** (p. 220)—think of one factor as the sum of two addends, multiply each addend by the other factor, and then add the products
- **multistep problem** (p. 222)—a problem that requires more than one operation to solve

Vocabulary Cards

Have students use the Vocabulary Cards on *Teacher's Resource Book* pages TR151–154 for the key terms in the chapter. The cards can be added to a file of mathematics terms.

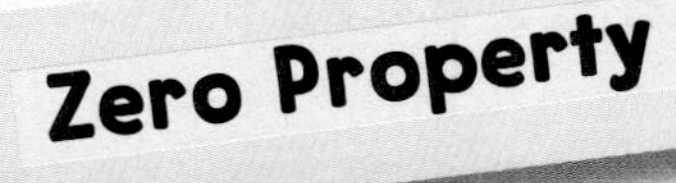

Multimedia Math Glossary

For vocabulary support, visit **www.harcourtschool.com/mathglossary**

Math Journal

Have students define the key vocabulary terms: *Associative (Grouping) Property of Multiplication, Identity Property, Zero Property, Distributive Property,* and *multistep problem.* Have students use their own words and give an example of each.

MATH Word Work

Objective To reinforce vocabulary concepts
Use after Lesson 11.4.

Materials *For each pair* color tiles, large sheet of paper

Students can make posters to describe each of the multiplication properties in Lesson 4. Have students explore making arrays with color tiles to find a way to model each of the properties. Then have them draw their arrays on a poster to display their models. Have students write a description of each property using their arrays. Make sure students make a model for each of the following properties: *Identity Property, Zero Property, Commutative (Order) Property, Associative (Grouping) Property,* and *Distributive Property.*

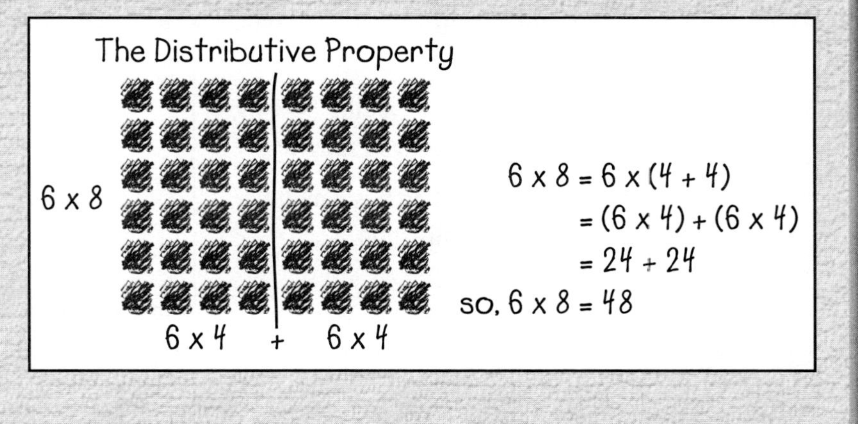

Multiplication Facts and Patterns

Mathematics Across the Grades

LOOKING BACK • Prerequisite Skills

To be ready for Chapter 11, students should have the following understandings and skills:

- **Skip-Count by Tens**—skip-count by tens to continue a pattern or find missing numbers in a pattern
- **Find Missing Factors**—find missing factors in multiplication sentences

Check What You Know

Use page 211 to determine students' knowledge of prerequisite concepts and skills.

Intervention

Help students prepare for the chapter by using the intervention resources described on TE page 211.

LOOKING AT CHAPTER 11 • Essential Skills

Students will

- multiply with 9 and 10.
- recognize the rule in a linear pattern and extend the pattern.
- **multiply with 3 factors and use the Associative (Grouping) Property of Multiplication.**
- use multiplication properties such as the Identity, Zero, Commutative, and Distributive Properties.
- solve multistep problems by using basic multiplication facts, addition, and subtraction.

Example

$4 \times (3 \times 3) = \blacksquare$

Model	Algorithm
■■■ ■■■ ■■■ ■■■ ■■■ ■■■ ■■■ ■■■ ■■■ ■■■ ■■■ ■■■	$4 \times (3 \times 3) =$ $4 \times 9 = 36$

LOOKING AHEAD • Applications

Students will apply what they learn in Chapter 11 to the following new concepts:

- Write Expressions (Chapter 13)
- Multiply Multiples of 10 (Chapter 29)
- Divide by 9 and 10 (Chapter 14)
- Multiply 2-Digit Numbers (Chapter 29)

Differentiated Instruction

Meeting the Needs of All Learners

Extra Support	Activities for All	Enrichment
Alternative Teaching Strategy TE Lessons 11.1, 11.2, 11.3, 11.4, 11.5 **ESOL/ESL** TE Lessons 11.1, 11.2, 11.3, 11.4, 11.5 **Special Needs** TE Lessons 11.3, 11.4	**Cross-Curricular Connections** **Math:** TE Lesson 11.1 **Reading:** TE Lesson 11.5 **Social Studies:** Chapter Opener **Vocabulary:** TE p. 210B, PE/TE p. 211 **Writing:** TE Lesson 11.5	**Advanced Learners** TE Lesson 11.2, 11.3, 11.4 **Early Finishers** TE Lesson 11.1, 11.5

Combination and Multi-age Classrooms

Grade 2	Grade 3	Grade 4
Skills Trace Across the Grades		
Relate addition and multiplication; use arrays to make models; explore sizes of equal groups; make specific numbers of groups.	**Multiply with 9 and 10; practice multiplication facts through 10; identify and write the rule for a number pattern; use multiplication properties.**	Relate multiplication and division; multiply and divide facts to 12; use multiplication properties; write expressions with multiplication and division.
Instructional Strategies		
Students on this level may require more time to build conceptual understanding. **Assignments** **Grade 3 Pupil Edition** • Have students work in pairs for Lessons 11.1, 11.3, and 11.4. Skip Lessons 11.2 and 11.5. **Grade 2 Pupil Edition**—pages 521–528	Students on this level should be able to complete all the lessons in the Pupil Edition and all the activities in the Teacher's Edition with minimal adjustments. **Assignments** **Grade 3 Pupil Edition**—pages 210–225	Students on this level will probably require less time to build conceptual understanding. **Assignments** **Grade 3 Pupil Edition** • Compact Lessons 11.3 and 11.4 **Grade 4 Pupil Edition**—pages 162–201

CHAPTER 11

Multiplication Facts and Patterns

Introducing the Chapter

Tell students that in this chapter they will learn how to multiply with 9 and 10. Ask them about how much 9 full-grown Samoyeds would weigh. about 450 pounds

Using Data

To begin the study of this chapter, have students

- Determine how much 9 American Eskimo puppies weigh. 90 ounces
- Determine which weighs more: 2 Alaskan Malamute puppies or 3 Siberian Husky puppies. 3 Siberian Husky puppies
- Determine which weighs more: a Siberian Husky and an American Eskimo puppy or an Alaskan Malamute and a Samoyed puppy? an Alaskan Malamute and a Samoyed puppy

Problem Solving Project

Purpose To use multiplication facts to solve a problem

Grouping partners

Background Adult sled dogs usually weigh between 40 and 80 pounds. A warm undercoat and a protective outer coat allow sled dogs to sleep comfortably outdoors in extremely cold weather.

UNDERSTAND • PLAN • SOLVE • CHECK

Have students

- Write a word problem about the weight of 9 American Eskimo puppies.
- Exchange problems with a partner to solve.
- Check each other's solutions. Check students' work.

Suggest that students place the problems in their portfolios.

Graphing Investigations
Begin Week 11.

CHAPTER 11

Multiplication Facts and Patterns

FAST FACT • SOCIAL STUDIES Dogsled teams were used to deliver mail in places such as Michigan, Minnesota, Wisconsin, and Alaska. Large teams of dogs could pull 400 to 500 pounds of mail.

PROBLEM SOLVING A full-grown Samoyed sled dog weighs about 50 pounds. A team of 10 Samoyeds weighs about 500 pounds. What would 10 newborn Samoyed puppies weigh? 100 ounces

WEIGHT OF A NEWBORN PUPPY

Siberian Husky	
Alaskan Malamute	
American Eskimo	
Samoyed	

Key: Each [symbol] = 2 ounces.

Anchorage, Alaska

210

WHY LEARN MATH?

Mushers are people who race sleds pulled by teams of dogs. The number of dogs in a team ranges from 3 to 10. A musher uses multiplication to figure out the weight of his or her team of dogs. If there are 9 dogs in a team and each dog weighs about 70 pounds, how much do the dogs weigh altogether? about 630 pounds

Family Involvement Activities

These activities provide:

- Letter to the Family
- Math Vocabulary
- Family Game
- Practice (Homework)

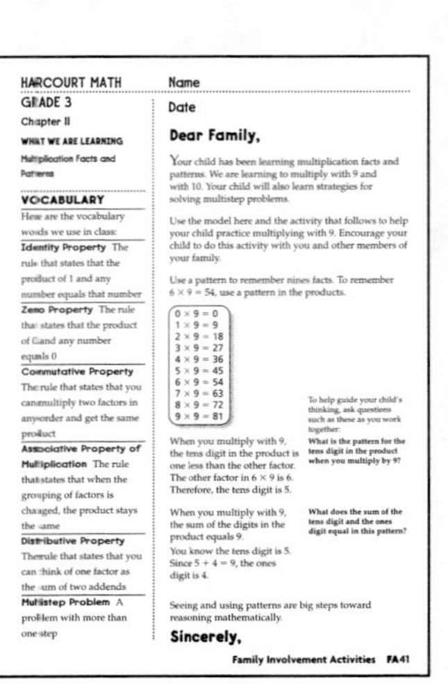

HARCOURT MATH
GRADE 3
Chapter 11
WHAT WE ARE LEARNING
Multiplication Facts and Patterns

VOCABULARY
Here are the vocabulary words we use in class:
Identity Property The rule that states that the product of 1 and any number equals that number
Zero Property The rule that states that the product of 0 and any number equals 0
Commutative Property The rule that states that you can multiply two factors in any order and get the same product
Associative Property of Multiplication The rule that states that when the grouping of factors is changed, the product stays the same
Distributive Property The rule that states that you can think of one factor as the sum of two addends
Multistep Problem A problem with more than one step

Name
Date

Dear Family,

Your child has been learning multiplication facts and patterns. We are learning to multiply with 9 and with 10. Your child will also learn strategies for solving multistep problems.

Use the model here and the activity that follows to help your child practice multiplying with 9. Encourage your child to do this activity with you and other members of your family.

Use a pattern to remember nines facts. To remember $6 \times 9 = 54$, use a pattern in the products.

$0 \times 9 = 0$
$1 \times 9 = 9$
$2 \times 9 = 18$
$3 \times 9 = 27$
$4 \times 9 = 36$
$5 \times 9 = 45$
$6 \times 9 = 54$
$7 \times 9 = 63$
$8 \times 9 = 72$
$9 \times 9 = 81$

To help guide your child's thinking, ask questions such as these as you work together:

When you multiply with 9, the tens digit in the product is one less than the other factor. The other factor in 6×9 is 6. Therefore, the tens digit is 5.

What is the pattern for the tens digit in the product when you multiply by 9?

When you multiply with 9, the sum of the digits in the product equals 9. You know the tens digit is 5. Since $5 + 4 = 9$, the ones digit is 4.

What does the sum of the tens digit and the ones digit equal in this pattern?

Seeing and using patterns are big steps toward reasoning mathematically.

Sincerely,

Family Involvement Activities FA41

Family Involvement Activities, p. FA41

Use this page to help you review and remember important skills needed for Chapter 11.

SKIP-COUNT BY TENS

Continue the pattern.

1. 10, 20, 30, 40, ■, ■ **50, 60**
2. 30, 40, 50, 60, 70, ■, ■ **80, 90**

Skip-count by tens to find the missing numbers.

3. 3, 13, 23, ■, ■, 53, ■, ■, 83, ■ **33, 43, 63, 73, 93**
4. 7, 17, 27, ■, ■, 57, ■, 77, ■, ■ **37, 47, 67, 87, 97**
5. 5, 15, 25, ■, ■, 55, ■, ■, ■ **35, 45, 65, 75, 85**
6. 64, 54, 44, ■, ■, ■, ■ **34, 24, 14, 4**

FIND MISSING FACTORS

Find the missing factor.

7. ■ × 4 = 32 **8**
8. 5 × ■ = 35 **7**
9. ■ × 6 = 36 **6**
10. 2 × ■ = 18 **9**
11. 7 × ■ = 28 **4**
12. ■ × 8 = 16 **2**
13. 5 × ■ = 45 **9**
14. ■ × 4 = 36 **9**
15. ■ × 4 = 24 **6**
16. 6 × ■ = 54 **9**
17. 3 × ■ = 24 **8**
18. ■ × 8 = 64 **8**
19. 5 × ■ = 40 **8**
20. 9 × ■ = 9 **1**
21. ■ × 4 = 0 **0**
22. 7 × ■ = 56 **8**

VOCABULARY POWER

REVIEW

product [prä′dəkt] *noun*

A product in mathematics is the answer to a multiplication problem. Tell another meaning for *product* that you find in your social studies book.
Possible answer: something that people make or grow, often to sell

PREVIEW

Associative Property
Identity Property
Zero Property
Distributive Property
multistep problem

GO ON-LINE www.harcourtschool.com/mathglossary

Assessing Prior Knowledge

Use the **Check What You Know** page to determine whether your students have mastered the prerequisite skills critical for this chapter.

Intervention

- **Diagnose and Prescribe**
  Evaluate your students' performance on this page to determine whether intervention is necessary or if enrichment is appropriate. Options that provide instruction, practice, and a check are listed in the chart below.

CHECK WHAT YOU KNOW RESOURCES

Intervention Copying Masters or CD-ROMs

Enrichment Copying Masters

VOCABULARY POWER

For activities and information about the vocabulary in this chapter, see page 210B.

Were students successful with CHECK WHAT YOU KNOW?

IF . . . NO THEN . . . INTERVENE — INTERVENTION OPTIONS — IF . . . YES THEN . . . ENRICH

Skill/Items	Missed more than	Intervene with
Skip-Count by Tens, 1–6	2	• *Intervention*, Skill 61
Find Missing Factors, 7–22	5	• *Intervention*, Skill 62

Skill/Items	Missed fewer than	Enrich with
Skip-Count by Tens, 1–6	3	• *Intervention*, Enrichment p. IN30
Find Missing Factors, 7–22	6	• *Intervention*, Enrichment p. IN30

Multiply with 9 and 10

Lesson Planning

Objective To multiply with 9 and 10

Materials *For each student* hundred charts, p. TR14; colored pencils

NCTM Standards
1. Number and Operations
6. Problem Solving
8. Communication
10. Representation

Math Background

These ideas will help students multiply with 9 and 10.

- Skip-count by tens to multiply with 10.
- To multiply with 9, find the 10's fact and subtract the other factor.
- When you multiply the numbers 2–9 by 9, the tens digit of the product is 1 less than the other factor.
- For every product of a 9's fact through 10×9, the sum of the digits is 9.

Warm-Up Resources

Use the number of hours between 11:00 A.M. and 2:00 P.M. to write 5 multiplication sentences.
Possible answers: $2 \times 3 = 6$, $3 \times 3 = 9$, $4 \times 3 = 12$, $7 \times 3 = 21$, $8 \times 3 = 24$

Daily Facts Practice

Have students practice addition and subtraction facts by completing Set A of *Teacher's Resource Book*, p. TR91.

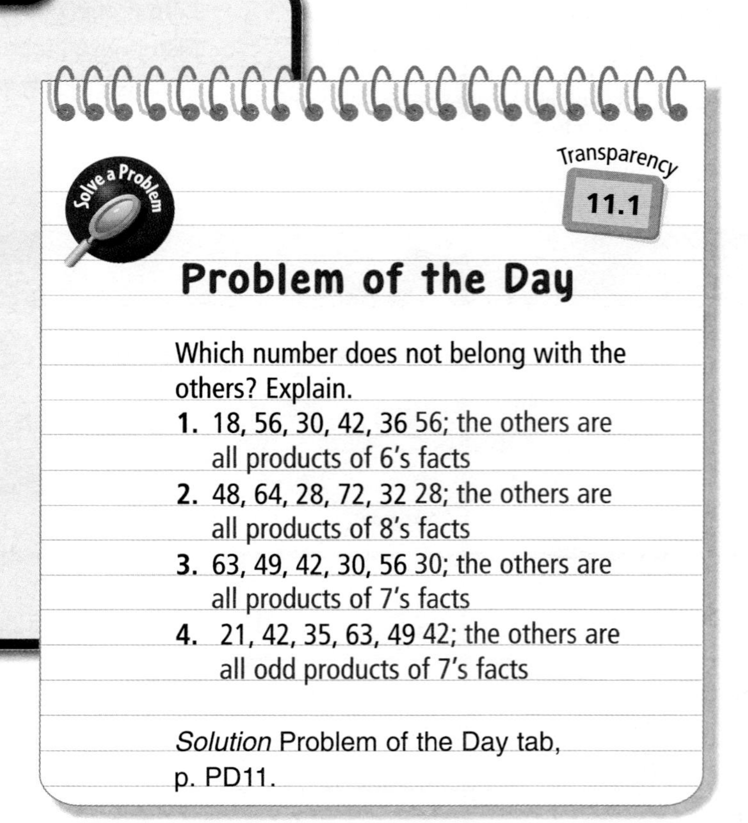

Transparency 11.1

Problem of the Day

Which number does not belong with the others? Explain.

1. 18, 56, 30, 42, 36 56; the others are all products of 6's facts
2. 48, 64, 28, 72, 32 28; the others are all products of 8's facts
3. 63, 49, 42, 30, 56 30; the others are all products of 7's facts
4. 21, 42, 35, 63, 49 42; the others are all odd products of 7's facts

Solution Problem of the Day tab, p. PD11.

Intervention and Extension Resources

Alternative Teaching Strategy

MATERIALS *For each group* 60 counters

Show students how to **use facts of 10 to find facts of 9** by using counters.

- Have students make 10 groups of 2 counters and find the product by counting. Display $10 \times 2 = 20$.
- Ask: How many counters should be taken away to show 9 groups of 2? 2 Have students take away 1 group of 2. Display $9 \times 2 = 20 - 2$, so $9 \times 2 = 18$.
- Ask: How could you use 10 groups of 6 counters to find 9×6? Possible answer: 9×6 would be 6 less than the product of 10×6.

See also page 214.

KINESTHETIC

BODILY/KINESTHETIC

Multistep and Strategy Problems

The following multistep or strategy problems are provided in Lesson 11.1:

Page	Item
214	58, 60

Technology Link

Intervention, *Skill 61*

The Harcourt Learning Site www.harcourtschool.com

Harcourt Mega Math The Number Games, *Up, Up, and Array,* Level C; **Ice Station Exploration,** *Arctic Algebra,* Level C

Math Jingles® CD 3–4 • *Track 6*

Math Connection

Help students **practice writing number sentences using 10's facts to find products of 9's facts**. Display the following number sentences:

$1 \times 9 = (1 \times 10) - 1 = 9$

$2 \times 9 = (2 \times 10) - 2 = 18$

Have students continue writing number sentences in this pattern through 9×9. Ask: Is there another method you can use to multiply 10×9? Explain. Possible answer: using the Commutative Property, 10×9 is the same as $9 \times 10 = 90$.

VISUAL; LOGICAL/MATHEMATICAL

Early Finishers

Have students **find products with 9 as a factor**.

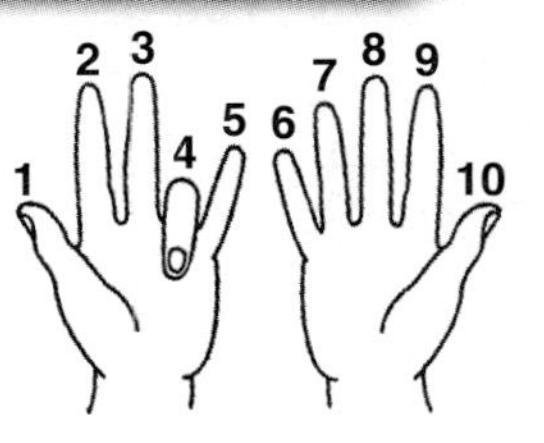

- Display $4 \times 9 =$ ■.
- Have students extend both hands, palms toward them, and count each finger as shown.
- Have students bend down the fourth finger. The number of fingers to the left of the bent finger tells how many tens are in the product. The number of fingers to the right tells how many ones. So, $4 \times 9 = 36$.
- Have students find additional products of 9's facts. Check students' work.

BODILY/KINESTHETIC

Lesson 11.1 Organizer

Objective To multiply with 9 and 10

Materials *For each student* hundred charts, p. TR14; colored pencils

1 INTRODUCE

QUICK REVIEW provides review of prerequisite skills.

WHY LEARN THIS? You can use 10's facts to find 9's facts. *Share the lesson objective with students.*

2 TEACH

Guided Instruction

- *Have students read the first page of the Learn section.*
  What addition sentence could you write for 5 × 10? 10 + 10 + 10 + 10 + 10 = 50
  What is another way to skip-count to find 5 × 10? Skip-count by 5s ten times.
  How can you find the product of 5 × 10 by looking at the first factor? Add a zero in the ones place to the first factor to find the product 50.
  REASONING What is the product of 37 × 10? of 681 × 10? Explain. 370; 6,810; find each product by adding a zero in the ones place to the first factor.

LESSON 1

Multiply with 9 and 10

Quick Review

1. $4 \times 8 = \blacksquare$ 32
2. $7 \times 5 = \blacksquare$ 35
3. $8 \times 0 = \blacksquare$ 0
4. $3 \times 6 = \blacksquare$ 18
5. $6 \times 7 = \blacksquare$ 42

Learn

TIMBER! Beavers cut down trees with their large front teeth. If 5 beavers each cut down 10 trees, how many trees did they cut down in all?

$5 \times 10 = \blacksquare$

One Way You can skip-count by tens 5 times.

0 5 10 15 20 25 30 35 40 45 50

Think: 10, 20, 30, 40, 50

So, $5 \times 10 = 50$.

Another Way Use a pattern to multiply by 10.

The product of 1 and any number equals that number.

$0 \times 1 = 0$
$1 \times 1 = 1$
$2 \times 1 = 2$
$3 \times 1 = 3$
$4 \times 1 = 4$
$5 \times 1 = 5$
$6 \times 1 = 6$
$7 \times 1 = 7$
$8 \times 1 = 8$
$9 \times 1 = 9$
$10 \times 1 = 10$

The product of 10 and any factor equals the other factor followed by a zero.

$0 \times 10 = 0$
$1 \times 10 = 10$
$2 \times 10 = 20$
$3 \times 10 = 30$
$4 \times 10 = 40$
$5 \times 10 = \blacksquare$
$6 \times 10 = 60$
$7 \times 10 = 70$
$8 \times 10 = 80$
$9 \times 10 = 90$
$10 \times 10 = 100$

So, $5 \times 10 = 50$. The beavers cut down 50 trees in all.

▲ When beavers cut down trees, they eat the bark and use the branches to build homes in the water.

×	0	1	2	3	4	5	6	7	8	9	10
0	0	0	0	0	0	0	0	0	0	0	0
1	0	1	2	3	4	5	6	7	8	9	10
2	0	2	4	6	8	10	12	14	16	18	20
3	0	3	6	9	12	15	18	21	24	27	30
4	0	4	8	12	16	20	24	28	32	36	40
5	0	5	10	15	20	25	30	35	40	45	50
6	0	6	12	18	24	30	36	42	48	54	60
7	0	7	14	21	28	35	42	49	56	63	70
8	0	8	16	24	32	40	48	56	64	72	80
9	0	9	18	27	36	45	54	63	72	81	90
10	0	10	20	30	40	50	60	70	80	90	100

REASONING

- How can you use skip-counting to find 6×10?
  count by 10's six times: 10, 20, 30, 40, 50, 60

212

Reteach 11.1

Multiply with 9 and 10

You can use facts of 10 to find facts of 9.

$8 \times 9 =$ __?__

First think of the facts of 10.	Then find 8 × 9.
Skip-count by tens 9 times. 10, 20, 30, 40, 50, 60, 70, 80, 90 So, 1 × 10 = 10 5 × 10 = 50 2 × 10 = 20 6 × 10 = 60 3 × 10 = 30 7 × 10 = 70 4 × 10 = 40 8 × 10 = 80 9 × 10 = 90	The 10's fact that can help me is **8 × 10 = 80** Next, subtract the first factor, 8. **80 − 8 = 72** Since 80 − 8 = 72, 8 × 9 = 72.

You can use patterns to find facts of 9.

- The tens digit is one less than the number being multiplied by 9.
  $8 \times 9 =$ __72__
- The sum of the digits in the product is **9**. $7 + 2 = 9$

Find the product.

1. 7 × 10 = __70__	2. 9 × 10 = __90__	3. 6 × 10 = __60__
70 − 7 = __63__	90 − 9 = __81__	60 − 6 = __54__
7 × 9 = __63__	9 × 9 = __81__	6 × 9 = __54__

4. 3 × 9 = __27__ 5. 5 × 10 = __50__ 6. 9 × 8 = __72__
7. 0 × 9 = __0__ 8. 1 × 10 = __10__ 9. 9 × 5 = __45__
10. 2 × 9 = __18__ 11. 9 × 7 = __63__ 12. 4 × 10 = __40__
13. 1 × 9 = __9__ 14. 10 × 3 = __30__ 15. 9 × 3 = __27__

Reteach RW57

Practice 11.1

Multiply with 9 and 10

Find the product.

1. 9 × 5 = 45 2. 10 × 9 = 90 3. 10 × 6 = 60 4. 10 × 8 = 80 5. 9 × 4 = 36
6. 9 × 6 = 54 7. 10 × 5 = 50 8. 10 × 3 = 30 9. 7 × 9 = 63 10. 10 × 2 = 20
11. 9 × 3 = 27 12. 10 × 4 = 40 13. 9 × 9 = 81 14. 10 × 7 = 70 15. 8 × 9 = 72

16. 8 × 10 = __80__ 17. 9 × 2 = __18__ 18. 1 × 10 = __10__
19. 1 × 9 = __9__ 20. 9 × 10 = __90__ 21. 9 × 5 = __45__
22. 10 × 2 = __20__ 23. 10 × 8 = __80__ 24. 9 × 7 = __63__

Find the missing factor.

25. __0__ × 8 = 0 26. __10__ × 2 = 20 27. 7 × __1__ = 7
28. 9 × __2__ = 6 × 3 29. 5 × 8 = __4__ × 10 30. __4__ × 9 = 6 × 6

Complete each table.

	Multiply by 9	
31.	9	81
32.	8	72

	Multiply by 7	
33.	6	42
34.	8	56

	Multiply by 10	
35.	7	70
36.	9	90

Mixed Review

Add or subtract.

37. \$8.09 − \$3.55 = \$4.54
38. \$7.00 − \$6.99 = \$0.01
39. \$5.55 + \$4.44 + \$3.33 = \$13.32
40. \$1.29 + \$1.39 + \$1.49 = \$4.17

Practice PW57

Multiply with 9

Lynn's class made 7 animal posters. The students drew 9 animals on each poster. How many animals did they draw in all?

$7 \times 9 = ■$

Lynn and Jeff use different ways to find 7×9.

Lynn

I'll think of the 10's fact first.

$7 \times 10 = 70$

Next, I'll subtract the first factor, 7.

$70 - 7 = 63$

Since $70 - 7 = 63$, $7 \times 9 = 63$.

Jeff

I'll use a pattern in the products of the 9's facts.

$7 \times 9 = ■$

- The tens digit will be 1 less than the factor 7.
- The sum of the digits in the product will be 9.

So, $7 \times 9 = 63$.

$0 \times 9 = 0$
$1 \times 9 = 9$
$2 \times 9 = 18$
$3 \times 9 = 27$
$4 \times 9 = 36$
$5 \times 9 = 45$
$6 \times 9 = 54$
$7 \times 9 = ■$
$8 \times 9 = 72$
$9 \times 9 = 81$

So, Lynn's class drew 63 animals.

MATH IDEA You can use facts you already know or a pattern to find 9's facts.

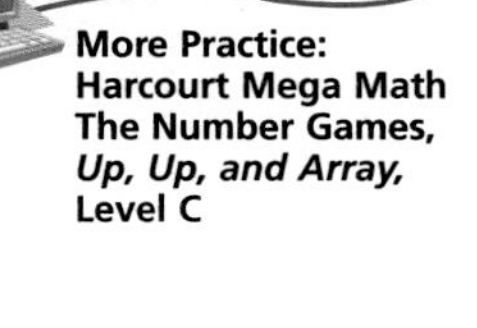

Technology Link

More Practice: Harcourt Mega Math The Number Games, *Up, Up, and Array,* Level C

Check

1. Explain how to use a 10's fact to find 3×9. $3 \times 10 = 30$; $30 - 3 = 27$.
2. Explain how to use a pattern to find 6×9. The tens digit of the product is 5; the sum of the digits of the product is 9; so $6 \times 9 = 54$.

Find the product.

3. $3 \times 10 = ■$ 30
4. $10 \times 6 = ■$ 60
5. $■ = 7 \times 9$ 63
6. $1 \times 9 = ■$ 9
7. $8 \times 9 = ■$ 72
8. $■ = 9 \times 2$ 18
9. $4 \times 10 = ■$ 40
10. $2 \times 10 = ■$ 20

Find the missing factor.

11. $■ \times 7 = 63$ 9
12. $5 \times ■ = 30$ 6
13. $10 \times ■ = 60$ 6
14. $■ \times 6 = 48$ 8
15. $■ \times 9 = 90$ 10
16. $6 \times ■ = 24$ 4
17. $■ \times 8 = 64$ 8
18. $9 \times ■ = 45$ 5

LESSON CONTINUES

North Carolina Standards **1.03** Develop fluency with multiplication from 1×1 to 12×12 and division to two-digit by one-digit numbers using: a) Strategies for multiplying and dividing numbers. *also* **5.01**

- *Discuss the two ways of multiplying with 9.*

How do 10's facts help you multiply with 9? Possible answers: Find the product of the 10's fact and subtract the other factor to find the product of the 9's fact.

In Jeff's way of multiplying with 9, how can you find the product by writing an addition sentence? $6 + ■ = 9$. The first addend is the tens digit, which is one less than the first factor. The sum is 9. The missing addend is the ones digit of the product. $6 + 3 = 9$, so $7 \times 9 = 63$.

Look at the 9's facts. What pattern do you see in the ones digits of the products? As the first factors increase by 1, the ones digits in the products decrease by 1.

3 PRACTICE

Guided Practice

Do Check Exercises 1–18 with your students. Identify students who are having difficulty and choose appropriate lesson resources to provide assistance.

Challenge 11.1

Combination Challenge

Use the numbers and symbols in each circle to make 4 different number sentences. Each number and symbol can be used only once in a sentence, but they can be used in more than one sentence. The first problem is done for you. Possible answers are given. Check students' sentences.

1. $3 \times 9 = 27$; $3 \times 4 = 12$; $3 \times 7 = 21$; $2 \times 7 = 14$ (circle: 3 9 1 × = 4 2 7)
2. $0 \times 4 = 0$; $4 \times 4 = 16$; $10 \times 4 = 40$; $1 \times 4 = 4$ (circle: 0 4 1 × = 0 4 6)
3. $1 \times 9 = 9$; $0 \times 9 = 0$; $9 \times 9 = 81$; $10 \times 9 = 90$ (circle: 9 0 1 × = 0 8 9)
4. $4 \times 9 = 36$; $7 \times 9 = 63$; $7 \times 7 = 49$; $6 \times 9 = 54$ (circle: 7 5 9 6 × = 4 3 7)
5. $2 \times 9 = 18$; $8 \times 9 = 72$; $7 \times 2 = 14$; $8 \times 2 = 16$ (circle: 2 9 1 × = 8 4 6 7)
6. $7 \times 9 = 63$; $6 \times 9 = 54$; $8 \times 7 = 56$; $4 \times 9 = 36$ (circle: 7 9 6 × = 4 5 8 3)
7. $5 \times 9 = 45$; $10 \times 4 = 40$; $10 \times 5 = 50$; $5 \times 1 = 5$ (circle: 5 0 9 1 × = 4 5 0 4)
8. $8 \times 8 = 64$; $8 \times 6 = 48$; $10 \times 6 = 60$; $10 \times 8 = 80$ (circle: 0 8 1 6 × = 6 8 4 0)

Challenge CW57

Problem Solving 11.1

Multiply with 9 and 10

Understand → Plan → Solve → Check

Write the correct answer.

1. Victor had a math test. He was not sure of the answer to $5 \times 9 =$ __?__. He thought it was either 45 or 54. Which answer should Victor write? **45**
2. The Ace Company sponsors 4 soccer teams. There are 9 players on each team. How many players does the company sponsor in all? **36 players**
3. Last year, Brad traveled for 2 weeks in Ohio and another 2 weeks in Texas. How many days did he travel altogether? **28 days**
4. A box of individual instant oatmeal packets contains 10 packets of each of 7 flavors. How many packets are there? **70 packets**

Choose the letter of the correct answer.

5. Look at the number line. Which numbers belong where the stars are?
   140 150 160 170 180 190 200 210 220
   A 142 and 192 C 147 and 217
   (B) 145 and 205 D 140 and 200
6. What number is represented by these base-ten blocks?
   (F) 158 H 851
   G 518 J 913
7. What number should be subtracted from 60 to find the product of 6×9?
   A 10 (C) 6
   B 9 D 5
8. Which number below is the ones digit of the product in all the multiplication facts of 10?
   F 10 H 1
   G 5 (J) 0
9. **Write About It** Describe the strategy you used to choose the correct answer for Problem 1.
   Possible answer: The tens digit in the product is one less than the factor being multiplied by 9.

Problem Solving PS57

COMMON ERROR ALERT

When multiplying with 10 and subtracting to find a 9's fact, students may subtract 9 instead of the other factor. Have students use counters as they model multiplying with 9. For example, have them make 10 groups of 6 counters and then subtract 1 group to show 60 − 6 and 9 × 6.

Incorrect	Correct
9 × 6 = ■	9 × 6 = ■
10 × 6 = 60	10 × 6 = 60
60 − 9 = 51	60 − 6 = 54
9 × 6 = 51	9 × 6 = 54

Independent Practice

Note that Exercises 58 and 60 are **multistep or strategy problems.** Assign Exercises 19–60.

MULTISTEP OR STRATEGY PROBLEM To solve Exercise 58, students can multiply 3 times the number of pieces, 10, and 2 times the number of pieces, 8, and then add the products to find the total number of pieces of pie.

SCAFFOLDED INSTRUCTION Use the prompts on Transparency 11 to guide instruction for the multistep or strategy problem in Exercise 60.

Practice and Problem Solving

Extra Practice, page 224, Set A

Find the product.

19. ■ = 10 × 4 **40**
20. 4 × 8 = ■ **32**
21. 9 × 8 = ■ **72**
22. ■ = 8 × 6 **48**
23. 9 × 9 = ■ **81**
24. ■ = 7 × 10 **70**
25. 10 × 10 = ■ **100**
26. 2 × 8 = ■ **16**
27. 10 × 8 **80**
28. 9 × 4 **36**
29. 5 × 10 **50**
30. 8 × 8 **64**
31. 9 × 3 **27**
32. 7 × 8 **56**
33. 4 × 3 **12**
34. 10 × 1 **10**
35. 8 × 3 **24**
36. 6 × 9 **54**
37. 9 × 7 **63**
38. 10 × 6 **60**

Find the missing factor.

39. ■ × 6 = 0 **0**
40. 10 × ■ = 20 **2**
41. ■ × 7 = 28 **4**
42. 5 × ■ = 4 × 10 **8**
43. ■ × 2 = 12 + 8 **10**
44. 6 × 6 = ■ × 4 **9**

Copy and complete each table.

	Multiply by 10.		
45.	6	■	**60**
46.	8	■	**80**

	Multiply by 8.		
47.	5	■	**40**
48.	7	■	**56**

	Multiply by 9.		
49.	8	■	**72**
50.	9	■	**81**

Compare. Write <, >, or = for each ●.

51. 10 × 6 ● 75 − 15 **=**
52. 9 × 9 ● 10 × 8 **>**
53. 7 × 9 ● 10 × 7 **<**
54. 8 × 9 ● 9 × 8 **=**
55. 16 + 40 ● 9 × 6 **>**
56. 10 × 10 ● 50 + 50 **=**

57. **FAST FACT** • SOCIAL STUDIES The beaver was adopted as the New York state animal in 1975. How many years ago was that? **Possible answer: In 2004: 29 years ago**

58. Malcolm cut 3 pies into 10 pieces each and 2 pies into 8 pieces each. How many pieces of pie did he have in all? **46 pieces**

59. **What's the Error?** Describe Mike's error. Then solve the problem correctly. **It should be 40 − 4 = 36; 9 × 4 = 36.**

Mike
9 x 4 = ■
Think: 10 x 4 = 40
40 − 9 = 31
So, 9 x 4 = 31.

60. Emiko had 4 sheets with 10 animal stickers on each. After she gave some stickers away, she had 37 left. How many stickers did she give away? **3 stickers**

214

Alternative Teaching Strategy

Scaffolded Instruction

PURPOSE Students use different strategies to multiply with 9 and 10 and explore the relationship between 10's facts and 9's facts.

MATERIALS *For each pair* ones and tens blocks

Step 1
Display 5 × 10 and ask students to use the ones blocks to model the problem in two ways. Have them make one model using equal groups and one model using an array.

Step 2
Display 5 × 9. Ask students how they could change each of their models to show this problem. Have students subtract 1 block from each of their groups to show 5 groups of 9. Then have them subtract one column of their array to show 5 rows of 9.

Equal Groups
5 x 10 = 50

5 x 9 = (5 x 10) − 5 = 45

Array
5 x 10 = 50

5 x 9 = (5 x 10) − 5 = 45

Step 3
Have students find the product 5 × 9. Point out that the product is the same as 5 × 10 minus 5.

Step 4
Instruct students to repeat Steps 1, 2, and 3 to show the 10's and 9's facts for 6, 7, 8, and 9.

Step 5
Ask students to describe any patterns they see in the products. Then ask: How can you use 10's facts to help you find 9's facts? Find the product of the 10's fact first and then subtract the other factor.

Getting Ready for the EOG Test

61. Jon sold 6 boxes of cards for a fund raiser. Each box had 10 cards. How many cards did he sell altogether? C

A 6
B 16
C 60
D 70

62. Dawn sold 7 planters. Three planters had 9 flowers and 4 planters had 10 flowers. How many flowers did she sell in all? A

A 67
B 64
C 57
D 53

Problem Solving LINKUP . . . to Reading

STRATEGY • CLASSIFY AND CATEGORIZE
When you *classify* information, you group similar information. When you *categorize,* you name the groups that you have classified.

MATERIALS: hundred charts, colored pencils

Shade the multiples of 2, 3, 4, 5, 6, and 7 on your charts.

1	2	3	4	5	6	7	8	9	10
11	12	13	14	15	16	17	18	19	20
21	22	23	24	25	26	27	28	29	30
31	32	33	34	35	36	37	38	39	40
41	42	43	44	45	46	47	48	49	50
51	52	53	54	55	56	57	58	59	60
61	62	63	64	65	66	67	68	69	70
71	72	73	74	75	76	77	78	79	80
81	82	83	84	85	86	87	88	89	90
91	92	93	94	95	96	97	98	99	100

For 1–6, use your hundred charts. Tell if the statement is *true* or *false*. If the statement is false, tell why.

3. False; If both numbers are odd, the product is odd. If one number is odd and one number is even, the product is even.

1. Even numbers have even multiples. true
2. Odd numbers have odd and even multiples. true
3. The product of any number and an odd number is an odd number. See above.
4. The product of any number and an even number is an even number. true
5. The product of any number and 6 can be even or odd. False; 6 is an even number and when one number is even, the product is even.
6. The product of 9 and 6 is an even number. true

Problem Solving LINKUP . . . to Reading

- *Have students shade the multiples on the hundred charts different colors.*
  What pattern do you notice in the multiples of 3? Possible answer: The multiples alternate from odd to even.

4 ASSESS

Summarize the lesson by having students:

DISCUSS What strategies could you use to find the number of days in 10 weeks? Possible answers: Use what I know about place value. 7 tens = 70; skip-count by 10s seven times to find $7 \times 10 = 70$.

WRITE Describe how to use two different strategies to find 8 × 9. Possible answers: find $8 \times 10 = 80$ and then subtract 8 from 80 to find $8 \times 9 = 72$; find 72 by using the pattern that the tens digit is one less than the factor 8 and the sum of the digits is 9.

LESSON QUIZ

Transparency 11.1

Find the product.

1. $6 \times 9 = \blacksquare$ 54
2. $\blacksquare = 3 \times 10$ 30
3. 10×8 — 80
4. 9×9 — 81

Lesson 11.2

Algebra: Find a Rule

Lesson Planning

Objective To recognize a rule in a linear pattern and extend the pattern

NCTM Standards

1. Number and Operations
2. Algebra
6. Problem Solving
7. Reasoning and Proof
8. Communication
10. Representation

Math Background

Experiences with finding a rule will help students' understanding of algebra.

- You can use a table to show a number pattern that describes a relationship between two numbers.
- Writing a rule is a readiness activity for algebra.
- Words are used to express the rule or equation; later, variables will be used.

Warm-Up Resources

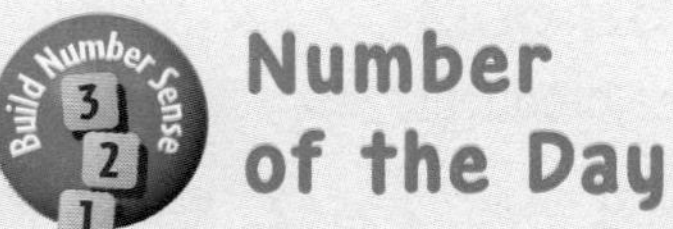

The number of the day is the number of pennies in a dime. Use this number to write and solve 5 multiplication sentences. Possible answers: $2 \times 10 = 20$, $9 \times 10 = 90$, $5 \times 10 = 50$, $4 \times 10 = 40$, $1 \times 10 = 10$

Daily Facts Practice

Have students practice addition and subtraction facts by completing Set B of *Teacher's Resource Book*, p. TR91.

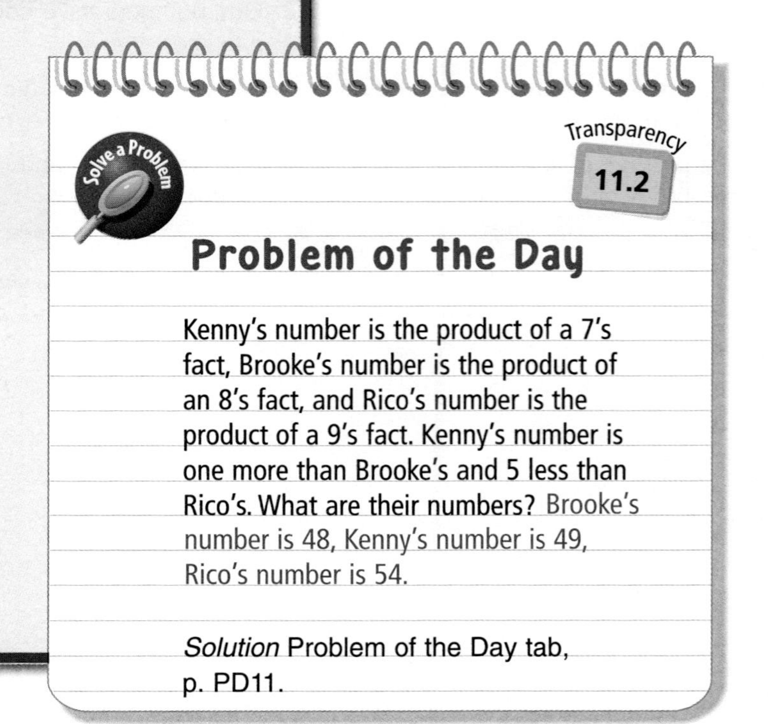

Problem of the Day

Kenny's number is the product of a 7's fact, Brooke's number is the product of an 8's fact, and Rico's number is the product of a 9's fact. Kenny's number is one more than Brooke's and 5 less than Rico's. What are their numbers? Brooke's number is 48, Kenny's number is 49, Rico's number is 54.

Solution Problem of the Day tab, p. PD11.

Intervention and Extension Resources

Alternative Teaching Strategy

Help students **make tables with multiplication patterns**. Ask them to think of real-world patterns, such as the number of desks in each row in the classroom or the number of legs on a spider.

- Have students work in pairs to make a table showing their pattern.
- Have them label each row and complete the first 5 columns of the first row.
- Instruct them to complete the first 2 numbers in the second row and leave the last 3 columns blank.
- Ask students to exchange tables, find the next 3 numbers in the pattern, and write the rule. Check students' work.

VISUAL

LOGICAL/MATHEMATICAL

Multistep and Strategy Problems

The following multistep or strategy problem is provided in Lesson 11.2:

Page	Item
217	9

ESOL/ESL

ESOL/ESL

Help students **build understanding of multiplication rules**. Explain that a rule is a procedure for solving a mathematical problem.

Display the following table:

Dogs	1	2	3	4	5
Legs	4	8	12	16	20

Have students take turns reading each column of the table in the following way: *One dog has four legs, two dogs have eight legs*, and so on.

Ask students to find the rule for the pattern. multiply number of dogs by 4 Then ask students to continue the pattern. How many legs do 6 dogs have? 24 7 dogs? 28

Have students repeat the activity, finding the rule for the number of dogs' ears. Check students' work.

KINESTHETIC, AUDITORY

LOGICAL/MATHEMATICAL

Advanced Learners

Challenge small groups of students to **practice finding a rule by playing a game**. The first student thinks of a rule, such as multiply by 4, but does not tell the group. The second student says a number, such as 5. The first student mentally performs the rule and says only the result, 20. A third student says a different number, such as 6. Again, the first student performs the same rule and says only the result, 24. Play continues until a student discovers the rule. Have students change roles. Check students' work.

AUDITORY

LOGICAL/MATHEMATICAL

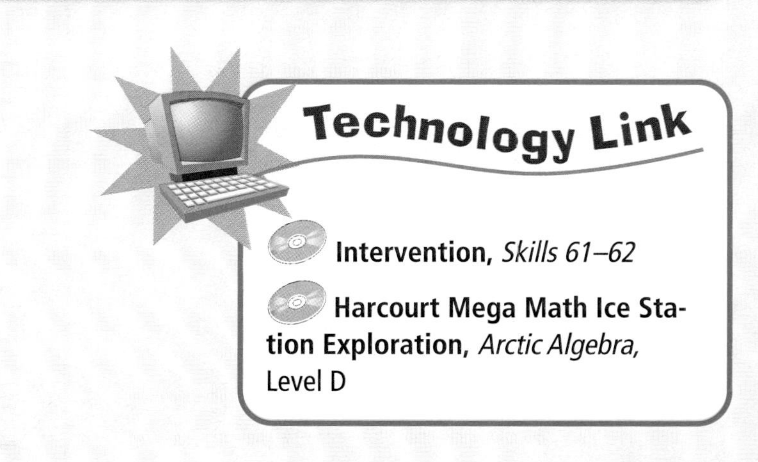

Technology Link

Intervention, *Skills 61–62*

Harcourt Mega Math Ice Station Exploration, *Arctic Algebra,* Level D

Lesson 11.2 Organizer

Objective To recognize a rule in a linear pattern and extend the pattern

Quick Review provides review of prerequisite skills.

Why Learn This? You can write a rule to continue a pattern, such as multiply by 5 to find the number of nickels in a given number of quarters. *Share the lesson objective with students.*

2 TEACH

Guided Instruction

- *Ask students to read the Learn section.*
  How does the table help you find a rule for the pattern? Possible answer: by showing the numbers in an organized way so that the pattern is clear
  What is another way that you could describe a rule for the pattern? Possible answer: skip-count by 4s as many times as the number of horses.
- *Have students look at the Example.*
  What does the table show? the cost of different numbers of loaves of bread
  Reasoning If 9 loaves of bread cost $27, how much does each loaf cost? $3

3 PRACTICE

Guided Practice

Do Check Exercises 1–2 with your students. Identify students who are having difficulty and choose appropriate lesson resources to provide assistance.

LESSON 2

Algebra: Find a Rule

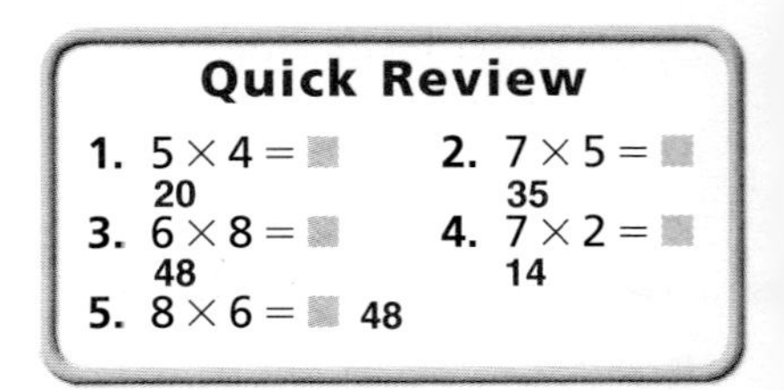

Learn

CLIP CLOP Horses wear a horseshoe on each of their 4 hooves. How many horseshoes are needed for 6 horses?

Think: 1 horse needs 4 horseshoes.
2 horses need 8 horseshoes.
3 horses need 12 horseshoes, and so on.

Look for a pattern. Write a rule.

Horses	1	2	3	4	5	6
Horseshoes	4	8	12	16	20	■

Pattern: The number of horseshoes equals the number of horses times 4.

Rule: Multiply the number of horses by 4.

Since $6 \times 4 = 24$, then 24 horseshoes are needed for 6 horses.

MATH IDEA You can write a rule to describe a number pattern in a table.

Technology Link
More Practice: Harcourt Mega Math Ice Station Exploration, *Arctic Algebra*, Level D

Example

Write a rule to find the cost of the bread.

Loaves of bread	1	2	4	5	7	9
Cost	$3	$6	$12	$15	$21	$27

Rule: Multiply the number of loaves of bread by $3.

- How can you use the rule to find the cost of 3 loaves of bread? **3 loaves of bread × $3 = $9.**

Check

1. **Explain** how you could use a rule to find the number of horseshoes on 8 horses. **Multiply the number of horses by 4; 8 × 4 = 32; 32 horseshoes**

216

Reteach 11.2

Algebra: Find a Rule

Each person in Bob's computer lab has 10 fingers. There are 8 people in his computer lab. How many fingers is this?

Think: **1** person has 10 fingers.
2 people have 20 fingers.
3 people have 30 fingers.

Organize your work in a table. Look for a pattern. Write a rule.

People	1	2	3	4	5	6	7	8
Fingers	10	20	30	40	50	60	70	?

Pattern	Rule
The number of fingers equals the number of people times 10.	Multiply the number of people by 10.

Since $8 \times 10 = 80$, then there are 80 fingers in the computer lab.

Write a rule for each table. Then complete the table.
Possible rules are given.

1.

Chairs	1	2	3	4	5	6
Legs	4	8	12	16	**20**	**24**

Rule: Multiply chairs by 4.

2.

Dollars	4	5	6	7	8	9
Dimes	40	50	60	**70**	**80**	**90**

Rule: Multiply dollars by 10.

3.

Toys	1	2	3	4	5	6
Rings	2	4	6	8	**10**	**12**

Rule: Multiply toys by 2.

4.

Quarters	4	5	6	7	8
Nickels	20	25	30	**35**	**40**

Rule: Multiply quarters by 5.

5.

Couches	1	2	3	4	5
Cushions	4	8	12	**16**	**20**

Rule: Multiply couches by 4.

6.

Quizzes	5	6	7	8	9
Answers	30	36	42	**48**	**54**

Rule: Multiply quizzes by 6.

RW58 Reteach

Practice 11.2

Algebra: Find a Rule

Write a rule for each table. Then complete the table. **Possible rules are given.**

1.

Flutes	2	3	4	5	6
Trumpets	6	9	12	**15**	**18**

Rule: **Multiply flutes by 3.**

2.

Cups	1	2	3	4	5	6
Ounces	8	16	24	**32**	**40**	**48**

Rule: **Multiply cups by 8.**

3.

Plates	5	6	7	8	9	10
Bowls	10	12	14	16	**18**	**20**

Rule: **Multiply plates by 2.**

4.

Plants	4	5	6	7	8	9
Flowers	24	30	36	**42**	**48**	**54**

Rule: **Multiply plants by 6.**

5. Each box holds 4 toys. How many toys do 5 boxes hold?

Boxes	1	2	3	4	5
Toys	4	8	**12**	**16**	**20**

Rule: **Multiply boxes by 4.**

6. Four shelves hold 36 toys. How many toys do 9 shelves hold?

Shelves	4	5	6	7	8	9
Toys	36	45	**54**	**63**	**72**	**81**

Rule: **Multiply shelves by 9.**

Mixed Review

Find the elapsed time.

7. 7:00 P.M. to 8:30 P.M. **1 hour 30 minutes**
8. 4:00 A.M. to noon **8 hours**
9. 9:00 A.M. to 1:00 P.M. **4 hours**
10. 6:30 P.M. to 10:15 P.M. **3 hours 45 minutes**

Use mental math to find the sum.

11. 52 + 48 + 24 + 26 = **150**
12. 17 + 13 + 16 + 14 = **60**
13. 51 + 49 + 47 + 53 = **200**
14. 19 + 21 + 15 + 15 = **70**

PW58 Practice

2. Write a rule for the table. Then copy and complete the table. **Multiply nickels by 5.**

Nickels	1	2	3	4	5	6	7	8	9	10
Pennies	5	10	15	■	■	■	■	■	■	■
				20	**25**	**30**	**35**	**40**	**45**	**50**

Practice and Problem Solving

Extra Practice, page 224, Set B

Write a rule for each table. Then copy and complete the table. **Possible rules are given.**

3. Multiply spiders by 8; 32, 40, 48
4. Multiply toy cars by $2; $8, $10, $12

3.

Spiders	1	2	3	4	5	6
Legs	8	16	24	■	■	■

4.

Toy cars	1	2	3	4	5	6
Cost	$2	$4	$6	■	■	■

5.

Tables	3	4	5	7	8	9
Legs	12	16	20	■	■	■

Multiply tables by 4; 28, 32, 36

6.

Guitars	2	3	5	6	7	8
Strings	12	18	30	■	■	■

Multiply guitars by 6; 36, 42, 48

For 7–8, use the table below.

Dimes	1	2	3	4	5	6	7	8	9	10
Nickels	2	4	6	■	■	■	■	■	■	■

7. Write a rule to find the number of nickels. Copy and complete the table. **Rule: Multiply dimes by 2; 8, 10, 12, 14, 16, 18, 20**

8. **REASONING** How many dimes can you trade for 18 nickels? How many nickels can you trade for 8 dimes? **9 dimes; 16 nickels**

9. **REASONING** Yogurt comes in packages of 6 cups. How many packages are needed to serve 23 students each a cup of yogurt? **4 packages**

10. Each pudding pack costs $4. How much do 5 packs cost? Make a table and write a rule to find your answer. **Check students' tables. Rule: Multiply the number of packs by $4; 5 packs cost $20.**

Getting Ready for the EOG Test

11. The table shows how many people can ride in rafts. If this pattern continues, how many people can ride in 10 rafts? **D**

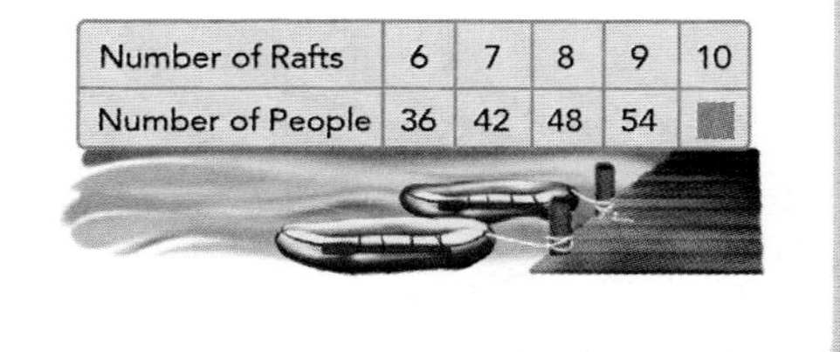

Number of Rafts	6	7	8	9	10
Number of People	36	42	48	54	■

A 18 **C** 48
B 36 **D** 60

Independent Practice

Note that Exercise 9 is a **multistep or strategy problem.** Assign Exercises 3–10.

Summarize the lesson by having students:

DISCUSS How do you find a rule for a pattern? Possible answer: Look at the top numbers in the pattern and determine how they relate to the bottom numbers.

WRITE What rule could you use to help you find the number of tires on 9 cars? Make a table. Multiply the number of cars by 4. Check students' work.

LESSON QUIZ

Transparency 11.2

Write a rule for each table. Then copy and complete the table.

1.

ants	1	2	3	4	5	6
legs	6	12	18	■	■	■

Multiply ants by 6. 24, 30, 36

2.

quarters	3	4	5	6	7	8
nickels	15	20	25	■	■	■

Multiply quarters by 5. 30, 35, 40

North Carolina Standards 1.03 Develop fluency with multiplication from 1 × 1 to 12 × 12 and division to two-digit by one-digit numbers using: a) Strategies for multiplying and dividing numbers. *also* **5.01**

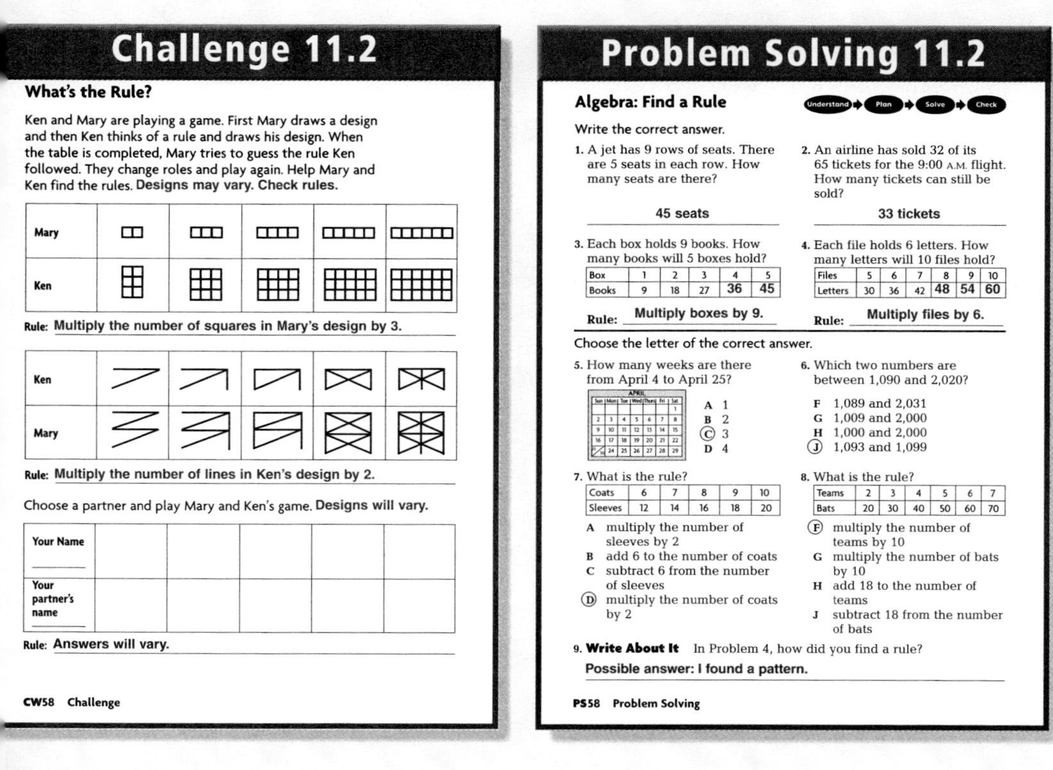

Challenge 11.2

What's the Rule?

Ken and Mary are playing a game. First Mary draws a design and then Ken thinks of a rule and draws his design. When the table is completed, Mary tries to guess the rule Ken followed. They change roles and play again. Help Mary and Ken find the rules. **Designs may vary. Check rules.**

Rule: **Multiply the number of squares in Mary's design by 3.**

Rule: **Multiply the number of lines in Ken's design by 2.**

Choose a partner and play Mary and Ken's game. **Designs will vary.**

Your Name					
Your partner's name					

Rule: **Answers will vary.**

CW58 Challenge

Problem Solving 11.2

Algebra: Find a Rule

Understand ➔ Plan ➔ Solve ➔ Check

Write the correct answer.

1. A jet has 9 rows of seats. There are 5 seats in each row. How many seats are there?

45 seats

2. An airline has sold 32 of its 65 tickets for the 9:00 A.M. flight. How many tickets can still be sold?

33 tickets

3. Each box holds 9 books. How many books will 5 boxes hold?

Box	1	2	3	4	5
Books	9	18	27	**36**	**45**

Rule: **Multiply boxes by 9.**

4. Each file holds 6 letters. How many letters will 10 files hold?

Files	5	6	7	8	9	10
Letters	30	36	42	**48**	**54**	**60**

Rule: **Multiply files by 6.**

Choose the letter of the correct answer.

5. How many weeks are there from April 4 to April 25?

A 1
B 2
(C) 3
D 4

6. Which two numbers are between 1,090 and 2,020?

F 1,089 and 2,031
G 1,009 and 2,000
H 1,000 and 2,000
(J) 1,093 and 1,099

7. What is the rule?

Coats	6	7	8	9	10
Sleeves	12	14	16	18	20

A multiply the number of sleeves by 2
B add 6 to the number of coats
C subtract 6 from the number of sleeves
(D) multiply the number of coats by 2

8. What is the rule?

Teams	2	3	4	5	6	7
Bats	20	30	40	50	60	70

(F) multiply the number of teams by 10
G multiply the number of bats by 10
H add 18 to the number of teams
J subtract 18 from the number of bats

9. **Write About It** In Problem 4, how did you find a rule?
Possible answer: I found a pattern.

PS58 Problem Solving

Lesson 11.3

Algebra: Multiply with 3 Factors

Lesson Planning

PROFESSIONAL DEVELOPMENT

Objective To multiply with 3 factors and use the Associative Property of Multiplication

NCTM Standards

1. Number and Operations
2. Algebra
6. Problem Solving
7. Reasoning and Proof
8. Communication
10. Representation

Math Background

These ideas will help students understand how to multiply with 3 factors and use the Associative Property of Multiplication.

- Use groups of arrays to show multiplication sentences with 3 factors.
- Use parentheses to group the two factors that will be multiplied first.
- When there are 3 or more factors, it does not matter how they are grouped; the product remains the same.

Vocabulary

Associative Property of Multiplication When the grouping of factors is changed, the product remains the same.

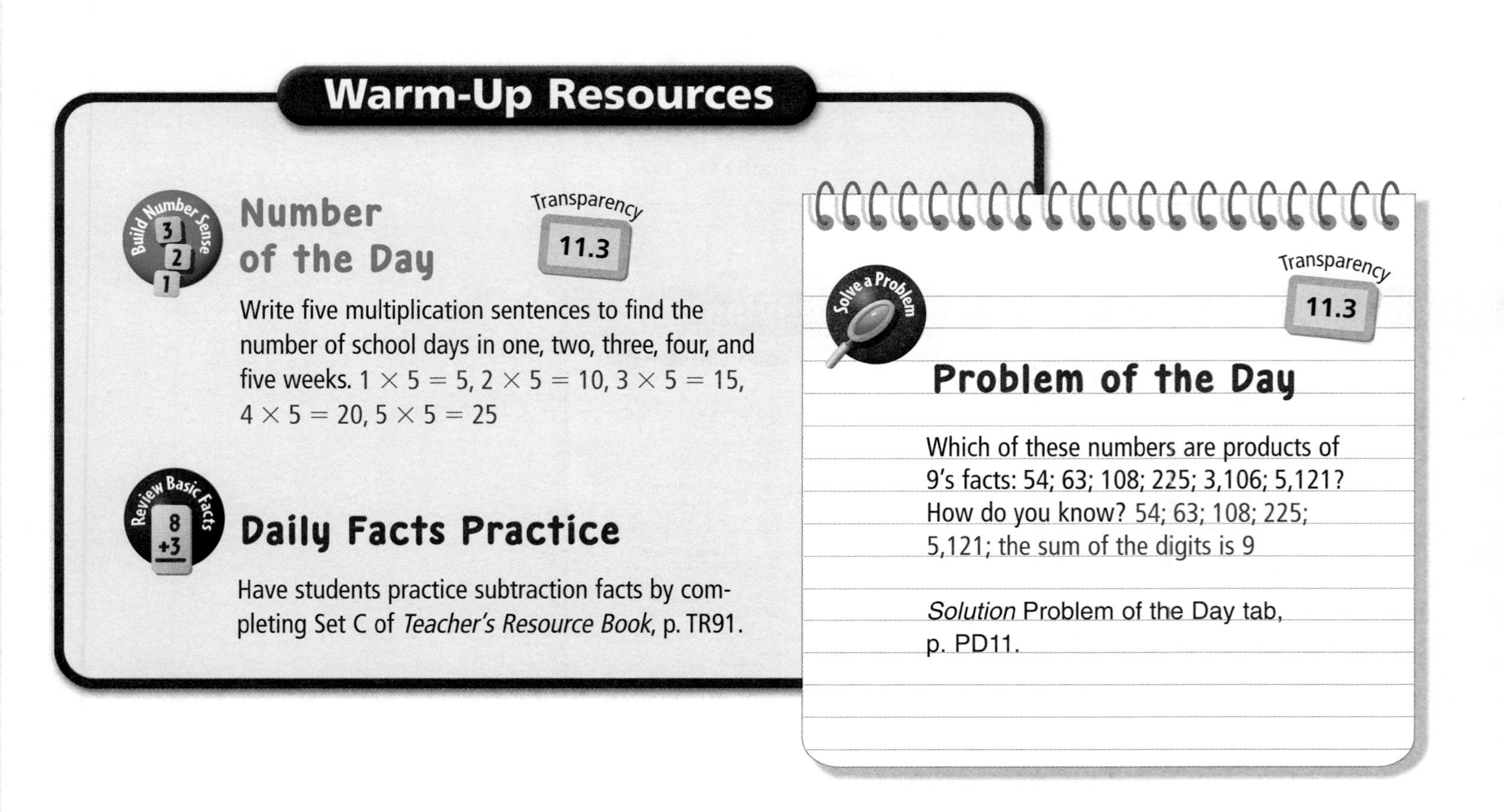

Warm-Up Resources

Number of the Day

Transparency 11.3

Write five multiplication sentences to find the number of school days in one, two, three, four, and five weeks. $1 \times 5 = 5$, $2 \times 5 = 10$, $3 \times 5 = 15$, $4 \times 5 = 20$, $5 \times 5 = 25$

Daily Facts Practice

Have students practice subtraction facts by completing Set C of *Teacher's Resource Book*, p. TR91.

Problem of the Day

Transparency 11.3

Which of these numbers are products of 9's facts: 54; 63; 108; 225; 3,106; 5,121? How do you know? 54; 63; 108; 225; 5,121; the sum of the digits is 9

Solution Problem of the Day tab, p. PD11.

REACHING ALL LEARNERS

Intervention and Extension Resources

Alternative Teaching Strategy

MATERIALS *For each pair* 3 spinners: two with four sections labeled 0–3, p. TR67; one with 6 sections labeled 4–9, p. TR68

Help students **practice multiplication with 3 factors.**

- Tell students that each number on the spinners is a factor.
- Have one student spin each spinner.
- The partner writes a multiplication sentence using the 3 numbers as factors, shows a grouping using parentheses, and finds the product.
- Have partners reverse roles and continue until each partner has taken 5 turns. Check students' work.

KINESTHETIC

BODILY/KINESTHETIC

Multistep and Strategy Problems

The following multistep or strategy problem is provided in Lesson 11.3:

Page	Item
219	30

Special Needs

Help students **model multiplying with 3 factors.**

Display the following multiplication sentences:

$(2 \times 2) \times 3 = 12$

$2 \times (2 \times 3) = 12$

Tell students that they can make groups of arrays to find each product. Arrange 12 students into 3 groups. Have each group stand in 2 rows of 2. Ask: Which sentence does this grouping represent? $(2 \times 2) \times 3 = 12$

Select another 12 students to show the second number sentence. Ask classmates to work together to identify the arrangement. Students should make 2 groups of 2 rows of 3 people.

Have students compare the two groupings. Ask: What do you notice about the two groups of students? The total number of students is the same. The grouping is different.

KINESTHETIC

LOGICAL/MATHEMATICAL

Advanced Learners

Challenge students to **find the missing factor in problems with 3 factors.**

Display the following incomplete number sentences:

$\blacksquare \times 2 \times 3 = 24$ 4 $7 \times \blacksquare \times 2 = 14$ 1

$3 \times 3 \times \blacksquare = 81$ 9 $2 \times \blacksquare \times 4 = 48$ 6

Ask students to find each missing factor. Then have students write their own number sentences with missing factors and exchange with a partner to solve. Check students' work.

VISUAL

LOGICAL/MATHEMATICAL

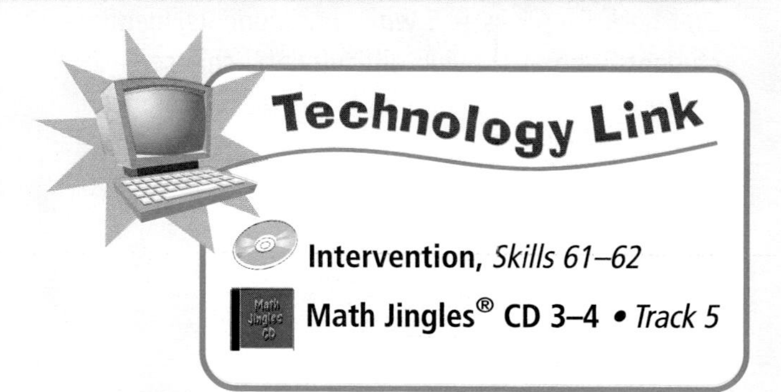

Technology Link
Intervention, *Skills 61–62*
Math Jingles® CD 3–4 • *Track 5*

Lesson 11.3 Organizer

Objective To multiply with 3 factors and use the Associative Property of Multiplication

Vocabulary Associative Property of Multiplication

Quick Review provides review of prerequisite skills.

Why Learn This? When you multiply three factors, one way of grouping them may be easier to multiply than another. *Share the lesson objective with students.*

2 TEACH

Guided Instruction

- *Have students read the Learn section.*
  What does each factor in the problem represent? 3: number of months Julia has been taking riding lessons; 2: number of hours she rides during each lesson; 4: number of lessons each month
  Why do you multiply 3 × 2 × 4 to find the total number of hours that Julia has ridden a horse? Multiply the number of months by the number of hours by the number of lessons to find the total.
- *Ask students to read the Math Idea.*
  How can the Associative Property of Multiplication help you multiply with 3 factors? Possible answer: You can group the factors in ways that make them easier to multiply.

Modifying Instruction Have students use square tiles to model the arrays shown.

Guided Practice

Do Check Exercises 1–5 with your students. Identify students who are having difficulty and choose appropriate lesson resources to provide assistance.

LESSON 3

Algebra: Multiply with 3 Factors

Quick Review

1. $2 \times 2 = \blacksquare$ 4
2. $4 \times 7 = \blacksquare$ 28
3. $3 \times 2 = \blacksquare$ 6
4. $6 \times 5 = \blacksquare$ 30
5. $9 \times 4 = \blacksquare$ 36

VOCABULARY

Associative Property of Multiplication

Learn

PRACTICE, PRACTICE . . . Julia has been taking horseback riding lessons for 3 months. At each lesson she rides for 2 hours. If she has 4 lessons each month, for how many hours has she ridden?

$$3 \times 2 \times 4 = \blacksquare$$

MATH IDEA The Associative Property of Multiplication, or Grouping Property, states that when the grouping of factors is changed, the product remains the same.

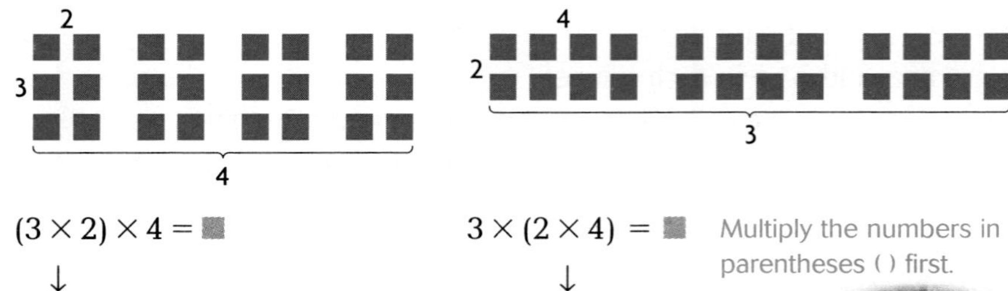

$(3 \times 2) \times 4 = \blacksquare$
↓
6 $\times 4 = 24$

$3 \times (2 \times 4) = \blacksquare$
↓
$3 \times$ 8 $= 24$

Multiply the numbers in parentheses ( ) first.

So, Julia has ridden for 24 hours.

Check

1. **Tell** which numbers you would multiply first to find $7 \times 2 \times 3$ mentally. **Possible answer: Find 2 × 3 = 6, then 7 × 6 = 42.**

Find each product.

2. $(2 \times 4) \times 1 = \blacksquare$ 8
3. $2 \times (1 \times 3) = \blacksquare$ 6
4. $2 \times (4 \times 2) = \blacksquare$ 16
5. $(3 \times 3) \times 2 = \blacksquare$ 18

Reteach 11.3

Algebra: Multiply with 3 Factors

The **Associative Property of Multiplication** states that when the grouping of factors is changed, the product remains the same.

$3 \times 2 \times 5 =$?

Multiply the first two factors first.	Multiply the numbers in ( ) first.	Multiply the last two factors first.
$(3 \times 2) \times 5 =$? ↓ **6** $\times 5 = 30$		$3 \times (2 \times 5) =$? ↓ $3 \times$ **10** $= 30$

Find each product.

1. $(7 \times 1) \times 3 =$? ↓ 7 $\times 3 =$ 21
2. $8 \times (5 \times 2) =$? ↓ $8 \times$ 10 $=$ 80
3. $(3 \times 3) \times 6 =$? ↓ 9 $\times 6 =$ 54
4. $(1 \times 3) \times 9 =$ 27
5. $(2 \times 4) \times 5 =$ 40
6. $4 \times (2 \times 2) =$ 16
7. $9 \times (0 \times 9) =$ 0
8. $(1 \times 5) \times 10 =$ 50
9. $(3 \times 9) \times 0 =$ 0
10. $2 \times (3 \times 3) =$ 18
11. $4 \times (4 \times 2) =$ 32
12. $7 \times (2 \times 3) =$ 42
13. $8 \times (2 \times 1) =$ 16
14. $(5 \times 2) \times 9 =$ 90
15. $(1 \times 8) \times 4 =$ 32
16. $4 \times (2 \times 3) =$ 24
17. $(3 \times 2) \times 2 =$ 12
18. $6 \times (2 \times 3) =$ 36
19. $(8 \times 1) \times 8 =$ 64
20. $10 \times (3 \times 2) =$ 60
21. $(0 \times 7) \times 10 =$ 0
22. $6 \times (4 \times 2) =$ 48
23. $(3 \times 3) \times 3 =$ 27
24. $2 \times (2 \times 2) =$ 8
25. $(1 \times 1) \times 1 =$ 1
26. $4 \times (2 \times 4) =$ 32
27. $(2 \times 4) \times 9 =$ 72

Reteach RW59

Practice 11.3

Algebra: Multiply with 3 Factors

Find each product.

1. $(3 \times 2) \times 3 =$ 18
2. $6 \times (4 \times 2) =$ 48
3. $(3 \times 3) \times 5 =$ 45
4. $(2 \times 2) \times 8 =$ 32
5. $(1 \times 4) \times 7 =$ 28
6. $4 \times (7 \times 1) =$ 28
7. $6 \times (0 \times 7) =$ 0
8. $(3 \times 3) \times 10 =$ 90
9. $(7 \times 1) \times 8 =$ 56

Use parentheses. Find the product.

10. $3 \times 3 \times 6 =$ 54
11. $4 \times 4 \times 2 =$ 32
12. $9 \times 3 \times 2 =$ 54
13. $7 \times 2 \times 2 =$ 28
14. $2 \times 4 \times 7 =$ 56
15. $4 \times 9 \times 1 =$ 36
16. $4 \times 2 \times 5 =$ 40
17. $3 \times 2 \times 10 =$ 60
18. $4 \times 2 \times 7 =$ 56

Find the missing factor.

19. $(8 \times$ 0 $) \times 8 = 0$
20. 6 $\times (3 \times 2) = 36$
21. (1 $\times 4) \times 3 = 12$
22. $6 \times (3 \times$ 3 $) = 54$
23. $(3 \times 3) \times$ 10 $= 90$
24. 8 $\times (5 \times 2) = 80$
25. (6 $\times 1) \times 1 = 6$
26. $4 \times ($ 2 $\times 4) = 32$
27. $(2 \times 4) \times$ 8 $= 64$

Mixed Review

Write the m ssing number that makes each sentence true.

28. $9 +$ 11 $= 20$
29. $8 =$ 11 $- 3$
30. 31 $+ 13 = 44$
31. $560 = 200 +$ 360

Write $<$, $>$, or $=$ for each ○.

32. 544 (=) 544
33. 5,106 (>) 5,099
34. 467 + 3 (<) 471

Complete the pattern.

35. 6, 12, 18 24, 30, 36, 42, 48
36. 39, 49, 59, 69, 79, 89, 99
37. 75, 70, 65, 60, 55, 50, 45, 40

Practice PW59

Practice and Problem Solving

Extra Practice, page 224, Set C

Find each product.

6. $(4 \times 2) \times 5 = \blacksquare$ **40**
7. $(3 \times 3) \times 6 = \blacksquare$ **54**
8. $8 \times (2 \times 2) = \blacksquare$ **32**
9. $(6 \times 1) \times 2 = \blacksquare$ **12**
10. $\blacksquare = 5 \times (7 \times 1)$ **35**
11. $\blacksquare = 3 \times (3 \times 3)$ **27**
12. $\blacksquare = (2 \times 3) \times 5$ **30**
13. $\blacksquare = (5 \times 2) \times 7$ **70**
14. $(4 \times 2) \times 4 = \blacksquare$ **32**

Use parentheses. Find the product.

15. $6 \times 1 \times 8 = \blacksquare$ **48**
16. $9 \times 2 \times 1 = \blacksquare$ **18**
17. $\blacksquare = 7 \times 4 \times 2$ **56**
18. $\blacksquare = 9 \times 8 \times 0$ **0**
19. $6 \times 5 \times 2 = \blacksquare$ **60**
20. $4 \times 2 \times 9 = \blacksquare$ **72**

Find the missing factor.

28. Possible answer: Since (9 × 2) × 2 is the same as 9 × (2 × 2), 18 × 2 is the same as 9 × (2 × 2).

21. $(1 \times \blacksquare) \times 8 = 64$ **8**
22. $(2 \times 4) \times \blacksquare = 24$ **3**
23. $42 = 7 \times (\blacksquare \times 2)$ **3**
24. $2 \times 4 \times \blacksquare = 8$ **1**
25. $2 \times 4 \times \blacksquare = 40$ **5**
26. $14 = \blacksquare \times 2 \times 7$ **1**
27. Jed has three $1 bills, 5 quarters, and 2 nickels. How much money does he have? **$4.35**
28. **REASONING** Explain why 18×2 is the same as $9 \times (2 \times 2)$. **See above.**
29. Ross made 2 cakes for each of 3 friends. In each cake he used 3 apples. How many apples did he use? **18 apples**
30. **ALGEBRA** Darla had 2 singing lessons a month for 2 months. She learned the same number of songs at each lesson. She learned 12 songs in all. How many songs did she learn at each lesson? **3 songs**

31. Possible answer: Numbers can be multiplied in any order without changing the product. 2 × 3 × 4 = (2 × 3) × 4 or 6 × 4 = 24; or 2 × (3 × 4) = 2 × 12 = 24

31. **Vocabulary Power** One meaning for the word *property* is "any of the special features that belong to something." Use the numbers 2, 3, and 4 to explain the Associative Property of Multiplication. **See above.**

Getting Ready for the EOG Test

32. Jody has bags of shells. Each bag has 6 shells. She gives 3 bags to each of 2 friends. How many shells does Jody give away? **C**

A 11   C 36
B 30   D 42

North Carolina Standards 1.03 Develop fluency with multiplication from 1 × 1 to 12 × 12 and division to two-digit by one-digit numbers using: a) Strategies for multiplying and dividing numbers. *also* **1.04**

Challenge 11.3

Missing Factors

Here are some Multiplication Squares to challenge your multiplication skills! Fill in the missing factors to complete the squares. **Possible answers are given.**

1.

×	3	5	9
2 × 4	24	40	72
3 × 3	27	45	81
5 × 2	30	50	90

2.

×	4	10	7
2 × 3	24	60	42
3 × 3	36	90	63
8 × 0	0	0	0

3.

×	2	8	9
2 × 5	20	80	90
1 × 7	14	56	63
3 × 3	18	72	81

4.

×	6	8	3
2 × 2	24	32	12
3 × 2	36	48	18
9 × 1	54	72	27

5.

×	6	4	0
3 × 3	54	36	0
7 × 1	42	28	0
2 × 2	24	16	0

6.

×	10	8	6
3 × 3	90	72	54
1 × 5	50	40	30
4 × 2	80	64	48

7.

×	2	4	5
9 × 1	18	36	45
1 × 7	14	28	35
2 × 5	20	40	50

8.

×	2	4	6
2 × 2	8	16	24
1 × 5	10	20	30
2 × 3	12	24	36

Problem Solving 11.3

Algebra: Multiply with 3 Factors

Understand → Plan → Solve → Check

Write the correct answer.

1. Any number minus ___?___ equals the same number. **zero**
2. Does $3 \times 2 \times 4$ have the same product as $8 \times 3 \times 1$? **yes**
3. Joseph's uncle gave him $35 on his seventh birthday and $40 on his eighth birthday. How much did his uncle give him in all? **$75**
4. Write a multiplication sentence with 3 factors that is equal to the product of $5 \times 2 \times 9$. **Possible answer: 3 × 3 × 10**

Choose the letter of the correct answer.

5. Josh did 3 pushups. Lyle did 4 pushups. Angie did 3 pushups. How many pushups did they do in all?
   (A) 10   B 13   C 36   D 343
6. Linda has 2 flower beds that have 5 rows of 6 petunias each. How many petunias does she have?
   F 13   G 16   H 32   (J) 60
7. Which has a product of 18?
   A $3 \times 3 \times 4$
   B $3 \times 2 \times 4$
   (C) $3 \times 3 \times 2$
   D $1 \times 9 \times 9$
8. Polly bought 54 stickers. She made 9 greeting cards. Each greeting card had 5 stickers on it. How many stickers were left over?
   F 99   G 40   (H) 9   J 0
9. **Write About It** Describe the strategy you used to answer Problem 4.
   Possible answer: I found the product of 5 × 2 × 9 to be 90. I know that 9 × 10 = 90. So, I wrote 9 as the product of 3 × 3.

COMMON ERROR ALERT

After they multiply the grouped factors, students may forget to multiply by the third factor. To correct this, have students cross off each factor as they multiply.

Independent Practice

Note that Exercise 30 is a **multistep or strategy problem.** Assign Exercises 6–31.

ALGEBRAIC THINKING Encourage students to write a number sentence to help them complete Exercise 30.

Vocabulary Power Discuss with students other ways the word *property* is used. What kinds of things do students think of as their property? Possible answer: property is something that belongs to someone; check students' answers: a bicycle, books, games, toys

4 ASSESS

Summarize the lesson by having students:

DISCUSS Explain how you would group the factors to find 7 × 2 × 5. Possible answer: $7 \times (2 \times 5)$; $7 \times 10 = 70$; I know that $2 \times 5 = 10$, and it's easy to multiply any number by 10.

WRITE Without multiplying, explain how you can tell if one product, (2 × 4) × 9 or 4 × (9 × 2), is greater. The products are equal. The factors are all the same but are grouped differently. The order and the grouping of factors don't change the product.

LESSON QUIZ

Transparency 11.3

Find each product.

1. $(2 \times 3) \times 7 = \blacksquare$ 42
2. $\blacksquare = 4 \times (4 \times 2)$ 32
3. $8 \times (5 \times 2) = \blacksquare$ 80
4. $\blacksquare = (3 \times 3) \times 9$ 81

Lesson 11.4

Algebra: Multiplication Properties

Lesson Planning

Objective To use multiplication properties to find products

NCTM Standards

1. Number and Operations
2. Algebra
6. Problem Solving
7. Reasoning and Proof
8. Communication
10. Representation

Math Background

These ideas will help students understand and use multiplication properties.

- The Identity Property states that the product of 1 and any number always equals that number.
- The Zero Property states that the product of 0 and any number always equals zero.
- The Commutative Property states that you can multiply two factors in either order and the product will remain the same.
- The Associative Property states that the grouping of factors can change, but the product will remain the same.
- The Distributive Property states that multiplying a sum by a number is the same as multiplying each addend in the sum by the number and then adding the products.

Vocabulary

Identity Property The product of 1 and any number equals that number.

Zero Property The product of 0 and any number equals 0.

Distributive Property In a problem with 2 factors, it is possible to break apart one factor and multiply each part by the second factor.

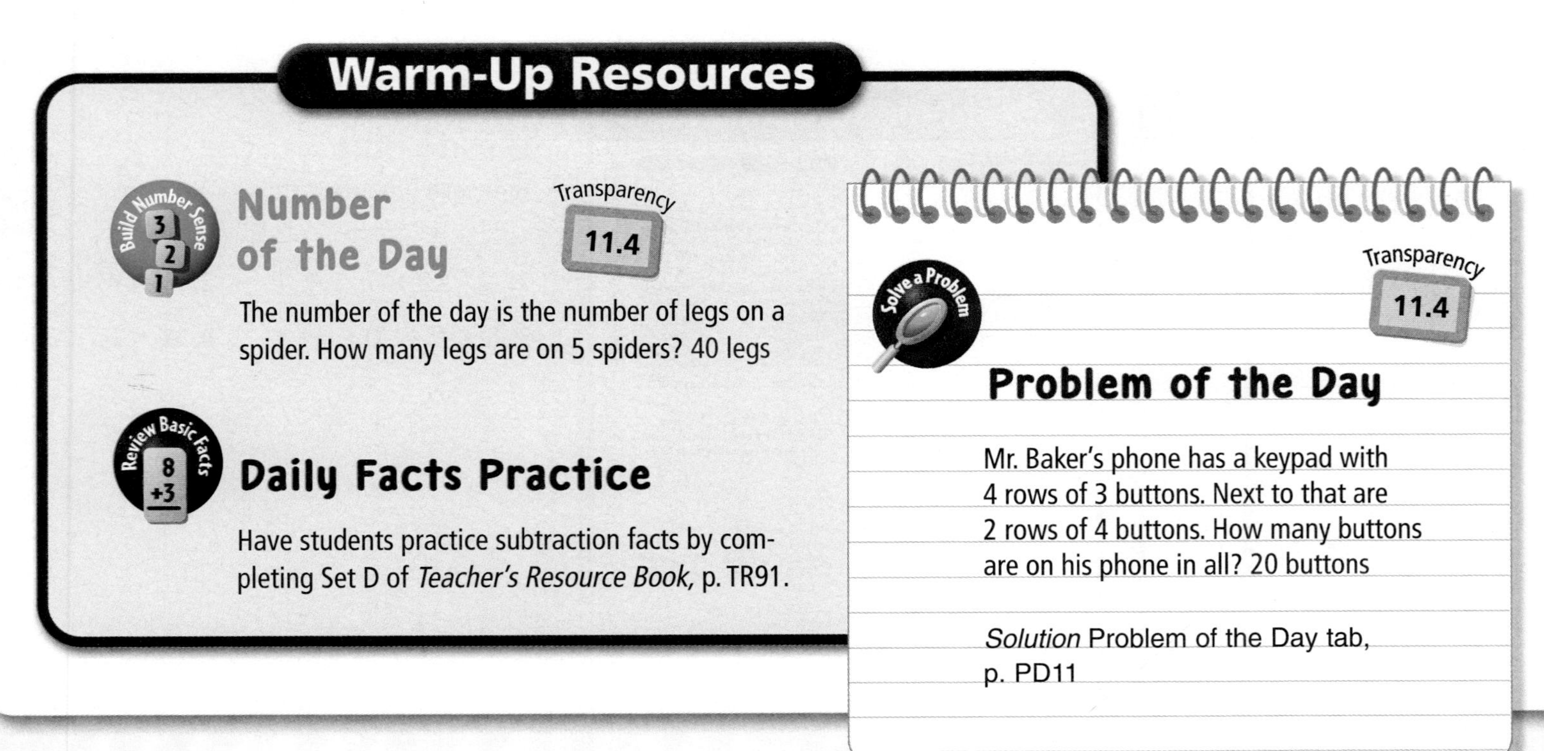

Warm-Up Resources
Build Number Sense
Number of the Day
Transparency 11.4
The number of the day is the number of legs on a spider. How many legs are on 5 spiders? 40 legs
Review Basic Facts
Daily Facts Practice
Have students practice subtraction facts by completing Set D of Teacher's Resource Book, p. TR91.
Solve a Problem
Transparency 11.4
Problem of the Day
Mr. Baker's phone has a keypad with 4 rows of 3 buttons. Next to that are 2 rows of 4 buttons. How many buttons are on his phone in all? 20 buttons
Solution Problem of the Day tab, p. PD11

Intervention and Extension Resources

Alternative Teaching Strategy

MATERIALS *For each student* connecting cubes

Name each of the properties and have one student give an explanation using words and a second student model each property using cubes. For the Zero Property, have students draw 3 circles and then try to put 0 cubes in each of the circles. Then have students draw 0 circles and try to put 3 cubes in them. They should readily see that any number times 0 will always equal 0. Continue discussing each property and having students model it.

KINESTHETIC

VISUAL/SPATIAL, BODILY/KINESTHETIC

Multistep and Strategy Problems

The following multistep or strategy problem is provided in Lesson 11.4:

Page	Item
221	33

Special Needs

MATERIALS *For each group* index cards, markers

Have students use flash cards to practice the multiplication facts. When they encounter a fact that they have trouble remembering, have them make their own flash card for that fact using an index card. On the back of the card, have students draw a picture or describe a strategy to help them learn the fact. Encourage students to use their flash cards to practice multiplication facts. Some students might benefit from working with a partner who is proficient in basic facts.

VISUAL

LOGICAL/MATHEMATICAL, INTERPERSONAL

Advanced Learners

MATERIALS *For each student* grid paper

Have students make a word search or crossword puzzle using the name of each property. Make copies of the puzzles and place them at a center for other students to solve.

VISUAL

VERBAL/LINGUISTIC, INTRAPERSONAL

Lesson 11.4 Organizer

Objective To use multiplication properties to find products

Vocabulary Identity Property, Zero Property, Distributive Property

QUICK REVIEW provides review of prerequisite skills.

WHY LEARN THIS? You can find products faster and easier by using multiplication properties. *Share the lesson objective with students.*

2 TEACH

Guided Instruction

- *Have students look at the first two properties.*
  Tell what each property means in your own words. Give an example of each. Possible answer: Identity Property: Any number times 1 equals that number; Zero Property: Zero times any number always equals zero.
- *Have students look at the Commutative and Associative Properties.*
  For the Commutative Property, tell how the two arrays are alike. Possible answer: The two arrays look the same except that one is turned a different way. Both arrays have 8 squares.
  For the Associative Property, are there the same number of cubes in each set of arrays? Explain. Yes. They both have 18 cubes.
- *Have the students look at the Distributive Property.*
  REASONING How can the word *distribute* help you understand this property? Possible answer: *Distribute* means "divide and hand out." One of the two numbers is divided into two parts and then each part is multiplied separately.

LESSON 4

Algebra: Multiplication Properties

Quick Review

1. 6×3 18
2. 9×1 9
3. 2×8 16
4. 4×4 16
5. 3×5 15

Vocabulary

Identity Property
Zero Property
Distributive Property

Learn

You can use multiplication properties to help you find products.

Identity Property The product of 1 and any number equals that number.

$1 \times 5 = 5$

Zero Property The product of 0 and any number equals 0.

$3 \times 0 = 0$

Commutative Property You can multiply two factors in any order and get the same product.

$2 \times 4 = 8$ $4 \times 2 = 8$

Associative Property You can group factors in different ways and get the same product.

$(2 \times 3) \times 3 = ■$
$6 \times 3 = 18$

$2 \times (3 \times 3) = ■$
$2 \times 9 = 18$

Distributive Property You can think of one factor as the sum of two addends. Then multiply each addend by the other factor and add the products.

Find 5×7.

Think: $5 \times 7 = 5 \times (3 + 4)$
$= (5 \times 3) + (5 \times 4)$
$= 15 + 20$

So, $5 \times 7 = 35$.

Make an array.

7

5

$5 \times 7 = ■$

Break the array into two smaller arrays.

$5 \times 3 + 5 \times 4$

220

Reteach 11.4

Multiplication Properties

The table shows properties that can help you multiply.

Property	Example
Identity Property The product of 1 and any number equals that number.	$4 \times 1 = 4$ $1 \times 4 = 4$
Zero Property The product of 0 and any number equals 0.	$0 \times 2 = 0$ $2 \times 0 = 0$
Commutative Property You can multiply two factors in any order and get the same product.	$3 \times 4 = 12$ $4 \times 3 = 12$
Associative Property You can group factors in different ways and get the same product.	$(3 \times 2) \times 4 = 3 \times (2 \times 4)$ $6 \times 4 = 3 \times 8$ $24 = 24$
Distributive Property You can think of one factor as the sum of two addends. Multiply each addend by the other factor and add the products.	$4 \times 6 = 4 \times (1 + 5)$ $= (4 \times 1) + (4 \times 5)$ $= 4 + 20$ $= 24$

Find each missing number. Write *Identity, Zero, Commutative, Associative,* or *Distributive* to tell what property of multiplication is shown.

1. $2 \times 7 =$ 14
   $7 \times 2 =$ 14
   Commutative
2. $8 \times 0 =$ 0
   Zero
3. $1 \times 9 =$ 9
   Identity
4. $3 \times 9 = 3 \times (4 +$ 5 $)$
   $= (3 \times$ 4 $) + (3 \times$ 5 $)$
   $=$ 12 $+$ 15
   $=$ 27
   Distributive
5. $2 \times (2 \times 5) =$ 20
   $(2 \times 2) \times 5 =$ 20
   Associative

Practice 11.4

Multiplication Properties

Find the product. Tell which property you used to help you. Properties may vary.

1. $8 \times 7 =$ 56 Commutative Property
2. $1 \times 6 =$ 6 Identity Property
3. $(2 \times 3) \times 4 =$ 24 Associative Property
4. $7 \times 0 =$ 0 Zero Property
5. $5 \times (2 \times 4) =$ 40 Associative Property
6. $9 \times 1 =$ 9 Identity Property
7. $9 \times 8 =$ 72 Commutative Property
8. $(2 \times 6) \times 3 =$ 36 Associative Property
9. $0 \times 4 =$ 0 Zero Property
10. $1 \times 5 =$ 5 Identity Property
11. $8 \times 0 =$ 0 Zero Property
12. $7 \times 6 =$ 42 Commutative Property

Write the missing number.

13. $4 \times 3 =$ 3 $\times 4$
14. $5 \times 9 = (5 \times 3) + (5 \times$ 6 $)$
15. $3 \times (2 \times 6) = (3 \times$ 2 $) \times 6$
16. $(8 \times 2) \times 4 =$ 8 $\times (2 \times 4)$
17. 6 $\times 9 = 9 \times 6$
18. $4 \times 7 = ($4 $\times 5) + ($4 $\times 2)$

Mixed Review

Solve.

19. $4.57 + $7.39 = $11.96
20. $9.03 − $2.54 = $6.49
21. $26.88 + $75.42 = $102.30
22. $50.00 − $24.99 = $25.01

Round each number to the nearest thousand.

23. 2,463 2,000
24. 8,711 9,000
25. 932 1,000
26. 4,300 4,000
27. 6,514 7,000
28. 7,820 8,000

Check

1. **Explain** how the Commutative Property helps you find 8×5 when you know that $5 \times 8 = 40$. **You can multiply two numbers in any order and get the same product, so $8 \times 5 = 40$.**

Find the product. Tell which property you used to help you.
Properties may vary.

2. 9×0 **0**
3. 1×7 **7**
4. 3×8 **24**
5. 6×9 **54**
6. 6×1 **6**
7. 7×8 **56**
8. 0×5 **0**
9. 7×7 **49**
10. $(2 \times 3) \times 5$ **30**
11. $(4 \times 4) \times 2$ **32**
12. $3 \times (2 \times 7)$ **42**
13. $2 \times (3 \times 8)$ **48**

Practice and Problem Solving

Extra Practice, page 224, Set D

Find the product. Tell which property you used to help you.
Properties may vary.

14. 0×6 **0**
15. 9×4 **36**
16. 8×1 **8**
17. 8×9 **72**
18. 5×9 **45**
19. 6×6 **36**
20. 7×4 **28**
21. 8×8 **64**
22. $(4 \times 2) \times 3$ **24**
23. $2 \times (4 \times 5)$ **40**
24. $5 \times (2 \times 3)$ **30**
25. $(3 \times 3) \times 9$ **81**

Write the missing number for each ■.

26. $6 \times 7 = ■ \times 6$ **7**
27. $2 \times (3 \times 5) = (■ \times 3) \times 5$ **2**
28. $5 \times ■ = 1 \times 5$ **1**
29. $9 \times 5 = ■ \times 9$ **5**
30. $3 \times 5 = (3 \times ■) + (3 \times 2)$ **3**
31. $■ \times 7 = 7 \times 4$ **4**
32. **Write About It** Explain how you can use the Distributive Property to find 7×8. Draw an array to show your answer. **Possible answer: $8 = 4 + 4$, so $7 \times 8 = (7 \times 4) + (7 \times 4)$. $7 \times 4 = 28$ and $28 + 28 = 56$, so $8 \times 7 = 56$.**
33. **REASONING** On Tuesday Kim bought 4 shirts for $8 each. On Friday she bought more of the same shirts. In the two days, she spent $48. How many shirts did she buy on Friday? Explain. **$48 – $32 = $16, and 2 × $8 = $16, so Kim bought 2 shirts on Friday.**

Getting Ready for the EOG Test

34. Roland's dog, Junior, eats 1 pound of dog food each day. How long will it take for Junior to eat a 10-pound bag of dog food? **D**

   A 1 day
   B 3 days
   C 5 days
   D 10 days

North Carolina Standards 1.04 Use basic properties (identity, commutative, associative, order of operations) for addition, subtraction, multiplication, and division. *also* **1.03a**

Challenge 11.4

Property Match Game

Play with a partner.

Materials: Expression cards shown below; scissors

How to Play:
- Cut apart the expression cards and place them facedown on a table.
- Players take turns. Turn over two cards. Determine whether the cards are an example of a multiplication property. If so, name the property. If not, place the cards back on the table facedown.
- If the property is named correctly, keep the cards. If not, place the cards back on the table facedown.
- When all the cards have been picked up, the player with more cards wins the game!

5×6	$(2 \times 2) + (2 \times 7)$	7
2×9	0×7	$8 \times (4 \times 2)$
9×1	$(7 \times 2) \times 5$	$(3 \times 2) \times 4$
0	$(4 \times 5) + (4 \times 3)$	6×5
$(8 \times 4) \times 2$	$7 \times (2 \times 5)$	7×1
$3 \times (2 \times 4)$	1×9	4×8

Make up your own set of cards. Trade with another pair of classmates, and play again.

CW60 Challenge

Problem Solving 11.4

Multiplication Properties

Understand → Plan → Solve → Check

Write the correct answer.

1. When 6 is multiplied by a number, the product is 6. What is that number? **1**
2. Write this amount as you would read it. $9.22 **nine dollars and twenty-two cents**
3. Sasha bought 4 packages of muffins. Each package contains 9 muffins. How many muffins did Sasha buy? **36 muffins**
4. Jacob pinned 5 rows of 3 photos each on his bulletin board. How else could he have arranged the photos so that they are in equal rows? **3 rows of 5 photos each**

Choose the letter of the correct answer.

5. Tim packed 8 books in each of 3 boxes. Each book weighs 2 pounds. Which multiplication property could you use to help find the total weight of the boxes?
   A Commutative Property
   B Distributive Property
   C Identity Property
   (D) Associative Property
6. Lori left for school at 7:30 A.M. She got to school at 7:55 A.M. How long did it take Lori to get to school?
   F 20 minutes
   (G) 25 minutes
   H 30 minutes
   J 35 minutes
7. Which shows the Zero Property of Multiplication?
   A $0 \times 1 = 1$
   B $0 \times 1 = 1 \times 0$
   (C) $7 \times 0 = 0$
   D $7 \times 0 = 7$
8. It snowed for 15 days in January, 12 days in February, and 3 days in March. How many days did it snow in all?
   F 18 days
   G 27 days
   (H) 30 days
   J 33 days
9. **Write About It** How could you use the Distributive Property to help you solve Problem 3? **Possible answer: Think of 9 as 4 + 5. Multiply 4 × 4 and 4 × 5 and add the products.**

PS60 Problem Solving

3 PRACTICE

Guided Practice

Do Check Exercises 1–13 with your students. Identify students who are having difficulty and choose appropriate lesson resources to provide assistance.

Independent Practice

Note that Exercise 33 is a **multistep or strategy problem.** Assign Exercises 14–33.

Have students identify number sentences in the exercises that are examples of the properties shown on page 220.

4 ASSESS

Summarize the lesson by having students:

DISCUSS What is the difference between multiplying a number by 1 and adding 1 to a number? Multiplying a number by 1 does not change the number but adding 1 to a number increases the number by 1.

WRITE Explain the difference between the Commutative and the Associative Properties. Possible answer: The Commutative Property says that you can multiply 2 factors in either order and get the same product. The Associative Property says that you can multiply 3 factors in any order and get the same product.

LESSON QUIZ

Find the product. Tell what property you used to help you.

1. 7×1 7; Identity Property
2. 9×0 0; Zero Property
3. 8×4 32; Commutative Property
4. $(3 \times 2) \times 6$ 36; Associative Property

Write the missing number for each.

5. $7 \times 8 = 8 \times ■$ 7
6. $1 \times (4 \times 5) = (■ \times 4) \times 5$ 1

Lesson 11.5

Problem Solving Skill
Multistep Problems

Lesson Planning

PROFESSIONAL DEVELOPMENT

Objective To solve multistep problems using basic multiplication facts, addition, and subtraction

Lesson Resources Reading Transparency 11; Intervention • Problem Solving, Strategy/Skill 11

NCTM Standards
1. Number and Operations
6. Problem Solving
8. Communication
10. Representation

Math Background
These ideas will help students understand how to solve multistep problems using multiplication, addition, and subtraction.

- A multistep problem contains two or more related problems that have to be solved to find the answer.
- Two different operations may have to be used to solve a multistep problem.

Vocabulary
multistep problem a problem requiring more than one step to solve

Warm-Up Resources

Number of the Day

Write 4 different number sentences in which the number that represents the month of August is the product, sum, or difference. Possible answers: $9 - 1 = 8$; $2 \times 4 = 8$; $5 + 3 = 8$; $16 - 8 = 8$

Daily Facts Practice

Have students practice subtraction facts by completing Set E of *Teacher's Resource Book*, p. TR91.

Solve a Problem

Transparency 11.5

Problem of the Day

The difference between two numbers is 6. The product of the numbers is 40. What are the numbers? 10 and 4

Solution Problem of the Day tab, p. PD11.

Intervention and Extension Resources

Alternative Teaching Strategy

Help students work together in groups to **write multistep problems** such as the example that follows.

Jamie made 9 plates of muffins for the bake sale.

Jamie put 8 muffins on each plate.

Jamie sold 7 plates of muffins.

Jamie made 2 extra plates of muffins for her friends.

Assign each group two operations: either multiplication and addition or multiplication and subtraction. Tell students to choose the sentences they need to write a multistep problem that can be solved by using their operations. Have a student from each group read his or her problem aloud for the class to solve. Check students' work.

AUDITORY

LOGICAL, MATHEMATICAL

Reading Strategy

Draw Conclusions Tell students that when you look at information in a problem and use what you already know, you can draw conclusions to solve the problem. Read the following problem:

There are 3 red marbles in each red bag and 5 blue marbles in each blue bag. Kelly has 2 red bags and 1 blue bag. Does she have more red marbles or blue marbles?

Display the following column headings:

Look at the Information   Use What You Already Know

Help students fill in the columns and draw a conclusion to solve the problem. For example, Information: 3 red marbles in each red bag, Kelly has 2 red bags; You Know: $2 \times 3 = 6$. $6 > 5$, so Kelly has more red marbles.

Transparency 11 **Reading Transparency 11**

Multistep and Strategy Problems

The following multistep or strategy problems are provided in Lesson 11.5:

Page	Item
223	1–8

Writing in Mathematics

Have students **write a multistep word problem**. Encourage them to write a problem that can be solved by using two different operations. Have students exchange problems with a partner and solve. Check students' work.

Early Finishers

Have students **draw a picture to solve a multistep problem**. Read students the following problem:

Andrea brought 4 packages of hamburger buns to the family picnic. Each package held 8 buns. There were 6 buns left. How many buns were eaten? 26; check students' work.

VISUAL

VISUAL, SPATIAL

Intervention • Problem Solving, *Strategy/Skill 11*

Lesson 11.5 Organizer

Objective To solve multistep problems using basic multiplication facts, addition, and subtraction

Vocabulary multistep problem

Lesson Resources Reading Transparency 11; Intervention • Problem Solving, Strategy/Skill 11

1 INTRODUCE

QUICK REVIEW provides review of prerequisite skills.

WHY LEARN THIS? You can solve complicated word problems. *Share the lesson objective with students.*

2 TEACH

Guided Instruction

- *Ask students to read the problem.*
  How do you know that this is a multistep problem? Possible answer: Touchdowns and field goals are worth a different number of points.
  What information do you need to solve the problem? the number of field goals and touchdowns scored and the total number of points scored for each
  Which operations will you use to solve the problem? multiplication and addition
- *Have students look at Steps 1, 2, and 3.*
  How do you know to multiply in Step 2? Each field goal is worth 3 points.
  How do you know to add in Step 3? You need to combine the touchdown and field goal points to find the total number of points.

MODIFYING INSTRUCTION You may choose to have students use calculators to help them solve multistep problems.

- *Have students discuss the Talk About It question.*
  REASONING What if the referees decided that one of the field goals didn't count? How could you find the total number of points scored? Possible answer: Subtract 3 points from the total. $18 - 3 = 15$

LESSON 5

Problem Solving Skill
Multistep Problems

UNDERSTAND › PLAN › SOLVE › CHECK

KNOW THE SCORE Jeff's team scored 6 points for a touchdown but missed the extra point. Then they scored 3 points for each of 4 field goals. How many points did they score in all?

To find how many points in all, you must solve a **multistep problem**, or a problem with more than one step.

Quick Review

1. $(2 \times 3) \times 4 = \blacksquare$ 24
2. $(5 \times 1) \times 7 = \blacksquare$ 35
3. $4 + 16 + 5 = \blacksquare$ 25
4. $7 + 8 + 2 = \blacksquare$ 17
5. $3 \times (4 \times 2) = \blacksquare$ 24

VOCABULARY
multistep problem

Example

STEP 1

Find how many points were scored by touchdowns.	1 touchdown was scored. Each touchdown = 6 points. $1 \times 6 = 6$ 6 points were scored in touchdowns.

STEP 2

Find how many points were scored by field goals.	4 field goals were scored. Each field goal = 3 points. $4 \times 3 = 12$ 12 points were scored in field goals.

STEP 3

Find how many points were scored in all.	Add the points scored by touchdowns and field goals. $6 + 12 = 18$ So, 18 points were scored in all.

Talk About It

- Does it matter if you find the points scored in touchdowns first or the points scored in field goals first? Explain.
  No; the order in which you add does not change the answer.

222

Reteach 11.5

Problem Solving Skill
Multistep Problems

A multistep problem is a problem which needs more than one step in order to solve it.

To earn money for a vacation, Bryan walked 3 dogs. Rene walked 4 dogs. They got paid $2 for each dog they walked. How much money did they earn in all?

Step 1 Find how much money Bryan earned.	3 × $2 = $6 Bryan earned $6.
Step 2 Find how much money Rene earned.	4 × $2 = $8 Rene earned $8.
Step 3 Find how much money they earned in all.	$6 + $8 = $14 So, they earned $14 in all.

Solve.

1. Paul read 315 pages in 3 days. He read 109 the first day and 105 the second day. How many pages did he read the third day?
   Step 1 How much did Paul read altogether on the first and second days? 214
   Step 2 How many pages did he read the third day? 101
2. Rita bought 4 cartons of eggs. Each carton had 8 eggs. Her family ate 10 of the eggs. How many eggs were left?
   Step 1 How many eggs did Rita buy? 32
   Step 2 How many eggs were left? 22
3. Robbie earns $2 for each car she washes. She earns $6 for each car she waxes. Robbie washed 4 cars and waxed 3 cars. How much did she earn? $26
4. Nancy drove 400 miles in 3 days. She drove 113 miles on each of the first 2 days. How many miles did she drive on the third day? 174 miles

Reteach RW61

Practice 11.5

Problem Solving Skill
Multistep Problems

Solve.

1. Taylor bought 6 used books that cost $2 each. He also bought 3 used books that cost $4 each. How much did Taylor spend on used books? $24
2. Tina has 3 rows of 8 rocks in her rock collection. She wants to double her collection. How many rocks will Tina have when she doubles her collection? 48 rocks
3. Howard has $138 and Tess has $149. They need a total of $250 to buy a recliner chair for their father. How much more money do they have than they need? $37
4. To raise money for school, Megan sold 8 magazine subscriptions. Parker sold 7 subscriptions. Each subscription raises $5 for the school. How much money did they raise in all? $75
5. The Romers drove 613 miles in 3 days. They drove 251 miles the first day and 168 miles the second day. How far did they drive on the third day? 194 miles
6. Two friends are comparing money. Bert has 8 quarters and 7 dimes. Ernie has 10 quarters and 7 nickels. Who has the most money? How much more money than his friend does he have? Ernie; $0.15

Mixed Review

Continue the pattern.

7. 20, 40, 60, 80, ?, ?, ? 100, 120, 140
8. 12, 14, 15, 17, 18, 20, ?, ? 21, 23

Find the product.

9. $(2 \times 3) \times 9 =$ 54
10. $6 \times (3 \times 3) =$ 54

Practice PW61

Problem Solving Practice

Solve.

1. To raise money for the school, Lucia sold 9 boxes of cards. Ginger sold 7 boxes. Each box cost $3. How much money did they raise in all? **$48**

2. The Wilsons drove 598 miles in 3 days. They drove 230 miles the first day and 175 miles the second day. How far did they go the third day? **193 miles**

Kelsey bought 3 boxes of tacos. Each box had 6 tacos. Then she gave 4 tacos away.

3. Which shows the first step you take to find how many tacos Kelsey had left? **C**
   A $3 + 6 = 9$
   B $6 - 3 = 3$
   C $3 \times 6 = 18$
   D $3 \times 4 = 12$

4. How many tacos did Kelsey have left? **G**
   F 12
   G 14
   H 18
   J 22

Mixed Applications

USE DATA For 5–7, use the pictograph.

5. How many students did NOT vote for hot dogs? **40 students**

6. How many students voted in all? **60 students**

7. **Write a problem** about the graph. Exchange with a partner and solve. **Check students' problems.**

8. **What's the Question?** Rob spent $30 for 4 tickets. He bought 3 children's tickets for $7 each and 1 adult ticket. The answer is $9. **How much did the adult ticket cost?**

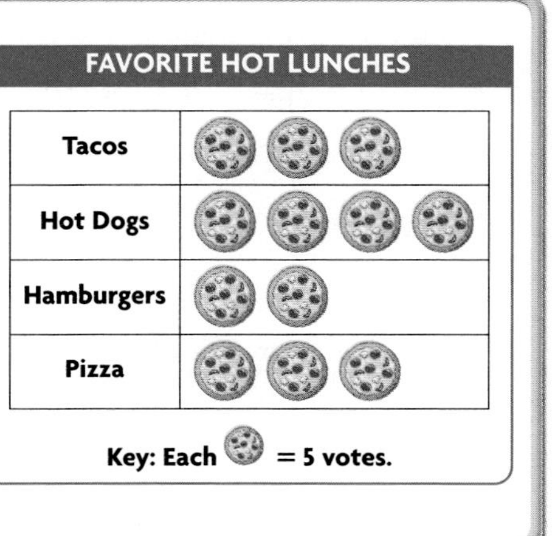

North Carolina Standards 1.06 Develop flexibility in solving problems by selecting strategies and using mental computation, estimation, calculators or computers, and paper and pencil.

3 PRACTICE

Guided Practice

Do Problem Solving Practice Exercises 1–4 with your students. Identify students who are having difficulty and choose appropriate lesson resources to provide assistance. Note that Exercises 1–4 are **multistep or strategy problems.**

Independent Practice

Note that Exercises 5–8 are **multistep or strategy problems.** Assign Exercises 5–8.

Summarize the lesson by having students:

DISCUSS How do you know Exercise 2 is a multistep problem? Possible answer: You must add to find the number of miles they drove on the first 2 days and subtract that number from the total number of miles.

WRITE Describe the steps you took to solve Exercise 1 on page 223. Step 1: Multiply. $9 \times \$3 = \$27$. Step 2: Multiply. $7 \times \$3 = \$21$. Step 3: Add the two amounts. $\$27 + \$21 = \$48$.

LESSON QUIZ

Transparency 11.5

Solve.

1. At the school bake sale, Jeremy sold 8 plates of cookies and Ashley sold 7 plates. If each plate cost $2, how much money did they earn in all? $30

2. Ms. Harrison traveled 1,556 miles on a train in three days. She traveled 347 miles on the first day and 790 miles on the second day. How many miles did she travel on the third day? 419 miles

Challenge 11.5

Special Delivery

In each problem, the mailboxes have the same number of letters inside. Write the total number of letters for each problem.

1. Key: = 5 letters — 17 letters
2. Key: = 10 letters — 34 letters
3. Key: = 8 letters — 39 letters
4. Key: = 9 letters — 25 letters
5. Key: = 7 letters — 20 letters
6. Key: = 9 letters — 51 letters
7. 4 × + — Key: = 3 letters — 14 letters
8. 3 × + — Key: = 8 letters — 28 letters
9. 6 × − — Key: = 5 letters — 27 letters
10. 8 × + — Key: = 9 letters — 77 letters

Challenge CW61

Reading Strategy 11.5

Sequence Information Understand → Plan → Solve → Check

When a problem gives you a lot of information, it is helpful to understand the order, or **sequence**, of events. Then you can group the related facts in a chart.

VOCABULARY sequence

Read the following problem.

► Mr. Jones drove from his house to his mother's house. He drove 75 miles before lunch. He drove 215 miles after lunch. He made a wrong turn. So he drove 22 miles back down the same road. Then he turned and drove 3 miles to his mother's house. How many miles was it to his mother's house?

1. Group the facts that are related in a chart. Complete the chart.

Numbers to Add	Numbers to Subtract
75 215 + 3	293 − 22

2. Solve the problem.
   75 + 215 + 3 = 293; 293 − 22 = 271 miles.

3. Describe the strategy you used.
   Possible answer: I used addition first, then subtraction.

Group the related facts. Complete the chart. Solve.

4. Melinda bought 4 boxes of cookies. Each box had 9 cookies. Then she gave 8 cookies away. How many cookies does she have left? 28 cookies

Numbers to multiply	Numbers to subtract
4 × 9 36	36 − 8 28

5. Tim sent 75 invitations on Monday and 35 on Tuesday. Sixty-eight people said they would attend. How many people did not say they would attend? 42 people

Numbers to add	Numbers to subtract
75 + 35 110	110 − 68 42

Reading Strategy PS61

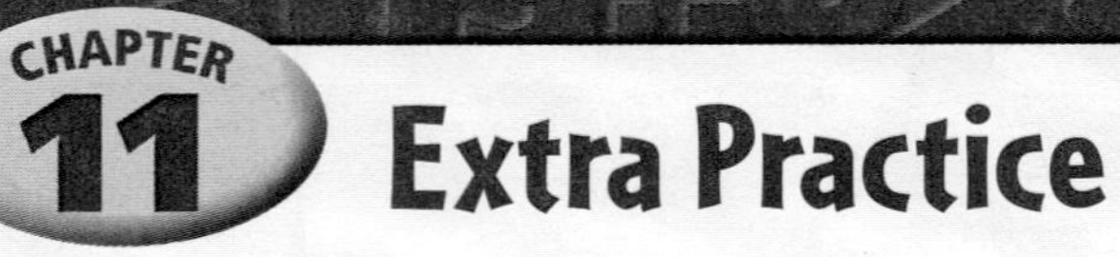

Extra Practice

Purpose To provide extra practice for the skills presented in this chapter

The blue page references in each set of exercises refer to the lesson pages where each skill is taught.

Internet Resources

Visit THE LEARNING SITE at **www.harcourtschool.com** for a listing of practice activities.

Extra Practice

Set A (pp. 212–215)

Find the product.

1. $9 \times 7 = \blacksquare$ 63
2. $6 \times 9 = \blacksquare$ 54
3. $6 \times 10 = \blacksquare$ 60
4. $10 \times 3 = \blacksquare$ 30
5. $3 \times 9 = \blacksquare$ 27
6. $8 \times 9 = \blacksquare$ 72
7. $10 \times 7 = \blacksquare$ 70
8. $9 \times 5 = \blacksquare$ 45

Find the missing factor.

9. $\blacksquare \times 9 = 36$ 4
10. $90 = 9 \times \blacksquare$ 10
11. $7 \times \blacksquare = 56$ 8
12. $21 = \blacksquare \times 7$ 3

Set B (pp. 216–217)

Write a rule for each table. Then copy and complete the table.

1.

Packs	1	2	3	4	5	6
Cards	4	8	12	■	■	■

multiply packs by 4; 16, 20, 24

2.

Bags	1	2	3	4	5	6
Oranges	6	12	18	■	■	■

multiply bags by 6; 24, 30, 36

3.

Cans	1	2	3	4	5	6
Tennis Balls	3	6	9	■	■	■

multiply cans by 3; 12, 15, 18

4.

Gloves	1	2	3	4	5	6
Fingers	5	10	15	■	■	■

multiply gloves by 5; 20, 25, 30

Set C (pp. 218–219)

Find each product.

1. $(4 \times 1) \times 3 = \blacksquare$ 12
2. $(3 \times 2) \times 3 = \blacksquare$ 18
3. $(5 \times 1) \times 5 = \blacksquare$ 25
4. $4 \times (2 \times 2) = \blacksquare$ 16
5. $10 \times (3 \times 3) = \blacksquare$ 90
6. $(6 \times 1) \times 7 = \blacksquare$ 42

Find the missing factor.

7. $(4 \times \blacksquare) \times 1 = 16$ 4
8. $5 \times (2 \times \blacksquare) = 20$ 2
9. $\blacksquare \times (7 \times 1) = 49$ 7

Set D (pp. 220–221)

Find the product. Tell which property you used to help you.
Properties may vary.

1. 0×7 0
2. 9×2 18
3. 1×8 8
4. 3×8 24
5. 5×9 45
6. 5×0 0
7. 4×8 32
8. 9×9 81
9. $(6 \times 2) \times 2$ 24
10. $(4 \times 5) \times 2$ 40
11. $2 \times (3 \times 5)$ 30
12. $(3 \times 8) \times 3$ 72

Review/Test

CHECK VOCABULARY AND CONCEPTS

Choose the best term from the box.

factor
Associative Property
multistep problem

1. A problem with more than one step is a _?_. (p. 222) **multistep problem**
2. The _?_ of Multiplication states that when the grouping of factors is changed, the product remains the same. (p. 218) **Associative Property**

CHECK SKILLS

Find the product. (pp. 212–215)

3. $9 \times 7 = ■$ **63**
4. $■ = 9 \times 4$ **36**
5. $6 \times 9 = ■$ **54**
6. $8 \times 9 = ■$ **72**
7. $10 \times 5 = ■$ **50**
8. $3 \times 10 = ■$ **30**
9. $■ = 9 \times 9$ **81**
10. $10 \times 7 = ■$ **70**

Write a rule for the table. Then copy and complete the table. (pp. 216–217) **multiply insects by 6**

11.

Insects	1	2	3	4	5	6	7
Legs	6	12	18	■	■	■	■
				24	**30**	**36**	**42**

Find each product. (pp. 218–219)

12. $(3 \times 1) \times 6 = ■$ **18**
13. $■ = 5 \times (2 \times 2)$ **20**
14. $(3 \times 3) \times 9 = ■$ **81**
15. $4 \times (2 \times 5) = ■$ **40**
16. $■ = (2 \times 4) \times 8$ **64**
17. $9 \times (4 \times 1) = ■$ **36**

Find the product. Tell which property you used to help you. (pp. 220–221)
Properties may vary.

18. 1×6 **6**
19. 2×9 **18**
20. 8×0 **0**
21. 7×8 **56**
22. 4×6 **24**
23. 5×9 **45**

CHECK PROBLEM SOLVING

Solve. (pp. 222–223)

24. In March, Mr. Holly's class raised \$176. In April, the students raised \$209. How much do they still need in order to raise \$500? **\$115**
25. Joe bought 5 guppies for \$3 each and 8 goldfish for \$2 each. How much did he spend? **\$31**

Review/Test

Purpose To check understanding of concepts, skills, and problem solving presented in Chapter 11

Using the Page

The Chapter 11 Review/Test can be used as a **review** or a **test**.

- Items 1–2 check understanding of concepts and new vocabulary.
- Items 3–23 check skill proficiency.
- Items 24–25 check students' abilities to choose and apply problem solving strategies to real-life multiplication problems.

Suggest that students place the completed Chapter 11 Review/Test in their portfolios.

Using the Assessment Guide

- Multiple-choice format of Chapter 11 Posttest—See *Assessment Guide*, pp. AG65–66.
- Free-response format of Chapter 11 Posttest—See *Assessment Guide*, pp. AG67–68.

Using Student Self-Assessment

The How Did I Do? survey helps students assess what they have learned and how they learned it. This survey is available as a copying master in *Assessment Guide*, p. AGxvii.

Chapter 11 Test, page 1

Choose the correct answer.

1. What is the missing factor?
   $■ \times 9 = 54$
   A 8 — B 7 — (C) 6 — D 5
2. Find the product.
   $3 \times (5 \times 2) = ■$
   F 56 — (G) 30 — H 13 — J 10
3. What is the rule for the table?

Packages	1	2	3	4	5	6
Flowers	6	12	18	24	30	36

   (A) Multiply the number of packages by 6.
   B Add 5 to the number of packages.
   C Subtract 5 from the number of flowers.
   D Multiply the number of packages by 5.

4. What is the rule for the table?

Weeks	1	2	3	4	5	6
Days	7	14	21	28	35	42

   F Multiply the number of days by 7.
   G Add 6 to the number of weeks.
   (H) Multiply the number of weeks by 7.
   J Subtract 6 from the number of days.

For 5–6, find the missing number for each ______.

5. $2 \times (4 \times 3) = (\_\_\_\_ \times 4) \times 3$
   (A) 2 — B 3 — C 4 — D 12
6. $7 \times \_\_\_\_ = 8 \times 7$
   F 1 — G 4 — (H) 8 — J 56

For 7–8, tell what property you would use to find the product.

7. 1×8
   A Associative Property
   (B) Identity Property
   C Distributive Property
   D Commutative Property
8. 9×4
   F Associative Property
   G Identity Property
   H Zero Property
   (J) Distributive Property

For 9–10, use this table.

Packages	1	2	3	4	5	6
Cupcakes	2	4	6	■	■	■

9. Which numbers complete the table?
   A 7, 8, 9 — (B) 8, 10, 12 — C 12, 14, 16 — D 9, 12, 15
10. Suppose you had 16 cupcakes. How many packages would you have?
   F 7 — (G) 8 — H 9 — J 10

Go On

Chapter 11 Test, page 2

11. Ellen has \$35. A pair of sunglasses sells for \$7. A hair bow sells for \$2. She buys 2 pairs of sunglasses and 4 hair bows. How much money does she have left?
   A \$3 — B \$7 — C \$8 — (D) \$13
12. The product of a number and 8 is 72. What is the number?
   (F) 9 — G 10 — H 64 — J 80
13. There are 4 cupcakes in each box. Each cupcake has 1 cherry on top. Crystal buys 5 boxes of cupcakes. How many cherries are there?
   A 9 — B 10 — (C) 20 — D 24
14. Adult tickets cost \$3 each. Student tickets cost \$2 each. How much will 5 adult tickets and 10 student tickets cost?
   (F) \$35 — G \$40 — H \$50 — J \$56
15. Which numbers complete the table?

Octopuses	3	4	5	6	7	8
Arms	24	32	40	■	■	■

   A 44, 48, 52
   B 45, 50, 55
   C 46, 52, 58
   (D) 48, 56, 64

16. Find the product.
   $(3 \times 3) \times 9 = ■$
   F 27 — G 71 — H 80 — (J) 81
17. Which symbol makes the number sentence true?
   $18 + 15 \bullet 3 \times 10$
   (A) $>$ — B $<$ — C $=$
18. Kate had 50 stickers. She gave 15 away on Monday and 24 on Tuesday. How many stickers does she have left?
   (F) 11 — G 21 — H 59 — J 81
19. A nickel has the same value as 5 pennies. John has 9 nickels. How many pennies would this be?
   A 14 — B 40 — (C) 45 — D 50
20. A restaurant sells roast beef sandwiches for \$5 each. There are 2 sandwiches in a bag. Which expression shows how much it would cost to buy 4 bags?
   (F) $(2 \times 5) \times 4$
   G $(4 + 2) \times 5$
   H $4 + (2 \times 5)$
   J $4 \times (2 + 5)$

Stop

Getting Ready for the EOG Test

Chapters 1–11

Using the Pages

These pages may be used to help students get ready for the North Carolina EOG Test. The test items are written in the same style and arranged in the same format as those on the EOG Test.

The pages are cumulative. They cover the standards from the North Carolina Mathematics Standard Course of Study that have been taught up to this point in the text or in a previous grade. Each Getting Ready for the EOG Test also reviews the North Carolina mathematics strands shown below.

- Number and Operations
- Measurement
- Geometry
- Data Analysis and Probability
- Algebra

These pages can be assigned at the end of the chapter as classwork or as a homework assignment. You may want to have students use individual recording sheets presented in a multiple-choice (standardized) format. A Test Answer Sheet is available as a blackline master in the *Assessment Guide* (p. AGlii).

You may wish to have students describe how they solved each problem and share their solutions.

Getting Ready for the EOG Test

NUMBER AND OPERATIONS

1. Mrs. Walsh bought 6 bags of oranges. Each bag contains 10 oranges. How many oranges did she buy? D

A 4
B 16
C 30
D 60

2. Which multiplication fact does the array show? B

★★★★★★★★★
★★★★★★★★★
★★★★★★★★★
★★★★★★★★★

A $2 \times 9 = 18$
B $4 \times 9 = 36$
C $8 \times 3 = 24$
D $4 \times 5 = 20$

3. Which number should Karen write to make the equation true? D

$(8 \times ■) \times 1 = 72$

A 4
B 7
C 8
D 9

4. Explain It Abby has 218 beads. Sasha has 53 beads. Abby says she has about 150 more beads than Sasha. Tell how Abby estimated the difference. See page 227.

MEASUREMENT AND GEOMETRY

5. The clock shows the time Milla woke up this morning. At what time did Milla wake up? A

A 7:25 A.M.
B 5:35 A.M.
C 7:35 P.M.
D 5:35 P.M.

6. These coins are in Jana's purse.

How much money is in Jana's purse? C

A $4.41
B $2.41
C $1.41
D $1.31

7. Explain It Lance bought a pen for $1.89 and a notebook for $1.09. He gave the clerk a $5 bill. About how much change did Lance receive? Explain how you found your answer. See page 227.

ALGEBRA

8. Which group shows numbers that are products of 9 and another number? **C**

A 3, 9, 18, 45
B 5, 3, 4, 6
C 18, 36, 27, 54
D 19, 29, 39, 49

9. One spider has 8 legs. How many legs do 6 spiders have in all? **D**

Spiders	1	2	3	4	5	6
Legs	8	16	24	32	40	■

A 6
B 8
C 32
D 48

10. The table shows how many bottles of hot sauce Vincent made. If the pattern continues, how many bottles will he make on Friday? **C**

VINCENT'S HOT SAUCE

Day	Bottles
Monday	9
Tuesday	18
Wednesday	27
Thursday	36

A 15
B 20
C 45
D 72

11. Explain It Name two ways you can use skip-counting to find 5×10. **See below.**

DATA ANALYSIS AND PROBABILITY

12. The pictograph shows the number of books read by 4 students. How many more books did Emma read than Jack? **A**

BOOKS READ

Emma	📘📘📘📘
Fran	📘📘📘
Gary	📘📘📘📘📘
Jack	📘📘

Key: 📘 equals 2 books.

A 4
B 3
C 2
D 1

TIP **Look for important words.** See item 13. Find the total number of books the students in each answer choice read. Compare the numbers to the number of books that Gary read.

13. Look at the pictograph above. Which students together read the same number of books as Gary? **A**

A Fran and Jack
B Jack and Emma
C Emma and Fran
D Fran, Jack, and Emma

14. Explain It Tell how you could use the symbols on the pictograph above to order the students from fewest to most books read. **See below.**

Chapters 1–11

Item Analysis

You may wish to use the item analysis to determine which North Carolina standards need additional review.

Item	North Carolina Standard	Lesson
1	1.03	11.1
2	1.03	11.1
3	1.04	11.1
4	1.06	5.1
5	(2) 2.02	7.1
6	Goal 2	6.1
7	Goal 2	6.4
8	5.01	11.1
9	5.01	10.2
10	5.01	11.1
11	5.01	11.1
12	(2) 4.01	Grade 2
13	(2) 4.01	Grade 2
14	(2) 4.01	Grade 2

SCORING RUBRIC
Explain It

2 Demonstrates a complete understanding of the problem and chooses an appropriate strategy to determine the solution

1 Demonstrates a partial understanding of the problem and chooses a strategy that does not lead to a complete and accurate solution

0 Demonstrates little understanding of the problem and shows little evidence of using any strategy to determine a solution

Explain It • Written Response

4. Possible answer: 218 rounds to 200, and 53 rounds to 50; $200 - 50 = 150$.

7. About \$2.00; possible answer: \$1.89 is about \$2.00; \$1.09 is about \$1.00; \$2.00 + \$1.00 = \$3.00; \$5.00 − \$3.00 = \$2.00.

11. Possible answer: count by fives ten times and count by tens five times.

14. Possible answer: the person with the fewest symbols, Jack, read the fewest books. The person with the most symbols, Gary, read the most books. The order from fewest to most is Jack, Fran, Emma, Gary.

It's in the Bag

Multiplication Rocks

Purpose To set up and solve multiplication equations

Materials *For each student* 24 small, flat rocks; a permanent marker; 1 paper lunch bag or 1 sandwich-size plastic bag with zip closure

Using the Page

Preparing the Materials

- Small, flat rocks can be collected by students or purchased from a store carrying garden supplies. Large beads or buttons in light colors may be used in place of rocks. Choose items that can be written upon. Small zip-lock bags or paper lunch bags can be bought inexpensively at discount stores.

Making the Project

- Have students prepare 2 sets of rocks by labeling them from 0–10 and using different-colored permanent markers to label and decorate them. Have students practice multiplication facts from 0 through 10. Suggest students add additional rocks to their collections as needed.

Extending the Project

- Have pairs use the multiplication rocks to have 1-minute fact drills. One student pulls out two numbers from the sack and states the product. This player continues for 1 minute, finding as many products as possible. The other player keeps time and uses a tally table to record the number of correct products. Players switch roles and repeat at least two times. Encourage students to try to beat their own scores each time they play.

IT'S IN THE BAG

Multiplication Rocks

PROJECT Use rocks to practice the multiplication facts.

Directions

1. Collect a variety of small, flat rocks.
2. Write a number from 0–10 on each rock. Make two sets of 0–10 rocks. *(Picture A)*
3. Write a × sign on one of the rocks.
4. Write an = sign on one of the rocks. *(Picture B)*
5. Label and decorate the bag.
6. Choose one rock from the bag and place it to the left of the × sign. Choose a second rock from the bag and place it to the right of the × sign. Place the = sign.
7. Then find the rocks in the bag to show the product. *(Picture C)*

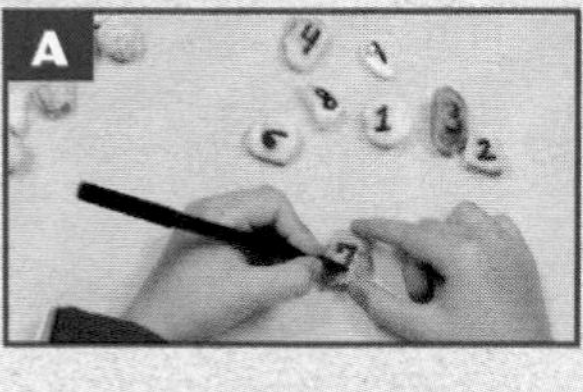
A

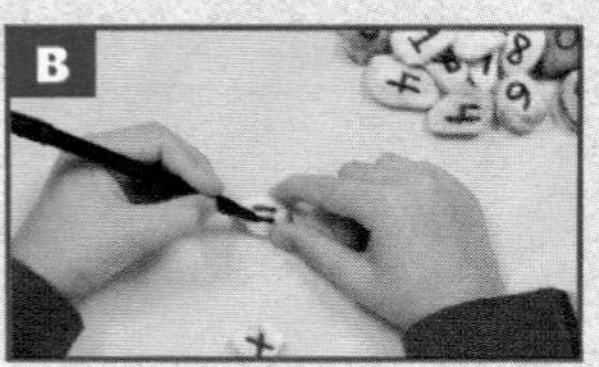
B

C

Challenge

Multiply with 11 and 12

There are 11 players on a soccer team. In a soccer game, there are two teams on the field. How many players are on the field?

2 × 11 = ■

You can use a multiplication table to find the product.

The product is found where the row for 2 and the column for 11 meet.

So, there are 22 players on the field.

×	0	1	2	3	4	5	6	7	8	9	10	11	12
0	0	0	0	0	0	0	0	0	0	0	0	0	0
1	0	1	2	3	4	5	6	7	8	9	10	11	12
2	0	2	4	6	8	10	12	14	16	18	20	22	24
3	0	3	6	9	12	15	18	21	24	27	30	33	36
4	0	4	8	12	16	20	24	28	32	36	40	44	48
5	0	5	10	15	20	25	30	35	40	45	50	55	60
6	0	6	12	18	24	30	36	42	48	54	60	66	72
7	0	7	14	21	28	35	42	49	56	63	70	77	84
8	0	8	16	24	32	40	48	56	64	72	80	88	96
9	0	9	18	27	36	45	54	63	72	81	90	99	108
10	0	10	20	30	40	50	60	70	80	90	100	110	120
11	0	11	22	33	44	55	66	77	88	99	110	121	132
12	0	12	24	36	48	60	72	84	96	108	120	132	144

Talk About It

- Explain how to use a multiplication table to find 6 × 12. The row for 6 and the column for 12 meet at the product 72.
- What patterns do you notice in the column for 12 of the multiplication table? Possible answers: the ones digits repeat the pattern 0, 2, 4, 6, 8; all of the products are even numbers.

Try It

Use the multiplication table to solve.

1. 3 × 11 = ■ 33 **2.** ■ = 7 × 11 77 **3.** ■ = 4 × 12 48

4. 8 × 11 = ■ 88 **5.** ■ = 6 × 11 66 **6.** 5 × 12 = ■ 60

7. 1 × 12 = ■ 12 **8.** ■ = 2 × 12 24 **9.** 9 × 12 = ■ 108

10. 12 × 7 = 84 **11.** 11 × 9 = 99 **12.** 11 × 5 = 55 **13.** 12 × 3 = 36 **14.** 12 × 8 = 96

Intervention and Extension Resources

Math Connection

Invite students to **learn about square numbers.** Remind students that numbers like 1, 4, 9, and 16 are called square numbers.

Tell them that ancient Greek mathematicians called numbers like 1, 3, 6, and 10 triangular numbers.

- Have students draw the next three numbers in the square and triangular number patterns and write the numbers. 25, 36, 49; 15, 21, 28
- Instruct students to choose a triangular number. Have them add it to the next greater triangular number. Ask: What do you notice about the sum? Possible answer: the sum is a square number.

VISUAL; VISUAL/SPATIAL

Challenge

Multiply with 11 and 12

Objective To extend the concepts and skills of Chapters 8–11

Using the Page

- *Direct students' attention to the first paragraph.*
  What array could you make to find 2 × 11? Possible answer: an array of 2 rows with 11 objects in each row
  How could you use the multiplication table to find 2 × 12? What is the product? Start at row 2 and look across until you reach the column 12. Where they meet is the product; 24.
- *Discuss the Talk About It question.*
  Using the pattern, explain how you could find 13 × 12. Possible answer: Add 12 to 144 to find 13 × 12, or 156.

Try It Before assigning the Try It exercises, remind students of the many ways they have learned to find products: break an array into known facts, use a multiplication table, use the Commutative Property of Multiplication, and use doubling when one of the factors is an even number.

Study Guide and Review

Purpose To help students review concepts and skills presented in Chapters 8–11

Using the Pages

Assessment Checkpoint

The Study Guide and Review includes content from Chapters 8–11.

Chapter 8

- 8.1 Algebra: Connect Addition and Multiplication
- 8.2 Multiply with 2 and 5
- 8.3 Hands On: Arrays
- 8.4 Multiply with 3
- 8.5 Problem Solving Skill: *Too Much/Too Little Information*

Chapter 9

- 9.1 Multiply with 1 and 0
- 9.2 Multiply with 4 on a Multiplication Table
- 9.3 Problem Solving Strategy: *Find a Pattern*
- 9.4 Practice Multiplication
- 9.5 Algebra: Missing Factors

Chapter 10

- 10.1 Multiply with 6
- 10.2 Multiply with 8
- 10.3 Problem Solving Skill: *Use a Pictograph*
- 10.4 Multiply with 7
- 10.5 Algebra: Practice the Facts

Chapter 11

- 11.1 Multiply with 9 and 10
- 11.2 Algebra: Find a Rule
- 11.3 Algebra: Multiply with 3 Factors
- 11.4 Algebra: Multiplication Properties
- 11.5 Problem Solving Skill: *Multistep Problems*

The blue page numbers in parentheses provided with each group of exercises indicate the pages on which the concept or skill was presented.

Study Guide and Review

VOCABULARY

Choose the best term from the box.

factors
Associative Property of Multiplication
Commutative Property of Multiplication

1. The _?_ means that two factors can be multiplied in any order. The product is the same. (p. 163)
   Commutative Property of Multiplication
2. The _?_ means that when the grouping of factors is changed, the product remains the same. (p. 218)
   Associative Property of Multiplication

STUDY AND SOLVE

Chapter 8

Use the Commutative Property of Multiplication.

Factors can be multiplied in any order. The product is the same.

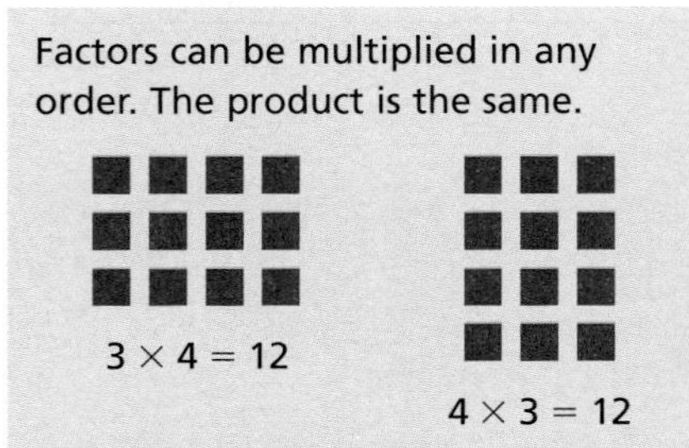

$3 \times 4 = 12$ $4 \times 3 = 12$

Find the product. (pp. 162–167)

3. $2 \times 3 = ■$ **6** $3 \times 2 = ■$ **6**
4. $3 \times 7 = ■$ **21** $7 \times 3 = ■$ **21**
5. $4 \times 5 = ■$ **20** $5 \times 4 = ■$ **20**
6. $3 \times 5 = ■$ **15** $5 \times 3 = ■$ **15**
7. $2 \times 7 = ■$ **14** $7 \times 2 = ■$ **14**

Chapter 9

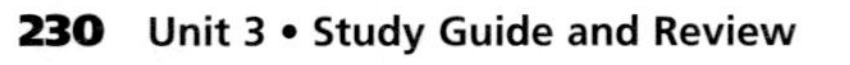

Find missing factors.

$■ \times 7 = 28$

The multiplication table on page 229 can help you. Look down the column for 7 to the product 28. Look left across the row from 28. The factor in that row is 4.

So, $4 \times 7 = 28$.

Find the missing factor. (pp. 186–187)

8. $■ \times 8 = 16$ **2**
9. $5 \times ■ = 30$ **6**
10. $9 \times ■ = 45$ **5**
11. $3 \times ■ = 3$ **1**
12. $4 \times ■ = 0$ **0**
13. $■ \times 3 = 15$ **5**
14. $■ \times 6 = 18$ **3**
15. $4 \times ■ = 36$ **9**

Chapter 10

Write multiplication facts with factors 6, 7, and 8.

You can double products of facts you already know to help you find products you don't know.

6 × 8 = ■
Think: 6 × 4 = 24
24 + 24 = 48, so 6 × 8 = 48.

Use the Commutative Property of Multiplication.
5 × 7 = ■
7 × 5 = 35, so 5 × 7 = 35.

Find the product. (pp. 194–197, 200–201)

16. 6 × 8 = ■ **48**
17. 7 × 6 = ■ **42**
18. 8 × 4 = ■ **32**
19. 6 × 6 = ■ **36**
20. 6 × 3 = ■ **18**
21. 4 × 8 = ■ **32**
22. 8 × 7 = ■ **56**
23. 8 × 8 = ■ **64**
24. 7 × 9 = ■ **63**
25. 7 × 7 = ■ **49**
26. 8 × 5 = ■ **40**
27. 7 × 4 = ■ **28**

Chapter 11

Find a rule for the pattern.

Write a rule for the pattern in the table.

Cars	1	2	3	4	5	6	7	8	9	10
Tires	4	8	12	16	20	■	■	■	■	■

Think: The number of tires is 4 times the number of cars.
Rule: Multiply by 4.

For 28–29, use the table below. (pp. 216–217)

Spiders	1	2	4	5	6	8
Legs	8	16	32	40	■	■

28. Write a rule for the table. **Multiply by 8.**

29. Use the rule from Exercise 28 to complete the table. **48, 64**

PROBLEM SOLVING PRACTICE

Solve. (pp. 168–169, 222–223)

30. Pencils are in packages of 4. Erasers are in packages of 7. Marian bought 16 pencils. How many packages of pencils did she buy? Is there too much or too little information? Explain. **4 packages; too much information; you don't need to know about the erasers.**

31. A box of cookies costs $3. A bag of nuts costs $2. Aimee bought 4 boxes of cookies and 7 bags of nuts for her friends. How much did she spend? **4 × $3 = $12, 7 × $2 = $14, $12 + $14 = $26**

Assessment Checkpoint

Portfolio Suggestions The portfolio represents the growth, talents, achievements, and reflections of the mathematics learner. Students might spend a short time selecting work samples for their portfolios and completing A Guide to My Math Portfolio from *Assessment Guide*, page AGxix.

You may want to have students respond to the following questions:

- **What new understanding of math have I developed in the past several weeks?**
- **What growth in understanding or skills can I see in my work?**
- **What can I do to improve my understanding of math ideas?**
- **What would I like to learn more about?**

For information on how to organize, share, and evaluate portfolios, see *Assessment Guide*, page AGxviii.

Use the item analysis in the **Intervention** chart to diagnose students' errors. You may wish to reinforce content or remediate misunderstandings by using the text pages or lesson resources.

Unit Test

- Multiple-choice format of Unit 3 Posttest–See *Assessment Guide*, pp. AG69–72.
- Free-Response format of Unit 3 Posttest–See *Assessment Guide*, pp. AG73–76.

Study Guide and Review Intervention • How to Help Options

Items	Text Pages	Reteach and Practice Resources
3–7	162–167	Worksheets for Lessons 8.3, 8.4
8–15	186–187	Worksheets for Lesson 9.5
16–27	194–197, 200–201	Worksheets for Lessons 10.1, 10.2, 10.4
28–29	216–217	Worksheets for Lesson 11.2
30–31	168–169, 222–223	Worksheets for Lessons 8.5, 11.5

UNIT 3

Performance Assessment

Purpose To provide performance assessment tasks for Chapters 8–11

Using the Page

- *Have students work individually or in pairs as an alternative to formal assessment.*
- *Use the performance indicators and work samples below to evaluate Tasks A–B.*

See *Performance Assessment* for

- a complete scoring rubric, p. PAx, for this unit.
- additional student work samples for this unit.
- copying masters for this unit.

You may suggest that students place completed Performance Assessment tasks in their portfolios.

Performance Indicators

Task A
A student with a Level 3 paper
✓ Makes and draws arrays.
✓ Writes multiplication sentences.
✓ Explains Order Property of Multiplication.

Task B
A student with a Level 3 paper
✓ Multiplies two factors.
✓ Compares products.
✓ Writes multiplication sentences.

PERFORMANCE ASSESSMENT

TASK A • CLASS PLAY

Materials: square tiles

You need to set up 24 chairs for people to watch the class play. You must put the chairs into rows with an equal number of chairs in each row.

a. Use square tiles to represent the chairs. Make arrays to show two possible ways to set up the chairs. Draw a picture of each array. **Check students' drawings.**

b. Write a multiplication sentence for each array. **Check students' work.**

c. Are the two multiplication sentences you wrote examples of the Order Property of Multiplication? Why or why not? **Answers will vary.**

School Play
Place-Auditorium
Date-October 6
Time-8:00pm

TASK B • A NEW GAME

You and a friend invent a new game using 2 spinners. You spin the pointer on each spinner. Use the numbers the pointers land on as factors to write a multiplication sentence. If a pointer lands on a shaded section, you can choose any number on that spinner as the factor. The winner of the round is the player with the greater product.

a. Your friend spins a 4 and a 5. You spin a 3 and a shaded section. Which numbers could you choose to make yourself the winner? **7, 8, or 9**

b. Write three multiplication sentences for factors you can spin on the spinners that give a product less than 20. **Possible answer: $1 \times 5 = 5$; $2 \times 6 = 12$; $0 \times 9 = 0$**

c. Suppose you want to change the game so that you can spin factors with products more than 100. What numbers would you put on the spinners? **Answers will vary.**

232 Unit 3 • Performance Assessment

Work Samples for Task A and Task B

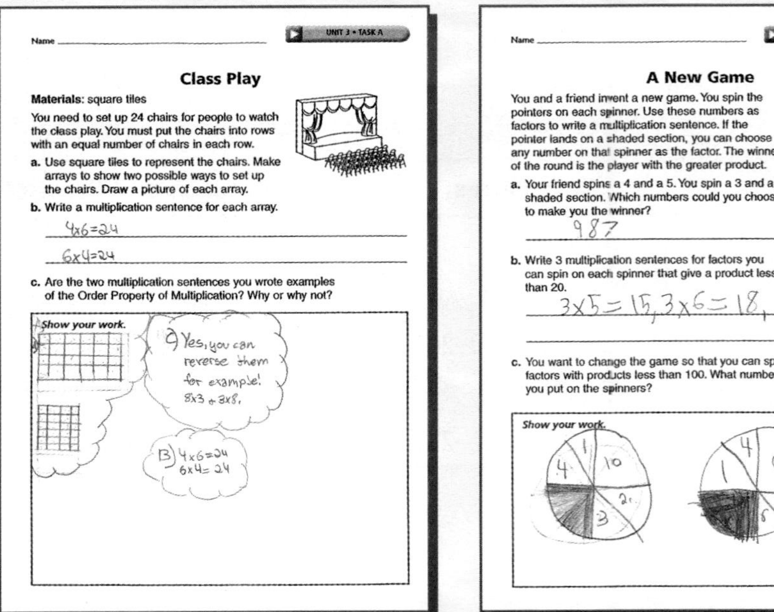

Name ______ UNIT 3 • TASK A

Class Play

Materials: square tiles

You need to set up 24 chairs for people to watch the class play. You must put the chairs into rows with an equal number of chairs in each row.

a. Use square tiles to represent the chairs. Make arrays to show two possible ways to set up the chairs. Draw a picture of each array.

b. Write a multiplication sentence for each array.

4x6=24

6x4=24

c. Are the two multiplication sentences you wrote examples of the Order Property of Multiplication? Why or why not?

Show your work.

C) Yes, you can reverse them for example! 8x3 + 3x8.

B) 4x6=24 6x4=24

Name ______ UNIT 3 • TASK B

A New Game

You and a friend invent a new game. You spin the pointers on each spinner. Use these numbers as factors to write a multiplication sentence. If the pointer lands on a shaded section, you can choose any number on that spinner as the factor. The winner of the round is the player with the greater product.

a. Your friend spins a 4 and a 5. You spin a 3 and a shaded section. Which numbers could you choose to make you the winner?

987

b. Write 3 multiplication sentences for factors you can spin on each spinner that give a product less than 20.

3x5=15, 3x6=18, 2x5=10

c. You want to change the game so that you can spin factors with products less than 100. What numbers would you put on the spinners?

Show your work.

Level 3 This student shows good understanding of arrays and writes two multiplication sentences, as directed. Explanations are included.

Level 3 This student's work demonstrates understanding of the task. The answers are accurate and complete.

Technology Linkup

The Learning Site • Multiplication Mystery

If you know your multiplication facts, it is easy to count groups of coins and other objects.

You can practice your multiplication facts at the Harcourt School Learning Site.

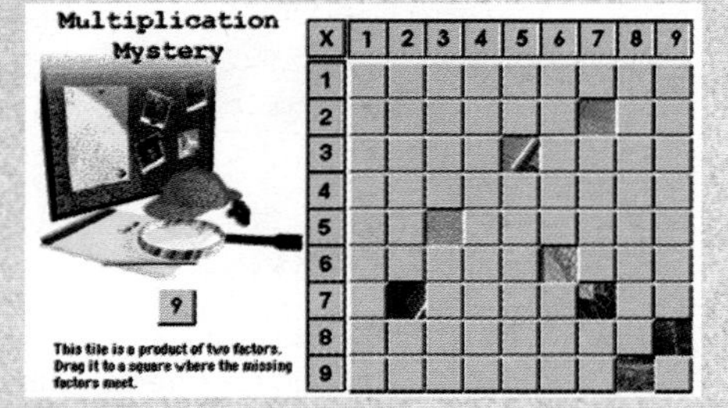

Multiplication Mystery
X 1 2 3 4 5 6 7 8 9
This tile is a product of two factors. Drag it to a square where the missing factors meet.

- Go to The Learning Site. **www.harcourtschool.com**
- Click on *Multiplication Mystery.*
- Drag the products into the multiplication table to uncover the picture.
- What picture did you uncover? **Possible answers: windmill, castle, black panther, kitten looking through fish bowl**

Practice and Problem Solving

Find the product.

1. $2 \times 10 = ■$ **20** **2.** $3 \times 5 = ■$ **15** **3.** $4 \times 2 = ■$ **8** **4.** $6 \times 2 = ■$ **12**

5. $7 \times 4 = ■$ **28** **6.** $5 \times 5 = ■$ **25** **7.** $2 \times 7 = ■$ **14** **8.** $3 \times 9 = ■$ **27**

Find the missing factor.

9. $4 \times ■ = 12$ **3** **10.** $■ \times 8 = 40$ **5** **11.** $■ \times 5 = 35$ **7** **12.** $10 \times ■ = 90$ **9**

13. $7 \times ■ = 42$ **6** **14.** $■ \times 7 = 63$ **9** **15.** $8 \times ■ = 56$ **7** **16.** $■ \times 3 = 24$ **8**

17. **Write a problem** involving two multiplication facts. **Check students' problems.**

18. **STRETCH YOUR THINKING** Joanne has 88 stickers. She has 7 sheets of 8 animal stickers. How many sheets of 8 stickers without animals does she have? **4 sheets**

GO ON-LINE **Multimedia Math Glossary** www.harcourtschool.com/mathglossary

Vocabulary Power Look up *Commutative Property of Multiplication* in the Multimedia Math Glossary. Write a problem that uses the examples shown in the glossary, and use counters to model it.

Check students' work.

Technology Linkup

Objective To practice multiplication facts

Using the Page

- *Have students read about The Learning Site.* **Explain how you uncover the picture.** by dragging the products to their correct location on the multiplication table
  Where would the product 45 go on the table? The product 45 would go where row 9 and column 5 meet or where row 5 and column 9 meet.

Using the Harcourt Learning Site

Students do not need to complete the entire multiplication table to have the picture revealed to them. You may wish to have students repeat the activity, uncovering a second picture, to give them additional practice before they complete the Practice and Problem Solving exercises. There are 4 different pictures to uncover.

Practice and Problem Solving

Encourage students to solve the exercises mentally, so that they can practice memorizing the facts. Extend the lesson by having students write facts with missing numbers and exchange with a partner to solve.

Multimedia Math Glossary

Commutative Property of Multiplication and all other vocabulary words in this unit can be found in the Harcourt Multimedia Math Glossary.
www.harcourtschool.com/mathglossary

Problem Solving
in North Carolina

Purpose To provide additional practice for concepts and skills in Chapters 8–11

Using the Page

NORTH CAROLINA CAMPGROUNDS

- *Direct students to the data in the table.* **How many tent symbols would be needed to show that a campground has 70 sites? Explain.** 7 tent symbols; $7 \times 10 = 70$.
- *After students have completed Exercise 2, ask:* **Which campground has 25 fewer sites than Cartoogechaye Creek?** Timberlake

Extension Encourage students to use the data on this page to write a multistep problem. Then have each student exchange problems with a classmate, and solve. Check students' work.

▲ Nantahala National Forest

Nantahala National Forest & Fontana Lake

CAMPING

North Carolina has over one million acres of national forests. Campers enjoy fishing, hiking, rock climbing, and swimming.

5. Possible answer: An Eagle's Landing; it has the fewest campsites, so there are the fewest people.

USE DATA For 1–5, use the pictograph.

1. Which campground has the most campsites? Which has the fewest campsites? **Adventure Trail; An Eagle's Landing**
2. How many more campsites does Adventure Trail have than An Eagle's Landing? **60 more campsites**
3. List the campgrounds from the one with the fewest campsites to the one with the most campsites. **An Eagle's Landing, Timberlake, Cartoogechaye Creek, Adventure Trail**
4. Suppose Timberlake Campground had 10 empty campsites. How many campsites were filled? **40 campsites were filled.**
5. **REASONING** Mike's family wants to stay at the campground with the fewest people. Which campground should they choose? Explain. **See above.**

NORTH CAROLINA CAMPGROUNDS	
Campground	Number of Sites
Adventure Trail	▲▲▲▲▲▲▲▲▲
An Eagle's Landing	▲▲▲
Cartoogechaye Creek	▲▲▲▲▲▲▲ and a half ▲
Timberlake	▲▲▲▲▲
Key: Each ▲ = 10 campsites.	

▼ Campers enjoy the waterfalls and rivers in Nantahala National Forest. The word *Nantahala* means "land of the midday sun."

FONTANA LAKE

The Fontana Lake area is known for some of the best walleye fishing in North Carolina. Visitors can fish, swim, and go whitewater rafting in the Fontana Lake area.

▲ The northern side of Fontana Lake is surrounded by the Great Smoky Mountains National Park. People can catch sunfish, catfish, and white bass in the lake.

▲ The walleye is a large freshwater fish. It is known for its large eyes.

USE DATA For 1 and 5, use the information on the sign.

1. The Collins family camped at Adventure Trail for 2 nights. There are 6 people in the family. What was the total cost? **$52**
2. At the campground, there are 7 tents with 4 people in each tent, and 9 tents with 5 people in each tent. How many campers are there in all? **73 campers**
3. Caroline and her family went whitewater rafting on the Nantahala River. There were 5 rafts. Each raft held 8 people. There were 22 adults in the group. How many rafters were children? **18 rafters**
4. Sean fished in Fontana Lake. He caught 4 walleyes the first day. He caught twice as many bass the second day. If he catches 6 walleyes or bass on the third day, how many fish will he have caught altogether? **18 fish**

Adventure Trail Campground

Fees
$22 per night for family of 4
$2 per night for each additional person

5. **Write About It** Write a problem using the data on the sign. Then trade problems with a classmate and solve. **Check students' answers.**

Using the Page

FONTANA LAKE

- *After students have completed Exercise 1, ask:* **Suppose the cost of the campsite is reduced to $18 and the cost for each additional person is raised to $3 per night. How much will the family of 6 save on the total cost? Explain.** $4; cost for 2 nights: $36; cost for 2 additional people for 2 days; $12. Total cost: $36 + $12 = $48; $52 – $48 = $4.
- *After students have completed Exercise 4, ask:* **How many walleye does Sean still need to catch if he wants to catch 25 fish altogether? Explain.** 7 fish; 25 − 18 = 7

Extension After students have completed Exercise 3, have them make a table to show how many people can fit in 6–10 rafts. Then have them write their own problem based on this data, exchange problems with a classmate, and solve. Check students' work.

Rafts	6	7	8	9	10
People	48	56	64	72	80

EOG TEST HANDBOOK

The tips and the problems on the following pages will help you succeed on the EOG Test.

Before working on the Getting Ready for the EOG Test problems and before taking the EOG Test, sharpen your test-taking skills by reviewing these pages. Here you can find tips such as how to get ready for the test, how to understand the directions, and how to keep track of time.

The problems in this section cover the strands of the North Carolina Mathematics Standard Course of Study. Use these problems to build your test-taking skills and to prepare for EOG success.

Tricky Triangles

Other Resources

Review addition, subtraction, multiplication, and division facts by taking the basic facts tests throughout the year to improve your memorization skills.

All the important measures used in this book are in this table. If you've forgotten exactly how many feet are in a mile, this table will help you.

This glossary will help you speak and write the language of mathematics. Use the glossary to check the definitions of important terms.

Use the index when you want to review a topic. It lists the page numbers where the topic is taught.

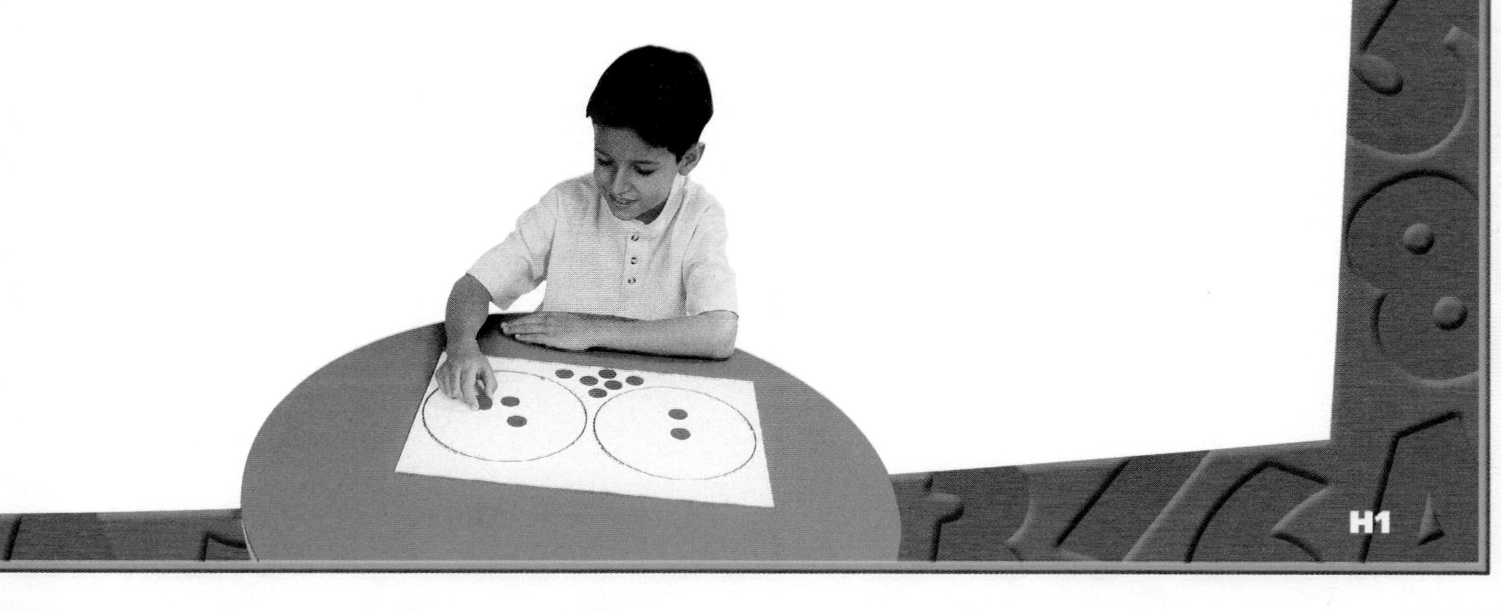

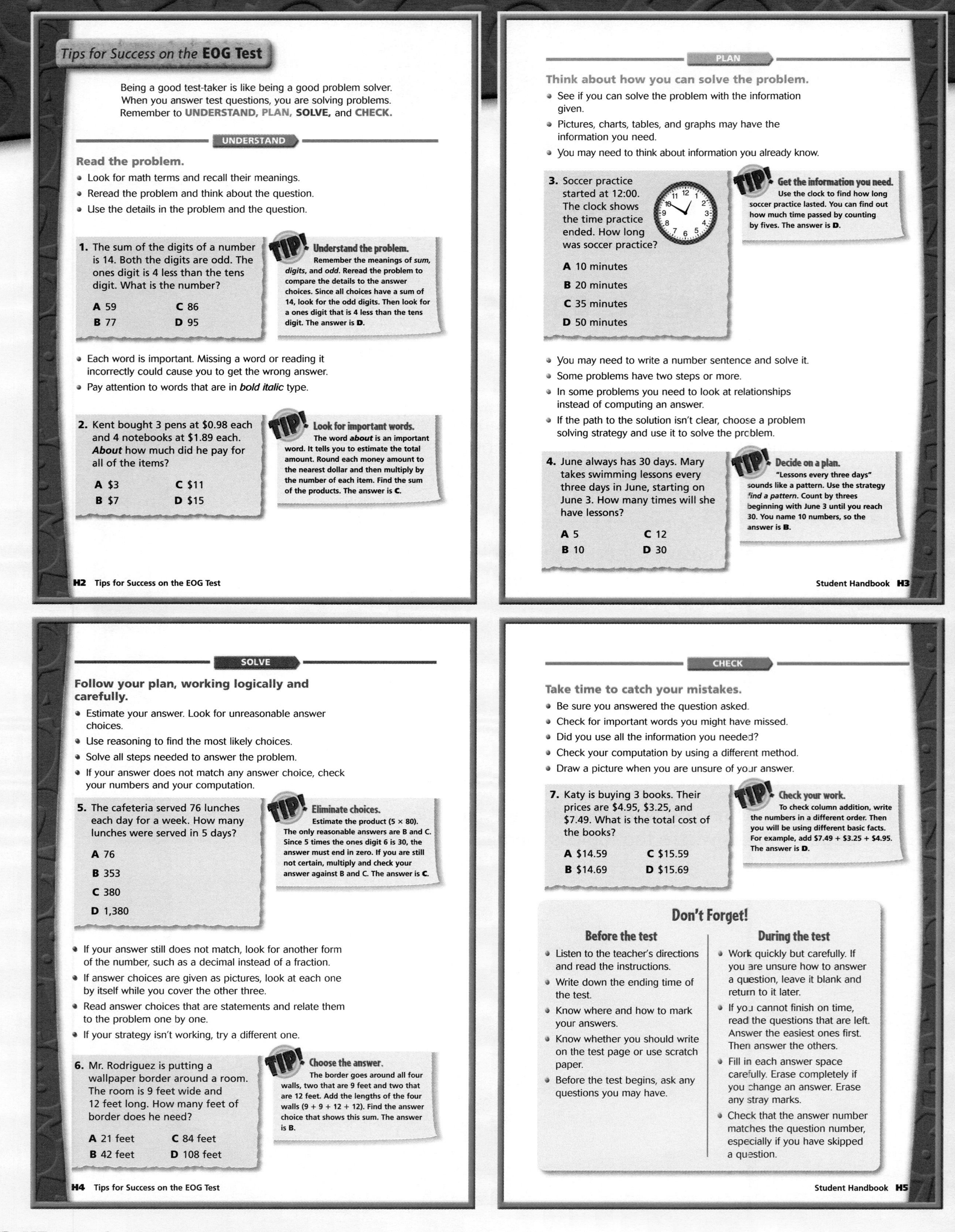

Tips for Success on the EOG Test

Being a good test-taker is like being a good problem solver. When you answer test questions, you are solving problems. Remember to **UNDERSTAND, PLAN, SOLVE,** and **CHECK.**

UNDERSTAND

Read the problem.

- Look for math terms and recall their meanings.
- Reread the problem and think about the question.
- Use the details in the problem and the question.

1. The sum of the digits of a number is 14. Both the digits are odd. The ones digit is 4 less than the tens digit. What is the number?

A 59 **C** 86
B 77 **D** 95

TIP! Understand the problem. Remember the meanings of *sum*, *digits*, and *odd*. Reread the problem to compare the details to the answer choices. Since all choices have a sum of 14, look for the odd digits. Then look for a ones digit that is 4 less than the tens digit. The answer is **D**.

- Each word is important. Missing a word or reading it incorrectly could cause you to get the wrong answer.
- Pay attention to words that are in ***bold italic*** type.

2. Kent bought 3 pens at $0.98 each and 4 notebooks at $1.89 each. ***About*** how much did he pay for all of the items?

A $3 **C** $11
B $7 **D** $15

TIP! Look for important words. The word ***about*** is an important word. It tells you to estimate the total amount. Round each money amount to the nearest dollar and then multiply by the number of each item. Find the sum of the products. The answer is **C**.

PLAN

Think about how you can solve the problem.

- See if you can solve the problem with the information given.
- Pictures, charts, tables, and graphs may have the information you need.
- You may need to think about information you already know.

3. Soccer practice started at 12:00. The clock shows the time practice ended. How long was soccer practice?

A 10 minutes
B 20 minutes
C 35 minutes
D 50 minutes

TIP! Get the information you need. Use the clock to find how long soccer practice lasted. You can find out how much time passed by counting by fives. The answer is **D**.

- You may need to write a number sentence and solve it.
- Some problems have two steps or more.
- In some problems you need to look at relationships instead of computing an answer.
- If the path to the solution isn't clear, choose a problem solving strategy and use it to solve the problem.

4. June always has 30 days. Mary takes swimming lessons every three days in June, starting on June 3. How many times will she have lessons?

A 5 **C** 12
B 10 **D** 30

TIP! Decide on a plan. "Lessons every three days" sounds like a pattern. Use the strategy *find a pattern*. Count by threes beginning with June 3 until you reach 30. You name 10 numbers, so the answer is **B**.

SOLVE

Follow your plan, working logically and carefully.

- Estimate your answer. Look for unreasonable answer choices.
- Use reasoning to find the most likely choices.
- Solve all steps needed to answer the problem.
- If your answer does not match any answer choice, check your numbers and your computation.

5. The cafeteria served 76 lunches each day for a week. How many lunches were served in 5 days?

A 76
B 353
C 380
D 1,380

TIP! Eliminate choices. Estimate the product (5 × 80). The only reasonable answers are B and C. Since 5 times the ones digit 6 is 30, the answer must end in zero. If you are still not certain, multiply and check your answer against B and C. The answer is **C**.

- If your answer still does not match, look for another form of the number, such as a decimal instead of a fraction.
- If answer choices are given as pictures, look at each one by itself while you cover the other three.
- Read answer choices that are statements and relate them to the problem one by one.
- If your strategy isn't working, try a different one.

6. Mr. Rodriguez is putting a wallpaper border around a room. The room is 9 feet wide and 12 feet long. How many feet of border does he need?

A 21 feet **C** 84 feet
B 42 feet **D** 108 feet

TIP! Choose the answer. The border goes around all four walls, two that are 9 feet and two that are 12 feet. Add the lengths of the four walls (9 + 9 + 12 + 12). Find the answer choice that shows this sum. The answer is **B**.

CHECK

Take time to catch your mistakes.

- Be sure you answered the question asked.
- Check for important words you might have missed.
- Did you use all the information you needed?
- Check your computation by using a different method.
- Draw a picture when you are unsure of your answer.

7. Katy is buying 3 books. Their prices are $4.95, $3.25, and $7.49. What is the total cost of the books?

A $14.59 **C** $15.59
B $14.69 **D** $15.69

TIP! Check your work. To check column addition, write the numbers in a different order. Then you will be using different basic facts. For example, add $7.49 + $3.25 + $4.95. The answer is **D**.

Don't Forget!

Before the test

- Listen to the teacher's directions and read the instructions.
- Write down the ending time of the test.
- Know where and how to mark your answers.
- Know whether you should write on the test page or use scratch paper.
- Before the test begins, ask any questions you may have.

During the test

- Work quickly but carefully. If you are unsure how to answer a question, leave it blank and return to it later.
- If you cannot finish on time, read the questions that are left. Answer the easiest ones first. Then answer the others.
- Fill in each answer space carefully. Erase completely if you change an answer. Erase any stray marks.
- Check that the answer number matches the question number, especially if you have skipped a question.

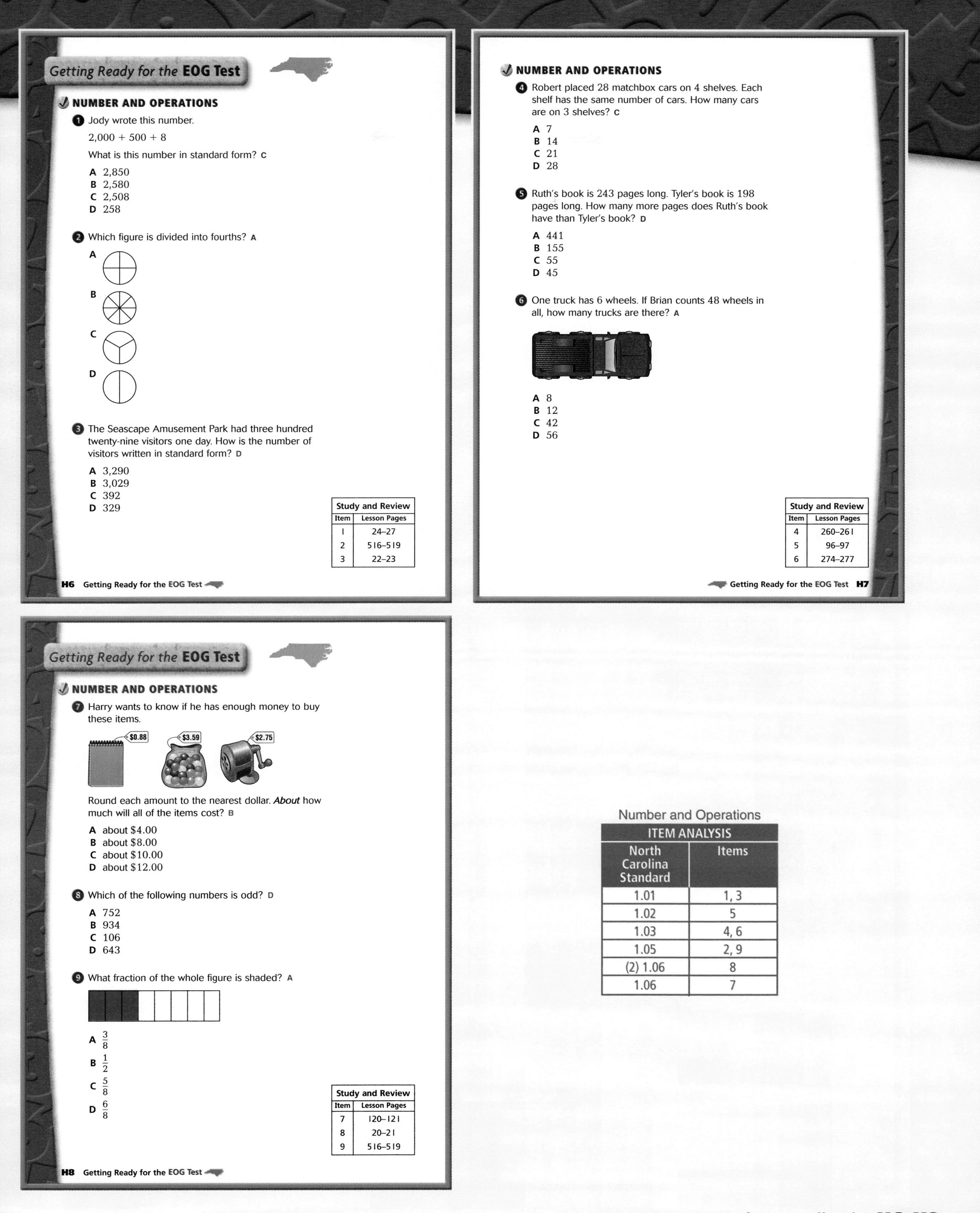

Getting Ready for the EOG Test

NUMBER AND OPERATIONS

1. Jody wrote this number.

   2,000 + 500 + 8

   What is this number in standard form? C

   A 2,850
   B 2,580
   C 2,508
   D 258

2. Which figure is divided into fourths? A

   A
   B
   C
   D

3. The Seascape Amusement Park had three hundred twenty-nine visitors one day. How is the number of visitors written in standard form? D

   A 3,290
   B 3,029
   C 392
   D 329

Study and Review	
Item	Lesson Pages
1	24–27
2	516–519
3	22–23

NUMBER AND OPERATIONS

4. Robert placed 28 matchbox cars on 4 shelves. Each shelf has the same number of cars. How many cars are on 3 shelves? C

   A 7
   B 14
   C 21
   D 28

5. Ruth's book is 243 pages long. Tyler's book is 198 pages long. How many more pages does Ruth's book have than Tyler's book? D

   A 441
   B 155
   C 55
   D 45

6. One truck has 6 wheels. If Brian counts 48 wheels in all, how many trucks are there? A

   A 8
   B 12
   C 42
   D 56

Study and Review	
Item	Lesson Pages
4	260–261
5	96–97
6	274–277

Getting Ready for the EOG Test

NUMBER AND OPERATIONS

7. Harry wants to know if he has enough money to buy these items.

   $0.88 $3.59 $2.75

   Round each amount to the nearest dollar. *About* how much will all of the items cost? B

   A about $4.00
   B about $8.00
   C about $10.00
   D about $12.00

8. Which of the following numbers is odd? D

   A 752
   B 934
   C 106
   D 643

9. What fraction of the whole figure is shaded? A

   A $\frac{3}{8}$
   B $\frac{1}{2}$
   C $\frac{5}{8}$
   D $\frac{6}{8}$

Study and Review	
Item	Lesson Pages
7	120–121
8	20–21
9	516–519

Number and Operations

ITEM ANALYSIS	
North Carolina Standard	Items
1.01	1, 3
1.02	5
1.03	4, 6
1.05	2, 9
(2) 1.06	8
1.06	7

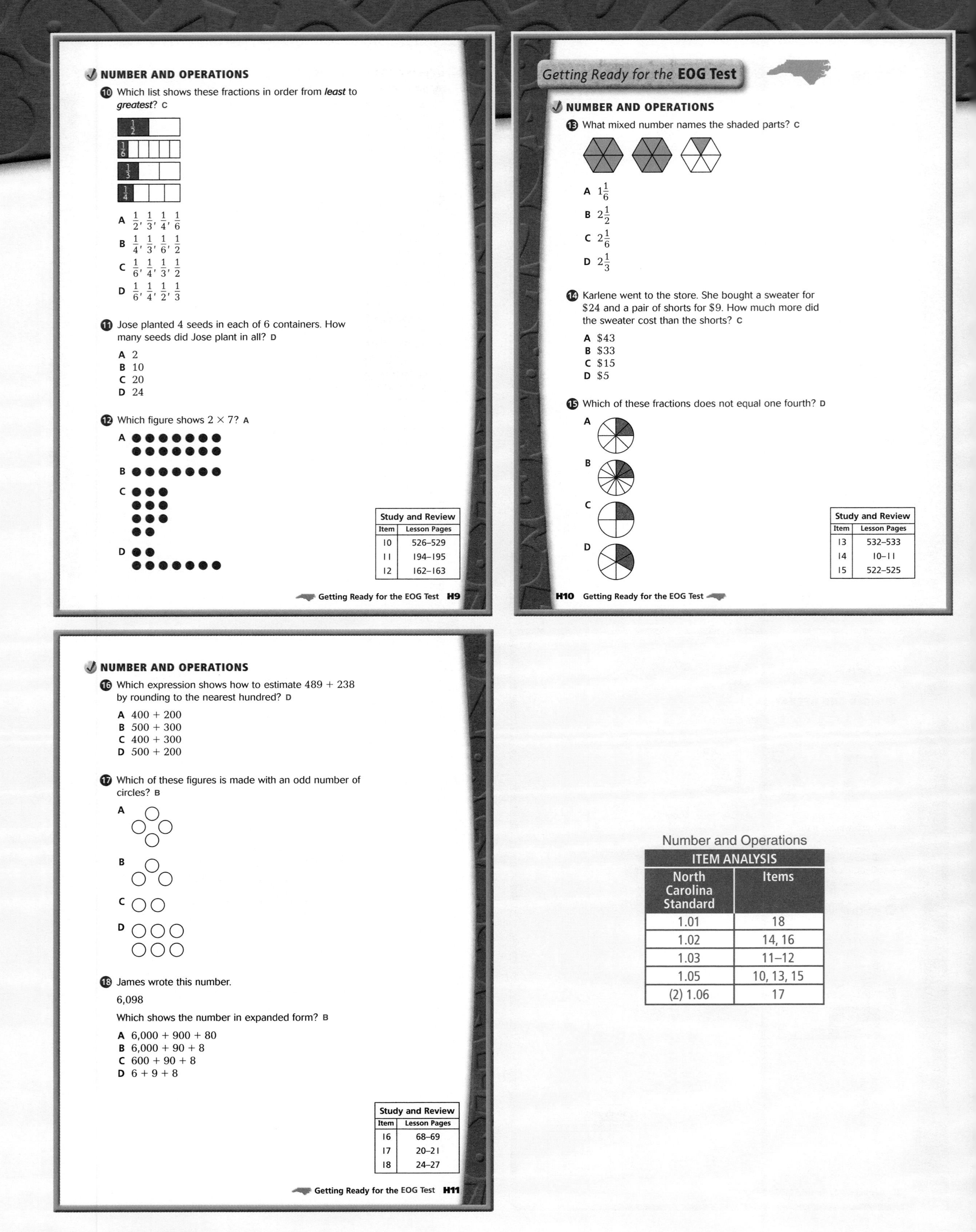

NUMBER AND OPERATIONS

10. Which list shows these fractions in order from *least* to *greatest*? C

A $\frac{1}{2}, \frac{1}{3}, \frac{1}{4}, \frac{1}{6}$
B $\frac{1}{4}, \frac{1}{3}, \frac{1}{6}, \frac{1}{2}$
C $\frac{1}{6}, \frac{1}{4}, \frac{1}{3}, \frac{1}{2}$
D $\frac{1}{6}, \frac{1}{4}, \frac{1}{2}, \frac{1}{3}$

11. Jose planted 4 seeds in each of 6 containers. How many seeds did Jose plant in all? D

A 2
B 10
C 20
D 24

12. Which figure shows 2×7? A

A
B
C
D

Study and Review	
Item	Lesson Pages
10	526–529
11	194–195
12	162–163

Getting Ready for the EOG Test

NUMBER AND OPERATIONS

13. What mixed number names the shaded parts? C

A $1\frac{1}{6}$
B $2\frac{1}{2}$
C $2\frac{1}{6}$
D $2\frac{1}{3}$

14. Karlene went to the store. She bought a sweater for \$24 and a pair of shorts for \$9. How much more did the sweater cost than the shorts? C

A \$43
B \$33
C \$15
D \$5

15. Which of these fractions does not equal one fourth? D

A
B
C
D

Study and Review	
Item	Lesson Pages
13	532–533
14	10–11
15	522–525

NUMBER AND OPERATIONS

16. Which expression shows how to estimate $489 + 238$ by rounding to the nearest hundred? D

A $400 + 200$
B $500 + 300$
C $400 + 300$
D $500 + 200$

17. Which of these figures is made with an odd number of circles? B

A
B
C
D

18. James wrote this number.

6,098

Which shows the number in expanded form? B

A $6,000 + 900 + 80$
B $6,000 + 90 + 8$
C $600 + 90 + 8$
D $6 + 9 + 8$

Study and Review	
Item	Lesson Pages
16	68–69
17	20–21
18	24–27

Number and Operations

ITEM ANALYSIS	
North Carolina Standard	Items
1.01	18
1.02	14, 16
1.03	11–12
1.05	10, 13, 15
(2) 1.06	17

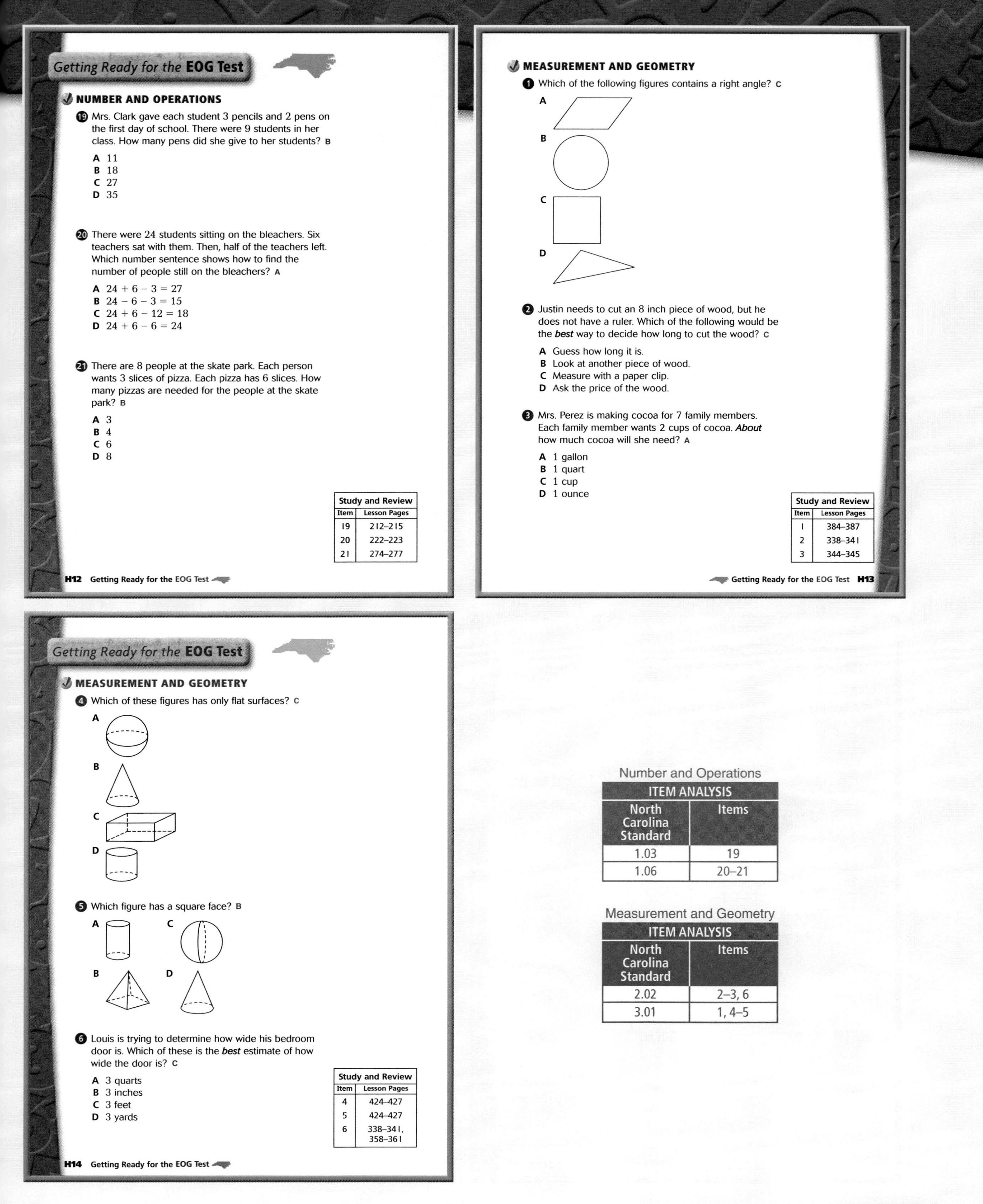

Getting Ready for the EOG Test

NUMBER AND OPERATIONS

19. Mrs. Clark gave each student 3 pencils and 2 pens on the first day of school. There were 9 students in her class. How many pens did she give to her students? B

A 11
B 18
C 27
D 35

20. There were 24 students sitting on the bleachers. Six teachers sat with them. Then, half of the teachers left. Which number sentence shows how to find the number of people still on the bleachers? A

A $24 + 6 - 3 = 27$
B $24 - 6 - 3 = 15$
C $24 + 6 - 12 = 18$
D $24 + 6 - 6 = 24$

21. There are 8 people at the skate park. Each person wants 3 slices of pizza. Each pizza has 6 slices. How many pizzas are needed for the people at the skate park? B

A 3
B 4
C 6
D 8

Study and Review	
Item	Lesson Pages
19	212–215
20	222–223
21	274–277

MEASUREMENT AND GEOMETRY

1. Which of the following figures contains a right angle? C

A
B
C
D

2. Justin needs to cut an 8 inch piece of wood, but he does not have a ruler. Which of the following would be the ***best*** way to decide how long to cut the wood? C

A Guess how long it is.
B Look at another piece of wood.
C Measure with a paper clip.
D Ask the price of the wood.

3. Mrs. Perez is making cocoa for 7 family members. Each family member wants 2 cups of cocoa. ***About*** how much cocoa will she need? A

A 1 gallon
B 1 quart
C 1 cup
D 1 ounce

Study and Review	
Item	Lesson Pages
1	384–387
2	338–341
3	344–345

Getting Ready for the EOG Test

MEASUREMENT AND GEOMETRY

4. Which of these figures has only flat surfaces? C

A
B
C
D

5. Which figure has a square face? B

A C
B D

6. Louis is trying to determine how wide his bedroom door is. Which of these is the ***best*** estimate of how wide the door is? C

A 3 quarts
B 3 inches
C 3 feet
D 3 yards

Study and Review	
Item	Lesson Pages
4	424–427
5	424–427
6	338–341, 358–361

Number and Operations

ITEM ANALYSIS	
North Carolina Standard	Items
1.03	19
1.06	20–21

Measurement and Geometry

ITEM ANALYSIS	
North Carolina Standard	Items
2.02	2–3, 6
3.01	1, 4–5

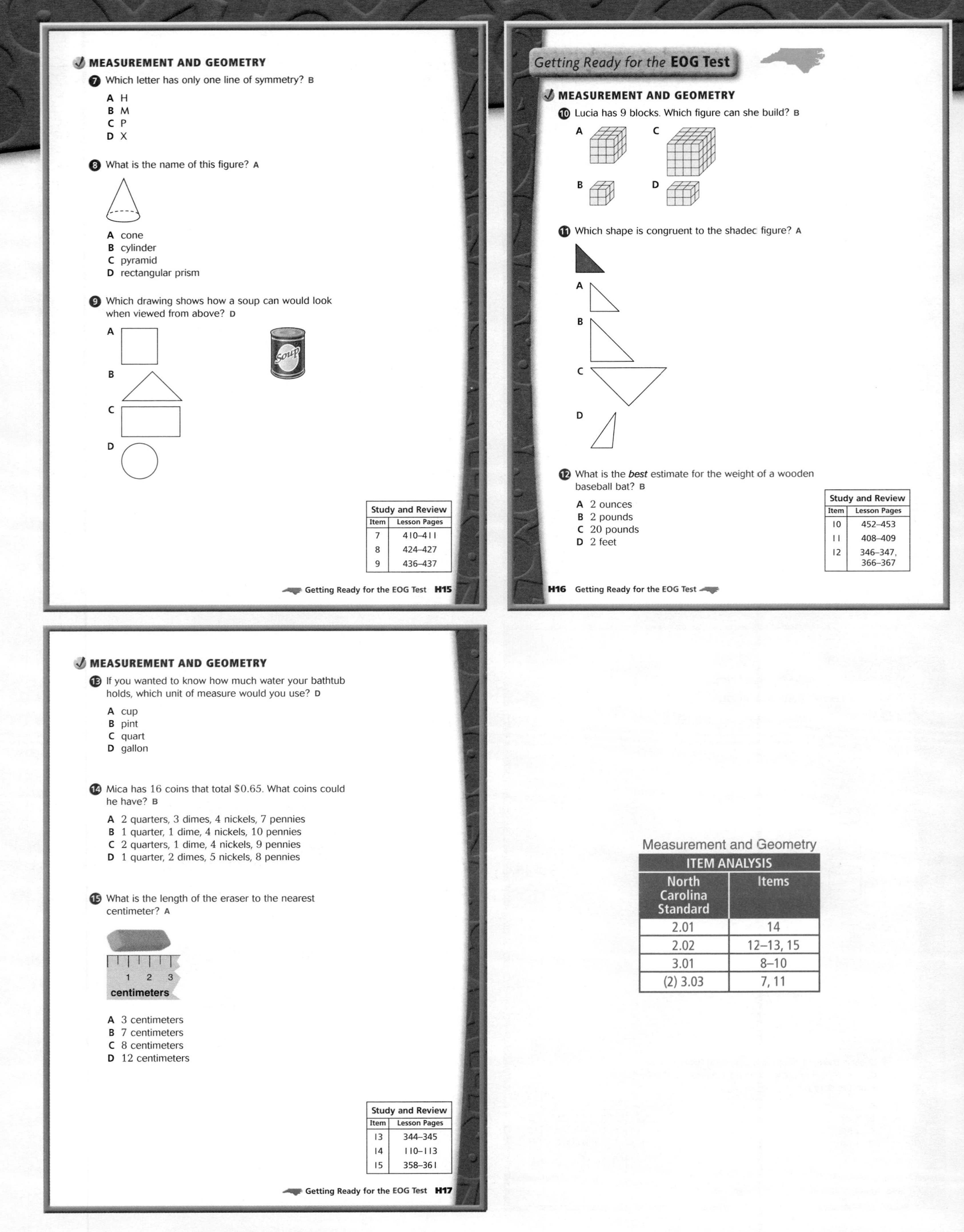

MEASUREMENT AND GEOMETRY

7. Which letter has only one line of symmetry? B

A H
B M
C P
D X

8. What is the name of this figure? A

A cone
B cylinder
C pyramid
D rectangular prism

9. Which drawing shows how a soup can would look when viewed from above? D

A
B
C
D

Study and Review	
Item	Lesson Pages
7	410–411
8	424–427
9	436–437

Getting Ready for the EOG Test

MEASUREMENT AND GEOMETRY

10. Lucia has 9 blocks. Which figure can she build? B

A
C
B
D

11. Which shape is congruent to the shaded figure? A

A
B
C
D

12. What is the *best* estimate for the weight of a wooden baseball bat? B

A 2 ounces
B 2 pounds
C 20 pounds
D 2 feet

Study and Review	
Item	Lesson Pages
10	452–453
11	408–409
12	346–347, 366–367

MEASUREMENT AND GEOMETRY

13. If you wanted to know how much water your bathtub holds, which unit of measure would you use? D

A cup
B pint
C quart
D gallon

14. Mica has 16 coins that total \$0.65. What coins could he have? B

A 2 quarters, 3 dimes, 4 nickels, 7 pennies
B 1 quarter, 1 dime, 4 nickels, 10 pennies
C 2 quarters, 1 dime, 4 nickels, 9 pennies
D 1 quarter, 2 dimes, 5 nickels, 8 pennies

15. What is the length of the eraser to the nearest centimeter? A

A 3 centimeters
B 7 centimeters
C 8 centimeters
D 12 centimeters

Study and Review	
Item	Lesson Pages
13	344–345
14	110–113
15	358–361

Measurement and Geometry

ITEM ANALYSIS	
North Carolina Standard	Items
2.01	14
2.02	12–13, 15
3.01	8–10
(2) 3.03	7, 11

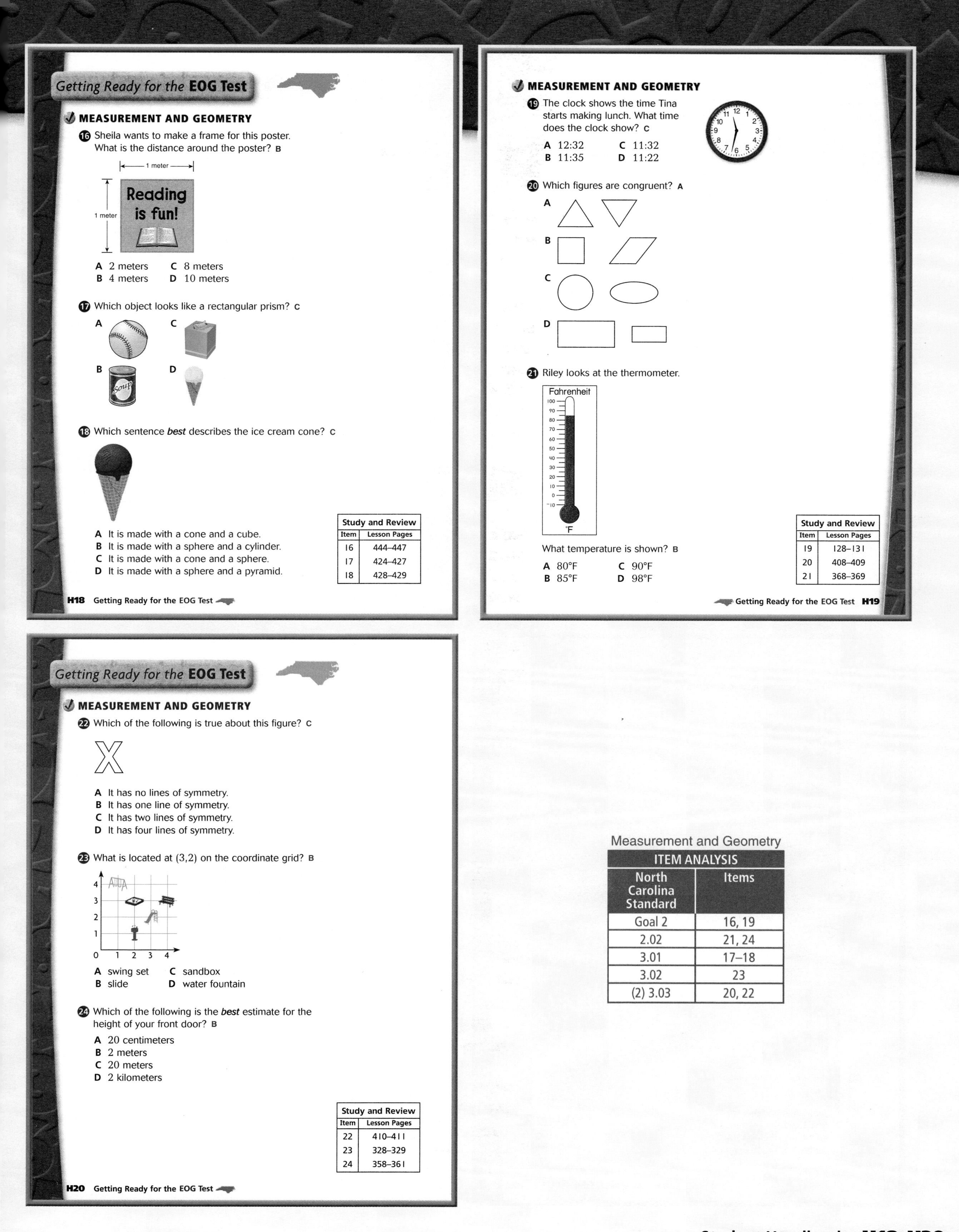

Getting Ready for the EOG Test

MEASUREMENT AND GEOMETRY

16. Sheila wants to make a frame for this poster. What is the distance around the poster? B

1 meter
1 meter
Reading is fun!

A 2 meters C 8 meters
B 4 meters D 10 meters

17. Which object looks like a rectangular prism? C

A C
B D

18. Which sentence *best* describes the ice cream cone? C

A It is made with a cone and a cube.
B It is made with a sphere and a cylinder.
C It is made with a cone and a sphere.
D It is made with a sphere and a pyramid.

Study and Review	
Item	Lesson Pages
16	444–447
17	424–427
18	428–429

MEASUREMENT AND GEOMETRY

19. The clock shows the time Tina starts making lunch. What time does the clock show? C

A 12:32 C 11:32
B 11:35 D 11:22

20. Which figures are congruent? A

A
B
C
D

21. Riley looks at the thermometer.

Fahrenheit
°F

What temperature is shown? B

A 80°F C 90°F
B 85°F D 98°F

Study and Review	
Item	Lesson Pages
19	128–131
20	408–409
21	368–369

Getting Ready for the EOG Test

MEASUREMENT AND GEOMETRY

22. Which of the following is true about this figure? C

X

A It has no lines of symmetry.
B It has one line of symmetry.
C It has two lines of symmetry.
D It has four lines of symmetry.

23. What is located at (3,2) on the coordinate grid? B

A swing set C sandbox
B slide D water fountain

24. Which of the following is the *best* estimate for the height of your front door? B

A 20 centimeters
B 2 meters
C 20 meters
D 2 kilometers

Study and Review	
Item	Lesson Pages
22	410–411
23	328–329
24	358–361

Measurement and Geometry

ITEM ANALYSIS	
North Carolina Standard	Items
Goal 2	16, 19
2.02	21, 24
3.01	17–18
3.02	23
(2) 3.03	20, 22

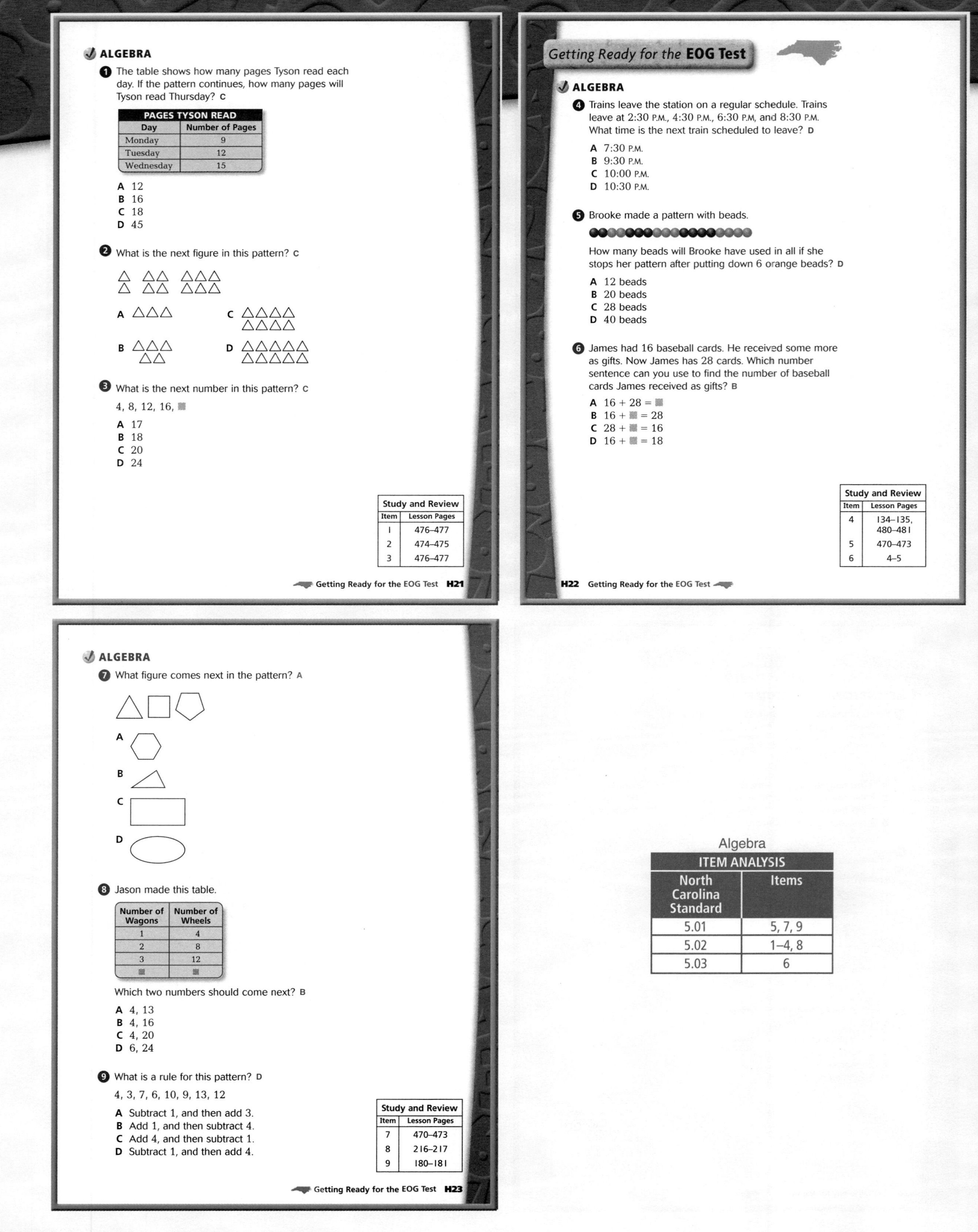

ALGEBRA

1. The table shows how many pages Tyson read each day. If the pattern continues, how many pages will Tyson read Thursday? C

PAGES TYSON READ	
Day	Number of Pages
Monday	9
Tuesday	12
Wednesday	15

A 12
B 16
C 18
D 45

2. What is the next figure in this pattern? C

A
B
C
D

3. What is the next number in this pattern? C

4, 8, 12, 16, ■

A 17
B 18
C 20
D 24

Study and Review	
Item	Lesson Pages
1	476–477
2	474–475
3	476–477

Getting Ready for the EOG Test H21

Getting Ready for the **EOG Test**

ALGEBRA

4. Trains leave the station on a regular schedule. Trains leave at 2:30 P.M., 4:30 P.M., 6:30 P.M, and 8:30 P.M. What time is the next train scheduled to leave? D

A 7:30 P.M.
B 9:30 P.M.
C 10:00 P.M.
D 10:30 P.M.

5. Brooke made a pattern with beads.

How many beads will Brooke have used in all if she stops her pattern after putting down 6 orange beads? D

A 12 beads
B 20 beads
C 28 beads
D 40 beads

6. James had 16 baseball cards. He received some more as gifts. Now James has 28 cards. Which number sentence can you use to find the number of baseball cards James received as gifts? B

A $16 + 28 = ■$
B $16 + ■ = 28$
C $28 + ■ = 16$
D $16 + ■ = 18$

Study and Review	
Item	Lesson Pages
4	134–135, 480–481
5	470–473
6	4–5

H22 Getting Ready for the EOG Test

ALGEBRA

7. What figure comes next in the pattern? A

A
B
C
D

8. Jason made this table.

Number of Wagons	Number of Wheels
1	4
2	8
3	12
■	■

Which two numbers should come next? B

A 4, 13
B 4, 16
C 4, 20
D 6, 24

9. What is a rule for this pattern? D

4, 3, 7, 6, 10, 9, 13, 12

A Subtract 1, and then add 3.
B Add 1, and then subtract 4.
C Add 4, and then subtract 1.
D Subtract 1, and then add 4.

Study and Review	
Item	Lesson Pages
7	470–473
8	216–217
9	180–181

Getting Ready for the EOG Test H23

Algebra

ITEM ANALYSIS	
North Carolina Standard	Items
5.01	5, 7, 9
5.02	1–4, 8
5.03	6

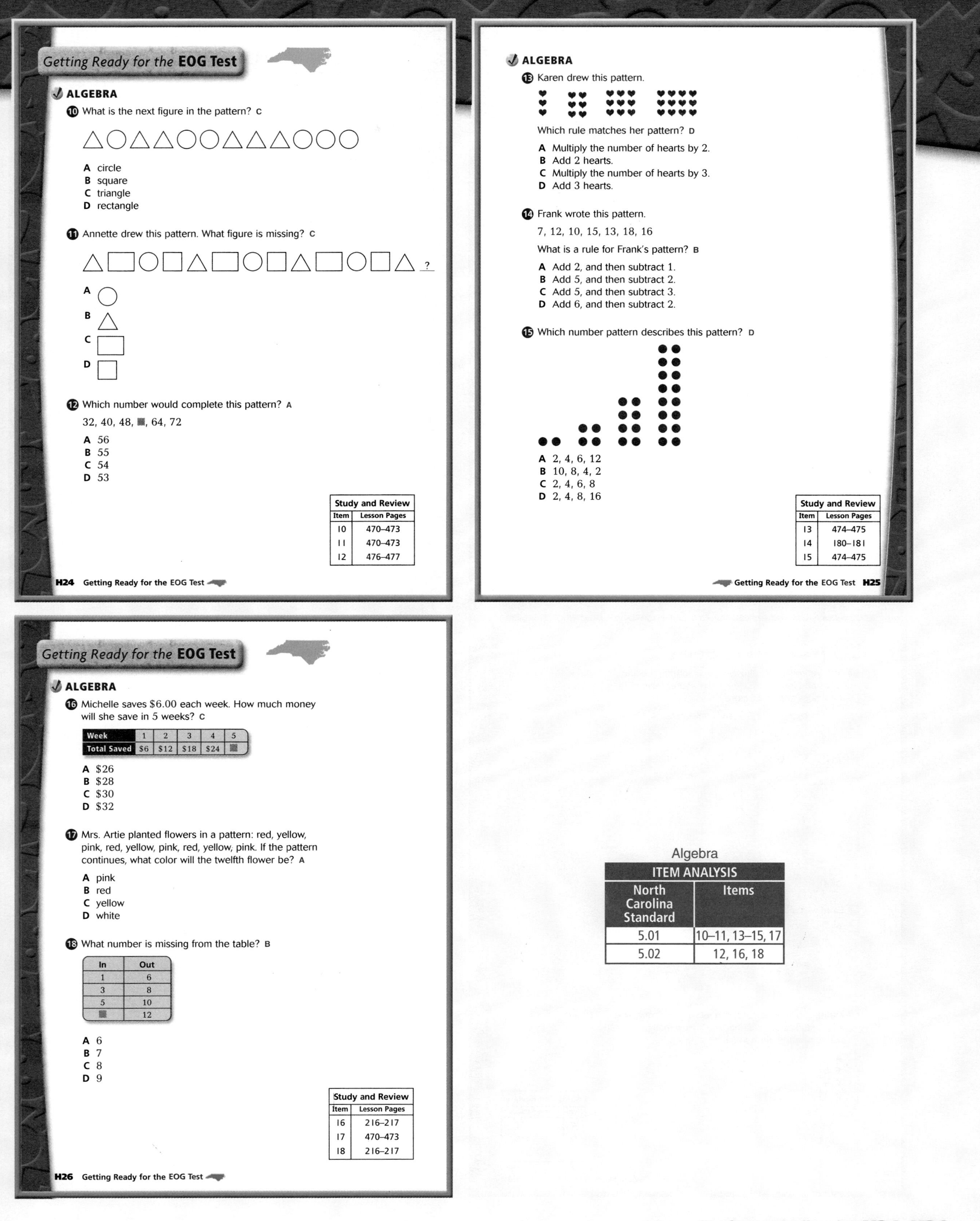

Getting Ready for the EOG Test

ALGEBRA

10 What is the next figure in the pattern? C

△○△△○○△△△○○○

A circle
B square
C triangle
D rectangle

11 Annette drew this pattern. What figure is missing? C

△▭○□△▭○□△▭○□△ ?

A ○
B △
C ▭
D □

12 Which number would complete this pattern? A

32, 40, 48, ■, 64, 72

A 56
B 55
C 54
D 53

Study and Review	
Item	**Lesson Pages**
10	470–473
11	470–473
12	476–477

ALGEBRA

13 Karen drew this pattern.

Which rule matches her pattern? D

A Multiply the number of hearts by 2.
B Add 2 hearts.
C Multiply the number of hearts by 3.
D Add 3 hearts.

14 Frank wrote this pattern.

7, 12, 10, 15, 13, 18, 16

What is a rule for Frank's pattern? B

A Add 2, and then subtract 1.
B Add 5, and then subtract 2.
C Add 5, and then subtract 3.
D Add 6, and then subtract 2.

15 Which number pattern describes this pattern? D

A 2, 4, 6, 12
B 10, 8, 4, 2
C 2, 4, 6, 8
D 2, 4, 8, 16

Study and Review	
Item	**Lesson Pages**
13	474–475
14	180–181
15	474–475

Getting Ready for the EOG Test

ALGEBRA

16 Michelle saves $6.00 each week. How much money will she save in 5 weeks? C

Week	1	2	3	4	5
Total Saved	$6	$12	$18	$24	■

A $26
B $28
C $30
D $32

17 Mrs. Artie planted flowers in a pattern: red, yellow, pink, red, yellow, pink, red, yellow, pink. If the pattern continues, what color will the twelfth flower be? A

A pink
B red
C yellow
D white

18 What number is missing from the table? B

In	Out
1	6
3	8
5	10
■	12

A 6
B 7
C 8
D 9

Study and Review	
Item	**Lesson Pages**
16	216–217
17	470–473
18	216–217

Algebra

ITEM ANALYSIS	
North Carolina Standard	**Items**
5.01	10–11, 13–15, 17
5.02	12, 16, 18

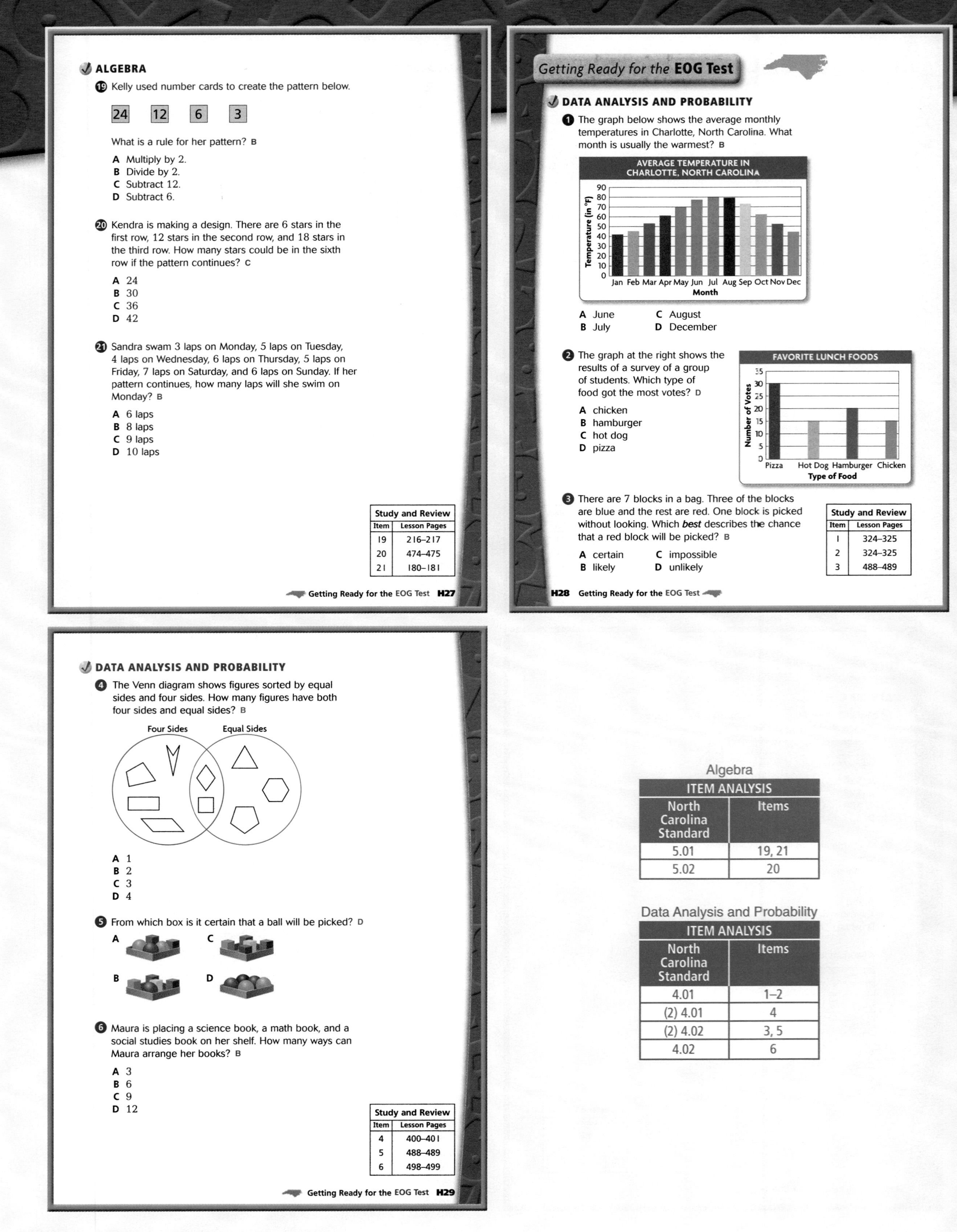

ALGEBRA

19. Kelly used number cards to create the pattern below.

24 12 6 3

What is a rule for her pattern? B

A Multiply by 2.
B Divide by 2.
C Subtract 12.
D Subtract 6.

20. Kendra is making a design. There are 6 stars in the first row, 12 stars in the second row, and 18 stars in the third row. How many stars could be in the sixth row if the pattern continues? C

A 24
B 30
C 36
D 42

21. Sandra swam 3 laps on Monday, 5 laps on Tuesday, 4 laps on Wednesday, 6 laps on Thursday, 5 laps on Friday, 7 laps on Saturday, and 6 laps on Sunday. If her pattern continues, how many laps will she swim on Monday? B

A 6 laps
B 8 laps
C 9 laps
D 10 laps

Study and Review	
Item	Lesson Pages
19	216–217
20	474–475
21	180–181

Getting Ready for the EOG Test H27

Getting Ready for the EOG Test

DATA ANALYSIS AND PROBABILITY

1. The graph below shows the average monthly temperatures in Charlotte, North Carolina. What month is usually the warmest? B

A June
B July
C August
D December

2. The graph at the right shows the results of a survey of a group of students. Which type of food got the most votes? D

A chicken
B hamburger
C hot dog
D pizza

3. There are 7 blocks in a bag. Three of the blocks are blue and the rest are red. One block is picked without looking. Which *best* describes the chance that a red block will be picked? B

A certain
B likely
C impossible
D unlikely

Study and Review	
Item	Lesson Pages
1	324–325
2	324–325
3	488–489

H28 Getting Ready for the EOG Test

DATA ANALYSIS AND PROBABILITY

4. The Venn diagram shows figures sorted by equal sides and four sides. How many figures have both four sides and equal sides? B

A 1
B 2
C 3
D 4

5. From which box is it certain that a ball will be picked? D

A B C D

6. Maura is placing a science book, a math book, and a social studies book on her shelf. How many ways can Maura arrange her books? B

A 3
B 6
C 9
D 12

Study and Review	
Item	Lesson Pages
4	400–401
5	488–489
6	498–499

Getting Ready for the EOG Test H29

Algebra

ITEM ANALYSIS	
North Carolina Standard	Items
5.01	19, 21
5.02	20

Data Analysis and Probability

ITEM ANALYSIS	
North Carolina Standard	Items
4.01	1–2
(2) 4.01	4
(2) 4.02	3, 5
4.02	6

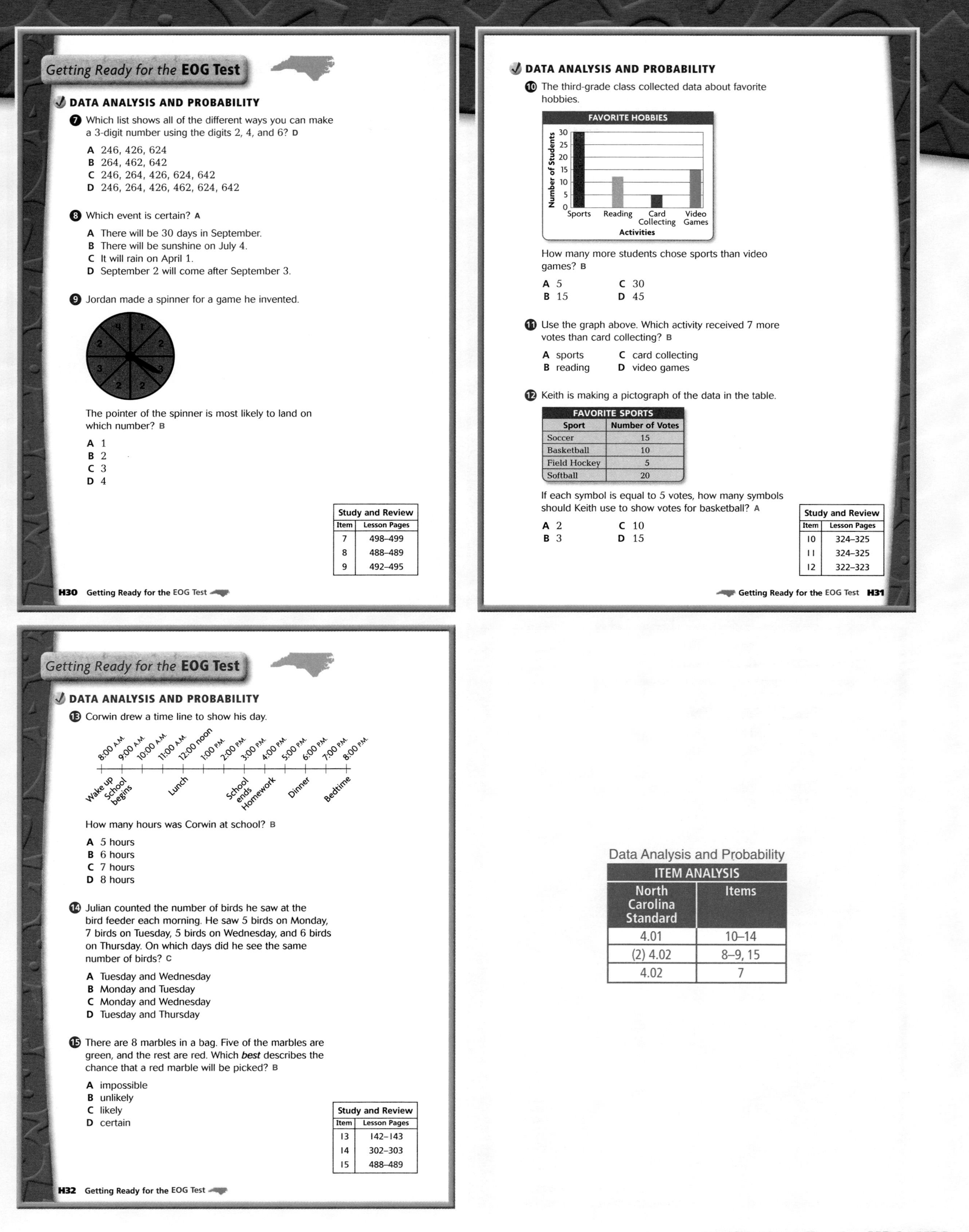

Getting Ready for the EOG Test

DATA ANALYSIS AND PROBABILITY

7. Which list shows all of the different ways you can make a 3-digit number using the digits 2, 4, and 6? D

A 246, 426, 624
B 264, 462, 642
C 246, 264, 426, 624, 642
D 246, 264, 426, 462, 624, 642

8. Which event is certain? A

A There will be 30 days in September.
B There will be sunshine on July 4.
C It will rain on April 1.
D September 2 will come after September 3.

9. Jordan made a spinner for a game he invented.

The pointer of the spinner is most likely to land on which number? B

A 1
B 2
C 3
D 4

Study and Review	
Item	Lesson Pages
7	498–499
8	488–489
9	492–495

DATA ANALYSIS AND PROBABILITY

10. The third-grade class collected data about favorite hobbies.

How many more students chose sports than video games? B

A 5 C 30
B 15 D 45

11. Use the graph above. Which activity received 7 more votes than card collecting? B

A sports C card collecting
B reading D video games

12. Keith is making a pictograph of the data in the table.

FAVORITE SPORTS	
Sport	Number of Votes
Soccer	15
Basketball	10
Field Hockey	5
Softball	20

If each symbol is equal to 5 votes, how many symbols should Keith use to show votes for basketball? A

A 2 C 10
B 3 D 15

Study and Review	
Item	Lesson Pages
10	324–325
11	324–325
12	322–323

Getting Ready for the EOG Test

DATA ANALYSIS AND PROBABILITY

13. Corwin drew a time line to show his day.

How many hours was Corwin at school? B

A 5 hours
B 6 hours
C 7 hours
D 8 hours

14. Julian counted the number of birds he saw at the bird feeder each morning. He saw 5 birds on Monday, 7 birds on Tuesday, 5 birds on Wednesday, and 6 birds on Thursday. On which days did he see the same number of birds? C

A Tuesday and Wednesday
B Monday and Tuesday
C Monday and Wednesday
D Tuesday and Thursday

15. There are 8 marbles in a bag. Five of the marbles are green, and the rest are red. Which *best* describes the chance that a red marble will be picked? B

A impossible
B unlikely
C likely
D certain

Study and Review	
Item	Lesson Pages
13	142–143
14	302–303
15	488–489

Data Analysis and Probability

ITEM ANALYSIS	
North Carolina Standard	Items
4.01	10–14
(2) 4.02	8–9, 15
4.02	7

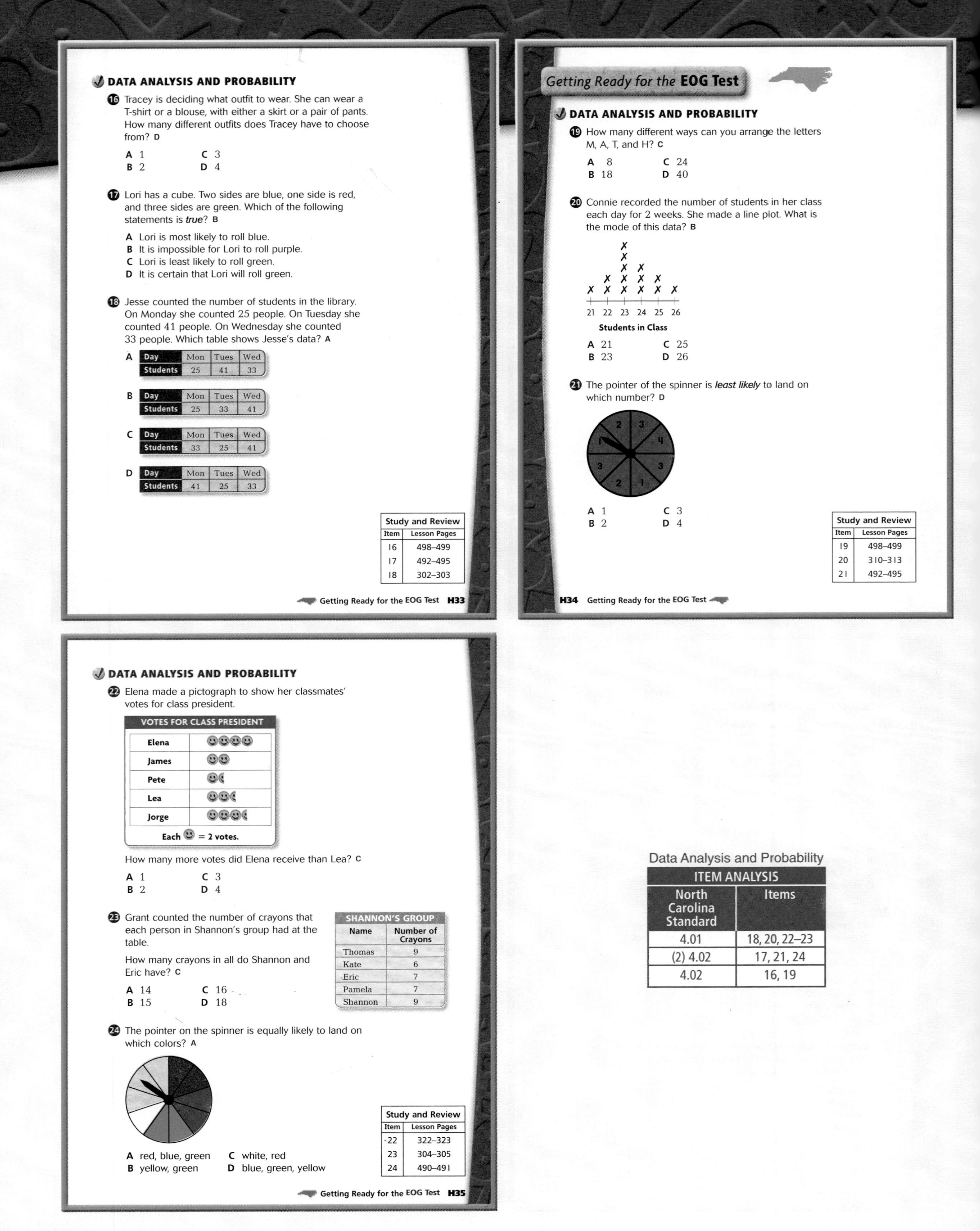

DATA ANALYSIS AND PROBABILITY

16. Tracey is deciding what outfit to wear. She can wear a T-shirt or a blouse, with either a skirt or a pair of pants. How many different outfits does Tracey have to choose from? D

A 1 C 3
B 2 D 4

17. Lori has a cube. Two sides are blue, one side is red, and three sides are green. Which of the following statements is *true*? B

A Lori is most likely to roll blue.
B It is impossible for Lori to roll purple.
C Lori is least likely to roll green.
D It is certain that Lori will roll green.

18. Jesse counted the number of students in the library. On Monday she counted 25 people. On Tuesday she counted 41 people. On Wednesday she counted 33 people. Which table shows Jesse's data? A

A

Day	Mon	Tues	Wed
Students	25	41	33

B

Day	Mon	Tues	Wed
Students	25	33	41

C

Day	Mon	Tues	Wed
Students	33	25	41

D

Day	Mon	Tues	Wed
Students	41	25	33

Study and Review	
Item	Lesson Pages
16	498–499
17	492–495
18	302–303

Getting Ready for the EOG Test

DATA ANALYSIS AND PROBABILITY

19. How many different ways can you arrange the letters M, A, T, and H? C

A 8 C 24
B 18 D 40

20. Connie recorded the number of students in her class each day for 2 weeks. She made a line plot. What is the mode of this data? B

A 21 C 25
B 23 D 26

21. The pointer of the spinner is *least likely* to land on which number? D

A 1 C 3
B 2 D 4

Study and Review	
Item	Lesson Pages
19	498–499
20	310–313
21	492–495

DATA ANALYSIS AND PROBABILITY

22. Elena made a pictograph to show her classmates' votes for class president.

VOTES FOR CLASS PRESIDENT	
Elena	
James	
Pete	
Lea	
Jorge	

Each ☺ = 2 votes.

How many more votes did Elena receive than Lea? C

A 1 C 3
B 2 D 4

23. Grant counted the number of crayons that each person in Shannon's group had at the table.

How many crayons in all do Shannon and Eric have? C

A 14 C 16
B 15 D 18

SHANNON'S GROUP	
Name	Number of Crayons
Thomas	9
Kate	6
Eric	7
Pamela	7
Shannon	9

24. The pointer on the spinner is equally likely to land on which colors? A

A red, blue, green C white, red
B yellow, green D blue, green, yellow

Study and Review	
Item	Lesson Pages
22	322–323
23	304–305
24	490–491

Data Analysis and Probability

ITEM ANALYSIS	
North Carolina Standard	Items
4.01	18, 20, 22–23
(2) 4.02	17, 21, 24
4.02	16, 19

ADDITION FACTS TEST

	K	L	M	N	O	P	Q	R
A	3 + 2 5	0 + 6 6	2 + 4 6	5 + 9 14	6 + 1 7	2 + 5 7	3 + 10 13	4 + 4 8
B	8 + 9 17	0 + 7 7	3 + 5 8	9 + 6 15	6 + 7 13	2 + 8 10	3 + 3 6	7 + 10 17
C	4 + 6 10	9 + 0 9	7 + 8 15	4 + 10 14	3 + 7 10	7 + 7 14	4 + 2 6	7 + 5 12
D	5 + 7 12	3 + 9 12	8 + 1 9	9 + 5 14	10 + 5 15	9 + 8 17	2 + 6 8	8 + 7 15
E	7 + 4 11	0 + 8 8	3 + 6 9	6 + 10 16	5 + 3 8	2 + 7 9	8 + 2 10	9 + 9 18
F	2 + 3 5	1 + 7 8	6 + 8 14	5 + 2 7	7 + 3 10	4 + 8 12	10 + 10 20	6 + 6 12
G	8 + 3 11	7 + 2 9	7 + 0 7	8 + 5 13	9 + 1 10	4 + 7 11	8 + 4 12	10 + 8 18
H	7 + 9 16	5 + 6 11	8 + 10 18	6 + 5 11	8 + 6 14	9 + 4 13	0 + 9 9	7 + 1 8
I	4 + 3 7	5 + 5 10	6 + 4 10	10 + 2 12	7 + 6 13	8 + 0 8	6 + 9 15	9 + 2 11
J	5 + 8 13	1 + 9 10	5 + 4 9	8 + 8 16	6 + 2 8	6 + 3 9	9 + 7 16	9 + 10 19

SUBTRACTION FACTS TEST

	K	L	M	N	O	P	Q	R
A	9 − 1 8	10 − 4 6	7 − 2 5	6 − 4 2	20 − 10 10	7 − 0 7	8 − 3 5	13 − 9 4
B	9 − 9 0	13 − 4 9	7 − 1 6	11 − 5 6	9 − 7 2	6 − 3 3	15 − 10 5	6 − 2 4
C	10 − 2 8	8 − 8 0	16 − 8 8	6 − 5 1	18 − 10 8	8 − 7 1	13 − 3 10	15 − 6 9
D	11 − 7 4	9 − 5 4	12 − 8 4	8 − 1 7	15 − 8 7	18 − 9 9	14 − 10 4	9 − 4 5
E	9 − 2 7	7 − 7 0	10 − 3 7	8 − 5 3	16 − 9 7	11 − 9 2	14 − 8 6	12 − 6 6
F	7 − 3 4	12 − 10 2	17 − 9 8	6 − 0 6	9 − 6 3	11 − 8 3	10 − 9 1	12 − 2 10
G	15 − 7 8	8 − 4 4	13 − 6 7	7 − 5 2	11 − 2 9	12 − 3 9	14 − 6 8	11 − 4 7
H	7 − 6 1	13 − 5 8	12 − 9 3	10 − 5 5	13 − 8 5	11 − 3 8	16 − 10 6	14 − 7 7
I	5 − 0 5	10 − 8 2	11 − 6 5	9 − 3 6	14 − 5 9	5 − 4 1	7 − 7 0	14 − 9 5
J	15 − 9 6	9 − 8 1	13 − 7 6	8 − 2 6	7 − 4 3	13 − 10 3	10 − 6 4	16 − 7 9

MULTIPLICATION FACTS TEST

	K	L	M	N	O	P	Q	R
A	$2 \times 7 = 14$	$0 \times 6 = 0$	$6 \times 6 = 36$	$9 \times 2 = 18$	$8 \times 3 = 24$	$3 \times 4 = 12$	$2 \times 8 = 16$	$6 \times 1 = 6$
B	$7 \times 7 = 49$	$5 \times 9 = 45$	$2 \times 2 = 4$	$7 \times 5 = 35$	$2 \times 3 = 6$	$10 \times 8 = 80$	$4 \times 10 = 40$	$8 \times 4 = 32$
C	$4 \times 5 = 20$	$5 \times 1 = 5$	$7 \times 0 = 0$	$6 \times 3 = 18$	$3 \times 5 = 15$	$6 \times 8 = 48$	$7 \times 3 = 21$	$9 \times 9 = 81$
D	$0 \times 9 = 0$	$6 \times 4 = 24$	$6 \times 10 = 60$	$1 \times 6 = 6$	$9 \times 8 = 72$	$4 \times 4 = 16$	$3 \times 2 = 6$	$9 \times 3 = 27$
E	$0 \times 7 = 0$	$9 \times 4 = 36$	$1 \times 7 = 7$	$9 \times 7 = 63$	$2 \times 5 = 10$	$7 \times 9 = 63$	$5 \times 6 = 30$	$5 \times 8 = 40$
F	$4 \times 3 = 12$	$6 \times 9 = 54$	$1 \times 9 = 9$	$7 \times 6 = 42$	$7 \times 10 = 70$	$6 \times 0 = 0$	$2 \times 9 = 18$	$10 \times 3 = 30$
G	$5 \times 3 = 15$	$1 \times 5 = 5$	$7 \times 1 = 7$	$3 \times 8 = 24$	$3 \times 6 = 18$	$8 \times 10 = 80$	$3 \times 9 = 27$	$6 \times 7 = 42$
H	$7 \times 4 = 28$	$7 \times 2 = 14$	$3 \times 7 = 21$	$2 \times 4 = 8$	$7 \times 8 = 56$	$4 \times 7 = 28$	$5 \times 10 = 50$	$8 \times 6 = 48$
I	$4 \times 6 = 24$	$5 \times 5 = 25$	$5 \times 7 = 35$	$3 \times 3 = 9$	$9 \times 6 = 54$	$8 \times 0 = 0$	$4 \times 9 = 36$	$8 \times 8 = 64$
J	$8 \times 9 = 72$	$6 \times 2 = 12$	$4 \times 8 = 32$	$9 \times 5 = 45$	$5 \times 4 = 20$	$0 \times 5 = 0$	$10 \times 6 = 60$	$9 \times 10 = 90$

DIVISION FACTS TEST

	K	L	M	N	O	P	Q	R
A	$1\overline{)1} = 1$	$3\overline{)9} = 3$	$2\overline{)6} = 3$	$2\overline{)4} = 2$	$1\overline{)6} = 6$	$3\overline{)12} = 4$	$5\overline{)15} = 3$	$7\overline{)21} = 3$
B	$6\overline{)24} = 4$	$8\overline{)56} = 7$	$5\overline{)40} = 8$	$6\overline{)18} = 3$	$6\overline{)30} = 5$	$7\overline{)42} = 6$	$9\overline{)81} = 9$	$5\overline{)45} = 9$
C	$5\overline{)30} = 6$	$2\overline{)16} = 8$	$3\overline{)21} = 7$	$7\overline{)35} = 5$	$3\overline{)15} = 5$	$9\overline{)9} = 1$	$8\overline{)16} = 2$	$9\overline{)63} = 7$
D	$4\overline{)32} = 8$	$9\overline{)90} = 10$	$4\overline{)8} = 2$	$8\overline{)48} = 6$	$9\overline{)54} = 6$	$3\overline{)18} = 6$	$10\overline{)50} = 5$	$6\overline{)48} = 8$
E	$7\overline{)28} = 4$	$3\overline{)0} = 0$	$5\overline{)20} = 4$	$4\overline{)24} = 6$	$7\overline{)14} = 2$	$3\overline{)6} = 2$	$5\overline{)50} = 10$	$10\overline{)60} = 6$
F	$9\overline{)18} = 2$	$4\overline{)36} = 9$	$5\overline{)25} = 5$	$7\overline{)63} = 9$	$1\overline{)5} = 5$	$8\overline{)32} = 4$	$9\overline{)45} = 5$	$6\overline{)54} = 9$
G	$2\overline{)14} = 7$	$8\overline{)24} = 3$	$4\overline{)4} = 1$	$5\overline{)40} = 8$	$3\overline{)9} = 3$	$4\overline{)12} = 3$	$7\overline{)56} = 8$	$8\overline{)72} = 9$
H	$5\overline{)35} = 7$	$1\overline{)4} = 4$	$8\overline{)64} = 8$	$5\overline{)10} = 2$	$8\overline{)40} = 5$	$2\overline{)12} = 6$	$6\overline{)42} = 7$	$10\overline{)70} = 7$
I	$7\overline{)49} = 7$	$9\overline{)27} = 3$	$10\overline{)90} = 9$	$3\overline{)27} = 9$	$9\overline{)36} = 4$	$4\overline{)20} = 5$	$9\overline{)72} = 8$	$8\overline{)80} = 10$
J	$8\overline{)0} = 0$	$4\overline{)28} = 7$	$2\overline{)10} = 5$	$7\overline{)70} = 10$	$1\overline{)3} = 3$	$10\overline{)80} = 8$	$6\overline{)60} = 10$	$10\overline{)100} = 10$

MULTIPLICATION AND DIVISION FACTS TEST

	K	L	M	N	O	P	Q	R
A	$2\overline{)18} = 9$	$8 \times 4 = 32$	$5\overline{)15} = 3$	$10 \times 6 = 60$	$8 \times 1 = 8$	$3\overline{)24} = 8$	$6\overline{)12} = 2$	$5 \times 8 = 40$
B	$8 \times 2 = 16$	$7\overline{)56} = 8$	$9\overline{)81} = 9$	$4 \times 10 = 40$	$7 \times 9 = 63$	$1\overline{)6} = 6$	$8\overline{)80} = 10$	$4 \times 9 = 36$
C	$6\overline{)36} = 6$	$8 \times 5 = 40$	$7 \times 7 = 49$	$10\overline{)90} = 9$	$5\overline{)45} = 9$	$6 \times 7 = 42$	$8\overline{)16} = 2$	$9 \times 9 = 81$
D	$10 \times 2 = 20$	$4\overline{)32} = 8$	$9\overline{)54} = 6$	$7 \times 8 = 56$	$9 \times 3 = 27$	$9\overline{)90} = 10$	$6\overline{)54} = 9$	$9 \times 4 = 36$
E	$8 \times 10 = 80$	$7 \times 6 = 42$	$8\overline{)64} = 8$	$2\overline{)20} = 10$	$9 \times 0 = 0$	$10 \times 10 = 100$	$3\overline{)36} = 12$	$10\overline{)100} = 10$
F	$4\overline{)40} = 10$	$8 \times 3 = 24$	$8 \times 6 = 48$	$9 \times 6 = 54$	$7\overline{)49} = 7$	$9\overline{)45} = 5$	$10 \times 3 = 30$	$9 \times 7 = 63$
G	$8\overline{)48} = 6$	$6\overline{)60} = 10$	$9 \times 2 = 18$	$5 \times 9 = 45$	$7\overline{)42} = 6$	$4\overline{)36} = 9$	$5 \times 10 = 50$	$9 \times 8 = 72$
H	$6 \times 5 = 30$	$8 \times 8 = 64$	$9\overline{)72} = 8$	$5\overline{)50} = 10$	$6 \times 9 = 54$	$8 \times 5 = 40$	$9\overline{)36} = 4$	$7\overline{)63} = 9$
I	$8\overline{)56} = 7$	$10\overline{)80} = 8$	$7 \times 8 = 56$	$10 \times 9 = 90$	$5\overline{)50} = 10$	$9 \times 5 = 45$	$10 \times 8 = 80$	$10\overline{)70} = 7$
J	$6 \times 8 = 48$	$10 \times 9 = 90$	$4\overline{)40} = 10$	$7\overline{)35} = 5$	$3 \times 6 = 18$	$8\overline{)56} = 7$	$9 \times 8 = 72$	$7 \times 5 = 35$

Basic Facts

Background

The Pupil Edition pages and the ideas described below have two purposes: to help students memorize basic facts and to reinforce and review the facts that students know. To make the most of practice sessions, do the following:

- *Begin practice as soon as students show an understanding of a fact's meaning and symbols.*
- *Before students drill, be sure they realize that their goal is memorization—not just getting an answer.*
- *Vary the practice to keep the interest of students.*
- *Keep practice sessions short and frequent. Schedule practice sessions almost every day.*
- *Motivate students by sharing your enthusiasm for practice activities. Reward efforts with praise.*

Activity Ideas

BOARD GAMES Students generate two numbers by using number cubes, spinners, number cards, or fact cards. Then students add, subtract, multiply, or divide the numbers to determine their moves on a game board.

TARGET GAMES Each student in a group generates three digits by using a spinner, rolling a number cube, or drawing cards from a box. The winner is the student who comes closest to a target number by combining the digits in an expression, such as $7 + 5 - 4$. During each turn, students make mental computations to find the best combination of digits.

CONCENTRATION Students make an array of cards face down and take turns trying to turn over pairs of cards that match. Matching cards might have the same answer ($4 + 7$ and $8 + 3$) or they might be related ($24 \div 8$ and 3×8).

WHAT'S THE QUESTION? Students place a set of numbered cards face down in rows. They take turns turning over a card and naming an expression equal to the number on the card.

Practice Ideas

ORAL PRACTICE Have students read aloud and answer the exercises in one row or column.

QUICK QUIZ Students record their answers for one or more rows or columns on lettered strips of paper.

WHOLE PAGE Students draw a lettered grid on their papers, like the grid on the pupil page, to record their answers. To prevent skipping exercises, they slide a paper or ruler beneath the rows or alongside the columns of exercises.

SELF-CHECK Each time students repeat a set of facts, they record the number correct on a table or graph. They set personal goals for weekly progress.

TIMED PRACTICE FOR AUTOMATICITY Students repeat a set of exercises over several days, using immediate recall to increase speed and accuracy.

HORIZONTAL FORMATS The addition, subtraction, and multiplication facts are shown in a vertical format. The division facts are shown in the "house" format. Students practice basic facts by rewriting and solving them in a horizontal format.

BASIC FACT STRATEGIES Students review the basic fact strategies for addition: *counting on, doubles* and *doubles plus one,* and *make a ten.* Students repeat with the strategies for subtraction: *counting back* and *doubles* and *doubles minus one.*

INVERSE OPERATIONS Students write the related subtraction fact for each addition fact and the related addition fact for each subtraction fact. They do the same for the multiplication and division facts.

FLASH CARDS AND OTHER GRAPHIC AIDS Students record the facts they miss and make flash cards to use for memorization. Students work in pairs to review those facts. As students read the cards and complete the facts, they separate the cards into facts they know and facts they do not know. They shuffle the do-not-know cards and continue until all the cards are in the do-know pile.

DESK SHEET Students make a desk sheet of a test by highlighting missed facts and taping the sheet to their desks. Students say each missed fact with the correct answer every time they sit down at their desks.

FACT FAMILIES Given one addition or subtraction fact or one multiplication or division fact, students write the other facts in the fact family.

MULTIPLICATION TABLES Students go through the multiplication facts and find all of the facts for 1, 2, 3, and so on. They fill in any missing facts. Then they rewrite all of the facts in their own multiplication table.

TABLE OF MEASURES

METRIC	CUSTOMARY
Length	
1 decimeter (dm) = 10 centimeters	1 foot (ft) = 12 inches (in.)
1 meter (m) = 100 centimeters	1 yard (yd) = 3 feet, or 36 inches
1 meter (m) = 10 decimeters	1 mile (mi) = 1,760 yards, or 5,280 feet
1 kilometer (km) = 1,000 meters	
Mass/Weight	
1 kilogram (kg) = 1,000 grams (g)	1 pound (lb) = 16 ounces (oz)
Capacity	
1 liter (L) = 1,000 milliliters (mL)	1 pint (pt) = 2 cups (c)
	1 quart (qt) = 2 pints
	1 gallon (gal) = 4 quarts

TIME	
1 minute (min) = 60 seconds (sec)	1 year (yr) = 12 months (mo), or about 52 weeks
1 hour (hr) = 60 minutes	1 year = 365 days
1 day = 24 hours	1 leap year = 366 days
1 week (wk) = 7 days	

MONEY
1 penny = 1 cent (¢)
1 nickel = 5 cents
1 dime = 10 cents
1 quarter = 25 cents
1 half dollar = 50 cents
1 dollar ($) = 100 cents

SYMBOLS
< is less than
> is greater than
= is equal to
≠ is not equal to
°F degrees Fahrenheit
°C degrees Celsius
(2,3) ordered pair

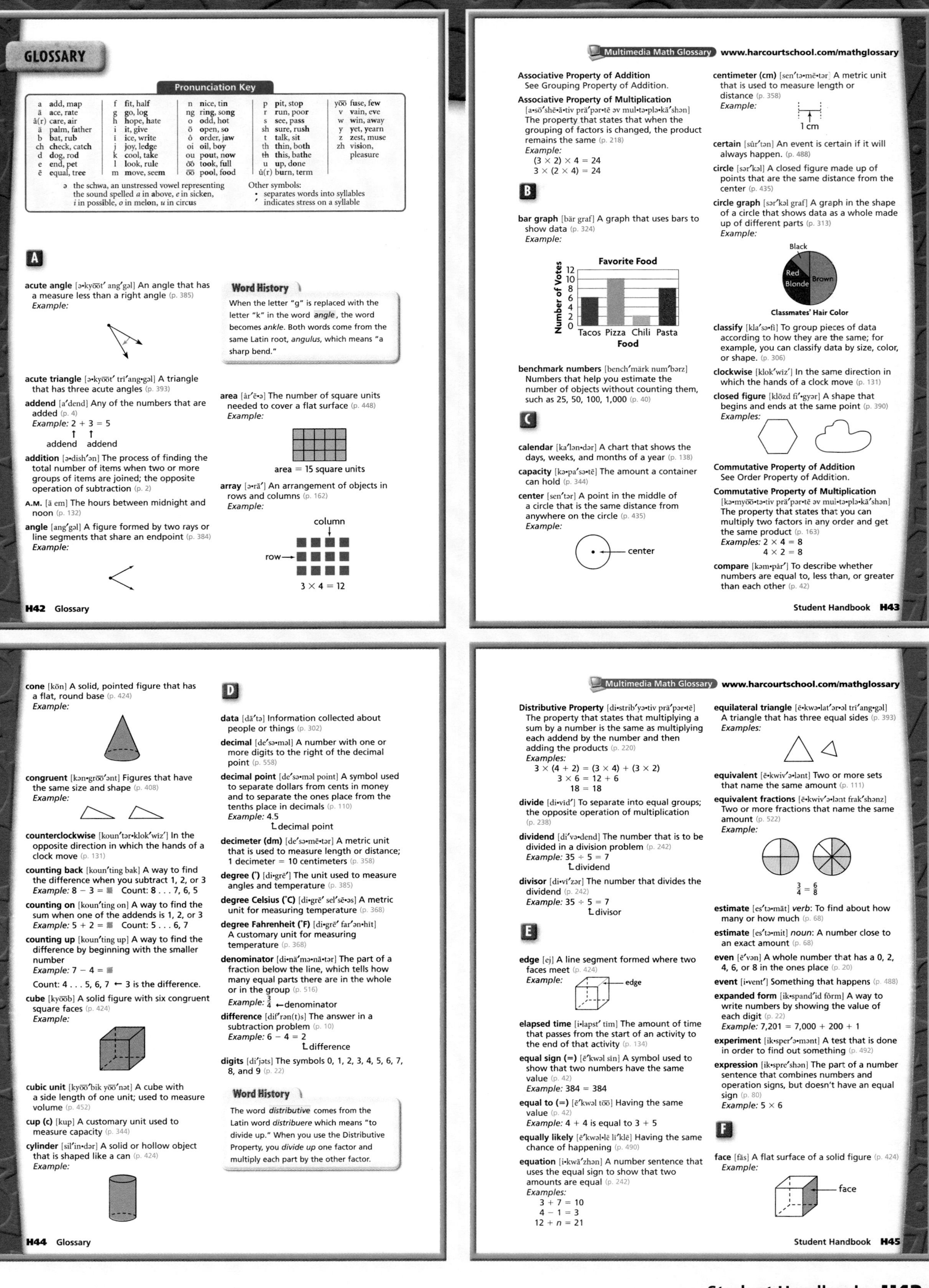

GLOSSARY

Pronunciation Key

a	add, map	f	fit, half	n	nice, tin	p	pit, stop	yo͞o	fuse, few
ā	ace, rate	g	go, log	ng	ring, song	r	run, poor	v	vain, eve
â(r)	care, air	h	hope, hate	o	odd, hot	s	see, pass	w	win, away
ä	palm, father	i	it, give	ō	open, so	sh	sure, rush	y	yet, yearn
b	bat, rub	ī	ice, write	ô	order, jaw	t	talk, sit	z	zest, muse
ch	check, catch	j	joy, ledge	oi	oil, boy	th	thin, both	zh	vision, pleasure
d	dog, rod	k	cool, take	ou	pout, now	th	this, bathe		
e	end, pet	l	look, rule	o͝o	took, full	u	up, done		
ē	equal, tree	m	move, seem	o͞o	pool, food	û(r)	burn, term		

ə the schwa, an unstressed vowel representing the sound spelled *a* in above, *e* in sicken, *i* in possible, *o* in melon, *u* in circus

Other symbols:
• separates words into syllables
ʹ indicates stress on a syllable

A

acute angle [ə•kyo͞otʹ angʹgəl] An angle that has a measure less than a right angle (p. 385)
Example:

Word History
When the letter "g" is replaced with the letter "k" in the word *angle*, the word becomes *ankle*. Both words come from the same Latin root, *angulus*, which means "a sharp bend."

acute triangle [ə•kyo͞otʹ triʹang•gəl] A triangle that has three acute angles (p. 393)

addend [aʹdend] Any of the numbers that are added (p. 4)
Example: 2 + 3 = 5
addend addend

addition [ə•dishʹən] The process of finding the total number of items when two or more groups of items are joined; the opposite operation of subtraction (p. 2)

A.M. [ā em] The hours between midnight and noon (p. 132)

angle [angʹgəl] A figure formed by two rays or line segments that share an endpoint (p. 384)
Example:

area [ârʹē•ə] The number of square units needed to cover a flat surface (p. 448)
Example:
area = 15 square units

array [ə•rāʹ] An arrangement of objects in rows and columns (p. 162)
Example:
column
row
3 × 4 = 12

Associative Property of Addition See Grouping Property of Addition.

Associative Property of Multiplication [ə•sōʹshē•ā•tiv präʹpər•tē əv mul•tə•plə•kāʹshən] The property that states that when the grouping of factors is changed, the product remains the same (p. 218)
Example:
(3 × 2) × 4 = 24
3 × (2 × 4) = 24

B

bar graph [bär graf] A graph that uses bars to show data (p. 324)
Example:

Favorite Food
Number of Votes
Tacos Pizza Chili Pasta
Food

benchmark numbers [benchʹmärk numʹbərz] Numbers that help you estimate the number of objects without counting them, such as 25, 50, 100, 1,000 (p. 40)

C

calendar [kaʹlən•dər] A chart that shows the days, weeks, and months of a year (p. 138)

capacity [kə•paʹsə•tē] The amount a container can hold (p. 344)

center [senʹtər] A point in the middle of a circle that is the same distance from anywhere on the circle (p. 435)
Example:
center

centimeter (cm) [senʹtə•mē•tər] A metric unit that is used to measure length or distance (p. 358)
Example:
1 cm

certain [sûrʹtən] An event is certain if it will always happen. (p. 488)

circle [sərʹkəl] A closed figure made up of points that are the same distance from the center (p. 435)

circle graph [sərʹkəl graf] A graph in the shape of a circle that shows data as a whole made up of different parts (p. 313)
Example:
Black
Red
Blonde
Brown
Classmates' Hair Color

classify [klaʹsə•fī] To group pieces of data according to how they are the same; for example, you can classify data by size, color, or shape. (p. 306)

clockwise [klokʹwīzʹ] In the same direction in which the hands of a clock move (p. 131)

closed figure [klōzd fiʹgyər] A shape that begins and ends at the same point (p. 390)
Examples:

Commutative Property of Addition See Order Property of Addition.

Commutative Property of Multiplication [kə•myo͞oʹtə•tiv präʹpər•tē əv mul•tə•plə•kāʹshən] The property that states that you can multiply two factors in any order and get the same product (p. 163)
Examples: 2 × 4 = 8
4 × 2 = 8

compare [kəm•pârʹ] To describe whether numbers are equal to, less than, or greater than each other (p. 42)

cone [kōn] A solid, pointed figure that has a flat, round base (p. 424)
Example:

congruent [kən•gro͞oʹənt] Figures that have the same size and shape (p. 408)
Example:

counterclockwise [koun•tər•klok•wīzʹ] In the opposite direction in which the hands of a clock move (p. 131)

counting back [kounʹting bak] A way to find the difference when you subtract 1, 2, or 3
Example: 8 − 3 = ■ Count: 8 . . . 7, 6, 5

counting on [kounʹting on] A way to find the sum when one of the addends is 1, 2, or 3
Example: 5 + 2 = ■ Count: 5 . . . 6, 7

counting up [kounʹting up] A way to find the difference by beginning with the smaller number
Example: 7 − 4 = ■
Count: 4 . . . 5, 6, 7 ← 3 is the difference.

cube [kyo͞ob] A solid figure with six congruent square faces (p. 424)
Example:

cubic unit [kyo͞oʹbik yo͞oʹnət] A cube with a side length of one unit; used to measure volume (p. 452)

cup (c) [kup] A customary unit used to measure capacity (p. 344)

cylinder [silʹin•dər] A solid or hollow object that is shaped like a can (p. 424)
Example:

D

data [dāʹtə] Information collected about people or things (p. 302)

decimal [deʹsə•məl] A number with one or more digits to the right of the decimal point (p. 558)

decimal point [deʹsə•məl point] A symbol used to separate dollars from cents in money and to separate the ones place from the tenths place in decimals (p. 110)
Example: 4.5
decimal point

decimeter (dm) [deʹsə•mē•tər] A metric unit that is used to measure length or distance; 1 decimeter = 10 centimeters (p. 358)

degree (°) [di•grēʹ] The unit used to measure angles and temperature (p. 385)

degree Celsius (°C) [di•grēʹ selʹsē•əs] A metric unit for measuring temperature (p. 368)

degree Fahrenheit (°F) [di•grēʹ farʹən•hit] A customary unit for measuring temperature (p. 368)

denominator [di•näʹmə•nā•tər] The part of a fraction below the line, which tells how many equal parts there are in the whole or in the group (p. 516)
Example: $\frac{3}{4}$ ← denominator

difference [difʹrən(t)s] The answer in a subtraction problem (p. 10)
Example: 6 − 4 = 2
difference

digits [diʹjəts] The symbols 0, 1, 2, 3, 4, 5, 6, 7, 8, and 9 (p. 22)

Word History
The word *distributive* comes from the Latin word *distribuere* which means "to divide up." When you use the Distributive Property, you *divide up* one factor and multiply each part by the other factor.

Distributive Property [di•stribʹyə•tiv präʹpər•tē] The property that states that multiplying a sum by a number is the same as multiplying each addend by the number and then adding the products (p. 220)
Examples:
3 × (4 + 2) = (3 × 4) + (3 × 2)
3 × 6 = 12 + 6
18 = 18

divide [di•vidʹ] To separate into equal groups; the opposite operation of multiplication (p. 238)

dividend [diʹvə•dend] The number that is to be divided in a division problem (p. 242)
Example: 35 ÷ 5 = 7
dividend

divisor [di•viʹzər] The number that divides the dividend (p. 242)
Example: 35 ÷ 5 = 7
divisor

E

edge [ej] A line segment formed where two faces meet (p. 424)
Example:
edge

elapsed time [i•lapstʹ tīm] The amount of time that passes from the start of an activity to the end of that activity (p. 134)

equal sign (=) [ēʹkwəl sīn] A symbol used to show that two numbers have the same value (p. 42)
Example: 384 = 384

equal to (=) [ēʹkwəl to͞o] Having the same value (p. 42)
Example: 4 + 4 is equal to 3 + 5

equally likely [ēʹkwəl•lē līʹklē] Having the same chance of happening (p. 490)

equation [i•kwāʹzhən] A number sentence that uses the equal sign to show that two amounts are equal (p. 242)
Examples:
3 + 7 = 10
4 − 1 = 3
12 + *n* = 21

equilateral triangle [ē•kwə•latʹər•əl triʹang•gəl] A triangle that has three equal sides (p. 393)
Examples:

equivalent [ē•kwivʹə•lənt] Two or more sets that name the same amount (p. 111)

equivalent fractions [ē•kwivʹə•lənt frakʹshənz] Two or more fractions that name the same amount (p. 522)
Example:
$\frac{3}{4} = \frac{6}{8}$

estimate [esʹtə•māt] *verb*: To find about how many or how much (p. 68)

estimate [esʹtə•mit] *noun*: A number close to an exact amount (p. 68)

even [ēʹvən] A whole number that has a 0, 2, 4, 6, or 8 in the ones place (p. 20)

event [i•ventʹ] Something that happens (p. 488)

expanded form [ik•spandʹid fôrm] A way to write numbers by showing the value of each digit (p. 22)
Example: 7,201 = 7,000 + 200 + 1

experiment [ik•sperʹə•mənt] A test that is done in order to find out something (p. 492)

expression [ik•spreʹshən] The part of a number sentence that combines numbers and operation signs, but doesn't have an equal sign (p. 80)
Example: 5 × 6

F

face [fās] A flat surface of a solid figure (p. 424)
Example:
face

fact family [fakt fam′ə•lē] A set of related addition and subtraction, or multiplication and division, number sentences (pp. 2, 246)
Example:
4 × 7 = 28   28 ÷ 7 = 4
7 × 4 = 28   28 ÷ 4 = 7

factor [fak′tər] A number that is multiplied by another number to find a product (p. 160)
Example: 3 × 8 = 24
↑ ↑
factor factor

flip [flip] A movement of a figure to a new position by flipping the figure over a line (p. 414)
Example:

foot (ft) [fŏŏt] A customary unit used to measure length or distance;
1 foot = 12 inches (p. 342)

fraction [frak′shən] A number that names part of a whole or part of a group (p. 516)
Example:
$\frac{1}{3}$

Word History
A *fraction* is a part of a whole, or a whole that is broken into pieces. *Fraction* comes from the Latin word *frangere,* which means "to break".

frequency table [frē′kwen•sē tā′bəl] A table that uses numbers to record data (p. 302)
Example:

FAVORITE COLOR	
Color	Number
blue	10
red	7
green	8
yellow	4

front-end estimation [frunt-end es•tə•mā′shən] A method of estimating a sum or difference by using the front digit of the number and adding zeros for the other digits (p. 68)
Example:
4,496 → 4,000
+3,745 → +3,000
7,000

G

gallon (gal) [ga′lən] A customary unit for measuring capacity; 1 gallon = 4 quarts (p. 344)

gram (g) [gram] A metric unit that is used to measure mass (p. 366)

greater than (>) [grā′tər than] A symbol used to compare two numbers, with the greater number given first (p. 42)
Example: 6 > 4

grid [grid] Horizontal and vertical lines on a map (p. 328)

Grouping Property of Addition [grōōp′ing prä′pər•tē əv ə•dish′ən] A rule stating that you can group addends in different ways and still get the same sum (p. 6)
Example:
4 + (2 + 5) = 11 and
(4 + 2) + 5 = 11

Grouping Property of Multiplication [grōōp′ing prä′pər•tē əv mul•tə•plə•kā′shən] The property that states that when the grouping of factors is changed, the product remains the same (p. 218)
Example:
3 × (4 × 1) = 12 and
(3 × 4) × 1 = 12

H

half hour [haf our] 30 minutes (p. 129)
Example: Between 4:00 and 4:30 is one half hour.

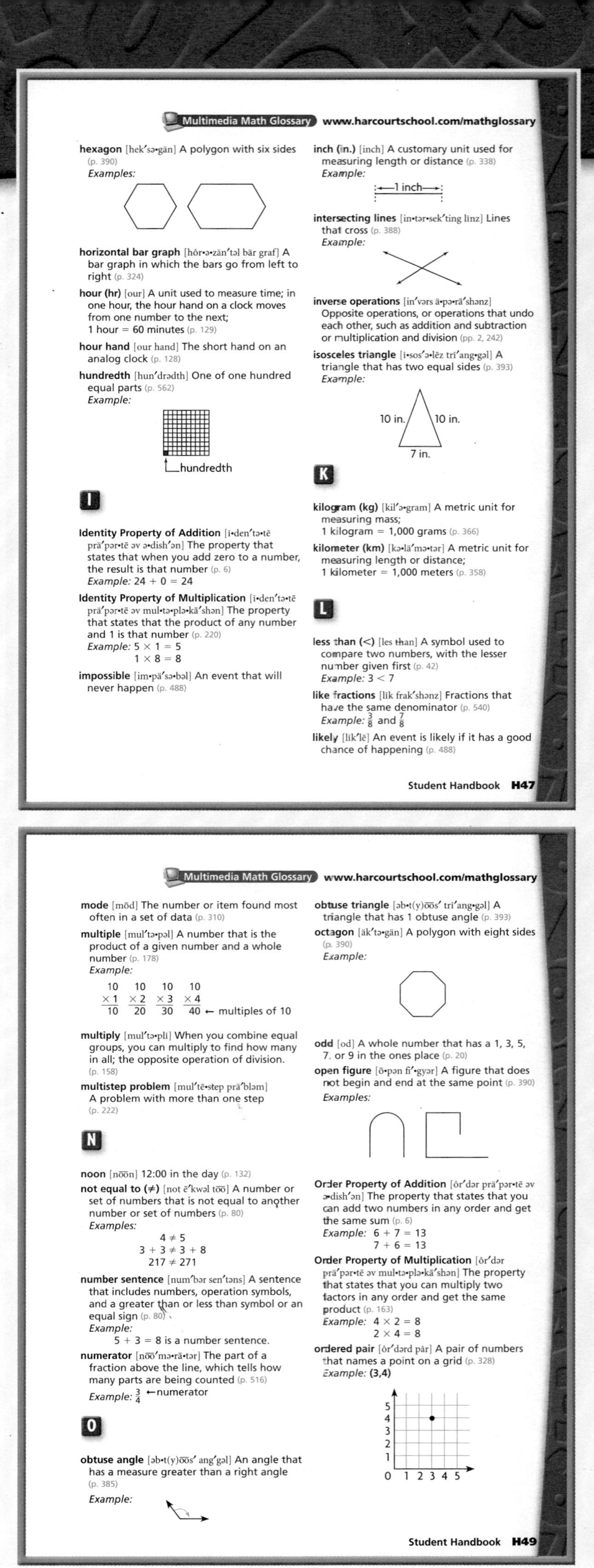

hexagon [hek′sə•gän] A polygon with six sides (p. 390)
Examples:

horizontal bar graph [hôr•ə•zän′təl bär graf] A bar graph in which the bars go from left to right (p. 324)

hour (hr) [our] A unit used to measure time; in one hour, the hour hand on a clock moves from one number to the next;
1 hour = 60 minutes (p. 129)

hour hand [our hand] The short hand on an analog clock (p. 128)

hundredth [hun′drədth] One of one hundred equal parts (p. 562)
Example:
hundredth

I

Identity Property of Addition [ī•den′tə•tē prä′pər•tē əv ə•dish′ən] The property that states that when you add zero to a number, the result is that number (p. 6)
Example: 24 + 0 = 24

Identity Property of Multiplication [ī•den′tə•tē prä′pər•tē əv mul•tə•plə•kā′shən] The property that states that the product of any number and 1 is that number (p. 220)
Example: 5 × 1 = 5
1 × 8 = 8

impossible [im•pä′sə•bəl] An event that will never happen (p. 488)

inch (in.) [inch] A customary unit used for measuring length or distance (p. 338)
Example:
1 inch

intersecting lines [in•tər•sek′ting līnz] Lines that cross (p. 388)
Example:

inverse operations [in′vərs ä•pə•rā′shənz] Opposite operations, or operations that undo each other, such as addition and subtraction or multiplication and division (pp. 2, 242)

isosceles triangle [ī•sos′ə•lēz trī′ang•gəl] A triangle that has two equal sides (p. 393)
Example:
10 in. 10 in.
7 in.

K

kilogram (kg) [kil′ə•gram] A metric unit for measuring mass;
1 kilogram = 1,000 grams (p. 366)

kilometer (km) [kə•lä′mə•tər] A metric unit for measuring length or distance;
1 kilometer = 1,000 meters (p. 358)

L

less than (<) [les than] A symbol used to compare two numbers, with the lesser number given first (p. 42)
Example: 3 < 7

like fractions [līk frak′shənz] Fractions that have the same denominator (p. 540)
Example: $\frac{3}{8}$ and $\frac{7}{8}$

likely [līk′lē] An event is likely if it has a good chance of happening (p. 488)

line [līn] A straight path extending in both directions with no endpoints (p. 384)
Example:

Word History
The word *line* comes from *linen,* a thread spun from the fibers of the flax plant. In early times thread was held tight to mark a straight line between two points.

line graph [līn graf] A graph that uses a line to show how data change over time (p. 330)
Example:
Temperature
Degrees (°F): 0, 10, 20, 30, 40, 50, 60, 70, 80
Month: Jan, Feb, Mar, Apr, May

line of symmetry [līn əv sim′ə•trē] An imaginary line on a figure that when the figure is folded on this line, the two parts match exactly (p. 410)
Example:
line of symmetry

line plot [līn plŏt] A graph that records each piece of data on a number line (p. 310)
Example:

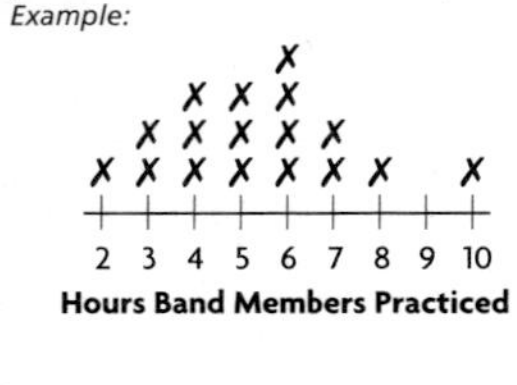

line segment [līn seg′mənt] A part of a line that includes two points, called endpoints, and all of the points between them (p. 384)
Example:

liter (L) [lē′tər] A metric unit for measuring capacity; 1 liter = 1,000 milliliters (p. 364)

M

mass [mas] The amount of matter in an object (p. 366)

mean [mēn] The number found by dividing the sum of a set of numbers by the number of addends (p. 314)
Example:
Find the mean for: 2, 3, 5, 5, 6, and 9
2 + 3 + 5 + 5 + 6 + 9 = 30
30 ÷ 6 = 5
The mean is 5.

median [mē′dē•ən] The middle number in an ordered list of numbers (p. 314)
1, 3, 4, 6, 7
median

meter (m) [mē′tər] A metric unit for measuring length or distance;
1 meter = 100 centimeters (p. 358)

midnight [mid′nīt] 12:00 at night (p. 132)

mile (mi) [mīl] A customary unit for measuring length or distance; 1 mile = 5,280 feet (p. 342)

milliliter (mL) [mil′ə•lē•tər] A metric unit for measuring capacity (p. 364)

minute (min) [min′it] A unit used to measure short amounts of time; in one minute, the minute hand moves from one mark to the next (p. 128)

minute hand [mi′nət hand] The long hand on an analog clock (p. 128)

mixed number [mikst num′bər] A number represented by a whole number and a fraction (p. 532)
Example: $4\frac{1}{2}$

mode [mōd] The number or item found most often in a set of data (p. 310)

multiple [mul′tə•pəl] A number that is the product of a given number and a whole number (p. 178)
Example:
10 10 10 10
×1 ×2 ×3 ×4
10 20 30 40 ← multiples of 10

multiply [mul′tə•plī] When you combine equal groups, you can multiply to find how many in all; the opposite operation of division. (p. 158)

multistep problem [mul′tē•step prä′bləm] A problem with more than one step (p. 222)

N

noon [nōōn] 12:00 in the day (p. 132)

not equal to (≠) [not ē′kwəl tōō] A number or set of numbers that is not equal to another number or set of numbers (p. 80)
Examples:
4 ≠ 5
3 + 3 ≠ 3 + 8
217 ≠ 271

number sentence [num′bər sen′təns] A sentence that includes numbers, operation symbols, and a greater than or less than symbol or an equal sign (p. 80)
Example:
5 + 3 = 8 is a number sentence.

numerator [nōō′mə•rā•tər] The part of a fraction above the line, which tells how many parts are being counted (p. 516)
Example: $\frac{3}{4}$ ←numerator

O

obtuse angle [əb•t(y)ōōs′ ang′gəl] An angle that has a measure greater than a right angle (p. 385)
Example:

obtuse triangle [əb•t(y)ōōs′ trī′ang•gəl] A triangle that has 1 obtuse angle (p. 393)

octagon [äk′tə•gän] A polygon with eight sides (p. 390)
Example:

odd [od] A whole number that has a 1, 3, 5, 7, or 9 in the ones place (p. 20)

open figure [ō•pən fi′gyər] A figure that does not begin and end at the same point (p. 390)
Examples:

Order Property of Addition [ôr′dər prä′pər•tē əv ə•dish′ən] The property that states that you can add two numbers in any order and get the same sum (p. 6)
Example: 6 + 7 = 13
7 + 6 = 13

Order Property of Multiplication [ôr′dər prä′pər•tē əv mul•tə•plə•kā′shən] The property that states that you can multiply two factors in any order and get the same product (p. 163)
Example: 4 × 2 = 8
2 × 4 = 8

ordered pair [ôr′dərd pâr] A pair of numbers that names a point on a grid (p. 328)
Example: **(3,4)**
0 1 2 3 4 5

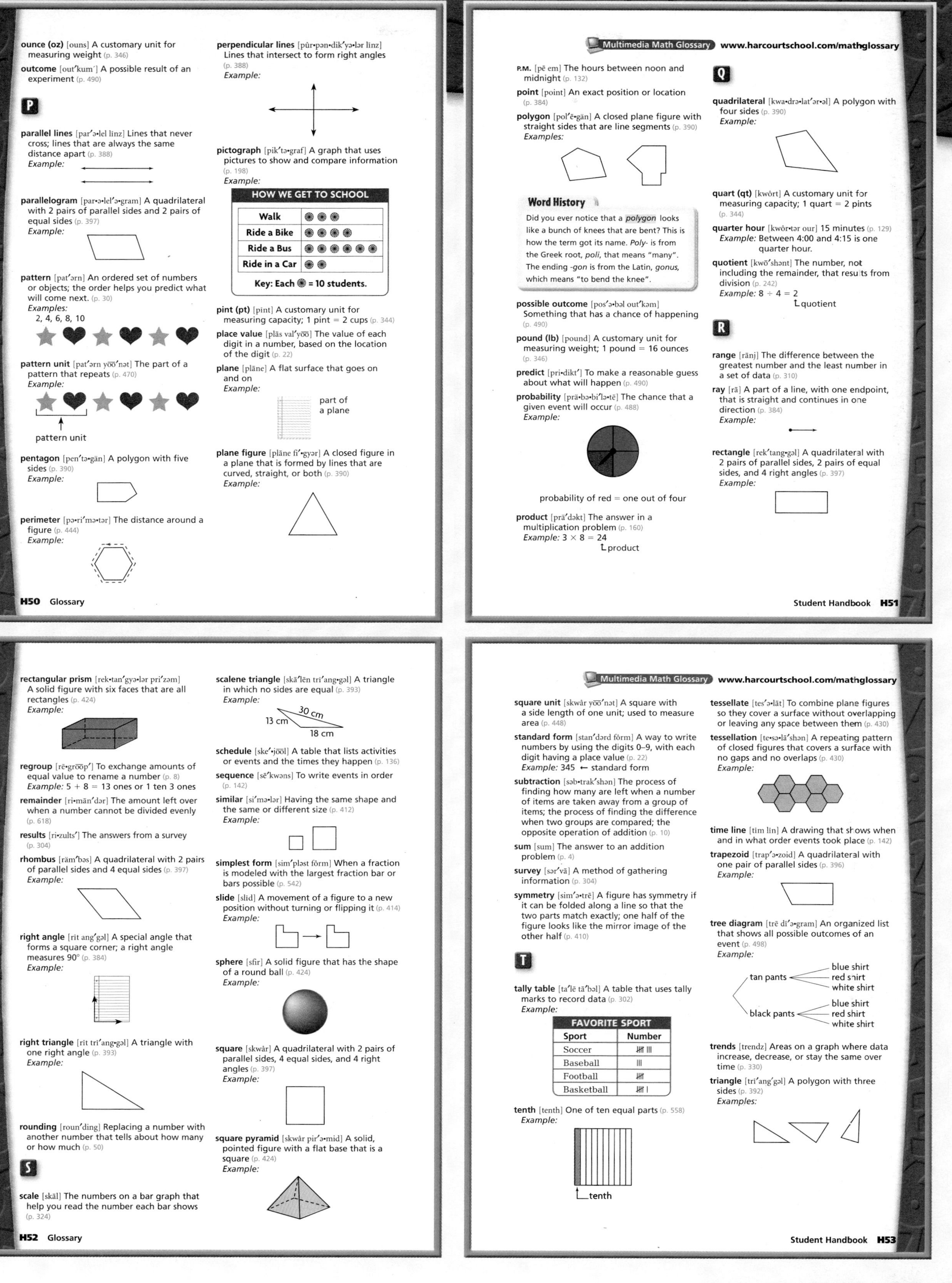

ounce (oz) [ouns] A customary unit for measuring weight (p. 346)

outcome [out'kum'] A possible result of an experiment (p. 490)

P

parallel lines [par'ə•lel linz] Lines that never cross; lines that are always the same distance apart (p. 388)
Example:

parallelogram [par•ə•lel'ə•gram] A quadrilateral with 2 pairs of parallel sides and 2 pairs of equal sides (p. 397)
Example:

pattern [pat'ərn] An ordered set of numbers or objects; the order helps you predict what will come next. (p. 30)
Examples:
2, 4, 6, 8, 10

pattern unit [pat'ərn yo͞o'nət] The part of a pattern that repeats (p. 470)
Example:
pattern unit

pentagon [pen'tə•gän] A polygon with five sides (p. 390)
Example:

perimeter [pə•ri'mə•tər] The distance around a figure (p. 444)
Example:

perpendicular lines [pûr•pən•dik'yə•lər linz] Lines that intersect to form right angles (p. 388)
Example:

pictograph [pik'tə•graf] A graph that uses pictures to show and compare information (p. 198)
Example:

HOW WE GET TO SCHOOL	
Walk	❋ ❋ ❋
Ride a Bike	❋ ❋ ❋
Ride a Bus	❋ ❋ ❋ ❋ ❋ ❋
Ride a Car	❋ ❋

Key: Each ❋ = 10 students.

pint (pt) [pint] A customary unit for measuring capacity; 1 pint = 2 cups (p. 344)

place value [plās val'yo͞o] The value of each digit in a number, based on the location of the digit (p. 22)

plane [plān] A flat surface that goes on and on
Example:
part of a plane

plane figure [plān fi'gyər] A closed figure in a plane that is formed by lines that are curved, straight, or both (p. 390)
Example:

H50 Glossary

Multimedia Math Glossary www.harcourtschool.com/mathglossary

P.M. [pē em] The hours between noon and midnight (p. 132)

point [point] An exact position or location (p. 384)

polygon [pol'ē•gän] A closed plane figure with straight sides that are line segments (p. 390)
Examples:

Word History

Did you ever notice that a *polygon* looks like a bunch of knees that are bent? This is how the term got its name. *Poly-* is from the Greek root, *poli*, that means "many". The ending *-gon* is from the Latin, *gonus*, which means "to bend the knee".

possible outcome [pos'ə•bəl out'kəm] Something that has a chance of happening (p. 490)

pound (lb) [pound] A customary unit for measuring weight; 1 pound = 16 ounces (p. 346)

predict [pri•dikt'] To make a reasonable guess about what will happen (p. 490)

probability [prä•bə•bil'lə•tē] The chance that a given event will occur (p. 488)
Example:
probability of red = one out of four

product [prä'dəkt] The answer in a multiplication problem (p. 160)
Example: 3 × 8 = 24
product

Q

quadrilateral [kwa•drə•lat'ər•əl] A polygon with four sides (p. 390)
Example:

quart (qt) [kwôrt] A customary unit for measuring capacity; 1 quart = 2 pints (p. 344)

quarter hour [kwôr•tər our] 15 minutes (p. 129)
Example: Between 4:00 and 4:15 is one quarter hour.

quotient [kwō'shənt] The number, not including the remainder, that results from division (p. 242)
Example: 8 ÷ 4 = 2
quotient

R

range [rānj] The difference between the greatest number and the least number in a set of data (p. 310)

ray [rā] A part of a line, with one endpoint, that is straight and continues in one direction (p. 384)
Example:

rectangle [rek'tang•gəl] A quadrilateral with 2 pairs of parallel sides, 2 pairs of equal sides, and 4 right angles (p. 397)
Example:

Student Handbook H51

rectangular prism [rek•tan'gyə•lər pri'zəm] A solid figure with six faces that are all rectangles (p. 424)
Example:

regroup [rē•gro͞op'] To exchange amounts of equal value to rename a number (p. 8)
Example: 5 + 8 = 13 ones or 1 ten 3 ones

remainder [ri•mān'dər] The amount left over when a number cannot be divided evenly (p. 618)

results [ri•zults'] The answers from a survey (p. 304)

rhombus [räm'bəs] A quadrilateral with 2 pairs of parallel sides and 4 equal sides (p. 397)
Example:

right angle [rit ang'gəl] A special angle that forms a square corner; a right angle measures 90° (p. 384)
Example:

right triangle [rit tri'ang•gəl] A triangle with one right angle (p. 393)
Example:

rounding [roun'ding] Replacing a number with another number that tells about how many or how much (p. 50)

S

scale [skāl] The numbers on a bar graph that help you read the number each bar shows (p. 324)

scalene triangle [skā'lēn tri'ang•gəl] A triangle in which no sides are equal (p. 393)
Example:
30 cm
13 cm
18 cm

schedule [ske'•jo͞ol] A table that lists activities or events and the times they happen (p. 136)

sequence [sē'kwəns] To write events in order (p. 142)

similar [si'mə•lər] Having the same shape and the same or different size (p. 412)
Example:

simplest form [sim'pləst fôrm] When a fraction is modeled with the largest fraction bar or bars possible (p. 542)

slide [slid] A movement of a figure to a new position without turning or flipping it (p. 414)
Example:

sphere [sfir] A solid figure that has the shape of a round ball (p. 424)
Example:

square [skwâr] A quadrilateral with 2 pairs of parallel sides, 4 equal sides, and 4 right angles (p. 397)
Example:

square pyramid [skwâr pir'ə•mid] A solid, pointed figure with a flat base that is a square (p. 424)
Example:

H52 Glossary

Multimedia Math Glossary www.harcourtschool.com/mathglossary

square unit [skwâr yo͞o'nət] A square with a side length of one unit; used to measure area (p. 448)

standard form [stan'dərd fôrm] A way to write numbers by using the digits 0–9, with each digit having a place value (p. 22)
Example: 345 ← standard form

subtraction [səb•trak'shən] The process of finding how many are left when a number of items are taken away from a group of items; the process of finding the difference when two groups are compared; the opposite operation of addition (p. 10)

sum [sum] The answer to an addition problem (p. 4)

survey [sər'vā] A method of gathering information (p. 304)

symmetry [sim'ə•trē] A figure has symmetry if it can be folded along a line so that the two parts match exactly; one half of the figure looks like the mirror image of the other half (p. 410)

T

tally table [ta'lē tā'bəl] A table that uses tally marks to record data (p. 302)
Example:

FAVORITE SPORT	
Sport	Number
Soccer	卌 |||
Baseball	|||
Football	卌
Basketball	卌 |

tenth [tenth] One of ten equal parts (p. 558)
Example:
tenth

tessellate [tes'ə•lāt] To combine plane figures so they cover a surface without overlapping or leaving any space between them (p. 430)

tessellation [te•sə•lā'shən] A repeating pattern of closed figures that covers a surface with no gaps and no overlaps (p. 430)
Example:

time line [tim lin] A drawing that shows when and in what order events took place (p. 142)

trapezoid [trap'ə•zoid] A quadrilateral with one pair of parallel sides (p. 396)
Example:

tree diagram [trē di'ə•gram] An organized list that shows all possible outcomes of an event (p. 498)
Example:
tan pants — blue shirt, red shirt, white shirt
black pants — blue shirt, red shirt, white shirt

trends [trendz] Areas on a graph where data increase, decrease, or stay the same over time (p. 330)

triangle [tri'ang'gəl] A polygon with three sides (p. 392)
Examples:

Student Handbook H53

turn [tûrn] A movement of a figure to a new position by rotating the figure around a point (p. 414)
Example:

U

unit cost [yo͞o′nit kôst] The cost of one item when several items are sold for a single price (p. 297)

unlikely [ən•līk′lē] An event is unlikely if it does not have a good chance of happening. (p. 488)

V

variable [vâr′ē•ə•bəl] A symbol or a letter that stands for an unknown number (p. 243)

> **Word History**
>
> **Variable** The word *vary* comes from the Latin, *variabilis,* meaning "changeable." At first the word applied to changes of color, as in the speckled fur of animals. Eventually the word was used for things that involve change of any kind.

Venn diagram [ven dī′ə•gram] A diagram that shows relationships among sets of things (p. 400)
Example:

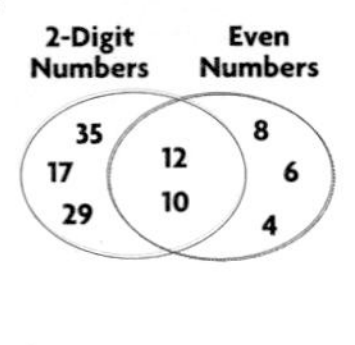

vertex [vûr′teks] The point at which two or more line segments meet in a plane figure or where three or more edges meet in a solid figure (p. 424)
Examples:

vertex

vertex

vertical bar graph [vûr′ti•kəl bär graf] A bar graph in which the bars go up from bottom to top (p. 324)

volume [väl′yəm] The amount of space a solid figure takes up (p. 452)

W

whole number [hōl nəm′bər] One of the numbers 0, 1, 2, 3, 4, ... The set of whole numbers goes on without end.

word form [wûrd form] A way to write numbers by using words (p. 22)
Example: The word form of 212 is two hundred twelve.

Y

yard (yd) [yärd] A customary unit for measuring length or distance; 1 yard = 3 feet (p. 342)

Z

Zero Property of Multiplication [zir′ō prä′pər•tē əv mul•tə•plə•kā′shən] The property that states that the product of zero and any number is zero (p. 220)
Example: $0 \times 6 = 0$

HARCOURT

Math

Problem of the Day

This section provides complete solutions for the **Problem of the Day** in each lesson plan. The problems include all types—one-step, multi-step, applied, process, nonroutine, open-ended, and puzzle problems—and provide options for students to develop their ability to use logical reasoning to choose and apply problem-solving strategies to varied and interesting situations.

The **Problem of the Day** for a lesson is also available on the Daily Transparency.

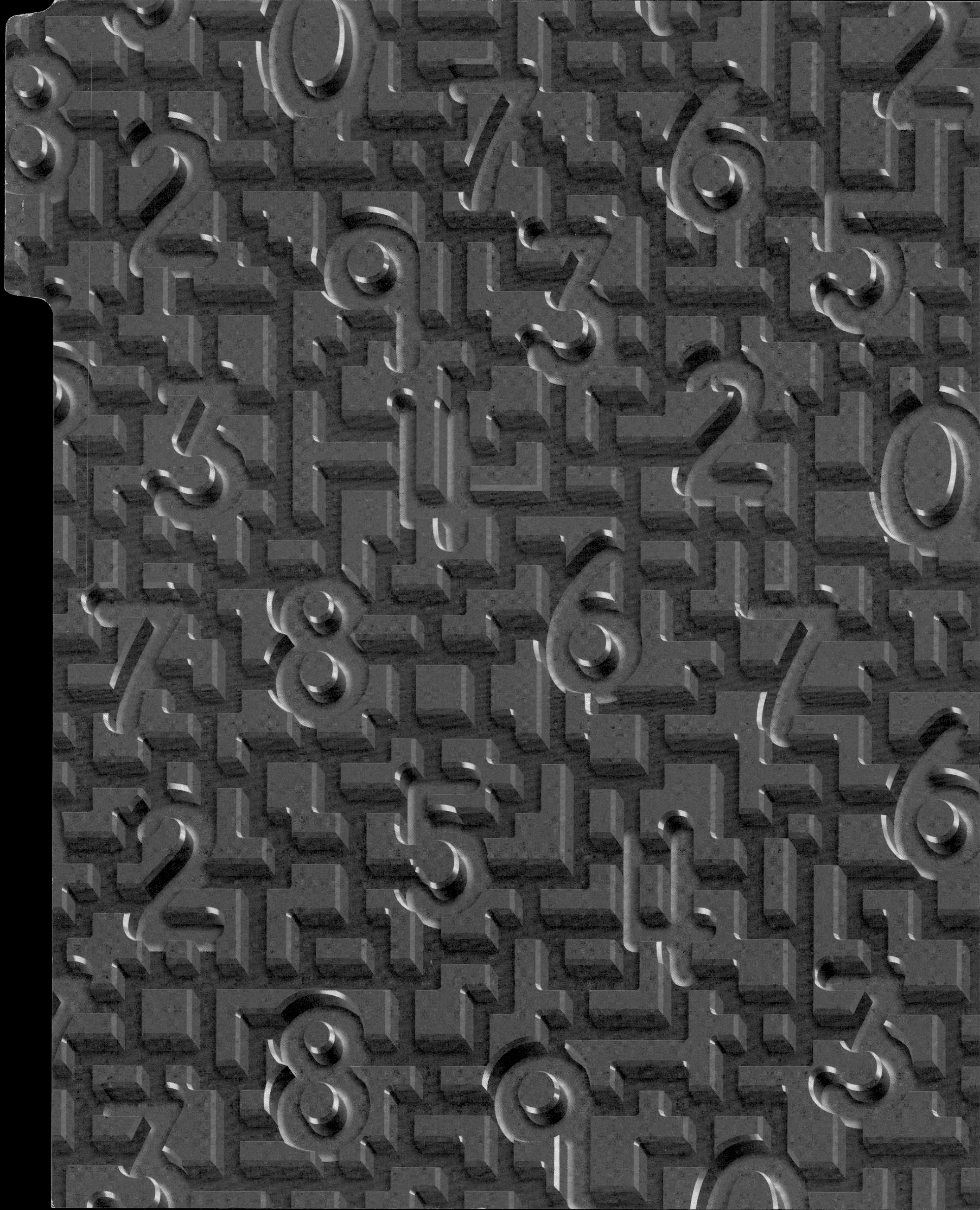

Problem of the Day

Chapter 1 Answer Key

Lesson 1.1

Problem

Yolanda's dog had 9 puppies. Yolanda gave away 3 puppies. How many does she have left?

Solution

Strategy: Write a Number Sentence

Write a number sentence to find the number of puppies Yolanda has left: $9 - 3 = 6$.

6 puppies

Lesson 1.2

Problem

Evan had 20 cents. Then he borrowed a dime from his sister and a nickel from his brother. How much money does he have now?

Solution

Strategy: Act It Out

Use play coins to act out the problem. Start with 2 dimes, or 20 cents. Add 1 dime, or 10 cents. Then add 1 nickel, or 5 cents. 3 dimes and 1 nickel = \$0.30 + \$0.05.

35 cents

Lesson 1.3

Problem

Ravi had 10 comic books in his collection. Now he has only 7 comic books. What could he have done?

Solution

Strategy: Use Logical Reasoning

If Ravi has fewer comic books now than he did before, then something was done with the comic books that he no longer has.

Possible answer: He gave 3 away.

Lesson 1.4

Problem

Pablo joined 5 red cubes and 6 blue cubes. Then he joined 4 yellow cubes and 3 green cubes. How many cubes did Pablo join in all?

Solution

Strategy: Draw a Picture

Draw a picture to show each set of cubes being joined. Count the cubes in your picture to find the total number of cubes.

18 cubes

Lesson 1.5

Problem

Megan's cat climbed 6 feet up a tree. Then she climbed down 3 feet and up another 5 feet. How many feet up the tree was Megan's cat?

Solution

Strategy: Draw a Diagram

Draw a diagram, similar to a number line, to show how the cat moves up and down the tree.

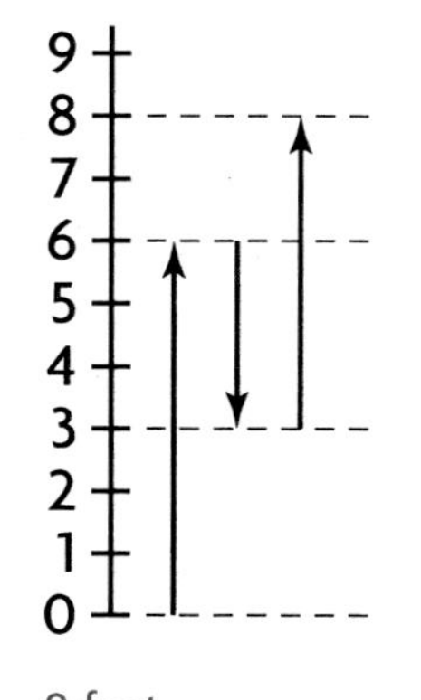

8 feet

Lesson 1.6

Problem

Marcella is setting up chairs for Parent Night. Can she skip-count by 5s to arrange 32 chairs in equal rows? Explain.

Solution

Strategy: Make a Table

Make a table showing the number of rows and the total number of chairs used.

Rows	1	2	3	4	5	6	7
Chairs	5	10	15	20	25	30	35

No; possible answer: when you skip-count from 0 by 5s, the ones digit is either 0 or 5.

Chapter 2 Answer Key

Lesson 2.1

Problem

Look at the hundred chart on page 21. Find all the numbers that have a one in the ones place. What pattern do you see? Why do these numbers form a pattern on a hundred chart?

Solution

Strategy: Use Logical Reasoning

All of the numbers with a one in the ones place are in the first column.

Possible answer: The rows all have ten numbers, therefore each new row begins with a one added to ten or to a certain number of tens.

Lesson 2.2

Problem

On what day does this month end? Could you skip-count by twos on your calendar, beginning with the first day of the month, and land on the last day? Explain.

Solution

Strategy: Find a Pattern

Begin with the first day of the month and skip-count by twos.

1, 3, 5, 7, ...

The pattern is that the numbers are all odd.

If the month ends with a day that is an odd number (29 or 31), yes. If it ends with an even number (28 or 30), no. If you skip-count by twos and begin with an odd number, you will end with an odd number.

Lesson 2.3

Problem

Shawn and Andrea each start at 99 on a hundred chart and count back to zero. Shawn counts back by sixes and Andrea by fives. What numbers do they both say? What is the last number each says?

Solution

Strategy: Make an Organized List

Shawn: 99, 93, 87, 81, 75, 69, 63, 57, 51, 45, 39, 33, 27, 21, 15, 9, 3

Andrea: 99, 94, 89, 84, 79, 74, 69, 64, 59, 54, 49, 44, 39, 34, 29, 24, 19, 14, 9, 4

They both say: 99, 69, 39, 9

Shawn's last number is 3; Andrea's is 4.

Lesson 2.4

Problem

The sum of the digits in a two-digit number is 13. The tens digit is greater than the ones. What three numbers could this be?

Solution

Strategy: Predict and Test

94, 85, 76 $9 + 4 = 13, 9 > 4; 8 + 5 = 13, 8 > 5; 7 + 6 = 13, 7 > 6$

Lesson 2.5

Problem

Katie signed up for a karate class. It lasts for five weeks and meets two times each week. Use skip-counting to find out how many classes she will have in all.

Solution

Strategy: Make a Model

Use a number line to skip-count by 2's for 5 weeks.

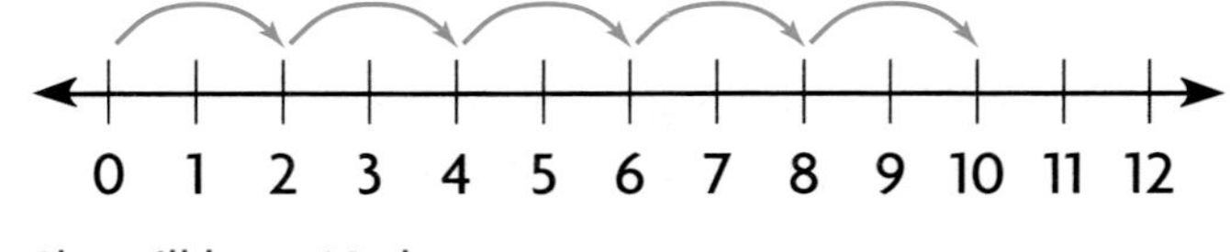

She will have 10 classes.

Lesson 2.6

Problem

Kim's zip code is an odd number. All five digits in the zip code are different. The last digit is the sum of the other four digits. The first digit is one more than the second, and the second is one more than the third. What is Kim's zip code?

Solution

Strategy: Predict and Test

Kim's zip code is 43209. 4 is one more than 3; 3 is one more than 2; $4 + 3 + 2 + 0 = 9$; all 5 digits are different; 43209 is an odd number.

Chapter 3 Answer Key

Lesson 3.1

Problem

Rearrange the digits in 57,070 to form at least 12 different numbers. Read them to a classmate.

Solution

Strategy: Make an Organized List

Any 12 of the following solutions:

77,500 75,700 77,050 75,070 77,005 75,007
70,750 57,700 50,770 70,705 57,070 50,707
70,570 57,007 50,077 70,507 70,075 70,057

Lesson 3.2

Problem

Samantha is swimming across a lake to reach a diving platform that is 18 yards away. Every time she swims 6 yards, the waves push her back 2 yards. At this rate, how many times must she swim forward 6 yards to reach the platform?

Solution

Strategy: Write a Number Sentence

1st time: $6 - 2 = 4$

2nd time: $4 + 6 = 10, 10 - 2 = 8$

3rd time: $8 + 6 = 14, 14 - 2 = 12$

4th time: $12 + 6 = 18$

So, Samantha must swim 6 yards forward 4 times.

Lesson 3.3

Problem

Both Holly and Mike have 12 base-ten blocks. Mike has an equal number of hundreds, tens, and ones blocks. Holly has 3 tens and 5 ones, and the others are hundreds. Who can model the greater number?

Solution

Strategy: Make a Model

If Mike has equal numbers of hundreds, tens, and ones blocks, he will have 4 of each to form the number 444. If Holly has 3 tens and 5 ones, she will need 4 hundreds to have 12 blocks. She can form the number 435. 444 is greater than 435, so Mike can model the greater number.

Lesson 3.4

Problem

Josh's house is between Fran's house and the school. Kay lives the closest to the school. Their houses are at 846, 862, and 822 Main Street. The school is at 826 Main Street. What is the house number of each student?

Solution

Strategy: Draw a Picture

On their pictures, students should order the numbers from least to greatest.

822	826	846	862
Kay	school	Josh	Fran

Lesson 3.5

Problem

Find the number whose thousands value is the same as the thousands value in 4,106; whose hundreds value is the same as the hundreds value in 2,039; whose tens value is the same as the tens value in 4,303; and whose ones value is the same as the ones value in 6,288.

Solution

Strategy: Make a Table

Thousands	Hundreds	Tens	Ones
4	1	0	6
2	*0*	3	9
4	3	*0*	3
6	2	8	*8*

4,008

Lesson 3.6

Problem

Sue wrote all the numbers that can be rounded to 60. Lee wrote all the numbers that can be rounded to 600. Who wrote more numbers? How many more numbers?

Solution

Strategy: : Make an Organized List

Sue: 55, 56, 57, 58, 59, 60, 61, 62, 63, 64

10 numbers

Lee: 550, 551, 552, 553, 554, 555, 556, 557, 558, 559, 560, 561, 562, 563, 564, 565, 566, 567, 568, 569, 570, 571, 572, 573, 574, 575, 576, 577, 578, 579, 580, 581, 582, 583, 584, 585, 586, 587, 588, 589, 590, 591, 592, 593, 594, 595, 596, 597, 598, 599, 600, 601, 602, 603, 604, 605, 606, 607, 608, 609, 610, 611, 612, 613, 614, 615, 616, 617, 618, 619, 620, 621, 622, 623, 624, 625, 626, 627, 628, 629, 630, 631, 632, 633, 634, 635, 636, 637, 638, 639, 640, 641, 642, 643, 644, 645, 646, 647, 648, 649

100 numbers

$100 - 10 = 90$

Lee wrote 90 more numbers than Sue.

Chapter 4 Answer Key

Lesson 4.1

Problem

To find the sum of a 2-addend number sentence, Josh thinks of 5 + 5 + 1. For the same number sentence, Augie thinks of 6 + 6 − 1. What is the 2-addend number sentence?

Solution

Strategy: Use Logical Reasoning

One of the numbers must have been 5 and the other 6. Each found a sum of 11.

The number sentence is 5 + 6 = 11 or 6 + 5 = 11.

Lesson 4.2

Problem

Tim and Lauren each have 10 base-ten blocks. Tim has 1 more tens block than Lauren. Lauren has the same number of tens as ones. What is the sum of their numbers?

Solution

Strategy: Make a Model

	Tens	Ones	Total
Lauren	5	5	10
Tim	6	4	10
Sum	11	9	

Lauren + Tim = sum

55 + 64 = 119

Lesson 4.3

Problem

Add down and across.

2	9	7	?
4	6	1	?
?	?	?	?

35	43	?
29	36	?
?	?	?

Solution

Strategy: Write a Number Sentence

2 + 9 + 7 = 18 35 + 43 = 78

4 + 6 + 1 = 11 29 + 36 = 65

6 + 15 + 8 = 29 64 + 79 = 143

Students should find the same numbers (29 and 143) as the final sums both down and across.

Lesson 4.4

Problem

The digits 0–9 are used only once in either an addend or the sum. Write the missing digits.

$$\begin{array}{r} \blacksquare\,8\,\blacksquare \\ +\ \blacksquare\,\blacksquare\,\blacksquare \\ \hline 1{,}0\,5\,3 \end{array}$$

Solution

Strategy: Predict and Test

$$\begin{array}{r} 789 \\ +264 \\ \hline 1{,}053 \end{array} \quad \begin{array}{r} 284 \\ +769 \\ \hline 1{,}053 \end{array} \quad \begin{array}{r} 784 \\ +269 \\ \hline 1{,}053 \end{array} \quad \begin{array}{r} 289 \\ +764 \\ \hline 1{,}053 \end{array}$$

Lesson 4.5

Problem

To find this secret number, add the greatest whole number that rounds to 50 and the least number that rounds to 80. What is the secret number? Make up a secret number of your own for a classmate to solve.

Solution

Strategy: Make a Model

Students may use a number line.

The greatest number that rounds to 50 is 54.

The least number that rounds to 80 is 75.

54 + 75 = 129

129 is the secret number.

Lesson 4.6

Problem

Pedro's number has as many tens as Sandra's number has ones and as many ones as Sandra's number has tens. If Pedro subtracts 9 from his number and Sandra adds 9 to her number, they will each have the same number, 22. What are their numbers?

Solution

Strategy: Write a Number Sentence

Pedro: ■ − 9 = 22

Sandra: ■ + 9 = 22

Pedro, 31 (31 − 9 = 22); Sandra, 13 (13 + 9 = 22)

Chapter 5 Answer Key

Lesson 5.1

Problem

The sum of the digits in a 3-digit number is 6. If the digits are rearranged to make a new number, 321, the difference between the two numbers is 198. What is the number?

Solution

Strategy: Predict and Test

123 → 1 + 2 + 3 = 6 (Add the three digits)

123 → 321 (Reverse the three digits)

321 – 123 = 198

123

Lesson 5.2

Problem

Subtract the greatest number that rounds to ten from the least number that rounds to 30. What is the answer?

Solution

Strategy: Make a Model

Use a number line.

The greatest number that rounds to ten is 14.

The least number that rounds to 30 is 25.

25 – 14 = 11

Lesson 5.3

Problem

Lee, Brandon, and Kate each picked the same number of apples. Lee picked 8 yellow apples, and Brandon picked 3 yellow apples. Kate picked 5 yellow apples and 7 red apples. How many red apples did Lee pick? How many red apples did Brandon pick?

Solution

Strategy: Write an Equation

	Yellow		Red		Total
Kate:	5	+	7	=	12
Lee:	8	+	?	=	12
Brandon:	3	+	?	=	12

Lee picked 4 red apples; Brandon picked 9 red apples.

Lesson 5.4

Problem

Tasha planned to read 100 pages over the weekend. She read 33 pages on Friday and 45 pages on Saturday. How many pages will she have to read on Sunday to meet her goal?

Solution

Strategy: Write a Number Sentence

Write a number sentence to find the total number of pages Tasha read on Friday and Saturday: 33 + 45 = 78. Then, write a number sentence to find the number of pages she will have to read on Sunday to meet her goal: 100 – 78 = 22.

22 pages

Lesson 5.5

Problem

Subtract down and across.

900	340	?
503	108	?
?	?	?

Solution

Strategy: Write a Number Sentence

900	–	340	=	560
–503	–	108	=	395
397	–	232	=	165

Lesson 5.6

Problem

Craig has 3 dimes and 4 pennies in one pocket and 5 dimes and 8 pennies in the other pocket. If he exchanges 10 pennies for one dime, how many dimes and pennies does he have? What is the value of the coins?

Solution

Strategy: Act It Out

Students use coins to find the solution.

Dimes	Pennies
3	4
5	8
8	12 (change to 1 dime, 2 pennies)

Craig will have 9 dimes and 2 pennies; the value is 92¢.

Chapter 6 Answer Key

Lesson 6.1

Problem

Use a dollar sign, a decimal point, and the digits 0, 4, and 8. Write as many different amounts of money as you can. List the coins and bills that would equal each amount.

Solution

Strategy: Make an Organized List

Order the sums from least to greatest.

One solution:

$0.48 1 quarter, 2 dimes, 3 pennies

$0.84 2 quarters, 3 dimes, 4 pennies

$4.08 4 one-dollar bills, 1 nickel, 3 pennies

$4.80 4 one-dollar bills, 3 quarters, 1 nickel

$8.04 1 five-dollar bill, 3 one-dollar bills, 4 pennies

$8.40 1 five-dollar bill, 3 one-dollar bills, 1 quarter, 1 dime, 1 nickel

Lesson 6.2

Problem

In her left hand, Jessica has two coins of the same kind. In her right hand, she has 5 coins that are all alike but that are different from the coins in her left hand. She has an equivalent amount of money in each hand. How much money does she have in all?

Solution

Strategy: Predict and Test/Make a Table

Left Hand	Right Hand	Equivalent
2 pennies ($0.02)	5 nickels ($0.25)	No
2 nickels ($0.10)	5 pennies ($0.05)	No
2 quarters ($0.50)	5 dimes ($0.50)	Yes

With the third combination, Jessica has $0.50 in each hand, so she has $1.00 in all.

Lesson 6.3

Problem

Ahmed has 2 coins of one kind and 2 of another. Katie has different coins, but she also has 2 of one kind and 2 of another. Ahmed has 22¢ more than Katie. What coins does each have if they both have less than $1.00?

Solution

Strategy: Predict and Test

Ahmed has 2 quarters and 2 pennies—52¢.

Katie has 2 dimes and 2 nickels—30¢.

Lesson 6.4

Problem

Dylan has 7 coins, but he is not able to give his friend change if the friend gives him a nickel, a dime, a quarter, or a half dollar. What coins might Dylan have?

Solution

Strategy: Predict and Test

He may have 1 quarter, 1 dime, 1 nickel, and 4 pennies; he may have 7 half dollars.

Lesson 6.5

Problem

Phillip has 457 pennies in the piggy bank in his room. He trades some of the pennies in for three $1 bills. How many pennies does he have left?

Solution

Strategy: Write an Equation

One dollar = 100 pennies

3 dollars = 300 pennies

457 – 300 = 157

Phillip has 157 pennies left.

Chapter 7 Answer Key

Lesson 7.1

Problem

In how many ways can a digital clock show the time using the digits 1, 2, and 3 without repeating any digit? Write each time.

Solution

Strategy: Make an Organized List

Hours	Minutes	
1	23	23 minutes after 1
1	32	32 minutes after 1
2	13	13 minutes after 2
2	31	31 minutes after 2
3	12	12 minutes after 3
3	21	21 minutes after 3

6 ways: 1:23, 1:32, 2:13, 2:31, 3:12, 3:21

Lesson 7.2

Problem

When Mr. Smith asked what time it was, Holly said that it was 4 minutes before 11, Tom said 10:56, Kim said 4 minutes before 10, and Marcus said 56 minutes after 10. Three students answered correctly. Whose answer is incorrect?

Solution

Strategy: Use Logical Reasoning

Kim's answer is incorrect.

Lesson 7.3

Problem

In numbers which are palindromes, the digits are in the same order from left to right as they are from right to left. On a digital clock, 1:01 is a palindrome number. We read: 1 minute after 1. Write at least 5 palindrome numbers for a digital clock.

Solution

Strategy: Make an Organized List

1:01	2:02	3:03	4:04	5:05	6:06
7:07	8:08	9:09	10:01		
1:11	2:12	3:13	4:14	5:15	6:16
7:17	8:18	9:19	11:11		

There are 57 possible answers. Check that students have at least 5.

Lesson 7.4

Problem

Lucas is painting a poster with the words HELP KEEP AMERICA GREEN on it. It takes him 5 minutes to paint each giant letter. If he starts at 10:15 A.M., will he be finished before lunch at noon? How do you know?

Solution

Strategy: Draw a Picture

Students can draw a picture of a clock and count by fives to find the answer.

Yes, he will be finished before noon. He will finish at 11:55 A.M.

Lesson 7.5

Problem

To find the secret number, add the number of months in a year as many times as there are days in a week. From that sum, subtract the number of minutes in an hour. Is the secret number the number of minutes in an hour, the number of hours in a day, or the number of days in a year?

Solution

Strategy: Write an Equation

$12 + 12 + 12 + 12 + 12 + 12 + 12 = 84$

$84 - 60 = 24$

The secret number is 24, the number of hours in a day.

Lesson 7.6

Problem

Hilary's birthday is exactly 6 weeks before Henry's. Rosa is 40 days older than Hilary. Hilary's birthday is the last day of April. When are Rosa's and Henry's birthdays?

Solution

Strategy: Use Logical Reasoning

Students can use a calendar. Hilary's birthday is April 30. Count back 40 days to find Rosa's birthday on March 21. Start at April 30 and count by weeks to find Henry's birthday on June 11.

Rosa's birthday is on March 21 and Henry's birthday is on June 11.

Chapter 8 Answer Key

Lesson 8.1

Problem

Darrell is buying a notepad for 75¢. He wants to pay for it with coins that are all the same kind. What type of coins and how many of each could Darrell use to pay for the notepad?

Solution

Strategy: Predict and Test

Because of the five ones in 75, he can't use all half dollars or dimes since their ones digit would always be 0.

He can use 3 quarters, 15 nickels, or 75 pennies.

Lesson 8.2

Problem

Complete each pattern. Describe the patterns in your own words.

2, ■, ■, 17, 22, ■, 32

2, ■, 8, ■, 32, 64

Solution

Strategy: Look for a Pattern

If necessary, give these hints:

From left to right, are the numbers becoming greater or less? greater

What do you do to numbers to make them become greater? add or multiply

What number do you think was added each time in the first pattern? 5

The missing numbers are 7, 12, and 27.

By what number were the numbers multiplied in the second pattern? by 2

The missing numbers are 4 and 16.

Lesson 8.3

Problem

Maria has a secret number. She says it when she counts by twos and threes. She does not say it when she counts by fours. What could the number be?

Solution

Strategy: Make an Organized List

Write the numbers she would say when counting by twos, threes, and fours:

counting by twos: 2, 4, 6, 8, 10, 12, 14, 16, 18, 20

counting by threes: 3, 6, 9, 12, 15, 18, 21

counting by fours: 4, 8, 12, 16, 20

When counting by twos and threes, she says 6, 12, and 18. However, since she also says 12 when counting by fours, 12 cannot be her secret number.

Possible answers: 6, 18

Lesson 8.4

Problem

I am a number between 30 and 40. You say my name when you count by threes. You also say my name when you count by twos. What number am I?

Solution

Strategy: Make an Organized List

multiples of 3: 33, 36, 39

multiples of 4: 32, 36

You are number 36.

Lesson 8.5

Problem

Find three people in your class who are the same age in years. Use a calendar to help you put them in order from oldest to youngest.

Solution

Strategy: Make a Model

Make a calendar, placing each student's name in the month in which he or she was born. Then, list the students beginning with the student who was born earliest in the year.

Answers will vary.

Chapter 9 Answer Key

Lesson 9.1

Problem

Write the numbers 0–8 so that the sum of each connected line of three numbers is 15.

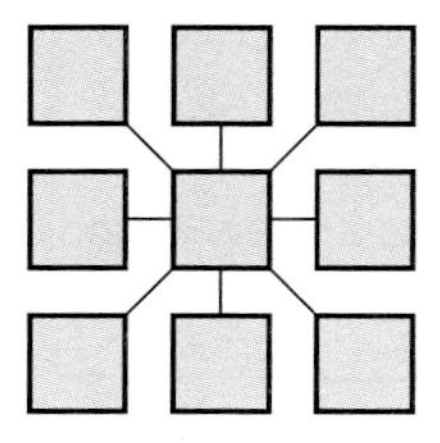

Solution

Strategy: Make an Organized List

Begin with 0, and write 3 digits with a sum of 15.

$0 + 7 + 8 = 15$

$1 + 6 + 8 = 15$

$2 + 5 + 8 = 15$

$3 + 4 + 8 = 15$

If students still have difficulty, ask: Which number is used in each sum? 8 Which box in the diagram is used each time? middle box Several solutions are possible, but all should have 8 in the middle box.

Possible Solution: First row: 4, 0, 1; Second row: 5, 8, 2; Third row: 6, 7, 3.

Lesson 9.2

0	■	■	6	8
10	■	14	■	■
■	22	■	26	■
■	■	■	■	■

Problem

Complete this chart. By what number did you count? What pattern do you see in the ones digits?

Solution

Strategy: Find/Use a Pattern

Count by twos.

Chart answers: 1st row: 2, 4; 2nd row: 12, 16, 18; 3rd row: 20, 24, 28; 4th row: 30, 32, 34, 36, 38

Skip-counted by twos; possible answers: they are all even; they increase by 2; the numbers 0, 2, 4, 6, and 8 repeat.

Lesson 9.3

Problem

Amy started at 0 and skip-counted by 3 until she reached 30. Lila started at 0 and skip-counted by 4 until she reached 32. What numbers did Amy and Lila both count?

Solution

Strategy: Make a Table

Numbers Amy counted: 0, 3, 6, 9, 12, 15, 18, 21, 24, 27, 30

Numbers Lila counted: 0, 4, 8, 12, 16, 20, 24, 28, 32

Numbers they both counted: 12, 24

Lesson 9.4

Problem

If you multiply Andy's age by 3 and add 1, you'll get 16. How old is Andy?

Solution

Strategy: Write an Equation

$16 - 1 = 15$

$15 \div 3 = 5$

5 years old

Lesson 9.5

Problem

The answer to a multiplication problem is 12. What could the factors be?

Solution

Strategy: Write a Number Sequence

$1 \times 12 = 12$

$2 \times 6 = 12$

$3 \times 4 = 12$

1 and 12, 2 and 6, 3 and 4

Chapter 10 Answer Key

Lesson 10.1

Problem

Jill has 4 nickels and 7 pennies. Jonathan has twice as many nickels and three times as many pennies as Jill. How much money does Jonathan have?

Solution

Strategy: Solve a Simpler Problem
First find the number of nickels and pennies Jonathan has. He has twice as many nickels as Jill. $2 \times 4 = 8$ nickels. He has three times as many pennies as Jill. $3 \times 7 = 21$ pennies. Find the value of 8 nickels and 21 pennies. 8 nickels are worth 5¢ each. So, $8 \times 5 = 40$¢.
40¢ + 21¢ = 61¢. He has 61¢.

Lesson 10.2

Problem

Every time his football team scored a touchdown, worth 6 points, Will kicked an extra point, worth 1 point. Will's team won 56 to 28 scoring only touchdowns and extra points. How many extra points did Will kick?

Solution

Strategy: Make an Organized List

TD		EP		Score	Total Score
6	+	1	=	7	7
6	+	1	=	7	14
6	+	1	=	7	21
6	+	1	=	7	28
6	+	1	=	7	35
6	+	1	=	7	42
6	+	1	=	7	49
6	+	1	=	7	56

Will kicked 8 extra points.

Lesson 10.3

Problem

Jason watered the plants in his vegetable garden every fourth day. If he began on March 3, how many times did he water the plants during the month of March?

Solution

Strategy: Make an Organized List
List the dates Jason watered the plants, beginning with March 3:
Mar 3, Mar 7, Mar 11, Mar 15, Mar 19, Mar 23, Mar 27, Mar 31. There are 8 dates in the list.
Jason watered the plants 8 times in March.

Lesson 10.4

Problem

Signs are placed every 6 miles along a road. There is a sign at the beginning of the road and a sign at the end. If there are 8 signs in all on the road, how long is the road?

Solution

Strategy: Draw a Picture
Draw a picture of the road. Draw 8 signs on the road, starting at the beginning.

0 6 12 18 24 30 36 42

Write 0 underneath the first sign. Then skip-count by sixes from 0 until you reach the last sign. That number is the length of the road in miles. 42 miles

Lesson 10.5

Problem

On grid paper, Gina wrote the numbers 1–99, putting 8 numbers in each row. What is the last number she wrote on the third line? What multiplication fact does this show? Where did she write the number 56? What is the greatest two-digit number she wrote in the ninth row?

Solution

Strategy: Make a Model

1	2	3	4	5	6	7	8
9	10	11	12	13	14	15	16
17	18	19	20	21	22	23	24
25	26	27	28	29	30	31	32
33	34	35	36	37	38	39	40
41	42	43	44	45	46	47	48
49	50	51	52	53	54	55	56
57	58	59	60	61	62	63	64
65	66	67	68	69	70	71	72
73	74	75	76	77	78	79	80
81	82	83	84	85	86	87	88
89	90	91	92	93	94	95	96
97	98	99					

24 is the last number in the third line. It shows $3 \times 8 = 24$. She wrote 56 as the last number in the 7th row. 72 is the greatest two-digit number in the 9th row.

Chapter 11 Answer Key

Lesson 11.1

Problem

Which number does not belong with the others? Explain.

1. 18, 56, 30, 42, 36
2. 48, 64, 28, 72, 32
3. 63, 49, 42, 30, 56
4. 21, 42, 35, 63, 49

Solution

Strategy: Use Logical Reasoning

1. 56; the others are all products of 6's facts
2. 28; the others are all products of 8's facts
3. 30; the others are all products of 7's facts
4. 42; the others are all odd products of 7's facts

Lesson 11.2

Problem

Kenny's number is the product of a 7's fact, Brooke's number is the product of an 8's fact, and Rico's number is the product of a 9's fact. Kenny's number is one more than Brooke's and 5 less than Rico's. What are their numbers?

Solution

Strategy: Write a Number Sentence

Use a multiplication table. Compare the numbers in row 7 and row 8 to see what number in row 7 is one more than a number in row 8. 49 is 1 more than 48.

Brooke's number is 48.
Kenny's number is 49.
Rico's number is 54 (49 + 5).

Lesson 11.3

Problem

Which of these numbers are products of 9's facts: 54; 63; 108; 225; 3,106; 5,121? How do you know?

Solution

Strategy: Write a Number Sentence

If the sum of the digits of a number is 9, the number is the product of a 9's fact.

$5 + 4 = 9$, so 54 is the product of a 9's fact.
$6 + 3 = 9$, so 63 is the product of a 9's fact.
$1 + 0 + 8 = 9$, so 108 is the product of a 9's fact.
$2 + 2 + 5 = 9$, so 225 is the product of a 9's fact.
$3 + 1 + 0 + 6 = 10$, so 3,105 is NOT the product of a 9's fact.
$5 + 1 + 2 + 1 = 9$, so 5,121 is the product of a 9's fact.

54, 63, 108, 225, and 5,121 are all products of 9's facts; the sum of the digits is 9.

Lesson 11.4

Problem

Mr. Baker's phone has a keypad with 4 rows of 3 buttons. Next to that are 2 rows of 4 buttons. How many buttons are on his phone in all?

Solution

Strategy: Draw a Picture

Sketch arrays to draw a picture of the keypad.

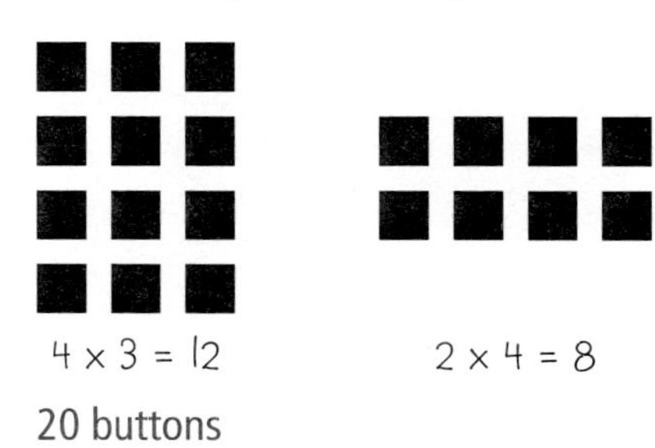

4 × 3 = 12 2 × 4 = 8

20 buttons

Lesson 11.5

Problem

The difference between two numbers is 6. The product of the numbers is 40. What are the numbers?

Solution

Strategy: Predict and Test

Choose two numbers whose difference is 6. Try 9 and 3. Multiply to find the product. $9 \times 3 = 27$, not 40.
Try 10 and 4. $10 \times 4 = 40$. So, 10 and 4 are the numbers.

10 and 4

Teaching Notes

Additional Ideas:

Good Questions to Ask:

Additional Resources:

Notes for Next Time:

HARCOURT

Math

The scope and sequence shows the development of all strands of math across the grades—Kindergarten through Grade 6. In addition there is a detailed scope and sequence specific to the grade level.

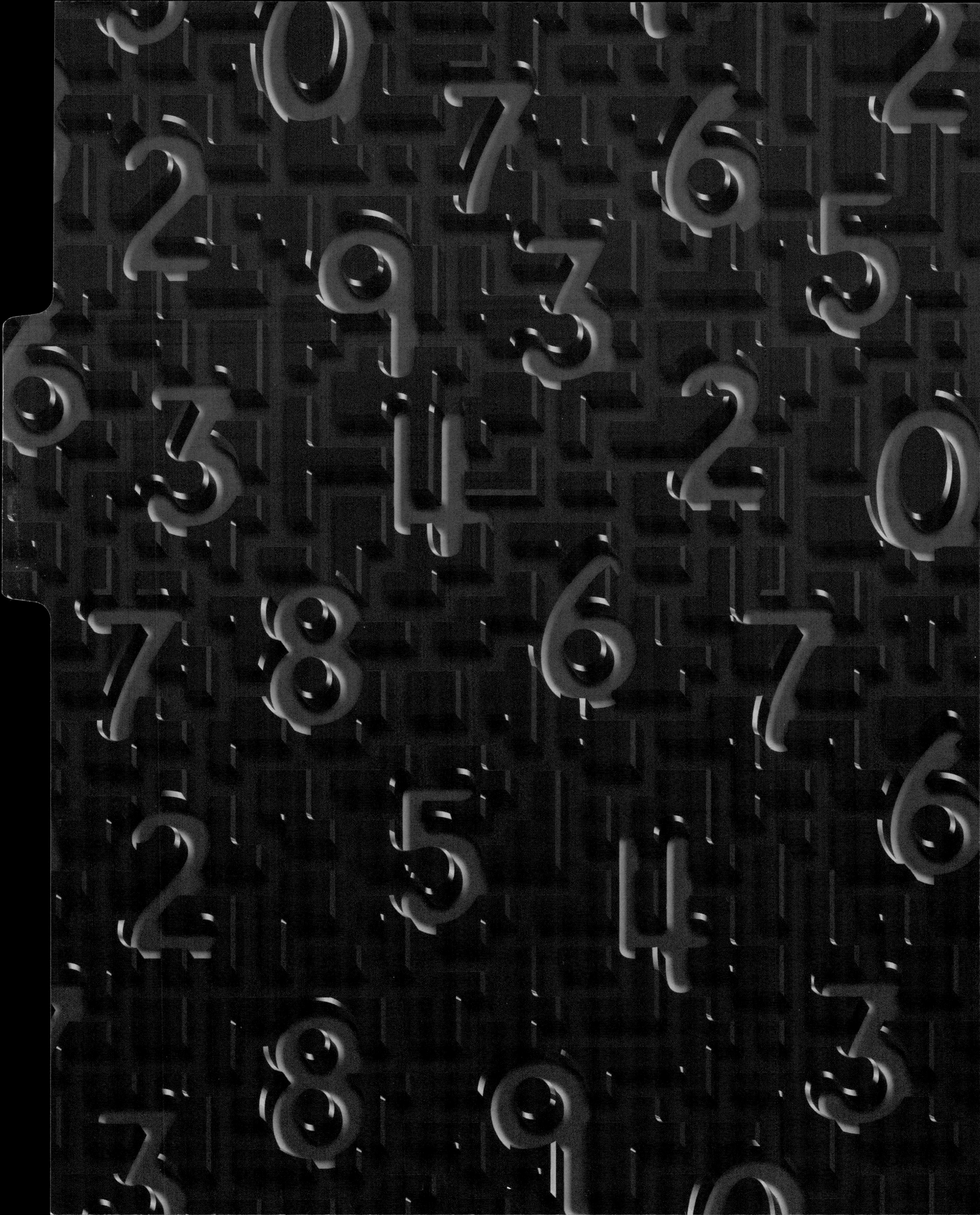

Scope and Sequence

NUMBER SENSE, CONCEPTS, AND OPERATIONS

NUMBER SENSE AND CONCEPTS	K	1	2	3	4	5	6
WHOLE NUMBERS							
Meaning of numbers	●	●	●	●	●	●	▲
Read and write numbers							
to 30	●	▲					
to 100		●	●	▲	▲		
to 1,000			●	●	▲	▲	▲
in the ten thousands				●	●	▲	▲
in the hundred thousands				●	●	▲	▲
in the millions					●	●	▲
in the billions						●	▲
Count	●	●	●	●			
Place value							
tens and ones	●	●	●				
to 100		●	●	▲	▲		
to 1,000			●	●	▲		
to 10,000				●	●	●	▲
in the hundred thousands				●	●	●	▲
in the millions					●	●	▲
in the billions						●	▲
Expanded form	●	●	●	●	●	●	▲
Compare and order							
to 10 (with objects)	●	▲					
to 100 (using symbols)		●	●	▲	▲	▲	▲
to 1,000 (using symbols)			●	●	●	▲	▲
to 10,000 (using symbols)				●	●	●	▲
to 100,000 (using symbols)				●	●	●	▲
in the millions (using symbols)					●	●	▲
in the billions (using symbols)						●	▲
Make reasonable estimates	●	●	●	●	●	●	●
Rounding							
to nearest ten, hundred, or thousand			●	●	●	●	●
to nearest ten thousand through nearest million					●	●	●
Even/odd	●	●	●	●	▲	▲	▲
Ordinal numbers	●	●	●				
Multiples				●	●	●	●
Divisibility					●	●	●
Prime and composite					●	●	●
Least common multiple						●	●
Common factors						●	●
Greatest common factor						●	●
Powers and exponents						●	●
Factor whole numbers					●	●	●
Prime factors					●	●	●
Prime factorization						●	●
Square numbers and square roots					●	●	●

● Teach ▲ Reinforce and Maintain

NUMBER SENSE AND CONCEPTS

WHOLE NUMBERS

Meaning of numbers 20–21, 22–23, 24–27

Read and write numbers

to 1,000 22–23, 24–27

in the ten thousands 32–33

in the hundred thousands 32–33

Count 22–23, 24–27

Place value

to 1,000 22–23, 24–27

to 10,000 32–33

in the hundred thousands 32–33

Expanded form 22–23, 24–27, 32–33

Compare and order

to 1,000 (using symbols) 42–45, 46–47

to 10,000 (using symbols) 42–43, 46–47, 48–49

to 100,000 (using symbols) 42–43, 46–47

Make reasonable estimates 40–41

Rounding

to nearest ten, hundred, or thousand 50–51, 52–53

Even/odd 20–21

Multiples 178–179

Type printed in red indicates that a topic is being introduced for the first time.

NUMBER SENSE, CONCEPTS, AND OPERATIONS

NUMBER SENSE AND CONCEPTS	K	1	2	3	4	5	6
MONEY							
Identify coins	●	●	●	●			
Value of coins	●	●	●	●	▲		
count and trade amounts		●	●	●			
make change			●	●	▲		
Value of collection of coins and bills		●	●	●	▲		
count and trade amounts		●	●	●	▲	▲	
make change				●	▲	▲	▲
Compare amounts and prices	●	●	●	●	▲	▲	▲
Equivalent amounts	●	●	●	●	▲	▲	▲
Use decimal notation and/or dollar and cents symbols		●	●	●	●	●	▲
DECIMALS							
Meaning of decimals				●	●	●	▲
Read and write decimals							
to tenths				●	●	●	▲
to hundredths				●	●	●	▲
to thousandths					●	●	▲
to ten-thousandths						●	▲
Locate on number line				●	●	●	▲
Relate to fractions				●	●	●	●
Decimal place value							
to tenths				●	●	●	▲
to hundredths				●	●	●	▲
to thousandths					●	●	▲
to ten-thousandths						●	▲
Compare and order							
to hundredths				●	●	●	●
to thousandths					●	●	●
to ten-thousandths						●	●
Equivalent decimals					●	●	●
Relate to percent					●	●	●
Decimals greater than 1				●	●	●	▲
Round					●	●	●
Terminating/repeating decimals							●
Scientific notation						●	●

● Teach ▲ Reinforce and Maintain

NUMBER SENSE AND CONCEPTS

MONEY

Identify coins 110–113
Value of coins
count and trade amounts 110–113
make change 118–119
Value of a collection of coins and bills
count and trade amounts 110–113
make change 118–119
Compare amounts and prices 116–117
Equivalent amounts 110–113, 114–115
Use decimal notation and/or dollar and cents symbols 110–113, 114–115, 116–117, 118–119, 120–121, 576–577, 578–579, 581–583, 584–585

DECIMALS

Meaning of decimals 558–559
Read and write decimals
to tenths 560–561
to hundredths 562–563
Locate on number line 566–567
Relate to fractions 558–559, 560–561, 562–563
Decimal place value
to tenths 560–561
to hundredths 560–561, 562–563
Compare and order
to hundredths 566–567
Decimals greater than 1 564–565

Type printed in red indicates that a topic is being introduced for the first time.

NUMBER SENSE, CONCEPTS, AND OPERATIONS

NUMBER SENSE AND CONCEPTS	K	1	2	3	4	5	6
FRACTIONS							
Meaning of fractions	●	●	●	●	●	▲	▲
Part of a whole	●	●	●	●	●	▲	▲
Part of a group		●	●	●	●	▲	▲
Read and write fractions		●	●	●	●	▲	▲
Locate on a number line				●	●	●	▲
Relate to decimals				●	●	●	●
Compare, unit fractions			●	●	▲	▲	▲
Compare, like denominators			●	●	●	●	●
Compare, unlike denominators				●	●	●	●
Fractions equal to 1 or greater			●	●	●	●	●
Mixed numbers				●	●	●	●
locate on number line				●	●	●	▲
Equivalent fractions			●	●	●	●	●
Order, like denominators				●	●	●	●
Order, unlike denominators				●	●	●	●
Simplest form				●	●	●	●
Least common denominator						●	●
Relate to percent						●	●
Reciprocals						●	●
Rational numbers							●
INTEGERS							
Opposites					●	●	●
Negative numbers					●	●	●
Meaning of integers					●	●	●
Integers on the number line					●	●	●
Absolute value						●	●
Compare and order					●	●	●
RATIONAL NUMBERS							
Meaning of rational numbers							●
Compare and order							●
Scientific notation						●	●

● Teach ▲ Reinforce and Maintain

NUMBER SENSE AND CONCEPTS

FRACTIONS

Meaning of fractions 516–519, 520–521
Part of a whole 516–519
Part of a group 520–521
Read and write fractions 516–519, 520–521
Locate on a number line 517–519
Relate to decimals 558–559
Compare, unit fractions 526–529
Compare, like denominators 526–529
Compare, unlike denominators 526–529, 530–531
Fractions equal to 1 or greater 532–533
Mixed numbers
locate on a number line 532–533
Equivalent fractions 522–523
Order, like denominators 526–529
Order, unlike denominators 526–529
Simplest form 542–543

Type printed in red indicates that a topic is being introduced for the first time.

NUMBER SENSE, CONCEPTS, AND OPERATIONS

NUMBER SENSE AND CONCEPTS	K	1	2	3	4	5	6
MEANING AND RELATIONSHIPS							
Meaning of whole numbers	●	●	●	●	●	●	▲
Number relationships	●	●	●	●	●	●	●
Meaning of fractions		●	●	●	●	●	▲
Meaning of decimals				●	●	●	▲
Equivalent forms of numbers		●	●	●	●	●	●
Effects of operations						●	●
Meaning of percent					●	●	●
Meaning of integers					●	●	●
Meaning of rational numbers							●
MENTAL MATH							
Skip-counting	●	●	●	●	▲	▲	
Use properties		●	●	●	●	●	●
Patterns, multiples, and powers of 10			●	●	●	●	●
Compatible numbers					●	●	●
ESTIMATE QUANTITIES							
Benchmarks	●	●	●	●	●	●	▲
Rounding			●	●	●	●	●

● Teach ▲ Reinforce and Maintain

NUMBER SENSE AND CONCEPTS

MEANING AND RELATIONSHIPS

Meaning of whole numbers 20–21, 22–23, 24–27

Number relationships 20–21, 30–31, 40–41, 42–45, 46–47

Meaning of fractions 516–519, 520–521

Meaning of decimals 558–559

Equivalent forms of numbers 522–523, 558–559, 560–561, 562–563

MENTAL MATH

Skip-counting 182–185

Use properties 6–7, 220–221

Patterns, multiples, and powers of 10 30–31, 63, 178–179, 180–181, 212–215, 216–217

ESTIMATE QUANTITIES

Benchmarks 40–41

Rounding 50–51, 52–53

Type printed in red indicates that a topic is being introduced for the first time.

NUMBER SENSE, CONCEPTS, AND OPERATIONS

CONCEPTS AND OPERATIONS	K	1	2	3	4	5	6
WHOLE NUMBERS							
Addition							
Meaning of addition	●	●	●	▲	▲	▲	▲
Concrete objects, numbers less than 10	●	●					
Addition facts (sums to 10)		●	●	▲			
Addition facts (sums to 20)		●	●	●	▲		
Basic-fact strategies							
counting on		●	●	▲			
doubles and doubles plus one		●	●	▲			
make a ten		●	●	▲			
Column addition		●	●	●	▲	▲	▲
Fact families/inverse relationship between + and −		●	●	●	▲	▲	▲
Properties		●	●	●	●	●	▲
3 or more addends		●	●	●	●	▲	▲
2-digit numbers, with/without regrouping		●	●	●	▲	▲	▲
using mental math		●	●	▲	▲	▲	▲
3-digit numbers			●	●	●	▲	▲
4-digit numbers				●	●	●	▲
Greater numbers					●	●	▲
Estimate sums			●	●	●	●	●
Subtraction							
Meaning of subtraction	●	●	●	▲	▲	▲	▲
Concrete objects, numbers less than 10	●	●					
Subtraction facts (differences from 10)		●	●	▲			
Subtraction facts (differences from 20)		●	●	●	▲		
Basic-fact strategies							
counting back		●	●	▲			
Missing addends		●	●	●	▲	▲	▲
2-digit numbers, with/without regrouping		●	●	●	▲	▲	▲
using mental math		●	●	▲	▲	▲	▲
3-digit numbers			●	●	▲	▲	▲
4-digit numbers				●	●	●	▲
Greater numbers					●	●	▲
With zeros		●	●	●	●	●	▲
Checking subtraction			●	●	●	▲	▲
Estimate differences		●	●	●	●	●	●

● Teach ▲ Reinforce and Maintain

CONCEPTS AND OPERATIONS

WHOLE NUMBERS

Addition

Addition facts (sums to 20) 2–3, 4–5, 6–7
Column addition 8–9, 70–71, 72–73
Fact families/inverse relationships between + and – 2–3, 4–5
Properties 6–7
3 or more addends 6–7
2-digit numbers, with/without regrouping 8–9
3-digit numbers 72–73, 74–75, 76–79
4-digit numbers 72–73, 74–75, 76–79
Estimate sums 68–69

Subtraction

Subtraction facts (differences from 20) 2–3
Missing addends 4–5
2-digit numbers, with/without regrouping 10–11
3-digit numbers 96–97, 98–101
4-digit numbers 96–97, 98–101
With zeros 92–95
Checking subtraction 90–91, 92–95, 96–97, 98–101
Estimate differences 88–89, 90–91, 92–95, 96–97, 98–101, 102–103

Type printed in red indicates that a topic is being introduced for the first time.

NUMBER SENSE, CONCEPTS, AND OPERATIONS

CONCEPTS AND OPERATIONS	K	1	2	3	4	5	6
Multiplication							
Meaning of multiplication			●	●	●	▲	▲
Multiplication facts for 2s, 5s, and 10s				●	●	▲	▲
Multiplication facts to 10 × 10				●	●	▲	▲
Multiplication facts to 12 × 12				●	●	▲	▲
Basic-fact strategies							
skip-counting				●	▲	▲	
break-apart numbers				●	●	●	
doubling				●	●		
Order Property				●	▲	▲	▲
Fact families/inverse relationship between × and ÷				●	▲	▲	▲
Estimate products				●	●	●	●
Multiples of 10				●	●	●	▲
Multidigit by 1-digit factor				●	●	●	▲
Multidigit by 2-digit factor					●	●	▲
Multidigit by 3-digit factor						●	▲
Multidigit by 4-digit factor						●	▲
Exponents						●	●
Properties				●	●	●	▲
Division							
Meaning of division			●	●	●	●	▲
Model and compute quotient			●	●	●	●	●
Division facts for 2s, 3s, 4s, 5s, 6s, 7s, 8s, 9s, 10s				●	●	▲	▲
Division facts for 11s and 12s				●	●	▲	▲
Missing factors				●	●	●	▲
Basic-fact strategies							
inverse operations				●	●	●	▲
Fact families				●	●	▲	
Remainders				●	●	●	▲
Interpret remainders				●	●	●	●
0 and 1 in division				●	▲	▲	▲
Multidigit by 1-digit divisor, no remainder				●	●	●	▲
Multidigit by 1-digit divisor, with remainder				●	●	●	▲
Multidigit by 2-digit divisor					●	●	▲
Zeros in the quotient					●	●	▲
Estimate quotients				●	●	●	▲
Divisibility					●	●	●
Determine unit cost				●	●	●	●

● Teach ▲ Reinforce and Maintain

CONCEPTS AND OPERATIONS

Type printed in red indicates that a topic is being introduced for the first time.

NUMBER SENSE, CONCEPTS, AND OPERATIONS

CONCEPTS AND OPERATIONS	K	1	2	3	4	5	6
MONEY							
Add	●	●	●	●	●	●	▲
Subtract	●	●	●	●	●	●	▲
Multiply				●	●	●	▲
Divide				●	●	●	▲
Estimate sums, differences, products, quotients			●	●	●	●	▲
DECIMALS							
Addition							
Meaning of addition				●	●	●	▲
Sums to two decimal places				●	●	●	●
Sums to three decimal places					●	●	●
Estimate sums					●	●	●
Subtraction							
Meaning of subtraction				●	●	●	▲
Differences to two decimal places				●	●	●	●
Differences to three decimal places					●	●	●
Estimate differences					●	●	●
Multiplication							
Meaning of multiplication						●	▲
Decimal by a whole number						●	●
Decimal by a decimal						●	●
By powers of 10						●	●
Place the decimal point						●	●
Place zeros in the product						●	●
Estimate products						●	●
Round products							●
Division							
Meaning of division					●	●	●
Decimal by a whole number						●	●
Decimal by a decimal						●	●
By powers of 10						●	●
Place the decimal point						●	●
Place zeros in the quotient						●	●
Estimate quotients (compatible numbers)						●	●
Round quotients							●
Repeating/terminating quotients							●

● Teach ▲ Reinforce and Maintain

CONCEPTS AND OPERATIONS

MONEY

Add 120–121, 580–583

Subtract 120–121, 580–581

Multiply 216–217

Divide 284–285

Estimate sums, differences, products, quotients 120–121, 580–583

DECIMALS

Addition

Meaning of addition 580–583

Sums to two decimal places 580–583

Subtraction

Meaning of subtraction 580–583

Differences to two decimal places 580–583

Type printed in red indicates that a topic is being introduced for the first time.

NUMBER SENSE, CONCEPTS, AND OPERATIONS

CONCEPTS AND OPERATIONS	K	1	2	3	4	5	6
FRACTIONS							
Addition							
Meaning of addition				●	●	●	▲
Like denominators				●	●	●	▲
Unlike denominators					●	●	●
Estimate sums						●	●
Mixed numbers					●	●	●
Subtraction							
Meaning of subtraction				●	●	●	▲
Like denominators				●	●	●	▲
Unlike denominators					●	●	●
Estimate differences						●	●
Mixed numbers					●	●	●
Mixed numbers with renaming						●	●
Multiplication							
Meaning of multiplication						●	●
Fraction by a whole number						●	●
Fraction by a fraction						●	●
Fraction and mixed number						●	●
Estimate products							●
Mixed numbers						●	●
Division							
Meaning of division						●	●
Fraction by a whole number						●	●
Whole number by a fraction						●	●
Fraction by a fraction						●	●
Estimate quotients							●
Mixed numbers						●	●
INTEGERS							
Meaning of addition and subtraction						●	●
Use a number line to compute							●
Add						●	●
Subtract						●	●
Multiply							●
Divide							●
ESTIMATE ANSWERS							
Rounding			●	●	●	●	●
Benchmarks			●	●	●	●	▲
Compatible numbers					●	●	●
Front-end				●	●	●	

● Teach ▲ Reinforce and Maintain

CONCEPTS AND OPERATIONS

FRACTIONS

Addition

Meaning of addition 540–541, 542–543

Like denominators 540–541, 542–543

Subtraction

Meaning of subtraction 544–545, 546–549

Like denominators 544–545, 546–549

ESTIMATE ANSWERS

Rounding 40–41

Benchmarks 68–69, 88–89, 608–611, 628–629

Front-end 68–69, 88–89

Type printed in red indicates that a topic is being introduced for the first time.

MEASUREMENT, GEOMETRY, AND SPATIAL SENSE

MEASUREMENT AND SPATIAL SENSE	K	1	2	3	4	5	6
CONCEPTS							
Choose appropriate tools/units to measure or draw			●	●	●	●	●
angles					●	●	●
parallel and perpendicular lines					●	●	▲
polygons and circles					●	●	▲
Precision/accuracy					●	●	●
LENGTH/DISTANCE							
Meaning of linear measurement	●	●	●	●	●	●	●
Direct comparison	●	●	●	●	●	●	●
Indirect comparison	●	●	●	●	●	●	●
Nonstandard objects/units	●	●	●	●	●	●	
Compare and order	●	●	●	●	●	●	▲
Estimate	●	●	●	●	●	●	▲
Customary units		●	●	●	●	●	●
measure to the nearest inch			●	●	▲	▲	▲
measure to fractional part of an inch				●	●	▲	▲
Metric units		●	●	●	●	●	●
measure to the nearest centimeter			●	●	▲	▲	▲
measure to the nearest millimeter					●	●	●
Relate units			●	●	●	●	●
choose appropriate units			●	●	●	●	●
Change units within a system				●	●	●	●
Compare/convert units between systems					●	●	●
Apply distance formula ($d = rt$)							●
Pythagorean Theorem							●
CAPACITY							
Meaning of capacity	●	●	●	●	●	●	▲
Nonstandard units	●	●	●	●	▲		
Compare and order	●	●	●	●	●	●	▲
Estimate	●	●	●	●	●	●	▲
Customary units		●	●	●	●	●	▲
Metric units		●	●	●	●	●	▲
Relate units			●	●	●	●	●
choose appropriate units			●	●	●	●	▲
Change units within a system				●	●	●	●
Compare/convert units between systems					●	●	●

● Teach ▲ Reinforce and Maintain

MEASUREMENT AND SPATIAL SENSE

CONCEPTS

Choose appropriate tools/units to measure or draw 342–343, 344–345, 346–347, 364–365, 366–367

LENGTH/DISTANCE

Meaning of linear measurement 338–341, 358–361

Direct comparison 363

Indirect comparison 341

Nonstandard objects/units 338–341

Compare and order 363

Estimate 338–341, 342–343

Customary units

measure to the nearest inch 338–341, 342–343

measure to fractional part of an inch 338–341, 342–343

Metric units

measure to the nearest centimeter 358–361

Relate units

choose appropriate units 342–343, 344–345, 346–347, 364–365, 366–367

Change units within a system 348–349

CAPACITY

Meaning of capacity 344–345

Nonstandard units 344–345

Compare and order 344–345

Estimate 344–345, 364–365

Customary units 344–345

Metric units 364–365

Relate units

choose appropriate units 344–345, 364–365

Change units within a system 348–349

Type printed in red indicates that a topic is being introduced for the first time.

MEASUREMENT, GEOMETRY, AND SPATIAL SENSE

MEASURING OBJECTS	K	1	2	3	4	5	6
WEIGHT/MASS							
Meaning of weight/mass	●	●	●	●	●	●	▲
Nonstandard units	●	●	●	●	▲	▲	
Compare and order	●	●	●	●	●	●	▲
Estimate	●	●	●	●	●	●	▲
Customary units		●	●	●	●	●	▲
Metric units		●	●	●	●	●	▲
Relate units			●	●	●	●	●
choose appropriate units			●	●	●	●	▲
Change units within a system				●	●	●	●
Compare/convert units between systems					●	●	●
TEMPERATURE							
Meaning of temperature	●	●	●	●	●	▲	▲
Read a thermometer: Fahrenheit and Celsius		●	●	●	●	●	▲
Meaning of negative numbers					●	●	●
Computing temperature changes				●	●	●	●
Change units between systems: Fahrenheit/Celsius							●

● Teach ▲ Reinforce and Maintain

MEASURING OBJECTS

Type printed in red indicates that a topic is being introduced for the first time.

MEASUREMENT, GEOMETRY, AND SPATIAL SENSE

MEASURING TIME	K	1	2	3	4	5	6
Concept of time	●	●	●	●	●	▲	▲
CLOCK							
As tool to measure time	●	●	●	●	●		
Sequence events	●	●	●	●	●		
Identify the times of everyday events	●	●	●	●	▲		
Tell and show time							
to the hour and half hour	●	●	●	●	▲		
to the quarter hour			●	●	▲		
to 5-minute and 1-minute intervals			●	●	●		
A.M. and P.M.			●	●	●	▲	▲
Relate minutes/hours, days/months, weeks/years		●	●	●	▲	▲	▲
Estimate time	●	●	●	●	▲		
Elapsed time			●	●	●	●	
Add and subtract units				●	●	●	
Schedules		●	●	●	●	●	
CALENDAR							
As tool to measure time	●	●	●	●	▲	▲	
Days of the week	●	●	●	●	▲		
Read	●	●	●	●	●		
Elapsed time			●	●	●	●	
MONEY							
Equivalent amounts	●	●	●	●	▲	▲	▲
Add	●	●	●	●	●	●	▲
Subtract	●	●	●	●	●	●	▲
Multiply				●	●	●	▲
Divide				●	●	●	▲
Estimate sums, differences, products, quotients			●	●	●	●	▲

● Teach ▲ Reinforce and Maintain

MEASURING TIME

Concept of time 128–131

CLOCK

As tool to measure time 128–131
Sequence events 142–143
Identify the times of everyday events 128–131, 132–133

Tell and show time

to the hour and half hour 128–131
to the quarter hour 128–131
to 5-minute and 1-minute intervals 128–131
A.M. and P.M. 132–133

Relate minutes/hours, days/months, weeks/years 128–141
Estimate time 128–131
Elapsed time 134–135
Add and subtract units 134–135
Schedules 136–137

CALENDAR

As a tool to measure time 138–141
Days of the week 138–141
Read 138–141
Elapsed time 138–141

MONEY

Equivalent amounts 110–113, 114–115
Add 120–121, 580–583
Subtract 120–121, 580–581
Multiply 216–217
Divide 284–285
Estimate sums, differences, products, quotients 120–121, 580–583

Type printed in red indicates that a topic is being introduced for the first time.

MEASUREMENT, GEOMETRY, AND SPATIAL SENSE

MEASUREMENT	K	1	2	3	4	5	6
PERIMETER							
Meaning of perimeter			●	●	●	●	●
Estimate and measure with nonstandard units				●	●	●	●
Measure			●	●	●	●	●
Add to find			●	●	●	●	●
Multiply and add to find				●	●	●	●
Apply formulas					●	●	●
square, rectangle, and compound figures					●	●	●
polygon/regular polygon					●	●	●
Use appropriate units of measure					●	●	●
Changing dimensions							●
CIRCUMFERENCE							
Estimate					●	●	●
Meaning of circumference					●	●	●
Find diameter or radius					●	●	●
Meaning of pi						●	●
Apply formula						●	●
Compare calculated and estimated							●
AREA							
Meaning of area		●	●	●	●	●	●
Estimate and measure with nonstandard units		●	●	●	●	●	●
Derive and apply formulas					●	●	●
squares, rectangles, and compound figures					●	●	●
parallelograms and triangles						●	●
trapezoids							●
circles						●	●
surface areas						●	●
nets						●	●
Use appropriate units of measure				●	●	●	●
Relate area and perimeter				●	●	●	●
Changing dimensions							●

● Teach ▲ Reinforce and Maintain

MEASUREMENT

Type printed in red indicates that a topic is being introduced for the first time.

MEASUREMENT, GEOMETRY, AND SPATIAL SENSE

MEASUREMENT	K	1	2	3	4	5	6
SURFACE AREA							
Meaning of surface area					●	●	●
Construct a cube and rectangular prism as patterns					●	●	▲
Apply formulas						●	●
prism						●	●
pyramid							●
cylinder							●
Use appropriate units of measure					●	●	●
VOLUME							
Meaning of volume			●	●	●	●	●
Estimate and measure with nonstandard units			●	●	●		
Estimate and measure					●	●	●
Apply formulas							
prisms					●	●	●
pyramids							●
cylinders							●
Compare formulas: rectangular prism/triangular prism/cylinder							●
Use appropriate units of measure					●	●	●
Relate perimeter, area, and volume						●	●
ANGLES							
Compare to right angle (greater than, less than, equal to)				●	●	●	●
Identify and classify			●	●	●	●	●
right, acute, obtuse				●	●	●	●
vertical, adjacent, complementary, supplementary							●
alternate interior, alternate exterior, interior, exterior, corresponding							●
Relate to $\frac{1}{4}$, $\frac{1}{2}$, and $\frac{3}{4}$ turns				●	●	●	●
Measure, draw, and construct						●	●
triangle: sum of measures of angles is 180°						●	●
rectangle: sum of measures of angles is 360°						●	▲
other polygons: sum of measures						●	▲
ALGEBRAIC THINKING							
Indirect measurement							●
similar figure applications							●

● Teach ▲ Reinforce and Maintain

MEASUREMENT

VOLUME

Meaning of volume 452–453

Estimate and measure with nonstandard units 452–455

ANGLES

Compare to right angle (greater than, less than, equal to) 384–385

Identify and classify

right, acute, obtuse 384–385, 400–401

Relate to $\frac{1}{4}$, $\frac{1}{2}$, and $\frac{3}{4}$ turns 414–415

Type printed in red indicates that a topic is being introduced for the first time.

MEASUREMENT, GEOMETRY, AND SPATIAL SENSE

GEOMETRY AND SPATIAL SENSE	K	1	2	3	4	5	6
CONCEPTS							
Position	●	●	●				
Attributes	●	●	●	●	●	●	●
Sides, vertices, edges, and faces		●	●	●	●	●	●
Points, lines, segments, angles, rays			●	●	●	●	●
parallel, perpendicular, and intersecting lines				●	●	●	●
skew lines							●
Congruence		●	●	●	●	●	●
Symmetry	●	●	●	●	●	●	●
line (bilateral)	●	●	●	●	●	●	●
point (rotational)					●	●	●
Transformations			●	●	●	●	●
Similarity				●	●	●	●
SOLID FIGURES							
Attributes and properties	●	●	●	●	●	●	●
Identify and describe common geometric objects	●	●	●	●	●	●	●
Identify, describe, and classify	●	●	●	●	▲	▲	▲
sphere, pyramid, cube, prism	●	●	●	●	▲	▲	▲
cone, cylinder	●	●	●	●	▲	▲	▲
Represent and visualize	●	●	●	●	●	●	▲
Build/take apart			●	●	●	●	▲
Identify or draw different views		●	●	●	●	●	●
Make nets				●	●	●	●
Measure							
volume				●	●	●	●
surface area					●	●	●

● Teach ▲ Reinforce and Maintain

GEOMETRY AND SPATIAL SENSE

CONCEPTS

Attributes 384–387, 388–389, 390–391, 392–395, 396–399, 400–401

Sides, vertices, edges, and faces 390–391, 424–427

Points, lines, segments, angles, rays 384–387

parallel, perpendicular, and intersecting lines 388–389

Congruence 408–409, 416–417

Symmetry

line (bilateral) 410–411

Transformations 414–415

Similarity 412–413

SOLID FIGURES

Attributes and properties 424–427

Identify and describe common geometric objects 424–427

Identify, describe, and classify

sphere, pyramid, cube, prism 424–427

cone, cylinder 424–427

Represent and visualize 424–427, 428–429, 432–435, 436–437

Build/take apart 432–435

Identify or draw different views 436–437

Make nets 434

Measure

volume 452–455

Type printed in red indicates that a topic is being introduced for the first time.

MEASUREMENT, GEOMETRY, AND SPATIAL SENSE

GEOMETRY AND SPATIAL SENSE	K	1	2	3	4	5	6
PLANE FIGURES							
Attributes and properties	●	●	●	●	●	●	●
triangle	●	●	●	●	●	●	●
quadrilaterals (rect., square, parall., rhombus, trap.)	●	●	●	●	●	●	●
Identify and describe common geometric objects	●	●	●	●	●	●	●
Identify, describe, and classify	●	●	●	●	●	●	●
rectangle, square, triangle, circle	●	●	●	●	●	●	●
pentagon, hexagon, octagon, decagon		●	●	●	●	●	●
Represent and visualize	●	●	●	●	●	●	●
Build/take apart			●	●	●	●	▲
Draw with appropriate tools							
parallel and perpendicular lines				●	●	●	●
angles				●	●	●	●
rectangles				●	●	●	●
triangles				●	●	●	●
quadrilaterals				●	●	●	●
Measure with appropriate tools							
angles					●	●	●
perimeter/circumference			●	●	●	●	●
area				●	●	●	●
Parts of a circle (radius, diameter, chord, central angle)					●	●	●
ALGEBRAIC THINKING							
Formulas				●	●	●	●
Graphing figures						●	●
Scatterplots							●
Correlations							●
Similar figure applications							●
indirect measurement							●

● Teach ▲ Reinforce and Maintain

GEOMETRY AND SPATIAL SENSE

PLANE FIGURES

Attributes and properties
- triangle 392–395
- quadrilaterals (rect., square, parall., rhombus, trap.) 396–399

Identify and describe common geometric objects 390–391

Identify, describe, and classify
- rectangle, square, triangle, circle 390–391, 392–395, 396–399
- pentagon, hexagon, octagon, decagon 390–391

Represent and visualize 390–391, 392–395, 396–399, 400–401

Build/take apart 390–391, 408–409, 410–411

Draw with appropriate tools
- parallel and perpendicular lines 388–391
- angles 384–385
- rectangles 498
- triangles 395
- quadrilaterals 498

Measure with appropriate tools
- perimeter/circumference 444–447
- area 448–449, 450–451

ALGEBRAIC THINKING

Formulas 449, 450–451, 453–455

Type printed in red indicates that a topic is being introduced for the first time.

MEASUREMENT, GEOMETRY, AND SPATIAL SENSE

GEOMETRY AND SPATIAL SENSE	K	1	2	3	4	5	6
VISUAL THINKING							
Patterns	●	●	●	●	●	●	●
tessellations				●	●	●	●
nets				●	●	●	●
Congruence		●	●	●	●	●	●
Symmetry	●	●	●	●	●	●	●
line (bilateral)	●	●	●	●	●	●	●
point (rotational)					●	●	●
Similarity				●	●	●	●
Transformations							
translations (slides)	●	●	●	●	●	●	●
reflections (flips)			●	●	●	●	●
rotations (turns)	●	●	●	●	●	●	●
dilations							●
solid figures							●
Representing							
building, drawing 3-D figures	●	●	●	●	●	●	●
different views					●	●	●
Perspective							
Networks							
COORDINATE GEOMETRY							
COORDINATE PLANE							
Ordered pairs			●	●	●	●	●
Graph points and figures					●	●	●
Graph linear relationships					●	●	●
Graph equations							●
Relations and functions						●	●
Identify functions							
linear functions						●	●
nonlinear functions							●
Translations, reflections, rotations						●	●

● Teach ▲ Reinforce and Maintain

GEOMETRY AND SPATIAL SENSE

VISUAL THINKING

Patterns
- tessellations 430–431
- nets 434

Congruence 408–409

Symmetry
- line (bilateral) 410–411

Similarity 412–413

Transformations
- translations (slides) 414–415
- reflections (flips) 414–415
- rotations (turns) 414–415

Representing
- building, drawing 3-D figures 428–429, 432–433

COORDINATE GEOMETRY

COORDINATE PLANE

Ordered pairs 428–429

Type printed in red indicates that a topic is being introduced for the first time.

ALGEBRAIC THINKING, ALGEBRA, AND FUNCTIONS

ALGEBRAIC THINKING AND PATTERNS	K	1	2	3	4	5	6
GEOMETRIC							
Identify, describe, compare	●	●	●	●	●	●	●
Extend	●	●	●	●	●	●	●
Create	●	●	●	●	●	●	●
COLOR/RHYTHMIC AND SYMBOLIC PATTERNS							
Describe-Write a rule			●	●	●	●	●
Identify and describe	●	●	●	●	●	●	●
Extend	●	●	●	●	●	●	●
Create	●	●	●	●	●	●	●
Transfer/Translate	●	●	●	●			
Correct		●	●				
LINEAR NUMBER							
Identify describe	●	●	●	●	●	●	●
Extend	●	●	●	●	●	●	●
Create			●	●	●	●	●
NUMERIC							
Describe/Write a rule			●	●	●	●	●
Identify and describe			●	●	●	●	●
Extend			●	●	●	●	●

● Teach ▲ Reinforce and Maintain

ALGEBRAIC THINKING AND PATTERNS

GEOMETRIC

Identify, describe, compare 470–473
Extend 470–473
Create 478–479

COLOR/RHYTHMIC AND SYMBOLIC PATTERNS

Describe/Write a rule 474–475, 476–477
Identify and describe 474–475, 476–477
Extend 474–475, 476–477
Create 478–479
Transfer/Translate 470–473

LINEAR NUMBER

Identify and describe 30–31, 63, 180–181, 476–477
Extend 30–31, 63, 180–181, 476–477
Create 30–31, 63, 180–181, 476–477

NUMERIC

Describe/Write a rule 30–31, 180–181, 470–473, 474–475, 476–477, 478–479, 480–481
Identify and describe 30–31, 180–181, 470–473, 474–475, 476–477, 478–479, 480–481
Extend 30–31, 180–181, 470–473, 474–475, 476–477

Type printed in red indicates that a topic is being introduced for the first time.

ALGEBRAIC THINKING, ALGEBRA, AND FUNCTIONS

ALGEBRA	K	1	2	3	4	5	6
CLASSIFY							
Identify and sort by attributes	●	●	●	●	●	●	●
determine objects that don't belong	●	●	●	●	●	●	●
PROPERTIES							
Of whole numbers		●	●	●	●	●	●
Associative and Commutative, of addition		●	●	●	●	▲	▲
Associative and Commutative, of multiplication				●	●	▲	▲
Distributive				●	●	●	●
Identity		●	●	●	●	▲	▲
EQUATIONS AND EXPRESSIONS							
Number sentences for addition and subtraction	●	●	●	●	●	●	●
Number sentences for multiplication and division			●	●	●	●	●
Use symbols: +, −, =, ≠	●	●	●	●	●	●	▲
Use symbols: ×, ÷			●	●	●	●	▲
Missing addend		●	●	●	●	●	●
Missing factor				●	●	●	●
Write numerical expressions			●	●	●	●	●
Evaluate numerical expressions		●	●	●	●	●	●
Match problem situation and expression				●	●	●	●
Formulas				●	●	●	●
Order of operations					●	●	●
Variables			●	●	●	●	●
geometric symbols			●	●	●	●	●
letters			●	●	●	●	●
Use parentheses				●	●	●	●
Write and evaluate algebraic expressions					●	●	●
with one variable					●	●	●
with two variables							●
with three variables							●
Write number sentence/equation for problem situation		●	●	●	●	●	●
Create problem situation for number sentence/equation		●	●	●	●	●	●

● Teach ▲ Reinforce and Maintain

ALGEBRA

CLASSIFY

Identify and sort by attributes 110–111, 306–307, 388–389, 408–409, 410–411, 412–413, 424–427

determine objects that don't belong 430–431

PROPERTIES

Of whole numbers

Associative and Commutative, of addition 6–7

Associative and Commutative, of multiplication 220–221

Distributive 220–221

Identity 220–221

EQUATIONS AND EXPRESSIONS

Number sentences for addition and subtraction 80–81, 92–95, 96–97

Number sentences for multiplication and division 250–251, 264–265

Use symbols: +, −, =, ≠ 80–81, 92–95, 96–97

Use symbols: ×, ÷ 250–251, 264–265

Missing addend 4–5

Missing factor 186–187, 280–283

Write numerical expressions 80–81, 250–251, 264–265

Evaluate numerical expressions 80–81, 250–251, 264–265

Match problem situation and expression 80–81, 92–95, 96–97, 250–251, 264–265

Formulas 348–349, 449, 450–451, 452–453

Variables

geometric symbols 4–5, 80–81, 186–187, 242–245, 264–265

letters 242–245

Use parentheses 6–7, 218–219

Write number sentence/equation for problem situation 80–81, 92–95, 96–97, 250–251, 264–265

Create problem situation for number sentence/equation 158–159, 160–161, 162–163, 164–167, 264–265

Type printed in red indicates that a topic is being introduced for the first time.

ALGEBRAIC THINKING, ALGEBRA, AND FUNCTIONS

ALGEBRA	K	1	2	3	4	5	6
Solve equations							
1-step addition and subtraction equations	●	●	●	●	●	●	●
1-step multiplication and division equations			●	●	●	●	●
modeling 2-step equations							●
equations with two variables					●	●	●
with integers						●	●
with rational numbers							●
linear equations					●	●	●
Use number sentence/equation to solve problem	●	●	●	●	●	●	●
Relate graphs and equations							●
Relate tables, graphs, and rules					●	●	●
INEQUALITIES							
Compare numbers	●	●	●	●	●	●	●
Inequality symbols		●	●	●	●	●	●
Algebraic inequality					●	●	●
Write inequality for problem situation					●	●	●
Solve inequalities					●	●	●
Use to solve problem					●	●	●

● Teach ▲ Reinforce and Maintain

ALGEBRA
Solve equations

1-step addition and subtraction equations 264–265

1-step multiplication and division equations 264–265

Use number sentence/equation to solve problem 80–81, 92–95, 96–97, 250–251, 264–265

INEQUALITIES

Compare numbers 42–43, 46–47, 116–117, 526–529, 530–531, 566–567

Inequality symbols 42–43, 46–47, 526–529, 530–531, 566–567

Type printed in red indicates that a topic is being introduced for the first time.

ALGEBRAIC THINKING, ALGEBRA, AND FUNCTIONS

ALGEBRA	K	1	2	3	4	5	6
PROPORTIONAL REASONING							
Ratio							
concept					●	●	●
read and write					●	●	●
equivalent ratios						●	●
cross products							●
rates, unit rates							●
Proportion							
meaning of proportion						●	●
solve proportions						●	●
applications							
indirect measurement							●
scale drawings, maps						●	●
similar figures						●	●
Percent							
meaning of percent					●	●	●
percent and decimals						●	●
percent and fractions						●	●
percents greater than 100%/less than 1%						●	●
find percent of a number						●	●
find percent one number is of another						●	●
estimate percents							●
applications							
circle graph						●	●
sales tax						●	●
simple interest							●
discount							●
NUMBER LINE							
Locate	●	●	●	●	●	●	●
Compare and order		●	●	●	●	●	●
Operations		●	●	●	●	●	●

● Teach ▲ Reinforce and Maintain

ALGEBRA

NUMBER LINE

Locate 42–45, 50–51, 52–53
Compare and order 42–45
Operations 164–167, 182–185, 212–215

Type printed in red indicates that a topic is being introduced for the first time.

ALGEBRAIC THINKING, ALGEBRA, AND FUNCTIONS

ALGEBRA AND FUNCTIONS	K	1	2	3	4	5	6
GRAPHING ON A NUMBER LINE							
Whole numbers					●	●	▲
Integers					●	●	●
Rational numbers					●	●	●
Inequalities					●	●	●
COORDINATE GRAPHING							
Ordered pairs			●	●	●	●	●
Coordinate plane							
1 quadrant			●	●	●	●	▲
4 quadrants					●	●	●
Relations						●	●
Functions						●	●
Linear equations						●	●
Nonlinear equations							●
FUNCTIONS AND RELATIONS							
Solve problems involving functions				●	●	●	●
Input-output tables		●	●	●	●	●	●
Graphs of functions						●	●
Write a rule		●	●	●	●	●	●
Graph from a rule							●
Linear functions							
with whole numbers				●	●	●	●
with integers							●
Applications							
measurement conversions				●	●	●	●
rates							●
proportions						●	●
distance/speed/time							●
unit cost				●	●	●	●

● Teach ▲ Reinforce and Maintain

ALGEBRA AND FUNCTIONS

Type printed in red indicates that a topic is being introduced for the first time.

DATA ANALYSIS AND PROBABILITY

DATA ANALYSIS AND STATISTICS	K	1	2	3	4	5	6
COLLECTING DATA							
Use systematic way to record	●	●	●	●	●	▲	▲
Pose question/collect data	●	●	●	●	●	▲	▲
Formulate question	●	●	●	●	●	▲	▲
Analyze question					●	●	●
Conduct survey	●	●	●	●	●	●	●
Sampling							●
determine when appropriate							●
bias							●
random						●	●
determine most representative						●	●
ORGANIZING DATA							
Sort objects/data and describe categories	●	●	●	●			
Tally table/chart	●	●	●	●	●	●	▲
Frequency table/chart			●	●	●	●	▲
cumulative frequency					●	●	▲
Organized list			●	●	●	●	●
Stem-and-leaf plot					●	●	▲
Line plot		●	●	●	●	●	▲
DISPLAYING DATA							
Objects	●	●	●				
Picture graph	●	●					
Pictograph			●	●	▲	▲	
Bar graph	●	●	●	●	●	●	▲
Line graph			●	●	●	●	▲
identify ordered pairs				●	●	●	▲
write ordered pairs				●	●	●	▲
graph ordered pairs				●	●	●	●
Circle graph				●	●	●	●
Histogram						●	●
Box-and-whisker graph							●
Scatterplot							●
Represent same data in different ways		●	●	●	●	●	●
Choose an appropriate graph					●	●	●

● Teach ▲ Reinforce and Maintain

DATA ANALYSIS AND STATISTICS

COLLECTING DATA

Use systematic way to record 302–303, 308–309, 322–323, 326–327, 490–491, 492–495, 498–499, 500–501

Pose question/collect data 302–303, 308–309

Formulate question 302–303, 305

Conduct survey 302–303, 305

ORGANIZING DATA

Sort objects/data and describe categories 110–111, 302–303, 306–307, 310–311, 388–389, 408–409, 410–411, 412–413, 424–427

Tally table/chart 302–303, 304–305, 308–309

Frequency table/chart 302–303

Organized list 500–501

Line plot 310–313

DISPLAYING DATA

Pictograph 198–199, 322–323

Bar graph 48–49, 324–325, 326–327

Line graph

identify ordered pairs 328–329

write ordered pairs 328–329

graph ordered pairs 326–327, 330–331

Circle graph 375

Represent same data in different ways 240–241, 313

Type printed in red indicates that a topic is being introduced for the first time.

DATA ANALYSIS AND PROBABILITY

DATA ANALYSIS AND STATISTICS	K	1	2	3	4	5	6
ANALYZING DATA							
Ask/answer questions about data	●	●	●	●	●	▲	▲
Interpret one-variable graphs	●	●	●	●	●	●	▲
Interpret two-variable graphs						●	●
Interpret tables	●	●	●	●	●	●	▲
Compare data	●	●	●	●	●	●	▲
Compare data sets of different sizes						●	▲
Compare/choose appropriate representations					●	●	●
Identify misleading graphs							●
Choose scale				●	●	●	●
Identify outliers					●	●	
Find range	●	●	●	●	●	●	▲
Measures of central tendency							
find mean (average)			●	●	●	●	▲
find median				●	●	●	▲
find mode	●	●	●	●	●	●	▲
compare/analyze measures						●	●
determine effects on measures of adding data						●	
Relate to conclusions the way data is displayed						●	●
Evaluate conclusions based on data					●	●	●
Make predictions	●	●	●	●	●	●	●
Make generalizations				●	●	●	●
Misleading graphs							●

● Teach ▲ Reinforce and Maintain

DATA ANALYSIS AND STATISTICS

ANALYZING DATA

Ask/answer questions about data 48–49, 302–303, 304–305, 306–307, 308–309, 322–323, 324–325, 328–329, 330–331

Interpret one-variable graphs 330–331

Interpret tables 302–303, 304–305, 308–309, 492–495

Compare data 48–49, 198–199, 324–325, 327–328

Choose scale 326–327

Find range 310–311

Measures of central tendency

find mean (average) 314–315

find median 314–315

find mode 310–313

Make predictions 488–489, 490–491, 496–497

Make generalizations 330–331, 496–497

Type printed in red indicates that a topic is being introduced for the first time.

DATA ANALYSIS AND PROBABILITY

PROBABILITY	K	1	2	3	4	5	6
CONCEPTS							
Likelihood of events	●	●	●	●	●	●	●
certain, likely, unlikely, impossible	●	●	●	●	●	●	●
more likely, equally likely, less likely	●	●	●	●	●	●	●
Fairness					●	●	▲
Randomness							●
FINDING OUTCOMES							
Outcomes		●	●	●	●	●	●
Tree diagram				●	●	●	●
Table/grid					●	●	●
Sample spaces							●
Arrangements/Permutations				●	●	●	●
Combinations				●	●	●	●
Fundamental Counting Principle							●
THEORETICAL PROBABILITY							
Meaning					●	●	●
Simple events				●	●	●	●
Compound events							●
Independent/dependent events							●
EXPERIMENTAL PROBABILITY							
Record possible outcomes			●	●	●	●	●
organized list				●	●	●	●
table/grid			●	●	●	●	●
tree diagram				●	●	●	●
Record outcomes during trials				●	●	●	●
Summarize/display results			●	●	●	●	●
Express verbally and numerically			●	●	●	●	●
Predict based on experiment or prior data			●	●	●	●	●
Simulations							●
Random numbers							●
REPRESENT PROBABILITY							
Verbally and numerically			●	●	●	●	●
Ratio, decimal, percent							●
Verify reasonableness							●
Of event not occurring (1 – P)							●
ODDS							●
in favor							●
against							●

● Teach ▲ Reinforce and Maintain

PROBABILITY

CONCEPTS
Likelihood of events
- certain, likely, unlikely, impossible 488–489
- more likely, equally likely, less likely 490–491, 492–493

FINDING OUTCOMES
Outcomes 490–491
Tree diagram 498–499
Arrangements/Permutations 500–501
Combinations 498–499

THEORETICAL PROBABILITY
Simple events 488–489

EXPERIMENTAL PROBABILITY
Record possible outcomes
- organized list 500–501
- table/grid 490–491
- tree diagram 498–499

Record outcomes during trials 490–491, 492–495, 496–497
Summarize/display results 490–491, 492–495, 496–497
Express verbally and numerically 490–491, 492–495, 496–497
Predict based on experiment or prior data 496–497

REPRESENT PROBABILITY
Verbally and numerically 488–489, 490–491, 492–495, 496–497, 498–499, 500–501

Type printed in red indicates that a topic is being introduced for the first time.

MATHEMATICAL REASONING

PROBLEM SOLVING PROCESS	K	1	2	3	4	5	6
SET UP/APPROACH PROBLEM							
Determine strategy	●	●	●	●	●	●	●
Determine materials	●	●	●	●	●	●	●
Model problem	●	●	●	●	●	●	●
Analyze problem							
relationships			●	●	●	●	●
relevant/irrelevant information			●	●	●	●	●
sequencing/prioritizing				●	●	●	●
patterns		●	●	●	●	●	●
Determine when to break into simpler parts				●	●	●	●
Formulate conjectures based on problem							●
SOLVE PROBLEM							
Use concrete objects	●	●	●	●	●	●	●
Use pictorial representation	●	●	●	●	●	●	●
Make calculations	●	●	●	●	●	●	●
Use results of simpler problem				●	●	●	●
Use mathematical notation/terms/clear language				●	●	●	●
Estimate solution graphically							●
EXPLAIN/JUSTIFY REASONING OR SOLUTION							
Explain reasoning with concrete objects	●	●	●	●	●	●	●
Explain reasoning with pictorial representations	●	●	●	●	●	●	●
Explain reasoning using a variety of methods				●	●	●	●
Defend reasoning		●	●	●	●	●	●
Check solution based on context	●	●	●	●	●	●	●
Justify procedure used		●	●	●	●	●	●
Use estimation to check			●	●	●	●	●
Defend solutions verbally and symbolically				●	●	●	●
Exact vs. estimated answers				●	●	●	●
GENERALIZE							
Between problems		●	●	●	●	●	●
Apply solution to similar problem				●	●	●	●
State/apply generalizations				●	●	●	●
Evaluate reasonableness in context of problem			●	●	●	●	●

● Teach ▲ Reinforce and Maintain

PROBLEM SOLVING PROCESS

SET UP/APPROACH PROBLEM

Determine strategy 28–29, 74–75, 114–115, 180–181, 286–287, 308–309, 322–323, 362–363, 400–401, 416–417, 480–481, 500–501, 530–531, 584–585

Determine materials 29, 75, 115, 181, 251, 287, 309, 323, 363, 401, 417, 481, 501, 531, 585

Model problem 70–71, 90–91, 92–95, 110–113, 158–159, 160–161, 162–163, 176, 182–185, 186, 194–195, 200–201, 238–239, 242–245, 368–369, 488–489, 516–519, 522–525, 530–531, 540–541, 544–545

Analyze problem

relationships 20–21, 30–31, 40–41, 42–45, 436–437

relevant/irrelevant information 168–169, 568–569

sequencing/prioritizing 142–143, 222–223

patterns 30–31, 63, 180–181, 470–473, 474–475, 476–477, 478–479, 480–481

Determine when to break into simpler parts 584–585

SOLVE PROBLEM

Use concrete objects 70–71, 90–91, 92–95, 162–163, 186, 194–195, 200–201, 238–239, 242–245, 516–519, 522–525, 530–531, 540–541, 542–543, 544–545

Use pictorial representation 91, 110–113, 116–117, 158–159, 160–161, 165, 176, 368–369, 488–489

Make calculations 76–79, 98–101, 240–241, 242–245, 246–249, 274–277, 278–279, 608–611, 626–627

Use results of simpler problem 584–585

Use mathematical notation/terms/clear language 42–43, 80–81, 96–97, 250–251, 264–265, 526–529, 566–567

EXPLAIN/JUSTIFY REASONING OR SOLUTION

Explain reasoning with concrete objects 70–71, 90–91, 162–163, 186, 194–195, 200–201, 238–239, 242–245, 516–519, 522–525, 526–529, 540–541, 544–545

Explain reasoning with pictorial representations 91, 110–113, 116–117, 158–159, 160–161, 165, 176, 182–185, 195, 368–369, 488–489

Explain reasoning using a variety of methods 90–91, 92–95, 110–113, 116–117, 158–159, 162–163, 177, 179, 187, 219, 326–327, 488–489, 490–491, 496–497, 516–519, 522–525, 526–529, 540–541, 544–545

Defend reasoning 70–71, 76–79, 90–91, 92–95, 110–113, 116–117, 158–159, 162–163, 177, 179, 187, 219, 326–327, 488–489, 490–491, 496–497, 516–519, 522–525, 526–529, 530–531, 540–541, 544–545, 608–611

Check solution based on context 90–91, 92–95, 98–101

Justify procedure used 76–79, 326–327, 342–347, 364–365, 488–489, 490–491, 496–497, 608–611

Use estimation to check 90–91, 92–95, 96–97, 98–101

Defend solutions verbally and symbolically 76–79, 342–347, 364–365, 488–489, 496–497, 608–611

Exact vs. estimated answers 102–103, 350–351

GENERALIZE

Between problems 348–349, 449, 450–451, 452–453

Apply solution to similar problem 348–349, 449, 450–451

State/apply generalizations 450–451, 452–453

Evaluate reasonableness in context of problem 348–349, 449, 450–451, 452–453, 550–551

Type printed in red indicates that a topic is being introduced for the first time.

MATHEMATICAL REASONING

PROBLEM SOLVING STRATEGIES/SKILLS	K	1	2	3	4	5	6
HEURISTIC		●	●	●	●	●	●
STRATEGIES							
Use logical reasoning	●	●	●	●	●	●	●
Predict and test	●	●	●	●	●	●	●
Make a table or graph	●	●	●	●	●	●	●
Find a pattern	●	●	●	●	●	●	●
Draw a picture or diagram	●	●	●	●	●	●	●
Write a number sentence		●	●	●			
Work backward			●	●	●	●	●
Break a problem into simpler parts/solve a simpler problem			●	●	●	●	●
Make a model or act it out	●	●	●	●	●	●	●
Write an equation					●	●	●
Make an organized list			●	●	●	●	●
Choose a strategy		●	●	●	●	●	●
SKILLS							
Identify relationships			●	●	●	●	●
Estimate or exact answer		●	●	●	●	●	●
Sequence events				●	▲	▲	▲
Too much/too little information			●	●	●	●	●
Multistep problems		●	●	●	●	●	●
Choose the operation	●	●	●	●	●	●	●
Draw conclusions		●	●	●	●	●	●
Interpret the remainder				●	●	●	●
Use a graph	●	●	●	●	●	●	●
Make generalizations				●	●	●	●
Sequence information				●	●	●	●
Evaluate reasonableness of answers		●	●	●	●	●	●
Use a table		●	●	▲	▲	▲	▲
Use a formula					●	●	●
Make decisions						●	●
Sequence and prioritize information						●	●
Relevant or irrelevant information						●	●
APPLICATIONS							
Number Sense	●	●	●	●	●	●	●
Algebra and Functions	●	●	●	●	●	●	●
Measurement and Geometry	●	●	●	●	●	●	●
Statistics, Data Analysis, and Probability	●	●	●	●	●	●	●

● Teach ▲ Reinforce and Maintain

PROBLEM SOLVING STRATEGIES/SKILLS

HEURISTIC

STRATEGIES

- Use logical reasoning 28–29
- Predict and test 74–75
- Make table or graph 114–115, 308–309, 322–323, 362–363
- Find a pattern 180–181, 480–481
- Draw a picture or diagram 400–401
- Write a number sentence 250–251
- Work backward 286–287
- Break a problem into simpler parts/solve a simpler problem 584–585
- Make a model or act it out 416–417, 530–531
- Make an organized list 500–501
- Choose a strategy 76–77, 98–101

SKILLS

- Identify relationships 436–437
- Estimate or exact answer 102–103, 350–351
- Sequence events 142–143
- Too much/too little information 168–169, 568–569
- Multistep problems 222–223
- Choose the operation 12–13, 266–267, 606–607
- Draw conclusions 624–625
- Interpret the remainder 624–625
- Use a graph 48–49, 198–199
- Make generalizations 450–451
- Sequence information 142–143
- Evaluate reasonableness of answers 550–551

APPLICATIONS

- Number Sense 12–13, 28–29, 74–75, 102–103, 168–169, 180–181, 250–251, 266–267, 286–287, 530–531, 550–551, 568–569, 584–585, 606–607, 624–625
- Algebra and Functions 436–437, 450–451, 480–481
- Measurement and Geometry 114–115, 142–143, 350–351, 362–363, 400–401, 416–417
- Statistics, Data Analysis, and Probability 48–49, 198–199, 308–309, 322–323, 500–501

Type printed in red indicates that a topic is being introduced for the first time.

MATHEMATICAL REASONING

REASONING	K	1	2	3	4	5	6
CRITICAL THINKING AND LOGICAL REASONING							
Classify and sort	●	●	●	●	●	●	●
Identify, extend, and use patterns	●	●	●	●	●	●	●
Order and sequence	●	●	●	●	●	●	●
Make generalizations		●	●	●	●	●	●
Compare and contrast	●	●	●	●	●	●	●
Draw conclusions		●	●	●	●	●	●
Use logical reasoning	●	●	●	●	●	●	●
Make and test predictions	●	●	●	●	●	●	●
Explain and justify answers	●	●	●	●	●	●	●
Evaluate evidence and conclusions				●	●	●	●
Interpret charts, tables, and graphs	●	●	●	●	●	●	●
Check reasonableness of results	●	●	●	●	●	●	●
VISUAL THINKING AND LOGICAL REASONING							
Spatial relationships	●	●	●	●	●	●	●
Visual patterns	●	●	●	●	●	●	●
Use visual representations to solve problems	●	●	●	●	●	●	●
DECISION MAKING							
Decide when to estimate				●	●	●	●
Decide on a computation method			●	●	●	●	●
Decide whether answer is reasonable	●	●	●	●	●	●	●
Choose from options or alternatives		●	●	●	●	●	●
CREATIVE THINKING							
Solve nonroutine problems		●	●	●	●	●	●
Generate problems	●	●	●	●	●	●	●
Choose alternative ways to solve problems		●	●	●	●	●	●

● Teach ▲ Reinforce and Maintain

REASONING

CRITICAL THINKING AND LOGICAL REASONING

Classify and sort 110–111, 302–303, 306–307, 310–311, 388–389, 408–409, 410–411, 412–413, 424–427

Identify, extend, and use patterns 30–31, 63, 180–181, 470–473, 474–475, 476–477, 478–479, 480–481

Order and sequence 42–43, 46–47, 526–529, 566–567

Make generalizations 348–349, 449, 450–451, 452–453, 550–551

Compare and contrast 42–43, 46–47, 526–529, 566–567

Draw conclusions 304–305, 306–307, 308–309, 310–313, 324–325, 330–331, 488–489, 490–491, 492–495, 496–497, 624–625

Use logical reasoning 28–29

Make and test predictions 488–489, 490–491, 496–497

Explain and justify answers 70–71, 90–91, 92–95, 110–113, 116–117, 158–159, 160–161, 162–163, 177, 179, 187, 219, 326–327, 488–489, 490–491, 496–497, 516–519, 522–525, 526–529, 530–531, 540–541, 542–543, 544–545

Evaluate evidence and conclusions 76–79, 326–327, 342–347, 364–365, 366–367, 488–489, 490–491, 496–497, 608–611

Interpret charts, tables, and graphs 48–49, 114–115, 198–199, 304–305, 306–307, 308–309, 310–313, 322–323, 324–325, 330–331, 362–363, 507

Check reasonableness of results 90–91, 92–95, 96–97, 98–101, 550–551

VISUAL THINKING AND LOGICAL REASONING

Spatial relationships 384–387, 388–389, 390–391, 408–409, 410–411, 412–413, 414–415, 424–427, 428–429, 430–431, 432–435

Visual patterns 470–471, 474–475

Use visual representations to solve problems 70–71, 90–91, 92–95, 110–113, 116–117, 158–159, 160–161, 162–163, 176, 182–185, 186, 194–195, 196–197, 200–201, 238–239, 242–245, 368–369, 488–489, 516–519, 522–525, 526–529, 530–531, 540–541, 542–543, 544–545

DECISION MAKING

Decide when to estimate 350–351

Decide on a computation method 12–13, 74–75, 102–103, 168–169, 266–267, 606–607

Decide whether answer is reasonable 90–91, 92–95, 96–97, 98–101, 550–551

Choose from options or alternatives 194–195, 196–197, 202–205

CREATIVE THINKING

Solve nonroutine problems 27, 45, 79, 101, 131, 141, 167, 185, 205, 245, 249, 283, 341, 361, 387, 427, 473

Generate problems 75, 89, 158–159, 160–161, 162–163, 164–167, 251, 264–265, 363, 521

Choose alternative ways to solve problems 194–195, 196–197, 202–205, 341, 348, 532–533

Type printed in red indicates that a topic is being introduced for the first time.

MATHEMATICAL REASONING

PROCESSES	K	1	2	3	4	5	6
COMMUNICATION							
Drawing	●	●	●	●	●	●	●
Writing		●	●	●	●	●	●
Talking	●	●	●	●	●	●	●
CONNECTIONS							
Mathematical	●	●	●	●	●	●	●
Cross-curricular	●	●	●	●	●	●	●
Everyday	●	●	●	●	●	●	●
MULTIPLE REPRESENTATIONS							
Different manipulatives	●	●	●	●	●	●	●
Different models	●	●	●	●	●	●	●
Manipulatives and models	●	●	●	●	●	●	●
Manipulatives, words, and symbols	●	●	●	●	●	●	●
Models, words, and symbols	●	●	●	●	●	●	●
TOOLS							
Calculator	●	●	●	●	●	●	●
Software	●	●	●	●	●	●	●
Manipulatives	●	●	●	●	●	●	●
Measuring tools	●	●	●	●	●	●	●
ruler		●	●	●	●	●	●
protractor					●	●	●
Compass					●	●	●

● Teach ▲ Reinforce and Maintain

PROCESSES

COMMUNICATION

Drawing 91, 110–113, 116–117, 158–159, 160–161, 165, 176, 182–185, 368–369, 488–489

Writing 73, 78, 115, 239, 241, 343, 347, 351, 367, 494, 517, 533

Talking 93, 118, 183, 186, 198, 213, 241, 258, 342, 348, 492

CONNECTIONS

Mathematical 27, 45, 79, 101, 131, 141, 167, 185, 205, 245, 249, 283, 341, 361, 387, 427, 473

Cross-curricular 95, 113, 215, 277, 313, 395, 399, 435, 447, 495, 519, 525, 529, 549, 583, 605, 611, 623

Everyday 18, 38, 66, 86, 108, 126, 156, 174, 192, 210, 236, 256, 272, 300, 320, 336, 356, 382, 406, 422, 442, 468, 486, 514, 538, 556, 574, 598, 616

MULTIPLE REPRESENTATIONS

Different manipulatives 70–71, 90–91, 92–95, 162–163, 186, 194–195, 196–197, 200–201, 238–239, 242–245, 516–519, 522–525, 526–529, 530–531, 540–541, 542–543, 544–545

Different models 516–519, 522–525, 526–529, 530–531, 540–541

Manipulatives and models 342–343, 516–519, 522–525, 526–529, 530–531, 540–541

Manipulatives, words, and symbols, 516–519, 522–525, 526–529, 530–531, 540–541

Models, words, and symbols 70–71, 90–91, 92–95, 162–163, 186, 194–195, 196–197, 200–201, 238–239, 242–245, 516–519, 522–525, 526–529, 530–531, 540–541, 542–543, 544–545

TOOLS

Calculator 63, 76–79, 98–101, 153, 297, 595, 608–611, 626–627, 639

Software 2, 8, 22, 24, 43, 70, 77, 91, 111, 119, 158, 162, 182, 200, 213, 216, 233, 242, 247, 261, 274, 281, 311, 325, 330, 379, 465, 489, 493, 511, 547, 580, 603, 619

Manipulatives 70–71, 90–91, 92–95, 162–163, 186, 194–195, 196–197, 200–201, 238–239, 242–245, 516–519, 522–525, 526–529, 530–531, 540–541, 542–543, 544–545

Measuring tools

ruler 338–341, 342–343, 358–361

Type printed in red indicates that a topic is being introduced for the first time.

HARCOURT

Math

Review of Research

As the content and pedagogy of *Harcourt Math* was developed, the primary goal of the authors, advisors, editors, and reviewers was to ensure the accuracy of the mathematical content and the validity of the pedagogical approach. Research about effective ways to develop children's mathematical competencies, to intervene to help those children whose performance levels were below expectation, and to provide teachers with suggested instructional strategies was consulted and used as the basis for developing the philosophy of the program and organizational structure of the chapters and lessons in the program.

In the following section, best practices as documented by research are defined; supporting studies are cited and described; and the ways in which these best practices are implemented in the program are shown. Research summaries for the following best practices are included:

What Research Says About . . .
Intervention

Overview

Intervention in this research review is defined as "the set of strategies that a teacher uses to accommodate students' diverse skill levels, interests, and learning preferences and to maximize learning for all students." Intervention is closely related to an approach to teaching known as differentiated instruction. Intervention includes specific accommodations made for individual students, but this report explores intervention as a system and presents the overarching principles that support such a system.

Though built on long-standing beliefs and practices, intervention and differentiated instruction are relatively new concepts, and at this time no specific educational research has been done on the effectiveness of intervention or differentiated instruction as a holistic, systematic approach. However, research in the areas of neurology, psychology, education, and other fields supports various components of the approach. These principles form the basis of this research review.

Research Findings

Intervention is based on a set of principles that, when put into practice, yield increased learning for all students. These principles are supported by decades of research in such areas as neurobiology, psychology, anthropology, and education. The principles discussed in this review are the following:

- Assessment is a tool for instruction.
- Students at all levels learn best when they face a moderate challenge.
- The human brain is designed to seek meaning and recognize patterns, and it has a limited focus.
- Varied classroom activities accommodate and motivate various learning profiles.

Proponents of intervention emphasize that in order for these principles to produce positive results, the following two structural components must be established:

- For intervention methods adopted in individual classrooms to be successful, a school must have the resources and attitude to support them (Kame'enui and Simmons, 1998).
- Schools and teachers must reexamine the purpose of assessment and use it as a building block for an intervention or differentiated instruction program.

According to Tomlinson (1999), assessment is essential to differentiated instruction in that it provides each student with an entry point for instruction—and from that entry point teachers should lead each student on an individualized course.

Assessment is a tool for instruction.

In an article that draws specifically from examples in the area of elementary mathematics, Beattie and Algozzine (1982) outlined the following steps that a teacher can follow in incorporating into instruction the information learned from diagnostic tests.

1. Determine from diagnostic test results not just students' scores but also the types of items for which correct or incorrect responses were provided.

2. Form tentative conclusions about the nature of each student's abilities.
3. Administer informal, teacher-created tests that target the identified area of weakness to determine the incorrect processes in which a student may be engaging.
4. Analyze content and process, and then begin remediation.

The authors warn, however, that a few experiences with a task will not yield complete understanding and that mere repetition will also not be of much benefit. The authors suggest varying the activities that foster the targeted skill area and providing four examples.

The integration of assessment and instruction can be achieved by two methods presented by Valencia and Wixson (1991): *alternative methods* and *scaffolding approaches*. The alternative-methods approach involves having a student try out several distinct alternatives to solving a problem. The scaffolding approach involves modifying different levels of support, from the least assistance to increasing assistance, as a student engages in a task. An effective system of evaluation to accompany the alternative-methods approach is to compare a student's performance, motivation, or knowledge during and after the administration of the different interventions. To accompany the scaffolding approaches, evaluation should focus on a comparison of the student's learning, performance, motivation, or knowledge at various levels of support for the purpose of finding an optimal level—one that presents appropriate challenge without frustration. The authors also note that interviewing students following the intervention can be a source of valuable information, and they provide sample questions that can be included in such an interview.

Students at all levels learn best when they face a moderate challenge.

Csikszentmihalyi, Rathunde, and Whalen (1993) studied the relationship between challenge and skill during moments in a classroom when students were engaged in academic work. They concluded that "only when challenges and skills were felt to be high and working in tandem did all the varied components of well-being—cognitive, emotional, and motivation—come together for the students. Concentration was far above its normal classroom level, and self-esteem, potency, and involvement also reached their highest levels" (p. 186). The engagement of skills without challenge maintained high esteem, though esteem was lower than in the first scenario. Challenge without skill maintained attention, but esteem dropped significantly. The worst profile was when both challenge and skill were absent—but the study also showed that this situation, which occurred when students were reading, watching films, or listening to lectures, accounted for 29 percent of all classroom experiences. The authors also found that teenagers were willing to accept challenges and overcome obstacles when the problems were interesting and the necessary skills were within the individual's reach.

The human brain is designed to seek meaning and recognize patterns, and it has a limited focus.

According to Howard (2000) in a survey of cognitive research, two effective ways to organize information and focus attention are the use of *advanced organizers* and *chunking*. In a summary of research findings by Walter Kintsch (1994), Howard states that advanced organizers presented before students interact with a text increase learning. The type of learning that occurs is dependent upon the arrangement of the organizers. When organizers are arranged in the same way as the target text, students score higher on recall of information. When organizers are arranged differently from the target text, comprehension scores are raised. A different arrangement, Howard notes, forces more participation from the learner, yielding a deeper understanding. Howard also points to research done by G. A. Miller in 1956 that demonstrated that seven pieces of new and unassociated pieces of information is the maximum that most individuals can handle at a time. Howard recommends that information be presented in "chunks" of no more than seven items, which students must master before another chunk is introduced.

Varied classroom activities accommodate and motivate various learning profiles.

Dunn, Beaudry, and Klavas (1989) reviewed a number of correlational studies and experimental research studies on instructional environments, as well as perceptual, sociological, time-of-day, and mobility preferences, and concluded that students' achievement increases when teaching methods match their learning styles. For example, eight studies throughout the late 1970s and 1980s revealed that when students were taught with *resources that initially matched* their preferred modalities, the students' scores increased; when those same students were reinforced with *resources that mismatched* their modalities, their scores increased even more.

Recommended Instructional Practices

The following best practices are derived from the research literature:

- Provide opportunities for enrichment for all students.
- Provide graphic or pictorial organizers for texts, notes, and concepts, and encourage students to develop their own.
- Organize curriculum around concepts and ideas, and for each concept identify essential questions, not facts.
- Regularly relate concepts and skills to students' own lives.
- Present no more than seven units of information to students at a time, and allow for that set to be recalled and reinforced before moving on.
- Identify the essence, or most important aspect, of a concept or body of information, and focus students' attention on it.
- Vary the ways in which students interact with concepts and information and demonstrate skills and knowledge.

How the Research Is Implemented in *Harcourt Math*

Intervention is the cornerstone on which *Harcourt Math* was developed. The assessment program is designed to provide teachers with diagnostic instruments of various types to determine each child's mathematical strengths and weaknesses. These assessments are linked to program-specific materials that provide review, reteaching, and remediation so that the teacher at each grade level has the necessary materials to meet the wide range of learning abilities found in every classroom.

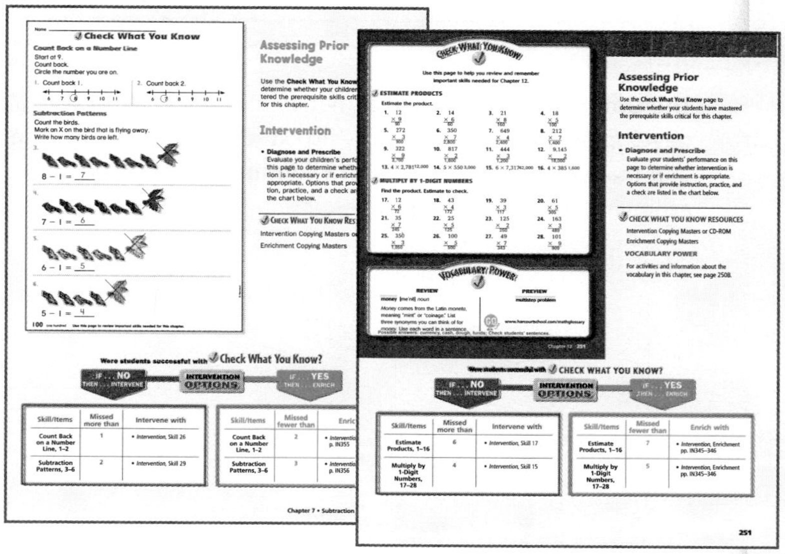

The Check What You Know assessment is a tool for instruction. It helps teachers define each student's strengths and weaknesses on prerequisite skills for each chapter and identify the student's entry point for instruction in the chapter.

Chapters in the Pupil Edition are organized around a key mathematical idea. Before students begin work in each chapter, there is an assessment tool called Check What You Know that helps students review and recall prerequisite skills critical for success in the chapter. This diagnostic instrument provides the teacher with information about students' areas of strength and weakness. For each of these prerequisite skills, there is an intervention strategy in the *Intervention • Skills*, which may be used to help the student before beginning instruction.

In addition, the *Teacher's Edition* contains suggestions throughout each lesson to vary classroom instruction to match students' preferred learning modalities, learning styles, and interests. These activities provide a balanced program designed to develop students' conceptual understanding, skill proficiency, and problem solving abilities.

Were students successful with Check What You Know?

IF . . . NO THEN . . . INTERVENE — INTERVENTION OPTIONS — IF . . . YES THEN . . . ENRICH

Skill/Items	Missed more than	Intervene with
Count Back on a Number Line, 1–2	1	• *Intervention,* Skill 26
Subtraction Patterns, 3–6	2	• *Intervention,* Skill 29

Skill/Items	Missed fewer than	Enrich with
Count Back on a Number Line, 1–2	2	• *Intervention,* Enrichment p. IN355
Subtraction Patterns, 3–6	3	• *Intervention,* Enrichment p. IN356

The Options provide varied activities that foster development of the skills on which students need assistance and that can help students make continuous progress toward achieving grade level objectives.

Through the use of *Harcourt Math,* teachers can help students move along a continuum of continuous progress based on careful diagnosis of strengths and weaknesses. The goal of the program is prevention rather than remediation.

These activities provide visual, verbal, and symbolic representation of key concepts and skills targeted as essential prerequisite skills for grade level work. Notice that the level of scaffolding support is modified as students work through the problems. The Independent Practice has a quiz at the end to assess whether the student has been successful.

References

Beattie, J., and B. Algozzine. (1982). Testing for teaching. *Arithmetic Teacher*, 30, 47–51.

Csikszentmihalyi, M., K. Rathunde, and S. Whalen. (1993). *Talented Teenagers: The Roots of Success and Failure.* New York: Cambridge University Press.

Dunn, R., J. Beaudry, and A. Klavas. (1989). Survey of research on learning styles. *Educational Leadership*, 46, (6), 50–58.

Howard, P. (2000). *The Owner's Manual for the Brain.* Austin, TX: Bard Press.

Kame'enui, E. J., and D.C. Simmons. (1998). Beyond effective practice to schools as host environments: Building and sustaining a schoolwide intervention model in beginning reading. *Oregon School Study Council Bulletin*, 41, (3), 3–24.

Kintsch, W. (1994). *Text Comprehension, Memory, and Learning. American Psychologist*, 49, (4), 294–303.

Tomlinson, C. A. (1999). *The Differentiated Classroom: Responding to the Needs of All Learners.* Alexandria, VA: Association for Supervision and Curriculum Development.

Valencia, S. W., and K. K. Wixson. (1991). Diagnostic teaching. *Reading Teacher*, 44, 420–423.

What Research Says About . . .

The Value of Visual Images in the Learning Process

Overview

Visual learning has been defined as "the acquisition and construction of knowledge as a result of interaction with visual phenomena." While the use of visual images abounds in many content areas, in mathematics we most readily turn to the use of charts, graphs, pictorial representations, and concrete models as visual aids to the learning process.

Research Findings

Through several studies of older learners, we know something about learning from visual models. Barsalou (1992) describes visual modeling as a process in which specific visual attributes and relationships are analogous to the actual physical parts and relationships in the situations they represent. Visuals help learners isolate and identify important material, recall prior knowledge, provide interaction with content, and enhance information acquisition (Dwyer et al, 1987). Winn (1987) also summarizes the advantages of visuals, noting that they make the abstract more concrete. It is the concreteness that stimulates the imaginal process.

Despite the data provided by these researchers, particularly by the prolific Dwyer, we cannot generalize all of their findings to younger students of mathematics yet. There is a need for further research. Instead, we must rely at this point on reports and naturalistic observations from elementary mathematics classrooms.

Using visuals enhances concept development and skill development and increases students' interest in a topic.

Korithoski and Korithoski (1993) gave fifth-grade students hands-on activities to help them understand the concept of arithmetic mean and gain experience in using mathematical models. The majority of students in this study came from classrooms in which use of manipulatives and hands-on learning had not been common practice. For most of the students, the concept of division was related more to an algorithmic process than to an activity in which physical objects were actually being distributed. The sequence of instruction consisted of the following steps:

1. Finding the mean by using models and redistributing them to show the mean
2. Using a number-line model representing candy pieces in a container along with movement along a number line with no remainders
3. Using a number-line model with all pieces not represented
4. Using only movement along a number line with no remainders
5. Using movement along a number-line model only with remainders
6. Calculating the mean with the algorithm with no model while making intuitive connections with the models used previously

The authors observed that many unexpected benefits occurred by looking at these concepts from a different perspective. The fifth graders enjoyed the experience, since determining the arithmetic mean was anchored in real time and space with objects that already had meaning to the students. The activity also involved the class in meaningful discourse, which led to valuable insights as to how the students reasoned and thought through problems. Finally, the authors noted that the students were active in their learning process, too busy developing an understanding of the concepts to notice the passage of time.

Visuals provide students clearer mental images and help them develop a deeper and more permanent understanding.

Englert and Sinicrope (1994) used graphic area models of multiplication to provide students with visual, concrete representations to teach two-digit multiplication. Fourth-grade teacher Englert observed that as her students made the transition from multiplication by a single-digit number to that by a two-digit number, the students became confused. Rather than using strategies that were based on their understanding of place value, the students tended to create nonsensical algorithms.

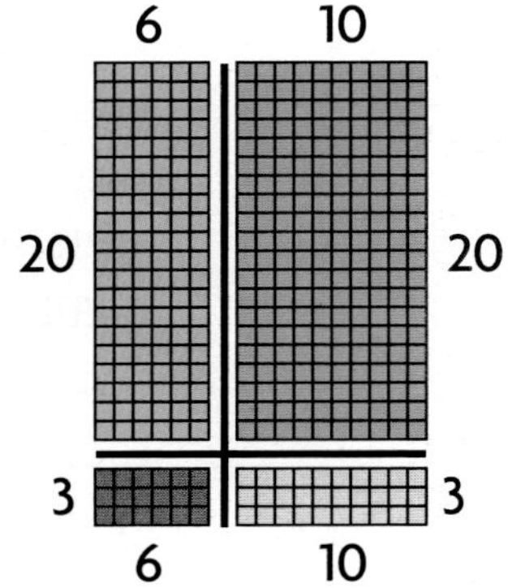

Englert and Sinicrope felt that Englert's students needed a concrete representation of the process before they could move on to the abstract. Englert cites in her report (Kennedy, 1986, 6), which advocated the use of manipulatives: "Students who see and manipulate a variety of objects have clearer mental images and can represent abstract ideas more completely." Yet Englert also considered the warning by Heddens (1986, 14): "Simply using manipulatives… is not sufficient; teachers must guide children to develop skills in thinking."

Since Schultz (1991) recommends using an area model, Englert used this semi-concrete model to enable students to develop the mental images necessary to reason abstractly. The fourth graders began by reviewing graphic area models, with the drawings showing the partial products. Next, they enhanced their models by using colors to represent the partial products. The third step was to draw the rectangular area on graph paper to represent the problem and then go on to partition this rectangle through use of color to represent place values. Students began to see patterns and solve problems of increasing difficulty and to make more observations. Although the time spent in developing the multiplication algorithm using the visual approach took longer than a more traditional approach, Englert felt that less time was needed for review and reteaching. It also provided "meaningfulness," something Brownell (1986) stressed as important to the learning of mathematics. Because multiplication was meaningful, the students had a deeper and more permanent understanding.

Skemp (1971) said using models and manipulatives is necessary for children to abstract concepts into appropriate mathematical structures, enabling them to learn more advanced mathematics. Therefore, Englert and Sinicrope believe the extra time invested in using this model for whole-number multiplication has both immediate and long-term benefits.

Bennett and Nelson (1994) worked with sixth graders who were learning to understand applications of percents, using a 10 x 10 grid to visualize the "parts per hundred" aspect of percent. This visual model offered a means of representing given information as well as suggesting different approaches to finding solutions. Once students have a visual image of percents and recognize that 100 percent is represented by one whole square, or unit square, and that 1 percent is represented by one small square, or one-hundredth of a unit square, then 10 x 10 grids can be shaded to illustrate percents accordingly.

Exploring their desire to have the school cafeteria serve pizza more often, students in Julia Mason's fourth-grade class carried out experiments to determine probabilities by using the visual tools of spinners and charts. The fourth graders had the opportunity to formulate this problem from an issue they found compelling, one that involved probability, prediction, modeling, and simulation. On the basis of the data they gathered, the students decided that their "lunch wheel spinners" gave them more favorable results. Mason also noted that the activity produced a number of valid and creative student approaches to the problem posed and enabled her to identify students who still had serious misconceptions about probability.

Hershkowitz and Markovits (1992) developed a 36-unit mathematics curriculum for third graders that introduced students to basic visual concepts and applied visual abilities and visual thinking to learning tasks such as ratio and proportion and numerical intuition. Begun as a continuing study of 25 pairs of matched classes when these children were preschoolers (1985–87), the study noted that students' counting strategies dropped dramatically, whereas the use of three estimation strategies increased, with the most dramatic increase occurring in global estimation. Though this study only provides naturalistic observations of students' success, its longitudinal aspect provides insight.

In conclusion, we once again call for further study of visual learning by young mathematics students. As we pursue instructional practices using these visual tools, we also need to consider Clark's view (1983, 1994). He argues that it is not the medium that causes gains in learning but the instructional strategy embedded in the media presentation.

Recommended Instructional Practices

The following best practices are derived from the research literature:

- Visuals should be used when students need to learn concrete concepts or when they must identify spatial relationships.

- Visuals are very useful in learning tasks which involve memory. The information received from visuals appears to remain longer in memory.
- Visuals should be incorporated to give a real-life meaningfulness to student learning.
- Concrete materials can be an effective aid to students' thinking and to successful teaching, but effectiveness is contingent on teachers' continual efforts to emphasize understanding, not just doing.

How the Research Is Implemented in *Harcourt Math*

Visuals are used throughout *Harcourt Math* to facilitate students' understanding of concepts and the mathematics that underlies each of the mathematical procedures. Questions that encourage students to reason about the visuals are included in the Pupil Edition, and questions in the Guided Instruction in the *Teacher's Edition* provide the scaffolding essential to derive meaning from visuals.

Visuals are also used to help students appreciate the usefulness of mathematics in everyday activities. Engaging students' interest in mathematics is a critical variable in assuring their engagement in daily lessons and in motivating them to put forth the effort in mathematics necessary for successful progress.

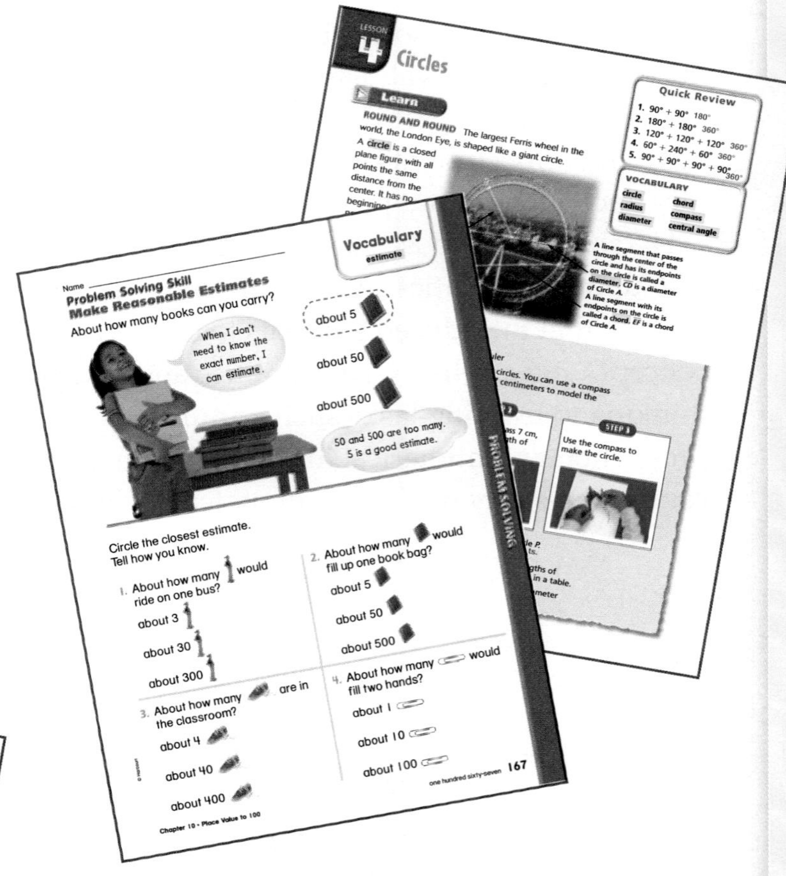

The use of real-life visuals to illustrate concepts and skills makes mathematics more meaningful and helps students see the usefulness of mathematics in everyday experiences.

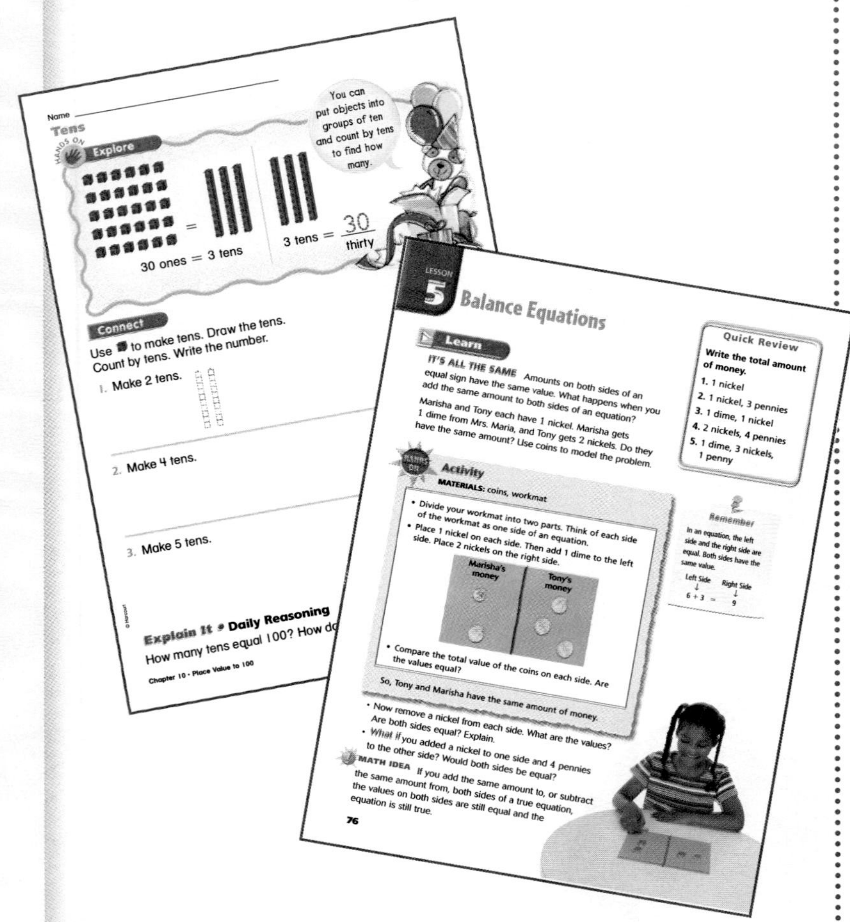

The use of visuals provides a clear mental image and enhances understanding of a concept. Students' interest levels are higher when they are involved in using visuals as learning tools.

In this media age, children live in a visual world. However, many of these visuals pass rapidly before children's eyes, and little learning results. Teaching children to read visuals and to link visuals and text is critical to their academic success. Visuals in mathematics are powerful teaching tools that children need to learn to "read" and use as they develop their mathematical abilities

References

Barsalou, Lawrence (1992). *Cognitive Psychology: An Overview for Cognitive Scientists*. Hillsdale, NJ: Lawrence Erlbaum Associates.

Bennett, A. B., Jr., and T. L. Nelson (1994). A conceptual model for solving percent problems. *Mathematics Teaching in the Middle School*, 1, (1), 20–25.

Brownell, W. A. (1986). *AT* classic: The revolution in Arithmetic. *Arithmetic Teacher*, 34, (2), 38–42.

Clark, R. E. (1994b). Media and method. *Educational Technological Research and Development*, 42, (3), 7–10.

_________. (1994a). Media will never influence learning. *Educational Technological Research and Development*, 42, (2), 21–29.

_________. (1983). Reconsidering research on learning from media. *Review of Educational Research*, 53, 445–459.

Dwyer, F. M., ed. (1987). *Enhancing Visualized Instruction—Recommendations for Practitioners*. State College, PA: Learning Services.

_________. (1978). *Strategies for Improving Visual Learning*. State College, PA: Learning Services.

_________. (1972). *A Guide for Improving Visualized Instruction*. State College, PA: Learning Services.

Englert, G. R., and R. Sinicrope (1994). Making connections with two-digit multiplication. *Arithmetic Teacher*, 41, (8), 446–448.

Heddens, J. W. (1986). Bridging the gap between the concrete and the abstract. *Arithmetic Teacher*, 33, (6), 14–17.

Hershkowitz, R., and Z. Markovits (1992). Conquer mathematics concepts by developing visual thinking. *Arithmetic Teacher*, 39, (9), 38–41.

Kennedy, L. M. (1986). A rationale. *Arithmetic Teacher*, 33, (6), 6–7.

Korithoski, T., and P. Korithoski (1993). Mean or meaningless. *Arithmetic Teacher*, 41, (4), 194–197.

Schultz, J. E. (1991). Area models—Spanning the mathematics of grades 3–9. *Arithmetic Teacher*, 39, (2), 42–46.

Skemp, R. S. (1971). *The Psychology of Learning Mathematics*. Harmondsworth, England: Penguin Books.

Winn, W. (1987). Charts, graphs, and diagrams in educational materials. In D. M. Willows and H. A. Houghton (Eds.), *The Psychology of Illustration: Basic Research* (Vol. 1). New York: Springer-Verlag.

Explicit Instruction:

Delivering Instruction That Is Clear and Direct

Overview

Explicit instruction is a procedure for making specific skills or strategies known to a learner. The teacher is charged with presenting material in such a way as to focus the student's attention on something specific to be learned (Wilkinson, 1999). Several terms are used in the literature for this concept. These terms include direct instruction, direct teaching, explicit teaching, explicit instruction, and direct explanation. In addition, recent research literature focuses on using alternatives in instruction including explicit instruction, self-directed learning, exploratory learning, discovery, and constructivism (Rieber, 1991; Guskey and Passaro, 1992).

Bangert-Downs and Bankert (1990, 8) reviewed 250 articles on teaching critical thinking as a general process and as a specific tool in several content area domains. Twenty studies were suitable for a meta-analysis; each of the 20 compared a group that received explicit instruction with a group that did not. Bangert-Downs and Bankert state, "It is most striking that the studies reviewed in this meta-analysis so consistently produced findings favorable to explicit instruction in critical thinking". These studies included students at the elementary, secondary, and post-secondary levels. Bangert-Downs and Bankert stress the importance of teaching young children to assess the "trustworthiness" of a statement. They suggest that children in younger grades benefit greatly from explicit instruction more than older students who have been making "trustworthiness" judgments for a longer time.

Lester (1983), in his review of trends and issues in mathematical problem solving research, stated that the role of the teacher is often overlooked in research studies. He recommends that research be directed toward understanding how the teacher affects problem solving behavior. He suggests including the teacher as a variable in research studies rather than ignoring or factoring out the teacher.

Research Findings

Explicit instruction is an effective strategy for teaching basic math skills and procedures.

Past and current instructional innovations use explicit teaching. Peterson, Swing, Braverman, and Buss (1981) taught a short unit on probability to fifth- and sixth-grade students. The teaching method followed a direct instructional model. After viewing themselves on videotape, students were interviewed about their thought processes during the lesson. The results showed that students who used specific cognitive strategies such as relating what was being taught to prior knowledge did better on an achievement test. Higher-ability students reported specific understandings and/or cognitive strategies, whereas lower-ability students gave vague reasons for what they did or did not understand.

Din (1998) developed individualized programs for students aged 7–16 who were referred for help in math by their parents. After three weeks of instruction, all 19 students showed significant improvement in basic math skills. The program provided direct instruction in numeration concepts, computational procedures, multiplication tables, and application.

Explicit instruction in interpreting the language used in word problems helps students select the correct algorithm to solve.

Stein (1998) examined understanding of word problems in mathematics. She found that after explicit instruction designed to help students interpret the language used in word problems, students were better able to select the correct algorithm to solve them. Stein stressed that students need to attend to the specific language used in a problem. Students used a math story chart based on Polya's four-step model. This chart helped them interpret language used in mathematical word problems (Polya, 1957). Polya's first step, Tell (the information given in the problem), formed the foundation for explicit teaching of problem solving.

Rudnitsky, Etheredge, Freeman, and Gilbert (1995) explicitly taught 401 students in Grades 3 and 4 a structured sequence of problem solving steps. These steps, (1) understand the problem, (2) make a plan, (3) use the plan, and (4) check the answer, are similar to Polya's four-step model. One group of students also wrote their own story problems. Results showed significantly higher problem solving scores for students in the structured-sequence-plus-writing group. This group also performed significantly better on a retention test ten weeks later.

Explicit instruction in writing about mathematics increases students' conceptual understanding, procedural knowledge, and mathematical communication.

Several studies examined writing as part of learning mathematics. In research with 540 fifth-grade students, Niemi (1996) found that students who received explicit instruction showed higher levels of principled understanding of fractions. Students were told that they were going to do a TV demonstration and had to write an explanation of everything a fifth-grade student should know about fractions. They were given a set of guiding questions to help them with their explanations. The students who had explicit instruction on fraction principles expressed more principles in their explanations. Even with a very short time period, $7\frac{1}{2}$ days, students' understanding was sensitive to cognitive changes.

Jurdah and Abu Zein (1998) compared two groups of upper-elementary students. One group wrote in math journals for 7–10 minutes at the end of math class three times a week for 12 weeks. Students in the journal-writing group had significantly higher posttest scores at the level of conceptual understanding, procedural knowledge, and mathematical communication. An important result was that teachers could intercede, provide supportive responses, and plan an explicit lesson based on students' perceived weaknesses.

In conclusion, explicit teaching appears to have favorable instructional consequences. Regardless of whether it is called explicit instruction, direct instruction, direct teaching, explicit teaching, or direct explanation, students benefit from instruction that is direct, explicit, and clearly stated.

Recommended Instructional Practices

The following best practices are derived from the research literature:

- Procedures based on Polya's four-step model are effective: (1) understand the problem, (2) devise a plan, (3) carry out the plan, (4) look back.
- It is useful to use a chart to show the series of steps to follow to solve a problem or complete a mathematical procedure.
- Writing about mathematics helps students understand both the "how" and the "why" of a mathematical procedure.

- Writing in mathematics is useful to improve mathematical communication, an area of instruction that is sometimes neglected.
- It is useful to observe learners as they work through problems and then to explicitly reteach the steps as needed.
- Short, intensive periods of explicit strategy instruction can have lasting effects.

How the Research Is Implemented in *Harcourt Math*

The structure of *Harcourt Math* lends itself to explicit teaching. Throughout the program, mathematical skills and procedures are clearly presented with models, explanations, and questions that can be used by the teacher to focus students' attention on key concepts and procedures. The *Teacher's Edition* facilitates explicit teaching through the use of guided instruction.

The development of problem solving skills and strategies is explicitly done through a four-step process modeled on Polya's work. Not only are these four steps developed in the Pupil Edition, but a *Problem Solving Think Along*, a format that is integral to the program, provides questions that help the students apply Polya's four-step process and record their thinking as they work through the steps.

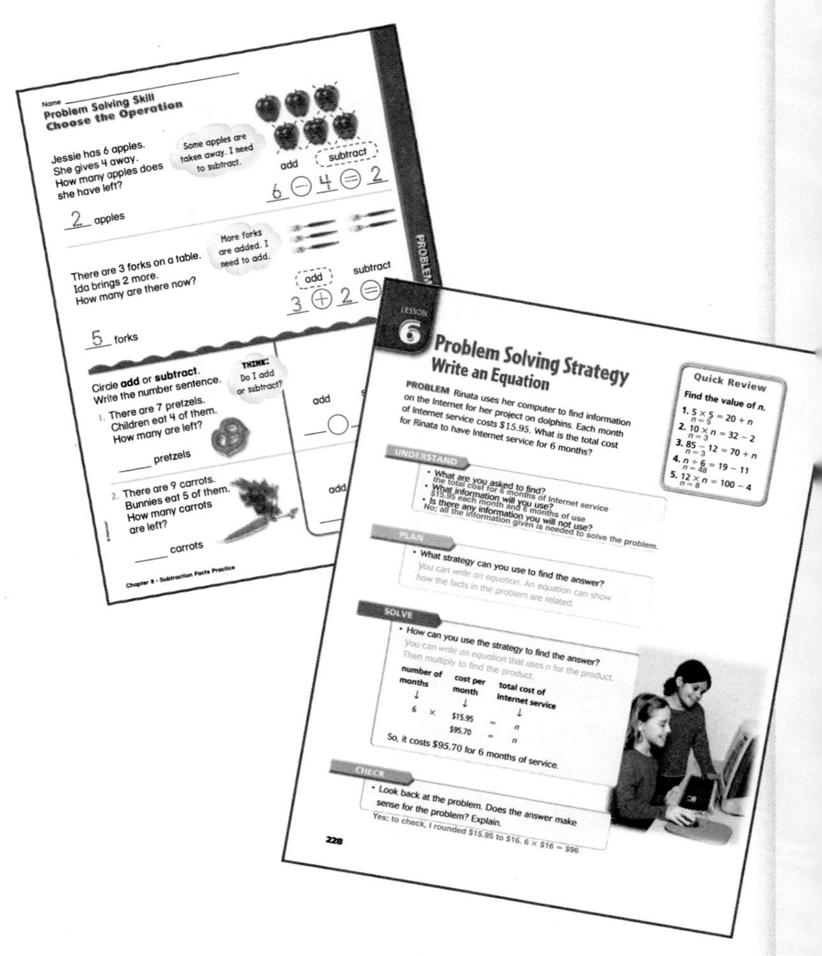

Name
Problem Solving Skill
Choose the Operation

Jessie has 6 apples. She gives 4 away. How many apples does she have left?
Some apples are taken away. I need to subtract.
add subtract
6 − 4 = 2
2 apples

There are 3 forks on a table. Ida brings 2 more. How many are there now?
More forks are added. I need to add.
add subtract
3 + 2 =
5 forks

Circle add or subtract. Write the number sentence.
THINK: Do I add or subtract?
1. There are 7 pretzels. Children eat 4 of them. How many are left?
____ pretzels
2. There are 9 carrots. Bunnies eat 5 of them. How many carrots are left?
____ carrots

Chapter 8 • Subtraction Facts Practice

LESSON 6
Problem Solving Strategy
Write an Equation

PROBLEM Rinata uses her computer to find information on the Internet for her project on dolphins. Each month of Internet service costs $15.95. What is the total cost for Rinata to have Internet service for 6 months?

UNDERSTAND
- What are you asked to find?
- What information will you use?
- Is there any information you will not use?

PLAN
- What strategy can you use to find the answer?
You can write an equation. An equation can show how the facts in the problem are related.

SOLVE
- How can you use the strategy to find the answer?
You can write an equation that uses n for the product. Then multiply to find the product.

number of months		cost per month		total cost of Internet service
6	×	$15.95	=	n
		$95.70	=	n

So, it costs $95.70 for 6 months of service.

CHECK
- Look back at the problem. Does the answer make sense for the problem? Explain.
Yes; to check, I rounded $15.95 to $16. 6 × $16 = $96

Quick Review
Find the value of n.
1. 5 × 5 = 20 + n
2. 10 × n = 32 − 2
3. 85 − 12 = 70 + n
4. n ÷ 6 = 19 − 11
5. 12 × n = 100 − 4

228

Explicit instruction in interpreting the language of word problems, in planning and solving the problem, and in checking the solution for reasonableness by using the four-step process—Understand, Plan, Solve, and Check—helps students select the correct operation and equation to solve the problem.

Writing is a part of students' daily work. Daily exercise sets require that students write their own problems, explanations of how they solved a given problem, justifications for their solutions, and conclusions and generalizations drawn from the mathematics they are learning. The use of a journal is encouraged, and teachers are given concrete suggestions for the types of entries that might be included.

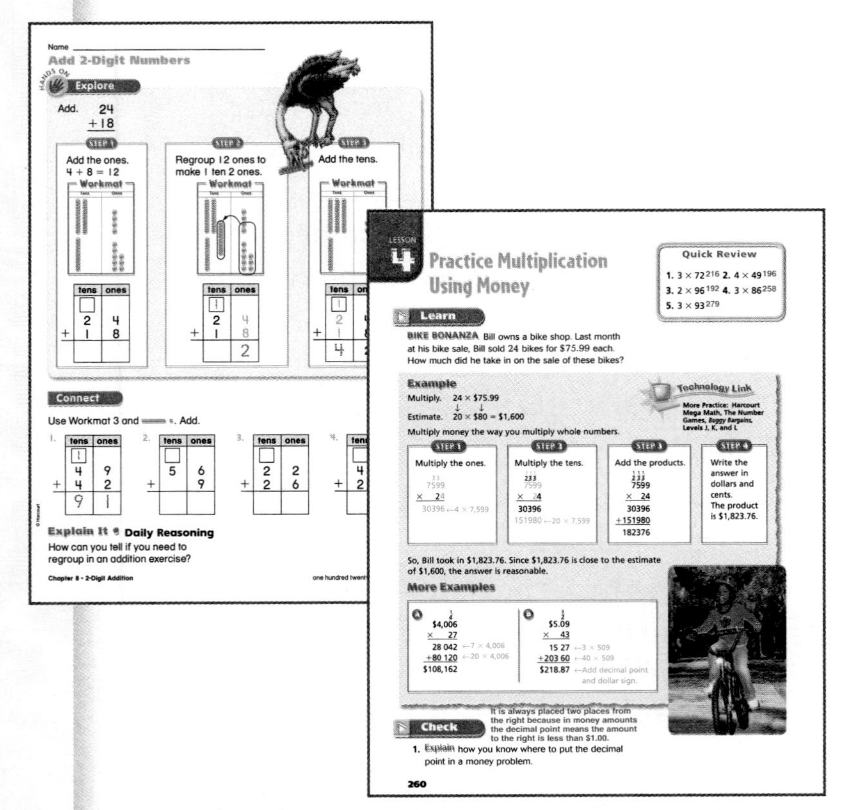

Name
Add 2-Digit Numbers
Explore
Add. 24 + 18
STEP 1: Add the ones. 4 + 8 = 12
STEP 2: Regroup 12 ones to make 1 ten 2 ones.
STEP 3: Add the tens.
Connect
Use Workmat 3 and tens ones. Add.
Explain It • Daily Reasoning
How can you tell if you need to regroup in an addition exercise?
Chapter 8 • 2-Digit Addition

LESSON 4
Practice Multiplication Using Money

Quick Review
1. 3 × 72 (216) 2. 4 × 49 (196)
3. 2 × 96 (192) 4. 3 × 86 (258)
5. 3 × 93 (279)

Learn
BIKE BONANZA Bill owns a bike shop. Last month at his bike sale, Bill sold 24 bikes for $75.99 each. How much did he take in on the sale of these bikes?

Example
Multiply. 24 × $75.99
Estimate. 20 × $80 = $1,600
Multiply money the way you multiply whole numbers.
STEP 1: Multiply the ones.
STEP 2: Multiply the tens.
STEP 3: Add the products.
STEP 4: Write the answer in dollars and cents. The product is $1,823.76.

So, Bill took in $1,823.76. Since $1,823.76 is close to the estimate of $1,600, the answer is reasonable.

More Examples
A: $4,006 × 27 = 28 042 + 80 120 = $108,162
B: $5.09 × 43 = 15 27 + 203 60 = $218.87

It is always placed two places from the right because in money amounts the decimal point means the amount to the right is less than $1.00.

Check
1. Explain how you know where to put the decimal point in a money problem.

260

Explicit step-by-step instruction that includes hands-on experiences, visual models, verbal descriptions of the process, and symbolic notation helps students both understand and apply algorithmic procedures.

The goal of the pedagogical approach in *Harcourt Math* is to provide a balance of suggested instructional strategies with explicit instruction forming the core of the suggested strategies so that teachers can be assured that they can guide students' mathematical development efficiently and effectively.

References

Bangert-Downs, R. L., and E. Bankert (1990). *Meta-analysis of effects of explicit instruction for critical thinking*. Paper presented at the annual meeting of the American Educational Research Association, Boston, April 16–20, 1990. 12 pp. (ERIC Document Reproduction Service No. ED 328 614.)

Din, F. S. (1998). *Direct instruction in remedial math instructions*. Paper presented at the National Conference on Creating the High Quality School, Arlington, VA, March 25–28, 1998. 14 pp. (ERIC Document Reproduction Service No. ED 417 955.)

Guskey, T. R., and P. D. Passaro (1992). *How mastery learning can address our nation's science education needs*. Paper presented at the annual meeting of the American Educational Research Association, San Francisco, April 10–14, 1992. 35 pp. (ERIC Document Reproduction Service No. ED 370 760.)

Jurdah, M., and R. Abu Zein (1998). The effect of journal writing on achievement in and attitudes toward mathematics. *School Science and Mathematics*, 98, (8), 412–419.

Lester, F. K., Jr. (1983). Trends and issues in mathematical problem-solving research. In R. Lesh and M. Landau (Eds.), *Acquisition of Mathematics Concepts and Processes* (pp. 229–257). New York: Academic Press.

Niemi, D. (1996). A fraction is not a piece of pie: Assessing exceptional performance and deep understanding in elementary school mathematics. *Gifted Child Quarterly*, 40, 70–80.

Peterson, P. L., S. R. Swing, M. T. Braverman, and R. Buss (1981). *Students' aptitudes and their reports of cognitive processes during direct instruction*. Paper presented at the annual meeting of the American Educational Research Association, Los Angeles, April 13–17, 1981. 45 pp. (ERIC Document Reproduction Service No. ED 211 234.)

Polya, G. (1957). *How to Solve It: A New Aspect of Mathematical Method*. Princeton, NJ: Princeton University Press.

Rieber, L. P. (1991). Computer-based microworlds: A bridge between constructivism and direct instruction. In M. R. Simonson and C. Hargrave (Eds.), *Proceedings of the Association for Educational Communications and Technology*, Orlando, FL, February 13–17, 1991. 18 pp. (ERIC Document Reproduction Service No. ED 335 007.)

Rudnitsky, A. M., S. Etheredge, J. M. Freeman, and T. Gilbert (1995). Learning to solve addition and subtraction word problems through a structure-plus-writing approach. *Journal for Research in Mathematics Education*, 26, 467–486.

Stein, M. G. (1998). *Strategic learning: The implications of language in successful math problem-solving*. 40 pp. (ERIC Document Reproduction Service No. ED 416 501.)

Wilkinson, L. (1999). An introduction to the explicit teaching of reading. In J. Hancock (Ed.), *The Explicit Teaching of Reading* (pp. 1–12). Newark, DE: International Reading Association.

The Use of Manipulatives, or Concrete Materials

Overview

In the mathematics classroom, manipulatives include such objects as counters, base-ten blocks, fraction rods, three-dimensional geometric models, geoboards, tangrams, and spinners. (See, for example, National Council of Teachers of Mathematics (2000), pp. 70 and 162.) Most research supports the view that such materials are effective in assisting students to develop new concepts by working from the concrete to the more abstract. When used appropriately by teachers, these materials, therefore, tend to lead to students having better understanding, achievement, and attitude.

Research Findings

The use of manipulatives increases students' conceptual understanding and achievement in mathematics.

There are a number of studies that show that the use of manipulatives (or concrete materials) can increase students' understanding of mathematical concepts and, hence, their achievement in mathematics overall. These studies range across all grade levels, from kindergarten to college, and across many mathematical topics, including basic computation, geometry, and algebra. They also compare the use of manipulatives with traditional textbook presentations, with the use of diagrams, and with computer presentations. Most of these studies demonstrate that using manipulatives has a positive effect on students' achievement, although a few studies show little effect. (See, for example, Chester, Davis, and Reglin (1991), Hiebert and Wearne (1992), and Peck and Connell (1991) for positive results, and Thompson's (1992) discussion of the inconsistencies among similar studies.)

Earlier work is summarized by Sowell (1989) in a meta-analysis combining the results of 60 studies that compare the effects of using manipulatives with the effects of using more abstract instruction. Sowell concludes "that mathematics achievement is increased through the long-term use of concrete instructional materials and that students' attitudes toward mathematics are improved when they have instruction with concrete materials provided by teachers knowledgeable about their use. Instruction with pictures and diagrams does not appear to differ in effectiveness from instruction with symbols."

Two main points emerge from these conclusions:

- Long-term use of manipulatives is important for success.
- Teachers need to have clear purposes for using manipulatives in a particular situation.

A discussion of more recent studies that address these two issues follows.

Several researchers have surveyed teachers about the nature and extent of the use of manipulatives in their classrooms. Gilbert and Bush (1988) asked teachers of Grades 1–3 about 11 different materials and discovered that overall use was only moderate and decreased from Grade 1 to Grade 3. In a follow-up study, after the publication of the NCTM standards (National Council of Teachers of Mathematics, 1989) that recommended the use of manipulatives, Hatfield (1994) found that little had changed. In her survey of K–6 teachers, she found limited use of manipulatives and diminishing use through the grades. Even the use of fraction bars, which are of more relevance in Grades 4–6, declined in these higher grades. Such results were confirmed more recently in a survey of Grades 1–6 by Marlow and Inman (1997), who found that, while counters were commonly used, other manipulatives such as fraction rods, geoboards, and geometric models were not often used by students in the classrooms of the teachers surveyed. Marlow and Inman also asked about barriers to the use of manipulatives and found that the main reasons for not using manipulatives were low parent expectations, lack of materials, discipline problems, and lack of preparation time.

Effective use of manipulatives is dependent upon teachers' guidance of students' interaction between the manipulatives and the concept or skill represented by the manipulatives.

The second point noted above in connection with Sowell's meta-analysis may also help explain those studies in which results were not positive about the use of manipulatives: the context in which particular manipulatives are used is very important and varies from class to class. Meira (1998) suggests that the link between manipulatives and learning is mediated by students' prior knowledge, culture, and so forth, and that therefore context is vital in determining the interaction between the concrete materials and students' skills acquisition. Linked to this is the finding of Schram, Felman-Nemser, and Ball (1990) that the teachers in their study did not discriminate among concrete materials and assumed students' seeing or touching such materials automatically produced understanding. These authors suggest that an important role for textbooks lies in developing teachers' understanding of the appropriate use of manipulatives.

Manipulatives should be used frequently and over the long term to ensure gains in achievement.

The research literature suggests very strongly that students who use manipulatives in their mathematics classrooms frequently and over the long term will gain in understanding, achievement, and attitude. Therefore, teachers should incorporate the use of concrete materials much more into their instruction, but not indiscriminately. Careful thought is needed to make the manipulatives appropriate to the teaching purpose and to the students—and with the first of these, teachers can be assisted by well-written textbooks. However, teachers will always need to monitor the effectiveness of particular manipulatives and switch to others when the need arises, either to apply to the whole class or to adapt to individual students' learning styles. In addition, change is needed to alter the prevailing attitude among teachers that manipulatives are for young students only. Students of all ages need concrete support with new abstract ideas (e.g., in algebra or coordinate geometry), and teachers at all grade levels should provide suitable manipulative materials to introduce any new concept that will benefit from their use.

Recommended Instructional Practices

The following best practices are derived from the research literature:

- Manipulatives should be used frequently and over the long term to help students understand concepts and procedures.
- Teachers should monitor their students' use of manipulatives to determine whether one manipulative is more effective than another for individual students.
- The link between the use of manipulatives and learning is facilitated by the teacher's use of questions that help students see the relationship of the manipulatives to the concept that is being modeled.

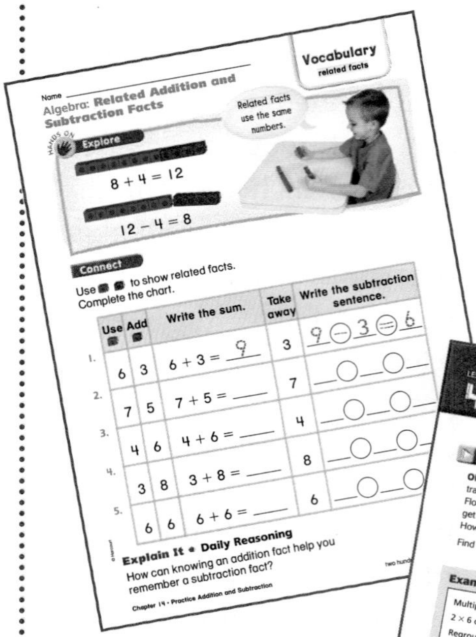

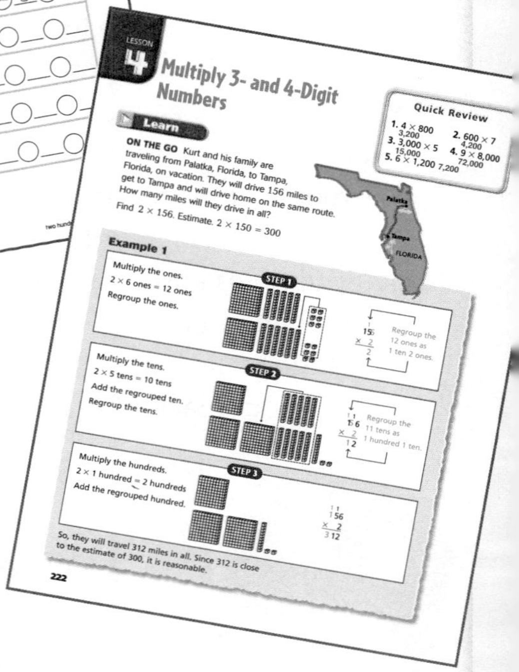

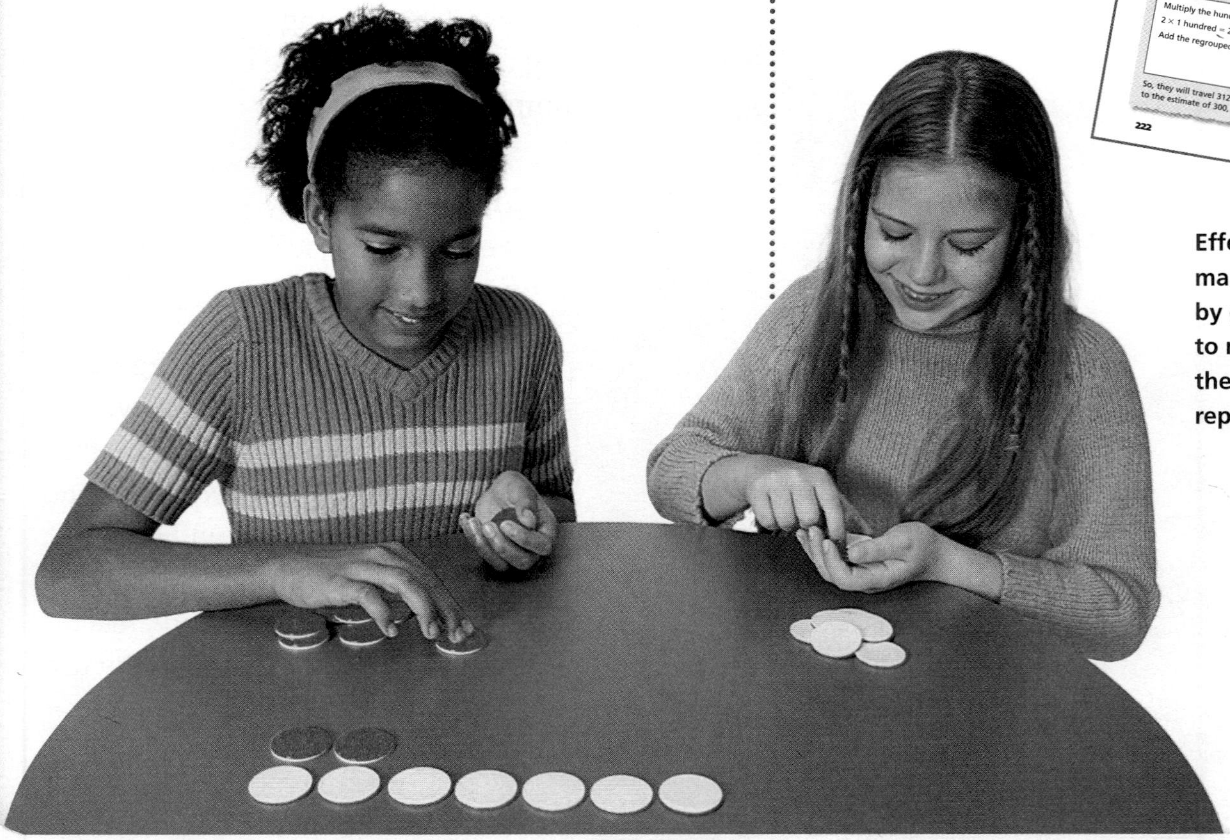

Effective use of manipulatives is assured by guiding students in how to make a model and how the manipulative model represents a concept or skill.

How the Research Is Implemented in *Harcourt Math*

Manipulatives are used throughout the grade levels to facilitate students' development of conceptual understanding of key concepts in each of the mathematical strands. The use of a wide variety of manipulatives is suggested. Learning experiences with manipulatives are accompanied by questions in the Pupil Edition that help students interact with the models to better understand concepts and procedures. Questions provided in the *Teacher's Edition* help teachers facilitate the interaction between the use of manipulatives and the concepts modeled.

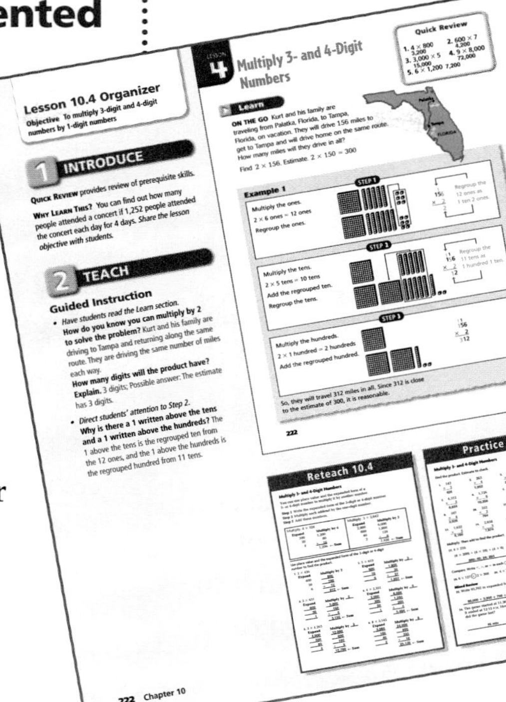

Lesson 10.4 Organizer

Objective To multiply 3-digit and 4-digit numbers by 1-digit numbers

1 INTRODUCE

QUICK REVIEW provides review of prerequisite skills.

WHY LEARN THIS? You can find out how many people attended a concert if 1,252 people attended the concert each day for 4 days. *Share the lesson objective with students.*

2 TEACH

Guided Instruction

- *Have students read the Learn section.* **How do you know you can multiply by 2 to solve the problem?** Kurt and his family are driving to Tampa and returning along the same route. They are driving the same number of miles each way. **How many digits will the product have? Explain.** 3 digits; Possible answer: The estimate has 3 digits.
- *Direct students' attention to Step 2.* **Why is there a 1 written above the tens and a 1 written above the hundreds?** The 1 above the tens is the regrouped ten from the 12 ones, and the 1 above the hundreds is the regrouped hundred from 11 tens.

LESSON 4 Multiply 3- and 4-Digit Numbers

Quick Review

1. 4 × 800 3,200
2. 600 × 7 4,200
3. 3,000 × 5 15,000
4. 9 × 8,000 72,000
5. 6 × 1,200 7,200

Learn

ON THE GO Kurt and his family are traveling from Palatka, Florida, to Tampa, Florida, on vacation. They will drive 156 miles to get to Tampa and will drive home on the same route. How many miles will they drive in all?

Find 2 × 156. Estimate. 2 × 150 = 300

Example 1

STEP 1 Multiply the ones. 2 × 6 ones = 12 ones. Regroup the ones. Regroup the 12 ones as 1 ten 2 ones.

STEP 2 Multiply the tens. 2 × 5 tens = 10 tens. Add the regrouped ten. Regroup the tens. Regroup the 11 tens as 1 hundred 1 ten.

STEP 3 Multiply the hundreds. 2 × 1 hundred = 2 hundreds. Add the regrouped hundred.

So, they will travel 312 miles in all. Since 312 is close to the estimate of 300, it is reasonable.

222

Reteach 10.4

Practice 10.4

222 Chapter 10

Guided Instruction helps teachers guide students' interaction between the manipulatives and the concept or skill represented by the manipulatives.

References

Chester, J., J. Davis, and G. Reglin (1991). *Math manipulatives use and math achievement of third-grade students.* (ERIC Document Reproduction Service No. ED 339 591.)

Gilbert, R. K., and W. S. Bush (1988). Familiarity, availability, and use of manipulative devices in mathematics at the primary level. *School Science and Mathematics*, 88, (6), 459–469.

Hatfield, M. M. (1994). Use of manipulative devices: Elementary school cooperating teachers self-report. *School Science and Mathematics*, 94, (6), 303–309.

Hiebert, J., and D. Wearne (1992). Links between teaching and learning place value with understanding in first grade. *Journal for Research in Mathematics Education*, 23, (2), 98–122.

Marlow, L., and D. Inman (1997). *Status report on teaching in the elementary school: Math, science, and social studies*. Paper presented at a meeting of the Eastern Educational Research Association, Hilton Head, SC, February 1997.

Meira, L. (1998). Making sense of instructional devices: The emergence of transparency in mathematical activity. *Journal for Research in Mathematics Education*, 29, (2), 121–142.

National Council of Teachers of Mathematics (1989). *Curriculum and Evaluation Standards for School Mathematics*. Reston, VA: author.

National Council of Teachers of Mathematics (2000). *Principles and Standards for School Mathematics*. Reston, VA: author.

Peck, D. M., and M. L. Connell (1991). Using physical materials to develop mathematical intuition in fraction part-whole situations. *Focus on Learning Problems in Mathematics*, 13, (4), 3–12.

Schram, P., S. Felman-Nemser, and D. L. Ball (1990). *Thinking about teaching subtraction with regrouping: A comparison of beginning and experienced teachers' responses to textbooks*. Research Report 89–5, East Lansing, MI: National Center for Research on Teacher Education.

Sowell, E. J. (1989). Effects of manipulative materials in mathematics instruction. *Journal for Research in Mathematics Education*, 20, (6), 498–505.

Thompson, P. W. (1992). Notations, conventions, and constraints: Contributions to effective uses of concrete materials in elementary mathematics. *Journal for Research in Mathematics Education*, 23, (2), 123–147.

What Research Says About . . .

The Use of Practice or Review to Improve Performance and Retention

Overview

Studies have demonstrated that in many areas of learning, there is a considerable amount of forgetting over time. In mathematics instruction, this is of special concern because of the building-block nature of math instruction. As Geary (1994) discusses, education in mathematics must focus on both procedural skills and conceptual knowledge, and one of the primary ways to develop foundational skills is through practice.

Research has demonstrated that practice is important for reinforcing students' knowledge and for preparing students to move on to new topics and types of problems. Although both word problems and drill-type problems have been demonstrated to lead to higher performance, research addresses the greater effectiveness of higher-level word problems and worked examples to review, rather than large amounts of frequent review of lower-level drill-type problems.

Research Findings

There are numerous studies that show that review helps students retain knowledge and improve performance. Much of the early research was done in the field of cognitive psychology, but more recent research demonstrates that the results of these studies can be generalized and applied specifically to the instruction of mathematics topics.

In mathematics instruction, review is especially important for the development of automaticity with basic math facts. Once facts have been learned to the point that they can be used automatically, students are able to focus on higher-level problem solving and allocate their attention to the other components of task performance. Studies also show that the type of review is important. Although drill-type review does help retention, it helps more for retention of lower-level concepts, while more thought-provoking questions help higher-level retention and generalizability.

Practice/Review is important for retention and automaticity.

In their reviews of research in mathematics, both Geary (1994) and Suydam and Dessart (1980) conclude that practice is essential for mastering skills and developing the automaticity that will allow these skills to be used routinely in other practices.

A number of research studies have addressed the importance of practice for skill retention. Bahrick and Hall (1991) studied 1,726 individuals to examine the life span retention of content acquired in math courses. The study found that talent and achievement had some impact, but the primary variable for success was practice that had occurred over time. Individuals who had learned the math content over a short period without practice over time showed declines in mathematics performance.

Ausubel (1966) studied the specific timing of reviews to determine whether early review (after one day) was more or less effective than delayed review (after seven days). He found that both produced results and that one did not seem more effective than the other. As a result, he concluded that both serve a purpose—the early review to consolidate the knowledge and the delayed review to allow students to relearn any forgotten information.

Although the inclusion of regular early and delayed review is only one variable in the experimental design used by Good and Grouws in their 1979 study, this study supports the idea that review at regular intervals is significant for the retention of mathematical knowledge. This study of Grade 4 math students determined that those receiving an experimental instructional program that included regular reviews—daily, weekly, and monthly—performed significantly higher on math achievement than did a control group not receiving the experimental instruction.

Goldman, Mertz, and Pellegrino (1989) concluded that repeated exposure to basic addition facts over a 12-week practice period increased the speed and accuracy of responses among Grade 3 and 4 students, thereby indicating the increased likelihood of direct retrieval as a result of practice.

In a series of experiments conducted primarily with Grade 8 students, Cooper and Sweller (1987) found that practice with algebraic word problems enhanced schema acquisition and automation, allowing students to solve both similar test problems and related transfer problems. The development of automation, which led to the ability to transfer skills to new types of problems, took more time than the development of schema acquisition, essentially background knowledge in one type of problem. Cooper and Sweller theorize that familiarity with the basic operations necessary for solving problems allowed the students to use greater cognitive capacity to deal with those parts of the problem that are unfamiliar.

Thought-provoking questions are important types of review questions.

Burns (1960) studied whether thought-provoking review questions would help retention of learning when spaced throughout arithmetic instruction in Grade 6. Interested in evaluating both the achievement and the attitudes of students involved, Burns determined that the inclusion of thought-provoking questions, rather than repetitive drill, encouraged discussion, improved performance, and proved more interesting to students.

In a 1980 study, Lee randomly assigned 60 seventh-grade students to experimental groups receiving different types of review questions and review passages. Groups received either word-type review questions, which required a thorough understanding of concepts and the application of these concepts to new situations; calculation-type review questions, which required comprehension of a narrower range of concepts and rules; or no review questions. Review questions of both types were found to facilitate retention. The group given word-type review questions received the highest score on a posttest of math aptitude, followed by those given calculation-type review questions, followed by the no-review group.

Although Cooper and Sweller's 1987 study did not specifically address using worked problems (sample problems that show the steps of the process already worked out) versus student-worked practice problems, they concluded by comparing the results of their 1987 study with previous research studies on practice that the use of worked examples may help speed up the process of automation as a result of practice.

Recommended Instructional Practices

The following best practices are derived from the research literature:

- Practice and regular review should be incorporated into daily lesson planning to encourage automaticity with mathematical skills.
- Practice should involve the use of a variety of problems and a mixture of procedures.

- Depending on the instructional goals, effective review can include basic drill-type items, worked problems, or more thought-provoking word-type review problems.
- Including worked problems and models enhance the development of automaticity.

How the Research Is Implemented in *Harcourt Math*

In Grades 1 and 2, the Daily Routine in each lesson helps children review prior-taught skills, and spaced reviews throughout the student text provide ongoing review of critical skills. In Grades 3 through 6, every lesson begins with a Quick Review. These reviews of a lesson's prerequisite skills and of prior-taught skills cover a wide range of key mathematical topics and represent a mixture of procedures and skills.

Quick Review

1. 14 + 14
2. 12 + 21
3. 42 + 25
4. 90 + 18
5. 25 + 49

Daily Routine

Calendar

Have children use a calendar to count back and tell the date of a special event that happened 1, 2, or 3 days ago. (Make sure that the starting date is between 4 and 20.)

- **What is today's date?**
- **What happened 3 days ago?**
- **What was the date?**

OCTOBER

Regular reviews in every lesson help students develop automaticity with skills in all strands of mathematics.

Models that show the step-by-step application of algorithmic procedures, and worked examples that show the variety of possible types of problems within a procedure are included throughout the program. These models are often accompanied by pictures of manipulatives to allow students to deepen their conceptual understanding of a procedure as they apply the steps in the procedure. At the end of a group of chapters that cover a major mathematical topic, a

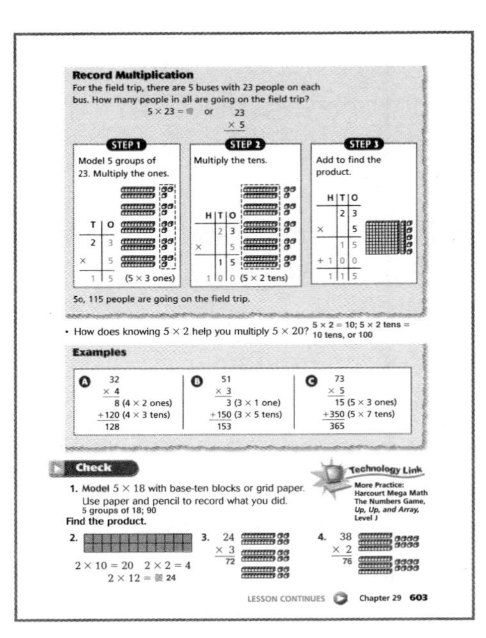

Record Multiplication

For the field trip, there are 5 buses with 23 people on each bus. How many people in all are going on the field trip?

5 × 23 = ■ or 23 × 5

STEP 1: Model 5 groups of 23. Multiply the ones. 15 (5 × 3 ones)

STEP 2: Multiply the tens. 100 (5 × 2 tens)

STEP 3: Add to find the product. 15 + 100 = 115

So, 115 people are going on the field trip.

- How does knowing 5 × 2 help you multiply 5 × 20? 5 × 2 = 10; 5 × 2 tens = 10 tens, or 100

Examples

A. 32 × 4: 8 (4 × 2 ones) + 120 (4 × 3 tens) = 128

B. 51 × 3: 3 (3 × 1 one) + 150 (3 × 5 tens) = 153

C. 73 × 5: 15 (5 × 3 ones) + 350 (5 × 7 tens) = 365

Check

1. Model 5 × 18 with base-ten blocks or grid paper. Use paper and pencil to record what you did. 5 groups of 18; 90

Find the product.

2. 2 × 10 = 20 2 × 2 = 4 2 × 12 = ■ 24
3. 24 × 3 = 72
4. 38 × 2 = 76

Technology Link — More Practice: Harcourt Mega Math The Numbers Game, *Up, Up, and Array,* Level J

LESSON CONTINUES Chapter 29 603

Step-by-step procedures shown with models and worked examples provide thought-provoking examples that deepen students' understanding of a procedure and make practice more effective in building toward automaticity.

Study Guide and Review shows worked examples of the types of problems on which students should develop automaticity with page references to help students review if necessary.

In Grades 3 through 6, practice exercises for every lesson include a variety of problems. Basic drill-type items are included in lessons emphasizing basic fact acquisition and procedural fluency. Thought-provoking word problems that apply the procedure, skill, or concept taught in the lesson and that review prior-taught skills are included in every lesson. The emphasis in many of these problems is on logical reasoning; solving multistep problems; and explaining, justifying, and proving solutions. Exercises that require writing questions given a possible solution, writing problems with given conditions, and analyzing errors develop students' conceptual and procedural knowledge of mathematics.

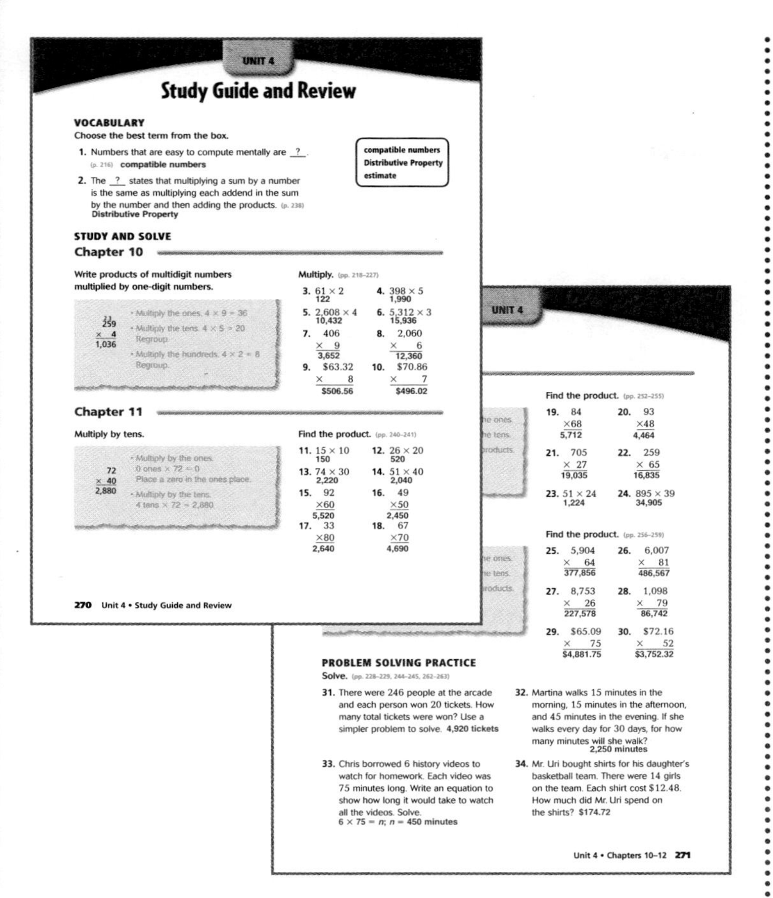

UNIT 4

Study Guide and Review

VOCABULARY

Choose the best term from the box.

compatible numbers
Distributive Property
estimate

1. Numbers that are easy to compute mentally are _?_. (p. 216) compatible numbers
2. The _?_ states that multiplying a sum by a number is the same as multiplying each addend in the sum by the number and then adding the products. (p. 238) Distributive Property

STUDY AND SOLVE

Chapter 10

Write products of multidigit numbers multiplied by one-digit numbers.

Multiply. (pp. 218–227)

3. 61×2 122
4. 398×5 1,990
5. $2,608 \times 4$ 10,432
6. $5,312 \times 3$ 15,936
7. 406×9 3,652
8. $2,060 \times 6$ 12,360
9. $\$63.32 \times 8$ $506.56
10. $\$70.86 \times 7$ $496.02

Chapter 11

Multiply by tens.

Find the product. (pp. 240–241)

11. 15×10 150
12. 26×20 520
13. 74×30 2,220
14. 51×40 2,040
15. 92×60 5,520
16. 49×50 2,450
17. 33×80 2,640
18. 67×70 4,690

270 Unit 4 • Study Guide and Review

UNIT 4

Find the product. (pp. 252–255)

19. 84×68 5,712
20. 93×48 4,464
21. 705×27 19,035
22. 259×65 16,835
23. 51×24 1,224
24. 895×39 34,905

Find the product. (pp. 256–259)

25. $5,904 \times 64$ 377,856
26. $6,007 \times 81$ 486,567
27. $8,753 \times 26$ 227,578
28. $1,098 \times 79$ 86,742
29. $\$65.09 \times 75$ $4,881.75
30. $\$72.16 \times 52$ $3,752.32

PROBLEM SOLVING PRACTICE

Solve. (pp. 228–229, 244–245, 262–263)

31. There were 246 people at the arcade and each person won 20 tickets. How many total tickets were won? Use a simpler problem to solve. 4,920 tickets
32. Martina walks 15 minutes in the morning, 15 minutes in the afternoon, and 45 minutes in the evening. If she walks every day for 30 days, for how many minutes will she walk? 2,250 minutes
33. Chris borrowed 6 history videos to watch for homework. Each video was 75 minutes long. Write an equation to show how long it would take to watch all the videos. Solve. $6 \times 75 = n$; $n = 450$ minutes
34. Mr. Uri bought shirts for his daughter's basketball team. There were 14 girls on the team. Each shirt cost $12.48. How much did Mr. Uri spend on the shirts? $174.72

Unit 4 • Chapters 10–12 271

Review over a chunk of instruction on a concept and related skills helps students make their learning more permanent. Providing worked examples with page references to lessons in which that skill or concept is taught ensures that students can find help that will allow them to be successful with the practice.

Mixed Strategy Practice

6. Four students are standing in line. Jane is standing 2 meters behind Kara and 1 meter in front of Chrissy. Chrissy is standing an equal distance between Kara and Paul. How far away is the first student standing from the last?
7. A computer lab has 8 rows of computers. Each row has 4 computers. There are also 4 computers grouped in the center of the room. How many computers are in the lab?
8. Karen left her house at the time shown on the clock. She arrived at Kaitlyn's house 15 minutes later. They spent 30 minutes eating lunch and then took a 15-minute walk. At what time did they fin[ish their wa]lk?
9. Jason took 3 courses while attending camp at a sea life park. The total cost for the 3 courses was $138.33. Use the chart to find the cost of the "Get All Wet!" course.

Sea Life Camp

Course	Cost
Wild Animals	$52.9[…]

Problem Solving • Logical Reasoning

6. There are 4 green cubes and 4 yellow cubes in a bowl. What could you do to make pulling a yellow cube likely?

______

______

______

Review of word problems involves choosing and using strategies taught throughout the program, solving logical reasoning and multistep problems, and applying skills and concepts learned earlier.

References

Ausubel, D. P. (1966). Early versus delayed review in meaningful learning. *Psychology in the Schools*, 3, 195–198.

Bahrick, H. P., and L. K. Hall (1991). Lifetime maintenance of high school mathematics content. *Journal of Experimental Psychology: General*, 120, 22–33.

Burns, P. C. (1960). Intensive review as a procedure in teaching arithmetic. *Elementary School Journal*, 60, 205–211.

Cooper, G., and J. Sweller (1987). Effects of schema acquisition and rule automation on mathematical problem-solving transfer. *Journal of Educational Psychology*, 79, 347–362.

Geary, D. C. (1994). *Children's Mathematical Development: Research and Practical Applications*. Washington, D.C.: American Psychological Association.

Goldman, S. R., D. L. Mertz, and J. W. Pellegrino (1989). Individual differences in extended practice functions and solution strategies for basic addition facts. *Journal of Educational Psychology*, 81, 481–496.

Good, T. L., and D. A. Grouws (1979). The Missouri Mathematics Effectiveness Project: An experimental study in fourth-grade classrooms. *Journal of Educational Psychology*, 71, 355–362.

Lee, H. (1980). The effects of review questions and review passages on transfer skills. *Journal of Educational Research*, 73, 330–335.

Suydam, M. N., and D. J. Dessart (1980). Skill learning. In Shumway, R. (Ed.), *Research in Mathematics Education*. Reston, VA: National Council of Teachers of Mathematics.

What Research Says About . . .

Overview

Most educational experts agree that effective lesson closure is essential to good teaching. In analyzing lesson plan models used over the past 150 years, Kelly (1997) found that closure was included in more than half of the lesson types. Closure gives students an opportunity to think and talk about what they have learned and a chance to internalize the skills and content taught.

Closure is generally considered one of the last steps in a lesson, but its exact placement in the instructional sequence varies from model to model. In some instructional planning models, closure is paired with an initial, introductory step called a set. Set activities prepare students for the upcoming instruction, and closure summarizes the lesson. Romberg and Wilson (1973) recommend a variation of this model with lesson parts called an advance organizer and a post organizer. They explain that when mathematics teachers finish a presentation, "closing with a concise summarization is usually desirable."

Others contend that closure can occur at any time throughout a lesson when a teacher wants to clarify key points and check whether students are understanding. So, it can be done in intervals instead of as a final conclusion to the lesson.

A review of the literature also reveals two contrasting styles of closure. Some experts (Hunter, 1991) recommend an explicit, teacher-directed approach to closure that is concerned primarily with restating or summarizing what has been taught. Others advocate a more reflective, student-centered approach that engages students in a variety of activities such as repeating important concepts, summarizing critical points, questioning procedures used in the lesson, giving assignments, projecting future activities, and acknowledging student contributions to the lesson (Bailey, 1980).

Research Findings

Researchers who have surveyed existing instructional practices have found that teachers often do not use closure effectively. Wolf and Supon (1994) noted that teachers often provide all the pertinent information to convey a concept but then quickly conclude by assigning homework or telling students to get out the necessary materials for the next subject. Likewise, in a case study of math instruction, Welch (1978) found that a lesson frequently consisted of a review of the previous lesson, some explanation of new materials, the assignment of new problems, and teacher coaching, without any closure.

Is closure effective? Does closure enhance students' learning? Because of the complexity of the teaching-learning process, it is difficult to isolate a single instructional variable such as closure and assess its effect on students' learning. Consequently, we must rely on the results of correlational studies and learning theory to deduce the value of closure.

A variety of closure strategies should be a regular and consistent part of lesson planning.

Rosenshine and Meister (1994) analyzed the results of 16 studies and found that closure activities appeared to help students perform better on measures used in the studies. These closure strategies included summarization, summary writing, and question generation.

Drawing on schema theory, Romberg (1992) recommends closure as a way to help students make connections between newly learned concepts and previously acquired knowledge. He calls for having students learn *how* as opposed to learning *what* in mathematics. Welch also calls for an emphasis on learning *how* as opposed to learning *what*.

Paul, Binker, and Weil (1995) contend that one of the main goals of math instruction is to get students to think independently as problem solvers and to use their problem solving abilities to make sense of the world. Teachers can promote such thinking, they suggest, through closure activities that include questioning *how* and *why* a math concept or skill is useful and by having students pose problems to other students as extended practice.

Recommended Instructional Practices

The following best practices are derived from the research literature:

- Make closure a regular and consistent part of lesson planning.
- Use a variety of closure strategies or activities. Some may be more explicit, teacher-directed activities such as repeating important concepts, summarizing critical points, and making connections between the new lesson and previous lessons; others may be more reflective, learner-centered activities such as encouraging students to question procedures used in the lesson, having students explain how and why the concept may be applied to real-life situations, and engaging students in discussions to validate their own thinking.
- Offer students opportunities to demonstrate their knowledge in a variety of ways through oral, written, and graphic summarization.
- Use closure, when appropriate, throughout a lesson to clarify key points and check student understanding.
- Use closure as a decision-making tool for deciding which students have fully grasped the concept of the lesson and can move on and which students could profit from additional review or reteaching.

How the Research Is Implemented in *Harcourt Math*

Closure is a regular and consistent part of every lesson plan. Step 4 of the lesson plan provides a variety of closure activities—oral discussion; skill check; and written explanations, such as generalizations or restatements of the big idea of the lesson, or problem solving activities that require reasoning and justification.

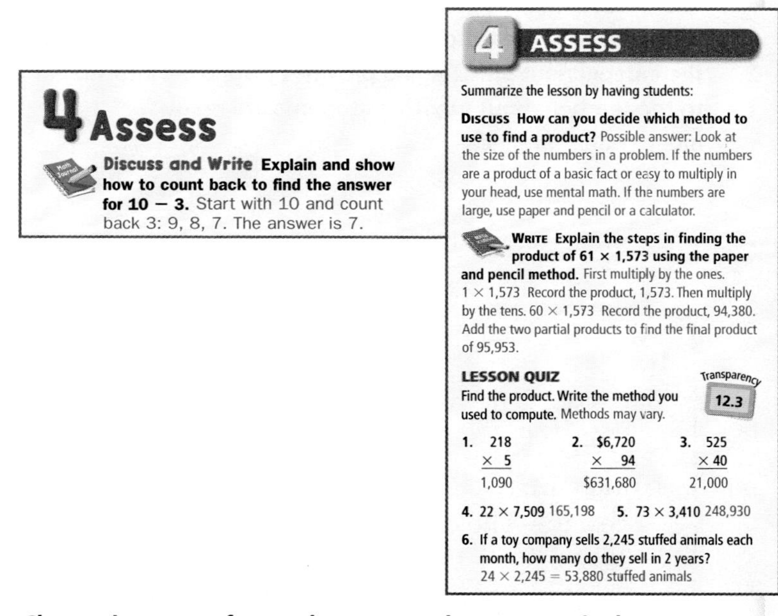

4 Assess

Discuss and Write Explain and show how to count back to find the answer for 10 − 3. Start with 10 and count back 3: 9, 8, 7. The answer is 7.

4 ASSESS

Summarize the lesson by having students:

DISCUSS How can you decide which method to use to find a product? Possible answer: Look at the size of the numbers in a problem. If the numbers are a product of a basic fact or easy to multiply in your head, use mental math. If the numbers are large, use paper and pencil or a calculator.

WRITE Explain the steps in finding the product of 61 × 1,573 using the paper and pencil method. First multiply by the ones. 1 × 1,573 Record the product, 1,573. Then multiply by the tens. 60 × 1,573 Record the product, 94,380. Add the two partial products to find the final product of 95,953.

LESSON QUIZ Transparency 12.3

Find the product. Write the method you used to compute. Methods may vary.

1. 218 × 5 = 1,090 **2.** $6,720 × 94 = $631,680 **3.** 525 × 40 = 21,000

4. 22 × 7,509 165,198 **5.** 73 × 3,410 248,930

6. If a toy company sells 2,245 stuffed animals each month, how many do they sell in 2 years? 24 × 2,245 = 53,880 stuffed animals

Closure is a part of every lesson. Students are actively involved in summarizing the content of the lesson through oral discussion and through writing.

In addition, closure is developed throughout the lessons through the use of reasoning questions, Math Idea statements, and a short section called Check that guides students in applying the lesson skills and concepts before moving to independent practice.

Students participate in many different kinds of activities that help them develop their understanding of the connections among mathematical ideas and that encourage them to use different ways to demonstrate their understanding and knowledge of the mathematics they are learning.

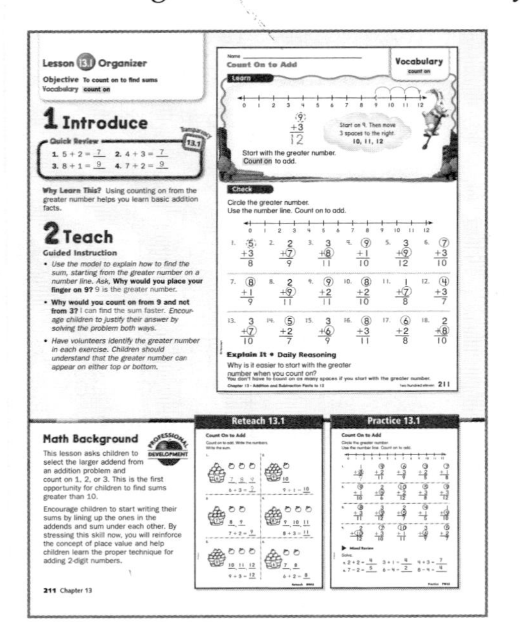

The Guided Instruction in the *Teacher's Edition* provides closure within the lesson. Closure helps students prepare for the independent practice and provides diagnostic information to the teacher about whether students are ready for independent practice.

The wide variety of closure activities and their placement throughout the lesson and at the end of every lesson provide important ongoing information about students' progress and provide solid data that teachers can use to make decisions about individual students' needs and effective ways to plan future lessons based on overall class achievement and needs.

In Grades 3-6, certain lessons in a sequence of lessons on a related topic provide opportunities within the lesson to summarize and bring closure to math ideas. Every lesson includes a Check set of exercises and problems that provide closure to the instructional part of the lesson and a bridge to the independent practice section of the lesson.

References

Bailey, G. D. (April 1980). Set and closure revisited. *NASSKP Bulletin*, 64, (435), 103–110.

Hunter, M. (October 1991). Forum: Generic lesson design—The case for. *The Science Teacher*, 58, (7), 26–28.

Kelly, K. B. (1997). *Evolution/role of lesson plans in instructional planning*. Paper presented at the Eighth Annual Reading/Literacy Conference, Bakersfield, CA. (ERIC Document Reproduction Services No. ED 414 261.)

Paul, R., A. J. A. Binker, and D. Weil (1995). *Critical Thinking: Handbook K–3: A Guide for Remodelling Lesson Plans in Language Arts, Social Studies, and Science*. Santa Rosa, CA: Foundation for Critical Thinking.

Romberg, T. A. (1992). Mathematics learning and teaching: What we have learned in ten years. In C. Collins and J. Mangieri (Eds.), *Teaching Thinking: An Agenda for the Twenty-First Century* (pp. 49–64). Hillsdale, NJ: Lawrence Erlbaum Associates.

Romberg, T. A., and J. W. Wilson (March 1973). The effect of an advanced organizer, cognitive set, and post organizer on the learning and retention of written materials. *Journal for Research in Mathematics Education*, 4, (2), 68–76.

Rosenshine, B., and C. Meister (Winter 1994). Reciprocal teaching: A review of the research. *Review of Educational Research*, 64, (4), 479–530.

Welch, W. (1978). Science education in Urbanville: A case study. In R. Stake and J. Easley (Eds.), *Case Studies in Science Education* (pp. 515–533). Urbana: University of Illinois.

Wolf, P., and V. Supon (1994). *Winning through student participation in lesson closure.* (ERIC Document Reproduction Services No. ED 368 694.)

HARCOURT

Math

Professional Handbook

- **Section 1**

  Articles by respected mathematicians describe the conceptual foundations of key math topics.

- **Section 2**

  Articles by the authors of *Harcourt Math* describe the philosophy and research base that guided the development of the program and provide examples of implementation of the philosophy.

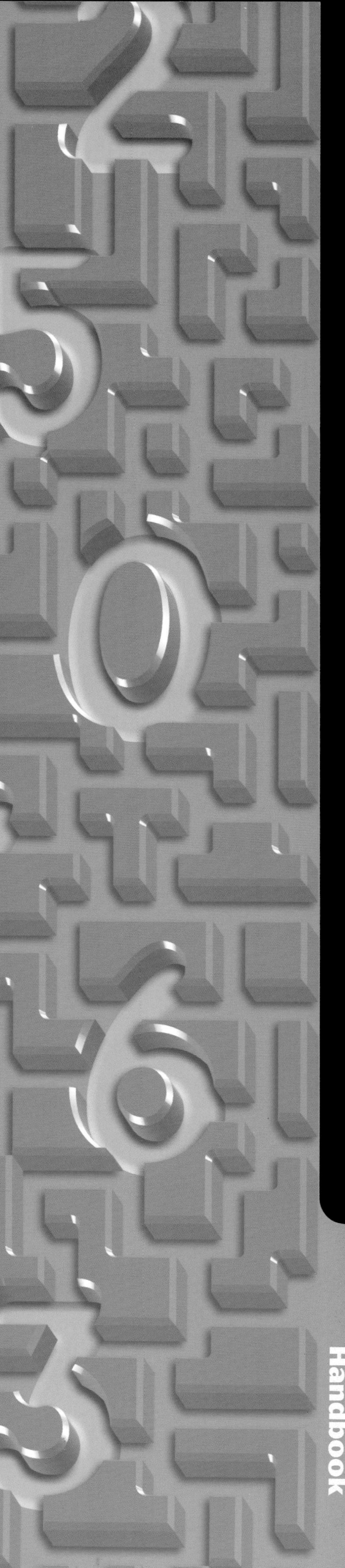

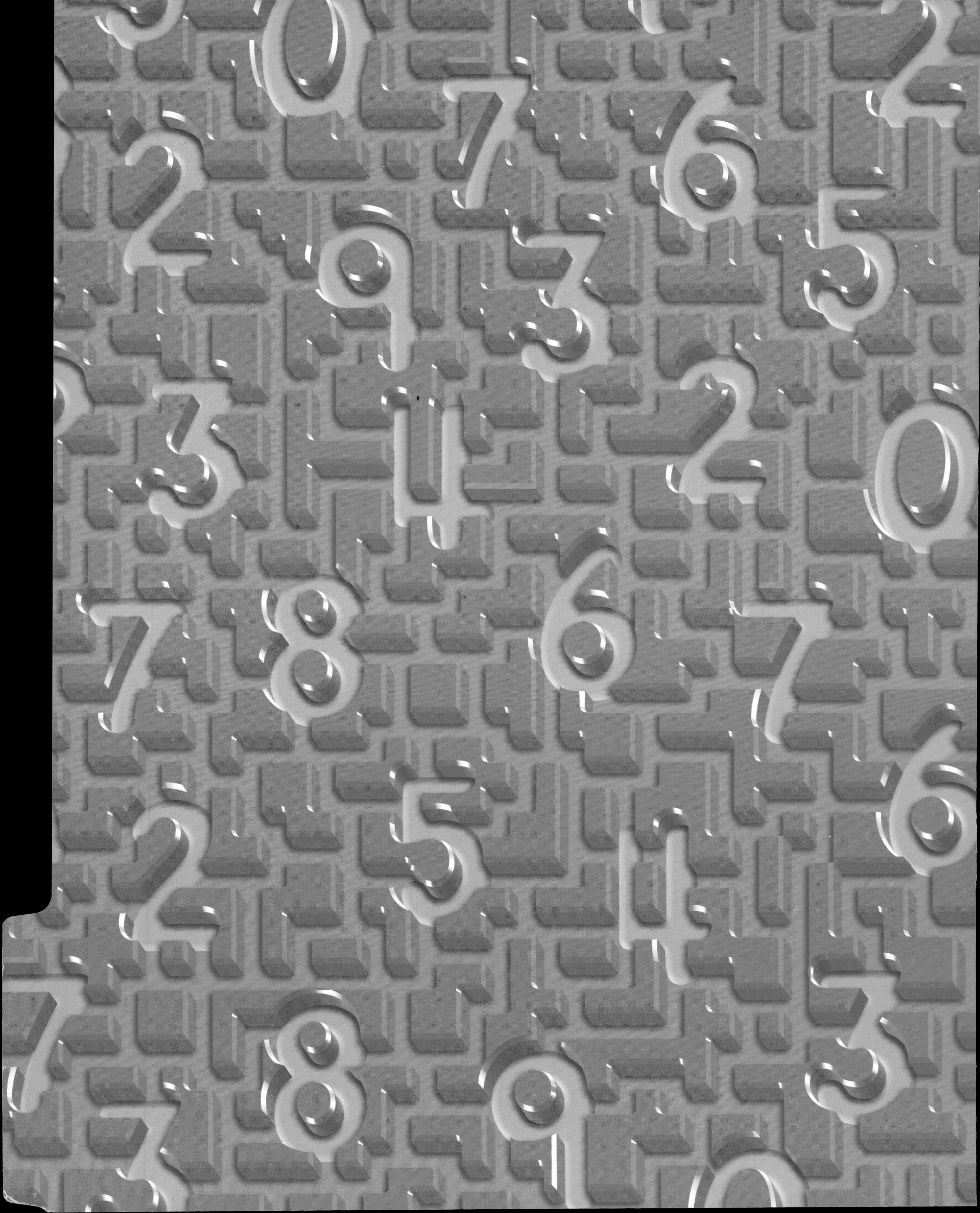

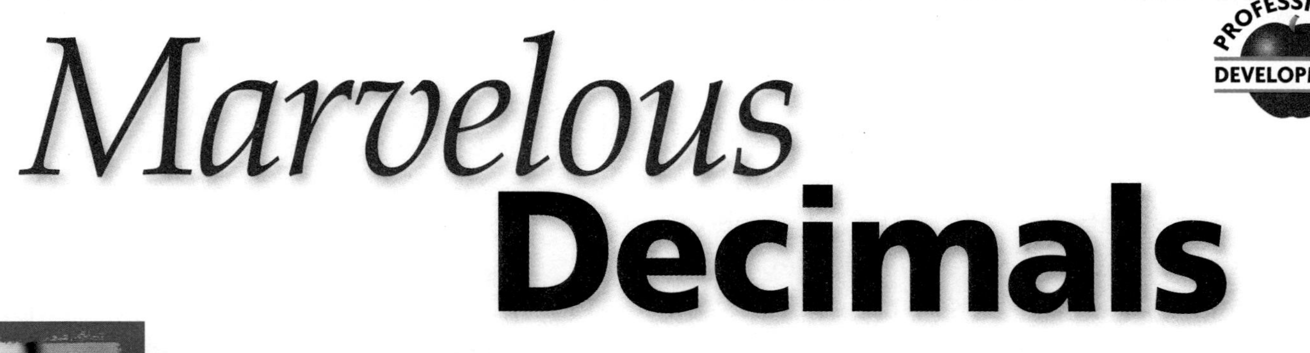

Marvelous Decimals

by Roger Howe

It is hard to see clearly how wonderful something as familiar as our decimal number system really is, but pause a moment to contemplate its marvels.

Of the many virtues of the decimal system, consider the following six:

1. **Efficiency** It represents numbers with astounding (in a sense, perfect) compactness and efficiency.
2. **Sophistication** It is highly sophisticated. It uses all the operations of basic algebra (addition, multiplication, and exponentiation [raising to powers]) merely to represent numbers.
3. **Ease of calculation** It makes calculations fast and simple to perform. More technically, it supports efficient, general, easily implemented algorithms for calculation.
4. **Ease of comparison** It is compatible with our ideas of ordering and magnitude. We can easily tell which of two decimal numbers is larger.
5. **Ease of approximation** It deals smoothly with errors and approximation.
6. **Scale independence** It scales easily, allowing representation of arbitrarily small numbers as well as arbitrarily large ones by essentially the same scheme. The arithmetic operations are scale-independent.

That the decimal system does so much so well and so easily makes it a marvel for users, but it presents a challenge for educators. All the structure built into decimals, and all the benefits they confer, are hard to appreciate without both extended practice and extended thought. It takes a long time for a student to unpack the intellectual treasure chest we know as the decimal place-value number system, and it takes careful guidance from teachers to strike the right balance between helping students master the mechanics of decimal computation and providing them with insight into the various computational recipes that have been developed. However, done right, attention to concepts can provide a solid foundation for computation. It can make the sometimes seemingly arcane procedures of arithmetic appear as pragmatic solutions to essential problems.

History of the Decimal Place-Value System

Let's look briefly at the history of the development of the decimal number system and its possible effects on mathematics and science. The decimal system took a long time to develop. After several thousand years of precursors, this way of writing numbers was invented in India in about A.D. 500. It was adopted and developed by Islamic scholars and finally introduced into Europe in the late Middle Ages. An early pioneer and promoter of decimal notation in Europe was Leonardo of Pisa, also known as Fibonacci. Before Fibonacci, Roman numerals were used to keep records and calculation was done with a counting board. Use of decimals gradually displaced Roman numerals and became standard by the fifteenth century. Although the effects of a change of practice such as the transition from Roman numerals to decimals are diffuse and subtle to gauge, some writers attribute to decimals both a significant role in the European commercial boom of the late Middle Ages and Renaissance and a great stimulus to science and mathematics.

This collection of articles surveys a few highlights of the features of the decimal system listed above. This article discusses the first two items—efficiency and sophistication. The following articles discuss how the sophisticated structure built into decimal numbers promotes efficient arithmetic and how it allows for estimation.

The Efficiency of the Decimal Place-Value System

Writing Numbers Let's look first at writing numbers. The earliest representations of numbers were simple tallies: one mark for one object of some sort. So to indicate 10, it would take 10 tally marks: I I I I I I I I I I. Our decimal system represents up to 9 objects with just one symbol, but that does not begin to reveal its efficiency. As we use more digits, the system gets increasingly efficient. Each additional digit increases our descriptive reach *tenfold*. One digit can tell us the number of people in a typical nuclear family. With two digits, we can name the number of people in an extended family or in a typical school classroom. With three digits, we can specify the number of students in a moderate-sized school. Four digits allow us to name the populations of a large public high school, a moderate-sized college, or a small town. Five digits can number the largest campuses of state universities or large towns and small cities. With six digits, we can count the populations of sizable cities (San Francisco, Cleveland) and some states (Delaware, Wyoming). Seven digits allow us to name the populations of New York City and Paris, most states, and many countries. Using eight digits, we can number the populations of the largest cities (Tokyo, Mexico City, São Paulo), states (California, New York), and most countries (England, Canada, Argentina, Nigeria). Nine digits count the people in large countries like the United States, Japan, or Indonesia—all but China and maybe India. With ten digits, the same number as tallies to count our fingers, we can record the entire human population of the world. With ten digits, we can also write an arbitrary U.S. telephone number. This efficient representation lets us dial anyone in the country in a matter of seconds. (Of course, we will probably get the person's answering machine.)

The principle behind this efficiency is the same principle that makes language work. Start with a small set of basic symbols and create an arbitrarily large vocabulary by making lists formed from the basic symbols—that is, by putting several basic symbols in sequential order. Thus, spoken words are sequences (in time) of basic sounds (called phonemes by linguists). In English and other languages that use an alphabet, the same system governs writing. Each written word is a sequence (on the page) of letters that encode spoken sounds. So, the decimal system is merely the application to numbers of a general technique for presenting information. We can call it the *alphabetic principle* or *digitization.* The decimal system, however, embodies digital representation at its ultimate. It represents every (positive whole) number, with no exceptions and in exactly one way for each—no misses, no repetitions. This contrasts with the situation for language. There are many sequences of letters and many sequences of syllables that do not make words, but rather only nonsense. Additionally, there is more than one way to pronounce or spell some words.

The Sophistication of the Decimal Number System

Very Round Numbers Admirable as it is, the representational efficiency of our decimal notation hardly touches on the sophistication of the system as a way of representing numbers specifically, rather than some other indefinitely large collection, such as words or telephone numbers. In assigning telephone numbers, we are not really using the numbers as numbers—they are just labels. It doesn't make any sense to add, multiply, or round off telephone numbers. We could just as well use any collection of symbols to write telephone numbers. There still is a (redundant) labeling of the telephone buttons also by letters, which these days is exploited by firms with 800 numbers to provide customers with a catchy mnemonic for remembering how to call them—for example, 1-800-CALL-XYZ. Numbers are convenient for labeling things, but they are much more. They have a rich structure—arithmetic operations, ordering, and magnitude—that makes them much more valuable than a simple list. The decimal system is admirably compatible with all these structures. This compatibility comes out of the sophisticated way the decimal system uses algebraic operations and principles for the mere task of writing numbers. The basis of the system is numbers of a very special type—a single digit followed by zeros. We will call such numbers "very round." Thus, 7,000; 30; 600,000; 200; 5; and 800,000,000,000 are very round numbers.

Every positive whole number is a sum of very round numbers—one for each decimal place. Indeed, the digits in a given number tell us how to express it as a sum of very round numbers. The following examples show 742 and 3,805 expressed in this way. When we teach children to express numbers in this way, we call it *expanded form.*

$$742 = 700 + 40 + 2$$
$$3{,}805 = 3{,}000 + 800 + 5$$

Notice that in 3,805 the zero in the tens place indicates that no very round number with only one zero is needed. This is the place-value principle in action. We record the absence of the multiple of 10 in order to signal that the 8 is representing 800, not 80. Very round numbers are the purest expression of the place-value principle. They are the elements from which all numbers are formed. Thus the zero, which might seem wasteful since it stands for nothing, is the key to making decimal place-value representation work. We will call the very round numbers used to form a general decimal whole number the *very round components* of the number. Thus, the very round components of 742 are 700, 40, and 2.

Structure of Very Round Numbers The use of addition in writing numbers is supplemented by the use of multiplication in forming the very round numbers. Each very round number is the product of a digit times a power of 10 as shown in the following examples.

$$700 = 7 \times 100$$
$$40 = 4 \times 10$$
$$3{,}000 = 3 \times 1{,}000$$

Of course, this is also true for the single digits such as $2 = 2 \times 1$, etc., but we don't usually bother to make this explicit.

Each very round number with digit 1 is a power of 10—the product of 10 multiplied by itself repeatedly. The number of multiplications by 10 is just the number of zeros as shown in the following examples.

$1 = 10^0$

$10 = 10^1$

$100 = 10 \times 10 = 10^2$

$1{,}000 = 10 \times 10 \times 10 = 10^3$

Polynomials in the Variable "10" If we take into account the multiplicative structure of the very round numbers, in addition to the additive structure of non-round numbers, we see that every decimal number is composed from a very limited collection of basic components. In fact, every decimal number is made by combining just the digits and 10 by means of the basic operations of algebra—addition, multiplication, and exponentiation (raising to powers). Here is how this looks for our examples of 742 and 3,805.

$$\begin{aligned} 742 &= 700 + 40 + 2 \\ &= (7 \times 100) + (4 \times 10) + (2 \times 1) \\ &= 7 \times 10^2 + 4 \times 10^1 + 2 \times 10^0 \\ 3{,}805 &= 3{,}000 + 800 + 5 \\ &= (3 \times 1{,}000) + (8 \times 100) + (5 \times 1) \\ &= 3 \times 10^3 + 8 \times 10^2 + 5 \times 10^0 \end{aligned}$$

Thus, simply to record numbers, our decimal system implicitly uses all the operations of basic algebra. Furthermore, the expressions we use to write decimal numbers are of a kind familiar from algebra. A quantity that is formed by taking some number, raising it to various powers, and multiplying by some coefficients and summing is referred to as a *polynomial*. Thus, we see that decimal notation is a shorthand device for expressing numbers as "polynomials in 10." This way of describing our familiar decimal notation may seem to be making something simple complicated, but the similarity is not superficial. There are strong parallels between decimal numbers and polynomials, not only in the way of writing them but also in calculations and other properties. The standard procedures for addition, multiplication, and so forth, exploit the structure just elaborated. Furthermore, the "Laws of Algebra" are heavily involved in justifying and comparing algorithms for computation. Understanding and appreciation of the decimal system is greatly enhanced by recognition of this pervasive role of algebra.

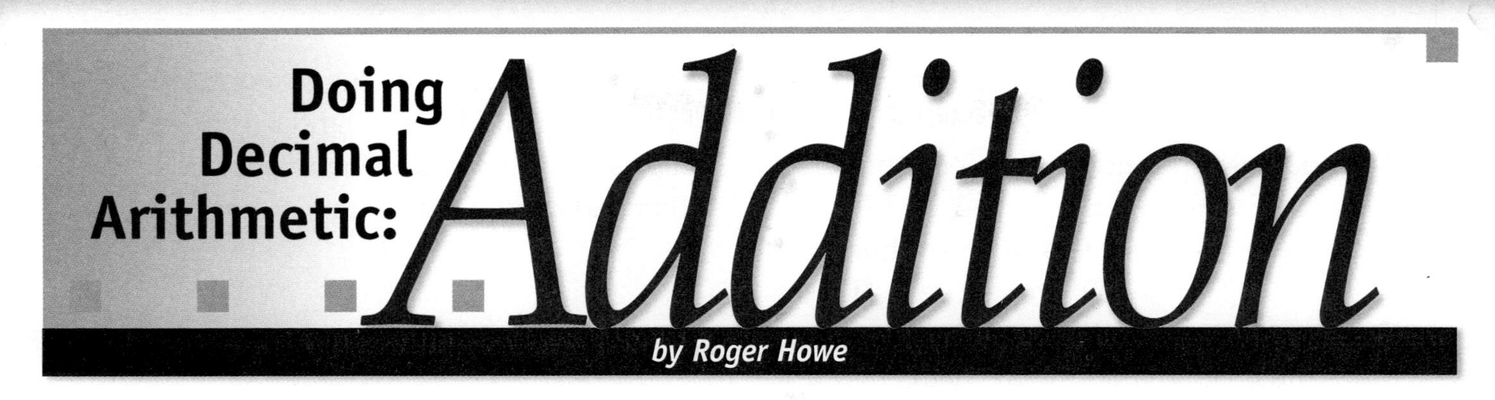

Doing Decimal Arithmetic: Addition

by Roger Howe

The article "Marvelous Decimals" (pp. PH1–PH4), describes the algebraic sophistication that our standard decimal notation brings to the writing of numbers. Decimal numbers implicitly treat ordinary whole numbers as "polynomials in 10." What do we get from this algebraic sophistication? We get remarkable power, not only to record but also to manipulate numbers, to perform the usual operations of arithmetic. We get *ease of calculation in the form of efficient, easily implemented algorithms.* Addition and multiplication are essentially combinations of single-digit operations (plus keeping track of decimal places). More exactly, we add or multiply general numbers by appropriate combinations of additions or multiplications of very round numbers, and these essentially amount to calculations with single-digit numbers. Let's see what this means for addition.

Adding Very Round Numbers

Remember that a "very round number" is a number with a single digit followed by zeros: 9; 40; 100; 20,000; 600,000,000, and so forth. The general principle behind addition of decimal numbers is that every addition can be done by an appropriate combination of additions of very round numbers. So, let's examine the sum of two very round numbers.

Let's call the number of digits in a very round number the *length of the number*. Adding very round numbers is interesting only when both numbers have the same length. To add very round numbers of different lengths, all we do is to put the leading digit of each number in its place in the sum. For example, 7,000 + 40 = 7,040. This procedure holds for the sums of many very round numbers, as long as they all have different lengths. For example, 3,000 + 800 + 5 = 3,805. This is, of course, the basic principle that is used to express a general whole number as a sum of its very round components. Students refer to this expression of a number as *expanded form*. However, when we add two very round numbers of the same length, such as 3,000 + 2,000 = 5,000; or 40 + 40 = 80; or 700 + 600 = 1,300, it is not a simple matter of recording digits in appropriate places. Instead, we see that we essentially have to do a single-digit addition and also keep track of the number of zeros in the very round summands. Treating the above examples more formally, we see these processes taking place:

$$3{,}000 + 2{,}000 = (3 \times 1{,}000) + (2 \times 1{,}000) = (3 + 2) \times 1{,}000 = 5 \times 1{,}000 = 5{,}000$$

$$40 + 40 = (4 \times 10) + (4 \times 10) = (4 + 4) \times 10 = 8 \times 10 = 80$$

$$700 + 600 = (7 \times 100) + (6 \times 100) = (7 + 6) \times 100 = 13 \times 100 = 1{,}300$$

The crucial fact we need to know to find the sum is a single-digit addition—an "addition fact." Another way of thinking about factoring out the power of 10 is to treat the power of 10 as a unit. Thus, for 3,000 + 2,000 = 5,000, we can say, "Three thousands plus two thousands makes five thousands," in analogy with "Three apples plus two apples makes five apples." If the sum of the digits of the numbers we are adding is less than 10, the sum will again be very round and will be the same length as the two original numbers. However, if the sum of the digits is 10 or larger, the sum of the very round numbers will be longer than the original numbers and may not be very round. If we have to do further calculations with it, we should decompose it into a sum of its very round components. This would lead us to write:

$$700 + 600 = 1{,}300 = 1{,}000 + 300$$

We can now continue the computation, using the 1,000 and the 300 individually, as called for. This, of course, is the source of "carrying," or "regrouping."

Adding Any Whole Numbers

To add two general numbers, we decompose each of them into their very round components and add components with the same length. Thus, to compute 26 + 53, we write:

$$26 + 53 = (20 + 6) + (50 + 3) =$$
$$(20 + 50) + (6 + 3) = 70 + 9 = 79$$

This example is very simple. It has only two-digit addends and requires no carrying or regrouping. Before looking at more complicated examples, the following points should be made. First, although we have written everything on a line, with liberal use of parentheses, what we have done, in essence, is the same as the standard procedure for this addition. Standard procedure tells us to line the numbers up one under the other and add each column:

$$\begin{array}{r} 26 \\ +53 \\ \hline 79 \end{array}$$

We see that the process of alignment and column-wise operation forces us to add the 6 and 3 and the 20 and 50 (represented only by the digits, with the zeros being implicit in the location of the digit in the tens column). Thus, the standard procedure is a way to achieve automatically what we have done explicitly. Although we will not do it in each case, all the illustrations that follow also translate in similar fashion into the standard format.

Second, we should take note of all the rearrangement we have done to get from (20 + 6) + (50 + 3) to (20 + 50) + (6 + 3). These rearrangements are, of course, recognized as being legitimate by anyone experienced with arithmetic. More formally, they are justifiable by means of some of the Laws of Algebra. Specifically, this rewriting used the Commutative and Associative Laws for addition several times. Also, as discussed above, in the addition 20 + 50 = 70, we are implicitly invoking the Distributive Law, which connects addition and multiplication. The Distributive Law is the law that allows us to factor out the 10 in the process.

$$20 + 50 = (2 \times 10) + (5 \times 10) =$$
$$(2 + 5) \times 10 = 7 \times 10 = 70$$

Since the purpose of this article is not to give a formal treatment of arithmetic, but only to discuss some key ideas, we usually do not mention these Laws of Algebra again. However, they are implicitly involved in virtually all arithmetic calculations, and a full understanding of decimal arithmetic does involve fluency with these Laws.

As previewed on page PH6, sometimes the sum of two digits is 10 or larger, and results in a sum that and has one more digit than the original numbers. This results in "carrying," or "regrouping." We must decompose the result into its very round components and combine the longer one with the original components of that length. Thus,

$$76 + 53 = (70 + 6) + (50 + 3) =$$
$$(70 + 50) + (6 + 3) =$$
$$120 + 9 = 100 + 20 + 9 = 129$$

This is quite a transparent process if the carrying only affects the largest power of 10 as above. If the overflow occurs in a smaller place, the overflow from one sum must be combined with the sum for the next higher place-value position.

$$26 + 57 = (20 + 6) + (50 + 7) =$$
$$(20 + 50) + (6 + 7) = 70 + 13 =$$
$$70 + (10 + 3) = (70 + 10) + 3 =$$
$$80 + 3 = 83$$

In adding multi-digit numbers, the need to carry, or regroup, may affect several places, and there may be a cascade effect, whereby an overflow at one place affects several larger places, as in

$$146 + 57 = (100 + 40 + 6) + (50 + 7) =$$
$$100 + (40 + 50) + (6 + 7) =$$
$$100 + 90 + 13 = 100 + 90 + (10 + 3) =$$
$$100 + (90 + 10) + 3 = 100 + 100 + 3 =$$
$$200 + 3 = 203$$

Despite these complications, the principle is clear. All additions can be done by suitable combinations of additions of very round numbers.

Ease of Calculation

It is also important that this "suitable combination" involves only a fairly small number of additions. To add any two numbers under 1,000 (three-digit numbers), we need at most three basic additions and perhaps three more to allow for carrying, or regrouping (six at most). To add two numbers under 10,000, it is only slightly worse—a maximum of eight one-digit additions. Compare this with the effort of counting the objects in a set made by joining two sets, each with several thousand objects! Just as it eases the labor of writing numbers, decimal notation reduces the effort needed for addition. Furthermore, we should remember that all the complications are inherent already in one-digit addition—$7 + 6 = 13$ is greater than 10, and we can't help that. Our decimal system accommodates this fact of life as gracefully as one could hope.

Extra Efficiency of the Standard Algorithm

The standard format for doing the last addition is:

$$\begin{array}{r} {\scriptstyle 1\,1} \\ 146 \\ +\ 57 \\ \hline 203 \end{array}$$

The ones above the 4 and the 1 represent the regroupings. They remind us to convert 10 ones to a ten and 10 tens to a hundred and to then add these newly created larger units to the ones already there.

The standard algorithm is much more compact and involves much less writing than the computation at the left. The reason for the compactness is twofold.

- First, rather than explicitly performing the space-consuming decomposition of each number into very round numbers, the standard procedure forces this by lining up the numbers according to their place values and prescribing column addition.

- Second, the standard procedure goes from right to left, adding the ones and regrouping a 10, if necessary, *before* adding the tens, with this process being repeated similarly for each place-value position.

This short-circuits the space-consuming recombination and recalculation steps in our first version. **Thus, the standard procedure is designed for compactness and efficiency of exact calculation.**

Flexibility for Mental Math and Estimation

However, the principle that our computation emphasizes—that multi-digit addition is a combination of additions of very round numbers of the same length—is worth understanding. For one thing, it allows us to think flexibly about addition. It shows us that the operations needed to compute the sum may be done in many orders—thanks to the Commutative and Associative Laws. The standard procedure picks one order—the order that keeps rewriting to a minimum. However, other orders are possible and may sometimes be useful. In particular, with mental math, it often seems more natural to start by adding the places farthest to the left, since these are the largest parts of the numbers being added. Thus, to add 146 and 57 mentally, many people would start by adding 140 + 50 to get 190, and then add the 6 + 7 = 13 to the result, getting 190 + 13 = 203. The point is that the 190 is much larger than the 13, so with just that part of the addition completed, you already know "most of" the answer. If you did not need to know the exact answer, but just approximately how large the sum is, you could say that it is "about 190" or "about 200" (since it is clearly more than 190, and 200 is a very round number). By contrast, the standard procedure starts by computing the ones place, which is the smallest part of the answer, and doesn't find the main part of the result until the end of the calculation. The same ideas let us quickly estimate the size of a multi-digit sum, so that we can check an answer on a calculator for reasonableness. This is discussed more thoroughly in "Estimation and Arithmetic" (pp. PH17–PH20).

Doing Decimal Arithmetic: Multiplication

by Roger Howe

In the article "Doing Decimal Arithmetic: Addition" (pp. PH5–PH8), we saw how decimal notation provides a framework for efficient addition. The story with multiplication is similar, but in some ways more remarkable. Everything again depends on combining operations on very round numbers.

Multiplying Very Round Numbers

Recall that very round numbers are numbers consisting of a single digit followed by some zeros. Examples are 2,000 and 4 and 90. They may also be described as a single-digit number times a power of 10. Multiplying very round numbers amounts to multiplying the digits, plus keeping track of the powers of 10. More precisely, to multiply two very round numbers, we multiply their digits, then on the right we append as many zeros as are in both factors together. Here are some examples of multiplications of very round numbers:

$$20 \times 40 = (2 \times 10) \times (4 \times 10) = (2 \times 4) \times (10 \times 10) = 8 \times 100 = 800;$$
$$30 \times 3{,}000 = (3 \times 10) \times (3 \times 1{,}000) = (3 \times 3) \times (10 \times 1{,}000) = 9 \times 10{,}000 = 90{,}000;$$
$$600 \times 7 = (6 \times 100) \times 7 = (6 \times 7) \times 100 = 42 \times 100 = 4{,}200 = 4{,}000 + 200$$

As the last example shows, when the product of the two digits is 10 or more, the product of the very round numbers may not be very round, and in any case will have one more digit than when the product is less than 10. This is not an essential problem, but it is one source of regrouping in the standard procedures for multiplication.

One case that might cause confusion is when one of the digits is 5 and the other is even. When this happens, the product of the digits will be a multiple of 10 and so the whole product will be very round, and it will seem to have an extra zero. But this case is computed in the same way as all the others. The "extra" zero is contributed by the product of the digits. Thus, in the examples below, the extra zero in the second product results because $5 \times 4 = 20$:

$$50 \times 300 = (5 \times 10) \times (3 \times 100) = (5 \times 3) \times (10 \times 100) = 15 \times 1{,}000 = 15{,}000, \text{ but}$$
$$50 \times 400 = (5 \times 10) \times (4 \times 100) = (5 \times 4) \times (10 \times 100) = 20 \times 1{,}000 = 20{,}000$$

Multiplying Any Whole Numbers

Once we know how to multiply very round numbers, the Distributive Law tells us what to do to multiply general multi-digit numbers. To multiply two numbers, we should multiply every very round component of one factor by every very round component of the other and add the products together. As an example, take first a one-digit by two-digit multiplication:

$$2 \times 34 = 2 \times (30 + 4) = 60 + 8 = 68$$

Here all the single-digit products were less than 10. If some product is more than 10, it must be decomposed into its very round components, resulting in regrouping:

$$2 \times 37 = 2 \times (30 + 7) = 60 + 14 = 60 + (10 + 4) = (60 + 10) + 4 = 70 + 4 = 74$$

To multiply a pair of multi-digit numbers, we must remember to multiply *each* term of one by *each* term of the other and then add *all* the products together. Thus,

$$\begin{aligned} 21 \times 23 &= (20 + 1) \times (20 + 3) \\ &= 20 \times 20 + 1 \times 20 + 20 \times 3 + 1 \times 3 \\ &= 400 + 20 + 60 + 3 = 400 + 80 + 3 = 483 \end{aligned}$$

If one wants to proceed very carefully, the second equality can be accomplished in stages:

$$\begin{aligned} 21 \times 23 &= 21 \times (20 + 3) = 21 \times 20 + 21 \times 3 \\ &= (20 + 1) \times 20 + (20 + 1) \times 3 \\ &= 20 \times 20 + 1 \times 20 + 20 \times 3 + 1 \times 3 \end{aligned}$$

Comparing with the Standard Algorithm

As with addition, our way of writing the multiplication parallels the standard procedure. For the standard procedure, we write the numbers under one another just as we did for addition. Then we multiply the top number by each digit of the bottom number and "move the product to the left" in order to take account of the fact that we are really multiplying not only by a single digit but also by a power of 10. The moving-over procedure is the bookkeeping step that reminds us of the power of 10, which is an implicit factor in the product.

$$\begin{array}{r} 21 \\ \times\ 23 \\ \hline 63 \\ +\ 42 \\ \hline 483 \end{array}$$

Here the 42 really means 420 = 400 + 20, the first two summands in our expanded computation, and 63 = 60 + 3 accounts for the last two summands. Thus, the standard procedure automatically organizes several summands from the extended form of the product into single multi-digit numbers, which are then added according to the standard procedures for addition. Perhaps we should emphasize that we could add the four products, 400, 20, 60, and 3, in any order whatsoever without changing the answer—the rules of addition let us do that. We have written them in the order we did, precisely to allow easy comparison with the standard algorithm.

The Need for Regrouping

In this example, we used small digits to avoid the complications of regrouping. Regrouping comes from two sources:

1. when we need to decompose a product larger than 10
2. when the sum of terms with a given power of 10 is greater than 10

(Note that the first problem is essentially the same as in addition, but it is more prominent with multiplication than with addition because the product of two one-digit numbers tends to be larger than the sum.) For example,

$$\begin{aligned} 24 \times 41 &= (20 + 4) \times (40 + 1) = \\ &= 800 + 160 + 20 + 4 = 800 + (100 + 60) + 20 + 4 \\ &= (800 + 100) + (60 + 20) + 4 = 900 + 80 + 4 = 984 \end{aligned}$$

In the example at the bottom of the previous page, the product 4×4 is greater than 10. Even if all products are less than 10, however, the fact that several products are multiplied by the same power of 10 can produce regrouping:

$$
\begin{aligned}
23 \times 32 &= (20 + 3) \times (30 + 2) \\
&= 600 + 90 + 40 + 6 = 600 + 130 + 6 \\
&= 600 + (100 + 30) + 6 \\
&= (600 + 100) + 30 + 6 = 700 + 30 + 6 = 736
\end{aligned}
$$

Here, the products involving the factor 10 are 3×30 and 20×2. Although each is less than 100, they sum to more than 100, resulting in regrouping.

Typically, both causes of regrouping will occur in the same product, making even a two-digit calculation fairly lengthy if carried out in the step-by-step manner we have been using. Here is an example.

$$
\begin{aligned}
36 \times 67 &= (30 + 6) \times (60 + 7) \\
&= 1{,}800 + 360 + 210 + 42 \\
&= 1{,}800 + (300 + 60) + (200 + 10) + (40 + 2) \\
&= 1{,}000 + (800 + 300 + 200) + (60 + 10 + 40) + 2 \\
&= 1{,}000 + 1{,}300 + 110 + 2 \\
&= 1{,}000 + (1{,}000 + 300) + (100 + 10) + 2 \\
&= (1{,}000 + 1{,}000) + (300 + 100) + 10 + 2 \\
&= 2{,}000 + 400 + 10 + 2 = 2{,}412
\end{aligned}
$$

Comparing this with the standard procedure helps us to appreciate the high degree of compression the latter achieves.

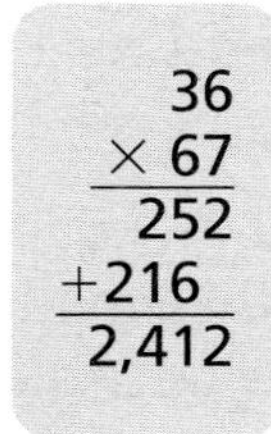

(Note that the relation between our long procedure and the standard one is the same as in the first examples: the first two products of the long method, 1,800 and 360, sum to make 2,160, and the second two products, 210 and 42, sum to make 252. These are the two partial products of the standard procedure, which are added to find the full product. All the intermediate steps in the long method are to accomplish the needed regrouping.) The downside of this compacting of the task of multiplication is that the final procedure is far from transparent. It takes considerable time and effort on the part of the teacher to make sure that students understand why it works.

Multiplication Is More Complex than Addition

We see in the previous examples that the tendency of products of one-digit numbers to be larger than their sums complicates multiplication by producing more regrouping. There is another more fundamental way in which multiplication is more complex than addition. To add two multi-digit numbers, the number of very round additions (not including regrouping) that must be done is only the number of digits in the smaller of the summands. However, to multiply the same two numbers, the number of one-digit multiplications that must be done is the *product* of the number of digits in the two numbers. Further, the multiplications must be followed by a roughly equal number of additions. The following examples, in which each digit is a 1, involve no regrouping, so each product of very round components contributes a 1 to some digit of the product. The sum of the digits in the final product therefore tells us the total number of very round multiplications involved.

$$
\begin{aligned}
11 \times 11 &= (10 + 1) \times (10 + 1) = 100 + 10 + 10 + 1 \\
&= 100 + 20 + 1 = 121
\end{aligned}
$$

$$
\begin{aligned}
111 \times 111 &= (100 + 10 + 1) \times (100 + 10 + 1) \\
&= 10{,}000 + 1{,}000 + 100 + 1{,}000 + 100 + 10 + 100 + 10 + 1 \\
&= 10{,}000 + 2{,}000 + 300 + 20 + 1 \\
&= 12{,}321
\end{aligned}
$$

In the first product, the digit sum is $1 + 2 + 1 = 4$, and in the second it is $1 + 2 + 3 + 2 + 1 = 9$. Thus, multiplying two 3-digit numbers involves 9 very round multiplications, more than twice as much work as the four multiplications for multiplying two 2-digit numbers. Multiplying two 4-digit numbers will require 16 multiplications, or four times as many as for 2-digit numbers. (The reader may enjoy finding the product $1{,}111 \times 1{,}111$.)

Flexibility for Mental Math and Estimation

Thus multiplication is intrinsically more complex than addition; but it can still be accomplished with remarkably little work relative to the size of the numbers involved, and just as in the writing of numbers, this efficiency improves as the size of the numbers increases. When the necessary operations are organized for efficiency by following one of the standard algorithms, the multiplication of three- and four-digit numbers—yielding products into the tens of millions—can be accomplished quickly by hand.

Hence, with multiplication as with addition, the decimal system supports efficient arithmetic. This is probably the feature of it that is most explicitly appreciated, and it forms the core of mathematics instruction in the elementary grades. In teaching, it is important to keep in mind that the compactness and sophistication that make the decimal system so powerful also present roadblocks for most children as they try to learn it. The considerable structure, both explicit and implicit, used in building the decimal system must be unpacked mentally by each child and then repacked. Failure to grasp, at least in some implicit form, the features discussed above, as well as the underlying Laws of Algebra, will impede further learning.

Just as for addition, the "long form" of multiplication that we have used in our discussion is, of course, a good deal more cumbersome than the usual method taught for finding products. It has also the same advantages, both for letting us see what is going on in forming a product and for promoting flexible thinking about multiplication. As with addition, one advantage with the long form is that we can use it to relate the usual procedure to mental math. In this multiplication:

$$21 \times 23 = 20 \times 20 + 1 \times 20 + 20 \times 3 + 1 \times 3 = 400 + 20 + 60 + 3 = 400 + 80 + 3 = 483$$

the usual procedure begins with computing $60 + 3 = 63$. This is done for the same reason that addition is done from left to right—to minimize rewriting. But as in addition, this means that we are paying attention to the smallest parts of the product first. If one is interested in knowing how large something is, it makes sense to pay attention to the largest parts first. In the multiplication above, it is clear that the product 20×20, of the longest very round components, is the largest. Next in size are the products of the longest very round component of one number with the next-to-longest component of the other number. The product of the single digits is the smallest of the four terms. So, if we were multiplying 21×23 mentally, we would first compute $20 \times 20 = 400$, and we would already have an idea of the size of the number. Then we would make a correction by adding $1 \times 20 + 20 \times 3 = 20 + 60 = 80$. Finally, we would add the $1 \times 3 = 3$. If the product of the digits in the smaller products is greater than 10, regrouping is necessary, and the largest digit may be affected. Still, the simple one-digit multiplication of the two longest very round components can give us an idea of what the total product will be. This provides a useful check that the numbers we get from a calculator are plausible. These ideas are discussed more carefully in "Estimation and Arithmetic" (pp. PH17–PH20).

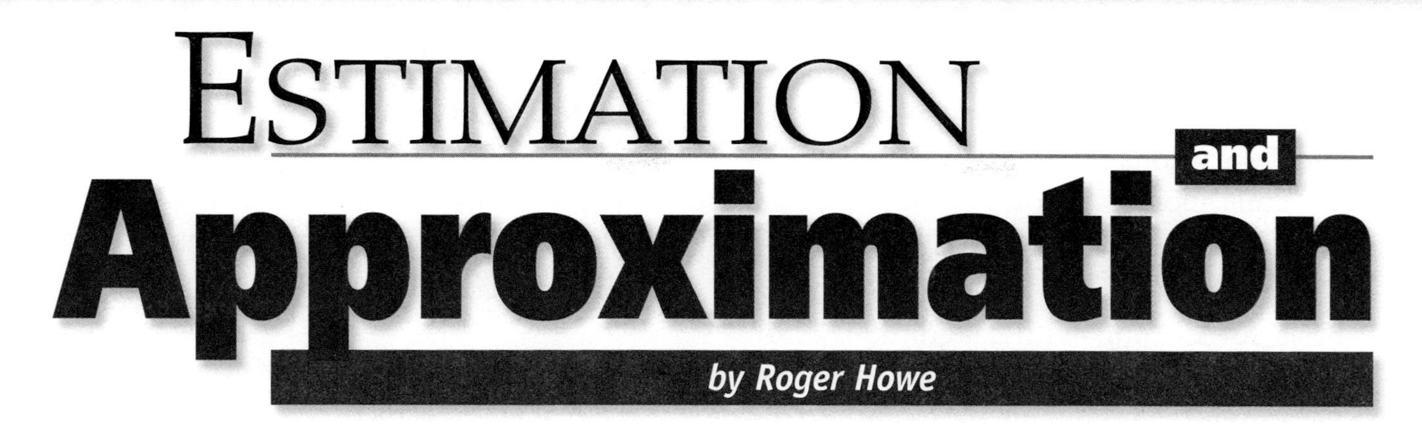

ESTIMATION and Approximation

by Roger Howe

In the articles "Doing Decimal Arithmetic: Addition" and "Doing Decimal Arithmetic: Multiplication" (pp. PH5–PH12), we see how decimal notation makes arithmetic easy. Ease of computation is very important, but the decimal system does much more for us. Estimation and approximation are almost as important as exact calculation. Many decisions we make depend on knowing only a number's approximate size—roughly how large it is—rather than knowing exactly what the number is. But estimation is not merely practical. In fact, we cannot avoid dealing with approximation and estimation. Essentially all real-life numbers—numbers that come from measurements or from some sort of data collection process—are not exact. They are subject to errors of many kinds—errors of measurement, errors of processing, and so on. They may even refer to quantities that are not well defined, that is, quantities that refer to an *ideal* situation can only be approximated in real life.

One example of approximation is the measurement of the "radius of the Earth." To mention the radius of the Earth is to implicitly treat the Earth as a sphere. But it is not exactly a sphere in the mathematical sense. It is slightly flattened at the poles, and it has a bulge near Hawaii. And, of course, it has wrinkles—mountain ranges and deep undersea trenches. (Mount Everest would fit easily into the Marianas Trench near the Philippines and still be well underwater.) It also has bumps—volcanoes such as Mauna Loa in Hawaii. These deviations from the shape of a sphere are small in a relative sense. If the Earth were the size of a billiard ball, it would look as round as the billiard ball and be even smoother. But the deviations do limit the accuracy with which we can speak of "the radius of the Earth." They mean that the "radius of the Earth" is not a definite number. That does not mean that it is not a useful number to think and talk about, but it does mean that we have to tolerate imprecision in this phenomenon, as in most. The ability to think approximately is more valuable in many situations than the ability to calculate exactly, although it is much less represented in the mathematics curriculum.

MAGNITUDE

The decimal system readily adapts to dealing with magnitude, error, and approximation. Just as with arithmetic, the very round numbers are the key. Very round numbers are numbers with a single leading digit followed by zeros—numbers like 70; 50,000; and 200. Every number is a sum of very round numbers encoded by the digits of the number. For example,

2,345 = 2,000 + 300 + 40 + 5. We call 2,000 and 300 and 40 and 5 the *very round components* of 2,345. (See "Marvelous Decimals," pp. PH1–PH4 for more details about very round numbers.)

ORDERING NUMBERS

The basis for dealing with magnitude, error, and approximation is this very simple principle: **Of the very round components of a number, the longest is the largest.** In fact, it is larger than all of the shorter very round components put together. This is true, no matter what the components are—even if the digit in the longest component is only a 1 and the digit in the next component is a 9. (Of course, this is more obvious if the situation is reversed!) Thus, the most important piece of information about the size of a (positive, whole) decimal number is the number of digits needed to represent it—the more digits, the larger the number. Any two-digit number is larger than any one-digit number, any three-digit number is larger than any two-digit number, and so on. The extreme cases are 10 > 9, or 100 > 99, or 1,000 > 999, etc. In recognition of the key role that the number of digits plays in determining the size of numbers, it is sometimes referred to as the *order of magnitude* of the number. In the less formal language of the financial world, the idea is captured in terms like "six-figure salary."

After order of magnitude, the next most important item is the leading, or first, or leftmost, digit—the digit of the longest very round component. Among numbers of the same order of magnitude, the one with the larger leading digit is larger. For example,

6,048 > 5,873   60,481 > 58,738

604,813 > 587,386

If a four-digit number begins with 2, it is at least 2 times as large as any three-digit number. If it begins with 6, it is at least six times as large, and so forth.

Making finer distinctions between numbers is not much harder. If two numbers have the same order of magnitude and the same leading digit, then the one with the larger second (from left) digit is the larger number: 85 > 83 and 8,524 > 8,396. If the first two digits are the same, then size is determined by the third digit, and if these are also the same, by the fourth digit, then the fifth, etc. For example,

854 > 852   85,475 > 85,468

8,547,521,673 > 8,547,511,384

Except for the restriction that the numbers should have the same length, this is the same principle of ordering used in dictionaries—*lexicographic order.* However, in mathematics it is not an arbitrary convention, but a natural consequence of the meaning of decimal notation.

APPROXIMATION

The principles used for comparing numbers also help us approximate numbers effectively. We can rephrase the main observation about magnitude by saying that the longest very round component of a number contains most of the information about its size. Indeed, the longest very round component of a number is always more than half of the number. For example, in the following decompositions, the first term is always larger than the second:

154 = 100 + 54   7,633 = 7,000 + 633

100 > 54   7,000 > 633

495,852 = 400,000 + 95,852

400,000 > 95,852

This means that, if we just drop the second term, we still have most of the original number left. (The larger the first digit, the truer this is. If the first digit is a 9, we still have at least 90 percent of the number left.) In short, the information provided by just the first digit already gives us a reasonable idea of what the actual number is.

If we retain more digits of the number, the accuracy of the approximation improves rapidly. If we retain the first two digits, we will always have at least 90 percent of the number. If we retain the first three digits, we have at least 99 percent of the number, and at least 99.9 percent of it with the first four digits. For example,

$$400{,}000 > 95{,}852 \qquad 490{,}000 > 10 \times 5{,}852$$
$$495{,}000 > 100 \times 852$$

In fact, these statements are very conservative, because they must remain true for the worst cases, such as 19 or 109 or 1,009, when the first few digits are as small as they can be and the remaining digits are as large as they can be. This conservatism is imposed on us by the fact that single digits can represent a nine-fold range in size. Frequently, the first digit by itself will give 90 percent of the number, and the first two digits will give close to 99 percent. In any case, retaining only the first few digits of a decimal number already captures most of the number, and the accuracy of approximation increases rapidly with the additional number of digits retained. Specifically, the possible error decreases by a factor of 10 with each additional retained digit. The approximation process consisting of replacing the rightmost digits of a number with zeros is commonly called *rounding,* or more specifically, *rounding down,* since dropping the final digits always gives a number smaller than the original one. There are other types of rounding, including "rounding up" and "rounding to the nearest," that give slight refinements and that are useful in some situations, but all three types of rounding are qualitatively similar.

Absolute and Relative Accuracy

How good an approximation is good enough? This depends on context. Approximation is inherently a thornier issue than equality, because it is not a "yes-no" kind of issue. It involves matters of judgment. It involves consideration of context. In order to say whether one number is a "good approximation" of another number, we need to know what we want from the number, what we will use it for, what kind of inference might be made from it, and similar issues. A whole field of applied mathematics, known as numerical analysis, is devoted to understanding issues of approximation. Despite possible pitfalls, we cannot escape dealing with approximation because all numbers derived from measurement are necessarily known only approximately. Automatic computation also requires attention to error and approximation because computers can represent numbers only to a certain level of accuracy.

In situations involving error and approximation, there is frequently an implicit unit. Something is large or small according to whether it is larger or smaller than this unit. Confusion can result when people discussing an issue have different ideas about what the unit is. Thus, in a discussion of waste in government, people usually get excited when they hear that "millions of dollars" are being wasted on something. This is because, in thinking about "millions of dollars," people tend to compare this figure with amounts they are familiar with, such as their own salary. Relative to most people's everyday experience, a million dollars is a lot of money. However, the federal budget is currently well over a trillion dollars ($1,000,000,000,000), and a million dollars ($1,000,000) is only one-millionth of a trillion. I do not wish in any way to defend waste in government, but I would argue that here the relevant unit is the total federal budget, and the question to ask is "What portion of the total is being wasted?" If you expect government spending to be 99 percent efficient, which is probably never the case, you would still expect it to waste 10 billion dollars ($10,000,000,000) out of a trillion. Millions just don't show up. If the government is wasting only a few million, we should be overjoyed.

Even when we know clearly what the correct unit is, there are other issues. An important one is the kind of computation that will be done using a given number. In some spectacular examples from numerical analysis, a seemingly simple computation blows up a seemingly negligible error to such an extent that the answer becomes meaningless. This kind of magnification can also happen in the real world—for example, in weather. Future weather can be very sensitive to small changes in current conditions. This sensitivity may put a serious limit on how good our weather predictions can possibly be. Thus, the issue of approximation in general is complex.

We can discuss only a few general principles and simple situations. Two quite different types of accuracy are used frequently in discussing approximation. It is important to be able to distinguish between them and to tell whether one or the other is appropriate. One is *absolute accuracy,* in which errors are compared to a fixed number and amounts smaller than the fixed number are ignored. This is seen often in financial statements, which often give figures stated in units of a thousand dollars. The other kind is *relative accuracy,* in which errors are compared to the number being approximated. Relative accuracy is what is proposed above as the appropriate kind of accuracy to be considered in a discussion of government waste.

In rounding numbers, absolute accuracy refers to the number of digits that we neglect. Relative accuracy refers to the number of digits we retain. The retained digits are called *significant digits.* For example, if we round 4,286,419 to 4,286,000, we have absolute accuracy to the thousands and relative accuracy to four significant digits. The type of accuracy that is the more relevant depends on the context.

We should note a possible ambiguity in rounding. The usual convention in dealing with rounded numbers is that the non-zero digits are accurate (except that the last digit may be off by one) and that the digits represented by zeros could have been more or less anything. However, it might happen that the last significant digit is a zero. Then the number appears to be less accurate than it is. Thus, 4,280,419 rounded to the thousands is 4,280,000, and under usual conventions, this looks as if it is rounded to ten thousands. Sometimes context can tell us that some zeros at the end of a rounded number are in fact significant, but without further information, one assumes that they represent deleted or unknown digits.

Equipped with the language of significant digits, we again ask, "How accurate is accurate enough?" When measuring physical quantities, each additional significant digit is hard won. In many situations, one or two significant digits are enough to be useful. The usefulness of percents is based on the fact that, frequently, when discussing amounts that are part of some whole, anything less than one one-hundredth of the total is small enough to be negligible. Specifying percentages is akin to having two significant figures of accuracy. To have more than four significant digits takes painstaking work, and frequently even four-digit significance is not realistic. Consider again the example of the radius of the Earth. Since this is approximately 4,000 miles, four significant figures would specify it to at least the nearest mile. However, the difference in altitude between the deepest sea trenches and the highest mountains is over 10 miles. In this situation, and many others involving physical quantities, four significant figures of accuracy are simply not attainable.

ESTIMATION and Arithmetic

by Roger Howe

In the article "Estimation and Approximation" (pp. PH13–PH16), the issues of approximation and, in particular, the technique of rounding are discussed. The present article will discuss how rounding interacts with arithmetic—specifically, with the basic operations of addition and multiplication of positive whole numbers.

ROUNDING SIMPLIFIES ARITHMETIC

Since all decimal arithmetic is based on single-digit arithmetic, rounding simplifies the mechanics of the arithmetic operations. In the addition of round numbers, the zeros can just be carried along. For example:

$$87 + 37 = 124 \text{ and } 87{,}000 + 37{,}000 = 124{,}000$$

This means that when we round off numbers, it becomes less work to add them. It is easier to add 87,000 and 37,000 than to add 87,266 and 37,495.

Zeros on the end of rounded numbers are also easy to deal with in multiplication. They can just be deleted and then reinserted after the multiplication is done. The total number of added zeros in the product is the sum of the numbers of zeros ending the two factors. For example:

$$200 \times 34 = (2 \times 100) \times 34 = (2 \times 34) \times 100 = 68 \times 100 = 6{,}800$$
$$20 \times 340 = (2 \times 10) \times (34 \times 10) = (2 \times 34) \times (10 \times 10) = 68 \times 100 = 6{,}800$$
$$2 \times 3{,}400 = 2 \times (34 \times 100) = (2 \times 34) \times 100 = 68 \times 100 = 6{,}800$$

So, rounding simplifies multiplication. It is easier to compute 20×340 than to compute 23×345. As with multiplication of very round numbers, zeros created by the product of the non-round parts of the numbers may seem to be "extra zeros." They make it seem that there are more zeros than normal. But they do not change the process. One simply has to keep in mind that the "extra" zeros come from the multiplication of the retained digits. In the multiplication $20 \times 350 = (2 \times 10) \times (35 \times 10) = (2 \times 35) \times (10 \times 10) = 70 \times 100 = 7{,}000$, the final result has three zeros. One zero came from the product 2×35, and the other two zeros, one from the 20 and one from the 350, were appended to the end of the 70.

Accuracy of Rounded Arithmetic

Although rounding simplifies arithmetic, it introduces a new issue. If we add or multiply numbers that are only approximations of actual quantities, we must ask how well the result approximates the actual sum or product. Since a full discussion of this question gets rather involved, only a few basic observations are given here.

Recall the two types of accuracy—absolute and relative—discussed in "Estimation and Approximation." Although both apply to the same rounding process, they are quite different ways of thinking about error. *Absolute error* refers to the number of decimal places ignored in rounding, while *relative error* refers to the number of decimal places that are retained. Suppose we round 49,248 down to 49,200. To describe the absolute accuracy of this, we would say we have rounded (down) to the hundreds place. To describe the relative accuracy, we would say that we have retained three significant digits.

In doing addition, absolute accuracy is the relevant consideration. The main point is that the absolute accuracy of a sum can be no better than the worst absolute accuracy of the addends. For example, consider the sum 4,300 + 280 = 4,580. This sum appears to be rounded to the tens place. However, since 4,300 is standing for any number between 4,300 and 4,399 (since we are talking about rounding down), and 280 means a number between 280 and 289, all we know about the true sum is that it is between 4,580 and 4,688. This cannot actually be represented by a single rounded number according to standard conventions, but we frequently fudge it and write it as 4,600. If we decide to represent it by a single decimal number, 4,600 is the best choice. Certainly the third digit of accuracy that is implied by the formal sum is unwarranted.

This principle is the source of humor in the story of a family visiting a natural history museum. After looking at the skeleton of a huge dinosaur, they approached the guard in the room to ask how old it was. He answered, "70 million and 12 years."

They replied, "Oh, that's very old! How do you know?"

He answered, "Well, when I started working here, they told me that it was 70 million years old, and I've been here 12 years, so now it must be 70 million and 12."

In a case in which two numbers of substantially different sizes are being added, the need to round both to the same absolute accuracy can result in seemingly paradoxical situations that involve ignoring fairly large numbers. For example, in adding the rounded numbers 40,000 + 2,800, where 40,000 has been rounded to the nearest 10,000, the 2,800 must also be rounded to that place, which means that it will round to 0! It can be very difficult to round 42,800 back to 40,000, completely writing off the 2,800. However, retaining the extra digits in the formally correct sum creates a false impression of accuracy.

For products, the parallel principle is that *relative* accuracy of a product can be no better than the *least* relative accuracy of the factors. In standard arithmetic, 80 × 74 = 5,920. However, if 80 is standing for some number between 80 and 89, then even if the 74 is completely accurate, the number 5,920 is standing for some number between 80 × 74 and 89 × 74 = 6,586. We see from the large range of possibilities in the hundreds and smaller places that it makes no sense to state a result with more than one significant digit. Even the first digit may not be completely certain, but if we want to represent the product by a single number, 6,000 is as good as we can do. The extra digits of implied accuracy in the value 5,920 are quite misleading. When using a calculator, we need to make extra effort to keep in mind that most of the digits in the rapidly produced result of a multiplication may be meaningless.

If nothing further is to be done with a number, retaining meaningless digits may do little harm—it produces some unnecessary mental clutter, but there is no reason to think that the four-digit number 5,920 is a worse approximation of the actual number it represents than 6,000 is. The real problem with retaining meaningless digits is that they may produce a false sense of accuracy, leading us to use them in calculations whose results are meaningless and misleading. This is particularly likely to happen when we do subtraction. Suppose we have two numbers, 5,920 and 6,160, neither of which is accurate to more than one significant digit but for which we have retained three digits. If we now subtract them, we get 240, but since the two numbers involved are, in fact, only accurate to the nearest 1,000, this number is totally meaningless—none of its digits represent any reality. If we now use this number in further computations, whatever we produce will be nonsense. Calculators are quite willing to produce this kind of nonsense at the push of a button. It is up to us to know when to round off.

Ballpark Estimates Using Rounding

We can use the fact that rounding simplifies arithmetic to estimate a sum or a product by doing the same operation on rounded numbers. This gives us the opportunity to check that a calculation done on a calculator is roughly correct. Such checks can guard against gross errors when we punch in the numbers to be operated on. We can simplify the arithmetic as much as we want, depending on how accurate we want our check to be. The fewer digits we retain, the easier our check computation will be. Unfortunately, it will also be less accurate. The simplest thing to check would be when we retain only the largest very round component of a number. As we have noted already in "Doing Decimal Arithmetic: Addition" and "Doing Decimal Arithmetic: Multiplication," the sum or the product of the largest very round components represents the largest single contribution to the sum. However, due to regrouping, this single very round contribution may not determine even the leading digit in the actual sum. This problem is worse for multiplication than for addition. Consider the product for

$$
\begin{aligned}
14 \times 65 &= (10 + 4) \times (60 + 5) \\
&= (10 \times 60) + (4 \times 60) + (10 \times 5) + (4 \times 5) \\
&= 600 + 240 + 50 + 20 \\
&= 910
\end{aligned}
$$

We see that, of the four products of very round components, the largest is $10 \times 60 = 600$. However, the next two terms, $4 \times 60 = 240$ and $10 \times 5 = 50$, raise the amount from 600 to near 900, and the last term, $4 \times 5 = 20$, actually puts the total over 900. Thus, although the leading product gives a substantial chunk of the final product, the other terms contribute enough so that it is a matter of judgment as to whether the 600 is a "good approximation" of the actual product. Such judgments might be challenging to young students just learning multiplication.

One way to eliminate the need for such judgments is to sandwich the actual result between two products of rounded approximations to the original factors. This would create a "ballpark" in which the exact answer should lie. This strategy relies on the following basic properties of addition and multiplication:

- When adding two numbers, if either number increases, the sum also increases.
- When multiplying two positive numbers, if either number increases, the product also increases.

These facts are referred to as *monotonicity* of addition and multiplication, respectively. The monotonicity properties suggest the following strategy for getting "ballparks" in which a sum or a product of two numbers should lie. This strategy involves rounding up as well as rounding down. Rounding up is slightly more complicated than rounding down but is still quite simple. To round down, drop the last (meaning rightmost) digits of a number and replace them with zeros. In rounding up, do the same but also add a 1 to the last non-rounded digit of the number. This will always produce a number larger than the original. Thus, 47,283 rounded down to the thousands is 47,000. Rounded up to the thousands, it is 48,000. Effectively, we have written $47{,}283 = 47{,}000 + 283$, and replaced 283 by 1,000 to do the rounding up. Rounded down to the hundreds, 47,283 is 47,200; rounded up it is 47,300. Occasionally, rounding up will create a regrouping situation, and one or more digits could turn over, creating zeros that actually represent significant digits. Thus, 49,936 rounded up to the thousands is $49{,}000 + 1{,}000 = 50{,}000$. Rounded up to the hundreds, it is $49{,}900 + 100 = 50{,}000$—the same as rounding up to the thousands. In our application, this will not cause problems.

Here is the "ballpark estimation strategy" for sums or products of two positive whole decimal numbers.

---

1. Round the numbers down (to any desired accuracy).
2. Round the numbers up (to any desired accuracy).
3. Do the same operation (that is, add or multiply) on the rounded numbers (on the two rounded up numbers and on the two rounded down numbers) as specified for the original numbers.
4. The actual sum or product should lie between the two answers calculated in Step 3 above.

Of course, the simplest arithmetic will result if the rounding leaves only one significant digit. Here are some examples. For the product $14 \times 65 = 910$, the rounded down product is $10 \times 60 = 600$ and the rounded up product is $20 \times 70 = 1{,}400$. We have $600 < 910 < 1{,}400$, showing that the product is in the right ballpark. Of course, in this case, 1,400 is more than twice as large as 600, so the ballpark is rather large! But this is to some extent unavoidable. When the leading digit is a 1, the longest very round component says less about the number than when the leading digit is greater than 1.

Here is another example, using larger leading digits. Consider the product $43 \times 826 = 35{,}518$. Round up and down to one significant digit. Rounding down gives $40 \times 800 = 32{,}000$. Rounding up gives $50 \times 900 = 45{,}000$. We do indeed have $32{,}000 < 35{,}518 < 45{,}000$, as we must if we had done the actual multiplication correctly. If we round 826 to two significant digits, the ballpark rounded down is $40 \times 820 = 32{,}800$ and rounded up is $50 \times 830 = 41{,}500$. So, we have $32{,}800 < 35{,}518 < 41{,}500$. If we round 826 to one significant digit and leave 43 at two significant digits, the ballpark is $43 \times 800 = 34{,}400$ and $43 \times 900 = 38{,}700$. If we retain two significant digits in both factors, the ballpark is $43 \times 820 = 35{,}260$ and $43 \times 830 = 35{,}690$. With one-digit accuracy in both factors, the ballpark includes numbers with a leading digit of either 3 or 4. It did not completely determine even the first digit, although it limited the possibilities to 3 or 4. With two-digit accuracy in both factors, we also have two-digit accuracy in the product. Thus, we can narrow the ballpark as much as we want at the price of doing more work. The true answer must always lie in the ballpark.

A "BLIND SPOT" IN THE ORDER OF OPERATIONS

by Liping Ma

Liping Ma is a mathematics educator and researcher. She was an elementary school teacher in China before moving to the United States in 1988. She later attended Michigan State University and Stanford University as a doctoral student. In addition to her experiences as a mathematics teacher, she is the mother of two children who attend schools in the United States. Her many experiences with the educational systems of both countries have given her a unique perspective. In the following essay, she shares her concern about a "blind spot" she has noticed in the way many American educators address the order of operations in expressions or equations.

Many teachers in the United States are fond of using the mnemonic phrase "**P**lease **E**xcuse **M**y **D**ear **A**unt **S**ally." This mnemonic is intended to be a helpful reminder of the order in which operations should be addressed in expressions or equations. "Always do **p**arentheses first, **e**xponents second, then **m**ultiplication, then **d**ivision, then **a**ddition, and then **s**ubtraction." However, using this mnemonic can cause confusion and can lead to an incorrect answer. Consider, for example, this problem.

$$5 - 3 + 2 = \blacksquare$$

If we follow the mnemonic, it means that we should add $3 + 2$ first and then subtract that answer from 5. Then our result would be 0, which is incorrect. The correct answer is 4. Do $5 - 3$ first, then add 2. To help clarify the rationale for the priority of the operations, I've provided the following hypothetical discussion between two teachers.

Teacher A: This morning, one of my students asked me why we use "Please Excuse My Dear Aunt Sally" to determine the order of operations. I wasn't really sure of the answer. Is the priority order of operations really so arbitrary?

Teacher B: I don't think it is arbitrary. In fact, I think using that mnemonic can sometimes lead to errors. First, let's think about the four basic operations: addition, subtraction, multiplication, and division. If I asked you to put the four operations into two groups, what would you do?

Teacher A: I would put addition and subtraction in one group, since I know they are closely related: $2 + 3 = 5$ gives you $5 - 3 = 2$ or $5 - 2 = 3$. I would put multiplication and division in another group. They are also closely related: $2 \times 3 = 6$ gives you $6 \div 3 = 2$ or $6 \div 2 = 3$. Also, children learn addition and subtraction first at about the same time, and then they learn multiplication and division.

Teacher B: There is a name for the relationship of the operations in each group—*inverse operation*. Addition and subtraction are a pair of inverse operations, and multiplication and division are another pair of inverse operations. And the operation of squaring a number, for example $2^2 = 4$, and the operation of finding a square root, for example $\sqrt{4} = 2$ forms yet another pair of inverse operations.

Teacher A: Inverse operations? So we put operations that are inverses of each other in the same group? Interesting!

Teacher B: Have you ever noticed that subtracting a number is the same as adding its negative?[1] For example, $5 - 3 = 5 + (^{-}3)$. On the other hand, dividing a number is equivalent to multiplying by its reciprocal. For example, $10 \div 2 = 10 \times \frac{1}{2}$.

Teacher A: I see! In this sense, we can say that addition and subtraction are essentially the same operation, and multiplication and division are essentially the same operation. That is why there is no priority between addition and subtraction and between multiplication and division! But I still don't understand why some operations have priority over others.

Teacher B: Well, you just mentioned that addition and subtraction are closely related, and so are multiplication and division. How about addition and multiplication? Do you see any connections between them?

Teacher A: Yes. Multiplication is like adding the same number many times. But I think multiplication is much more powerful than addition. For example, to know how much 7 times 5 is, we do $5 + 5 + 5 + 5 + 5 + 5 + 5$ with addition and 7×5 with multiplication. The latter is much more efficient—not to mention what would happen if we were using big numbers.

Teacher B: Now let me ask you to solve a word problem. Suppose that your school has 45 fourth graders and 32 fifth graders, and each fourth grader has 4 books and each fifth grader has 7 books. How many books do all the fourth and fifth graders have?

[1] This is why in an equation with only addition and subtraction, the position of a number can be changed if the number is given the appropriate sign.

Teacher A: This is a three-step problem. I first do $45 \times 4 = 180$, get the number of fourth graders' books, then do $32 \times 7 = 224$, get the number of fifth graders' books, and then do $180 + 224 = 404$ to get all the books for the two grades.

Teacher B: But can you put the three steps in one equation?

Teacher A: I haven't thought about it.

Teacher B: Putting them together you get $45 \times 4 + 32 \times 7 = 404$ books. Doesn't this look more efficient and concise than the three separate equations?

Teacher A: Now I see. Because multiplication has priority over addition, we are able to deal with two chunks of computation in one equation. Otherwise, we can only deal with individual operations. So, this equation has two layers— one layer deals with multiplication and the other deals with addition.

Teacher B: I like the word "chunk." The problems that mathematics deals with may be much more complicated than the word problem I just gave you. But with the priority system, an equation can have many more layers. So it can deal with chunks, sub-chunks, even several layers of sub-chunks.

Teacher A: Oh, I remember what I learned in high school. In addition to parentheses ( ), there are also brackets [ ] and braces { }. They all have priority over all operations, though there is no fixed order in which they are handled. When parentheses, brackets, and braces are in an equation, there can be as many as six "layers" in the equation.

Teacher B: Yes. Of course, in elementary school our students learn a brief version of this priority system with only three layers.

Teacher A: This short version is: do parentheses first, multiplication *and* division second, and addition *and* subtraction last. I believe that once students learn this version well and feel comfortable with it, they will be ready to face the whole operation system when they learn more advanced mathematics.

Teacher B: I think your brief version makes lots of sense. From this version, young students will learn an important concept of mathematics operations.

Teacher A: Actually, it is from your explanation! Thank you so much!

Models for FRACTIONS

The study of fractions is the deepest and most interesting part of elementary school arithmetic. It builds on all the work that has happened earlier and sets the stage for algebra. A teacher should have several models handy to help students understand the basic concepts. With practice one gets better at seeing which model will help a given student the most in a certain situation.

BY TOM ROBY

The "slices of pie" model (or "pizza" model, though pizzas come in different shapes) is almost a cliché—but for good reason. It's easier to visualize $\frac{1}{3}$ of a circle accurately and distinguish it from $\frac{1}{4}$ of a circle than it is to grasp the same fractions in a bar model. At some level this seems to be hardwired into students' minds, but it also is trained by the clock reading that students begin as soon as they get to school. The "pie" shape also works well for adding fractions since it is easy to visualize and conceptualize pieces of pie being subdivided into smaller pieces to form common denominators.

Another important model for fractions is the number line. It helps students see how the new numbers they are learning relate to familiar ones. It gives a geometric feeling to addition in that adding $\frac{1}{3}$ to $\frac{1}{2}$ can be seen as starting $\frac{1}{3}$ to the right of zero and proceeding another $\frac{1}{2}$ unit to the right. The number line also becomes essential later in the mathematical sequence when working with positive and negative fractions. The slice of pie can still be used, but only if one can convince students to think of "pie demerits," or some way that a slice of pie can count negatively!

For a concrete practical model, it's hard to beat money. Students can draw on their direct experience. It is probably worth asking students to think about why we call the twenty-five cent piece a "quarter." For a student having trouble with some concept, asking a similar question in a monetary context can pay real dividends. For example, if adding fractions is a stumbling block, give students the problem $\frac{1}{2} + \frac{1}{4}$. Ask them to tell you what they would get if they added a half-dollar to a quarter. When they answer "seventy-five cents," respond with "Good, now what's that in quarters?" "How can we see it, thinking only in quarters?" "Can I trade my half-dollar for something equivalent?" The disadvantage of money is that it only models well those fractions corresponding to the kinds of money we have—halves, fourths, tenths, twentieths, and hundredths. Just try modeling $\frac{1}{3} + \frac{1}{7}$ using money! This illustrates why it is critical for students to move beyond this model to more general ones as soon as they are able.

For a hands-on practical model, use strips of paper. Students can draw lines to divide a strip into three equal segments and then shade the first two segments. Now fold the paper along the $\frac{1}{3}$ line so that the shaded portion is folded on top of itself. Fold that in half again. When unfolded, the paper will have fold marks at $\frac{1}{6}$, $\frac{2}{6}$ (or $\frac{1}{3}$), and $\frac{3}{6}$ (or $\frac{1}{2}$). This helps students see the equivalent fractions. An extra folding in half will produce twelfths, and so on.

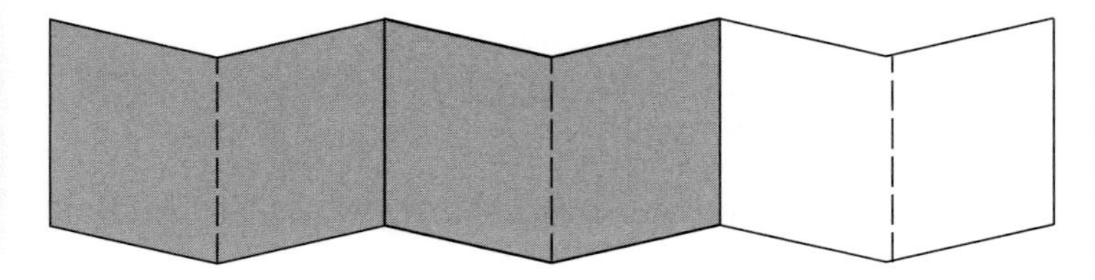

Paper or geometric models are excellent for helping students understand the reason underlying the rule for multiplication of fractions:

$$\text{product} = \frac{\text{product of numerators}}{\text{product of denominators}}$$

For example, to model $\frac{3}{4} \times \frac{2}{3}$, divide a (not too thin) strip of paper into thirds, starting from the left edge. Fold it in half, this time top to bottom, so that the fold runs through the middle of the strip. One more top-to-bottom fold will place fold marks at heights $\frac{1}{4}$, $\frac{1}{2}$, and $\frac{3}{4}$. Now unfold the paper and shade the small rectangles that fall within the lower three horizontal strips and the leftmost two vertical strips. You should get something like this:

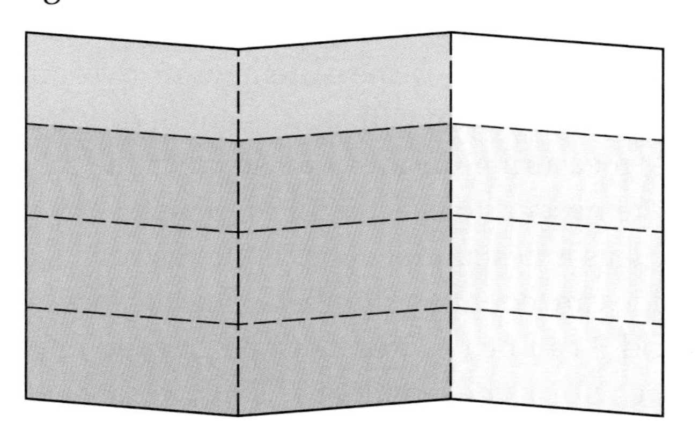

In this example, $\frac{3}{4}$ represents the fraction along the left side, and $\frac{2}{3}$ represents the fraction running along the bottom. So, the product of the numerators represents the number of rectangles that get shaded, and the product of the denominators represents the total number of small rectangles.

$$\frac{3}{4} \times \frac{2}{3} = ?$$

$$\frac{3 \times 2 \text{ number of shaded rectangles}}{4 \times 3 \text{ total number of small rectangles}}$$

We divide the number of shaded rectangles by the total number of rectangles to get the product.

$$\frac{3 \times 2}{4 \times 3} = \frac{6}{12}, \text{ or } \frac{1}{2}$$

Actual paper isn't necessary to show this model to students—a carefully drawn picture will do. This is faster when reviewing the concept, but the paper folding drives the concept home when students are learning it for the first time. It's important that students work with strips of paper on their own to model a couple of multiplication problems after they have seen it presented. Then they will never have any trouble with the rule for multiplying fractions.

Visual models are helpful even for whole numbers and their operations. Because fractions are harder to conceptualize, few students can be successful in using them without the benefits of visual models of several types.

GEOMETRY and Measurement

by David G. Wright

In order to teach geometry to young children, teachers must develop competence in the following areas:

- **Developing spatial sense, including an understanding of one, two, and three dimensions,**
- **Understanding basic shapes and their properties,**
- **Communicating geometric ideas,**
- **Understanding length, area, and volume.**

CBMS Mathematical Education of Teachers Project, Draft Report March, 2000

Geometry is visual and beautiful. It is a strand in mathematics in which precise definitions give meaning to shapes, measurements, and even addition and multiplication of numbers. In this article we look at understanding measurement of length, area, and volume and developing spatial sense.

Linear Measurement—Measuring One Dimension

The number of units needed to measure a line segment depends on the basic unit chosen. The basic unit can be an inch, a foot, a yard, a centimeter, a meter, or a kilometer. It can even be the length of a paper clip. Whatever the basic unit of length, students should know that a length of 3 means that when 3 of the basic units are abutted, the total length is the length of the object being measured. The 3 units cover the whole length, but they do not overlap. As simple as this idea is, it must be completely understood by students before any other discussion of measurement of length, area, or volume takes place.

What do we mean when we say that an object has a length of $3\frac{2}{7}$? If one of our unit lengths is divided into seven equal pieces, the length of any one of them is $\frac{1}{7}$. The length of two of them abutted has a length of $\frac{2}{7}$. Thus, a length of $3\frac{2}{7}$ means that if three unit lengths and two $\frac{1}{7}$ lengths are abutted, the resulting length is the same as that of the object being measured. So, we see that linear measurement gives a geometric understanding to fractions. It also gives a geometric meaning to the addition of fractions. The sum of $\frac{4}{3}$ and $\frac{7}{2}$ is simply the length of two line segments of lengths $\frac{4}{3}$ and $\frac{7}{2}$ when they are abutted. Linear measure is also used to measure the perimeter of a polygon and the circumference of a circle.

Area Measurement—Measuring Two Dimensions

Now let us consider measurement of area—a measurement of two dimensions. The unit of measurement is now a square with a side length of 1. We call such a square a *unit square.* Thus, measuring the area of a shape is the same as saying how many unit squares are needed to exactly fill the shape so that the squares abut but do not overlap. This is best understood in the case of a rectangle in which the lengths of the sides are counting numbers. For instance, a rectangle with sides of lengths 2 and 3 can be covered with no overlaps by two rows of 3 copies of the unit square with a side length of 1. Thus, the area of this rectangle is 2×3, or 6 square units.

In general, the area of a rectangle is the product of the lengths of the sides, or the dimensions of length and width. This works even for fractional lengths and gives meaning to the multiplication of fractions. For instance, consider a rectangle with sides of lengths $\frac{2}{7}$ and $\frac{3}{5}$. What could the area of this rectangle be? The first thing that should be noticed is that it must be less than 1 square unit because it fits inside a unit square. So, the answer should be a fraction of a unit square. But what fraction is it? Consider a unit square and divide the vertical side into 7 equal pieces (the denominator of one dimension—$\frac{2}{7}$) and the horizontal side into 5 equal pieces (the denominator of the second dimension—$\frac{3}{5}$). Using the divisions on the vertical side, slice the square into 7 equal rectangles. Now, using the divisions on the vertical side, slice each of the 7 equal rectangles into 5 equal pieces. Thus, we have $5 \times 7 = 35$ equal rectangles that do not overlap filling the unit square. So, the area of any one of these rectangles must be $\frac{1}{35}$. Furthermore, a rectangle with sides of lengths $\frac{2}{7}$ and $\frac{3}{5}$ is filled up with 6 of these rectangles (the product 2×3), each of which has an area of $\frac{1}{35}$. So, we can see that the area of the rectangle is $\frac{6}{35}$, or the product $\frac{2}{7} \times \frac{3}{5}$. This example gives a geometric meaning to the product of two fractions.

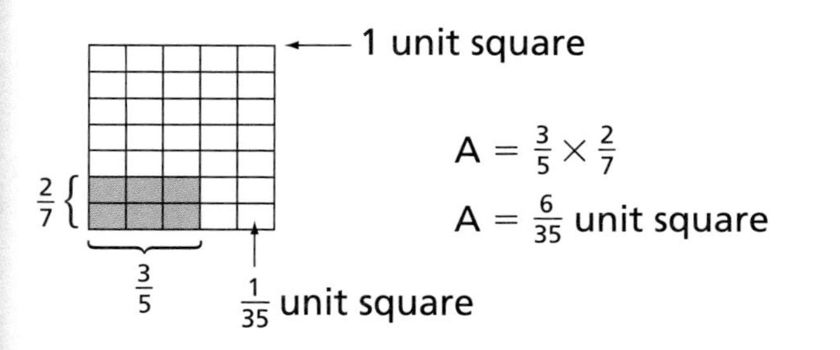

Area is also used to measure triangles. A triangle cannot be filled up by unit squares without some cutting. A simpler way to get the area of a right triangle is to find the area of two copies. These two copies can fit together to form a rectangle. The area of each right triangle is half the area of the rectangle.

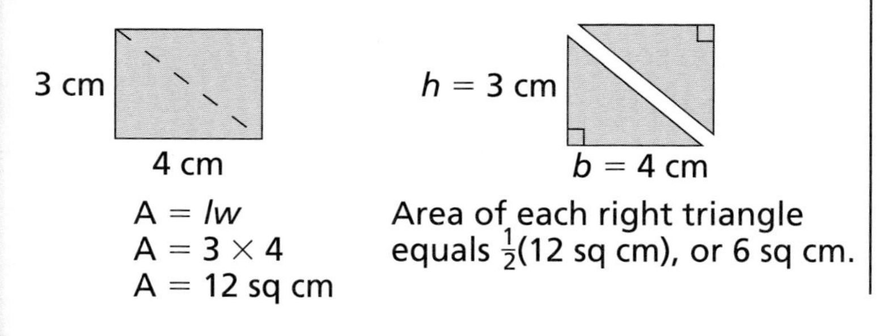

In general, knowing how to find the area of right triangles enables you to find the area of any triangle by looking at the sum or difference of areas of right triangles. The area of the following triangle *BDF* placed inside a rectangular grid can be found by computing the area of the rectangle and then subtracting the area of the right triangles.

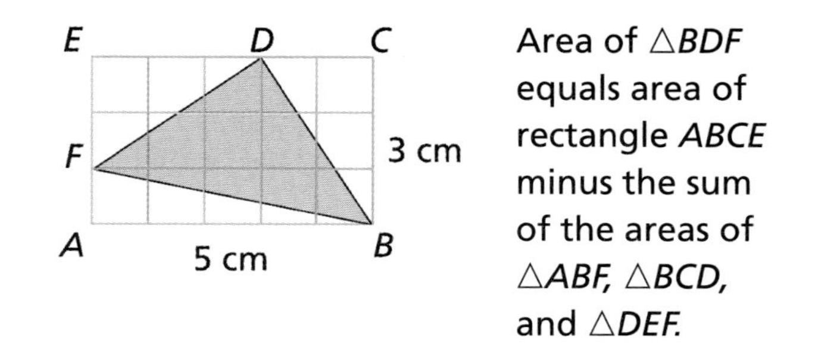

Area also measures other plane shapes, like parallelograms, trapezoids, and other polygons. These areas can be computed by breaking the shape, or an even larger shape, into triangles or rectangles that do not overlap and then computing the area of each piece.

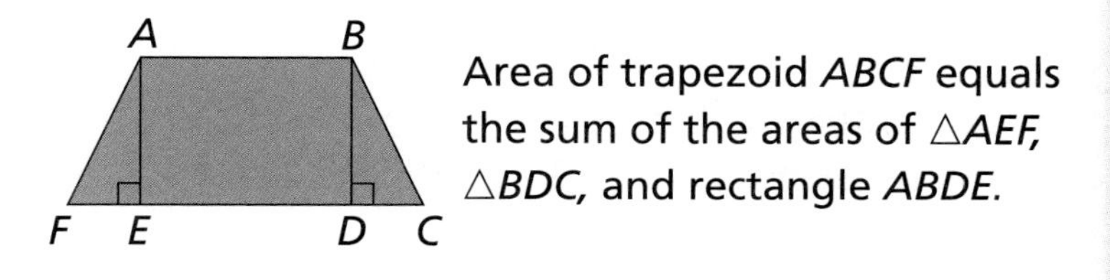

A
B
F
E
D
C
Area of trapezoid ABCF equals the sum of the areas of △AEF, △BDC, and rectangle ABDE.

We also find area of a circle (technically inside the circle). The area of a circle cannot be computed as above. A precise description about how area is computed requires the ideas of calculus, but the following picture shows that a circle can be cut to almost form a rectangle whose height is the radius and whose base is half the circumference. The area of this "rectangle" is the area of the circle. Since the circumference is $2 \times \pi \times$ radius, we can see that the formula for the area of the circle is πr^2.

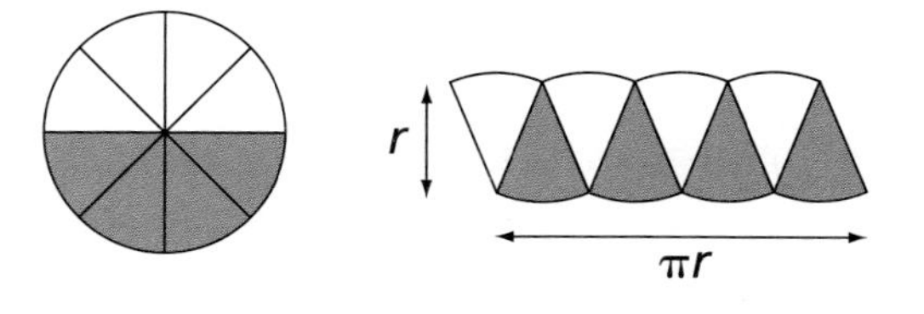

Area also measures the surface of a solid. This is most easily done for a solid like a square pyramid, where the faces are triangles and the base is a square. Finding the surface area of a solid requires finding the area of each of the faces of the solid and finding the sum of the areas.

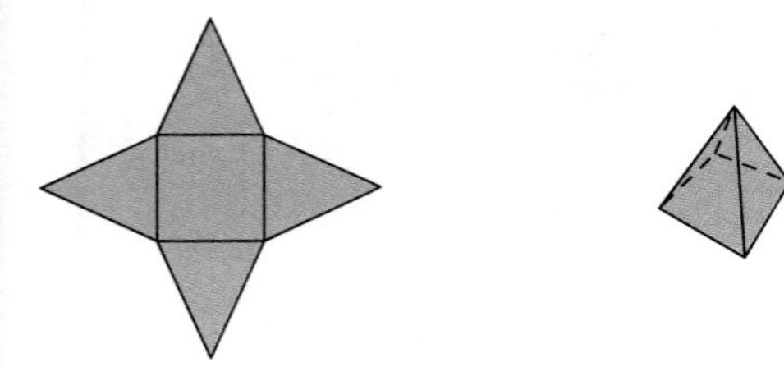

Surface area of a square pyramid equals area of square base plus the sum of the areas of the four triangular faces.

Volume Measurement—Measuring Three Dimensions

The volume of a solid is computed by finding how many unit cubes (where each edge is length 1) are needed to fill the solid with no gaps or overlaps. This is most easily done for a rectangular prism (box) where each of the edges has a natural number for a length. For example, a box whose edge lengths are 2, 3, and 4 has two layers, each of which contains $3 \times 4 = 12$ cubes. So the total volume is $2 \times 3 \times 4 = 24$ cubic units.

We measure volume for other solid objects, such as cones, pyramids, and spheres (filled in). If the previous examples are well understood, the idea of volume should not be too difficult. However, except for the rectangular prism, the volume formulas are a bit harder to explain.

Developing Spatial Sense—Understanding One, Two, and Three Dimensions

Spatial sense is "the ability to form a mental image of an object or set of objects, to recognize the structure of such objects, and to decompose those objects into component parts and recombine them in correct relation to one another" (CBMS Mathematical Education of Teachers Project, Draft Report, March 2000). Much of what went on in our discussion of understanding length, area, and volume also required the use of spatial sense. Here is an excellent problem that will help develop spatial sense.

A number of white cubes with an edge length of 1 are fitted together to build a cube with an edge length of 3. The outside of this cube is painted red. How many unit cubes have been painted on

at least one face?
exactly one face?
exactly two faces?
exactly three faces?

Repeat the problem for cubes with edge lengths of 4, 5, or some other number greater than 3.

There are various strategies for solving the first question. One is to carefully count the painted unit cubes in some order so as to find the total and not have any repetitions. A simpler strategy is to notice that the volume of the cube is 27. When the painted cubes are taken away, there is only one cube remaining. So, the number of painted cubes is 26.

Basic two- and three-dimensional shapes have mathematical definitions. A rectangle, for instance, is a quadrilateral (four-sided polygon) with right angles. From this definition, it follows that a square is also a rectangle. It is important for students to know that a square is a special kind of rectangle. A square is a rectangle in which all the sides have equal length. A rectangle may or may not be a square depending on whether the sides have equal length. A triangle is a polygon with 3 sides. Since the definition says nothing about equal sides, students need to be exposed to a variety of triangles so that they do not get the idea that all triangles must be equilateral. Through such experience students can learn to communicate geometric ideas and to form mental images of shapes so that they understand the component parts of the shapes and their relationships.

CONCEPTUAL UNDERSTANDING
The Power of Models and Visuals

by Evan Maletsky

Conceptual understanding is the foundation upon which mathematical thinking is built. For students to be good critical thinkers and effective problem solvers in mathematics, they need both understanding and skill in dealing with the concepts they have been taught. How do we build a solid understanding of mathematical concepts in our classrooms?

Models—Powerful Tools for Building Understanding

Many abstract concepts have their beginnings in concrete, hands-on experiences. This is especially true when it comes to the learning process that takes place in the mathematics classroom. Models offer powerful tools for developing solid understanding of mathematical concepts.

Sometimes, the best models for the classroom are made from the simplest of things. A 2-in. × 8-in. strip of paper may not look like much to work with at first glance. But it may, in fact, be just the needed visual model to give meaning to an otherwise abstract concept.

Have students fold the strip in half and in half again, open it up, and look at the unfolded strip. What mathematical ideas would you want your students to see when they look at this unfolded strip?

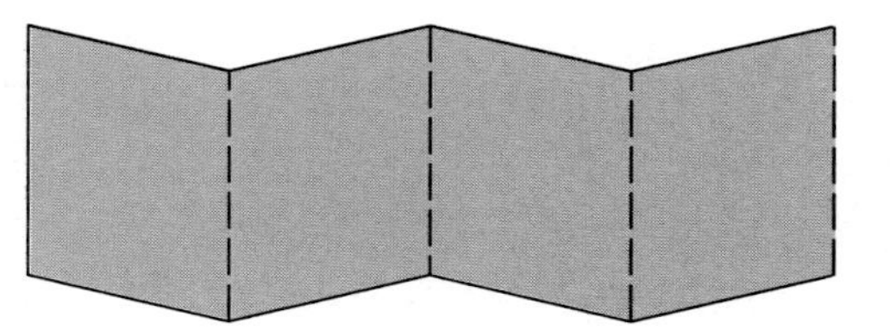

Compare the areas of the newly formed squares with that of the original rectangle. Each of the 2-in. squares has $\frac{1}{4}$ the area of the original rectangle, but it does not have $\frac{1}{4}$ of the perimeter. Many students confuse area with perimeter, and many think that the terms mean the same thing. Understanding the one-dimensional property of perimeter and comparing it with the two-dimensional property of area is fundamental to an understanding of the concepts of both perimeter and area. This model can serve to reinforce these key concepts.

Of course, there is much more that students need to see in this folded strip of paper. For example, everyone sees the 4 squares, but not everyone sees the other 6 rectangles that are there. To help students see all 10 rectangles, label the four square parts, in order, as A, B, C, and D. Then use the letters to name the different rectangles.

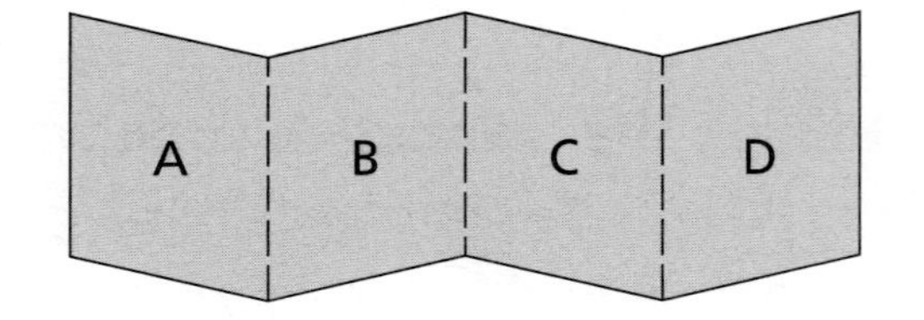

Rectangles: **ABCD, ABC, BCD**
AB, BC, CD, A, B, C, and D

Identify 1 rectangle made from all four squares, 2 rectangles from three squares, 3 rectangles from two squares, and 4 rectangles from one square. One quickly sees the sum of the number of rectangles, 1 + 2 + 3 + 4 = 10. If the strip were folded into five parts, there would be 1 + 2 + 3 + 4 + 5 = 15 rectangles. As shown in the table, the number of rectangles shows a nice pattern involving the triangular numbers.

Number of creases	0	1	2	3	4	5	6
Number of parts	1	2	3	4	5	6	7
Number of rectangles	1	3	6	10	15	21	28

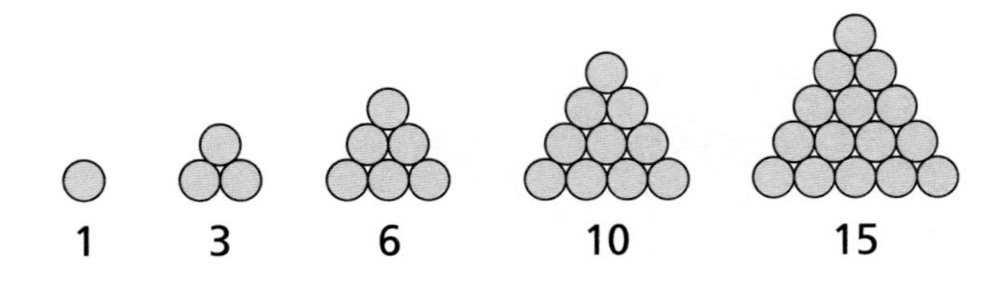

In general, fold the strip into n connected parts and use the formula $\frac{n(n+1)}{2}$ to find the total number of rectangles. This number is a triangular number.

This same two-dimensional flat strip can easily be folded into models that are three-dimensional when studying the concept of volume. Use 1-inch wooden cubes as units of volume. Fill the models of a 2-in. cube and a 1-in. × 3-in. × 2-in. rectangular prism. Use these volumes to estimate that of a triangular prism.

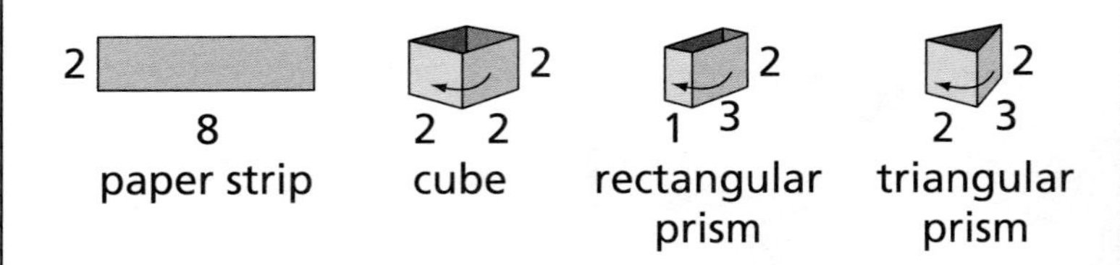

This activity sets in motion the development of the relationship of linear dimensions to volume. With different folding patterns, prisms of other shapes can easily be constructed and explored by your students. This same strip of paper, folded in different ways, creates models of prisms with different volumes. Fold it into eight equal 1-in. parts to form a prism with a regular octagon as a base. Its volume will be greater than that of the cube. For the maximum volume, don't fold it at all. Just curl it around to form a cylinder.

Models help bring in the dynamics of geometry. Only by seeing the action and change that comes from forming these different solids will students really begin to understand fully the concept of volume.

Visuals—A Way of Seeing Mathematics

Many arithmetic and algebraic concepts are abstractions in the eyes of the students because they don't see any reality in these concepts. Here is where models can offer visual support to numerical ideas.

Consider for a moment the concept of percent. Many students struggle with percent. They've been taught the computational algorithms, but what do they see? Even many of those who get the correct numerical results to percent problems have little if anything to say about what those numbers mean.

Think again about our folded strip. If the whole strip represents 100 percent, then each of the four squares is a visual model for 25 percent. The squares can be combined with the eye to show 50 percent and 75 percent as well.

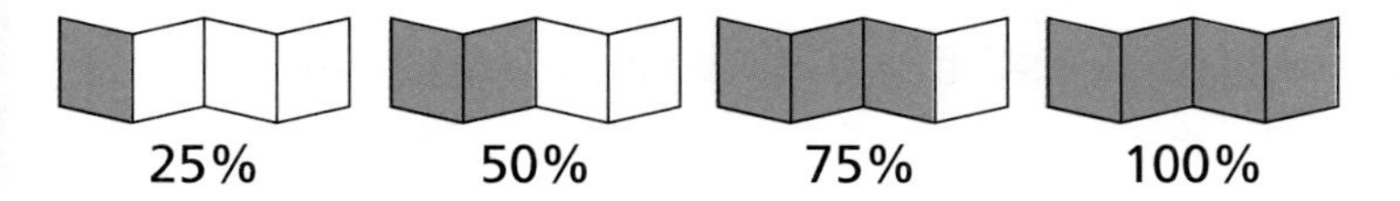

Of course, if a small square represents the whole, or 100 percent, then, from the very same model, we can see 100 percent, 200 percent, 300 percent, and 400 percent. But then, we can assign any value at all to the squares or to the strip. Suppose we call the whole strip the number 12. Then, through areas, we quickly see the numbers 3, 6, and 9 as well.

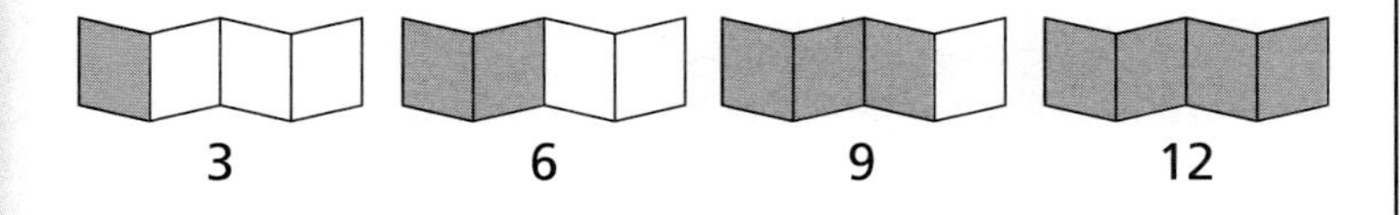

Maybe your students see even more. The same number of squares are shaded to show both 9 and 75 percent. Does this mean that 75 percent of 12 is 9? Clearly, it does.

On one of the past National Assessment of Educational Progress tests, eighth graders were asked to find 75 percent of 12. Sadly, less than half answered correctly. One wonders what it was that they saw, if anything, in trying to do this problem.

Our students need to develop good number sense. That comes from more than just practice in computation. It requires a vast and varied set of experiences that include concrete models and visual images of number relationships. This is especially important when it comes to estimation.

As an example, consider again our paper strip. Have each student fold it at some random point of their choice. Then assign some number to the area of the original strips and have the students estimate the corresponding number for the areas of the two parts. Watch how they work. Note if they do any computation. Ask them to write down the process they use. See if they use rounding or compatible numbers or just wild guesses. The results may well be very revealing.

If the original rectangle were assigned an area of 492, how would you go about estimating the areas of the two parts shown below?

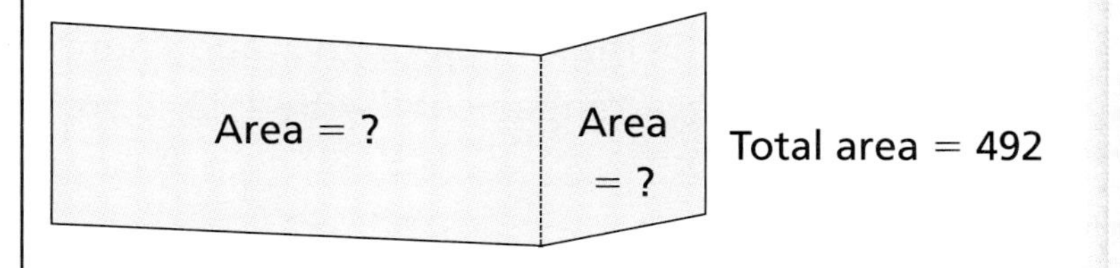

Concrete to Pictorial to Abstract

Models and visuals play a critical part in the concrete and pictorial stages of learning. They are essential to building the conceptual understanding that is needed, ultimately, to do abstract thinking. In *Harcourt Math* the approach to building mathematical concepts is to provide learning experiences based on reasoning before presenting practice. Throughout the years, mathematics has been the model for logic and reasoning. The foundation for success in this arena is built on the understanding of the basic concepts developed in the elementary school years.

Think again about our folded strip. This time, number the squares 1, 2, 3, and 4 on one side and 5, 6, 7, and 8 on the other side, with the 8 behind the 1. Now tear the strip apart into four squares, numbered front and back. Think of the numbers as digits, and ask some arrangement questions to reinforce the concept of place value.

- How many two-digit numbers can be formed with the digit 2 in the tens place?

- Do you see why the number 27 cannot be formed?

- What are the 24 different three-digit numbers possible with 2 in the tens place?
- What are the 48 different four-digit numbers possible with 2 in the tens place?

Adapt the example to any grade level you desire. Simplify the problem by using only the digits 1, 2, 3, and 4 on one side. At a more challenging level, make the problem a cooperative learning activity in which students use the digits 1 through 8 and count all possible arrangements with 1, 2, 3, or 4 digits.

one-	two-	three-	four-digit choices
8 +	8×6 +	$8 \times 6 \times 4$ +	$8 \times 6 \times 4 \times 2$

$= 8 + 48 + 192 + 384 = 632$

Moving from a simple modeling of two-digit numbers and the place-value concept at the concrete stage, this activity can quickly take us into the visual and abstract stages of mathematical reasoning.

At every level, a mathematics program must offer a rich blend of concept development, skill-oriented activities, and problem-solving opportunities. *Harcourt Math* captures these ideas in a new and refreshing way. It is the best way to reach and teach our students mathematics.

Mathematics and the mathematical experience must tickle the senses as well as sharpen and stretch the mind. It is through handling, seeing, and thinking experiences that students can sense the excitement, appreciate the beauty, and share in the creativity of the subject.

References

National Council of Teachers of Mathematics (1989). *Curriculum and Evaluation Standards for School Mathematics.* Reston, Virginia.

National Council of Teachers of Mathematics (2000). *Principles and Standards for School Mathematics.* Reston, Virginia.

National Council of Teachers of Mathematics (1991). *Professional Standards for Teaching Mathematics.* Reston, Virginia.

Sobel, M., and E. Maletsky (1999). *Teaching Mathematics: A Sourcebook of Aids, Activities, and Strategies.* Needham Heights, Massachusetts: Allyn and Bacon.

Effective Practice: Memorizing the Number Facts

by Grace M. Burton

Almost everyone agrees that children need to memorize the number facts. Indeed, when teachers and parents talk, one of the most frequently asked questions about school mathematics is, "How can I get the children to stop counting on their fingers?" After nearly a century of educational research, some strategies for assuring memorization have been developed. You may wish to consider them as you plan your mathematics program. To encourage the memorization of number facts:

$3 \times 5 = 15$

- **Build understanding first.** All of us memorize more easily when we understand what is to be memorized. This necessary understanding can be developed when children have many chances to model the facts with real objects and to illustrate the meaning of the facts with pictures.
- **Make clear that the goal is memorization.** When children are told to "learn their facts," it may not be obvious to them that adults mean they should immediately produce a sum or product when given two numbers. While there is a time in early instruction when "figuring out" is important, direct recall is the final goal, and children should be aware of this.
- **Have children thoroughly explore the Commutative and the Identity Properties for addition and multiplication.** When children truly believe that 3×6 and 6×3 (or $3 + 6$ and $6 + 3$) have the same answer, their memorization task is cut in half. When they accept that the sum of any number plus 0 is the number they started with (and that any number times 1 is the number they started with), there are 19 fewer addition or multiplication facts to be memorized.

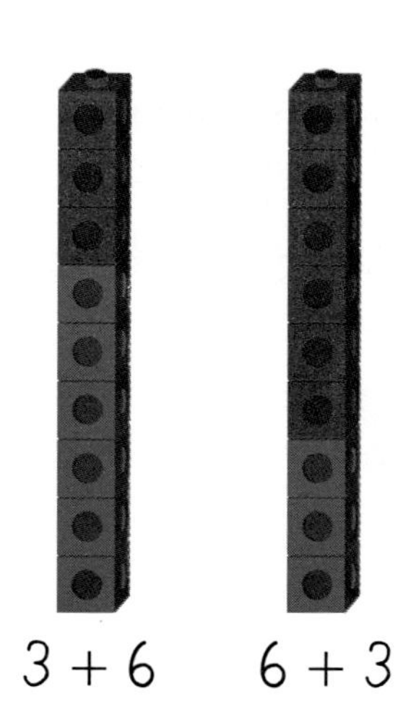

$3 + 6$ $6 + 3$

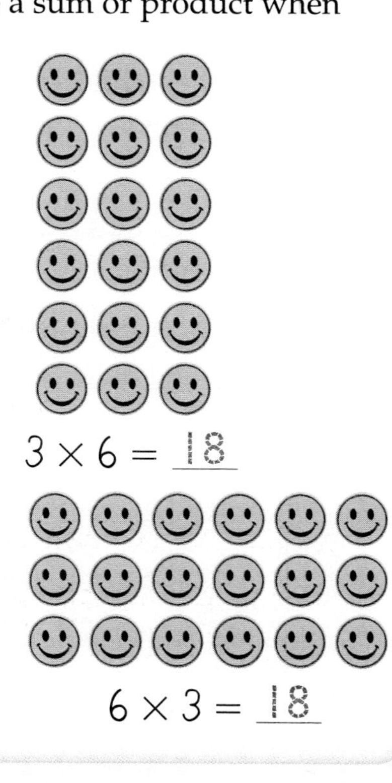

$3 \times 6 = 18$

$6 \times 3 = 18$

- **Assign memorization of the easier facts first.** Facts with 1, 2, or 3 as addends or factors provide important helps in memorization.

Easier Facts

+	0	1	2	3	4	5	6	7	8	9
0	0	1	2	3	4	5	6	7	8	9
1	1	2	3	4	5	6	7	8	9	10
2	2	3	4	5	6	7	8	9	10	11
3	3	4	5	6	7	8	9	10	11	12
4	4	5	6	7	8	9	10	11	12	13
5	5	6	7	8	9	10	11	12	13	14
6	6	7	8	9	10	11	12	13	14	15
7	7	8	9	10	11	12	13	14	15	16
8	8	9	10	11	12	13	14	15	16	17
9	9	10	11	12	13	14	15	16	17	18

- **Focus on only a small group of facts at a time.** Anyone faced with memorizing 100 items might feel overwhelmed. Asking that five or fewer items be memorized seems (and is) a much more doable assignment. These might be a fact family or a set of addends that have the same sum.

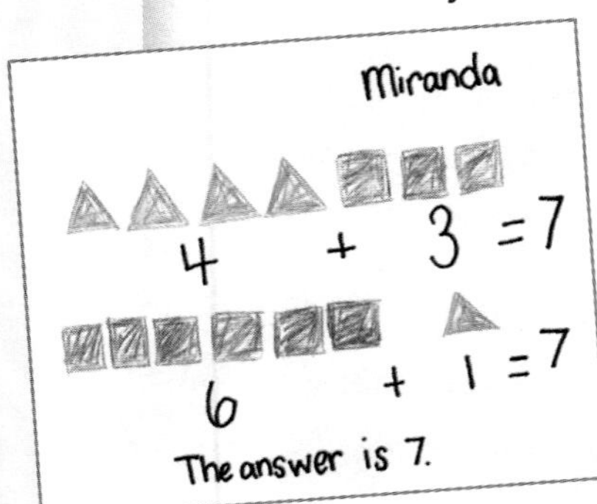
Miranda
4 + 3 = 7
6 + 1 = 7
The answer is 7.

- **Encourage parents to "hear" a few facts frequently.** You may wish to provide parents with an assigned "fact family" or set of facts for each week and suggest that they use some of the time they are in the car with their children or doing chores together to review these facts.

- **Have children keep a private record of the facts that they have memorized.**

Facts I Know by Heart

×	0	1	2	3	4	5	6	7	8	9
0	~~0~~	~~0~~	~~0~~	~~0~~	~~0~~	~~0~~	~~0~~	~~0~~	~~0~~	~~0~~
1	~~0~~	~~1~~	~~2~~	~~3~~	~~4~~	~~5~~	~~6~~	~~7~~	~~8~~	~~9~~
2	~~0~~	~~2~~	~~4~~	~~6~~	~~8~~	~~10~~	~~12~~	~~14~~	~~16~~	~~18~~
3	~~0~~	~~3~~	~~6~~	~~9~~	12	~~15~~	18	21	24	27
4	~~0~~	~~4~~	~~8~~	12	16	~~20~~	24	28	32	36
5	~~0~~	~~5~~	~~10~~	15	20	~~25~~	30	35	40	45
6	~~0~~	~~6~~	~~12~~	18	24	~~30~~	36	42	48	54
7	~~0~~	~~7~~	~~14~~	21	28	~~35~~	42	49	56	63
8	~~0~~	~~8~~	~~16~~	24	32	~~40~~	48	56	64	72
9	~~0~~	~~9~~	~~18~~	27	36	~~45~~	54	63	72	81

By providing children with these strategies for memorizing addition and multiplication facts, teachers and parents can work together to empower children with a potent tool for mathematics investigation and problem solving.

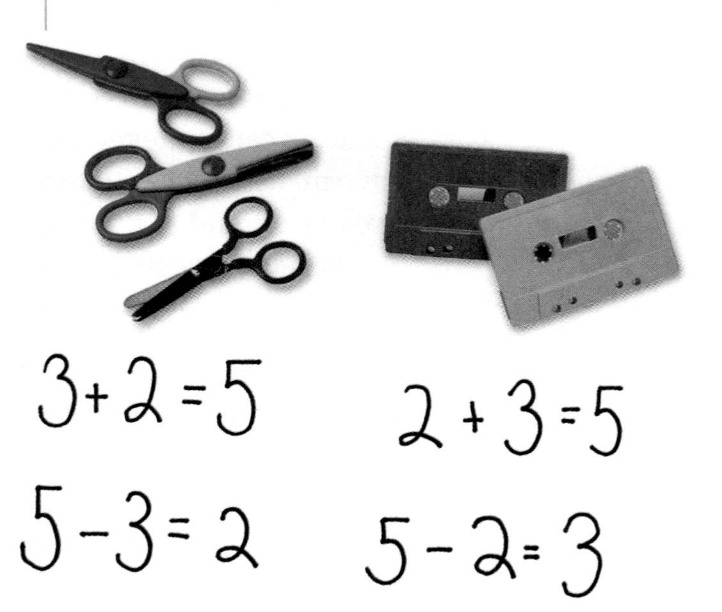
3 + 2 = 5
2 + 3 = 5
5 − 3 = 2
5 − 2 = 3

References

Ashlock, Robert B. (1998). *Error Patterns in Computation.* Seventh Edition. Columbus, Ohio: Merrill.

Rathmell, Edward C. "Using Thinking Strategies to Teach the Basic Facts." In *Developing Computational Skills,* edited by Marilyn N. Suydam. Reston, Virginia: NCTM, 1978.

Thornton, Carol A. and Smith, Paula J. "Action Research: Strategies for Learning Subtraction Facts," *Arithmetic Teacher*, 35 (April 1988), 8–11.

Thorndike, E. L. (1925). *The Psychology of Arithmetic.* New York: Macmillan.

Van de Walle, John A. (1998). *Elementary and Middle School Mathematics: Teaching Developmentally.* Third Edition. New York: Longman.

Effective Practice:

Building Computational and Procedural Efficiency

by Grace M. Burton

Some teachers and parents believe that when children are learning to use the whole-number algorithms for addition, subtraction, multiplication, and division, the more practice they do, the more likely they will learn. Educational research suggests that there are more effective strategies to accomplish efficiency with the whole-number algorithms. While practice is indeed important, there are ways to structure this practice so that children develop competency with the standard algorithms in an efficient way.

To encourage efficiency in the use of whole-number algorithms, you may wish to incorporate some of these research-based ideas:

- **Use realistic contexts to build understanding.** When children see a need for mathematics in their own lives, they are more apt to believe that there is a reason to apply themselves to learning. Teachers can help children appreciate the usefulness of algorithms when they present story problems of interest and when they ask children to write story problems for which a given algorithm is appropriate.

Brad gets an allowance of $12 each week. Sylvia's allowance is $50 a month. How much money does each receive in a year? Who gets more money? How much more?

- **Ensure that the required number facts have been memorized.** Even children who "know their facts" profit from practice on a regular basis. Setting a time for a quick review of a few facts, such as first thing every morning, helps them keep facts "at the ready." Playing games that require the use of number facts is also a good idea. Instant recall of the facts allows children to concentrate on the steps in the algorithms without having to stop to figure out a needed number fact.

- **Choose models that closely mirror the base-ten system.** When the link between the model and the written symbols is clear, children more easily make the connection between actions with real objects and the written record of those actions. Therefore, using materials based on our base-ten system that illustrate that one 10 equals ten 1s, etc., is crucial. Efficient teaching of the standard algorithms calls for extensive use of materials, such as base-ten blocks, sticks of ten connecting cubes, or bean sticks. The most effective way to use these materials is to have children model the problem with the materials, write the algorithm to be completed, and then record step-by-step what they do with the materials.

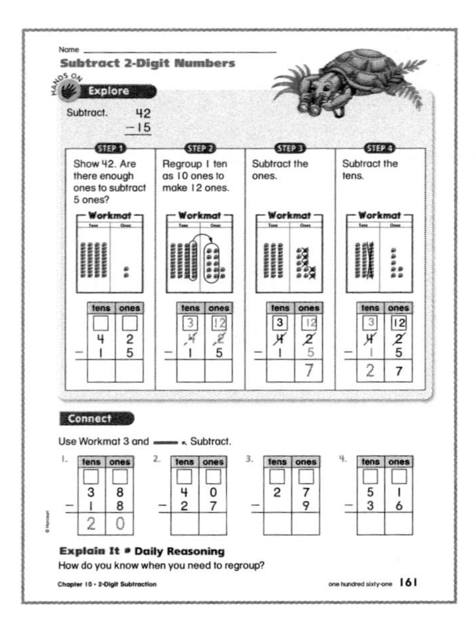
Name

Subtract 2-Digit Numbers

HANDS ON **Explore**

Subtract. $42 - 15$

STEP 1 Show 42. Are there enough ones to subtract 5 ones?

STEP 2 Regroup 1 ten as 10 ones to make 12 ones.

STEP 3 Subtract the ones.

STEP 4 Subtract the tens.

	tens	ones
	3	12
	~~4~~	~~2~~
−	1	5
	2	7

Connect

Use Workmat 3 and ▬ •. Subtract.

1. 38 − 18 = 20
2. 40 − 27
3. 27 − 9
4. 51 − 36

Explain It • Daily Reasoning

How do you know when you need to regroup?

Chapter 10 • 2-Digit Subtraction — one hundred sixty-one 161

- **Encourage children to estimate answers before computing or to check the reasonableness of their computation.** Helping children decide what a reasonable answer to an example might be will help alert them to answers that are not reasonable. Directly teaching and frequently reviewing estimation strategies encourage students to thoughtfully consider their answers. Estimation is a particularly important real-life skill, since most adults estimate rather than compute to find exact answers to solve everyday problems.

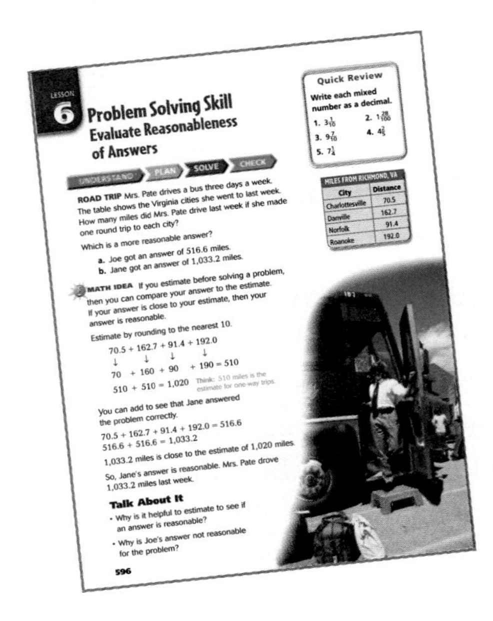
LESSON 6

Problem Solving Skill
Evaluate Reasonableness of Answers

UNDERSTAND · PLAN · SOLVE · CHECK

ROAD TRIP Mrs. Pate drives a bus three days a week. The table shows the Virginia cities she went to last week. How many miles did Mrs. Pate drive last week if she made one round trip to each city?

Which is a more reasonable answer?

a. Joe got an answer of 516.6 miles.
b. Jane got an answer of 1,033.2 miles.

MATH IDEA If you estimate before solving a problem, then you can compare your answer to the estimate. If your answer is close to your estimate, then your answer is reasonable.

Estimate by rounding to the nearest 10.

$70.5 + 162.7 + 91.4 + 192.0$
$70 + 160 + 90 + 190 = 510$
$510 + 510 = 1{,}020$ Think: 510 miles is the estimate for one-way trips.

You can add to see that Jane answered the problem correctly.

$70.5 + 162.7 + 91.4 + 192.0 = 516.6$
$516.6 + 516.6 = 1{,}033.2$

1,033.2 miles is close to the estimate of 1,020 miles.

So, Jane's answer is reasonable. Mrs. Pate drove 1,033.2 miles last week.

Talk About It

- Why is it helpful to estimate to see if an answer is reasonable?
- Why is Joe's answer not reasonable for the problem?

Quick Review

Write each mixed number as a decimal.

1. $3\frac{1}{10}$ 2. $1\frac{28}{100}$ 3. $9\frac{7}{10}$ 4. $4\frac{2}{5}$ 5. $7\frac{1}{4}$

MILES FROM RICHMOND, VA	
City	Distance
Charlottesville	70.5
Danville	162.7
Norfolk	91.4
Roanoke	192.0

596

- **Check for understanding after a few examples have been completed.** Whenever children practice a skill, it is easier to acquire proficiency if errors are caught early. The same is true when children are developing computational proficiency. Teachers who provide guided practice and diagnose for errors are supported in this strategy by years of research. In *Harcourt Math,* students are given exercises in which they must find and correct an error—an effective way to check whether students understand the concept or procedure well enough to detect and correct errors. Teachers are provided a *Common Error Alert* in some lesson plans in the *Teacher's Edition* to assist in the process of diagnosing and analyzing students' errors.

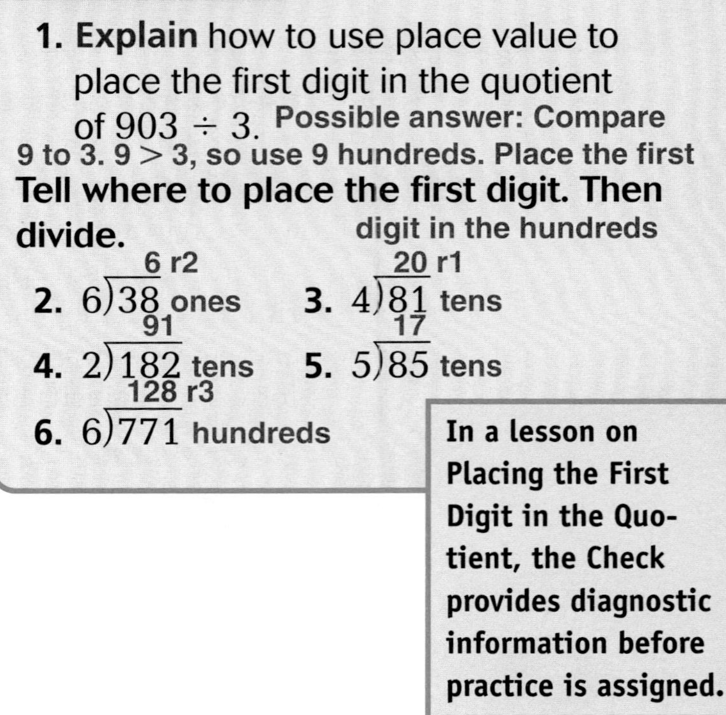
Check

1. **Explain** how to use place value to place the first digit in the quotient of $903 \div 3$. Possible answer: Compare 9 to 3. $9 > 3$, so use 9 hundreds. Place the first digit in the hundreds

Tell where to place the first digit. Then divide.

2. $6\overline{)38}$ 6 r2 ones
3. $4\overline{)81}$ 20 r1 tens
4. $2\overline{)182}$ 91 tens
5. $5\overline{)85}$ 17 tens
6. $6\overline{)771}$ 128 r3 hundreds

In a lesson on Placing the First Digit in the Quotient, the Check provides diagnostic information before practice is assigned.

- **Provide appropriate remedial instruction.** Once an error has been detected, it is often helpful to ask the child to model the algorithm with real materials, recording each step with pencil and paper. Diagnosing children's errors quickly is critical in order to prevent extensive repetition of that same error.

- **Enlist parents in your educational plan.** Keeping parents informed of your expectations and the strategies you use to meet them will help make you and the child's family partners in his or her learning.
- **Review all algorithms at frequent intervals.** Providing mixed reviews at regular intervals is a potent force to solidify what has been previously learned. You will want to do it often.

HARCOURT MATH
GRADE 5
Chapter 14
WHAT WE ARE LEARNING
Exponents and Prime Numbers

VOCABULARY
Here are the vocabulary words we use in class:
Exponent Shows how many times a number, called the **base**, is used as a factor.
exponent ↓ 6^4 ↑ base
Square number The product of a number and itself, expressed with the exponent 2.
Prime factorization The process of factoring a composite number into its prime components.
$12 = 2 \times 2 \times 3$
Factor tree A diagram that shows the factors of a number, then the factors of those numbers, and so on until only prime factors are left.

Name
Date

Dear Family,

Your child is learning new ways to show and describe numbers.

An exponent is a shortcut for showing that you multiplied the same number by itself again and again. For example, 10^4 stands for $10 \times 10 \times 10 \times 10$ or 10,000. Notice that the number of zeros and the exponent are the same.

To remember the meaning of *square number,* you can think of objects arranged in a square array.

$6^2 = 36$

A whole number may be either a prime number or a **composite number**. A **prime number** has two factors, 1 and itself. Other whole numbers are composite numbers.

prime numbers	composite numbers
$2 \rightarrow 1 \times 2$	$4 \rightarrow 1 \times 2 \times 2$ or 1×2^2
$3 \rightarrow 1 \times 3$	$6 \rightarrow 1 \times 2 \times 3$
$5 \rightarrow 1 \times 5$	$8 \rightarrow 1 \times 2 \times 2 \times 2$ or 1×2^3

You can write greater numbers in standard form
6,045,200
or in expanded form with exponents.

$(6 \times 10^6) + (4 \times 10^4) + (5 \times 10^3) + (2 \times 10^2)$

Use the pages that follow to practice these different ways to represent numbers.

Sincerely,

Family Involvement Activities FA53

The practice exercises and suggested activities in *Harcourt Math* were developed by the authors based on a study of the research. Therefore, as you use the program, you will have many options for presenting appropriate practice based on each individual student's mathematical strengths and weaknesses and their preferred learning modalities. The conceptual understanding of each of the algorithms is carefully developed prior to presenting practice on applying the procedure. Multifaceted practice requires that students demonstrate conceptual understanding, skill proficiency, and the ability to choose the correct algorithm and apply it in problem-solving situations. Review of the algorithm and its applications are woven throughout the program so that students can maintain their skill proficiency. When you use ideas from research to plan efficient practice in the whole-number algorithms, children, even those with special needs, are more likely to achieve success with this important mathematical goal.

References

Ashlock, Robert B. (1998). *Error Patterns in Computation.* Seventh Edition. Columbus, Ohio: Merrill.

Bley, Nancy, and Carol Thornton. (1989). *Teaching Mathematics to the Learning Disabled.* Second Edition. Austin: Pro-Ed.

Fuson, Karen, C. (1992). "Research on Whole Number Addition and Subtraction." In *Handbook of Research on Mathematics Teaching,* edited by Douglas A. Grows. New York: Maxwell Macmillan.

Suydam, Marilyn N. (ed.). (1978). *Developing Computational Skills.* Reston, Virginia: National Council of Teachers of Mathematics.

Van de Walle, John A. (1998). *Elementary and Middle School Mathematics: Teaching Developmentally.* Third Edition. New York: Longman.

Developing Algebraic Thinking

Preparation for Algebra Begins in Kindergarten

by Angela Giglio Andrews

Traditionally, algebra has been seen as a high school course—and as a significant mathematics hurdle that *only some* students successfully clear (Carroll). However, in today's world algebra can no longer be thought of as a subject for a select few. All students need to develop reasoning and problem-solving skills built upon exploration, conjecturing, modeling, explaining, and generalizing. These skills lay the foundation for the formal study of algebra (Steen, 1992). The responsibility for implementing these algebraic thinking skills begins with the kindergarten teacher. Fortunately, students already possess some natural algebraic understandings when they come to kindergarten. For instance, a kindergarten student, counting buttons in a collection, commented to her friend, "You know, I was just thinking. Whenever you add one to any number, you get the next number!" Her generalization about the patterns and relationships of the numbers she was exploring was intuitively algebraic in nature. Our responsibility is to recognize these natural algebraic intuitions and expand upon them.

As with any concept or skill, algebraic thinking will best develop when students experience it in various contexts and situations. We want our students to develop a feeling for and comfort with algebra that they will carry with them throughout their schooling. To reach this goal, we must pick and choose from a variety of activities that flow naturally from the mathematics we already have been teaching. We make these choices better when we recognize the algebraic potential of each activity.

We begin introducing the roots of algebra to our students when we have them **classify, pattern, and work with numbers.**

Classifying and Patterning

If mathematics is the study of patterns (Steen, 1988), then algebra is the mathematics of making *generalizations* about those patterns and relationships. Classification is about generalizing—the first step in algebra. When students classify, they must generalize attributes that are common to all the members of the set. A good way to help students learn to pattern objects by size, shape, texture, type, and other attributes is to do lots of sorting. Every sorting and classifying lesson contributes to our students' understanding of patterning which is the foundation for algebraic thinking. Patterns help develop inductive reasoning and make it possible to predict what is supposed to happen in math. If we do not teach students to look for patterns as a basic approach to understanding, learning math becomes much more difficult than it need be. For instance, the student who is learning to count to 100 and doesn't see the pattern of our base-ten number system has the hard task of learning 100 separate tasks in order. Starting in kindergarten, we immerse our students in the concept of pattern at calendar time, with rhythms and chants at music time, and with pattern cards in the interest center. Students generalize patterns with connecting cubes, orientations of craft sticks, and shapes of buttons. Using letters in order to provide a link between seemingly unrelated materials, we describe the patterns they create. (AAB may be their first algebraic expression in which symbols stand for relationships.) Patterning helps students begin to recognize "isomorphisms," or things that have the same structure but may not look the same. For instance, we help students translate color patterns such as "blue, blue, red," into shape patterns "circle, circle, square." Teachers need to help students expand their patterning skills to include reasoning about more complex patterns and explaining the generalizations they make about patterns in our base-ten number system (Kenney).

Working with Numbers

As students develop their understanding of arithmetic operations, they can be led to investigate properties of numbers and operations. While learning the doubles facts for addition, for example, a first grader noted that the sum of all doubles had to be even, because "they would always have a partner." Even young students make some generalizations about the properties of numbers. For instance, a kindergarten child may notice while constructing sums with connecting cubes that $2 + 3 = 5$ and $3 + 2 = 5$. The teacher might then ask if this could be true for all numbers. By verifying with concrete objects, the student would see that observation does not depend on any particular properties of these two numbers but rather the generalization also applies to any other pairs of numbers. The Order Property $a + b = b + a$, which the child is exploring informally, will later form the basis for memorizing basic addition and multiplication facts and even later to solving algebraic equations. The teacher's well-timed questions can lead students to see that the thinking they are doing about particular numbers can be generalized to many numbers. As teachers, we need to recognize that helping students to make such generalizations about numbers creates a bridge from arithmetic to algebraic thinking.

No other skill has been as closely tied to algebra as solving equations. The concept of representing unknown quantities can begin in kindergarten, using concrete objects, verbal descriptions, pictures, boxes ($3 + \blacksquare = 5$) or blanks ($\_\_ + 2 = 5$). Teachers can model and help students translate between these different representations. In working with equations, teachers should emphasize the equal (=) symbol as representing the concept of balance. (Younger students who may not understand balance can understand that *equals* means "is the same as.") Students' misunderstanding of the meaning of the equal sign is often a barrier to solving equations successfully. Many students believe that $4 + 5 =$ means "add 4 + 5," rather than "find the number that balances the equation."

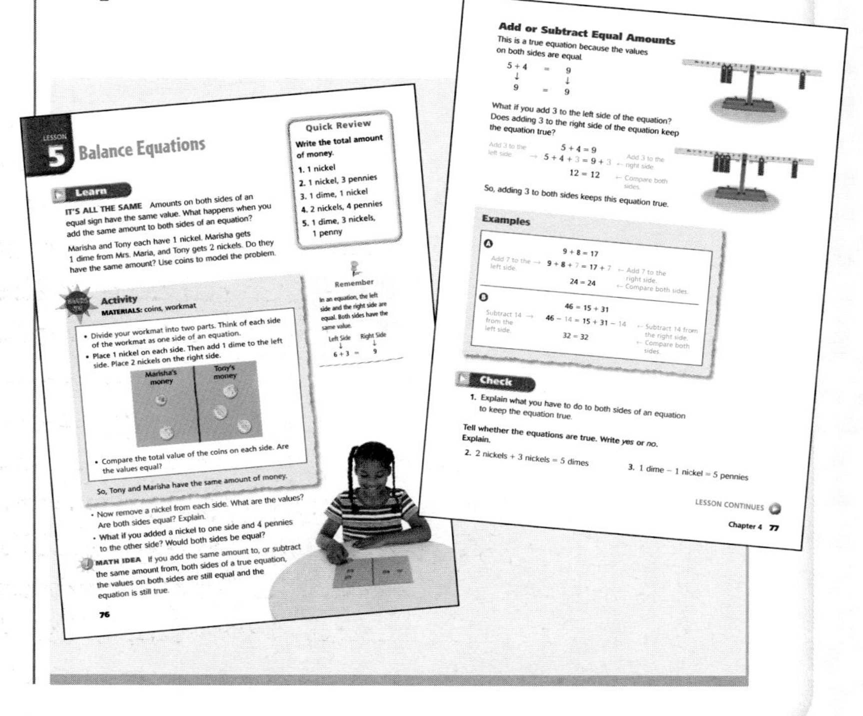
LESSON 5 Balance Equations

Learn

IT'S ALL THE SAME Amounts on both sides of an equal sign have the same value. What happens when you add the same amount to both sides of an equation?

Marisha and Tony each have 1 nickel. Marisha gets 1 dime from Mrs. Maria, and Tony gets 2 nickels. Do they have the same amount? Use coins to model the problem.

Quick Review
Write the total amount of money.
1. 1 nickel
2. 1 nickel, 3 pennies
3. 1 dime, 1 nickel
4. 2 nickels, 4 pennies
5. 1 dime, 3 nickels, 1 penny

Remember
In an equation, the left side and the right side are equal. Both sides have the same value.
Left Side ↓ 6 + 3 = Right Side ↓ 9

Activity
MATERIALS: coins, workmat
- Divide your workmat into two parts. Think of each side of the workmat as one side of an equation.
- Place 1 nickel on each side. Then add 1 dime to the left side. Place 2 nickels on the right side.

Marisha's money | Tony's money

- Compare the total value of the coins on each side. Are the values equal?

So, Tony and Marisha have the same amount of money.

- Now remove a nickel from each side. What are the values? Are both sides equal? Explain.
- What if you added a nickel to one side and 4 pennies to the other side? Would both sides be equal?

MATH IDEA If you add the same amount to, or subtract the same amount from, both sides of a true equation, the values on both sides are still equal and the equation is still true.

76

Add or Subtract Equal Amounts

This is a true equation because the values on both sides are equal.

5 + 4 = 9
↓ ↓
9 = 9

What if you add 3 to the left side of the equation? Does adding 3 to the right side of the equation keep the equation true?

5 + 4 = 9
Add 3 to the left side. → 5 + 4 + 3 = 9 + 3 ← Add 3 to the right side.
12 = 12 ← Compare both sides.

So, adding 3 to both sides keeps this equation true.

Examples

A
9 + 8 = 17
Add 7 to the left side. → 9 + 8 + 7 = 17 + 7 ← Add 7 to the right side.
24 = 24 ← Compare both sides.

B
46 = 15 + 31
Subtract 14 from the left side. → 46 − 14 = 15 + 31 − 14 ← Subtract 14 from the right side.
32 = 32 ← Compare both sides.

Check

1. Explain what you have to do to both sides of an equation to keep the equation true.

Tell whether the equations are true. Write *yes* or *no*. Explain.

2. 2 nickels + 3 nickels = 5 dimes
3. 1 dime − 1 nickel = 5 pennies

LESSON CONTINUES

Chapter 4 77

Test results show (Kieran) that students are much more successful solving equations when they have had experiences with number models with missing numbers in various formats, such as

___ = 8 + 2 4 + ___ = 10 ___ + 5 = 10 + 2

3 + 10 = ___ + 7 ■ + 5 = 9 + 2

In *Harcourt Math,* the development of algebraic thinking is a focus at every grade level. Algebra is a way of thinking, and the goal of the program is to develop children's abilities to think algebraically about the concepts and skills of mathematics and to apply algebraic thinking to solving problems of all types. Helping students understand mathematics from a perspective of identifying and describing patterns in both number and shape, making and testing generalizations, understanding the concept of equivalence as they memorize basic facts, developing proficiency with the algorithms, relating geometric concepts to algebraic concepts, and exploring the idea of function are some of the many ideas that are threads throughout the program.

The algebraic thinking introduced in the program beginning in kindergarten prepares the way for later formal instruction in algebra. By providing opportunities for our students to build confidence and competence, we help students see that algebra is something they can understand—not a hurdle to clear, but just another step along the way to mathematical literacy.

References

Carroll, Bill. *University of Chicago School Mathematics Project.*

Kenney, Patricia, and Ed Silver, Eds. (1997) *Results from the 6th Mathematics Assessment of the National Assessment of Educational Progress.* Reston, Va.: NCTM.

Kieran, C. (1992) "The learning and teaching of school algebra." *Handbook of Research on Mathematics Teaching and Learning.* New York: Macmillan.

Steen, L. A. (1992) "Does everybody need to study algebra?" *Basic Education 37.*

——— (1988) "The science of patterns." *Science* 240.

Problem Solving:

The Reason to Teach Mathematics

by Jan Scheer

Gerry and I have been friends since before his son, Jeremy, started school. Jeremy always had problems in math, and Gerry frequently called to ask for my advice, which was usually ignored. (You're never a hero in your own family or with your closest friends.) The trouble persisted, and Jeremy was sent to an "after-school program" where memorization was the primary learning approach.

Jeremy was at my home recently. Knowing that his class of 30 students would be taking a big bus trip, I inquired as to the number of buses that would be needed if a bus holds 20 students. Without taking a breath, Jeremy responded by saying, "That's easy! One and a half." While I stood dumbfounded, his dad marveled at how much Jeremy had learned at his "after-school program." I composed myself and asked Jeremy if he would take the half of the bus with the driver or the half without! Jeremy informed me that I was confusing him and left in a huff.

This incident really disturbed me. Although Jeremy could, indeed, divide 30 by 20 and get an answer of $1\frac{1}{2}$, he had no understanding of the problem. Understanding and application would indicate that in this case $\frac{30}{20}$ should proffer an answer of 2, not $1\frac{1}{2}$.

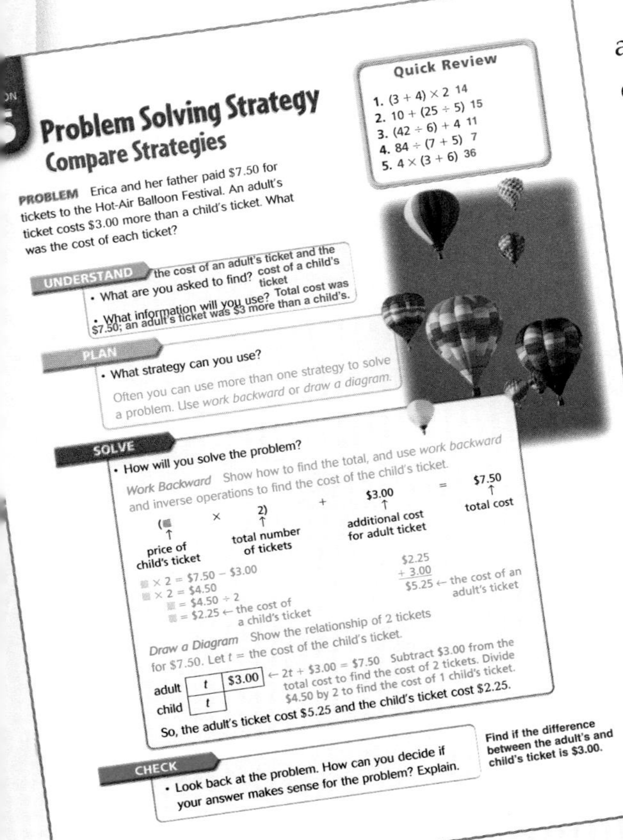

Problem Solving Strategy
Compare Strategies

PROBLEM Erica and her father paid $7.50 for tickets to the Hot-Air Balloon Festival. An adult's ticket costs $3.00 more than a child's ticket. What was the cost of each ticket?

Quick Review
1. (3 + 4) × 2 14
2. 10 + (25 ÷ 5) 15
3. (42 ÷ 6) + 4 11
4. 84 ÷ (7 + 5) 7
5. 4 × (3 + 6) 36

UNDERSTAND
- What are you asked to find? the cost of an adult's ticket and the cost of a child's ticket
- What information will you use? Total cost was $7.50; an adult's ticket was $3 more than a child's.

PLAN
- What strategy can you use?

Often you can use more than one strategy to solve a problem. Use *work backward* or *draw a diagram*.

SOLVE
- How will you solve the problem?

Work Backward Show how to find the total, and use *work backward* and inverse operations to find the cost of the child's ticket.

(■ × 2) + $3.00 = $7.50
price of child's ticket; total number of tickets; additional cost for adult ticket; total cost

■ × 2 = $7.50 − $3.00
■ × 2 = $4.50
■ = $4.50 ÷ 2
■ = $2.25 ← the cost of a child's ticket

$2.25 + 3.00 = $5.25 ← the cost of an adult's ticket

Draw a Diagram Show the relationship of 2 tickets for $7.50. Let *t* = the cost of the child's ticket.

adult	t	$3.00
child	t	

← 2t + $3.00 = $7.50 Subtract $3.00 from the total cost to find the cost of 2 tickets. Divide $4.50 by 2 to find the cost of 1 child's ticket.

So, the adult's ticket cost $5.25 and the child's ticket cost $2.25.

CHECK
- Look back at the problem. How can you decide if your answer makes sense for the problem? Explain.

Find if the difference between the adult's and child's ticket is $3.00.

256

In real life, when do we solve problems? I have never observed anyone in any place take out a pencil and paper to solve a long division problem. I have never seen anyone in a supermarket whip out base-ten blocks to figure which can of soup is the better buy. Nor have I seen anyone use fraction circles to determine what stock to purchase. But every day I see people who are using their mathematical understanding, experiences, and skills to deal with problem situations. They **understand** what the problem is; they **make a plan;** they **solve** the problem; and, finally, they **check** to be sure that their answer is reasonable. If Jeremy had followed this plan, he would have known that his answer was not reasonable.

In *Harcourt Math*, problem solving is part of every lesson. Many lessons present a problem as the vehicle for teaching a skill so that children can see the connection between the skill they are learning and its application. There are lessons devoted specifically to teaching children to use a problem solving strategy and helping them understand the types of problems for which that strategy is a good choice. Children practice problem solving in every lesson—problems that require skills taught earlier in their mathematics experiences, that require two or more steps to solve, that require reading and analyzing data, that require logical reasoning, and that apply the skill presently being taught.

The program helps children develop their abilities to think through a problem by focusing on questions that guide their understanding of the problem, their development of a plan as to which strategy to try or what approach to take, their solution of the problem, and their reflection on whether or not their answer is reasonable in the context of the problem. Reminders to use this process—**Understand, Plan, Solve,** and **Check**—are in every chapter. A Problem Solving Think Along provides a recording device for students as they address each of the above processes. This encourages the "stop and think" approach to solving problems rather than just random attempts. The teaching support that is part of *Harcourt Math* includes a Problem of the Day for every lesson—a rich problem that requires application of this thinking process. In addition, exercises in the practice sets for lessons require students to write their own word problems; write a question from given information; and explain, prove, and/or justify their solutions.

Harcourt Math has a strong focus on problem solving so that as children are becoming proficient with basic facts and the algorithmic procedures, they are seeing the usefulness of mathematics in solving problems that relate to their everyday experience. Children need to be taught that sometimes there can be more than one right answer; often, there can be more than one way to get the answer. They need to be able to use a variety of problem solving strategies. In short, we always need to be teaching children to **think.** ***Problem solving is not one reason to teach mathematics; it is the only reason to teach mathematics.***

PROBLEM SOLVING THINK ALONG

Name

Understand

1. Tell the problem in your own words.

2. What do you want to find out?

Plan

3. How will you solve the problem?

Solve

4. Show how you solved the problem.

Check

5. How can you check your answer?

TR124 Teacher's Resource Book

Name

PROBLEM SOLVING THINK ALONG

Problem Solving

Understand

1. Retell the problem in your own words.

2. List the information given.

3. Restate the question as a fill-in-the-blank sentence.

Plan

4. List one or more problem-solving strategies that you can use.

5. Predict what your answer will be.

Solve

6. Show how you solved the problem.

7. Write your answer in a complete sentence.

Check

8. Tell how you know your answer is reasonable.

9. Describe another way you could have solved the problem.

Problem Solving Think Along (written)

Teacher's Resource Book TR1

Instructional STRATEGIES: Best Practices Defined by Research

by Joyce McLeod

Instructional strategies used in the classroom usually mirror what teachers think about how children learn. So, choosing instructional strategies from among the best practices defined by research is based upon assumptions about learning and should reflect what is known about learning. The following research-based statements answer the question "What is learning?"

- Learning is goal-oriented.
- Learning is linking new information to prior knowledge.
- Learning is organizing information.
- Learning is acquiring a repertoire of cognitive and metacognitive structures.
- Learning occurs in phases yet is nonlinear.
- Learning is influenced by development (Jones, et al., 1987).

Best practices reflect these statements about learning. As we have learned more about how the brain functions as a learning organ and how learning modalities play a critical role in learning, our repertoire of best practices has been refined to reflect these understandings about learners.

Choosing appropriate instructional strategies in mathematics is a critical factor in ensuring that students make continuous progress. The hierarchical nature of the mathematics curriculum makes it imperative that teachers diagnose and intervene quickly to prevent severe deficits in children's mathematical development. In order to provide a balanced program, best practices for developing conceptual understanding, skill and procedural fluency, and reasoning and problem solving abilities must be aligned with the content. In addition, strategies that focus on effective learning modalities and memory strategies to ensure automaticity with the basic facts must be a part of the teacher's repertoire. Among the best practices for teaching mathematics, the following stand out:

- practice
- explicit instruction
- questioning strategies
- use of visuals
- reading and vocabulary development strategies
- use of manipulatives
- intervention

Let's look briefly at each of these best practices and how they are implemented in *Harcourt Math.*

Practice

Practice is important for reinforcing students' knowledge and for preparing students to move on to new topics and new types of problems. Review helps students retain knowledge and improve performance. In a review of research, Geary (1994) concludes that practice is essential for mastering skills and developing the automaticity that will allow these skills to be used routinely in other situations. Bahrick and Hall (1991) studied the life span retention of content acquired in math courses. Their study found that talent and achievement had some impact, but the primary variable for success was practice that had occurred over time. Individuals who had learned the math content over a short period without practice over time showed declines in performance.

—Daily Routine—

In *Harcourt Math,* practice and review are designed to reflect these research findings. In Grades 1 and 2, the Daily Routine in each lesson helps children review prior-taught skills, and spaced reviews throughout the student text provide ongoing review of critical skills. In Grades 3 through 6, every lesson begins with a Quick Review and ends with a lesson test prep. These reviews of lesson prerequisite skills and of prior-taught skills cover a wide range of key mathematical topics and represent a mixture of procedures and skills.

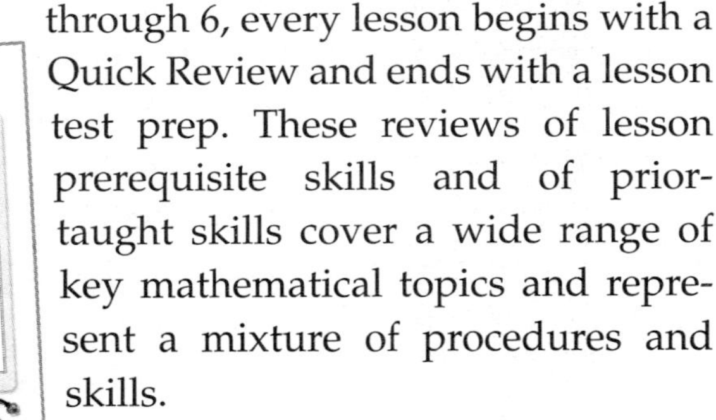

Models that show the step-by-step application of algorithmic procedures and worked examples showing the variety of possible types of problems within a procedure are included throughout the program. These models are often accompanied by pictures of manipulatives to allow students to deepen their conceptual understanding of a procedure as they apply the steps in the procedure. At the end of a group of chapters that cover a major mathematical topic, a Study Guide and Review shows worked examples of the types of problems in which students should develop automaticity, with page references to help students review if necessary.

In Grades 3 through 6, practice exercises for every lesson include a variety of problems. Basic drill-type items are included in lessons emphasizing basic fact acquisition and procedural fluency. Thought-provoking word problems that apply the procedure, skill, or concept taught in the lesson and that review prior-taught skills are included in every lesson. The emphasis in many of these problems is using logical reasoning; solving multistep problems; and explaining, justifying, and proving solutions. Exercises that require writing questions given a possible solution, writing problems with given conditions, and analyzing errors develop students' conceptual and procedural knowledge of mathematics.

Explicit Instruction

Explicit instruction is one of many terms that describe a teaching practice focused on making specific skills or strategies known to a learner. Explicit instruction involves explaining, demonstrating, and/or modeling mathematical concepts and procedures to students.

Liping Ma, in her book *Knowing and Teaching Elementary Mathematics,* emphasizes that in order for a teacher to instruct in mathematics, he or she must have these four properties of understanding:

- **Basic ideas** are the "simple but powerful basic concepts and principles of mathematics" that should be revisited and reinforced.

- **Connectedness** is the understanding of the connections between mathematical ideas that prevents students' learning from being fragmented and helps them see that math is a unified body of knowledge.
- **Multiple perspectives** are the different facets of an idea, the various approaches to the solution of a problem, and the explanations that students make of the different facets.
- **Longitudinal coherence** is the understanding of the whole mathematics curriculum that helps teachers understand what students have studied previously and what they are going to learn later (Ma, p. 122).

ed Instruction

Lift Off! with students.

do you know which operation to
se? The problem says that the two parts will
ined. Therefore, you add.

ıss the steps in Example 1.

is $\frac{1}{2}$ written as an equivalent fraction?
ıst be written as an equivalent fraction in
r to be added to $\frac{1}{6}$. **What is another name**
$\frac{3}{3}$? 1

In *Harcourt Math,* explicit instruction is facilitated by clear development in every lesson. In Grades 3–6, the instructional part of the student's lesson consists of vocabulary development, models and/or examples, and questions that help students connect new learning to previous learning, consider different approaches to thinking about a basic idea in mathematics, or choose different solution methods for a given problem. In Grades 1–2, the students' lessons show models and reinforce vocabulary. In the *Teacher's Edition* for all grade levels, explicit instruction is developed through Guided Instruction, which includes questions that help students connect the lesson topic to previously learned material, facilitate conceptual understanding and efficient skill development, and help students avoid common errors.

Questioning Strategies

All learning begins with questions. Questions cause interactions, and the quality of those interactions is determined by the character of the question. Questions are fundamental to teaching because they provide information, help students become more actively involved in a lesson, and guide students toward the highest levels of learning in which they apply what they have learned in a variety of ways.

Good questions focus students' attention on concepts, generalizations, laws, and principles and help them think critically and see relationships. In any one lesson, four or five good, open-ended questions challenge students to analyze, apply, react to, or reflect on content. Providing students time to answer (usually about a three- to four-second lapse following a question) results in more comprehensive, higher-quality answers (Rowe 1974).

In *Harcourt Math,* questions that guide students' thinking and help them analyze concepts and skills are included in the Pupil Edition. These questions are designed to help students develop strategies for solving problems and for memorizing basic facts, procedural processes, and key mathematical definitions. We know that memorizing something that is not understood or that has little meaning to an individual is virtually an impossible task. Think, for example, about your Social Security number. Memorizing and retaining that sequence of numbers in your long-term memory if it had no relevance to you would be impossible. You would have to memorize that sequence again and again if you were asked to repeat it at random or to use it in some isolated example. It would only become a part of your long-term memory and easily accessed if it had relevance for you and was connected to other experiences in your memory. So, good questions form the basis for helping students make connections and store information in their long-term memories so that they can easily access it when needed. The basic facts form a large part of the memories that we need to make permanent in students' long-term memories, and since memorizing what we do not understand is almost impossible, questioning for understanding forms the basis for memory.

Use of Visuals

Research clearly shows that the use of visuals enhances learning. Visuals help learners:

- isolate and identify important material.

- recall prior knowledge.
- provide interaction with content.
- enhance information acquisition (Dwyer, 1994).

Picture viewing is more exploratory than reading. Fixation durations are generally longer in picture viewing. Visuals serve as aids to memory because information received from visuals appears to remain longer in memory. Visuals also provide motivation when they give a real-life meaning to the mathematics. However, the most important aspect to remember about using visuals is that it is not the visual itself that causes gains in learning, but rather the instructional strategy in which the visual is embedded.

In *Harcourt Math,* visuals and accompanying questions and teaching suggestions are included throughout the program. Visuals are used to help teachers provide critical scaffolds to understanding and, therefore, memory. They are also used to help students appreciate the usefulness of mathematics in everyday activities. Our students live in a visual world, but many of these visuals pass rapidly before their eyes with very little learning occurring. So, teaching children to read visuals and to link visuals and text is a critical part of the focus in the program. The adage "Before you can see to learn, you must first learn to see," is taken seriously by the authors of this program.

Reading and Vocabulary Development Strategies

Reading in mathematics is critical for students' success. Mathematics is a language and a way of thinking. Therefore, teaching students to read mathematics for understanding and developing the unique vocabulary of mathematics are essential for success. Students' reading abilities in mathematics can be helped by relating their personal knowledge and experience to the information in the text, relating one part of the text to another, providing the lesson objective to students at the beginning of the lesson, and discussing the meaning of important new words (Ornstein, 1995).

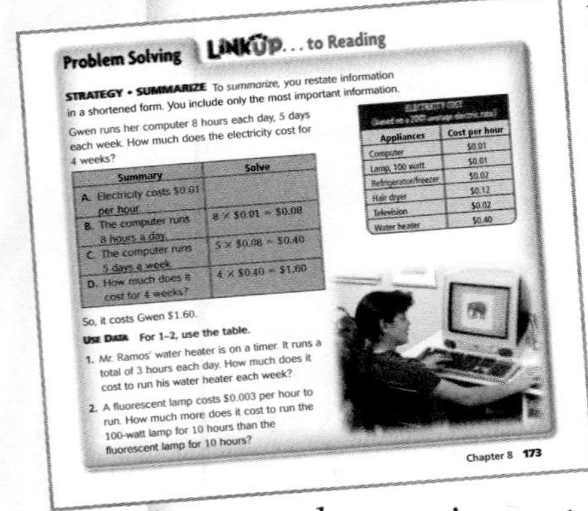

Problem Solving LINKUP... to Reading

STRATEGY • SUMMARIZE To *summarize,* you restate information in a shortened form. You include only the most important information.

Gwen runs her computer 8 hours each day, 5 days each week. How much does the electricity cost for 4 weeks?

Summary	Solve
A. Electricity costs $0.01 per hour	
B. The computer runs 8 hours a day.	8 × $0.01 = $0.08
C. The computer runs 5 days a week	5 × $0.08 = $0.40
D. How much does it cost for 4 weeks?	4 × $0.40 = $1.60

So, it costs Gwen $1.60.

Appliances	Cost per hour
Computer	$0.01
Lamp, 100 watt	$0.01
Refrigerator/freezer	$0.02
Hair dryer	$0.12
Television	$0.02
Water heater	$0.40

USE DATA For 1–2, use the table.

1. Mr. Ramos' water heater is on a timer. It runs a total of 3 hours each day. How much does it cost to run his water heater each week?
2. A fluorescent lamp costs $0.003 per hour to run. How much more does it cost to run the 100-watt lamp for 10 hours than the fluorescent lamp for 10 hours?

Chapter 8 173

In *Harcourt Math,* development of students' content reading skills forms a focus in the presentation of each lesson. Some of the helps to content-area include providing instructional objectives to focus students' thinking, providing a key question to guide the lesson development, identifying and defining key mathematical terms used in the lesson, and providing prompts to help students remember prior-taught material necessary for understanding the lesson. Review exercises throughout the program reinforce the content-area reading developed around each topic.

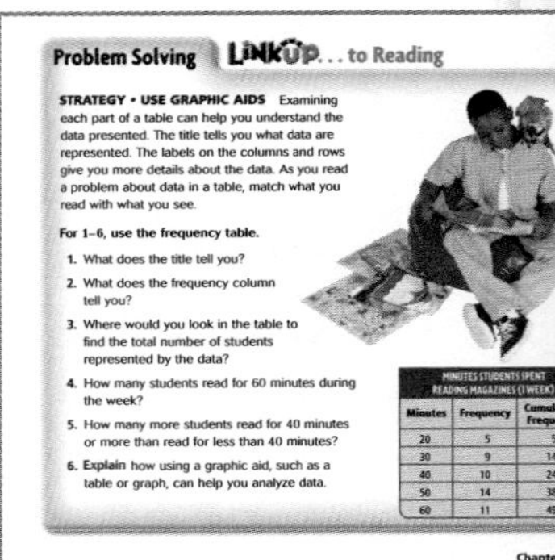

Problem Solving LINKUP... to Reading

STRATEGY • USE GRAPHIC AIDS Examining each part of a table can help you understand the data presented. The title tells you what data are represented. The labels on the columns and rows give you more details about the data. As you read a problem about data in a table, match what you read with what you see.

For 1–6, use the frequency table.

1. What does the title tell you?
2. What does the frequency column tell you?
3. Where would you look in the table to find the total number of students represented by the data?
4. How many students read for 60 minutes during the week?
5. How many more students read for 40 minutes or more than read for less than 40 minutes?
6. Explain how using a graphic aid, such as a table or graph, can help you analyze data.

MINUTES STUDENTS SPENT READING MAGAZINES (1 WEEK)

Minutes	Frequency	Cumula Freque
20	5	5
30	9	14
40	10	24
50	14	38
60	11	49

Chapte

Use of Manipulatives

Research supports the use of manipulatives to increase students' conceptual understanding and achievement in mathematics. Two main points that emerge from the research are:

- Long-term use of manipulatives is important for success.
- Teachers need to have clear purposes for using manipulatives in a particular situation (Sowell, 1989).

In *Harcourt Math,* manipulatives and the pictorial representations of manipulatives are used throughout the grade levels. Concepts are introduced through manipulative activities accompanied by questions that help students see the link between the concrete material or a pictorial representation and the mathematical idea being modeled. These structured manipulative activities demonstrate the purpose for using the manipulative and provide support to teachers in making the most efficient and effective use of manipulatives.

Basic-fact strategies and the procedures for each of the computational algorithms are developed through the use of manipulatives. These activities support memorization of basic facts and procedures because they provide concrete visuals that children can use to link related facts and procedures and, therefore, make the task of memorization easier. In the beginning, memorization of basic facts is best facilitated by use of basic-fact strategies supported by concrete experiences. As the goal of automaticity with the basic facts is reached, the basic-fact strategies are no longer used in the process of memorization but remain in the students' memories to act as helps for solving word problems. The same premise holds true as children develop automaticity with the basic algorithmic procedures.

Intervention

Intervention refers to a given set of strategies used by a teacher to accommodate the diverse skill levels, interests, and learning preferences of students. In order to meet the learning needs of all students, attention must be given to tailoring instruction so that the needs of auditory, visual, and kinesthetic learners are met; students' personal interests are considered; and instruction begins where students are. Carol Tomlinson, in her book *The Differentiated Classroom,* makes the following recommendations for differentiating instruction in the classroom:

- Build instruction around the essential concepts, principles, and skills of a subject.
- Attend to individual differences.
- Use assessment as today's means of understanding how to modify tomorrow's instruction.
- Use assessment data to modify the content students are to learn, the processes through which content is to be taught, and the product by which the students demonstrate what they have learned.

In *Harcourt Math,* intervention is woven through the program as the means by which teachers differentiate instruction. The variety of assessment instruments provides effective tools that help teachers diagnose students' strengths and weaknesses and allow them to make informed decisions about the classroom curriculum. In Grades 3–6, a Student Handbook in the back of the *Pupil Edition* provides intervention activities and exercises. *Intervention • Skills* links intervention activities to the grade-level content and, therefore, allows teachers to present grade-level content differentiated to meet the needs of all learners.

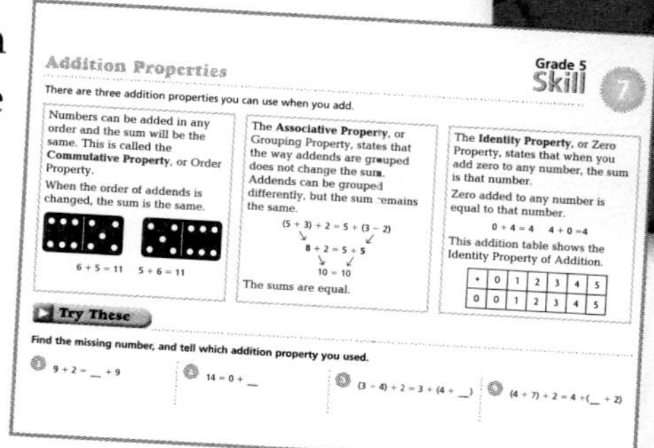

Addition Properties

Grade 5 Skill 7

There are three addition properties you can use when you add.

Numbers can be added in any order and the sum will be the same. This is called the **Commutative Property**, or Order Property.

When the order of addends is changed, the sum is the same.

6 + 5 = 11   5 + 6 = 11

The **Associative Property**, or Grouping Property, states that the way addends are grouped does not change the sum. Addends can be grouped differently, but the sum remains the same.

(5 + 3) + 2 = 5 + (3 + 2)

8 + 2 = 5 + 5

10 = 10

The sums are equal.

The **Identity Property**, or Zero Property, states that when you add zero to any number, the sum is that number.

Zero added to any number is equal to that number.

0 + 4 = 4   4 + 0 = 4

This addition table shows the Identity Property of Addition.

+	0	1	2	3	4	5
0	0	1	2	3	4	5

Try These

Find the missing number, and tell which addition property you used.

1. 9 + 2 = __ + 9
2. 14 = 0 + __
3. (3 + 4) + 2 = 3 + (4 + __)
4. (4 + 7) + 2 = 4 + (__ + 2)

The instructional strategies used in the classroom are an important determinant of students' achievement. The instructional strategies developed in *Harcourt Math* will help you make instructional decisions based on the goals of your classroom curriculum as mandated by your school or district, by the needs of each of your students, and by preparation for tests that your students are required to take.

References

Bahrick, H. P., & Hall, L. K. (1991). "Lifetime maintenance of high school mathematics content." *Journal of Experimental Psychology: General,* 120: 22–23.

Chuska, Kenneth. (1995). *Improving Classroom Questions.* Bloomington, Indiana: Phi Delta Kappa Educational Foundation.

Dwyer, Francis M., with Morre, David M. (1994). *Visual Literacy: A spectrum of visual learning.* Englewood Cliffs, New Jersey: Education Technology Publications.

Geary, D. C. (1994). *Children's Mathematical Development: Research and Practical Applications.* American Psychological Association. Washington, D.C.

Jones, B., Palincsar, A., Ogle, D., & Carr, E. (1987). *Strategic Teaching and Learning: Cognitive Instruction in the Content Areas.* Alexandria, Virginia: Association for Supervision and Curriculum Development.

Ma, Liping. (1999). *Knowing and Teaching Elementary Mathematics.* Mahwah, New Jersey: Lawrence Erlbaum Associates, Publisher.

Ornstein, Allan. (1995). *Strategies for Effective Teaching* (2nd Ed). Chicago: Brown & Benchmark Publishers.

Rowe, Mary Budd. "Wait-time and rewards as instruction variables: Their influence on language, logic, and fate control: Part I: Wait-time." *Journal of Research in Science Teachings* 11, no. 2: 81–84.

Sowell, E. J. (1989). "Effects of manipulative materials in mathematics instruction." *Journal for Research in Mathematics Education,* 29 (2), 121–142.

Tomlinson, Carol. (1999). *The Differentiated Classroom: Responding to the Needs of All Learners.* Alexandria, Virginia. Association for Supervision and Curriculum Development.

ASSESSMENT

An Integral Part of the Learning Process

by Lynda Luckie

Assessment is an integral part of the learning process. It can help us understand what students know, how well they know it, and the processes they use to reach their understanding. We must have a clear idea of what our students already know about mathematics in order to help guide instruction and plan for future learning. Many school districts across the country are developing higher standards and incorporating high stakes assessment. Often, the purpose of such assessment is to determine not only if students can compute, but also if they can think, reason, formulate ideas, and communicate mathematically. Assessment imbedded and integrated into instruction is a powerful tool to help us improve our teaching and students' learning.

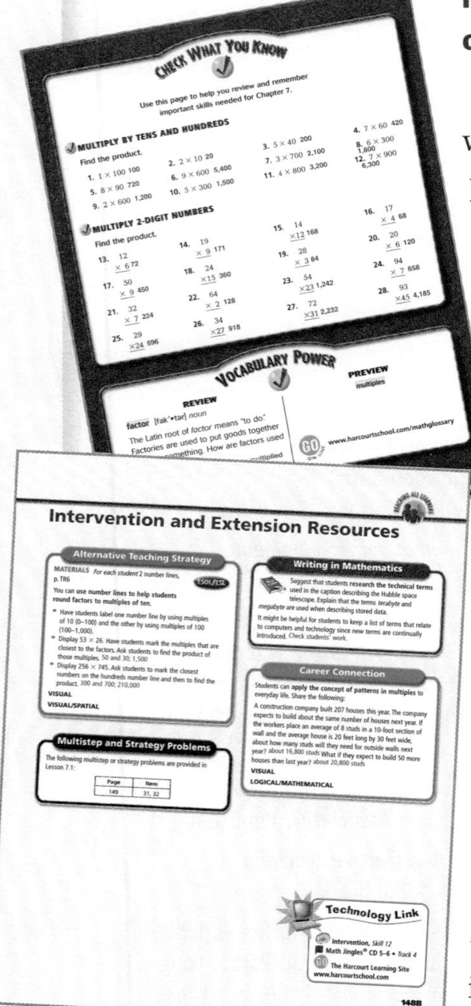

Entry-Level assessment is included in *Harcourt Math* to determine whether students enter a grade level with weaknesses and gaps in their skill proficiency and understanding or whether students show strengths and are, therefore, capable of thriving in a challenging curriculum. This entry-level assessment, designed to determine where students are in their skill development, conceptual understanding, and ability to solve problems, is provided at the beginning of each year. In addition, the *Check What You Know* at the beginning of each chapter provides an entry-level assessment for the content in that chapter. This assessment is linked to diagnostic and prescriptive information to assist the teacher in intervening to prevent students from experiencing failure with new material.

Progress monitoring is a part of every lesson. The third step of the lesson plan in *Harcourt Math* provides activities to check students' conceptual understanding and skill development, providing immediate diagnostic information to the teacher and immediate feedback to the student. In addition, end-of-chapter and end-of-unit progress monitoring provides students, their parents, and their teachers information as to whether students' learning has been connected with related mathematical ideas, can be used to solve problems, and, for skills, is progressing toward the level of automaticity.

Summative evaluation occurs at the end of each chapter, at the end of each unit, and at the end of the year. There are a variety of types of assessment instruments—multiple-choice tests, free-response tests, performance tasks, portfolio suggestions, and writing prompts—that may be used for summative evaluation. The assessment program in *Harcourt Math* is designed to develop a complete portrait of each student's mathematical development—conceptual development, skill proficiency, and problem solving ability. The underlying philosophy of the assessment program is described below.

Varied assessment tools help students value mathematics.

While a good assessment program helps teachers develop a solid plan for instruction and learning, it should also help students learn to value mathematics. Students' definitions and understanding of assessment dictate their perceptions of what we value. For instance, if assessment consists solely of computation-driven tests, then students will believe that is all we value. On the other hand, if we want students to value development of problem solving skills, reasoning, and mathematical communication, then we must find ways to make these connections more explicit for students (Davinoy, Bliem, and Mayfield). If we value strategies and thought processes, we must look at not only the "what" but also the "how."

Just as a balanced diet includes more than one food group, so does a balanced assessment program use more than one format. Students should be given opportunities in multiple formats to demonstrate what they know and can do. While the importance of computational skills should not be minimized, it is almost impossible to accurately assess students' understanding of the big ideas of mathematics without a variety of assessment tools. Indeed, some elements of mathematics learning can only be measured in ways other than multiple-choice tests (Stenmark, Mathematics Assessment NCTM). One of the most powerful arguments for implementing various assessment techniques is the value it has as a diagnostic tool for improved instruction.

Varied assessment tools prepare students for standardized tests.

Some useful assessment models include performance assessments, portfolios, math journals, individual or small-group projects, formal tests that include multiple-choice and free-response items, and self-assessment instruments. Good teaching also includes some informal student assessment such as observations and student interviews. Anecdotal record sheets and checklists can be very useful for this kind of documentation. Included in a balanced assessment program is a good preparation for local or national standardized testing. Exposure to and familiarity with the format and types of problems can be the key to building students' fluency and self-confidence in their abilities to take tests and perform well. Then the high-stakes tests will not be something for students to dread, but rather another opportunity to show what they know and can do.

Varied assessment tools provide useful diagnostic information to teachers about students' strengths and weaknesses.

Portfolios can be one of the best ways to present a clear, visible, continuous, and comprehensive picture of students' progress. It can be a way to showcase students' work. You may want to include several different types of assessment in portfolios, such as performance assessment tasks, paper-and-pencil tests, projects, and students' writing about mathematics. A suggestion for a writing piece is for students to record how they view themselves as mathematicians, both at the beginning and toward the end of the school year. You may see a huge difference in their perceptions over time. Many teachers find that students particularly enjoy selecting their best work to include in their portfolios. Moreover, a student portfolio can provide an invaluable communication tool as you conference with parents about their child's progress.

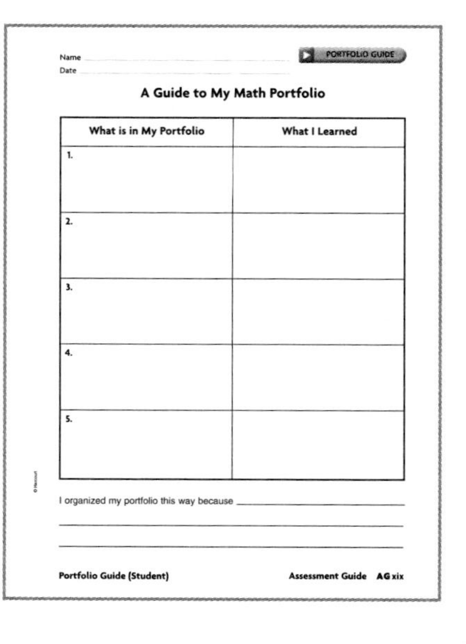

Name

Date

PORTFOLIO GUIDE

A Guide to My Math Portfolio

What is in My Portfolio	What I Learned
1.	
2.	
3.	
4.	
5.	

I organized my portfolio this way because

Portfolio Guide (Student) — Assessment Guide AG xix

Performance Assessment consists of presenting a mathematical task or project for students to work on and then making a determination of what they know and can do. This can be accomplished by using any combination of observations, student interviews, and rubrics that can be developed by teachers and/or by students. Performance assessments often incorporate a wide variety of mathematical skills and give evidence of a rich mathematics curriculum. As students work on these tasks, they become engaged in the activities and quickly learn that math is more than just learning how to complete an algorithm. They also learn that there is often more than one right answer and more than one way to solve a problem.

Math Journals provide invaluable insight into a student's progress. They can reveal understanding as well as attitudes and perceptions. Entries in a journal can be as simple and unstructured as responding to a prompt or can become more complex as students are asked to explain a mathematical process or justify an answer. As in their portfolios, students might record their changing view of themselves as mathematicians. Students should be encouraged to use pictures and diagrams to help explain their thinking. Many teachers use a math journal as a personal communication tool by responding in a student's journal and developing an ongoing conversation about mathematics. One caution to be considered is that students need to know that a journal entry is a viable part of the classroom mathematics program. If journals are never reviewed and never receive affirmation, then they will likely become just another chore in the minds of students.

Standardized and Free-Response Format Tests provide one way to diagnose your students' abilities to apply the skills and procedures of mathematics. These tests can be used before instruction on a topic is begun, to determine whether or not each student has the prerequisite skills for the new content. They can be used at the end of a sequence of lessons on a topic to determine whether an appropriate skill level has been attained. These tests can also assess students' abilities to apply skills and concepts in problem solving situations. Cumulative Review tests are a valuable way to measure remembering and retention over time of both conceptual and procedural knowledge and the ability to apply that knowledge in problem solving situations.

Name ____________ CHAPTER 16 TEST • PAGE 1

Choose the correct answer.

1. Which number is closest to $\frac{7}{10}$?
   A 0 C 1
   B $\frac{1}{2}$ D $1\frac{1}{2}$

For 2–5, ESTIMATE each sum or difference.

2. $\frac{7}{12} + \frac{3}{8}$
   F 0 H 1
   G $\frac{1}{2}$ J $1\frac{1}{2}$

3. $\frac{2}{10} - \frac{1}{6}$
   A 0 C 1
   B $\frac{1}{2}$ D $1\frac{1}{2}$

4. $\frac{8}{9} + \frac{2}{5}$
   F 0 H 1
   G $\frac{1}{2}$ J $1\frac{1}{2}$

5. $\frac{11}{12} - \frac{4}{7}$
   A 0 C 1
   B $\frac{1}{2}$ D $1\frac{1}{2}$

For 6–16, find the sum or difference in simplest form.

6. $\frac{1}{12} + \frac{7}{12}$
   F $\frac{4}{3}$ H $\frac{8}{24}$
   G $\frac{2}{3}$ J $\frac{1}{3}$

7. $\frac{4}{7} + \frac{2}{7}$
   A $\frac{6}{7}$ C $\frac{2}{7}$
   B $\frac{6}{14}$ D $\frac{2}{14}$

8. $\frac{5}{8} - \frac{3}{8}$
   F $\frac{8}{16}$ H $\frac{2}{16}$
   G $\frac{1}{4}$ J $\frac{1}{8}$

9. $\frac{5}{9} - \frac{2}{9}$
   A $\frac{2}{18}$ C $\frac{1}{3}$
   B $\frac{3}{18}$ D $\frac{7}{9}$

10. $\frac{5}{16} + \frac{3}{8}$
   F $\frac{8}{24}$ H $\frac{11}{16}$
   G $\frac{8}{16}$ J 1

Go On

Form A • Multiple Choice Assessment Guide AG109

Self-Assessment tools help you understand the attitudes and perceptions your students have about mathematics, their assessment of their own abilities to do mathematics, and their preferred ways of working. For many students, cooperative learning groups are an effective way for students to develop their problem solving abilities and their abilities to communicate about mathematics they are learning and to practice in order to develop skill and procedural fluency. Other students may work better individually for some of these types of activities. Self-assessment tools give you valuable information not only about the mathematics students are learning but also about the ways in which they prefer to learn.

Name ____________ Date ______ INDIVIDUAL END-OF-CHAPTER SURVEY
Chapter ____________

How Did I Do?

Write your response.

1. I thought the lessons in this chapter were ____________
2. The lesson I enjoyed the most was ____________
3. Something that I still need to work on is ____________
4. One thing that I think I did a great job on was ____________
5. I would like to learn more about ____________
6. Something I understand now that I did not understand before these lessons is ____________
7. I think I might use the math I learned in these lessons to ____________
8. The amount of effort I put into these lessons was ____________
   (very little some a lot)

End-of-Chapter Survey Assessment Guide AG xvii

The purpose of assessment should be to help students see the real-life application of mathematics.

As you develop your assessment program, keep in mind the big ideas. For example, what you want to assess should help you decide on the assessment tool. Whichever form you choose should embrace an "authentic assessment" mentality. In other words, assessment should help foster making a transition from what students learn in school to the mathematics they will need to know in "real life." There is also a very real place in your program for daily and periodic review of what students are learning. Curriculum should spiral and revisit ideas within the context of new material. For example, finding the area of given parcels of land can be imbedded in a problem solving task that involves representing data in a graph about national parks.

Building a Comprehensive Assessment Program in Your Classroom

If you are already using multiple forms of assessment, then you already realize the benefits. If not, one of the purposes of this article is to encourage you to begin to make some changes. The decision to make changes comes slowly and with deliberate effort. Some suggestions include:

- Take small steps.
- Try one new thing at a time.
- Allow yourself to make mistakes and adjustments.
- Collaborate with fellow teachers, parents, and students.
- Persevere until it becomes a natural, integrated component of your teaching.

Harcourt Math provides a varied toolbox of assessment instruments designed to provide ongoing diagnostic information about your students' strength and weaknesses. Students can only make progress in mathematics when teachers have varied sources of information about the abilities of their students. Your choice of assessment instruments should be linked to the kinds of information that you need to make your mathematics classroom a rich experience for your students; to prepare students for the standardized assessment required by your state, district, or school; and to provide both the student and his or her family members with a complete profile of the student's mathematical competency. The choices are many and varied and will allow you to continue to modify your assessment program to meet your needs and your students' needs and to document to parents, school administrators, and the community the richness of your classroom mathematics program.

Keep in mind that assessment should not be something we "do" after we "teach." Often we can assess students' learning in the process of teaching. Teachers do this every day. We watch students develop new skills and strategies as they become problem solvers. We know that we can imbed skill practice within tasks that are interesting and exciting for our students. We watch as students learn from each other and construct their own understanding on the foundation of what they already know, enabling them to transfer that knowledge to new situations. Based on these ongoing and informal observations that are supported in the daily lessons in *Harcourt Math*, teachers can make good choices as to which of the many and varied assessment options included with the program are right for their classroom. When teachers allow students to experience success in a variety of assessment formats, they confirm their belief that all students can learn, and they empower students to view themselves as mathematicians.

References

Stenmark, J. K. (1989). *Mathematics Assessment: Myths, Models, Good Questions, and Practical Suggestions.* Berkeley, California: University of California.

Davinroy, K. H., Bliem, C. L., & Mayfield, V. (1995) "How Does My Teacher Know What I Know?: Third Graders' Perceptions of Math, Reading, and Assesement." Boulder, Colorado: CRESST (National Center for Research on Evaluation, Standards, and Student Testing), University of Colorado.

Linking Home and School

Making Mathematics Part of the Family's Daily Routine

by Vicki Newman

School-home communication is one of the key components of an effective mathematics program. Parents have a better understanding of their child's mathematics program and become more supportive of a standards-based curriculum when the communication between school and home is ongoing. With a clear picture of what their child is learning at school and how they can provide support at home, families play a vital role in their child's mathematics education.

Children benefit when parents and teachers work together to emphasize the importance of mathematics in their children's daily lives. If children see a reason for studying math at school, they learn to value mathematics and develop a positive attitude and interest. The link between school and home is essential in ensuring a successful mathematics program. The following suggestions may help you foster the link between school and home and provide valuable information to parents.

- Identify grade-level mathematics content standards to provide parents with an outline of essential concepts and skills their child should know.
- Explain the goals of a balanced mathematics program through parent newsletters, parent conferences, or school bulletin boards. Have children share classroom projects and daily work that reflect how their mathematics program provides a balance between conceptual competence, computational and procedural competence, and mathematical reasoning.
- Help parents recognize their role and their child's role in learning mathematics. Suggest ways parents can support mathematics learning at school and extend learning experiences at home. Identify strategies parents can use at home to help their children with homework.
- Share information with parents regarding their child's progress in mathematics. Include samples of daily work and share the variety of assessment tools you frequently use to identify their child's progress.
- Encourage parents and the community to become involved in mathematics education by letting them know that their comments, concerns, and suggestions are valued.

The school-home link in *Harcourt Math* will help you implement these suggestions as you share the following materials with parents:

- **Family Involvement Activities** in kindergarten through Grade 2 outline the mathematics taught in each chapter, provide a list of the math vocabulary (with definitions) that will be introduced and reviewed, and give examples of the types of questions and problems children will be working on in the classroom. One important component of the school-home link is helping family members understand the thinking their child must do in order to be successful with the skills, concepts, and problem solving activities presented in the chapter. The *Family Involvement* materials include problems that children and their parents can solve together and a Family Fun activity that helps children see that mathematics can be fun and that solving math problems is a real-life skill. In addition, at the bottom of each of the lesson pages in the Pupil Edition, there is a Home Activity that describes the mathematics the child is learning and provides a suggestion for a way parents can help. All of these school-home links provide practical information that will help you involve parents as partners in supporting their child's progress in meeting mathematics standards.

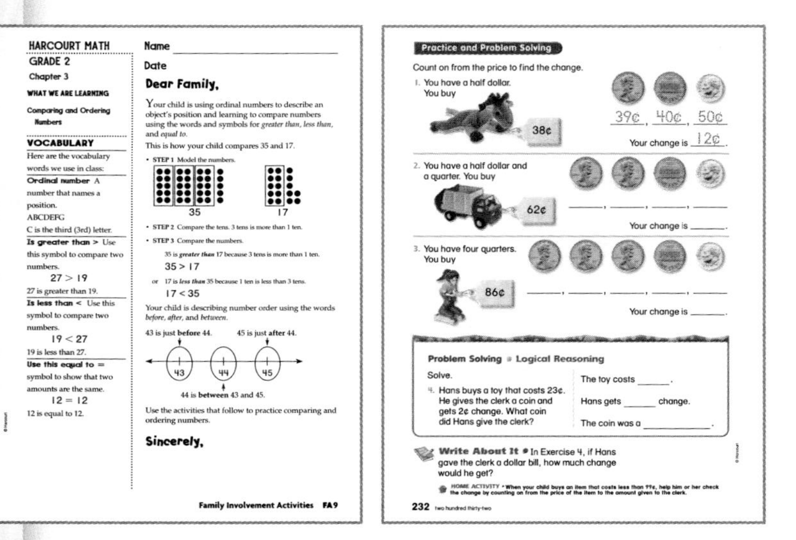

HARCOURT MATH
GRADE 2
Chapter 3
WHAT WE ARE LEARNING
Comparing and Ordering Numbers

VOCABULARY
Here are the vocabulary words we use in class:
Ordinal number A number that names a position.
ABCDEFG
C is the third (3rd) letter.
Is greater than > Use this symbol to compare two numbers.
27 > 19
27 is greater than 19.
Is less than < Use this symbol to compare two numbers.
19 < 27
19 is less than 27.
Use this equal to = symbol to show that two amounts are the same.
12 = 12
12 is equal to 12.

Name
Date
Dear Family,
Your child is using ordinal numbers to describe an object's position and learning to compare numbers using the words and symbols for *greater than*, *less than*, and *equal to*.
This is how your child compares 35 and 17.
- **STEP 1** Model the numbers.
35   17
- **STEP 2** Compare the tens. 3 tens is more than 1 ten.
- **STEP 3** Compare the numbers.
35 is ***greater than*** 17 because 3 tens is more than 1 ten.
35 > 17
or 17 is ***less than*** 35 because 1 ten is less than 3 tens.
17 < 35
Your child is describing number order using the words *before*, *after*, and *between*.
43 is just **before** 44.   45 is just **after** 44.
43   44   45
44 is **between** 43 and 45.
Use the activities that follow to practice comparing and ordering numbers.
Sincerely,

Family Involvement Activities FA9

Practice and Problem Solving
Count on from the price to find the change.
1. You have a half dollar. You buy 38¢
39¢, 40¢, 50¢
Your change is 12¢.
2. You have a half dollar and a quarter. You buy 62¢
___, ___, ___, ___
Your change is ___.
3. You have four quarters. You buy 86¢
___, ___, ___, ___, ___
Your change is ___.

Problem Solving • Logical Reasoning
Solve.
4. Hans buys a toy that costs 23¢. He gives the clerk a coin and gets 2¢ change. What coin did Hans give the clerk?
The toy costs ___.
Hans gets ___ change.
The coin was a ___.

Write About It • In Exercise 4, if Hans gave the clerk a dollar bill, how much change would he get?
HOME ACTIVITY • When your child buys an item that costs less than 99¢, help him or her check the change by counting on from the price of the item to the amount given to the clerk.
232 two hundred thirty-two

- **Family Involvement Activities** for Grades 3 through 6 also include a description of what the child will be learning, a list of vocabulary terms and definitions, and suggested ways for parents to help, including activities that provide more practice and a game that helps families have fun while helping their child with the mathematics they are learning at school.

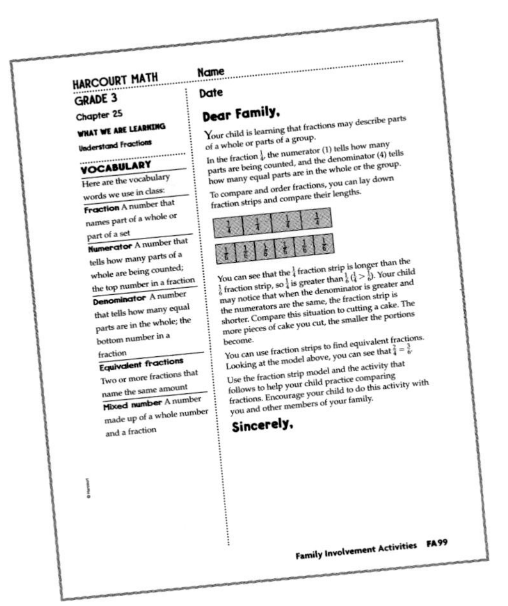

HARCOURT MATH
GRADE 3
Chapter 25
WHAT WE ARE LEARNING
Understand Fractions

VOCABULARY
Here are the vocabulary words we use in class:
Fraction A number that names part of a whole or part of a set
Numerator A number that tells how many parts of a whole are being counted; the top number in a fraction
Denominator A number that tells how many equal parts are in the whole; the bottom number in a fraction
Equivalent fractions Two or more fractions that name the same amount
Mixed number A number made up of a whole number and a fraction

Name
Date
Dear Family,
Your child is learning that fractions may describe parts of a whole or parts of a group.
In the fraction $\frac{1}{4}$, the numerator (1) tells how many parts are being counted, and the denominator (4) tells how many equal parts are in the whole or the group.
To compare and order fractions, you can lay down fraction strips and compare their lengths.
$\frac{1}{4}$ $\frac{1}{4}$ $\frac{1}{4}$ $\frac{1}{4}$
$\frac{1}{6}$ $\frac{1}{6}$ $\frac{1}{6}$ $\frac{1}{6}$ $\frac{1}{6}$ $\frac{1}{6}$
You can see that the $\frac{1}{4}$ fraction strip is longer than the $\frac{1}{6}$ fraction strip, so $\frac{1}{4}$ is greater than $\frac{1}{6}$ ($\frac{1}{4} > \frac{1}{6}$). Your child may notice that when the denominator is greater and the numerators are the same, the fraction strip is shorter. Compare this situation to cutting a cake. The more pieces of cake you cut, the smaller the portions become.
You can use fraction strips to find equivalent fractions. Looking at the model above, you can see that $\frac{2}{4} = \frac{3}{6}$.
Use the fraction strip model and the activity that follows to help your child practice comparing fractions. Encourage your child to do this activity with you and other members of your family.
Sincerely,

Family Involvement Activities FA99

Making Mathematics Part of the Family's Daily Routines

Parents can work with teachers to help their children see the relevance of mathematics in their everyday lives. When parents are filling out a mail-order form, figuring out how many days until a special family event, or calculating the mileage on a family trip, they can involve their children in these mathematical moments. "Parents' attitudes toward mathematics have an impact on how mathematics will be viewed by their children. The child whose parents show enthusiasm for mathematics in the home will be more likely to develop enthusiasm" (Brosnan et al., 329).

As children solve word problems in contexts that are meaningful, they become more confident in applying their math skills. When parents listen to their children explain how they solved a problem, they become more aware of the math concepts and skills their child is mastering. By helping their child apply classroom lessons in their home environment, parents become advocates of their child's education and develop a partnership with teachers that links school and home. The materials in *Harcourt Math* are designed to help you build that critical school-home link.

References

Brosnan, Patricia; Diamantis, Maria; and Hartog, Martin D. Feb. 1998. "Doing Mathematics with Your Child," *Teaching Children Mathematics,* Vol. 4, No. 6, pp. 326–330.

California Department of Education. 1999. *Mathematics Framework for California Schools, Kindergarten Through Grade Twelve.*

Ensign, Jacque. Feb. 1998. "Parents, Portfolios, and Personal Mathematics," *Teaching Children Mathematics,* Vol. 4, No. 6, pp. 331–337.

Follmer, Robin; Ford, Marilyn Sue; and Litz, Kathleen K. Feb. 1998. "School-Family Partnerships: Parents, Children, and Teachers Benefit!" *Teaching Children Mathematics,* Vol. 4, No. 6, pp. 310–312.

Moldavan, Carla C. Feb. 2000. "A Parent's Portfolio: Observing the Power of Matt, the Mathematician," *Teaching Children Mathematics,* Vol. 6, No. 6, pp. 372–374.

Mathematics for All *Doesn't Mean* Mathematics for Some!

by Jennie M. Bennett

The National Council of Teachers of Mathematics has a public service announcement that says "Do math and you can do anything." What does the reality for "doing math" mean for the youth of today? Today's mathematics opens doors to many opportunities, including entry into tomorrow's jobs—jobs that have not yet been defined. What does this mean for elementary classroom teachers?

Elementary teachers lay the mathematical foundation for students. This foundation must include developing students' mathematical thinking and infusing the elementary curriculum with algebraic concepts. Teachers must encourage students to pursue algebra and other higher mathematics courses at the secondary level and help students see that success in these higher-level courses will prepare them to participate fully in our ever-changing technological society. Students are now expected to achieve the higher standards set by the National Council of Teachers of Mathematics and by their local districts. High expectations are being placed on teachers to ensure that **all** students achieve these higher standards.

Teachers are being challenged to help every child achieve regardless of the child's academic ability. As teachers face this challenge, they must develop strategies to ensure that

- the needs of culturally different students are met;
- gender equity problems are identified and addressed;
- the needs of the mathematically gifted students are met; and
- students with special needs are included in the classroom curriculum.

All children have a thirst for knowledge. A thirst to learn mathematics is an opportunity for every child to participate fully in the classroom program and ultimately in the work force. For children of color, this opportunity is especially important.

The population of the United States is changing to reflect a more diverse society. In 1976, the nonwhite population of United States schools was 24 percent. By 1984, the population of nonwhite students in United States schools had increased to 29 percent. In the new millennium, the projected percent of nonwhite students will increase to between 30 percent and 40 percent (Tiedt and Tiedt, 1999). What do these statistics mean for teachers? The ever-changing cultural makeup of America means that teachers must fully address the challenges of equity and excellence. Both equity and excellence must be a part of a guide for students as well (Tomlinson, 1999).

Strategies for Addressing Equity and Excellence in the Classroom

When students arrive in the classroom, they do not leave their cultural backgrounds and experiences at the door. Mathematical ideas have natural cultural links for many students. Building on these links will help teachers include all children. In *Harcourt Math*, cultural contributions and experiences are embedded so that students can see the mathematical ideas and achievements of people from their own background and the backgrounds of their classmates. As defined by James Banks (Banks and Banks, 1993), this level of cultural integration is the lowest level. However, this level still remains important for students and teachers.

Encouraging culturally different students to participate in mathematics includes using the following instructional strategies:

- asking probing questions;
- allowing adequate wait time;
- engaging students in meaningful problem solving situations;
- asking them to explain their thinking;
- working in cooperative learning groups; and
- giving students positive feedback that helps them make progress.

Research states that multicultural education infused in classroom instruction impacts and supports individual esteem, teaches empathy for others, and provides equity for all students (Tiedt and Tiedt, 1999).

The issue of gender equity in the mathematics classroom continues to be deeply rooted in culture and tradition. Teachers must not let the stereotype that "girls cannot do much math" perpetuate in their classrooms from year to year. Girls can do math and should be presented the same rigorous activities that are presented to the boys in the class. They should be encouraged to participate in classroom activities and to freely communicate their mathematical thinking to their classmates. Teachers must be aware of and reduce factors in the classroom that do not equally enhance both boys' and girls' mathematical abilities.

Similarly, students with physical and mental challenges must have equal access to a high-quality mathematics instructional program. Barriers to their success in the mathematics classroom must be lowered. *Harcourt Math* offers inclusion opportunities so that lessons can be modified to allow these students to interact with other students and experience success in mathematics. The use of manipulatives addresses various learning styles and is an effective link to enable students with physical and mental challenges to succeed in the classroom.

The instruction of gifted and talented students also presents challenges. Many teachers are faced with including gifted students in the classroom instructional program, and they are challenged to meet the needs of these students and ensure that their potential is fully developed. The National Council of Teachers of Mathematics has broadened the definition of gifted and talented students to include "mathematically promising" students. Students showing mathematical promise come from all cultures and across all economic strata and have the potential to become problem solvers of the future (Bennett, 1999). Teachers need to make a special effort to challenge, encourage, and support promising students. *Harcourt Math* provides opportunities for students to develop their full capacities for learning mathematics.

The goal of *Harcourt Math* is to provide an instructional program that can be tailored to the instructional needs of every student. Some of the significant opportunities provided to students in the program are:

- providing problem solving activities at various levels of difficulty;
- asking students to make conjectures and justify their thinking;
- asking students to write about the mathematics they are learning and to write their own problems;
- having students use manipulatives to develop their conceptual understanding and model their thinking;
- asking students probing questions that require critical thinking and logical reasoning;
- having students use technology to develop both their conceptual understanding and skill proficiency; and
- having students work with their peers to share their thinking and build their knowledge.

Teachers play a pivotal role in providing quality learning experiences. It is through the expertise of the teacher that students learn mathematics and develop their full potential (NCTM, 2000). When teachers use *Harcourt Math*, they have opportunities to provide rich experiences to challenge each student. Some of the elements that teachers can use to form a consistent approach to developing their classroom instructional program are

- asking students at the end of each lesson to reflect on what they learned;
- asking students to explain and justify their answers to problem solving situations;
- enhancing students' styles of learning by engaging them in cooperative group work;
- using a variety of questioning strategies to build students' mathematical reasoning abilities;
- integrating culturally relevant connections;
- having students show multiple representations of concepts and problems;
- infusing algebraic thinking and introducing algebraic concepts in the early grades;
- engaging students in active, stimulating, and challenging mathematics; and
- communicating with parents about how to help their child at home.

Linking teachers, students, and parents to the mathematics developed in *Harcourt Math* ensures that all students, not just some of them, will be challenged to develop their mathematical abilities to their fullest potential.

References

Banks, James, and Cherry Banks. (1993). *Multicultural Education: Issues and Perspectives,* Second Edition. Boston: Allyn and Bacon.

Bennett, Jennie. (1999). "The Missing Link: Connecting Parents of Mathematically Promising Students to Schools." *Developing Mathematically Promising Students.* Reston, VA.: National Council of Teachers of Mathematics.

National Council of Teachers of Mathematics. (2000). *Principles and Standards for School Mathematics.* Reston, VA.: National Council of Teachers of Mathematics.

National Council of Teachers of Mathematics. (2000). *Changing the Faces of Mathematics: Perspectives on African Americans.* Reston, VA.: National Council of Teachers of Mathematics.

Tiedt, Pamela, and Iris Tiedt. (1999). *Multicultural Teaching: A Handbook of Activities, Information, and Resources,* Fifth Edition. Boston: Allyn and Bacon.

Tomlinson, Carol. (1999). *The Differentiated Classroom: Responding to the Needs of All Learners.* Alexandria, VA.: Association for Supervision and Curriculum Development.

Making Math Memorable: Brain-Compatible Learning

by Marilee Sprenger

It seems that the brain has a mind of its own. When the brain receives any information, including mathematical information, it sorts the information, discards information it doesn't believe is important, and places information that is meaningful in different pathways for later access. We used to believe that the brain took in all information and held it for later retrieval, but it is now believed that up to 99 percent of sensory input to the brain is simply dropped (Wolf, 2000).

How does the brain know what to keep and what to dispose of? Learning appears to take place under the following two conditions:

1. If the brain can connect new material to previously stored information, there is a stronger possibility for encoding. With prior knowledge, the brain has already set in place a network of information or ideas that help the new learning make sense. It is through this meaning-making that new memories can be stored for later access.
2. The other avenue for learning is to stimulate the brain with a novel situation or experience. When the brain experiences a new situation, novelty causes fresh stimulation that sparks attention. This novelty has an emotional component to it, and emotion drives attention and learning (Sylwester, 2000).

Brain-Compatible Learning in *Harcourt Math*

The Harcourt system for math instruction is an excellent approach to brain-compatible learning because the approach is consistent in leading the brain through the learning process. Consistency is a key to brain-compatible learning. The brain requires certain rituals, or parameters, that signal the brain that all is well. It thus feels safe to take in new, unanticipated experiences and new information for careful examination. Without this feeling of security, the brain may quickly initiate a stress response whenever a novel experience presents itself, preventing meaningful learning. When this need for security is met, information can be used at higher brain levels for complex thinking (Jensen, 1998).

The sequence of instruction in *Harcourt Math* helps create the ritual, and the individual components of each lesson allow new connections to be made. Each lesson begins by accessing prior knowledge, an activity that helps the child retrieve memories that will help him or her relate to the new material. Recall that one way we learn is to connect new information to previously stored information.

Reviewing skills is the next step in the lesson sequence. Optimal learning requires a state of "flow" in the brain (Jensen, 2000). This is a pattern of activity that combines challenge, skills, and desire. Students must feel that their skills are equal to the task at hand to allow them to work without stress. Reminding students of their previously learned and mastered skills aids them in attaining this state. The introduction of a lesson also includes an explanation of *why* the information is important to learn. It is through this understanding that students may be able to relate their learning to real-life situations.

The introduction provides a framework for learning the new material. *Harcourt Math* focuses on concrete, hands-on learning experiences. Research on brain development supports concrete learning as a hallmark of effective teaching. It is through concrete experiences that the brain can take steps toward higher-level thinking and abstraction (Sprenger, 1999). Modifications for meeting the needs of each individual learner are suggested at each step in the learning sequence. Since each brain is unique, provision for responding to that uniqueness is crucial. A variety of teaching strategies, as well as many opportunities for enrichment, pave the way for meeting the needs of each child. Activities are aimed at accommodating the different learning styles of students. Since many individuals learn better with visual representations, *Harcourt Math* emphasizes the use of pictures, graphs, and tables. For the kinesthetic, hands-on learner, activities using a variety of manipulatives are suggested. This exploration may be the simulation of a concept or skill that helps the brain that has no prior knowledge. If the meaning cannot be connected to stored memories, this method may create the understanding necessary for new learning and memory and allow the student options for taking the information into his or her brain in the most accessible format. Questioning strategies that follow the guided instruction allow the brain to connect more meaning to the learning.

Guided practice, a key step in the learning sequence in *Harcourt Math*, is necessary for complete learning and memory. Short-term memory is the first step in the process of retaining semantic learning (facts). Sometimes short-term memory is called immediate memory, and initially the area of the brain involved in this procedure holds information for only seconds. Immediate memory can be extended through a rehearsal process called working memory. Without this rote or elaborate rehearsal, memories are not stored and are easily forgotten (Squire and Kandel, 1999). It is only through this procedure that the information to be stored for the long term can be catalogued by a small structure in the brain called the hippocampus. Because of its size and its processing speed, large amounts of information cannot be stored quickly (Jensen, 2000). The process of encoding for long-term storage takes place over time. With each successive practice session, more of the learning can be placed in long-term storage. Independent practice allows for a second memory pathway to be utilized. This is procedural memory, which is sometimes called "muscle memory." Repetition of the process of problem solving allows the brain to store this information in another area of the brain. Storage in more memory pathways leads to better learning and easier retrieval.

Assessment is an ongoing process in *Harcourt Math*. Recent research emphasizes the importance of providing feedback to students on a regular basis. Feedback affects both attention and learning. It can also affect stress levels. In one study, students who were given no feedback had higher stress levels than those receiving negative feedback. It is more stressful for the brain to be uninformed than to be told that it needs improvement (Goleman, 1998). Multiple assessment methods provided in *Harcourt Math* create different types of feedback for both teacher and learner. By using multiple assessments, different memory pathways can be accessed separately or together. Students can discover that information has been stored in one way and that practice must be done for other storage processes. Self-assessment is also an excellent tool for feedback and greater understanding of the learning process. Results of self-assessment are metacognition and identification of new learning goals (Marzano, 2000).

Powerful Learning

The brain utilizes different areas for processing math. For instance, brain-imaging studies indicate that subtraction and multiplication activate separate brain regions (Talan, 1999). Fundamental knowledge that is stored through practice, such as the multiplication tables, provide one type of memory. Practical applications of a skill stimulate another memory pathway. With frequent feedback, these applications enhance both memory and recall. Greater effort is required for the application of skills, but understanding how learning relates in real-life situations stimulates cognition (Kessler, Learning Brain, 2000). Computer-assisted activities included in *Harcourt Math* aid in both drill and practice and practical applications.

Just as multiple memory pathways aid in retention and retrieval of memories, integrating disciplines also enhances memory. Students find more relevance in what they are learning through interdisciplinary and cross-disciplinary methods. They will see more easily how learning relates to real life and have more links to the learning (Jensen, 1998). In *Harcourt Math,* students are shown connections to other disciplines. Through science, social studies, health, physical education, or literature, students find many associations to activate their learning and memory.

As a classroom teacher, I often had to scramble to create lessons for advanced students, slower students, or just students who happened to retrieve information quickly and finished work early. Since my workload seemed to always be increasing, I hoped for a textbook series that would fill in these blanks for me. This series provides these resources. I cannot stress enough the importance of having activities and challenges for all students. The brain makes connections through active engagement, and the emotional brain responds well to the knowledge that its needs are being met.

Meeting needs of all involved is a strong point in *Harcourt Math*. I am not only referring to students. The series also provides information for teachers and parents that enhance each child's learning experience. The *Differentiated Instruction* provides the teacher necessary information to not only stay on track, but also to really know when students have the skills, understanding, and concepts to move forward. It's not just the usual "This is the end of the chapter; it's time to move on!"

Parents are also included in the program. Through *Family Involvement Activities*, parents and caregivers understand what the student is learning and can become involved in the process. This gives the entire program a cooperative effort and can give the student a sense of belonging, which is a basic brain instinct. The link between home and school is vital as parents and the home are the primary sources of comfort and happiness for most children (Kessler, 2000). Providing this connection strengthens the math program and the learning.

Back to the Basics of Learning

There are some basic principles of brain-based learning that should be examined by every educator. By understanding these principles and applying them, the classroom becomes an arena for rich experiences where standards are woven into large themes that students can relate to in many ways.

The brain learns through patterns. It looks for meaning by organizing and categorizing information. The brain can perceive and generate its own patterns. If information fits into an established pattern, the brain can apply the new learning and easily remember it. This principle is particularly relevant to math. It is necessary for students to be able to recognize patterns in problem solving. Since students are always seeking meaning through patterning, we must present material to help them identify and use patterns.

Emotions are critical to patterning. Any activity that creates an emotional tie causes the brain to release chemicals that enhance memory. Emotions cannot be separated from cognition; therefore, the emotional climate of the classroom must be monitored at all times. It is important that math be more than a verbal subject. Students need activities that invite emotion and, therefore, meaning. Each year teachers face students who may have internalized a pattern about math that is negative based on an earlier experience. It is particularly important that the teacher use as many resources as possible to change this thought pattern. It may be helpful to use *Technology Linkups* with these students. Or perhaps the *It's In The Bag* activities in the Pupil Editions will help students develop a positive feeling about math.

Learning is social. The brain learns better when it works in cooperation with other brains. For this reason, it is important to provide opportunities for group work. Dyads, triads, and small groups may provide the stimulation and meaning necessary for the learning to be made permanent. It may be through the experiences of others that students find the connection they need. The need for socialization may date back in history to times when people needed to be together for survival. The idea of safety in numbers may now be applied to math class!

Harcourt Math provides many opportunities for students to work together to solve problems. This group work provides two distinct opportunities to enhance learning. It gives students the chance to review concepts and skills, hear explanations from their peers rather than always from the teacher, and do some peer teaching. The students also have the opportunity to work on their social and emotional skills. This important arena needs to be cultivated and will result in stronger cognitive abilities (Kessler, 2000).

Learning involves conscious and unconscious processes. In memory terms this principle refers to the two most fundamental kinds of memory—implicit and explicit. *Implicit* memory occurs without conscious attention. That is to say that the memory is formed without much effort. *Explicit* memory requires conscious attention and is formed through the rehearsal process (Sprenger, 1999). In *Harcourt Math* we may see implicit learning through the *Problem of the Day* or *Number of the Day* activities in every lesson plan in the *Teacher's Editions*. As students enjoy problem solving together, they are conceptualizing the problem solving process.

Brains perceive both parts and wholes simultaneously. The left hemisphere of the brain handles details as one of its functions. The right hemisphere examines the big picture. The two hemispheres work together for complete understanding. It is through the integration of parts and wholes that students make connections. For instance, if students learn about graphs in math class, they might create a graph in geography that represents the amounts of rainfall in a given area over time.

Learning involves mind, body, and movement. Current research shows that some of our memories are stored in our bodies (Pert, 1997). Consequently, the more we involve the entire physiology, the better the learning and memory will be. Researchers have found that muscle tension varies a great deal during cognitive tasks. It appears that every mental task is also somewhat physical (Jensen, 2000). Whenever there is physical movement, heart and respiratory rates increase. This may also increase attention. So, when teaching a graphing lesson, rather than simply having students make a graph from given information, have students do a physical activity that can then be graphed. An activity such as this might involve mind, body, and movement.

High stress or threat can impair learning and even kill brain cells. This information has a great impact on teaching practice. Handling a classroom by threat is unfortunately not an uncommon practice. Threats and stress cause the brain to operate at a survival level where no higher-level thinking can take place. Students learn best when they are taught through ritual, novelty, and challenge. The brain also requires choice and feedback. If these practices were the norm in every classroom, there would be little need for threat or stress because students would be too busy learning to do anything inappropriate. Good curriculum and textbooks that provide these five necessities can lower stress for both teachers and students.

Brain Research–Not Just Another Fad

When I made my first brain-research-based presentation many years ago, the staff development director came up to me and said these words, "Brain research is here to stay!" We all know that in education there are some trends that come and go. Although we are learning new things about the brain on a daily basis, we have good information now to allow us to make better decisions about instructional strategies and classroom management. Teachers must make hundreds of decisions every day. Making them based on brain-based theories and applications that enhance learning and memory and provide for individual differences makes good sense. It also creates classrooms that make the mathematics experience a memorable one.

References

Goleman, Daniel. (1998). *Working with Emotional Intelligence*. New York, NY: Bantam.

Jensen, Eric. (2000). *Brain-Based Learning*. San Diego, CA: The Brain Store.

________. (2000). *Learning with the Body in Mind*. San Diego, CA: The Brain Store.

________. (1998). *Teaching with the Brain in Mind*. Alexandria, VA: A.S.C.D.

Kessler, Rachel. (2000). *Brain-Based Techniques Improve Test Scores*. San Diego, CA. The Learning Brain Newsletter.

________. (2000). *The Soul of Education*. Alexandria, VA: A.S.C.D.

Marzano, Robert J. (2000). *Transforming Classroom Grading*. Alexandria, VA: A.S.C.D.

Pert, Candace. (1997). *Molecules of Emotion*. New York: Scribner.

Sprenger, Marilee. (1999). *Learning and Memory: The Brain in Action*. Alexandria, VA: A.S.C.D.

Squire, Larry, and Eric Kandel. (1999). *Memory: From Mind to Molecules*. New York: Scientific American Library.

Sylwester, Robert. (2000) *A Biological Brain in a Cultural Classroom*. Thousand Oaks, CA: Corwin Press.

Talan, Jamie. (1999). "Simple division: Brain splits up math work." Seattle Times. Available online at: http://seattletimes.nwsource.com/news/nation-world/html98/math_19990507.html

Wolf, Pat. (2000). "Chalk Talk: From Discovery to the Blackboard." The Brain Connection to Education Spring Conference 2000. (audiocassette)

Teaching Notes

Additional Ideas:

Good Questions to Ask:

Additional Resources:

Notes for Next Time:

HARCOURT

Math

Bibliography and Index

The following bibliography contains references to:

- **Fiction and nonfiction books for students**
- **Technology resources**
- **Professional books and magazines**

These materials will assist you in creating an interesting learning environment. The references to literature are provided to help you work through your media center to acquire literature selections that you can use with *Harcourt Math*. The math activities developed to correlate to these books will help you build a math curriculum to meet the needs of all students.

The index contains information for both the Pupil Edition and Teacher Edition. The italicized entries are found in the Teacher Edition.

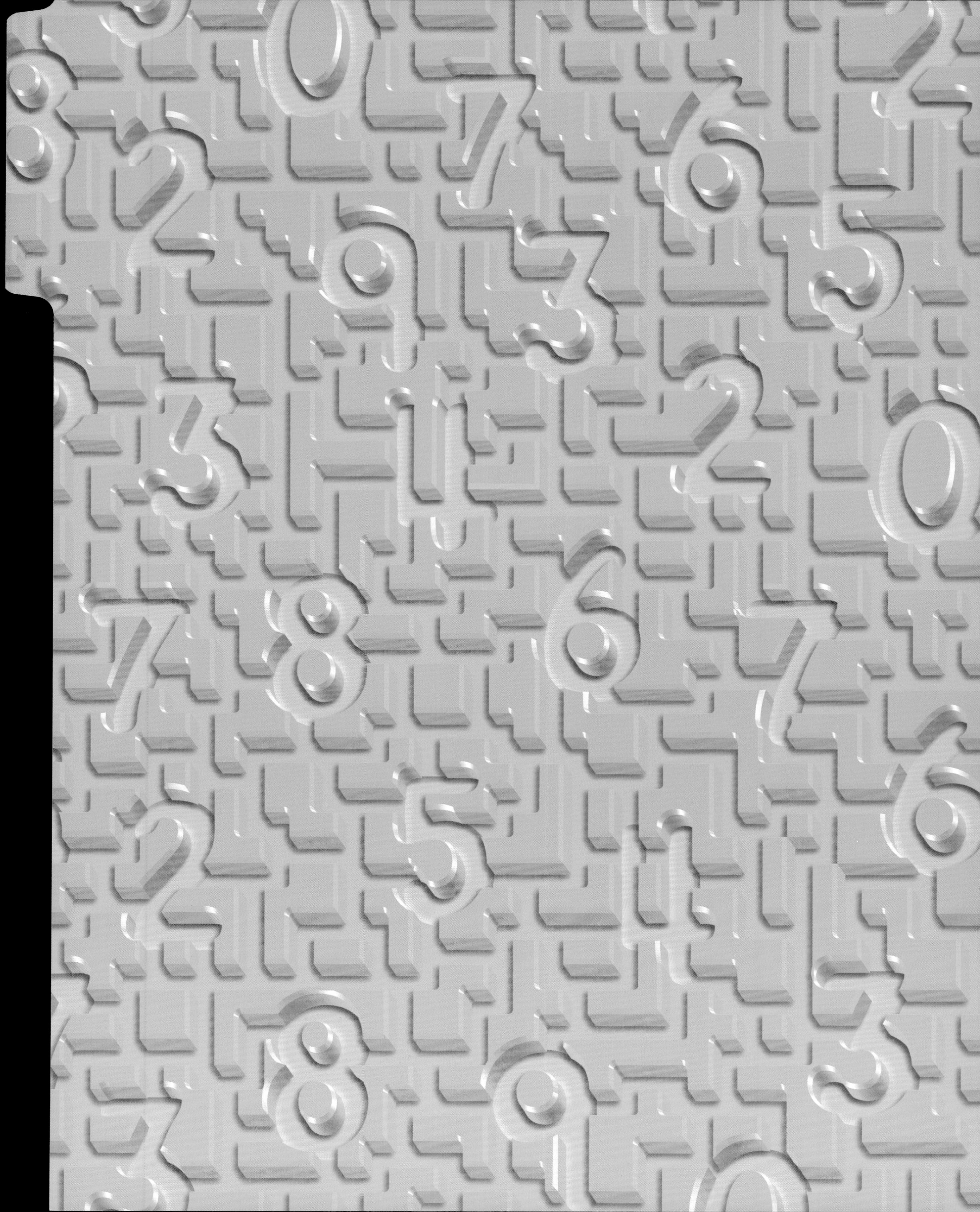

Bibliography

Books for Students

The Alaska Purchase. Cohen, Daniel. Millbrook, 1996.

Amanda Bean's Amazing Dream. Neuschwander, Cindy. Scholastic, 1998.

American History Math: 50 Problem-Solving Activities That Link Math to Key Events in U.S. History. Glasthal, Jacqueline B. Scholastic, 1996.

Anno's Mysterious Multiplying Jar. Anno, Masaichiro and Mitsumasa. Putnam, 1983.

Apollo 11. Stein, Conrad R. Children's Press, 1995.

Arithmetricks: 50 Easy Ways to Add, Subtract, Multiply, and Divide Without a Calculator. Julius, Edward H. Wiley & Sons, 1995.

A Bag Full of Pups. Gackenbach, Dick. Houghton Mifflin, 1983.

Bats, Bugs, and Biodiversity: Adventures in the Amazonian Rain Forest. Goodman, Susan E. Atheneum, 1995.

Beach Feet. Reiser, Lynn. William Morrow & Company, 1981.

Bicycle Race. Crews, Donald. Greenwillow Books, 1985.

Charlie and the Great Glass Elevator. Dahl, Roald. Puffin Books, 1998.

Chibi. Brenner, Barbara, and Julia Takaya. Clarion, 1996.

Class President. Hurwitz, Johanna. Scholastic, 1991.

A Cloak for the Dreamer. Friedman, Aileen. Scholastic, 1995.

Cool Math: Math Tricks, Amazing Math Activities, Cool Calculations, Awesome Math Factoids and More. Maganzini, Christi. Price Stern Sloan, Inc., 1997.

Counting on Frank. Clement, Rod. Gareth Stevens Publishing, 1991.

The Cuckoo Child. King-Smith, Dick. Hyperion Books for Children, 1993.

Discovering Graph Secrets. Markle, Sandra. Atheneum, 1997.

Discovering Math: Multiplication. Stienecker, David L. Benchmark Books, 1996.

Divide and Ride. Murphy, Stuart J. HarperCollins, 1997.

Do You Wanna Bet? Your Chance to Find Out About Probability. Cushman, Jean. Houghton Mifflin, 1991.

The Doorbell Rang. Hutchins, Pat. Greenwillow Books, 1986.

Each Orange Had 8 Slices. Giganti, Paul, Jr. Greenwillow Books, 1992.

Early Schools. Kalman, Bobbie D. Crabtree, 1982.

Earthquakes. Branley, Franklyn. Trophy Press, 1994.

Eating Fractions. McMillan, Bruce. Scholastic, 1991.

Exploring the Night Sky. Dickinson, Terence. Camden House, 1987.

Flatland. Abbott, Edwin A. Dover Publications, Inc., 1952.

Fourscore and 7: Investigating Math in American History. Franco, Betsy. Good Year Books, 1999.

Fraction Action. Leedy, Loreen. Holiday House, 1994.

Fraction Fun. Adler, David A. Holiday House, 1996.

Frogs, Toads, Lizards, and Salamanders. Parker, Nancy Winslow. Greenwillow Books, 1990.

Funny and Fabulous Fraction Stories. Greenberg, Dan. Scholastic, 1996.

G is for Googol. Schwartz, David M. Tricycle Press, 1998.

A Grain of Rice. Pittman, Helena Clare. Hastings House, 1986.

Grandfather Tang's Story. Tompert, Ann. Crown Publishers, 1990.

The Grapes of Math: Mind Stretching Math Riddles. Tang, Greg. Scholastic Press, 2001.

The Greedy Triangle. Burns, Marilyn. Scholastic, Inc., 1994.

Hey, New Kid! Duffey, Betsy. Viking, 1996.

How Big Is a Foot? Myller, Rolf. Young Yearling, 1991.

How Big Were the Dinosaurs? Most, Bernard. Harcourt Brace & Company, 1994.

How Many Days to America? Bunting, Eve. Clarion, 1988.

How Many Snails? Giganti, Paul, Jr. William Morrow & Company, 1996.

If You Made a Million. Schwartz, David M. Lothrop, Lee & Shepard, 1989.

Jigsaw Jackson. Birchman, David F. Lothrop, Lee & Shepard, 1996.

Keeping Time. Branley, Franklyn M. Houghton Mifflin, 1993.

Kids' Money Book. Godfrey, Neale S. Simon & Schuster, 1998.

The King's Equal. Paterson, Katherine. HarperCollins, 1992.

Lemonade for Sale. Murphy, Stuart J. HarperCollins, 1998.

The Librarian Who Measured the Earth. Lasky, Kathryn. Little, Brown and Company, 1994.

Lilly and Miss Liberty. Stevens, Carla. Little Apple, 1993.

The Man Who Counted: A Collection of Mathematical Adventures. Tahan, Malba. W. W. Norton & Company, 1993.

The Math Chef. D'Amico, Joan, and Karen Eich Drummond. John Wiley & Sons, 1997.

Math Counts: Capacity. Pluckrose, Henry. Children's Press, 1995.

Math Counts: Time. Pluckrose, Henry. Children's Press, 1995.

Math Curse. Scieszka, Jon. Penguin, 1995.

Math Mini Mysteries. Markle, Sandra. Atheneum, 1993.

Math Mysteries. Silbert, Jack. Scholastic, 1995.

Millions of Cats. Gág, Wanda. Sandcastle Books, 1988.

My Place in Space. Hirst, Robin and Sally. Orchard Books, 1992.

Nearer Nature. Arnosky, Jim. Midaya Press, 1996.

Nine for California. Levitin, Sonia. Orchard Books, 1996.

The Noonday Friends. Stolz, Mary. HarperCollins, 1995.

Old Home Day. Hall, Donald. Harcourt Brace & Company, 1996.

One Hundred Hungry Ants. Pinczes, Elinor J. Houghton Mifflin Company, 1993.

Paperboy. Kroeger, Mary Kay. Houghton Mifflin, 1996.

A Picture Book of Jesse Owens. Adler, David A. Holiday House, 1992.

Probability Pistachio. Murphy, Stuart S. Harper Trophy, 2001.

Pyramid. Macaulay, David. Houghton Mifflin, 1975.

The Quilt-Block History of Pioneer Days: With Projects Kids Can Make. Cobb, Mary. Millbrook, 1995.

Ready, Set, Hop! Murphy, Stuart J. HarperCollins, 1996.

Round Trip. Jonas, Ann. Greenwillow Books, 1983.

Selina and the Bear Paw Quilt. Smucker, Barbara. Dragonfly Books, 1999.

Shake, Rattle, and Roll!: Cool, and Educational, Things to Do With Dice. Onyshko, Dan. Penguin, 1997.

Shape Up! Adler, David. Holiday House, 1998.

Shaping the Earth. Patent, Dorothy Hinshaw. Clarion Books, 2000.

Sir Cumference and the First Round Table: A Math Adventure. Neuschwander, Cindy. Charlesbridge Publishing, 1997.

The Story of Maps and Navigation. Ganeri, Anita. Oxford University Press, 1997.

Summer Ice: Life Along the Antarctic Peninsula. McMillan, Bruce. Houghton Mifflin, 1995.

The Tarantula in My Purse. George, Jean Craighead. HarperCollins, 1996.

Too Many Kangaroo Things to Do! Murphy, Stuart J. HarperCollins, 1996.

The Toothpaste Millionaire. Merrill, Jean. Houghton Mifflin, 1972.

The Trading Game. Slote, Alfred. Harper Trophy, 1990.

The Trumpet of the Swan. White, E. B. HarperCollins, 1987.

Weather & Climate. Watt, Fiona, and Francis Wilson. EDC Publishing, 1992.

What Are You Figuring Now? A Story About Benjamin Banneker. Ferris, Jeri. Carolrhoda Books, 1988.

What Is a Wall, After All? Allen, Judy. Candlewick Press, 1993.

What's Faster Than a Speeding Cheetah? Wells, Robert E. Albert Whitman & Company, 1997.

Where Am I? The Story of Maps and Navigation. Smith, A. G. Stoddart Kids, 1997.

Zoo. Gibbons, Gail. Trophy Press, 1991.

Math Software

TITLE	PUBLISHER	DESCRIPTION	SYSTEM REQUIREMENTS
Harcourt Mega Math: Country Countdown	Harcourt	This program teaches students the concepts, facts, and thinking skills necessary to build math confidence and develop a strong, lasting understanding of math. **Math Topics** • Place Value • Addition • Subtraction • Comparing Number Sets • Time • Graphing	**PC:** Pentium II; Windows® 98, ME, XP Pro, 2000; 64MB RAM (128MB for Windows 2000) and XP SVGA; Sound Blaster® 16 or compatible sound card; 4X CD-ROM; 50 MB free hard drive space; Internet Explorer 5.5; Adobe Acrobat Reader 5.0 **Macintosh:** Macintosh G3; OS 8.6-9.2.2 or OS X 10.2.2; 64MB RAM with virtual memory enabled (128 for OS X); 800 × 600 resolution, thousands of color; 4X CD-ROM; 50 free hard drive space; Internet Explorer 5.5; Adobe Acrobat Reader 5.0
Harcourt Mega Math: The Number Games	Harcourt	This program teaches students the concepts, facts, and thinking skills necessary to build math confidence and develop a strong, lasting understanding of math. **Math Topics** • Money • Patterns • Multiplication • Division • Graphing	**PC:** Pentium II; Windows® 98, ME, XP Pro, 2000; 64MB RAM (128MB for Windows 2000) and XP SVGA; Sound Blaster® 16 or compatible sound card; 4X CD-ROM; 50 MB free hard drive space; Internet Explorer 5.5; Adobe Acrobat Reader 5.0 **Macintosh:** Macintosh G3; OS 8.6-9.2.2 or OS X 10.1.2; 64MB RAM with virtual memory enabled (128 for OS X); 800 × 600 resolution, thousands of color; 4X CD-ROM; 50 MB free hard drive space; Internet Explorer 5.5; Adobe Acrobat Reader 5.0
Harcourt Mega Math: Ice Station Exploration	Harcourt	This program teaches students the concepts, facts, and thinking skills necessary to build math confidence and develop a strong, lasting understanding of math. **Math Topics** • Plane Geometry • Solid Geometry • Linear Measurement • Algebra	**PC:** Pentium II; Windows® 98, ME, XP Pro, 2000; 64MB RAM (128MB for Windows 2000) and XP SVGA; Sound Blaster® 16 or compatible sound card; 4X CD-ROM; 50 MB free hard drive space; Internet Explorer 5.5; Adobe Acrobat Reader 5.0 **Macintosh:** Macintosh G3; OS 8.6-9.2.2 or OS X 10.1.2; 64MB RAM with virtual memory enabled (128 for OS X); 800 × 600 resolution, thousands of color; 4X CD-ROM; 50 MB free hard drive space; Internet Explorer 5.5; Adobe Acrobat Reader 5.0
Harcourt Mega Math: Fraction Action	Harcourt	This program teaches students the concepts, facts, and thinking skills necessary to build math confidence and develop a strong, lasting understanding of math. **Math Topics** • Fraction Concepts • Decimal Concepts • Fraction Operations • Probability	**PC:** Pentium II; Windows® 98, ME, XP Pro, 2000; 64MB RAM (128MB for Windows 2000) and XP SVGA; Sound Blaster® 16 or compatible sound card; 4X CD-ROM; 50 MB free hard drive space; Internet Explorer 5.5; Adobe Acrobat Reader 5.0 **Macintosh:** Macintosh G3; OS 8.6-9.2.2 or OS X 10.1.2; 64MB RAM with virtual memory enabled (128 for OS X); 800 × 600 resolution, thousands of color; 4X CD-ROM; 50 MB free hard drive space; Internet Explorer 5.5; Adobe Acrobat Reader 5.0
JumpStart Adventures 3rd Grade: Mystery Mountain	Knowledge Adventure	Students apply lessons in math and other curriculum areas while trying to defeat the schemes of a villain who is trying to use a time machine to alter the past. **Math Topics** • Addition • Subtraction • Multiplication • Estimation • Measurement • Problem Solving	**PC:** Windows 3.1/ 95/98, 486 DX2/ 66 MHz PC or higher; 16 MB RAM, 9 MB available on hard drive; quad-speed CD-ROM drive; 256-colors; Windows-compatible sound card **Macintosh:** Motorola 68040 40 MHz or Power PC Processor; System 7.5, 8 MB RAM, 9 MB available on hard drive; double-speed CD-ROM drive, 256-colors
JumpStart Adventures 4th Grade: Haunted Island	Knowledge Adventure	Students apply lessons in math and other curriculum areas to rescue 13 lost friends before they turn into freakish fiends forever! **Math Topics** • Equations • Multiplication • Subtraction • Fractions • Division • Addition • Decimals • Units of Measure	**PC:** Windows 95/98 486 DX2/66 MHz; 8 MB available, 9 MB available on hard drive; double-speed CD-ROM drive; SVGA 256-color graphics; MPC-compatible sound card **Macintosh:** 68040 40 MHz or Power PC Processor; System 7.1; 8 MB RAM, 9 MB available on hard drive; double-speed CD-ROM drive; 256-colors, 13″ monitor

Math Software

TITLE	PUBLISHER	DESCRIPTION	SYSTEM REQUIREMENTS
JumpStart Adventures 5th Grade: Jo Hammet, Kid Detective	Knowledge Adventure	While visiting the museum on a field trip, Jo Hammet uncovers a sinister plot to destroy all of the city's factories! Her mission (with student help) is to find clues leading to the capture of the mad genius, Dr. X. **Math Topics** • Fractions • Decimals • Equations • Division • Multiplication • Geometry • Ratios	**PC:** Windows 3.1/95/98, 486 DX/2 66; 16 MB RAM, 15 MB available on hard drive; double speed CD-ROM drive; 256-color SVGA graphics; MPC-compatible sound card **Macintosh:** Motorola 68040 25 MHz or Power Macintosh; System 7.1; 8 MB RAM, 15 MB available on hard drive; double-speed CD-ROM drive; 256-color graphics
The ClueFinders 5th Grade Adventure	The Learning Company	A sudden tsunami has shipwrecked the gang on an uncharted volcanic island, and Owen and Leslie have disappeared! Students collect the mysterious Cryp Tiles to solve the mystery before the volcano blows! **Math Topics** • Multiplication • Division • Geometry	**PC:** Pentium® 166 MHz or faster (Pentium® II 300 MHz or faster for XP); Windows® 95/98/Me/2000/XP 100 MB available on hard disk; 32 MB RAM (128 MB RAM for XP); 8X CD-ROM; High Color, 16-bit; Windows-compatible Sound card and speakers; mouse; Internet Access Printer recommended **Macintosh:** Power PC 180 MHz or faster; Mac OS 8.6-9x; 100 MB available on hard disk; 32 MB RAM; 8X CD-ROM; thousands color; 16-bit; sound card and speakers; mouse; Internet Access Printer
Carmen Sandiego Math Detective	The Learning Company	The program includes three levels of over 250 activities with thousands of math problems, as well as over 400 word problems and customizable problem sets. **Math Topics** • Numeration • Geometry • Measurement • Problem Solving	**PC:** Windows® 3.1; 486/66Mhz or better; 8MB RAM; 80MB Hard Drive; 256-colors; 2X CD-ROM; Windows compliant sound device; mouse **PC:** Windows® 95/98; 486/66Mhz or better, 16 MB RAM; 80MB Hard Drive; Super VGA (640 × 480) 256-colors; 4X CD-ROM; Windows compliant sound device **PowerMac™:** 16MB RAM, 20 MB Hard Drive; 256-colors, 4X CD-ROM; requires a 100 Mhz PowerPC or better
Community Construction Kit	Tom Snyder Productions	An opportunity for students to develop and create their own communities by designing historically accurate buildings and landscaping. **Math Topics** • Geometry • Map Skills • 3-D Concepts	**PC:** Windows 3.1/95/98/2000: IBM-compatible 486, 16 MB RAM, 256-colors; 640 × 480 resolution **Macintosh:** 68030 processor; Mac OS 7.1-9.x and OSX (classic mode), 8 MB, 256-colors; 640 × 480 resolution
Cornerstone ATS 3.2: Mathematics—Level B	The Learning Company	The process includes: Warm-up, Review, Quiz, Take Five, and Worksheet to demonstrate, guide, test, reinforce, and provide extra practice of concepts. **Math Topics** • Number Concepts • Percents • Whole Number Computation • Estimation • Fractions • Decimals • Data and Graphs	**PC:** Windows 95/98/2000, ME, NT 4.0 with Service Pack 5; 32 MB RAM; 4X CD-ROM; 640 × 480, 256-colors; hard disk; mouse; Windows compatible sound device and printer (optional). Supported Networks: Win NT 4.0 w/SP5, Novell NetWare 4.11, 5.0 **Macintosh:** PowerPC processor; Mac OS 7.5.5 or higher; 4X CD-ROM; 32 MB RAM (48 MB RAM if running an internet browser) plus virtual memory; 640 × 480, 256-colors; mouse; Macintosh compatible printer (optional). Supported Networks: Appleshare 6.3
The Cruncher 2.0	Knowledge Adventure	Program features include a full-featured spreadsheet, step-by-step animated tutorials, twenty cross-curricular projects and templates, colorful charts, and graphs. **Math Topics** • Spreadsheets • Graphs • Statistics • Surveys • Investments	**PC:** Windows 95/98; 486 66 MHz; 16 MB RAM; quad-speed CD-ROM; 640 × 480, 256-color SVGA graphics; Windows-compatible sound card **Macintosh:** Power Mac; System 7.5.1; 16 MB RAM; quad-speed CD-ROM drive; 14″ monitor; 640 × 480, 256-colors
Equivalent Fractions	Tenth Planet	Uses engaging multicultural themes to help students understand that fractions can be named in different but equivalent ways. **Math Topics** • Equivalent Fractions • Compare Fractions	**PC:** Windows 95/98, 486 or higher; OS 3.1 or higher; 16 MB RAM; 2 MB storage; CD-ROM required; 256 colors; incompatible with 2000 NP and XP **Macintosh:** 68040 processor or faster; OS 7.5 or higher; 8 MB RAM; 640 × 480 color monitor; 256-colors; Ethernet or faster network protocol

Math Software

TITLE	PUBLISHER	DESCRIPTION	SYSTEM REQUIREMENTS
Fraction Operations	Tenth Planet	Fraction Operations combines hands-on techniques with multimedia technology. Math concepts are presented in a variety of ways to accommodate a range of learning styles and ability levels. **Math Topics** • Common Denominators • Addition • Equivalent Fractions • Subtraction • Dividing Fractions • Multiplication	**PC:** Windows 95/98, 486 or higher; OS 3.1 or higher; 16 MB RAM; 2 MB storage; CD-ROM required; 256-colors; incompatible with 2000 NP and XP **Macintosh:** OS 7.5 or higher; 68040 processor or faster; 8 MB RAM; 640 × 480 color monitor; 256-colors; Ethernet or faster network protocol
Geometer's Sketchpad	Key Curriculum Press	The software allows students to create geometric figures that can be manipulated, transformed, and distorted while preserving geometric relationships. The software includes specific lessons for investigations, explorations, demonstrations, and constructions. **Math Topics** • Geometry • Visualization • Analysis • Informal Deduction	**PC:** Pentium®-based system or equivalent, Windows 95, NT 4 or later; 16MB RAM, CD-ROM drive **Macintosh:** Power Mac™-based system, Mac OS 8.6 or later; 16MB RAM, CD-ROM drive
The Graph Club	Tom Snyder Productions	The Graph Club is an easy-to-use graphing tool that can be used for self-directed exploration, lessons, and presentations, or creative class projects. **Math Topics** • Gather, Sort, and Classify • Interpret Tables and Graphs • Analyze Data and Graphs	**PC:** Windows 98/2000/NT/XP, Pentium 300MHz; 64 MB RAM; thousands of colors; 800 × 600 resolution; Network CD available **Macintosh:** PowerPC 100MHz; OS 8.6-9.X and OSX (native mode); 64 MB RAM; thousands of colors; 800 × 600 resolution; Network CD available
Graph Master	Tom Snyder Productions	Graph Master is a more powerful graphing program appropriate for students in grade 4 and up. The program allows students to analyze data by providing 9 different types of graphs, and many tools for comparing, filtering, and sorting data. **Math Topics** • Gather, Sort, and Classify • Interpret Tables and Graphs • Analyze Data and Graphs • Statistics	**PC:** Windows 95/98/2000/XP, IBM-compatible Pentium, 100 MHz; 32 MB RAM, 64 MB RAM is recommended; 256-colors, 800 × 600 resolution; Network CD available **Macintosh:** Power PC, 100 MHz; Mac OS 8.1-9.x and OSX (classic mode); 32 MB RAM, 64 MB RAM is recommended; 256-colors, 800 × 600 resolution; Network CD available
Math Blaster Ages 7-9	Knowledge Adventure	The program includes over 300 math lessons and 1000 math problems that focus on fundamental math skills, logic and problem-solving, and math confidence. Tracks student progress. **Math Topics** • Computation • Percents • Fractions • Estimation • Decimals • Number Patterns	**PC:** Windows 95/98; Pentium 90 MHz; 16 MB RAM (32 MB RAM recommended); 256-color SVGA graphics; quad-speed CD-ROM drive; Windows-compatible sound card **Macintosh:** Power Mac; system 7.5.3; 32 MB RAM; 640 × 480, 256-colors
Math Blaster Ages 9-12	Knowledge Adventure	Includes over 50,000 problems with 3 levels of play and 10 areas of skill development covering advanced math skills. **Math Topics** • Computation • Fractions • Estimation • Patterns • Integers	**PC:** Windows 95/98; Pentium 90 MHz; 16 MB RAM (32 MB RAM recommended); 16-bit high color graphics; 14" monitor; quad-speed CD-ROM drive; 16-bit sound card **Macintosh:** Power Mac; system 7.5.3; 32 MB RAM; quad-speed CD-ROM drive; 10MB available on hard drive; thousands of colors; 14" monitor; 16-bit sound card
Math Blaster Cross Terrain Challenge	Knowledge Adventure	Five critical-thinking activities focus on logical- and critical-thinking skills. **Math Topics** • Problem Solving • Numerical Coordinates • Decision Making • Directional Coordinates	**PC:** Windows 95/98/ME/2000; Pentium 200 MHz or higher; 32 MB RAM; high color 16-bit 800 × 600; 12X CD-ROM; Windows-compatible sound card **Macintosh:** G3 processor; Mac OS 8.1. 8.6, 9.1 (or higher); 64 MB RAM; 12X CD-ROM; thousands of colors, 800 × 600
Math Blaster Pre-Algebra	Knowledge Adventure	Earth's inhabitants are being "zapped" of their mathematical abilities by the magnetic brain invented by Dr. Dabble, the mad scientist. Students solve word problems involving pre-algebra and logical-thinking skills as they attempt to locate the disembodied brain in Dr. Dabble's mansion. **Math Topics** • Decimals • Factors • Integers • Fractions • Prime Numbers • Multiples • Percents	**PC:** Windows 95/98; 486 DX 33 MHz; 16 MB RAM; quad-speed CD-ROM drive; 640 × 480 256-colors SVGA graphics; 14" monitor; 16-bit sound card **Macintosh:** Power Mac; system 7.5; 16 MB RAM; quad-speed CD-ROM drive; 8MB available on hard drive; 256-colors; 14" monitor

Math Software

TITLE	PUBLISHER	DESCRIPTION	SYSTEM REQUIREMENTS
Math for the Real World	Knowledge Adventure	Students solve practical real-world problems as they travel the country with an up-and-coming rock band. **Math Topics** • Time • Money • Fractions • Logic • Charts	**PC:** Windows 95/98; 486/66 MHz or faster; 16 MB RAM; 4X CD-ROM drive; 256-colors; Windows-compatible sound card **Macintosh:** Power Mac; system 7.5.1; 16 MB RAM, 4X CD-ROM; hard drive; 256-colors; 14″ monitor
Math Workshop Deluxe	The Learning Company	Interface divides activities into beginning (downstairs) and more advanced (upstairs). Custom play option allows teachers to create their own "problem sets." **Math Topics** • Computation • Estimation • Logical Reasoning • Fractions • Spatial Visualization	**PC:** Windows 3.1 or 95; 486SX/33MHz; 8MB RAM; 4MB hard disk space; 2X CD-ROM; 640 × 480, 256-colors; Win-compatible sound card **Macintosh:** PowerPC; System 7.1.2; 12MB RAM (5MB free); 2.6MB hard disk space; 2X CD-ROM; 640 × 480, 256-colors; 13″ monitor
Thinkin' Things Collection 2	Edmark	Students are led to use logical reasoning and creative imagination as they perform various tasks in this engaging program. **Math Topics** • Critical Thinking • Spatial Awareness • Problem Solving • Perspective	**PC:** Windows 95/98, 486, Pentium or better, 33 MHZ or faster; 8 MB RAM, 12 MB available disk space; 2X CD-ROM; SVGA, 640 × 480, 16-bit color; Win-compatible sound card, Edmark TouchWindow, Microphone **Macintosh:** 68030, 68040 or PowerPC; OS 7.5.6-9.X, 4 MB, 5 MB for OS 7.5 or later; 8 MB recommended RAM, 12 MB RAM available disk space; 2X CD-ROM; 640 × 480, 256-colors; Edmark TouchWindow, Microphone
Thinkin' Things Collection 3	Edmark	This program allows students to use logical reasoning to solve various activities. They are encouraged to be creative in their solutions. **Math Topics** • Logical Reasoning • Analyze and Synthesize Information	**PC:** Windows 95/98, 486, Pentium® or better, 33 MHz or faster recommended; Hard disk with 2 MB free, 8 MB RAM required; 2X or faster CD-ROM drive; Super VGA graphics, 640 × 480, 256-colors; Windows-compatible sound card; Optional: Microphone, Edmark TouchWindow® **Macintosh:** 68030, 68040, or PowerPC; Mac 7.5.6-9.X; 4 MB RAM, 1900K unused, 5 MB for System 7.5 or later, 8 MB RAM recommended; 2X or faster CD-ROM drive; 256 or more colors, 13″ monitor or larger, Optional: Microphone, Edmark TouchWindow®
MindTwister Math	Edmark	MindTwister Math engages 1 to 3 players in a fast-paced format that involves both competition and cooperation. Best played with multiple players, the software provides an extensive review of third grade math skills. **Math Topics** • Place Value • Time and Money • Computation • Problem Solving • Geometry • Estimation and Mental Math • Fractions and Decimals • Patterns	**PC:** Win 95/98; Pentium or better (66 MHz recommended); Hard Disk with 40 MB free; 16 MB RAM; 2X CD-ROM drive; 640 × 480, 256-colors; Windows-compatible sound card **Macintosh:** Power Mac; OS 7.5.6-9.x or better; 12 MB RAM; Hard disk with 40 MB free; 2X CD-ROM drive; 640 × 480, 256-colors monitor
Stickybear Math II Deluxe	Optimum Resource	Designed to help students learn multiplication and division, from basic facts through multi-digit with regrouping. Visual aids are available to students, and the program offers a wide array of customization features for teachers. **Math Topics** • Multiplication • Division	**PC:** Pentium II 166 Mhz, Windows 95/98/2000*, XP*; 32 MB RAM, 4X CD-ROM drive or higher; 800 × 600 resolution, 256-colors **Macintosh:** Power PC or higher, System 7.6.1 through OS X; 16 MB RAM; 4X CD-ROM; 800 × 600 resolution, 256-colors **2000 and XP as Power User or Administrator only*
Stickybear's Math Splash	Optimum Resource	Four activities provide practice in computation. The program offers a number of customization features, including level of difficulty, optional auto-advance, and selection of problem types. **Math Topics** • Addition • Multiplication • Subtraction • Division	**PC:** Windows 486/66MHz, 16MB RAM; 2X CD-ROM drive; 800 × 600 resolution, 256-colors **Macintosh:** 68040 or Power PC; System 7.6.1 through OS X; 8 MB RAM; 2X CD-ROM; 800 × 600 resolution, 256-colors
Math Munchers Deluxe	The Learning Company	Students help the Math Munchers dodge a crew of troublesome troggles. Reinforces computation skills and math thinking skills. **Math Topics** • Computation • Math Thinking • Whole Numbers	**PC:** Win 3.1/95; 486SX/50MHz; 4MB RAM (8MB for Win95); 2X CD-ROM; 640 × 480, 256 colors; Win-compatible sound card **Macintosh:** 68040/20MHz/PowerPC; System 7.1; 5MB RAM; 2X CD-ROM; 13″ monitor, 640 × 480, 256-colors

Resources for Teachers

Baratta-Lorton, M. ***Mathematics Their Way: An Activity-Centered Mathematics Program for Early Childhood Education.*** Addison-Wesley, 1995.

Baratta-Lorton, R. ***Mathematics: A Way of Thinking.*** Addison-Wesley, 1977.

Benson, D. ***The Moment of Proof: Mathematical Epiphanies.*** Oxford University Press, 1999.

Berk, L., and A. Winsler. ***Scaffolding Children's Learning: Vygotsky and Early Childhood Education.*** National Association for the Education of Young Children, 1995.

Bloomer, A., and P. Carlson. ***Activity Math: Using Manipulatives in the Classroom.*** Addison-Wesley, 1993.

Bresser, R., and C. Holtzman. ***Developing Number Sense—Grades 3–6.*** Math Solutions Publications, 1999.

Bright, G., and J. Harvey. ***Basic Math Games.*** Dale Seymour Publications, 1987.

Brodie, J. P. ***Constructing Ideas About Large Numbers.*** Creative Publications, 1995.

Burk, D., A. Snider, and P. Symonds. ***Box It or Bag It Mathematics: Teachers' Resource Guide, First–Second.*** The Math Learning Center, 1988.

Burns, M. ***About Teaching Mathematics.*** Math Solutions Publications, 1993.

Burns, M. ***About Teaching Mathematics: A K–8 Resource.*** Math Solutions Publications, 1992.

Burns, M. ***A Collection of Math Lessons from Grades 6–8.*** Math Solutions Publications, 1990.

Burns, M. ***Math and Literature (K–3).*** Math Solutions Publications, 1992.

Burns, M. ***Math By All Means: Division, Grades 3 and 4.*** Math Solutions Publications, 1994.

Burns, M. ***Math By All Means: Multiplication, Grade 3.*** Math Solutions Publications, 1994.

Burns, M. ***Math By All Means: Probability, Grades 3 and 4.*** Math Solutions Publications, 1994.

Burns, M. ***MATH: Facing an American Phobia.*** Math Solutions Publications, 1998.

Burns, M. ***Probability, Grades 2–3.*** Math Solutions Publications, 1994.

Burns, M. ***This Book Is About Time.*** Yolla Bolly Press, 1978.

Burton, G. ***Towards a Good Beginning: Teaching Early Childhood Mathematics.*** Addison-Wesley, 1985.

Burton, G., D. Clements, et al. ***Addenda Series, Grades K–6.*** NCTM, 1991–1992.

Burton, G., et al. ***Addenda Series, Grades K–6, Number Sense and Operations.*** NCTM, 1993.

Butterworth, B. ***The Mathematical Brain.*** Macmillan, 1999.

Caine, R. and G. ***Unleashing the Power of Perceptual Change: The Potential of Brain-Based Teaching.*** ASCD, 1997.

Carpenter, T., E. Fennema, M. Franke, L. Levi, and S. Empson. ***Children's Mathematics—Cognitively Guided Instruction.*** Heinemann, 1999.

Cathcart. W., Y. Pothier, J. Vance, and N. Bezuk. ***Learning Mathematics in Elementary and Middle Schools.*** Merrill, 2000.

Childs, L., and L. Choate. ***Nimble with Numbers.*** Dale Seymour Publications, 1999.

Clapham, C. ***Concise Dictionary of Mathematics.*** Oxford University Press, 1996.

Coates, G., and J. Stenmark. ***Family Math for Young Children.*** Lawrence Hall of Science, 1997.

Coburn, T., et al. ***Addenda Series, Grades K–6, Patterns.*** NCTM, 1993.

Cohen, J. "The First 'R': Reflective Capacities." ***Educational Leadership,*** Vol. 57, ASCD, September 1999.

Cooney, M., ed. ***Celebrating Women in Mathematics and Science.*** NCTM, 1996.

Copley, J., ed. ***Mathematics in the Early Years.*** NCTM, 1999.

Cowan, T., and J. Maguire. ***Timelines of African-American History: 500 Years of Black Achievement.*** Berkley Publishing Group, 1994.

Crawford, M., and M. Witte. "Strategies for Mathematics: Teaching in Context." ***Educational Leadership,*** Vol. 57, ASCD, November 1999.

Curcio, F. "Developing Number Sense in the Middle Grades," ***Addenda Series.*** NCTM, 1991.

Curcio, F., and N. Bezuk, et al. ***Addenda Series, Grades 5–8, Understanding Rational Numbers and Proportions.*** NCTM, 1994.

Danielson, C., and L. Abrutyn. ***An Introduction to Using Portfolios in the Classroom.*** ASCD, 1997.

Del Grande, J., and L. Morrow. ***Addenda Series, Grades K–6, Geometry and Spatial Sense.*** NCTM, 1993.

Drake, S. ***Planning Integrated Curriculum.*** ASCD, 1993.

Eby, J., and E. Kujawa. ***Reflective Planning, Teaching and Evaluation: K–12.*** Merrill, 1994.

Elliott, P., ed. ***Communication in Mathematics, K–12 and Beyond (1996 Yearbook).*** NCTM, 1996.

Fennell, F., and D. Williams. "Decimal Dash," in ***The Arithmetic Teacher.*** NCTM, 1986.

Ferrini-Mundy, J., K. Graham, L. Johnson, and G. Mills, eds. ***Making Change in Mathematics Education: Learning from the Field.*** NCTM, 1998.

Flournoy, V., et al. ***The Patchwork Quilt.*** Scholastic, 1996.

Forte, I., and S. Schurr. ***Interdisciplinary Units and Projects for Thematic Instruction.*** Incentive Publications Inc., 1994.

Franco, B., et al. "Geometry Concentration," in ***Understanding Geometry***. Great Source Education Group, 1998.

Franco, B., et al. ***Understanding Geometry.*** Great Source Education Group, 1998.

Fuson, K. C., and Y. Kwon. "Korean Children's Understanding of Multidigit Addition and Subtraction." ***Child Development,*** Vol. 63, 491–506, 1992.

Garland, T. ***Fibonacci Fun: Fascinating Activities with Intriguing Numbers.*** Dale Seymour Publications, 1998.

Geary, D. C. ***Children's Mathematical Development: Research and Practical Applications.*** American Psychological Association, Washington, D.C., 1994.

Geary, D. C. "Reflections of Evolution and Culture in Children's Cognition: Implications for Mathematics Development and Mathematics Instruction." ***American Psychologist,*** Vol. 50, 24–27, 1995.

Geary, D. C., C. C. Bow-Tomas, and Y. Yao. "Counting Knowledge and Skill in Cognitive Addition: A Comparison of Normal and Mathematically Disabled Children." ***Journal of Experimental Child Psychology,*** Vol. 54, 372–91,1992.

Geary, D. C., et al. "A Biocultural Model of Academic Development," in ***Global Prospects for Education: Development, Culture, and Schooling.*** Edited by S. G. Paris and H. M. Wellman, Washington, D.C.: American Psychological Association, 1998.

Geary, D. C., et al. "Development of Arithmetical Competencies in Chinese and American Children: Influence of Age, Language, and Schooling." ***Child Development,*** Vol. 67, 2022–44, 1996.

Geary, D. C., and K. F. Widamin. "Numerical Cognition: On the Convergence of Componential and Psychometric Models." ***Intelligence,*** Vol. 16, 47–80, 1992.

Geddes, D., et al. ***Addenda Series, Grades 5–8, Geometry in the Middle Grades.*** NCTM, 1992.

Geddes, D., et al. ***Addenda Series, Grades 5–8, Measurement in the Middle Grades.*** NCTM, 1994.

Gelfand, I., and A. Shen. ***Algebra.*** Birkhauser, 1993.

Glassman, B., ed. ***Macmillan Visual Almanac.*** Blackbirch Press, 1996.

Glatzer, D., and J. Glatzer. ***Math Connections.*** Dale Seymour Publications, 1989.

Goldsmith, L., and J. Mark. "What Is Standards-Based Mathematics Curriculum?" ***Educational Leadership,*** Vol. 57, ASCD, November 1999.

Greenes, C., and G. Immerzeel. ***Problem Solving Focus: Time and Money.*** Dale Seymour Publications, 1993.

Grouws, D., ed. ***Handbook of Research on Mathematics Teaching and Learning.*** Macmillan, 1992.

Han, S. T., and B. Ford. ***The Master Revealed—A Journey with Tangrams.*** Cuisenaire, 1990.

Heaton, R. ***Teaching Mathematics to the New Standards: Relearning the Dance.*** Teachers College Press, 2000.

Henderson, J. ***Reflective Teaching: Becoming an Inquiring Educator.*** Macmillan, 1992.

Hiebert, J., T. Carpenter, E. Fennema, K. Fuson, D. Wearne, H. Murray, A. Olivier, and P. Humam. ***Making Sense: Teaching and Learning Mathematics with Understanding.*** Heinemann, 1997.

Hoffman, P. ***The Man Who Loved Only Numbers: The Story of Paul Erdos and the Search for Mathematical Truth.*** Hyperion, 1998.

House, P., and A. Coxford. ***Connecting Mathematics Across the Curriculum.*** NCTM, 1995.

Hynes, M. E., ed. ***Mission Mathematics: K–6.*** NCTM, 1997.

Irvin, J., ed. ***What Current Research Says to the Middle Level Practitioner.*** National Middle School Association, 1997.

Jacobs, H. ***Interdisciplinary Curriculum: Design and Implementation.*** ASCD, 1989.

Jurgens, H., E. Maletsky, H.O. Peitgen, T. Perciante, D. Saupe, and L. Yunker. ***Fractals for the Classroom: Strategic Activities, Vols. 1 & 2.*** NCTM. Copublished with Springer-Verlag, 1991-1992.

Kamii, C., and L. Housman. ***Young Children Reinvent Arithmetic: Implications of Piaget's Theory.*** Teachers College Press, 1999.

Kaplan, J. ***Basic Decimals.*** Educational Design, Inc., 1996.

Kaplan, J. ***Basic Fractions.*** Educational Design, Inc., 1996.

Kaplan, J. ***Strategies for Solving Math Word Problems.*** Educational Design, Inc., 1996.

Kenney, P., and E. Silver. ***Results from the Sixth Mathematics Assessment of the National Assessment of Educational Progress.*** NCTM, 1997.

Krause, M. ***Multicultural Mathematics Materials.*** NCTM, 1993.

Lamancusa, J. ***Kid Cash: Creative Money-Making Ideas.*** TAB Books, 1993.

Lee, M., and M. Miller. ***Great Graphing.*** Scholastic Professional Books, 1993.

Leutzinger, L., ed. ***Mathematics in the Middle.*** NCTM. Copublished with the National Middle School Association, 1998.

Levia, M., et al. "Oh How We've Changed!" in ***Addenda Series: Fourth Grade.*** NCTM, 1992.

Lindquist, M., et al. ***Making Sense of Data. Addenda Series, Grades K–6.*** NCTM, 1992.

Ma, Liping. ***Knowing and Teaching Elementary Mathematics.*** Lawrence Erlbaum Associates, 1999.

Madfes, T., project director. ***Learning from Assessment: Tools for Examining Assessment through Standards.*** (Includes PBS Mathline Video). NCTM, 1999.

Maletsky, E. ***Teaching with Student Math Notes.*** NCTM, 1993.

Mamchur, C. ***A Teacher's Guide to Cognitive Type Theory and Learning Style.*** ASCD, 1996.

The Math Learning Center. "Fractions on a Geoboard," in ***Opening Eyes to Mathematics, Volume 3.*** 1995.

McIntosh, A., B. Reys, R. Reys, and J. Hope. ***Number SENSE: Simple Effective Number Sense Experiences, Grades 4–6.*** Dale Seymour Publications, 1997.

Means, B., C. Chelener, and M. Knapp. ***Teaching Advanced Skills to At-Risk Students.*** Jossey-Bass Inc., 1991.

Mendlesohn, E. ***Teaching Primary Math with Music.*** Dale Seymour Publications, 1990.

Merrill, W. ***A Calculator Tutorial.*** Dale Seymour Publications, 1996.

Miller, D., and A. McKinnon. ***The Beginning School Mathematics Project.*** ASCD, 1995.

Miller, E. ***Read It! Draw It! Solve It! Problem Solving for Primary Grades.*** Dale Seymour Publications, 1997.

Morrison, P., and P. Morrison. ***Powers of Ten.*** W. H. Freeman and Company, 1982.

Morrow, L., ed. ***The Teaching and Learning of Algorithms in School Mathematics (1998 Yearbook).*** NCTM, 1998.

Moses, B. ***Algebraic Thinking, Grades K–12: Readings from NCTM's School-Based Journals and Other Publications.*** NCTM, 1999.

Myren, C. ***Posing Open-Ended Questions in the Primary Classroom.*** Teaching Resource Center, 1997.

Newman, V. ***Math Journals, Grades K–5.*** Teaching Resource Center, 1994.

Newman, V. ***Numbercises—A Fitness Program: Strategies for Addition and Subtraction.*** Teaching Resource Center, 1998.

Norton-Wolf, S. ***Base-Ten Block Activities.*** Learning Resources, 1990.

O'Connor, V., and M. Hynes. ***Mission Mathematics: 5–8.*** NCTM, 1997.

Ohanian, S. ***Garbage, Pizza, Patchwork Quilts, and Math Magic.*** W. H. Freeman and Company, 1992.

Olson, A. ***Mathematics Through Paper Folding.*** NCTM, 1975.

Pappas, T. ***Fractals, Googols and Other Mathematical Tales.*** Wild World Publishing/Tetra, 1993.

Pappas, T. ***The Magic of Mathematics—Discovering the Spell of Mathematics.*** Wild World Publishing/Tetra, 1994.

Parker, M., ed. ***She Does Math!—Real-Life Problems from Women on the Job.*** The Mathematical Association of America, 1995.

Perrone, V., ed. ***Expanding Student Assessment.*** ASCD, 1991.

Phillips, E., et al. ***Addenda Series, Grades 5–8, Patterns and Functions.*** NCTM, 1991.

Phillips, L. M., ed. ***Mathematics: Teacher Resource Handbook.*** Kraus International Publications, 1993.

Piccirilli, R. ***Mental Math: Computation Activities for Anytime.*** Scholastic Professional Books, 1996.

Pohl, V. ***How to Enrich Geometry Using String Designs.*** NCTM, 1986.

Pollard, J. ***Building Toothpick Bridges.*** Dale Seymour Publications, 1985.

Project AIMS. ***AIMS Activities.*** AIMS Educational Foundation, 1988–1995.

Reys, B., et al. ***Addenda Series, Grades 5–8.*** NCTM, 1991.

Rich, D. ***MegaSkills.*** Houghton Mifflin, 1992.

Richardson, K. ***Developing Number Concepts: Book 1, Counting, Comparing and Patterns.*** Dale Seymour Publications, 1999.

Richardson, K. ***Developing Number Concepts: Book 2, Addition and Subtraction.*** Dale Seymour Publications, 1999.

Richardson, K. ***Developing Number Concepts: Book 3, Place Value, Multiplication, and Division.*** Dale Seymour Publications, 1998.

Ringenberg, L. ***A Portrait of 2.*** NCTM, 1995.

Rommel, Carol A. ***Integrating Beginning Math & Literature.*** Incentive Publications, Inc., 1991.

Satariano, P. ***Storytime, Mathtime: Math Explorations in Children's Literature.*** Dale Seymour Publications, 1997.

Schechter, B. ***My Brain Is Open: The Mathematical Journeys of Paul Erdos.*** Simon & Schuster, 1998.

Scheidt, T. ***Fantasy Baseball.*** Giant Step Press, 1994.

Schifter, D., and C. Fosnot. ***Reconstructing Mathematics Education: Stories of Teachers Meeting the Challenge of Reform.*** Teachers College Press, 1993.

Schoenfeld, A. "When Good Teaching Leads to Bad Results: The Disasters of Well-Taught Mathematics Courses." ***Educational Psychologist,*** Vol. 23, 145–66, 1998.

Schullman, D., and E. Rebeka. ***Growing Mathematical Ideas in Kindergarten.*** Math Solutions Publications, 1999.

Schultz, K., et al. ***Mathematics for Every Young Child.*** Merrill, 1990.

Seymour, D. ***Getting Smarter Every Day.*** Prentice Hall, 1999.

Seymour, D. ***Probability Model Masters.*** Dale Seymour Publications, 1990.

Sheffield, L. ***Developing Mathematically Promising Students.*** NCTM, 1999.

Silverman, R., W. Welty, and S. Lyon. ***Case Studies for Teacher Problem Solving.*** McGraw-Hill, Inc., 1992.

Singer, Margie, et al. ***Between Never and Always***. Dale Seymour Publications, 1997.

Skinner, P. ***It All Adds Up!*** Math Solutions Publications (Adapted by permission of Addison-Wesley Longman, Australia), 1999.

Skinner, P. ***What's Your Problem? Posing and Solving Mathematical Problems, K–2.*** Heinemann, 1990.

Slavin, R. E., N. L. Karweit, and B. A. Wasik, eds. ***Preventing Early School Failure: Research, Policy, and Practice.*** Allyn and Bacon, 1994.

Sobel, M., and E. Maletsky. ***Teaching Mathematics: A Sourcebook of Aids, Activities, and Strategies.*** Allyn & Bacon, 1998.

Sonnabend, T. ***Mathematics for Elementary Teachers—An Interactive Approach.*** Saunders College Publishing, Harcourt Brace College Publishers, 1993.

Steen, L., ed. ***On the Shoulders of Giants—New Approaches to Numeracy.*** National Research Council, 1990.

Steen, L., ed. ***Why Numbers Count—Quantitative Literacy for Tomorrow's America.*** NCTM, 1997.

Stenmark, J., V. Thompson, and R. Cossey. ***Family Math.*** University of California, 1986.

Stenmark, J., ed. ***Mathematics Assessment: Myths, Models, Good Questions, and Practical Suggestions.*** NCTM, 1991.

Sternberg, R., and W. Williams. ***How to Develop Student Creativity.*** ASCD, 1996.

Stevenson, F. ***Exploratory Problems in Mathematics.*** NCTM, 1992.

Stewart, K., and K. Walker. ***20 Thinking Questions for Base-Ten Blocks, Grades 3–6.*** Creative Publications, 1995.

Stiff, L., and F. Curcio, eds. ***Developing Mathematical Reasoning in Grades K–12 (1999 Yearbook).*** NCTM, 1999.

Sylvester, R. ***A Celebration of Neurons—An Educator's Guide to the Human Brain.*** ASCD, 1995.

A Teacher's Guide to Performance-Based Learning and Assessment. Educators in Connecticut's Pomperaug Regional School District 15. ASCD, 1996.

Thiessen, D., and M. Mathias. ***The Wonderful World of Mathematics: A Critically Annotated List of Children's Books in Mathematics.*** NCTM, 1992.

Thornton, C., and N. Bley, eds. ***Windows of Opportunity: Mathematics for Students with Special Needs.*** NCTM, 1994.

Threewit, F. ***Estimation Destinations.*** Cuisenaire, 1994.

Tomlinson, Carol Ann. ***How to Differentiate Instruction in Mixed-Ability Classrooms.*** ASCD, 1995.

Trafton, P., and D. Thiessen. ***Learning Through Problems: Number Sense and Computational Strategies/A Resource for Teachers.*** Heinemann, 1999.

Van Cleave, J. "Graphing," ***Math for Every Kid: Easy Activities That Make Learning Math Fun.*** Wiley, 1991.

Van Cleave, J. ***Math for Every Kid: Easy Activities That Make Learning Math Fun.*** Wiley, 1991.

Van de Walle, J. ***Elementary and Middle School Mathematics: Teaching Developmentally, Third Edition.*** Dale Seymour Publications, 1997.

Walter, M. ***Boxes, Squares, and Other Things.*** NCTM, 1995.

Webb, N., and T. Romberg. ***Reforming Mathematics Education in America's Cities: The Urban Mathematics Collaborative Project.*** Teachers College Press, 1994.

Welchman-Tischler, R. ***How to Use Children's Literature to Teach Mathematics.*** NCTM, 1992.

Wu, H. "The 1997 Mathematics Standards War in California," in ***What Is at Stake at the K–12 Standards Wars?*** Edited by S. Stotsky. New York: Peter Lang Publishers, 1999.

Zaslavsky, C. ***Fear of Math—How to Get Over It and Get On with Your Life.*** Rutgers University Press, 1994.

Zaslavsky, C. ***Multicultural Math: Hands-On Math Activities from Around the World.*** Scholastic Professional Books,1994.

Zawojewski, J., et al. ***Addenda Series, Grades 5–8, Dealing with Data and Chance.*** NCTM, 1991.

Zemelman, S., H. Daniels, and A. Hyde. ***Best Practice: New Standards for Teaching and Learning in America's Schools.*** Heinemann, 1998.

BIBLIOGRAPHY FOR EXCERPTS FROM THE RESEARCH

Burton, G. M. "Patterning: Powerful Play," ***School Science and Mathematics,*** Vol. 82, 39–44, 1982.

Carpenter, T. P., J. M. Moser, and H. C. Bebout. "Representation of Addition and Subtraction Word Problems," ***Journal for Research in Mathematics Education,*** Vol. 24, 345–357, 1988.

Choate, L. D., and J. K. Okey. "Graphically Speaking: Primary-level Graphing Experiences. In A. P. Shulte and J. R. Smart (Eds.), ***Teaching Statistics and Probability: 1981 Yearbook*** (pp. 33–41). Reston, VA: National Council of Teachers of Mathematics, 1981.

Kilpatrick, J., J. Swafford, and F. Bradford, Eds. ***Adding It Up: Helping Children Learn Mathematics.*** Center for Education, Division of Behavioral and Social Sciences and Education, National Research Council. Washington, DC: National Academy Press, 2001.

Marzano, R. J., D. J. Pickering, and J. E. Pollock. ***Classroom Instruction that Works: Research-Based Strategies for Increasing Student Achievement.*** Alexandria, VA: Association for Supervision and Curriculum Development, 2001.

Van de Walle, J. A., and K. B. Watkins. "Early Development of Number Sense." In R. Jensen (Ed.), ***Research Ideas for the Classroom: Early Childhood Mathematics*** (pp. 127–150). New York: Macmillan, 1993.

Index

B

P

Y

Teaching Notes

Additional Ideas:

Good Questions to Ask:

Additional Resources:

Notes for Next Time:

HARCOURT

Math

NCTM Standards Correlations

This section contains the following:

- **Correlations to the NCTM Standards and Expectations**

These correlations demonstrate how *Harcourt Math* supports and aligns with the NCTM Content Standards. The chart indicates the lessons and chapters that correlate to each standard for the appropriate grade span.

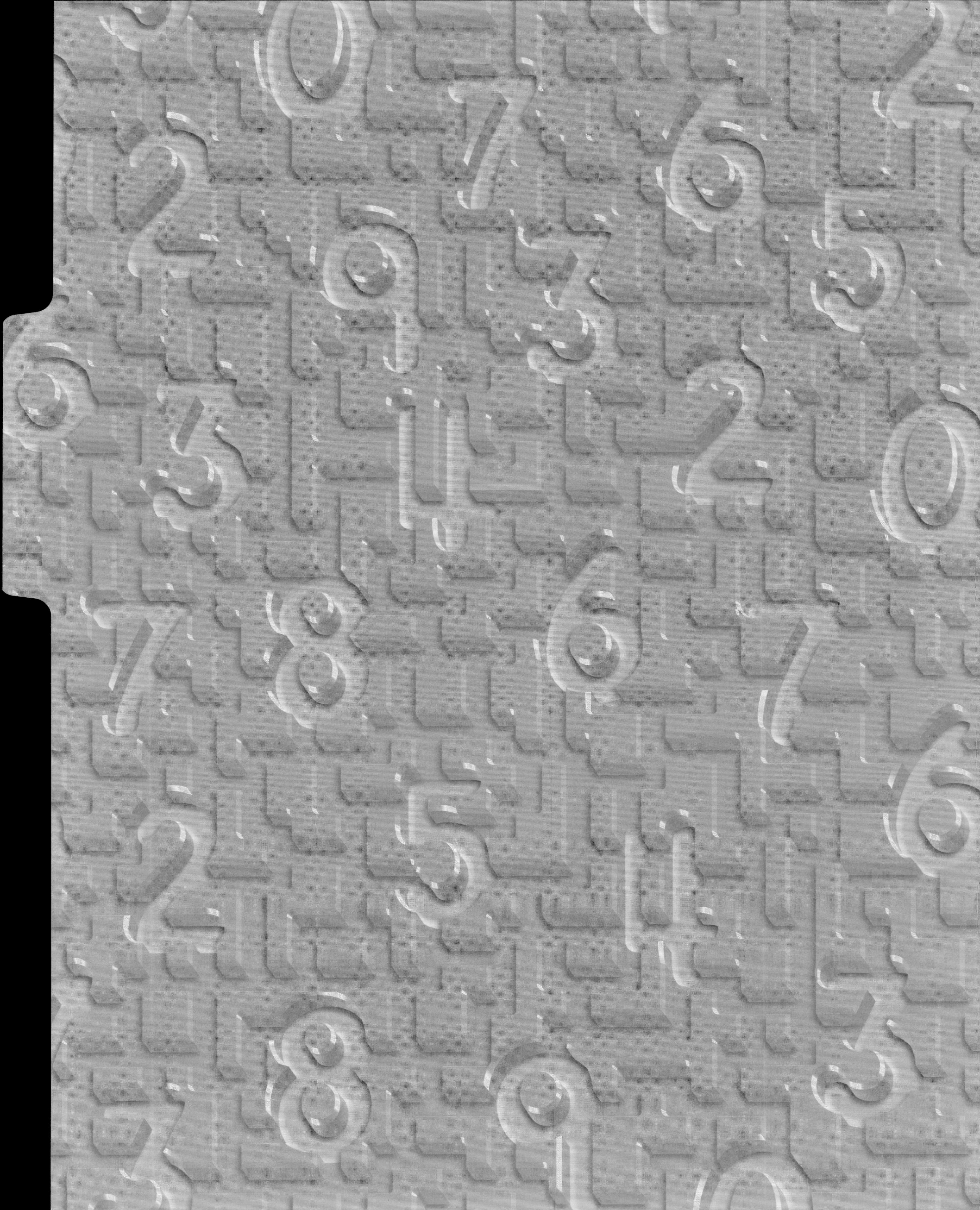

Correlations to NCTM Standards

STANDARD	GRADES 3–5 EXPECTATIONS	CORRELATION TO NCTM STANDARDS
Instructional programs from prekindergarten through grade 12 should enable all students to—	*In grades 3–5 all students should—*	
1. NUMBER AND OPERATIONS		
Understand numbers, ways of representing numbers, relationships among numbers, and number systems	• Understand the place-value structure of the base-ten number system and be able to represent and compare whole numbers and decimals; • recognize equivalent representations for the same number and generate them by decomposing and composing numbers; • develop understanding of fractions as parts of unit wholes, as parts of a collection, as locations on number lines, and as divisions of whole numbers; • use models, benchmarks, and equivalent forms to judge the size of fractions; • recognize and generate equivalent forms of commonly used fractions, decimals, and percents; • explore numbers less than 0 by extending the number line and through familiar applications; • describe classes of numbers according to characteristics such as the nature of their factors.	Lessons 1.1, 1.2, 1.3, 1.4, 1.5, 1.6, 2.1, 2.2, 2.3, 2.5, 2.6, 3.1, 3.2, 3.3, 3.4, 3.5, 3.6, 4.1, 4.2, 4.3, 4.4, 4.5, 4.6, 5.1, 5.2, 5.3, 5.4, 5.5, 5.6, 6.1, 6.2, 6.3, 6.4, 6.5, 7.1, 7.3, 7.4, 7.5, 7.6, 8.1, 8.2, 8.3, 8.4, 8.5, 9.1, 9.2, 9.3, 9.4, 9.5, 10.1, 10.2, 10.3, 10.4, 10.5, 11.1, 11.2, 11.3, 11.4, 11.5, 12.1, 12.2, 12.3, 12.4, 12.5, 13.1, 13.2, 13.3, 13.4, 13.5, 14.1, 14.2, 14.3, 14.4, 14.5, 15.1, 15.2, 15.3, 15.4, 15.5, 15.6, 16.1, 16.2, 16.3, 16.5, 17.1, 17.2, 17.3, 17.4, 17.5, 17.6, 18.1, 19.6, 22.1, 22.2, 22.3, 22.4, 23.3, 23.4, 23.5, 24.2, 24.3, 24.4, 24.5, 25.1, 25.2, 25.3, 25.4, 25.5, 25.6, 26.1, 26.2, 26.3, 26.4, 26.5, 27.1, 27.2, 27.3, 27.4, 27.5, 27.6, 28.1, 28.2, 28.3, 28.4, 29.1, 29.2, 29.3, 29.4, 30.1, 30.2, 30.3, 30.4, 30.5
Understand meanings of operations and how they relate to one another	• understand various meanings of multiplication and division; • understand the effects of multiplying and dividing whole numbers; • identify and use relationships between operations, such as division as the inverse of multiplication, to solve problems; • understand and use properties of operations, such as the distributivity of multiplication over addition.	
Compute fluently and make reasonable estimates	• develop fluency with basic number combinations for multiplication and division and use these combinations to mentally compute related problems, such as 30×50; • develop fluency in adding, subtracting, multiplying, and dividing whole numbers; • develop and use strategies to estimate the results of whole-number computations and to judge the reasonableness of such results; • develop and use strategies to estimate computations involving fractions and decimals in situations relevant to students' experience; • use visual models, benchmarks, and equivalent forms to add and subtract commonly used fractions and decimals;	

STANDARD	GRADES 3–5 EXPECTATIONS	CORRELATION TO NCTM STANDARDS
Instructional programs from prekindergarten through grade 12 should enable all students to—	*In grades 3–5 all students should—*	
1. NUMBER AND OPERATIONS ***(continued)***		
	• select appropriate methods and tools for computing with whole numbers from among mental computation, estimation, calculators, and paper and pencil according to the context and nature of the computation and use the selected method or tool.	
2. ALGEBRA		
Understand patterns, relations, and functions	• describe, extend, and make generalizations about geometric and numeric patterns; • represent and analyze patterns and functions, using words, tables, and graphs.	Lessons 1.1, 1.2, 1.3, 1.6, 2.5, 3.2, 4.3, 4.4, 4.5, 4.6, 5.3, 5.4, 5.5, 6.3, 6.5, 8.1, 8.2, 8.3, 8.4, 8.5, 9.1, 9.2, 9.3, 9.4, 9.5, 10.1, 10.2, 10.3, 10.4, 10.5, 11.2, 11.3, 11.4, 12.2, 12.3, 12.4, 12.5, 13.4, 14.1, 14.2, 14.3, 14.4, 15.3, 16.2, 16.4, 17.3, 17.4, 17.5, 18.2, 21.3, 22.1, 22.3, 22.4, 23.1, 23.2, 23.3, 23.4, 23.5, 24.1, 24.5, 25.1, 25.3, 27.4, 27.6, 28.1, 28.2, 28.3, 28.4, 29.1, 30.2
Represent and analyze mathematical situations and structures using algebraic symbols	• identify such properties as commutativity, associativity, and distributivity and use them to compute with whole numbers; • represent the idea of variable as an unknown quantity using a letter or a symbol; • express mathematical relationships using equations.	
Use mathematical models to represent and understand quantitative relationships	• model problem situations with objects and use representations such as graphs, tables, and equations to draw conclusions.	
Analyze change in various contexts	• investigate how a change in one variable relates to a change in a second variable; • identify and describe situations with constant or varying rates of change and compare them.	

STANDARD	GRADES 3–5 EXPECTATIONS	CORRELATION TO NCTM STANDARDS
Instructional programs from prekindergarten through grade 12 should enable all students to—	*In grades 3–5 all students should—*	
3. GEOMETRY		
Analyze characteristics and properties of two- and three-dimensional geometric shapes and develop mathematical arguments about geometric relationships	• identify, compare, and analyze attributes of two- and three-dimensional shapes and develop vocabulary to describe the attributes; • classify two- and three-dimensional shapes according to their properties and develop definitions of classes of shapes such as triangles and pyramids; • investigate, describe, and reason about the results of subdividing, combining, and transforming shapes; • explore congruence and similarity; • make and test conjectures about geometric properties and relationships and develop logical arguments to justify conclusions.	Lessons 19.1, 19.2, 19.3, 19.4, 19.5, 19.6, 20.1, 20.2, 20.3, 20.4, 20.5, 21.1, 21.2, 21.3, 21.4, 21.5, 22.1, 22.3, 22.4, 23.1, 23.2, 23.4
Specify locations and describe spatial relationships using coordinate geometry and other representational systems	• describe location and movement using common language and geometric vocabulary; • make and use coordinate systems to specify locations and to describe paths; • find the distance between points along horizontal and vertical lines of a coordinate system.	
Apply transformations and use symmetry to analyze mathematical situations	• predict and describe the results of sliding, flipping, and turning two-dimensional shapes; • describe a motion or series of motions that will show that two shapes are congruent; • identify and describe line and rotational symmetry in two- and three-dimensional shapes and designs.	
Use visualization, spatial reasoning, and geometric modeling to solve problems	• build and draw geometric objects; • create and describe mental images of objects, patterns, and paths; • identify and build a three-dimensional object from two-dimensional representations of that object; • identify and build a two-dimensional representation of a three-dimensional object; • use geometric models to solve problems in other areas of mathematics, such as number and measurement; • recognize geometric ideas and relationships and apply them to other disciplines and to problems that arise in the classroom or in everyday life.	

STANDARD	GRADES 3–5 EXPECTATIONS	CORRELATION TO NCTM STANDARDS
Instructional programs from prekindergarten through grade 12 should enable all students to—	*In grades 3–5 all students should—*	
4. MEASUREMENT		
Understand measurable attributes of objects and the units, systems, and processes of measurement	• understand such attributes as length, area, weight, volume, and size of angle and select the appropriate type of unit for measuring each attribute; • understand the need for measuring with standard units and become familiar with standard units in the customary and metric systems; • carry out simple unit conversions, such as from centimeters to meters, within a system of measurement; • understand that measurements are approximations and understand how differences in units affect precision; • explore what happens to measurements of a two-dimensional shape such as its perimeter and area when the shape is changed in some way.	Lessons 7.1, 7.2, 7.3, 7.4, 7.5, 7.6, 17.1, 17.2, 17.3, 17.4, 17.5, 17.6, 18.1, 18.2, 18.3, 18.4, 18.5, 22.1, 22.2, 22.3, 22.4
Apply appropriate techniques, tools, and formulas to determine measurements	• develop strategies for estimating the perimeters, areas, and volumes of irregular shapes; • select and apply appropriate standard units and tools to measure length, area, volume, weight, time, temperature, and the size of angles; • select and use benchmarks to estimate measurements; • develop, understand, and use formulas to find the area of rectangles and related triangles and parallelograms; • develop strategies to determine the surface areas and volumes of rectangular solids.	

STANDARD	GRADES 3–5 EXPECTATIONS	CORRELATION TO NCTM STANDARDS
Instructional programs from prekindergarten through grade 12 should enable all students to—	*In grades 3–5 all students should—*	
5. DATA ANALYSIS AND PROBABILITY		
Formulate questions that can be addressed with data and collect, organize, and display relevant data to answer them	• design investigations to address a question and consider how data-collection methods affect the nature of the data set; • collect data using observations, surveys, and experiments; • represent data using tables and graphs such as line plots, bar graphs, and line graphs; • recognize the difference in representing categorical and numerical data.	Lessons 3.2, 3.4, 3.5, 3.6, 6.2, 9.3, 10.3, 15.1, 15.2, 15.3, 15.4, 15.5, 15.6, 16.1, 16.2, 16.3, 16.4, 16.5, 19.6, 24.1, 24.2, 24.3, 24.4, 24.5, 24.6
Select and use appropriate statistical methods to analyze data	• describe the shape and important features of a set of data and compare related data sets, with an emphasis on how the data are distributed; • use measures of center, focusing on the median, and understand what each does and does not indicate about the data set; • compare different representations of the same data and evaluate how well each representation shows important aspects of the data.	
Develop and evaluate inferences and predictions that are based on data	• propose and justify conclusions and predictions that are based on data and design studies to further investigate the conclusions or predictions.	
Understand and apply basic concepts of probability	• describe events as likely or unlikely and discuss the degree of likelihood using such words as *certain, equally likely,* and *impossible*; • predict the probability of outcomes of simple experiments and test the predictions; • understand that the measure of the likelihood of an event can be represented by a number from 0 to 1.	

STANDARD	GRADES 3–5 EXPECTATIONS	CORRELATION TO NCTM STANDARDS
6. PROBLEM SOLVING		
Instructional programs from prekindergarten through grade 12 should enable all students to—	• Build new mathematical knowledge through problem solving • Solve problems that arise in mathematics and in other contexts • Apply and adapt a variety of appropriate strategies to solve problems • Monitor and reflect on the process of mathematical problem solving	Lessons 1.1, 1.2, 1.3, 1.4, 1.5, 1.6, 2.1, 2.2, 2.3, 2.4, 2.5, 2.6, 3.1, 3.2, 3.3, 3.4, 3.5, 3.6, 4.1, 4.2, 4.3, 4.4, 4.5, 4.6, 5.1, 5.2, 5.3, 5.4, 5.5, 5.6, 6.1, 6.2, 6.3, 6.4, 6.5, 7.1, 7.2, 7.3, 7.4, 7.5, 7.6, 8.1, 8.2, 8.3, 8.4, 8.5, 9.1, 9.2, 9.3, 9.4, 9.5, 10.1, 10.2, 10.3, 10.4, 10.5, 11.1, 11.2, 11.3, 11.4, 11.5, 12.1, 12.2, 12.3, 12.4, 12.5, 13.4, 13.5, 14.1, 14.2, 14.3, 14.4, 14.5, 15.1, 15.2, 15.3, 15.4, 15.5, 15.6, 16.1, 16.2, 16.3, 16.4, 16.5, 17.1, 17.2, 17.3, 17.4, 17.5, 17.6, 18.1, 18.2, 18.3, 18.4, 18.5, 19.1, 19.2, 19.3, 19.4, 19.5, 19.6, 20.1, 20.2, 20.3, 20.4, 20.5, 21.1, 21.2, 21.3, 21.4, 21.5, 22.1, 22.2, 22.3, 22.4, 23.1, 23.2, 23.3, 23.4, 23.5, 24.1, 24.2, 24.3, 24.4, 24.5, 24.6, 25.1, 25.2, 25.3, 25.4, 25.5, 25.6, 26.1, 26.2, 26.3, 26.4, 26.5, 27.1, 27.2, 27.3, 27.4, 27.5, 27.6, 28.1, 28.2, 28.3, 28.4, 29.1, 29.2, 29.3, 29.4, 30.1, 30.2, 30.3, 30.4, 30.5
7. REASONING AND PROOF		
Instructional programs from prekindergarten through grade 12 should enable all students to—	• Recognize reasoning and proof as fundamental aspects of mathematics • Make and investigate mathematical conjectures • Develop and evaluate mathematical arguments and proofs • Select and use various types of reasoning and methods of proof	Lessons 1.1, 1.2, 1.3, 1.5, 1.6, 2.1, 2.2, 2.3, 2.4, 2.6, 3.1, 3.2, 3.3, 3.4, 3.5, 3.6, 4.1, 4.2, 4.3, 4.4, 4.6, 5.2, 5.3, 5.4, 5.5, 5.6, 6.1, 6.2, 6.3, 6.4, 7.1, 7.2, 7.5, 7.6, 8.1, 8.2, 8.3, 8.4, 8.5, 9.1, 9.2, 9.3, 9.4, 10.1, 10.2, 10.4, 10.5, 11.2, 11.3, 11.4, 12.1, 12.2, 12.3, 12.4, 12.5, 13.1, 13.2, 13.3, 14.1, 14.2, 14.3, 14.4, 14.5, 15.1, 15.2, 15.3, 15.4, 15.6, 16.1, 16.2, 16.4, 17.2, 17.3, 17.4, 17.5, 17.6, 18.1, 18.2, 18.3, 18.4, 18.5, 19.1, 19.2, 19.3, 19.4, 19.5, 19.6, 20.1, 20.2, 20.3, 20.4, 20.5, 21.1, 21.3, 21.5, 22.1, 22.2, 22.3, 22.4, 23.1, 23.5, 24.1, 24.2, 24.3, 24.4, 24.5, 24.6, 25.1, 25.3, 25.4, 25.5, 25.6, 26.1, 26.2, 26.4, 26.5, 27.1, 27.2, 27.3, 27.4, 27.5, 28.1, 28.2, 28.3, 28.4, 29.1, 29.2, 29.3, 29.4, 30.2, 30.4, 30.5

STANDARD	GRADES 3–5 EXPECTATIONS	CORRELATION TO NCTM STANDARDS
8. COMMUNICATION		
Instructional programs from prekindergarten through grade 12 should enable all students to—	• Organize and consolidate their mathematical thinking through communication • Communicate their mathematical thinking coherently and clearly to peers, teachers, and others • Analyze and evaluate the mathematical thinking and strategies of others • Use the language of mathematics to express mathematical ideas precisely	Lessons 1.1, 1.2, 1.3, 1.4, 1.5, 1.6, 2.1, 2.2, 2.3, 2.4, 2.5, 2.6, 3.1, 3.2, 3.3, 3.4, 3.5, 3.6, 4.1, 4.2, 4.3, 4.4, 4.5, 4.6, 5.2, 5.3, 5.4, 5.5, 5.6, 6.1, 6.2, 6.3, 6.4, 6.5, 7.1, 7.2, 7.3, 7.4, 7.5, 7.6, 8.1, 8.2, 8.3, 8.4, 8.5, 9.1, 9.3, 10.1, 10.2, 10.4, 10.5, 11.1, 11.2, 11.3, 11.4, 11.5, 12.2, 12.3, 12.4, 12.5, 13.1, 13.2, 13.3, 13.4, 13.5, 14.1, 14.2, 14.3, 14.4, 14.5, 15.1, 15.2, 15.3, 15.4, 15.5, 15.6, 16.1, 16.2, 16.3, 16.4, 16.5, 17.2, 17.3, 17.4, 17.5, 17.6, 18.1, 18.2, 18.3, 18.4, 19.1, 19.2, 19.3, 19.4, 19.5, 19.6, 20.1, 20.2, 20.3, 20.4, 20.5, 21.1, 21.2, 21.3, 21.4, 21.5, 22.1, 22.2, 22.3, 22.4, 23.1, 23.2, 23.3, 24.1, 24.2, 24.3, 24.4, 24.5, 25.1, 25.2, 25.3, 25.4, 25.5, 25.6, 26.1, 26.2, 26.3, 26.4, 26.5, 27.1, 27.3, 27.4, 27.5, 27.6, 28.1, 28.2, 28.3, 28.4, 29.1, 29.2, 29.3, 29.4, 30.1, 30.2, 30.3, 30.4, 30.5
9. CONNECTIONS		
Instructional programs from prekindergarten through grade 12 should enable all students to—	• Recognize and use connections among mathematical ideas • Understand how mathematical ideas interconnect and build on one another to produce a coherent whole • Recognize and apply mathematics in contexts outside of mathematics	Lessons 1.2, 1.3, 1.4, 1.5, 1.6, 2.1, 2.2, 2.3, 2.4, 2.6, 3.1, 3.2, 3.3, 3.4, 3.5, 3.6, 4.2, 4.3, 4.4, 5.1, 5.3, 5.4, 5.5, 6.1, 7.4, 7.5, 7.6, 8.1, 8.4, 8.5, 9.4, 10.1, 10.2, 10.4, 10.5, 12.1, 12.2, 12.3, 12.4, 14.1, 14.2, 14.3, 14.4, 15.1, 15.2, 15.3, 15.4, 15.5, 15.6, 16.2, 16.4, 16.5, 17.1, 17.2, 17.4, 17.5, 17.6, 18.1, 18.2, 18.3, 18.4, 18.5, 19.1, 19.2, 19.4, 19.5, 21.1, 21.2, 22.2, 22.3, 23.5, 24.1, 24.2, 24.3, 24.4, 25.1, 25.2, 25.3, 25.4, 25.5, 25.6, 26.2, 26.3, 26.4, 26.5, 27.1, 27.2, 27.3, 27.4, 27.5, 27.6, 28.1, 28.2, 28.3, 29.1, 29.2, 29.3, 29.4
10. REPRESENTATION		
Instructional programs from prekindergarten through grade 12 should enable all students to—	• Create and use representations to organize, record, and communicate mathematical ideas • Select, apply, and translate among mathematical representations to solve problems • Use representations to model and interpret physical, social, and mathematical phenomena	Lessons 1.2, 1.3, 2.1, 2.2, 2.3, 2.4, 2.5, 2.6, 3.5, 3.6, 4.2, 4.3, 4.4, 4.5, 4.6, 5.2, 5.3, 5.6, 6.1, 6.2, 6.3, 6.4, 6.5, 7.2, 7.3, 7.4, 7.5, 7.6, 8.4, 9.2, 9.3, 9.4, 10.1, 10.2, 10.3, 10.4, 10.5, 11.1, 11.2, 11.3, 11.4, 11.5, 12.1, 12.3, 12.4, 12.5, 14.1, 14.2, 14.3, 14.4, 14.5, 15.1, 15.2, 15.3, 15.4, 15.5, 15.6, 16.1, 16.2, 16.3, 16.4, 16.5, 17.5, 18.2, 18.5, 19.1, 19.2, 19.3, 19.4, 19.5, 20.1, 20.2, 20.3, 20.4, 20.5, 21.1, 21.2, 21.3, 21.4, 21.5, 22.1, 22.2, 22.3, 22.4, 24.3, 24.4, 24.5, 24.6, 25.1, 25.2, 25.3, 25.4, 25.5, 25.6, 26.1, 26.2, 26.3, 26.4, 26.5, 27.1, 27.2, 27.3, 27.4, 27.5, 28.1, 28.3, 29.1, 29.2, 29.3, 29.4, 30.1, 30.2, 30.3

Teaching Notes

Additional Ideas:

Good Questions to Ask:

Additional Resources:

Notes for Next Time:

HARCOURT

North Carolina Mathematics Standard Course of Study Correlations

This section contains the following:

- **Correlations to the North Carolina Mathematics Standard Course of Study**

These correlations demonstrate how *Harcourt Math* supports and aligns with the North Carolina Mathematics Standard Course of Study. Page references for the Pupil and Teacher Editions follow each Objective.

Correlations to the North Carolina Mathematics Standard Course of Study

OBJECTIVE	PUPIL EDITION AND TEACHER EDITION PAGES
NUMBER AND OPERATIONS	
Competency Goal 1: The learner will model, identify, and compute with whole numbers through 9,999.	
1.01 Develop number sense for whole numbers through 9,999.	22–23, 24–27, 32–33, 40–41, 42–45, 46–47, 48–49, 50–51, 52–53, 116–117
a) Connect model, number word, and number using a variety of representations.	22–23, 24–27
b) Build understanding of place value (ones through thousands).	22–23, 24–27, 32–33
c) Compare and order.	42–45, 46–47, 48–49, 116–117
1.02 Develop fluency with multi-digit addition and subtraction through 9,999 using:	2–3, 4–5, 6–7, 8–9, 10–11, 12–13, 68–69, 70–71, 72–73, 88–89, 92–95, 96–97, 98–101, 102–103, 120–121
a) Strategies for adding and subtracting numbers.	2–3, 4–5, 6–7, 8–9, 10–11, 12–13, 92–95, 96–97, 120–121
b) Estimation of sums and differences in appropriate situations.	68–69, 88–89, 102–103
c) Relationships between operations.	2–3, 4–5
1.03 Develop fluency with multiplication from 1×1 to 12×12 and division up to two-digit by one-digit numbers using:	158–159, 160–161, 162–163, 164–167, 168–169, 176–177, 178–179, 182–185, 186–187, 194–195, 196–197, 198–199, 200–201, 202–205, 212–215, 216–217, 218–219, 220–221, 238–239, 240–241, 242–245, 246–249, 258–259, 260–261, 262–263, 274–277, 278–279, 280–283, 284–285, 600–601, 602–605, 608–611, 618–619, 620–623, 624–625
a) Strategies for multiplying and dividing numbers.	162–163, 178–179, 194–195, 212–213, 220–221, 600–601, 602–605
b) Estimation of products and quotients in appropriate situations.	608–611, 628–629, 635
c) Relationships between operations.	158–159, 240–241, 242–245
1.04 Use basic properties (identity, commutative, associative, order of operations) for addition, subtraction, multiplication, and division.	6–7, 164–167, 176–177, 218–219, 220–221

Source for North Carolina Mathematics Standard Course of Study: North Carolina Department of Public Instruction

OBJECTIVE	PUPIL EDITION AND TEACHER EDITION PAGES
NUMBER AND OPERATIONS	
1.05 Use area or region models and set models of fractions to explore part-whole relationships.	516–519, 520–521, 522–525, 526–529, 530–531, 532–533, 558–559, 560–561, 562–563, 564–565, 576–577, 578–579
a) Represent fractions concretely and symbolically (halves, fourths, thirds, sixths, eighths).	516–519, 520–521
b) Compare and order fractions (halves, fourths, thirds, sixths, eighths) using models and benchmark numbers (zero, one-half, one); describe comparisons.	526–529, 530–531
c) Model and describe common equivalents, especially relationships among halves, fourths, and eighths, and thirds and sixths.	522–525
d) Understand that the fractional relationships that occur between zero and one also occur between every two consecutive whole numbers.	532–533, 564–565
e) Understand and use mixed numbers and their equivalent fraction forms.	532–533
1.06 Develop flexibility in solving problems by selecting strategies and using mental computation, estimation, calculators or computers, and paper and pencil.	6–7, 12–13, 68–69, 76–79, 98–101, 168–169, 180–181, 222–223, 250–251, 266–267, 286–287, 362–363, 568–569, 584–585, 606–607, 608–611
MEASUREMENT	
Competency Goal 2: The learner will recognize and use standard units of metric and customary measurement.	
2.01 Solve problems using measurement concepts and procedures involving:	110–113, 114–115, 134–135, 136–137, 348–349
a) Elapsed time.	134–135, 136–137, 138–141, 142–143
b) Equivalent measures within the same measurement system.	110–113, 114–115, 348–349
2.02 Estimate and measure using appropriate units.	338–341, 342–343, 344–345, 346–347, 350–351, 358–361, 362–363, 364–365, 366–367, 368–369
a) Capacity (cups, pints, quarts, gallons, liters).	344–345, 364–365
b) Length (miles, kilometers).	338–341, 342–343, 358–361, 362–363
c) Mass (ounces, pounds, grams, kilograms).	346–347, 366–367
d) Temperature (Fahrenheit, Celsius).	368–369

OBJECTIVE	PUPIL EDITION AND TEACHER EDITION PAGES
GEOMETRY	
Competency Goal 3: The learner will recognize and use basic geometric properties of two- and three-dimensional figures.	
3.01 Use appropriate vocabulary to compare, describe, and classify two- and three-dimensional figures.	384–387, 388–389, 390–391, 392–395, 396–399, 400–401, 408–409, 410–411, 412–413, 416–417, 424–427, 428–429, 430–431, 432–435, 436–437
3.02 Use a rectangular coordinate system to solve problems.	328–329
a) Graph and identify points with whole number and/or letter coordinates.	328–329
b) Describe the path between given points on the plane.	328–329
DATA ANALYSIS AND PROBABILITY	
Competency Goal 4: The learner will understand and use data and simple probability concepts.	
4.01 Collect, organize, analyze, and display data (including circle graphs and tables) to solve problems.	198–199, 302–303, 304–305, 306–307, 308–309, 310–313, 314–315, 322–323, 324–325, 326–327, 330–331, 375, 498–499, 500–501
4.02 Determine the number of permutations and combinations of up to three items.	498–499, 500–501
4.03 Solve probability problems using permutations and combinations.	498–499, 500–501
ALGEBRA	
Competency Goal 5: The learner will recognize, determine, and represent patterns and simple mathematical relationships.	
5.01 Describe and extend numeric and geometric patterns.	4–5, 30–31, 180–181, 212–215, 216–217, 330–331, 470–473, 474–475, 476–477, 478–479, 480–481
5.02 Extend and find missing terms of repeating and growing patterns.	470–473, 474–475, 476–477, 480–481
5.03 Use symbols to represent unknown quantities in number sentences.	4–5, 178–179, 182–184, 186–187, 212–214, 242–245
5.04 Find the value of the unknown in a whole number sentence.	4–5, 80–81, 186–187, 194–195, 196–197, 242–245, 246–249

OBJECTIVE	PUPIL EDITION AND TEACHER EDITION PAGES
CONCEPTS/SKILLS TO MAINTAIN	
Addition and subtraction of multi-digit numbers	8–9, 10–11, 12–13, 70–71, 72–73, 76–79, 90–91, 92–95, 96–97, 98–101, 120–121
Length and time	128–131, 132–133, 134–135, 136–137, 338–341, 342–343, 350–351, 358–361, 362–363
Symmetry and congruence	408–409, 410–411, 416–417
Line plots, tallies, pictographs	198–199, 302–303, 306–307, 310–313, 488–489, 490–491, 492–495, 496–497
Venn diagrams	400–401

Teaching Notes

Additional Ideas:

Good Questions to Ask:

Additional Resources:

Notes for Next Time:

Teaching Notes

Additional Ideas:

Good Questions to Ask:

Additional Resources:

Notes for Next Time: